Select Material From

Genetics
From Genes to Genomes
FOURTH EDITION

Leland H. Hartwell
Fred Hutchinson Cancer Research Center

Leroy Hood
The Institute for Systems Biology

Michael L. Goldberg
Cornell University

Ann E. Reynolds
Fred Hutchinson Cancer Research Center

Lee M. Silver
Princeton University

 Learning Solutions

Boston   Burr Ridge, IL   Dubuque, IA   New York   San Francisco   St. Louis
Bangkok   Bogotá   Caracas   Lisbon   London   Madrid
Mexico City   Milan   New Delhi   Seoul   Singapore   Sydney   Taipei   Toronto

Select Material From
Genetics: From Genes to Genomes, Fourth Edition

Copyright © 2011 by The McGraw-Hill Companies, Inc. All rights reserved. Printed in the United States of America. Except as permitted under the United States Copyright Act of 1976, no part of this publication may be reproduced or distributed in any form or by any means, or stored in a data base retrieval system, without prior written permission of the publisher.

This book is a McGraw-Hill Learning Solutions textbook and contains select material from *Genetics: From Genes to Genomes*, Fourth Edition by Leland H. Hartwell, Leroy Hood, Michael L. Goldberg, Ann E. Reynolds and Lee M. Silver. Copyright © 2011, 2008, 2004, 2000 by The McGraw-Hill Companies, Inc. Reprinted with permission of the publisher. Many custom published texts are modified versions or adaptations of our best-selling textbooks. Some adaptations are printed in black and white to keep prices at a minimum, while others are in color.

1 2 3 4 5 6 7 8 9 0 TFR TFR 14 13 12

ISBN-13: 978-0-07-777073-0
ISBN-10: 0-07-777073-0
Part of:
ISBN-13: 978-0-07-777074-7
ISBN-10: 0-07-777074-9

Learning Solutions Consultant: Jill Albracht
Production Editor: Melissa Reinhardt
Printer/Binder: TFR Printing

About the Authors

Dr. Leland Hartwell is President and Director of Seattle's Fred Hutchinson Cancer Research Center and Professor of Genome Sciences at the University of Washington.

Dr. Hartwell's primary research contributions were in identifying genes that control cell division in yeast including those necessary for the division process as well as those necessary for the fidelity of genome reproduction. Subsequently, many of these same genes have been found to control cell division in humans and often to be the site of alteration in cancer cells.

Dr. Hartwell is a member of the National Academy of Sciences and has received the Albert Lasker Basic Medical Research Award, the Gairdner Foundation International Award, the Genetics Society Medal, and the 2001 Nobel Prize in Physiology or Medicine.

Dr. Lee Hood received an M.D. from the Johns Hopkins Medical School and a Ph.D. in biochemistry from the California Institute of Technology. His research interests include immunology, cancer biology, development, and the development of biological instrumentation (for example, the protein sequencer and the automated fluorescent DNA sequencer). His early research played a key role in unraveling the mysteries of antibody diversity. More recently he has pioneered systems approaches to biology and medicine.

Dr. Hood has taught molecular evolution, immunology, molecular biology, genomics and biochemistry and has co-authored textbooks in biochemistry, molecular biology, and immunology, as well as *The Code of Codes*—a monograph about the Human Genome Project. He was one of the first advocates for the Human Genome Project and directed one of the federal genome centers that sequenced the human genome. Dr. Hood is currently the president (and co-founder) of the cross-disciplinary Institute for Systems Biology in Seattle, Washington.

Dr. Hood has received a variety of awards, including the Albert Lasker Award for Medical Research (1987), the Distinguished Service Award from the National Association of Teachers (1998) and the Lemelson/MIT Award for Invention (2003). He is the 2002 recipient of the Kyoto Prize in Advanced Biotechnology—an award recognizing his pioneering work in developing the protein and DNA synthesizers and sequencers that provide the technical foundation of modern biology. He is deeply involved in K–12 science education. His hobbies include running, mountain climbing, and reading.

Dr. Michael Goldberg is a professor at Cornell University, where he teaches introductory genetics and human genetics. He was an undergraduate at Yale University and received his Ph.D. in biochemistry from Stanford University. Dr. Goldberg performed postdoctoral research at the Biozentrum of the University of Basel (Switzerland) and at Harvard University, and he received an NIH Fogarty Senior International Fellowship for study at Imperial College (England) and fellowships from the Fondazione Cenci Bolognetti for sabbatical work at the University of Rome (Italy). His current research uses the tools of *Drosophila* genetics and the biochemical analysis of frog egg cell extracts to investigate the mechanisms that ensure proper cell cycle progression and chromosome segregation during mitosis and meiosis.

Dr. Ann Reynolds is an educator and author. She began teaching genetics and biology in 1990, and her research has included studies of gene regulation in *E. coli,* chromosome structure and DNA replication in yeast, and chloroplast gene expression in marine algae. She is a graduate of Mount Holyoke College and received her Ph.D. from Tufts University. Dr. Reynolds was a postdoctoral fellow in the Harvard University Department of Molecular Biology and Genome Sciences at the University of Washington. She was also an author and producer of the laserdisc and CD-ROM *Genetics: Fundamentals to Frontiers.*

Dr. Lee M. Silver is a professor at Princeton University in the Department of Molecular Biology and the Woodrow Wilson School of Public and International Affairs. He has joint appointments in Princeton's Program in Science, Technology, and Environmental Policy, the Program in Law and Public Policy and the Princeton Environmental Institute. He received a Bachelor's and Master's degree in physics from the University of Pennsylvania, a doctorate in biophysics from Harvard University, postdoctoral training in mammalian genetics at the Sloan-Kettering Cancer Center, and training in molecular biology at Cold Spring Harbor Laboratory. Silver was elected a lifetime Fellow of the American Association for the Advancement of Science and was a recipient of an unsolicited National Institutes of Health MERIT award for outstanding research in genetics. He has been elected to the governing boards of the Genetics Society of America and the International Mammalian Genome Society, and is currently on the Board of Trustees of the American Council on Science and Health, the Advisory Board of The Reason Project, and the Scientific Advisory Board of the Institute of Systems Biology in Seattle.

Silver has published over 180 research articles in the fields of developmental genetics, molecular evolution, population genetics, behavioral genetics, and computer modeling. He is the lone author of three books: *Mouse Genetics: Concepts and Applications* (1995), *Remaking Eden* (1997) and *Challenging Nature* (2006). He has also published essays in *The New York Times*, *Washington Post*, *Time*, and *Newsweek International* and has appeared on numerous television and radio programs including the Charlie Rose Show, 20/20, 60 Minutes, PBS, NBC and ABC News, Nightline, NPR, and the Steven Colbert Report. Recently, Silver collaborated with the playwright Jeremy Kareken on the script of "Sweet, Sweet, Motherhood," which won first prize in the 2007 Two-headed Challenge from the Guthrie Theater, awarded to the best play written by a playwright and a non-theater partner.

Contributors

Genetics research tends to proceed down highly specialized paths. A number of experts in specific areas generously provided information in their areas of expertise. We thank them for their contributions to this edition of our text.

Claudio Alonso, *University of Sussex*
Jody Larson, *Instructional Designer, Textbook Development*
Martha Hamblin, *Cornell University*
Debra Nero, *Cornell University*

Brief Contents

Contents

PART I

Basic Principles: How Traits Are Transmitted   13

PART IV

How Genes Travel on Chromosomes   405

PART V

How Genes Are Regulated   519

PART VI

Beyond the Individual Gene and Genome   655

Preface

A Note from the Authors

The science of genetics is less than 150 years old, but its accomplishments within that short time have been astonishing. Gregor Mendel first described genes as abstract units of inheritance in 1865; his work was ignored and then "rediscovered" in 1900. Thomas Hunt Morgan and his students provided experimental verification of the idea that genes reside within chromosomes during the years 1910–1920. By 1944, Oswald Avery and his coworkers had established that genes are made of DNA. James Watson and Francis Crick published their pathbreaking structure of DNA in 1953. Remarkably, less than 50 years later (in 2001), an international consortium of investigators deciphered the sequence of the 3 billion nucleotides in the human genome. Twentieth century genetics made it possible to identify individual genes and to understand a great deal about their functions.

Today, scientists are able to access the enormous amounts of genetic data generated by the sequencing of many organisms' genomes. Analysis of these data will result in a deeper understanding of the complex molecular interactions within and among vast networks of genes, proteins, and other molecules that help bring organisms to life. Finding new methods and tools for analyzing these data will be a significant part of genetics in the twenty-first century.

Our fourth edition of *Genetics: From Genes to Genomes* emphasizes both the core concepts of genetics and the cutting-edge discoveries, modern tools, and analytic methods that will keep the science of genetics moving forward.

Our Focus—An Integrated Approach

Genetics: From Genes to Genomes represents a new approach to an undergraduate course in genetics. It reflects the way we, the authors, currently view the molecular basis of life.

We integrate:

- **Formal genetics:** the rules by which genes are transmitted.
- **Molecular genetics:** the structure of DNA and how it directs the structure of proteins.

- **Digital analysis, genomics, and proteomics:** recent technologies that allow a comprehensive analysis of the entire gene set and its expression in an organism.
- **Human genetics:** how genes contribute to health and diseases, including cancer.
- **The unity of life-forms:** the synthesis of information from many different organisms into coherent models.
- **Molecular evolution:** the molecular mechanisms by which biological systems and whole organisms have evolved and diverged.
- **Systems biology:** the multidisciplinary, integrated study of life processes that may lead to new ways to analyze, detect, and treat disease.

The strength of this integrated approach is that students who complete the book will have a strong command of genetics as it is practiced today by both academic and corporate researchers. These scientists are rapidly changing our understanding of living organisms, including ourselves. Ultimately, this vital research may create the ability to replace or correct detrimental genes—those "inborn errors of metabolism," as researcher Archibald Garrod called them in 1923, as well as the later genetic alterations that lead to the many forms of cancer.

The Genetic Way of Thinking

Modern genetics is a molecular-level science, but an understanding of its origins and the discovery of its principles is a necessary context. To encourage a genetic way of thinking, we begin the book by reviewing Mendel's principles and the chromosomal basis of inheritance. From the outset, however, we aim to integrate organism-level genetics with fundamental molecular mechanisms.

Chapter 1 presents the foundation of this integration by summarizing the main biological themes we explore. In Chapter 2, we tie Mendel's studies of pea-shape inheritance to the action of an enzyme that determines whether a pea is round or wrinkled. In the same chapter, we point to the relatedness of the patterns of heredity in all organisms. Chapters 3–5 cover extensions to Mendel, the chromosome theory of inheritance, and the fundamentals of gene linkage and mapping. Starting in Chapter 6, we focus on the physical characteristics of DNA, on mutations, and on how DNA encodes, copies, and transmits biological information.

Beginning in Chapter 9, we move into the digital revolution in DNA analysis with a look at modern genetics techniques, including gene cloning, hybridization, PCR, and microarrays. We explore how bioinformatics, an emergent analytical tool, can aid in string matching and in discovery of genome and proteome features.

The understanding of molecular and computer-based techniques carries into our discussion of chromosome specifics in Chapters 12–14, and also informs our analysis of gene regulation in Chapters 15, 16, and 17, the last of which provides an in-depth discussion of the cell cycle and its disruption in cancers. Chapter 18 describes the use of genetic tools at the molecular level to uncover the complex interactions of eukaryotic development.

Chapters 19 and 20 cover population genetics, with a view of how molecular tools have provided information on species relatedness and on genomes changes at the molecular level over time. Finally, in Chapter 21 we explore systems biology, an integrated field utilizing input from several disciplines. We consider the impact a systems approach could have on the identification and treatment of disease.

Throughout our book, we present the scientific reasoning of some of the ingenious researchers of the field—from Mendel, to Watson and Crick, to the collaborators on the Human Genome Project. We hope student readers will see that genetics is not simply a set of data and facts, but also a human endeavor that relies on contributions from exceptional individuals.

Student-Friendly Features

We have taken great pains to help the student make the leap to a deeper understanding of genetics. Numerous features of this book were developed with that goal in mind.

- *One Voice* Genetics: Genes to Genomes has a friendly, engaging reading style that helps students master the concepts throughout this book. The writing style provides the student with the focus and continuity required to make the book successful in the classroom.
- *Visualizing Genetics* The highly specialized art program developed for this book integrates

photos and line art in a manner that provides the most engaging visual presentation of genetics available. Our Feature Figure illustrations break down complex processes into step-by-step illustrations that lead to greater student understanding. All illustrations are rendered with a consistent color theme—for example, all presentations of phosphate groups are the same color, as are all presentations of mRNA.

- **Accessibility** Our intention is to bring cutting-edge content to the student level. A number of more complex illustrations are revised and segmented to help the student follow the process. Legends have been streamlined to highlight only the most important ideas, and throughout the book, topics and examples have been chosen to focus on the most critical information.
- *Problem Solving* Developing strong problem-solving skills is vital for every genetics student. The authors have carefully created problem sets at the end of each chapter that allow students to improve upon their problem-solving ability.
- **Solved Problems** which cover topical material with complete answers provide insight into the step-by-step process of problem solving.
- **Review Problems** offer more than 600 questions involving a variety of levels of difficulty that develop excellent problem-solving skills. The problems are organized by chapter section and in order of increasing difficulty within each section for ease of use by instructors and students. Answers to selected problems are in the back of the book. The companion Study Guide and Solutions Manual by Debra Nero (available separately) provides detailed analysis of strategies to solve all of the end-of-chapter problems.

Problems

Vocabulary

1. For each of the terms in the left column, choose the best matching phrase in the right column.

a. reciprocal translocation	1. lacking one or more chromosomes or having one or more extra chromosomes
b. gynandromorph	2. movement of short DNA elements
c. pericentric	3. having more than two complete sets of chromosomes
d. paracentric	4. exact exchange of parts of two nonhomologous chromosomes
e. euploids	5. excluding the centromere
f. polyploidy	6. including the centromere
g. transposition	7. having complete sets of chromosomes
h. aneuploids	8. mosaic combination of male and female tissue

Section 13.1

2. For each of the following types of chromosomal aberrations, tell: (i) whether an organism heterozygous for the aberration will form any type of loop in the chromosomes during prophase I of meiosis; (ii) whether a chromosomal bridge can be formed during anaphase I in a heterozygote, and if so, under what condition; (iii) whether an acentric fragment can be formed during anaphase I in a heterozygote, and if so, under what condition; (iv) whether the aberration can suppress meiotic recombination; and (v) whether the two chromosomal breaks responsible for the aberration occur on the same side or on opposite sides of a single centromere, or if the two breaks occur on different chromosomes.
   a. reciprocal translocation
   b. paracentric inversion
   c. small tandem duplication
   d. Robertsonian translocation
   e. paracentric inversion
   f. large deletion

3. In flies that are heterozygous for either a deletion or a duplication, there will be a looped-out region in a preparation of polytene chromosomes. How could you distinguish between a deletion or a duplication using polytene chromosome analysis?

Detailed List of Changes

Chapter 2

- New headings call out the Punnett square, product rule, sum rule, law of segregation, law of independent assortment, branched-line diagrams, testcrosses with dihybrids, and pedigrees to help readers to easily find the explanations of these basic genetics applications.

Chapter 3

- New headings call out the important examples of human ABO groups, seed coat patterns in lentils, and human histocompatibility groups.
- Headings for discussions of monomorphic-gene allele frequency versus polymorphic-gene allele frequency and recessive epistasis versus dominant epistasis allow student readers to more readily distinguish between these paired topics.
- The complementation-test discussion is identified with a new heading.

Chapter 5

- A major section groups information on the chi-square test and linkage analysis to highlight the importance of this tool.
- Recombination frequencies and tetrad analysis in fungi also are promoted to major-section treatment to facilitate topic management.

Chapter 6

- New figure 6.3 provides a clear depiction of bacterial transformation.
- New figure 6.14b depicts the specificity of DNA sequence interaction with DNA binding and regulatory proteins.

Chapter 8

- New heading scheme for the correlation between nucleotide sequence and amino acid sequence emphasizes findings as lines of evidence.
- Added headings call out exons and introns; mechanism of RNA splicing; and snRNPs and the spliceosome as subtopics.

Chapter 9

- New section on bioinformatics and how information technology, applied to genomic sequences, has transformed the practice of genetics.
- Presentation of the UCSC Genome Browser, a powerful web-based tool used by practicing geneticists to visualize a multitude of genomic features in images created on-the-fly.
- Figure 9.16 illustrates the application of the UCSC browser at different levels of genomic resolution from a whole chromosome down to the individual basepairs that distinguish the genome of James D. Watson.
- Figure 9.17 provides a visualization of the different degrees of sequence conservation that exist along the genome and across the phylogenetic tree.

Chapter 10

- Chapter 10 describes the most recent advances in the fields of genomics and proteomics.
- New table 10.1 shows the number of species of each organismal type that have been subjected to whole genome sequencing.
- New figure 10.1 shows the number of basepairs of sequence on each human chromosome that were deciphered in the first draft of a complete human genome.

Chapter 11

- Chapter 11 has been rewritten with a focus on individual variation at the whole genome level.
- Figure 11.2 illustrates the DNA sequence differences found in a comparison of the genomes of James D. Watson, J. Craig Venter, and an anonymous Chinese man.
- Figure 11.7 illustrates the genomic distribution of different types of allelic variants in the region of the gene responsible for cystic fibrosis.
- Several new figures illustrate the wide-spread distribution of a newly discovered, common form of genetic variation known as copy number polymorphisms (CNPs).

Chapter 12

- Reorganized and updated content on chromatin packaging and how it affects function.
- Updated coverage of the molecular characterization of heterochromatin and other alternative chromating structure.
- Updated information on the cohesin model for segregation of chromosomes.

Chapter 13

- Transposable elements are now described in a major section, highlighting the importance of their discovery and their characteristics in the genome.

- Evolutionary impact of genomic rearrangements, as shown by a speculative example, has become a major section.

Chapter 14

- Prokaryotic and organellar genetics are combined into one chapter for a more concise presentation of both areas.
- Additional information on metagenomic analysis of bacteria.
- Increased coverage of the evolution of pathogenic bacteria.

Chapter 15

- More in-depth coverage on the use of microarrays to analyze gene expression.
- Updates to global regulatory systems in bacteria.

Chapter 16

- Reorganization of material in the chapter to emphasize basic concepts of eukaryotic gene regulation.
- Increased coverage of post-transcriptional regulation.
- Increased coverage of RNAi.
- New information on chromatin remodeling.

Chapter 17

- The chapter has been reorganized to emphasize cancer's deviation from normal cell-cycle controls.
- A new overview section summarizes initiation of cell division, including components of signaling systems and mechanism of signal transduction.
- Added subheadings help identify information on isolation of cell-cycle mutants and their genetic analysis.

Chapter 18

- Analysis of genetic pathways has become a major topic.
- The section on gene interaction in a pathway has been expanded in this chapter and now includes both analysis of gene effects and use of double mutants. Two figures illustrate this expanded section.

Chapter 19

- Chapter 19 has been rewritten with an emphasis on genetic variation within and between human populations and stochastic models of population changes in allele frequency.
- New figure 19.4 illustrates the haplotype structure of whole population, whole human genomes.
- Two new figures illustrate the impact of population size on genetic drift of neutral alleles.
- New figure 19.9 models the likely impact of a small selective advantage.
- New figure 19.10 shows the worldwide geographic distribution of alleles associated with changes in human skin pigmentation.

Chapter 20

- Refocused the content on molecular evolution with fewer detailed examples of molecular evolution.

Chapter 21

- Revised, refocused content on the discipline of systems biology.
- More examples of how systems biology approaches are being used in medicine for diagnosis, treatment and development of new therapies.

Media and Supplements

Connect Genetics is a web-based assignment and assessment platform that gives students the means to better connect with their coursework, with their instructors, and with the important concepts that they will need to know for success now and in the future.

With Connect Genetics you can deliver assignments, quizzes and tests online. A robust set of questions and problems are presented and tied to the textbook's learning objectives. As an instructor, you can edit existing questions and author entirely new problems. Track individual student performance—by question, assignment or in relation to the class overall—with detailed grade reports. Integrate grade reports easily with Learning Management Systems (LMS) such as WebCT and Blackboard. And much more.

Connect Plus Genetics provides students with all the advantages of Connect Genetics, plus 24/7 online access to an eBook. Connect Plus Genetics allows students to practice important skills at their own pace and on their own schedule. Importantly, students' assessment results and instructors' feedback are all saved online—so students can continually review their progress and plot their course to success.

Flexible Options

McGraw-Hill eBooks offer a cheaper and eco-friendly alternative to traditional textbooks. By purchasing eBooks from McGraw-Hill students can save as much as 50% on selected titles delivered on the most advanced E-book platforms available. Contact your McGraw-Hill sales representative to discuss E-book packaging options.

Craft your teaching resources to match the way you teach! With McGraw-Hill Create™, www.mcgrawhillcreate.com, you can easily rearrange chapters, combine material from other content sources, and quickly upload content you have written like your course syllabus or teaching notes. Find the content you need in Create by searching through thousands of leading McGraw-Hill textbooks. Arrange your book to fit your teaching style. Create even allows you to personalize your book's appearance by selecting the cover and adding your name, school, and course information. Order a Create book and you'll receive a complimentary print review copy in 3–5 business days or a complimentary electronic review copy (eComp) via email in minutes. Go to www.mcgrawhillcreate.com today and register to experience how McGraw-Hill Create™ empowers you to teach *your* students *your* way.

Companion Website: www.mhhe.com/hartwell4
The text website includes:

- **Interactive Web Exercises** offer students an interactive way to analyze genetic data on the Web and complete exercises that test their understanding of the data.
- **Social and Ethical Issues** questions that require critical thinking analysis of the scientific issues that impact our society.
- **Portraits of Model Organisms.** Five **Genetic Portraits** are included on the book-specific website at www.mhhe.com/hartwell4 as easy-to-download PDF files. Each Genetic Portrait profiles a different model organism whose study has contributed to genetic research. The five selected were the ones chosen as the focus of the Human Genome Project.

They are:

Saccharomyces cerevisiae: Genetic Portrait of Yeast
Arabidopsis thaliana: Genetic Portrait of a Model Plant
Caenorhabditis elegans: Genetic Portrait of a Simple Multicellular Organism
Drosophila melanogaster: Genetic Portrait of the Fruit Fly
Mus musculus: Genetic Portrait of the House Mouse

We anticipate that instructors will choose to cover one or two portraits during the semester. Students may then use the specifics of the selected model organism to build an understanding of the principles and applications discussed in the book. The unique genetic manipulations and properties of each of the models make them important for addressing different biological questions using genetic analysis. In the portraits, we explain how biologists learned that the evolutionary relatedness of all organisms permits the extrapolation from a model to the analysis of other living forms. The portraits should thus help students understand how insights from one model organism can suggest general principles applicable to other organisms, including humans.

Presentation Center

In addition to the images from your book, this online digital library contains photos, artwork, animations, and other media from an array of McGraw-Hill textbooks that can be used to create customized lectures, visually enhanced tests and quizzes, compelling course websites, or attractive printed support materials.

Fully Developed Test Bank

All questions have been updated to fully align with the learning objectives and content of the text. Provided within a computerized test bank powered by McGraw-Hill's flexible electronic testing program EZ Test Online, instructors can create paper and online tests or quizzes in this easy to use program! A new tagging scheme allows you to sort questions by difficulty level, topic, and section. Imagine being able to create and access your test or quiz anywhere, at any time, without installing the testing software. Now, with EZ Test Online, instructors can select questions from multiple McGraw-Hill test banks or author their own, and then either print the test for paper distribution or give it online.

Solutions Manual/Study Guide

Extensively revised by Dr. Debra Nero of Cornell University, this manual presents the solutions to the end of chapter problems and questions along with the step-by-step logic of each solution. The manual also includes a synopsis, the objectives, and problem-solving tips for each chapter. Key figures and tables from the textbook are referenced throughout to guide student study.

Guided Tour

Integrating Genetic Concepts

Genetics: From Genes to Genomes takes an integrated approach in its presentation of genetics, thereby giving students a strong command of genetics as it is practiced today by academic and corporate researchers. Principles are related throughout the text in examples, essays, case histories, and Connections sections to make sure students fully understand the relationships between topics.

NEW! Chapter Outline

Every chapter now opens with a brief outline of the chapter's contents.

> **CHAPTER OUTLINE**
>
> - 13.1 Rearrangements of DNA Sequences
> - 13.2 Transposable Genetic Elements
> - 13.3 Rearrangements and Evolution: A Speculative Comprehensive Example
> - 13.4 Changes in Chromosome Number
> - 13.5 Emergent Technologies: Beyond the Karyotype

NEW! Summary Tables

After several major headings within the chapter, the authors have provided a short summary to help the students focus on the critical items of that section.

> Genetic studies of development in model organisms often provide key information that can be generalized to all eukaryotes. These studies can also illustrate how evolution has molded the action of conserved genes to produce diverse developmental programs in different species.

FAST FORWARD

Programmed DNA Rearrangements and the Immune System

The human immune system is a marvel of specificity and diversity. It includes close to a trillion B lymphocytes, specialized white blood cells that make more than a billion different varieties of antibodies (also called *immunoglobulins*, or *Igs*). Each B cell, however, makes antibodies against only a single bacterial or viral protein (called an *antigen* in the context of the immune response). The binding of antibody to antigen helps the body attack and neutralize invading pathogens.

One intriguing question about antibody responses is, How can a genome containing only 20,000–30,000 ($2–3 \times 10^4$) genes encode a billion (10^9) different types of antibodies? The answer is that programmed gene rearrangements, in conjunction with somatic mutations and the diverse pairing of polypeptides of different sizes, can generate roughly a billion binding specificities from a much smaller number of genes. To understand the mechanism of this diversity, it is necessary to know how antibodies are constructed and how B cells come to express the antibody-encoding genes determining specific antigen-binding sites.

The genetics of antibody formation produce specificity and diversity

All antibody molecules consist of a single copy or multiple copies of the same basic molecular unit. Four polypeptides make up this unit: two identical light chains, and two identical heavy chains. Each light chain is paired with a heavy chain (**Fig. A**). Each light

Figure A How antibody specificity emerges from molecular structure. Two heavy chains and two light chains held together by disulfide (–S–S–) bonds form the basic unit of an antibody molecule. Both heavy and light chains have variable (V) domains near their N termini, which associate to form the antigen-binding site. "Hypervariable" stretches of amino acids within the V domains vary extensively between antibody molecules. The remainder of each chain is composed of a C (constant) domain; that of the heavy chain has several subdomains (C_{H1}, hinge, C_{H2}, and C_{H3}).

and each heavy chain has a constant (C) domain and a variable (V) domain. The C domain of the heavy chain determines whether the antibody falls into one of five major classes (designated IgM, IgG, IgE, IgD, and IgA), which influence where and how an antibody functions. For example, IgM antibodies form early in an immune response and are anchored in the B-cell membrane; IgG antibodies emerge later and are secreted into the blood serum. The C domains of the light and heavy chains are not involved in determining the specificity of antibodies. Instead, the V domains of light and heavy chains come together to form the antigen-binding site, which defines an antibody's specificity.

The DNA for all domains of the heavy chain resides on chromosome 14 (**Fig. B**). This heavy-chain gene region consists of more than 100 V-encoding segments, each preceded by a promoter, several D (for diversity) segments, several J (for joining) segments, and nine C-encoding segments preceded by an enhancer (a short DNA segment that aids in the initiation of transcription by interacting with the promoter; see Chapter 16 for details). In all germ-line cells and in most somatic cells, including the cells destined to become B lymphocytes, these various gene segments lie far apart on the chromosome. During B-cell development, however, somatic rearrangements juxtapose random, individual V, D, and J segments together to form the particular variable region that will be transcribed. These rearrangements also place the newly formed variable region next to a C segment and its enhancer, and they further bring the promoter and enhancer into proximity, allowing transcription of the heavy-chain gene. RNA splicing removes the introns from the primary transcript, making a mature mRNA encoding a complete heavy-chain polypeptide.

The somatic rearrangements that shuffle the V, D, J, and C segments at random in each B cell permit expression of one, and only one, specific heavy chain. Without the rearrangements, antibody gene expression cannot occur. Random somatic rearrangements also generate the actual genes that will be expressed as light chains. The somatic rearrangements allowing the expression of antibodies thus generate enormous diversity of binding sites through the random selection and recombination of gene elements.

Several other mechanisms add to this diversity. First, each gene's DNA elements are joined imprecisely, which is perpetrated by cutting and splicing enzymes that sometimes trim DNA from or add nucleotides to the junctions of the segments they join. This imprecise joining helps create the hypervariable regions shown in Fig. A. Next, random somatic mutations in a rearranged gene's V region increase the variation of the antibody's V domain. Finally, in every B cell, two copies of a specific H chain that emerged from random DNA rearrangements combine with two copies of a specific L chain that also emerged from random DNA rearrangements to create molecules with a specific, unique binding site. The fact that any light chain can pair with any heavy chain exponentially increases the potential diversity of antibody types. For example, if there were 10^4 different light chains and 10^5 different heavy chains, there would be 10^9 possible combinations of the two.

Fast Forward Essays

This feature is one of the methods used to integrate the Mendelian principles presented early in the book with the molecular principles that will follow.

TOOLS OF GENETICS

Restriction Enzyme Recognition Sites

In many types of bacteria, the unwelcome arrival of viral DNA mobilizes minute molecular weapons known as **restriction enzymes.** Each enzyme has the twofold ability to (1) recognize a specific sequence of four to six base pairs anywhere within any DNA molecule and (2) sever a covalent bond in the sugar-phosphate backbone at a particular position within or near that sequence on each strand. When a bacterium calls up its reserve of restriction enzymes at the first sign of invasion, the ensuing shredding and dicing of selected stretches of viral DNA incapacitates the virus's genetic material and thereby restricts infection.

Since the early 1970s, geneticists have isolated more than 300 types of restriction enzymes and named them for the bacterial species in which they originate. EcoRI, for instance, comes from E. coli; Each enzyme recognizes a different base sequence and cuts the DNA strand at a precise spot in relation to that sequence. EcoRI recognizes the sequence 5′...GAATTC...3′ and cleaves between the G and the first A. The DNA of a bacteriophage called lambda (λ), for example, carries the GAATCC sequence recognized by EcoRI in five separate places; the enzyme thus cuts the linear lambda DNA at five points, breaking it

into six pieces with specific sizes. The DNA of a phage known as φX174, however, contains no EcoRI recognition sequences and is not cut by the enzyme.

Figure A illustrates EcoRI in action. Note that the recognition sequence in double-stranded DNA is symmetrical; that is, the base sequences on the two strands are identical when each is read in the 5′-to-3′ direction. Thus, each time an enzyme recognizes a short 5′-to-3′ sequence on one strand, it finds the exact same sequence in the 5′-to-3′ direction of the complementary antiparallel strand. The double-stranded recognition sequence is said to be palindromic; like the phrase "TAHITI HAT" or the number 1881, it reads the same backward and forward. (The analogy is not exact because in English only a single strand of letters or numbers is read in both directions, whereas in the DNA palindrome, reading in opposite directions occurs on opposite strands.)

Restriction enzymes made in other bacteria can recognize different DNA sequences and cleave them in different ways, as discussed in Chapter 9. When the weak hydrogen bonds between the strands dissociate, these cuts leave short, protruding single-stranded flaps known as **sticky,** or **cohesive, ends.** Like a tiny

Figure A EcoRI in action. The restriction enzyme EcoRI, recognizes a six-base-pair-long symmetrical sequence in double-stranded DNA molecules. The enzyme severs the phosphodiester bonds between the same two adjacent nucleotides on each DNA strand. Since the backbone cuts are offset from the center of the recognition site, the products of cleavage have sticky ends. Note that any sticky end produced by cleavage of any particular site in any one DNA molecule is complementary in sequence to any other sticky end made in another molecule.

Tools of Genetics Essays

Current readings explain various techniques and tools used by geneticists, including examples of applications in biology and medicine.

GENETICS AND SOCIETY

Stem Cells and Human Cloning

Stem cells are relatively undifferentiated cells that have the ability to divide indefinitely. Among their progeny are more stem cells as well as fully differentiated cells that eventually cease dividing. Embryonic stem (ES) cells, which are obtained from the undifferentiated inner-mass cells of a blastocyst (an early-stage embryo), are pluripotent. Their progeny can develop into many different cell types in the body. Adult stem cells, which are involved in tissue renewal and repair and are found in specific locations in the body, are multipotent: They can give rise only to specific types of cells. For example, hematopoietic stem cells in the bone marrow give rise to an array of red and white blood cells.

Although many investigators value embryonic stem cells because of their pluripotency, research with human embryonic stem cells is controversial because in order to start a stem cell culture, a blastocyst must be destroyed. Medical research with adult stem cells is relatively noncontroversial because these cells can be harvested from a patient's own tissues. However, adult stem cells have significant limitations. They are present in only minute quantities and are thus difficult to isolate, and they can give rise to only certain kinds of differentiated cells.

For medical researchers, the greatest excitement surrounding the use of embryonic stem cells is the potential for human **therapeutic cloning** to replace lost or damaged tissues. In a protocol known as somatic cell nuclear transfer, researchers create a cloned embryo by taking the nucleus of a somatic cell from one individual and inserting it into an egg cell whose own nucleus has been removed (**Fig. A**). This hybrid egg is then stimulated to begin embryonic divisions by treatment with electricity or certain ions. The embryo is not allowed to develop to term; instead, it is cultured for about five days in a petri plate to the blastocyst stage, at which point the ES cells in the inner cell mass are collected and placed in culture. The cultured ES cells can be induced to differentiate into many kinds of cells that might be of therapeutic value, such as nerve cells to treat Parkinson disease (Fig. A). One of the major advantages of therapeutic cloning is that the ES cells and the differentiated cells derived from them are genetically identical to the patient's own cells. Thus, there should be little chance of tissue rejection when these cells are transplanted into the patient's body.

Therapeutic cloning, which is specifically intended to produce stem cells for the treatment of ailing patients, must not be confused with **reproductive cloning,** a type of cloning designed to make genetically identical complete organisms. The idea here is to create a cloned embryo by the same method just described for therapeutic cloning. In this case, however, the embryo is implanted into the uterus of a foster mother and allowed to develop to term (Fig. A). Reproductive cloning has been successfully

Figure A Reproductive cloning and therapeutic cloning. Both procedures begin with the fusion of a somatic cell nucleus and an enucleated egg, producing a hybrid egg that divides in culture into an early embryo. In reproductive cloning, this embryo is implanted into a surrogate mother and allowed to develop until birth. In therapeutic cloning, the early embryo develops in culture to the blastocyst stage, when the embryonic stem (ES) cells are harvested. These ES cells can be induced to differentiate into various cell types.

Donor supplies unfertilized eggs.

Tissue cell donor

Cells from animal to be cloned are maintained in culture so they do not divide.

Egg cell

Somatic cell

Enucleated egg

Nucleus is removed.

Nucleus fuses with egg after electric current is applied.

The hybrid embryo grows for seven days.

Reproductive Cloning

Embryo is implanted into surrogate mother.

Cloned animal

Embryo grows into blastocyst.

Blastocyst

Therapeutic Cloning

ES cells removed and placed in culture.

ES cell culture

ES cell differentiation induced.

Nerve cells

Pancreatic cells

(Continued)

Genetics and Society Essays

Dramatic essays explore the social and ethical issues created by the multiple applications of modern genetic research.

Comprehensive Examples

Comprehensive Examples are extensive case histories or research synopses that, through text and art, summarize the main points in the preceding section or chapter and show how they relate to each other.

16.5 A Comprehensive Example: Sex Determination in *Drosophila*

Male and female *Drosophila* exhibit many sex-specific differences in morphology, biochemistry, behavior, and function of the germ line (**Fig. 16.29** on p. 576). By examining the phenotypes of flies with different chromosomal constitutions, researchers confirmed that the ratio of X to autosomal chromosomes (X:A) helps determine sex, fertility, and viability (**Table 16.2** on p. 576). They then carried out genetic experiments that showed that the X:A ratio influences sex through three independent pathways: One determines whether the flies look and ... e males or females; and ... determine whether ... ells develop as eggs or sp... ... compensation through ... ... n of X-linked genes in m...

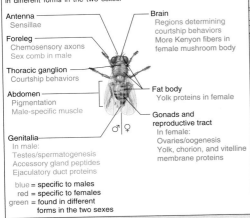

Figure 16.29 Sex-specific traits in *Drosophila*. Objects or traits shown in *blue* are specific to males. Objects or traits shown in *red* are specific to females. Objects or traits shown in *green* are found in different forms in the two sexes.

Antenna
Sensillae

Brain
Regions determining courtship behaviors
More Kenyon fibers in female mushroom body

Foreleg
Chemosensory axons
Sex comb in male

Thoracic ganglion
Courtship behaviors

Abdomen
Pigmentation
Male-specific muscle

Fat body
Yolk proteins in female

Gonads and reproductive tract
In female:
Ovaries/oogenesis
Yolk, chorion, and vitelline membrane proteins

Genitalia
In male:
Testes/spermatogenesis
Accessory gland peptides
Ejaculatory duct proteins

blue = specific to males
red = specific to females
green = found in different forms in the two sexes

TABLE 16.2		How Chromosomal Constitution Affects Phenotype in *Drosophila*
Sex Chromosomes	**X:A**	**Sex Phenotype**
Autosomal Diploids		
XO	0.5	Male (sterile)
XY	0.5	Male
XX	1.0	Female
XXY	1.0	Female
Autosomal Triploids		
XXX	1.0	Female
XYY	0.33	Male
XXY	0.66	Intersex

Connections

Medical geneticists have used their understanding of linkage, recombination, and mapping to make sense of the pedigrees presented at the beginning of this chapter (see Fig. 5.1 on p. 119). The X-linked gene for red-green colorblindness must lie very close to the gene for hemophilia A because the two are tightly coupled. In fact, the genetic distance between the two genes is only 3 m.u. The sample size in Fig. 5.1a was so small that none of the individuals in the pedigree were recombinant types. In contrast, even though hemophilia B is also on the X chromosome, it lies far enough away from the red-green colorblindness locus that the two genes recombine relatively freely. The colorblindness and hemophilia B genes may appear to be genetically unlinked in a small sample (as in Fig. 5.1b), but the actual recombination distance separating the two genes is about 36 m.u. Pedigrees pointing to two different forms of hemophilia, one very closely linked to colorblindness, the other almost not linked at all, provided one of several indications that hemophilia is determined by more than one gene (**Fig. 5.26**).

Refining the human chromosome map poses a continuous challenge for medical geneticists. The newfound potential for finding and fitting more and more DNA markers into the map (review the Fast Forward box in this chapter) enormously improves the ability to identify genes that cause disease, as discussed in Chapter 11.

Linkage and recombination are universal among lifeforms and must therefore confer important advantages to living organisms. Geneticists believe that linkage provides the potential for transmitting favorable combinations of genes intact to successive generations, while recombination produces great flexibility in generating new combinations of alleles. Some new combinations may help a species adapt to changing environmental conditions, whereas the inheritance of successfully tested combinations can preserve what has worked in the past.

Thus far, this book has examined how genes and chromosomes are transmitted. As important and useful as this knowledge is, it tells us very little about the structure and mode of action of the genetic material. In the next section (Chapters 6–8), we carry our analysis to the level of DNA, the actual molecule of heredity. In Chapter 6, we look at DNA structure and learn how the DNA molecule carries genetic information. In Chapter 7, we describe how geneticists defined the gene as a localized region of DNA containing many nucleotides that together encode the information to make a protein. In Chapter 8, we examine how the cellular machinery interprets the genetic information in genes to produce the multitude of phenotypes that make up an organism.

Figure 5.26 A genetic map of part of the human X chromosome.

Hunter syndrome
Hemophilia B

Fragile X syndrome

Hemophilia A

G6PD deficiency: Favism
Drug-sensitive anemia
Chronic hemolytic anemia

Colorblindness (several forms)
Dyskeratosis congenita
Deafness with stapes fixation
TKCR syndrome

Adrenoleukodystrophy
Adrenomyeloneuropathy

Emery muscular dystrophy
SED tarda
Spastic paraplegia, X-linked

Connections

Each chapter closes with a Connections section that serves as a bridge between the topics in the just-completed chapter and those in the upcoming chapter or chapters.

Visualizing Genetics

Full-color illustrations and photographs bring the printed word to life. These visual reinforcements support and further clarify the topics discussed throughout the text.

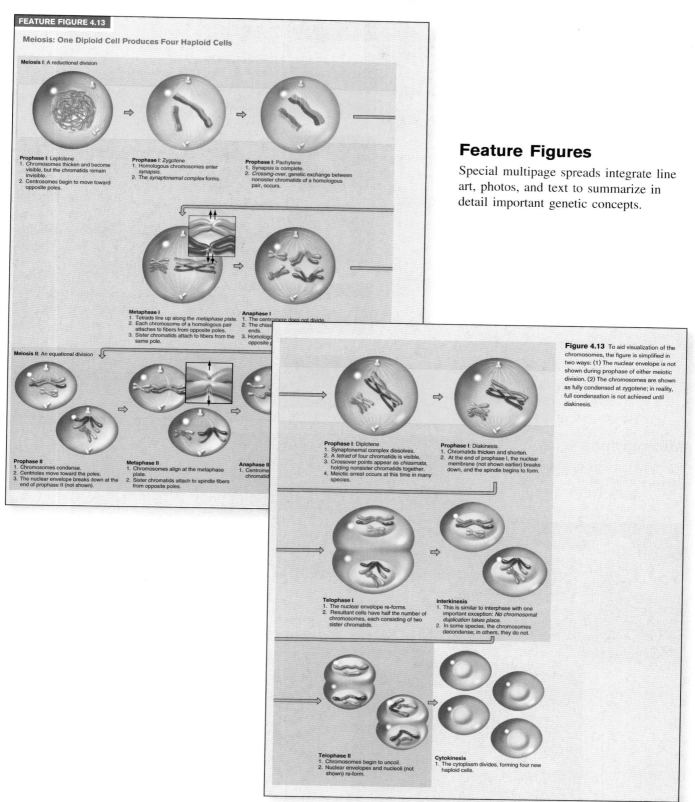

Feature Figures

Special multipage spreads integrate line art, photos, and text to summarize in detail important genetic concepts.

FEATURE FIGURE 4.13

Meiosis: One Diploid Cell Produces Four Haploid Cells

Meiosis I: A reductional division

Prophase I: Leptotene
1. Chromosomes thicken and become visible, but the chromatids remain invisible.
2. Centrosomes begin to move toward opposite poles.

Prophase I: Zygotene
1. Homologous chromosomes enter *synapsis*.
2. The *synaptonemal complex* forms.

Prophase I: Pachytene
1. Synapsis is complete.
2. *Crossing-over*, genetic exchange between nonsister chromatids of a homologous pair, occurs.

Metaphase I
1. Tetrads line up along the *metaphase plate*.
2. Each chromosome of a homologous pair attaches to fibers from opposite poles.
3. Sister chromatids attach to fibers from the same pole.

Anaphase I
1. The centromere does not divide.
2. The chias ends.
3. Homolog opposite p

Meiosis II: An equational division

Prophase II
1. Chromosomes condense.
2. Centrioles move toward the poles.
3. The nuclear envelope breaks down at the end of prophase II (not shown).

Metaphase II
1. Chromosomes align at the metaphase plate.
2. Sister chromatids attach to spindle fibers from opposite poles.

Anaphase II
1. Centrome chromatid

Figure 4.13 To aid visualization of the chromosomes, the figure is simplified in two ways: (1) The nuclear envelope is not shown during prophase of either meiotic division. (2) The chromosomes are shown as fully condensed at zygotene; in reality, full condensation is not achieved until diakinesis.

Prophase I: Diplotene
1. Synaptonemal complex dissolves.
2. A *tetrad* of four chromatids is visible.
3. Crossover points appear as *chiasmata*, holding nonsister chromatids together.
4. Meiotic arrest occurs at this time in many species.

Prophase I: Diakinesis
1. Chromatids thicken and shorten.
2. At the end of prophase I, the nuclear membrane (not shown earlier) breaks down, and the spindle begins to form.

Telophase I
1. The nuclear envelope re-forms.
2. Resultant cells have half the number of chromosomes, each consisting of two sister chromatids.

Interkinesis
1. This is similar to interphase with one important exception: *No chromosomal duplication takes place.*
2. In some species, the chromosomes decondense; in others, they do not.

Telophase II
1. Chromosomes begin to uncoil.
2. Nuclear envelopes and nucleoli (not shown) re-form.

Cytokinesis
1. The cytoplasm divides, forming four new haploid cells.

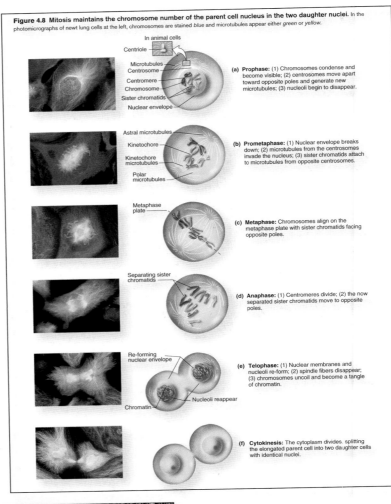

Figure 4.8 Mitosis maintains the chromosome number of the parent cell nucleus in the two daughter nuclei. In the photomicrographs of newt lung cells at the left, chromosomes are stained *blue* and microtubules appear either *green* or *yellow*.

In animal cells

(a) Prophase: (1) Chromosomes condense and become visible; (2) centrosomes move apart toward opposite poles and generate new microtubules; (3) nucleoli begin to disappear.

(b) Prometaphase: (1) Nuclear envelope breaks down; (2) microtubules from the centrosomes invade the nucleus; (3) sister chromatids attach to microtubules from opposite centrosomes.

(c) Metaphase: Chromosomes align on the metaphase plate with sister chromatids facing opposite poles.

(d) Anaphase: (1) Centromeres divide; (2) the now separated sister chromatids move to opposite poles.

(e) Telophase: (1) Nuclear membranes and nucleoli re-form; (2) spindle fibers disappear; (3) chromosomes uncoil and become a tangle of chromatin.

(f) Cytokinesis: The cytoplasm divides, splitting the elongated parent cell into two daughter cells with identical nuclei.

Process Figures

Step-by-step descriptions allow the student to walk through a compact summary of important details.

Micrographs

Stunning micrographs bring the genetics world to life.

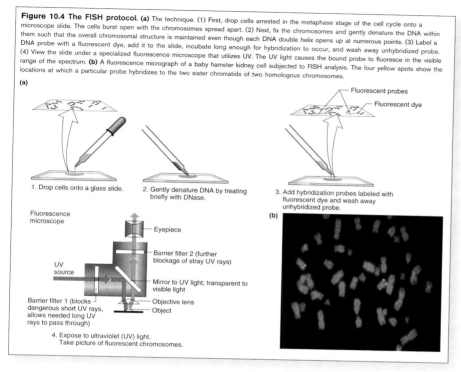

Figure 10.4 The FISH protocol. (a) The technique. (1) First, drop cells arrested in the metaphase stage of the cell cycle onto a microscope slide. The cells burst open with the chromosomes spread apart. (2) Next, fix the chromosomes and gently denature the DNA within them such that the overall chromosomal structure is maintained even though each DNA double helix opens up at numerous points. (3) Label a DNA probe with a fluorescent dye, add it to the slide, incubate long enough for hybridization to occur, and wash away unhybridized probe. (4) View the slide under a specialized fluorescence microscope that utilizes UV. The UV light causes the bound probe to fluoresce in the visible range of the spectrum. **(b)** A fluorescence micrograph of a baby hamster kidney cell subjected to FISH analysis. The four yellow spots show the locations at which a particular probe hybridizes to the two sister chromatids of two homologous chromosomes.

Experiment and Technique Figures

Illustrations of performed experiments andgenetic analysis techniques highlight how scientific concepts and processes are developed.

Comparative Figures

Comparison illustrations lay out the basic differences of often confusing principles.

Figure 3.8 Plant incompatibility systems prevent self-fertilization and thus promote outbreeding and allele proliferation. A pollen grain carrying a self-incompatibility allele that is identical to either of the two alleles carried by a potential female parent cannot grow a pollen tube; as a result, fertilization cannot take place.

Solving Genetics Problems

The best way for students to assess and increase their understanding of genetics is to practice through problems. Found at the end of each chapter, problem sets assist students in evaluating their grasp of key concepts and allow them to apply what they have learned to real-life issues.

problem-solving skills. The answers to select problems can be found in the back of this text.

Review Problems

Problems are organized by chapter section and in order of increasing difficulty to help students develop strong

Solved Problems

Solved problems offer step-by-step guidance needed to understand the problem-solving process.

Acknowledgements

The creation of a project of this scope is never solely the work of the authors. We are grateful to our colleagues around the world who took the time to review the previous edition and make suggestions for improvement. Their willingness to share their expectations and expertise was a tremendous help to us.

Edward Bernstine, *Bay Path College*
Miranda Brockett, *Georgia Institute of Technology*
Yury Chernoff, *Georgia Institute of Technology*
John Elder, *Valdosta State University*
Aboubaker Elkharroubi, *Johns Hopkins University*
David Foltz, *Louisiana State University*
Wayne Forrester, *Indiana University*
Kent Golic, *University of Utah–Salt Lake City*
Christine Gray, *University of Puget Sound*
Frank Healy, *Trinity University*
Nancy Hollingsworth, *Stony Brook University*
Jackie Horn, *Houston Baptist University*
Deborah Hoshizaki, *University of Nevada*
Jim Jaynes, *Thomas Jefferson University*
Mark Jensen, *University of Georgia*
Kathleen Karrer, *Marquette University*
Kevin Livingstone, *Trinity University*

Kirill Lobachev, *Georgia Institute of Technology, School of Biology*
Mark Meade, *Jacksonville State University*
Steve Mount, *University of Maryland*
Brian Ring, *Valdosta State University*
Agnes Southgate, *College of Charleston, SC*
Ed Stephenson, *University of Alabama*
Barbara Taylor, *Oregon State University*
Jim Thompson, *University of Oklahoma*
Tara N. Turley-Stoulig, *Southeastern Louisiana University*
Jennifer Waldo, *SUNY New Paltz*
Scott Weitze, *San Francisco State University*
Andrew Wood, *Southern Illinois University–Carbondale*

A special thank-you to Jody Larson and Martha Hamblin for their extensive feedback on this fourth edition. We would also like to thank the highly skilled publishing professionals at McGraw-Hill who guided the development and production of the fourth edition of **Genetics: From Genes to Genomes:** Janice Roerig-Blong for her sponsorship and support; Fran Schreiber for her organizational skills and tireless work to tie up all loose ends; and Vicki Krug, Sheila Frank and the entire production team for their careful attention to detail and ability to move the schedule along.

Genetics: The Study of Biological Information

Information can be stored in many ways including the patterns of letters and words in books and the sequence of nucleotides in DNA molecules.

Genetics, the science of heredity, is at its core the study of biological information. All living organisms—from single-celled bacteria and protozoa to multicellular plants and animals—must store, replicate, transmit to the next generation, and use vast quantities of information to develop, reproduce, and survive in their environments (**Fig. 1.1**). Geneticists examine how organisms pass biological information on to their progeny and how they use it during their lifetime.

This book introduces you to the field of genetics as currently practiced in the early twenty-first century. Several broad themes recur throughout this presentation. First, we know that biological information is encoded in DNA, and that the proteins responsible for an organism's many functions are built from this code. These elements interact to form complex systems by which function is controlled. We also have found that all living forms are closely related at the molecular level, and recent technology has revealed that genomes have a modular construction that has allowed rapid evolution of complexity. With the aid of high-speed computers and other technologies, we can now study genomes at the level of DNA sequence. Finally, our focus here is on human genetics and the application of genetic discoveries to human problems.

In the remainder of this chapter, we introduce these themes. Keep them in mind as you delve into the details of genetics.

1.1 DNA: The Fundamental Information Molecule of Life

The process of evolution has taken close to 4 billion years to generate the amazingly efficient mechanisms for storing, replicating, expressing, and diversifying biological information seen in organisms now inhabiting the earth. The linear DNA molecule stores biological information in units known as nucleotides. Within each DNA molecule, the sequence of the four letters of the DNA alphabet—G, C, A, and T—specify which proteins an organism will make as well as when and where protein synthesis will occur. The letters refer to the bases—guanine, cytosine, adenine, and thymine—that are components of the nucleotide building blocks of DNA. The DNA molecule itself is a double strand of nucleotides carrying complementary G–C or A–T base pairs (**Fig. 1.2**). These complementary base pairs can bind together through hydrogen bonds. The molecular complementarity of double-stranded DNA is its most important property and the key to understanding how DNA functions.

Figure 1.1 The biological information in DNA generates an enormous diversity of living organisms.

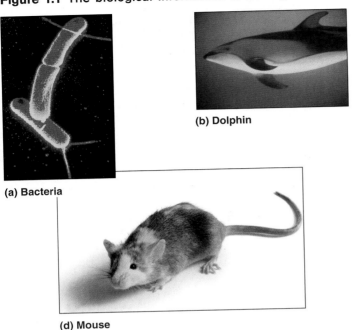

(a) Bacteria

(b) Dolphin

(c) Plants

(d) Mouse

(e) Humans

Figure 1.2 Complementary base pairs are a key feature of the DNA molecule.

A single strand of DNA is composed of nucleotide subunits each consisting of a deoxyribose sugar (depicted here as a *white pentagon*), a phosphate (depicted as a *yellow circle*), and one of four nitrogenous bases—adenine, thymine, cytosine, or guanine (designated as *lavender* or *green* A's, T's, C's, or G's). The chemical structure of the bases enables A to associate tightly with T, and C to associate tightly with G through hydrogen bonding. Thus the two strands are complementary to each other. The arrows labeled 5′ to 3′ show that the strands have opposite orientation.

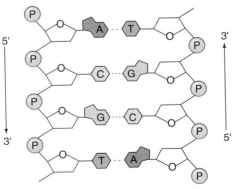

Figure 1.3 An automated DNA sequencer.

This instrument can sequence about 1,000,000 base pairs a day and newer technologies are 100 to 1000 times faster.

Although the DNA molecule is three-dimensional, most of its information is one-dimensional and digital. The information is one-dimensional because it is encoded as a specific sequence of letters along the length of the molecule. It is digital because each unit of information—one of the four letters of the DNA alphabet—is discrete. Because genetic information is digital, it can be stored as readily in a computer memory as in a DNA molecule. Indeed, the combined power of DNA sequencers (**Fig. 1.3**), computers, and DNA synthesizers makes it possible to interpret, store, replicate, and transmit genetic information electronically from one place to another anywhere on the planet. This information can then be used to synthesize an exact replica of a portion of the originally sequenced DNA molecule.

The DNA regions that encode proteins are called *genes.* Just as the limited number of letters in a written alphabet places no restrictions on the stories one can tell, so too the limited number of letters in the genetic code alphabet places no restrictions on the kinds of proteins and thus the kinds of organisms genetic information can define.

Within the cells of an organism, DNA molecules carrying the genes are assembled into *chromosomes:* organelles that package and manage the storage, duplication, expression, and evolution of DNA (**Fig. 1.4**). The entire collection of

Figure 1.4 One of 24 different types of human chromosomes. Each chromosome contains thousands of genes.

chromosomes in each cell of an organism is its *genome.* Human cells, for example, contain 24 distinct kinds of chromosomes carrying approximately 3×10^9 base pairs and roughly 20,000–30,000 genes. The amount of information that can be encoded in this size genome is equivalent to 6 million pages of text containing 250 words per page, with each letter corresponding to one *base pair,* or pair of nucleotides.

To appreciate the long journey from a finite amount of genetic information easily storable on a computer disk to the production of a human being, we must examine proteins, the molecules that determine how complex systems of cells, tissues, and organisms function.

> DNA, a macromolecular chain composed of four nucleic acids, is the repository of the genetic code. Genes are DNA regions that encode proteins.

1.2 Proteins: The Functional Molecules of Life Processes

Although no single characteristic distinguishes living organisms from inanimate matter, you would have little trouble deciding which entities in a group of 20 objects are alive. Over time, these living organisms, governed by the laws of physics and chemistry as well as a genetic program, would be able to reproduce themselves. Most of the organisms would also have an elaborate and complicated structure that would change over time—sometimes drastically, as when an insect larva metamorphoses into an adult. Yet another characteristic of life is the ability to move. Animals swim, fly, walk, or run, while plants grow toward or away from light. Still another characteristic is the capacity to adapt selectively to the environment. Finally, a key characteristic of living organisms is the ability to use sources of energy and matter to grow—that is, the ability to convert foreign material into their own body parts. The chemical and physical reactions that carry out these conversions are known as *metabolism.*

Figure 1.5 Proteins are polymers of amino acids that fold in three dimensions. The specific sequence of amino acids in a chain determines the precise three-dimensional shape of the protein. **(a)** Chemical formulas for two amino acids: alanine and tyrosine. All amino acids have a basic amino group (–NH) at one end and an acidic carboxyl group (–COOH) at the other. The specific side chain determines the amino acid's chemical properties. **(b)** A comparison of equivalent segments in the chains of two digestive proteins, chymotrypsin and elastase. The *red lines* connect sites in the two sequences that carry identical amino acids; the two chains differ at all the other sites shown. **(c)** Schematic drawings of the hemoglobin β chain (*green*) and lactate dehydrogenase (*purple*) show the different three-dimensional shapes determined by different amino acid sequences.

Hemoglobin β chain

Lactate dehydrogenase

Most properties of living organisms ultimately arise from the class of molecules known as *proteins*—large polymers composed of hundreds to thousands of amino acid subunits strung together in long chains; each chain folds into a specific three-dimensional conformation dictated by the sequence of its amino acids (**Fig. 1.5**). There

Figure 1.6 Diagram of the conversion of biological information from a one- to a three- and finally a four-dimensional state.

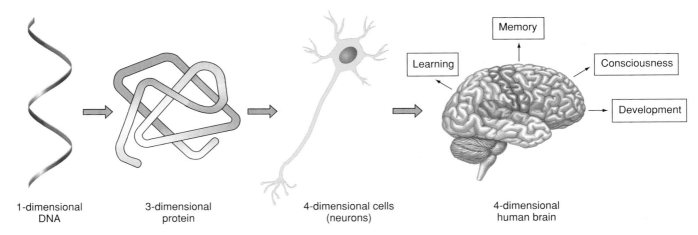

1-dimensional
DNA

3-dimensional
protein

4-dimensional cells
(neurons)

4-dimensional
human brain

are 20 different amino acids. The information in the DNA of genes dictates, via a genetic code, the order of amino acids in a protein molecule.

You can think of proteins as constructed from a set of 20 different kinds of snap beads distinguished by color and shape; if you were to arrange the beads in any order, make strings of a thousand beads each, and then fold or twist the chains into shapes dictated by the order of their beads, you would be able to make a nearly infinite number of different three-dimensional shapes. The astonishing diversity of three-dimensional protein structure generates the extraordinary diversity of protein function that is the basis of each organism's complex and adaptive behavior. The structure and shape of the hemoglobin protein, for example, allow it to transport oxygen in the bloodstream and release it to the tissues. The proteins myosin and actin can slide together to allow muscle contraction. Chymotrypsin and elastase are enzymes that help break down other proteins. Most of the properties associated with life emerge from the constellation of protein molecules that an organism synthesizes according to instructions contained in its DNA.

function both within individual cells and among groups of cells within an organism. Here we use **biological system** to mean any complex network of interacting molecules or groups of cells that function in a coordinated manner through dynamic signaling. Several layers of biological systems exist. The human pancreas, for example, is an isolated biological system that operates within the larger biological system of the human body and mind. A whole community of animals, such as a colony of ants that functions in a highly coordinated manner, is also a biological system.

The information that defines any biological system is four-dimensional because it is constantly changing over the three dimensions of space and the one dimension of time. One of the most complex examples of this level of biological information (other than an entire human being) is the human brain with its 10^{11} (100,000,000,000) neurons connected through perhaps 10^{18} (1,000,000,000,000,000,000) junctions known as synapses. From this enormous biological network, based ultimately on the information in DNA and protein, arise properties such as memory, consciousness, and the ability to learn (**Fig. 1.6**).

> Proteins, macromolecules containing up to 20 different amino acids in a sequence encoded in DNA, are responsible for most biological functions.

> A biological system is a network of interactions between molecules or groups of cells to accomplish coordinated function.

1.3 Complex Systems and Molecular Interactions

In addition to DNA and protein, a third level of biological information encompasses dynamic interactions among DNA, protein, and other types of molecules as well as interactions among cells and tissues. These complex interactive networks represent *biological systems* that

1.4 Molecular Similarities of All Life-Forms

The evolution of biological information is a fascinating story spanning the 4 billion years of earth's history. Many biologists think that RNA was the first information-processing molecule to appear. Very similar to DNA, RNA molecules are also composed of four subunits: the bases

G, C, A, and U (for uracil, which replaces the T of DNA). Like DNA, RNA has the capacity to store, replicate, mutate, and express information; like proteins, RNA can fold in three dimensions to produce molecules capable of catalyzing the chemistry of life. RNA molecules, however, are intrinsically unstable. Thus, it is probable that the more stable DNA took over the linear information storage and replication functions of RNA, while proteins, with their far greater capacity for diversity, preempted the functions derived from RNA's three-dimensional folding. With this division of labor, RNA became an intermediary in converting the information in DNA into the sequence of amino acids in protein (**Fig. 1.7a**). The separation that

placed information storage in DNA and biological function in proteins was so successful that all organisms alive today descend from the first organisms that happened upon this molecular specialization.

The evidence for the common origin of all living forms is present in their DNA sequences. All living organisms use essentially the same genetic code in which various triplet groupings of the 4 letters of the DNA and RNA alphabets encode the 20 letters of the amino acid alphabet. (**Fig. 1.7b**).

The relatedness of all living organisms is also evident from comparisons of genes with similar functions in very different organisms. For example, there is striking similarity between the genes for many proteins in bacteria, yeast, plants, worms, flies, mice, and humans (**Fig. 1.8**). Moreover, it is often possible to place a gene from one organism into the genome of a very different organism and see it function normally in the new environment. Human genes that help regulate cell division, for example, can replace related genes in yeast and enable the yeast cells to function normally.

One of the most striking examples of relatedness at this level of biological information was uncovered in studies of eye development. Both insects and vertebrates (including humans) have eyes, but they are of very different types (**Fig. 1.9**). Biologists had long assumed that the evolution of eyes occurred independently, and in many evolution textbooks, eyes are used as an example of *convergent evolution,* in which structurally unrelated but functionally analogous organs emerge in different species

Figure 1.7 RNA is an intermediary in the conversion of DNA information into protein via the genetic code. (a) The linear bases of DNA are copied through molecular complementarity into the linear bases of RNA. The bases of RNA are read three at a time, that is, as triplets, to encode the amino acid subunits of proteins. **(b)** The genetic code dictionary specifies the relationship between RNA triplets and the amino acid subunits of proteins.

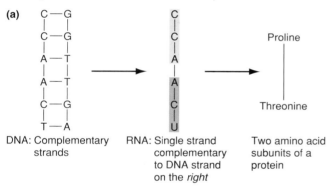

(a)

DNA: Complementary strands

RNA: Single strand complementary to DNA strand on the *right*

Two amino acid subunits of a protein

Proline

Threonine

(b)

Second letter

First letter / Third letter

	U	C	A	G	
U	UUU UUC } Phe UUA UUG } Leu	UCU UCC UCA UCG } Ser	UAU UAC } Tyr UAA Stop UAG Stop	UGU UGC } Cys UGA Stop UGG Trp	U C A G
C	CUU CUC CUA CUG } Leu	CCU CCC CCA CCG } Pro	CAU CAC } His CAA CAG } Gln	CGU CGC CGA CGG } Arg	U C A G
A	AUU AUC } Ile AUA AUG Met	ACU ACC ACA ACG } Thr	AAU AAC } Asn AAA AAG } Lys	AGU AGC } Ser AGA AGG } Arg	U C A G
G	GUU GUC GUA GUG } Val	GCU GCC GCA GCG } Ala	GAU GAC } Asp GAA GAG } Glu	GGU GGC GGA GGG } Gly	U C A G

Figure 1.8 Comparisons of gene products in different species provide evidence for the relatedness of living organisms. This chart shows the amino acid sequence for equivalent portions of the cytochrome C protein in six species: *Saccharomyces cerevisiae* (yeast), *Arabidopsis thaliana* (a weedlike flowering plant), *Caenorhabditis elegans* (a nematode), *Drosophila melanogaster* (the fruit fly), *Mus musculus* (the house mouse), and *Homo sapiens* (humans). Consult Fig. 1.5 for the key to amino acid names.

S. cerevisiae	GPNLHGIFGRHSGQVKGYSYTDANINKNVKW
A. thaliana	GPELHGLFGRKTGSVAGYSYTDANKQKGIEW
C. elegans	GPTLHGVIGRTSGTVSGFDYSAANKNKGVVW
D. melanogaster	GPNLHGLIGRKTGQAAGFAYTDANKAKGITW
M. musculus	GPNLHGLFGRKTGQAAGFSYTDANKNKGITW
H. sapiens	GPNLHGLFGRKTGQAPGYSYTAANKNKGIIW
	** *** . ** . * . * . ** . . . *

S. cerevisiae	DEDSMSEYLTNPKKYIPGTKMAFAGLKKEKDR
A. thaliana	KDDTLFEYLENPKKYIPGTKMAFGGLKKPKDR
C. elegans	TKETLFEYLLNPKKYIPGTKMVFAGLKKADER
D. melanogaster	NEDTLFEYLENPKKYIPGTKMIFAGLKKPNER
M. musculus	GEDTLMEYLENPKKYIPGTKMIFAGIKKKGER
H. sapiens	GEDTLMEYLENPKKYIPGTKMIFVGIKKKEER
	. . . ** ** ****** * * . ** . *

* Indicates identical and . indicates similar

Figure 1.9 The eyes of insects and humans have a common ancestor. (a) A fly eye and **(b)** human eye.

(a)   (b)

Figure 1.10 How genes arise by duplication and divergence. Duplications of ancestral *gene A* followed by mutations and DNA rearrangements have generated a family of related genes. The *dark blue* and *red* bands indicate the different exons of the genes while the *light blue* bands represent introns.

as a result of natural selection. Studies of a gene called the *Pax6* gene have turned this view upside down.

Mutations in the *Pax6* gene lead to a failure of eye development in both people and mice, and molecular studies have suggested that *Pax6* might play a central role in the initiation of eye development in all vertebrates. Remarkably, when the human *Pax6* gene is expressed in cells along the surface of the fruit fly body, it induces numerous little eyes to develop there. This result demonstrates that after 600 million years of divergent evolution, both vertebrates and insects still share the same main control switch for initiating eye development. (You will learn more about *Pax6* in Chapter 18.)

The usefulness of the relatedness and unity at all levels of biological information cannot be overstated. It means that in many cases, the experimental manipulation of organisms known as *model organisms* can shed light on complex networks in humans. If genes similar to human genes function in simple model organisms such as fruit flies or bacteria, scientists can determine gene function and regulation in these experimentally manipulable organisms and bring these insights to an understanding of the human organism. The same is true of the shared informational pathways such as DNA replication and protein synthesis. You can visit our website at www.mhhe.com/hartwell4 for detailed genetic portraits of five key model organisms: the yeast *S. cerevisiae,* the simple plant known as *A. thaliana,* the roundworm *C. elegans,* the fruit fly *D. melanogaster,* and the house mouse *M. musculus.*

> Living organisms exhibit marked similarities at the molecular level; certain genes have been carried through the evolution of widely divergent species.

1.5 The Modular Construction of Genomes

We have seen that roughly 20,000–30,000 genes direct human growth and development. How did such complexity arise? Recent technical advances have enabled

researchers to complete structural analyses of the entire genome of many organisms. The information obtained reveals that families of genes have arisen by duplication of a primordial gene; after duplication, mutations and rearrangements may cause the two copies to diverge from each other (**Fig. 1.10**). In both mice and humans, for example, five different hemoglobin genes produce five different hemoglobin molecules at successive stages of development, with each protein functioning in a slightly different way to fulfill different needs for oxygen transport. The set of five hemoglobin genes arose from a single primordial gene by several duplications followed by slight divergences in structure.

Duplication followed by divergence underlies the evolution of new genes with new functions. This principle appears to have been built into the genome structure of all eukaryotic organisms. The protein-coding region of most genes is subdivided into as many as 10 or more small pieces (called *exons*), separated by DNA that does not code for protein (called *introns*) as shown in Fig. 1.10. This modular construction facilitates the rearrangement of different modules from different genes to create new combinations during evolution. It is likely that this process of modular reassortment facilitated the rapid diversification of living forms about 570 million years ago (see Fig. 1.10).

The tremendous advantage of the duplication and divergence of existing pieces of genetic information is evident in the history of life's evolution (**Table 1.1**). *Prokaryotic* cells such as bacteria, which do not have a membrane-bounded nucleus, evolved about 3.7 billion years ago; *eukaryotic* cells such as algae, which have a membrane-bounded nucleus, emerged around 2 billion years ago; and multicellular eukaryotic organisms appeared 600–700 million years ago. Then, at about 570 million years ago, within the relatively short evolutionary time of roughly 20–50 million years known as the Cambrian

TABLE 1.1	Fossil Evidence for Some Major Stages in the Evolution of Life

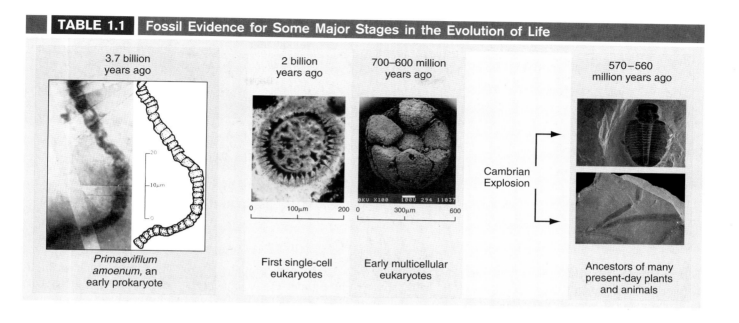

3.7 billion years ago	2 billion years ago	700–600 million years ago		570–560 million years ago
Primaevifilum amoenum, an early prokaryote	First single-cell eukaryotes	Early multicellular eukaryotes	Cambrian Explosion	Ancestors of many present-day plants and animals

explosion, the multicellular life-forms diverged into a bewildering array of organisms, including primitive vertebrates.

A fascinating question is, how could the multicellular forms achieve such enormous diversity in only 20–50 million years? The answer lies, in part, in the hierarchic organization of the information encoded in chromosomes. Exons are arranged into genes; genes duplicate and diverge to generate multigene families; and multigene families sometimes rapidly expand to gene superfamilies containing hundreds of related genes. In both mouse and human adults, for example, the immune system is encoded by a gene superfamily composed of hundreds of closely related but slightly divergent genes. With the emergence of each successively larger informational unit, evolution gains the ability to duplicate increasingly complex informational modules through single genetic events.

Probably even more important for the evolution of complexity is the rapid change of regulatory networks that specify how genes behave (that is, when, where, and to what degree they are expressed) during development. For example, the two-winged fly evolved from a four-winged ancestor not because of changes in gene-encoded structural proteins, but rather because of a rewiring of the regulatory network, which converted one pair of wings into two balancing organs known as haltere (**Fig. 1.11**).

Duplication of genes has allowed divergence of copies and the potential for evolution of new functions. In eukaryotes, separated exons composing a single gene allow potential rearrangements and rapid diversification.

Figure 1.11 Two-winged and four-winged flies. Geneticists converted a contemporary normal two-winged fly to a four-winged insect resembling the fly's evolutionary antecedent. They accomplished this by mutating a key element in the fly's regulatory network. Note the club-shaped halteres behind the wings of the fly at the top.

1.6 Modern Genetic Techniques

The complexity of living systems has developed over 4 billion years from the continuous amplification and refinement of genetic information. The simplest bacterial

Figure 1.12 Five model organisms whose genomes were sequenced as part of the Human Genome Project. The chart indicates genome size in millions of base pairs, or megabases (Mb). It also shows the approximate number of genes for each organism.

Organism	E. coli	S. cerevisiae	C. elegans	D. melanogaster	Mus musculus
Genome size: (in megabases)	4.5 Mb	16 Mb	100 Mb	130 Mb	3000 Mb
Number of genes	4500	6200	19,200	13,900	20,000–30,000

cells contain about 1000 genes that interact in complex networks. Yeast cells, the simplest eukaryotic cells, contain about 6000 genes. Nematodes (roundworms) and fruit flies contain roughly 14,000–19,000 genes; humans may have as many as 30,000 genes. The Human Genome Project, in addition to completing the sequencing of the entire human genome, has sequenced the genomes of *E. coli,* yeast, the nematode, the fruit fly, and the mouse (**Fig. 1.12**). Each of these organisms has provided valuable insights into biology in general and human biology in particular.

With modern genetic techniques, researchers can dissect the complexity of a genome piece by piece, although the task is daunting. The logic used in genetic dissection is quite simple: inactivate a gene in a model organism and observe the consequences. For example, loss of a gene for visual pigment produces fruit flies with white eyes instead of eyes of the normal red color. One can thus conclude that the protein product of this gene plays a key role in the development of eye pigmentation. From their study of model organisms, researchers are amassing a detailed picture of the complexity of living systems.

Even though the power of genetic techniques is astonishing, however, the complexity of biological systems is difficult to comprehend. Knowing everything there is to know about each of the human genes and proteins would not reveal how a human results from this particular ensemble. For example, the human nervous system is a network of 10^{11} neurons with perhaps 10^{18} connections. The complexity of the system is far too great to be encoded by a simple correspondence between genes and neurons or genes and connections. Moreover, the remarkable properties of the system, such as learning, memory, and personality, do not arise solely from the genes and proteins; network interactions and the environment also play a role. The goal of understanding higher-order processes that arise from interacting networks of genes, proteins, cells, and organs is one of the most challenging aspects of modern biology.

The new global tools of genomics—such as high-throughput DNA sequencers, genotypers, and large-scale DNA arrays (also called DNA chips)—have the capacity to analyze thousands of genes rapidly and accurately. These global tools are not specific to a particular system or organism; rather, they can be used to study the genes of all living things.

The DNA chip is a powerful example of a global genomic tool. Individual chips are subdivided into arrays of microscopic blocks that each contain a unique string of DNA units (**Fig. 1.13a**). When a chip is exposed to a complex mixture of fluorescently labeled nucleic acid—such as DNA or RNA from any cell type or sample—the unique string in each microscopic block can bind to and detect a specific complementary sequence. This type of binding is known as *hybridization* (**Fig. 1.13b**). A computer-driven microscope can then analyze the bound sequences of the hundreds of thousands of blocks on the chip, and special software can enter this information into a database (**Fig. 1.13c**).

The potential of DNA chips is enormous for both research and clinical purposes. Already chips with over 400,000 different detectors can provide simultaneous information on the presence or absence of 400,000 discrete DNA or RNA sequences in a complex sample. And they can do it within hours. Here is one example. Now that the sequence of all human genes is known, unique stretches of DNA representing each of the 20,000–30,000 human genes can be placed on a chip and used to determine the complete set of genes copied into RNA in any human cell type at any stage of development or differentiation. Computer-driven comparisons can contrast the genes expressed in different cell types, for example, in neurons versus muscle cells, making it possible to determine which genes contribute to the construction of various cell types. Scientists have already created catalogs of the genes expressed in different cell types and have discovered that some genes, called "housekeeping genes," are expressed in nearly all cell types, whereas other genes are expressed only in certain specialized cells. This

Figure 1.13 One use of a DNA chip. (a) Schematic drawing of the components of a DNA chip. **(b)** 1. Preparing complementary DNA, or cDNA, with a fluorescent tag from the RNA of a group of cells. 2. The hybridization of chip DNA to fluorescent cDNA from untreated and drug-treated cells. **(c)** Computerized analysis of chip hybridizations makes it possible to compare gene activity in any two types of cells.

(a) Schematic drawing of a DNA chip

(Chip microarray)

Segment of a chip

Spot containing copies of a single DNA molecule

Part of one DNA strand

DNA bases

(b) The detection of DNA-cDNA hybridization

1.

Cells are broken, RNA is extracted, the RNA is copied to produce complementary DNA (cDNA), and the cDNA is labeled with fluorescent tags. The cDNA represents genes that are active, that is, being converted to protein via RNA.

2. cDNA from untreated cells

cDNA

Pair of complementary bases

chip DNA

cDNA from treated cells

Examples of reactions

(c) Computer analysis to identify genes that respond to drug treatment

- Gene that strongly increased activity in treated cells
- Gene that strongly decreased activity in treated cells
- Gene that was equally active in treated and untreated cells
- Gene that was inactive in both groups

knowledge of the relation between particular genes and particular cell types is helping us understand how the cellular specialization necessary for the construction of all human organs arises.

In medicine, clinical researchers have used DNA chip technology to identify genes whose expression increases or decreases when tumor cells are treated with an experi-

mental cancer drug (Fig. 1.13b–c). Changes in the patterns of gene expression may provide clues to the mechanisms by which the drug might inhibit tumor growth. In a related but slightly different application of the same idea, researchers can assess the inherent differences between breast cancers that respond well to a particular drug therapy and those that do not (that is, that recur despite treatment). Using microarray analysis of patients' tumors can predict with considerable accuracy whether a specific drug will be effective against their particular type of cancer.

> Modern techniques such as computerized processing and mechanized sequencing, DNA amplification, and hybridization have provided knowledge of genomes at the sequence level.

1.7 Human Genetics

In the mid-1990s, a majority of scientists who responded to a survey conducted by *Science* magazine rated genetics as the most important field of science for the next decade. One reason is that the powerful tools of genetics open up the possibility of understanding biology, including human biology, from the molecular level up to the level of the whole organism.

The Human Genome Project, by changing the way we view biology and genetics, has led to a significant paradigm change: the systems approach to biology and medicine. The systems approach seeks to study the relationships of all the elements in a biological system as it undergoes genetic perturbation or biological activation (see Chapter 10). This is a fundamental change from the study of complex systems one gene or protein at a time.

Molecular studies may lead to predictive and preventive medicine

Over the next 25 years, geneticists will identify hundreds of genes with variations that predispose people to many types of disease: cardiovascular, cancerous, immunological, mental, metabolic. Some mutations will always cause disease; others will only predispose to disease. For example, a change in a specific single DNA base (that is, a change in one DNA unit) in the β-*globin* gene will nearly always cause sickle-cell anemia, a painful, life-threatening condition that leads to severe anemia. By contrast, a mutation in the *breast cancer 1 (BRCA1)* gene increases the risk of breast cancer to between 40% and 80% depending on the population in a woman carrying one copy of the mutation. This conditional state arises because the *BRCA1* gene interacts with environmental factors that affect the probability of activating the cancerous condition, and because various forms of other genes modify expression of the *BRCA1* gene. Physicians may be able to use DNA diagnostics—a collection of techniques for characterizing genes—to analyze an individual's DNA

for genes that predispose to some diseases. With this genetic profile, they may be able to write out a predictive health history based on probabilities for some medical conditions. Many people will benefit from genetically based diagnoses and forecasts.

As scientists come to understand the complex systems in which disease genes operate, they may be able to design therapeutic drugs to block or reverse the effects of mutant genes. If taken before the onset of disease, such drugs could prevent occurrence or minimize symptoms of the gene-based disease. Although the discussion here has focused on genetic conditions rather than infectious diseases, it is possible that ongoing analyses of microbial and human genomes will lead to procedures for controlling the virulence of some pathogens.

Many social issues need to be addressed

Although biological information is similar to other types of information from a strictly technical point of view, it is as different as can be in its meaning and impact on individual human beings and on human society as a whole. The difference lies in the personal nature of the unique genetic profile carried by each person from birth. Within this basic level of biological information are complex life codes that provide greater or lower susceptibility or resistance to many diseases, as well as greater or lesser potential for the expression of many physiologic, physical, and neurological attributes that distinguish people from each other. Until now, almost all this information has remained hidden away. But if research continues at its present pace, in less than a decade it will become possible to read a person's entire genetic profile, and with this information will come the power to make some limited predictions about future possibilities and risks.

As you will see in many of the Genetics and Society boxes throughout this book, society can use genetic information not only to help people but also to restrict their lives (for example, by denying insurance or employment). We believe that just as our society respects an individual's right to privacy in other realms, it should also respect the privacy of an individual's genetic profile and work against all types of discrimination. Indeed, in 2008 the federal government passed the Genetic Information Nondiscrimination Act prohibiting insurance companies and employers from discrimination on the basis of genetic tests.

Another issue raised by the potential for detailed genetic profiles is the interpretation or misinterpretation of that information. Without accurate interpretation, the information becomes useless at best and harmful at worst. Proper interpretation of genetic information requires some understanding of statistical concepts such as risk and probability. To help people understand these concepts, widespread education in this area will be essential. Children especially should learn the concepts and implications of modern human biology as a science of information.

Yet another pressing issue concerns the regulation and control of the new technology. With the sequencing of the entire human genome, the question of whether the government should establish guidelines for the use of genetic and genomic information, reflecting society's social and ethical values, remains in open debate.

To many people, the most frightening potential of the new genetics is the development of technology that can alter or add to the genes present within the *germ line* (reproductive cell precursors) of human embryos. This technology, referred to as "transgenic technology" in scientific discourse and "genetic engineering" in public discussions, has become routine in hundreds of laboratories working with various animals other than humans.

Some people caution that developing the power to alter our own genomes is a step we should not take, arguing that if genetic information and technology are misused, as they certainly have been in the past, the consequences could be horrific. Attempts to use genetic information for social purposes were prevalent in the early twentieth century, leading to enforced sterilization of individuals thought to be inferior, to laws that prohibited interracial marriage, and to laws prohibiting immigration of certain ethnic groups. The scientific basis of these actions has been thoroughly discredited.

Others agree that we must not repeat the mistakes of the past, but warn that if the new technologies could help children and adults lead healthier, happier lives, we need to think carefully about whether the reasons for objecting outright to their use are valid. Most agree that the biological revolution we are living through will have a greater impact on human society than any technological revolution of the past and that education and public debate are the key to preparing for the consequences of this revolution.

The focus on human genetics in this book looks forward into the new era of biology and genetic analysis. These new possibilities raise serious moral and ethical issues that will demand wisdom and humility. It is in the hope of educating young people for the moral and ethical challenges awaiting the next generation that we write this book.

> Advances in human genetics have great promise for the treatment or prevention of disease. Guidelines must be established, however, to prevent misuse of this knowledge.

Connections

Genetics, the study of biological information, is also the study of the DNA and RNA molecules that store, replicate, transmit, and evolve information for the construction of proteins. At the molecular level, all living things are closely related, and as a result, observations of model organisms as different as yeast and mice can provide insights into general biological principles as well as human biology.

Remarkably, more than 75 years before the discovery of DNA, Gregor Mendel, an Augustinian monk, delineated the basic laws of gene transmission with no knowledge of the molecular basis of heredity. He accomplished this by following simple traits, such as flower or seed color, through several generations of the pea plant (*Pisum sativum*). We now know that his findings apply to all sexually reproducing organisms. Chapter 2 describes Mendel's studies and insights, which became the foundation of the field of genetics.

ESSENTIAL CONCEPTS

1. The biological information fundamental to life is encoded in the DNA molecule.

2. Biological function emerges primarily from protein molecules.

3. Complex biological systems emerge from the functioning of regulatory networks that specify the behavior of genes and proteins.

4. All living forms are descended from a common ancestor and therefore are closely related at the molecular level.

5. The modular construction of genomes has allowed rapid evolution of biological complexity.

6. Modern genetic technology permits detailed analysis and dissection of biological complexity.

7. Application of modern technology to human genetics shows great promise for prediction, prevention, and treatment of disease.

On Our Website | vvww.mhhe.com/hartwell4

Annotated Suggested Readings and Links to Other Websites

- Additional information about DNA

- Conversion of DNA to RNA to protein
- More about systems biology and predictive/preventive medicine

Mendel's Principles of Heredity

Although Mendel's laws can predict the probability that an individual will have a particular genetic makeup, the chance meeting of particular male and female gametes determines an individual's actual genetic fate.

A quick glance at an extended family portrait is likely to reveal children who resemble one parent or the other or who look like a combination of the two (**Fig. 2.1**). Some children, however, look unlike any of the assembled relatives and more like a great, great grandparent. What causes the similarities and differences of appearance and the skipping of generations?

The answers lie in our **genes,** the basic units of biological information, and in **heredity,** the way genes transmit physiological, anatomical, and behavioral traits from parents to offspring. Each of us starts out as a single fertilized egg cell that develops, by division and differentiation, into a mature adult made up of 10^{14} (a hundred trillion) specialized cells capable of carrying out all the body's functions and controlling our outward appearance. Genes, passed from one generation to the next, underlie the formation of every heritable trait. Such traits are as diverse as the presence of a cleft in your chin, the tendency to lose hair as you age, your hair, eye, and skin color, and even your susceptibility to certain cancers. All such traits run in families in predictable patterns that impose some possibilities and exclude others.

Genetics, the science of heredity, pursues a precise explanation of the biological structures and mechanisms that determine inheritance. In some instances, the relationship between gene and trait is remarkably simple. A single change in a single gene, for example, results in sickle-cell anemia, a disease in which the hemoglobin molecule found in red blood cells is defective. In other instances, the correlations between genes and traits are bewilderingly complex. An example is the genetic basis of facial features, in which many genes determine a large number of molecules that interact to generate the combination we recognize as a friend's face.

Gregor Mendel (1822–1884; **Fig. 2.2**), a stocky, bespectacled Augustinian monk and expert plant breeder, discovered the basic principles of genetics in the mid–nineteenth century. He published his findings in 1866, just seven years after Darwin's *On the Origin of Species* appeared in print. Mendel lived and worked in Brünn, Austria (now Brno in the Czech Republic), where he examined the inheritance of clear-cut alternative traits in pea plants, such as purple versus white flowers or yellow versus green seeds. In so doing, he inferred genetic laws that allowed him to make verifiable predictions about which traits would appear, disappear, and then reappear, and in which generations.

CHAPTER OUTLINE

- 2.1 Background: The Historical Puzzle of Inheritance
- 2.2 Genetic Analysis According to Mendel
- 2.3 Mendelian Inheritance in Humans

Figure 2.1 A family portrait. The extended family shown here includes members of four generations.

Figure 2.2 Gregor Mendel. Photographed around 1862 holding one of his experimental plants.

Figure 2.3 Like begets like and unlike. A Labrador retriever with her litter of pups.

Mendel's laws are based on the hypothesis that observable traits are determined by independent units of inheritance not visible to the naked eye. We now call these units *genes*. The concept of the gene continues to change as research deepens and refines our understanding. Today, a gene is recognized as a region of DNA that encodes a specific protein or a particular type of RNA. In the beginning, however, it was an abstraction—an imagined particle with no physical features, the function of which was to control a visible trait by an unknown mechanism.

We begin our study of genetics with a detailed look at what Mendel's laws are and how they were discovered. In subsequent chapters, we discuss logical extensions to these laws and describe how Mendel's successors grounded the abstract concept of hereditary units (genes) in an actual biological molecule (DNA).

Four general themes emerge from our detailed discussion of Mendel's work. The first is that variation, as expressed in alternative forms of a trait, is widespread in nature. This genetic diversity provides the raw material for the continuously evolving variety of life we see around us. Second, observable variation is essential for following genes from one generation to the next. Third, variation is not distributed solely by chance; rather, it is inherited according to genetic laws that explain why like begets both like and unlike. Dogs beget other dogs—but hundreds of breeds of dogs are known. Even within a breed, such as Labrador retrievers, genetic variation exists: Two black dogs could have a litter of black, brown, and golden puppies (**Fig. 2.3**). Mendel's insights help explain why this is so. Fourth, the laws Mendel discovered about heredity apply equally well to all sexually reproducing organisms, from protozoans to peas to people.

2.1 Background: The Historical Puzzle of Inheritance

Several steps lead to an understanding of genetic phenomena: the careful observation over time of groups of organisms, such as human families, herds of cattle, or fields of corn or tomatoes; the rigorous analysis of systematically recorded information gleaned from these observations; and the development of a theoretical framework that can explain the origin of these phenomena and their relationships. In the mid–nineteenth century, Gregor Mendel became the first person to combine data collection, analysis, and theory in a successful pursuit of the true basis of heredity. For many thousands of years before that, the only genetic practice was the selective breeding of domesticated plants and animals, with no guarantee of what a particular mating would produce.

Artificial selection was the first applied genetic technique

A rudimentary use of genetics was the driving force behind a key transition in human civilization, allowing hunters and gatherers to settle in villages and survive as shepherds and farmers. Even before recorded history, people practiced applied genetics as they domesticated plants and animals for their own uses. From a large litter of semitamed wolves, for example, they sent the savage and the misbehaving to the stew pot while sparing the alert sentries and friendly companions for longer life and eventual mating. As a result of this **artificial selection**— purposeful control over mating by choice of parents for the next generation—the domestic dog (*Canis lupus familiaris*) slowly arose from ancestral wolves (*Canis lupus*). The oldest bones identified indisputably as dog (and not wolf) are a skull excavated from a 20,000-year-old Alaskan settlement. Many millennia of evolution guided by artificial selection have produced massive Great Danes and minuscule Chihuahuas as well as hundreds of other modern breeds of dog. By 10,000 years ago, people had begun to use this same kind of genetic manipulation to develop economically valuable herds of reindeer, sheep, goats, pigs, and cattle that produced life-sustaining meat, milk, hides, and wools.

Farmers also carried out artificial selection of plants, storing seed from the hardiest and tastiest individuals for the next planting, eventually obtaining strains that grew better, produced more, and were easier to cultivate and harvest. In this way, scrawny weedlike plants gradually, with human guidance, turned into rice, wheat, barley, lentils, and dates in Asia; corn, squash, tomatoes, potatoes, and peppers in the Americas; yams, peanuts, and gourds in Africa. Later, plant breeders recognized male and female organs in plants and carried out artificial pollination. An Assyrian frieze carved in the ninth century B.C., pictured in **Fig. 2.4,** is the oldest known visual record of this kind of genetic experiment. It depicts priests brushing the flowers of female date palms with selected male pollen. By this method of artificial selection, early practical geneticists produced several hundred varieties of dates, each differing in specific observable qualities, such as the fruit's size, color, or taste. A 1929 botanical survey of three oases in Egypt turned up 400 varieties of date-bearing palms, twentieth-century evidence of the natural and artificially generated variation among these trees.

Figure 2.4 The earliest known record of applied genetics. In this 2800-year-old Assyrian relief from the Northwest Palace of Assurnasirpal II (883–859 B.C.), priests wearing bird masks artificially pollinate flowers of female date palms.

Desirable traits sometimes disappear and reappear

In 1822, the year of Mendel's birth, what people in Austria understood about the basic principles of heredity was not much different from what the people of ancient Assyria had understood. By the nineteenth century, plant and animal breeders had created many strains in which offspring often carried a prized parental trait. Using such strains, they could produce plants or animals with desired characteristics for food and fiber, but they could not always predict why a valued trait would sometimes disappear and then reappear in only some offspring. For example, selective breeding practices had resulted in valuable flocks of merino sheep producing large quantities of soft, fine wool, but at the 1837 annual meeting of the Moravian Sheep Breeders Society, one breeder's dilemma epitomized the state of the art. He possessed an outstanding ram that would be priceless "if its advantages are inherited by its offspring," but "if they are not inherited, then it is worth no more than the cost of wool, meat, and skin." Which would it be? According to the meeting's recorded minutes, current breeding practices offered no definite answers. In his concluding remarks at this sheep-breeders meeting, the

Abbot Cyril Napp pointed to a possible way out. He proposed that breeders could improve their ability to predict what traits would appear in the offspring by finding the answers to three basic questions: What is inherited? How is it inherited? What is the role of chance in heredity?

This is where matters stood in 1843 when 21-year-old Gregor Mendel entered the monastery in Brünn, presided over by the same Abbot Napp. Although Mendel was a monk trained in theology, he was not a rank amateur in science. The province of Moravia, in which Brünn was located, was a center of learning and scientific activity. Mendel was able to acquire a copy of Darwin's *On the Origin of Species* shortly after it was translated into German in 1863. Abbot Napp, recognizing Mendel's intellectual abilities, sent him to the University of Vienna—all expenses paid—where he prescribed his own course of study. His choices were an unusual mix: physics, mathematics, chemistry, botany, paleontology, and plant physiology. Christian Doppler, discoverer of the Doppler effect, was one of his teachers. The cross-pollination of ideas from several disciplines would play a significant role in Mendel's discoveries. One year after he returned to Brünn, he began his series of seminal genetic experiments. **Figure 2.5** shows where Mendel worked and the microscope he used.

Mendel devised a new experimental approach

Before Mendel, many misconceptions clouded people's thinking about heredity. Two of the prevailing errors were particularly misleading. The first was that one parent contributes most to an offspring's inherited features; Nicolaas Hartsoeker, one of the earliest microscopists, contended in 1694 that it was the male, by way of a fully formed "homunculus" inside the sperm (**Fig. 2.6**). Another deceptive notion was the concept of *blended inheritance,* the idea that parental traits become mixed and forever changed in the offspring, as when blue and yellow pigment merge to green on a painter's palette. The theory of blending may have grown out of a natural tendency for parents to see a combination of their own traits in their offspring. While blending could account for children who look like a combination of their parents, it could not explain obvious differences between biological brothers and sisters nor the persistence of variation within extended families.

The experiments Mendel devised would lay these myths to rest by providing precise, verifiable answers to the three questions Abbot Napp had raised almost 15 years earlier: What is inherited? How is it inherited? What is the role of chance in heredity? A key component of Mendel's breakthrough was the way he set up his experiments.

Figure 2.5 Mendel's garden and microscope. (a) Gregor Mendel's garden was part of his monastery's property in Brno. **(b)** Mendel used this microscope to examine plant reproductive organs and to pursue his interests in natural history.

(a)

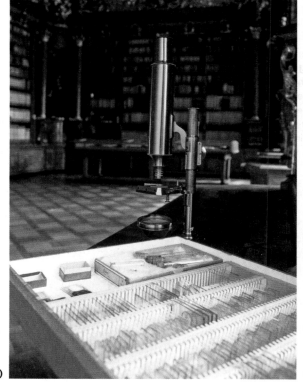

(b)

Figure 2.6 The homunculus: A misconception. Well into the nineteenth century, many prominent microscopists believed they saw a fully formed, miniature fetus crouched within the head of a sperm.

What did Mendel do differently from those who preceded him? First, he chose the garden pea *(Pisum sativum)* as his experimental organism (**Figs. 2.7a** and **b**). Peas grew well in Brünn, and with male and female organs in the same flower, they were normally self-fertilizing. In **self-fertilization** (or *selfing*), both egg and pollen come from the same plant. The particular anatomy of pea flowers, however, makes it easy to prevent self-fertilization and instead to **cross-fertilize** (or *cross*) two individuals by brushing pollen from one plant onto a female organ of another plant, as illustrated in **Fig. 2.7c.** Peas offered yet another advantage. For each successive generation, Mendel could obtain large numbers of individuals within a relatively short growing season. By comparison, if he had worked with sheep, each mating would have generated only a few offspring and the time between generations would have been several years.

Second, Mendel examined the inheritance of clear-cut alternative forms of particular traits—purple versus white flowers, yellow versus green peas. Using such "either-or" traits, he could distinguish and trace unambiguously the transmission of one or the other observed characteristic, because there were no intermediate forms. (The opposite of these so-called *discrete traits* are *continuous traits,* such as height and skin color in humans. Continuous traits show many intermediate forms.)

Third, Mendel collected and perpetuated lines of peas that bred true. Matings within such **pure-breeding lines** produce offspring carrying specific parental traits that remain constant from generation to generation. Mendel observed his pure-breeding lines for up to eight generations. Plants with white flowers always produced offspring with white flowers; plants with purple flowers produced only offspring with purple flowers. Mendel called constant but mutually exclusive, alternative traits, such as purple versus white flowers or yellow versus green seeds, "antagonistic pairs" and settled on

Figure 2.7 Mendel's experimental organism: The garden pea. (a) Pea plants with white flowers. **(b)** Pollen is produced in the anthers. Mature pollen lands on the stigma, which is connected to the ovary (which becomes the pea pod). After landing, the pollen grows a tube that extends through the stigma to one of the ovules (immature seeds), allowing fertilization to take place. **(c)** To prevent self-fertilization, breeders remove the anthers from the female parents (here, the white flower) before the plant produces mature pollen. Pollen is then transferred with a paintbrush from the anthers of the male parent (here, the purple flower) to the stigma of the female parent. Each fertilized ovule becomes an individual pea (mature seed) that can grow into a new pea plant. All of the peas produced from one flower are encased in the same pea pod, but these peas form from different pollen grains and ovules.

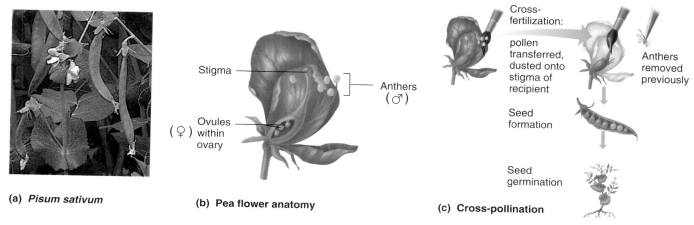

(a) *Pisum sativum*   **(b) Pea flower anatomy**   **(c) Cross-pollination**

seven such pairs for his study (**Fig. 2.8**). In his experiments, he not only perpetuated pure-breeding stocks for each member of a pair, but he also cross-fertilized pairs of plants to produce **hybrids,** offspring of genetically dissimilar parents, for each pair of antagonistic traits. Figure 2.8 shows the appearance of the hybrids he studied.

Fourth, being an expert plant breeder, Mendel carefully controlled his matings, going to great lengths to ensure that the progeny he observed really resulted from the specific fertilizations he intended. Thus he painstakingly prevented the intrusion of any foreign pollen and assured self- or cross-pollination as the experiment demanded. Not only did this allow him to carry out controlled breedings of selected traits, he could also make **reciprocal crosses.** In such crosses, he reversed the traits of the male and female parents, thus controlling whether a particular trait was transmitted via the egg cell within the ovule or via a sperm cell within the pollen. For example, he could use pollen from a purple flower to fertilize the eggs of a white flower and also use pollen from a white flower to fertilize the eggs of a purple flower. Because the progeny of these reciprocal crosses were similar, Mendel demonstrated that the two parents contribute equally to inheritance. "It is immaterial to the form of the hybrid," he wrote, "which of the parental types was the seed or pollen plant."

Fifth, Mendel worked with large numbers of plants, counted all offspring, subjected his findings to numerical analysis, and then compared his results with predictions based on his models. He was the first person to study inheritance in this manner, and no doubt his background in physics and mathematics contributed to this quantitative approach. Mendel's careful numerical analysis revealed patterns of transmission that reflected basic laws of heredity.

Finally, Mendel was a brilliant practical experimentalist. When comparing tall and short plants, for example, he made sure that the short ones were out of the shade of the tall ones so their growth would not be stunted. Eventually he focused on certain traits of the pea seeds themselves, such as their color or shape, rather than on traits of the plants arising from the seeds. In this way, he could observe many more individuals from the limited space of the monastery garden, and he could evaluate the results of a cross in a single growing season.

In short, Mendel purposely set up a simplified "black-and-white" experimental system and then figured out how it worked. He did not look at the vast number of variables that determine the development of a prize ram nor at the origin of differences between species. Rather, he looked at discrete traits that came in two mutually exclusive forms and asked questions that could be answered by observation and computation.

Figure 2.8 The mating of parents with antagonistic traits produces hybrids. Note that each of the hybrids for the seven antagonistic traits studied by Mendel resembles only one of the parents. The parental trait that shows up in the hybrid is known as the "dominant" trait.

Gregor Mendel performed genetic crosses in a systematic way, using mathematics to analyze the data he obtained and to predict outcomes of other experiments.

2.2 Genetic Analysis According to Mendel

In early 1865 at the age of 43, Gregor Mendel presented a paper entitled "Experiments on Plant Hybrids" before the Natural Science Society of Brünn. Despite its modest heading, it was a scientific paper of uncommon clarity and simplicity that summarized a decade of original observations and experiments. In it Mendel describes in detail the transmission of visible characteristics in pea plants, defines unseen but logically deduced units (genes) that determine when and how often these visible traits appear, and analyzes the behavior of genes in simple mathematical terms to reveal previously unsuspected principles of heredity.

Published the following year, the paper would eventually become the cornerstone of modern genetics. Its stated purpose was to see whether there is a "generally applicable law governing the formation and development of hybrids." Let us examine its insights.

Monohybrid crosses reveal units of inheritance and the law of segregation

Once Mendel had isolated pure-breeding lines for several sets of characteristics, he carried out a series of matings between individuals that differed in only one trait, such as seed color or stem length. In each cross, one parent carries one form of the trait, and the other parent carries an alternative form of the same trait. **Figure 2.9** illustrates one such mating. Early in the spring of 1854, for example, Mendel planted pure-breeding green peas and pure-breeding yellow peas and allowed them to grow into the **parental (P) generation.** Later that spring when the plants had flowered, he dusted the female stigma of "green-pea" plant flowers with pollen from "yellow-pea" plants. He also performed the reciprocal cross, dusting "yellow-pea" plant stigmas with "green-pea" pollen. In the fall, when he collected and separately analyzed the progeny peas of these reciprocal crosses, he found that in both cases, the peas were all yellow.

These yellow peas, progeny of the P generation, were the beginning of what we now call the **first filial (F₁)** generation. To learn whether the green trait had disappeared entirely or remained intact but hidden in these

Figure 2.9 Analyzing a monohybrid cross. Cross-pollination of pure-breeding parental plants produces F₁ hybrids, all of which resemble one of the parents. Self-pollination of F₁ plants gives rise to an F₂ generation with a 3:1 ratio of individuals resembling the two original parental types. For simplicity, we do not show the plants that produce the peas or that grow from the planted peas.

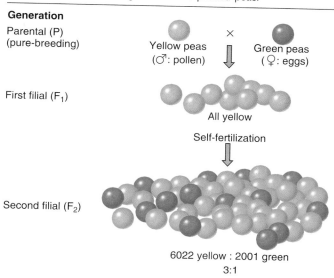

Generation

Parental (P)
(pure-breeding)

First filial (F₁)

Second filial (F₂)

Yellow peas
(♂: pollen)

Green peas
(♀: eggs)

All yellow

Self-fertilization

6022 yellow : 2001 green
3:1

F₁ yellow peas, Mendel planted them to obtain mature F₁ plants that he allowed to self-fertilize. Such experiments involving hybrids for a single trait are often called **monohybrid crosses.** He then harvested and counted the peas of the resulting **second filial (F₂)** generation, progeny of the F₁ generation. Among the progeny of one series of F₁ self-fertilizations, there were 6022 yellow and 2001 green F₂ peas, an almost perfect ratio of 3 yellow : 1 green. F₁ plants derived from the reciprocal of the original cross produced a similar ratio of yellow to green F₂ progeny.

Reappearance of the recessive trait

The presence of green peas in the F₂ generation was irrefutable evidence that blending had not occurred. If it had, the information necessary to make green peas would have been irretrievably lost in the F₁ hybrids. Instead, the information remained intact and was able to direct the formation of 2001 green peas actually harvested from the second filial generation. These green peas were indistinguishable from their green grandparents.

Mendel concluded that there must be two types of yellow peas: those that breed true like the yellow peas of the P generation, and those that can yield some green offspring like the yellow F₁ hybrids. This second type somehow contains latent information for green peas. He called the trait that appeared in all the F₁ hybrids—in this

FAST FORWARD

Genes Encode Proteins

Genes determine traits as disparate as pea shape and the inherited human disease cystic fibrosis. We now know that genes encode the proteins that cells produce and depend on for structure and function. As early as 1940, investigators had uncovered evidence suggesting that some genes determine the formation of enzymes, the proteins that catalyze specific chemical reactions. But it was not until 1991, 126 years after Mendel published his work, that a team of British geneticists was able to identify the gene for pea shape and to pinpoint how the enzyme it specifies influences a seed's round or wrinkled contour. About the same time, medical researchers in the United States identified the cys-

tic fibrosis gene. They discovered how a mutant allele causes unusually sticky mucus secretion and a susceptibility to respiratory infections and digestive malfunction, once again, through the protein the gene determines.

The pea shape gene encodes an enzyme known as SBE1 (for starch-branching enzyme 1), which catalyzes the conversion of amylose, an unbranched linear molecule of starch, to amylopectin, a starch molecule composed of several branching chains (**Fig. A**). The dominant *R* allele of the pea shape gene causes the formation of active SBE1 enzyme that functions normally. As a result, *RR* homozygotes produce a high proportion of branched

Figure A Round and wrinkled peas: How one gene determines an enzyme that affects pea shape. The *R* allele of the pea shape gene directs the synthesis of an enzyme that converts unbranched starch to branched starch, indirectly leading to round pea shape. The *r* allele of this gene determines an inactive form of the enzyme, leading to a buildup of linear, unbranched starch that ultimately causes seed wrinkling. The photograph at right shows two pea pods, each of which contains wrinkled (arrows) and round peas; the ratio of round to wrinkled in these two well-chosen pods is 9:3 (or 3:1).

case, yellow seeds—**dominant** (see Fig. 2.8) and the "antagonistic" green-pea trait that remained hidden in the F_1 hybrids but reappeared in the F_2 generation **recessive.** But how did he explain the 3:1 ratio of yellow to green F_2 peas?

Genes: Discrete units of inheritance

To account for his observations, Mendel proposed that for each trait, every plant carries two copies of a unit of inheritance, receiving one from its maternal parent and the other from the paternal parent. Today, we call these units of inheritance *genes.* Each unit determines the appearance of a specific characteristic. The pea plants in Mendel's collection had two copies of a gene for seed color, two copies of another for seed shape, two copies of a third for stem length, and so forth.

Mendel further proposed that each gene comes in alternative forms, and combinations of these alternative forms determine the contrasting characteristics he was studying. Today we call the alternative forms of a single gene **alleles.** The gene for pea color, for example, has yellow and green alleles; the gene for pea shape has round and wrinkled alleles. (The Fast Forward box "Genes Encode Proteins" on this page describes the biochemical and molecular mechanisms by which different alleles determine different forms of a trait.) In Mendel's monohybrid crosses, one allele of each gene was dominant, the other recessive. In the P generation, one parent carried two dominant alleles for the trait under consideration; the other parent, two recessive alleles. The F_1 generation hybrids carried one dominant and one recessive allele for the trait. Individuals having two different alleles for a single trait are **monohybrids.**

starch molecules, which allow the peas to maintain a rounded shape. In contrast, the enzyme determined by the recessive *r* allele is abnormal and does not function effectively. In homozygous recessive *rr* peas, sucrose builds up because less of it is converted into starch. The excess sucrose modifies osmotic pressure, causing water to enter the young seeds. As the seeds mature, they lose water, shrink, and wrinkle. The single dominant allele in *Rr* heterozygotes apparently produces enough of the normal enzyme to prevent wrinkling. In summary, a specific gene determines a specific enzyme whose activity affects pea shape.

The human disease of cystic fibrosis (CF) was first described in 1938, but doctors and scientists did not understand the biochemical mechanism that produced the serious respiratory and digestive malfunctions associated with the disease. As a result, treatments could do little more than relieve some of the symptoms, and most CF sufferers died before the age of 30.

In 1989, molecular geneticists found that the normal allele of the cystic fibrosis gene determines a protein that forges a channel through the cell membrane (**Fig. B**). This protein, called the c̲ystic f̲ibrosis t̲ransmembrane conductance r̲egulator (CFTR), controls the flow of chloride ions into and out of the cell. The normal allele of this gene produces a CFTR protein that correctly regulates the back-and-forth exchange of ions, which, in turn, determines the cell's osmotic pressure and the flow of water through the cell membrane. In people with cystic fibrosis, however, the two recessive alleles produce only an abnormal form of the CFTR protein. The abnormal protein cannot be inserted into the cell membranes, so patients lack functional CFTR chloride channels. The cells thus retain water, and a thick, dehydrated mucus builds up outside the cells. In cells lining the airways and the ducts of secretory organs such as the pancreas,

Figure B The cystic fibrosis gene encodes a cell membrane protein. A model of the normal CFTR protein that regulates the passage of chloride ions through the cell membrane. A small change in the gene that codes for CFTR results in an altered protein that prevents proper flow of chloride ions, leading to the varied symptoms of cystic fibrosis.

this single biochemical defect produces clogging and blockages that result in respiratory and digestive malfunction.

Identification of the cystic fibrosis gene brought not only a protein-based explanation of disease symptoms but also the promise of a cure. In the early 1990s, medical researchers placed the normal allele of the gene into respiratory tissue of mice with the disease. These mice could then produce a functional CFTR protein. Such encouraging results in these small mammals suggested that in the not-too-distant future, gene therapy might bestow relatively normal health on people suffering from this once life-threatening genetic disorder. Unfortunately, human trials of CFTR gene therapy have not yet achieved clear success.

The law of segregation

If a plant has two copies of every gene, how does it pass only one copy of each to its progeny? And how do the offspring then end up with two copies of these same genes, one from each parent? Mendel drew on his background in plant physiology and answered these questions in terms of the two biological mechanisms behind reproduction: gamete formation and the random union of gametes at fertilization. **Gametes** are the specialized cells—eggs within the ovules of the female parent and sperm cells within the pollen grains—that carry genes between generations. He imagined that during the formation of pollen and eggs, the two copies of each gene in the parent separate (or *segregate*) so that each gamete receives only one allele for each trait (**Fig. 2.10a**). Thus, each egg and each pollen grain receives only one allele for pea color (either yellow or green). At fertilization, pollen with one or the

other allele unites at random with an egg carrying one or the other allele, restoring the two copies of the gene for each trait in the fertilized egg, or **zygote** (**Fig. 2.10b**). If the pollen carries yellow and the egg green, the result will be a hybrid yellow pea like the F_1 monohybrids that resulted when pure-breeding parents of opposite types mated. If the yellow-carrying pollen unites with a yellow-carrying egg, the result will be a yellow pea that grows into a pure-breeding plant like those of the P generation that produced only yellow peas. And finally, if pollen carrying the allele for green peas fertilizes a green-carrying egg, the progeny will be a pure-breeding green pea.

Mendel's **law of segregation** encapsulates this general principle of heredity: *The two alleles for each trait separate (segregate) during gamete formation, and then unite at random, one from each parent, at fertilization.* Throughout this book, the term **segregation** refers to

Figure 2.10 The law of segregation. (a) The two identical alleles of pure-breeding plants separate (segregate) during gamete formation. As a result, each pollen grain or egg carries only one of each pair of parental alleles. **(b)** Cross-pollination and fertilization between pure-breeding parents with antagonistic traits result in F₁ hybrid zygotes with two different alleles. For the seed color gene, a *Yy* hybrid zygote will develop into a yellow pea.

(a) The two alleles for each trait separate during gamete formation.

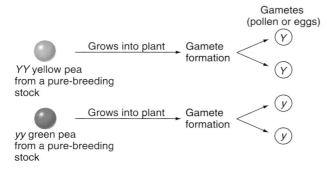

(b) Two gametes, one from each parent, unite at random at fertilization.

Y = yellow-determining allele of pea color gene
y = green-determining allele of pea color gene

such *equal segregation* in which one allele, and only one allele, of each gene goes to each gamete. Note that the law of segregation makes a clear distinction between organisms, whose cells have two copies of each gene, and gametes, which bear only a single copy of each gene.

The Punnett square

Figure 2.11 shows a simple way of visualizing the results of the segregation and random union of alleles during gamete formation and fertilization. Mendel invented a system of symbols that allowed him to analyze all his crosses in the same way. He designated dominant alleles with a capital *A, B,* or *C* and recessive ones with a lowercase *a, b,* or *c*. Modern geneticists have adopted this convention for naming genes in peas and many other organisms, but they often choose a symbol with some reference to the trait in question—a *Y* for yellow or an *R* for round. Throughout this book, we present gene symbols in italics. In Fig. 2.11, we denote the dominant yellow allele by a capital *Y* and the recessive green allele by a lower

Figure 2.11 The Punnett square: Visual summary of a cross. This Punnett square illustrates the combinations that can arise when an F₁ hybrid undergoes gamete formation and self-fertilization. The F₂ generation should have a 3:1 ratio of yellow to green peas.

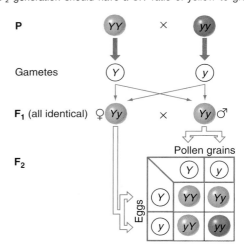

case *y*. The pure-breeding plants of the parental generation are either *YY* (yellow peas) or *yy* (green peas). The *YY* parent can produce only *Y* gametes, the *yy* parent only *y* gametes. You can see from the diagram why every cross between *YY* and *yy* produces exactly the same result—a *Yy* hybrid—no matter which parent (male or female) contributes which particular allele.

Next, to visualize what happens when the *Yy* hybrids self-fertilize, we set up a Punnett square (named after British mathematician Reginald Punnett, who introduced it in 1906; Fig. 2.11). The square provides a simple and convenient method for tracking the kinds of gametes produced as well as all the possible combinations that might occur at fertilization. As the Punnett square shows, each hybrid produces two kinds of gametes, *Y* and *y*, in a ratio of 1:1. Thus, half the pollen and half the eggs carry *Y*, the other half *y*. At fertilization, 1/4 of the progeny will be *YY*, 1/4 *Yy*, 1/4 *yY*, and 1/4 *yy*. Since the gametic source of an allele (egg or pollen) for the traits Mendel studied had no influence on the allele's effect, *Yy* and *yY* are equivalent. This means that 1/2 of the progeny are yellow *Yy* hybrids, 1/4 *YY* true-breeding yellows, and 1/4 true-breeding *yy* greens. The diagram illustrates how the segregation of alleles during gamete formation and the random union of egg and pollen at fertilization can produce the 3:1 ratio of yellow to green that Mendel observed in the F₂ generation.

Mendel's law of segregation states that alleles of genes separate during gamete formation and then come together randomly at fertilization. The Punnett square is one tool for analyzing allele behavior in a cross.

Mendel's results reflect basic rules of probability

Though you may not have realized it, the Punnett square illustrates two simple rules of probability—the product rule and the sum rule—that are central to the analysis of genetic crosses. These rules predict the likelihood that a particular combination of events will occur.

The product rule

The **product rule** states that the probability of two or more *independent events* occurring together is the *product* of the probabilities that each event will occur by itself. With independent events:

Probability of event 1 *and* event 2 =

Probability of event 1 × probability of event 2

Consecutive coin tosses are obviously independent events; a heads in one toss neither increases nor decreases the probability of a heads in the next toss. If you toss two coins at the same time, the results are also independent events. A heads for one coin neither increases nor decreases the probability of a heads for the other coin. Thus, the probability of a given combination is the product of their independent probabilities. For example, the probability that both coins will turn up heads is

$$1/2 \times 1/2 = 1/4$$

Similarly, the formation of egg and pollen are independent events; in a hybrid plant, the probability is 1/2 that a given gamete will carry Y and 1/2 that it will carry y. Because fertilization happens at random, the probability that a particular combination of maternal and paternal alleles will occur simultaneously in the same zygote is the product of the independent probabilities of these alleles being packaged in egg and sperm. Thus, to find the chance of a Y egg (formed as the result of one event) uniting with a Y sperm (the result of an independent event), you simply multiply 1/2 × 1/2 to get 1/4. This is the same fraction of YY progeny seen in the Punnett square of Fig. 2.11, which demonstrates that the Punnett square is simply another way of depicting the product rule.

The sum rule

While we can describe the moment of random fertilization as the simultaneous occurrence of two independent events, we can also say that two different fertilization events are mutually exclusive. For instance, if Y combines with Y, it cannot also combine with y in the same zygote. A second rule of probability, the **sum rule,** states that the probability of either of two such *mutually exclusive events* occurring is the *sum* of their individual probabilities. With mutually exclusive events:

Probability of event 1 *or* event 2 =

Probability of event 1 + probability of event 2

To find the likelihood that an offspring of a Yy hybrid self-fertilization will be a hybrid like the parents, you add 1/4 (the probability of maternal Y uniting with paternal y) and 1/4 (the probability of the mutually exclusive event where paternal Y unites with maternal y) to get 1/2, again the same result as in the Punnett square. In another use of the sum rule, you could predict the ratio of yellow to green F_2 progeny. The fraction of F_2 peas that will be yellow is the sum of 1/4 (the event producing YY) plus 1/4 (the mutually exclusive event generating Yy) plus 1/4 (the third mutually exclusive event producing yY) to get 3/4. The remaining 1/4 of the F_2 progeny will be green. So the yellow-to-green ratio is 3/4 to 1/4, or more simply, 3:1.

> In the analysis of a genetic cross, the product rule multiplies probabilities to predict the chance of a particular fertilization event. The sum rule adds probabilities to predict the proportion of progeny that share a particular trait such as pea color.

Further crosses verify the law of segregation

Although Mendel's law of segregation explains the data from his pea crosses, he performed additional experiments to confirm its validity. In the rigorous check of his hypothesis illustrated in **Fig. 2.12,** he allowed self-fertilization of all the plants in the F_2 generation and counted the types of F_3 progeny. Mendel found that the plants that developed from F_2 green peas all produced only F_3 green peas, and when the resulting F_3 plants self-fertilized, the next generation also produced green peas (not shown). This is what we (and Mendel) would expect of pure-breeding lines carrying two copies of the recessive allele. The yellow peas were a different story. When Mendel allowed 518 F_2 plants that developed from yellow peas to self-fertilize, he observed that 166, roughly 1/3 of the total, were pure-breeding yellow through several generations, but the other 352 (2/3 of the total yellow F_2 plants) were hybrids because they gave rise to yellow and green F_3 peas in a ratio of 3:1.

It took Mendel years to conduct such rigorous experiments on seven pairs of pea traits, but in the end, he was able to conclude that the segregation of dominant and recessive alleles during gamete formation and their random union at fertilization could indeed explain the 3:1 ratios he observed whenever he allowed hybrids to self-fertilize. His results, however, raised yet another question,

Figure 2.12 Yellow F$_2$ peas are of two types: Pure breeding and hybrid. The distribution of a pair of contrasting alleles (*Y* and *y*) after two generations of self-fertilization. The homozygous individuals of each generation breed true, whereas the hybrids do not.

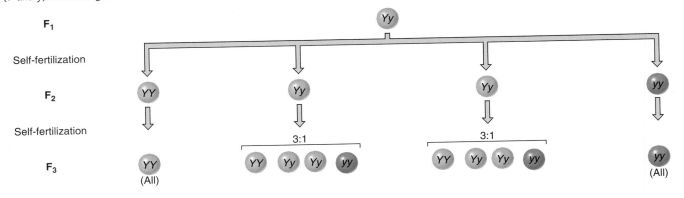

one of some importance to future plant and animal breeders. Plants showing a dominant trait, such as yellow peas, can be either pure-breeding (*YY*) or hybrid (*Yy*). How can you distinguish one from the other? For self-fertilizing plants, the answer is to observe the appearance of the next generation. But how would you distinguish pure-breeding from hybrid individuals in species that do not self-fertilize?

Testcrosses: A way to establish genotype

Before describing Mendel's answer, we need to define a few more terms. An observable characteristic, such as yellow or green pea seeds, is a **phenotype,** while the actual pair of alleles present in an individual is its **genotype.** A *YY* or a *yy* genotype is called **homozygous,** because the two copies of the gene that determine the particular trait in question are the same. In contrast, a genotype with two different alleles for a trait is **heterozygous;** in other words, it is a hybrid for that trait (**Fig. 2.13**). An individual with a homozygous genotype is a **homozygote;** one with a heterozygous genotype is a **heterozygote.** Note that the

phenotype of a heterozygote (that is, of a hybrid) defines which allele is dominant: Because *Yy* peas are yellow, the yellow allele *Y* is dominant to the *y* allele for green. If you know the genotype and the dominance relation of the alleles, you can accurately predict the phenotype. The reverse is not true, however, because some phenotypes can derive from more than one genotype. For example, the phenotype of yellow peas can result from either the *YY* or the *Yy* genotype.

With these distinctions in mind, we can look at the method Mendel devised for deciphering the unknown genotype, we'll call it *Y–*, responsible for a dominant phenotype; the dash represents the unknown second allele, either *Y* or *y*. This method, called the **testcross,** is a mating in which an individual showing the dominant phenotype, for instance, a *Y–* plant grown from a yellow pea, is crossed with an individual expressing the recessive phenotype, in this case a *yy* plant grown from a green pea. As the Punnett squares in **Fig. 2.14** illustrate, if the dominant phenotype in question derives from a homozygous

Figure 2.14 How a testcross reveals genotype. An individual of unknown genotype, but dominant phenotype, is crossed with a homozygous recessive. If the unknown genotype is homozygous, all progeny will exhibit the dominant phenotype, (*cross A*). If the unknown genotype is heterozygous, half the progeny will exhibit the dominant trait, half the recessive trait (*cross B*).

Figure 2.13 Genotype versus phenotype in homozygotes and heterozygotes. The relationship between genotype and phenotype with a pair of contrasting alleles where one allele (*Y*) shows complete dominance over the other (*y*).

Genotype for the Seed Color Gene	Phenotype
YY Homozygous dominant	Yellow
Dominant allele — Recessive allele *Yy* Heterozygous	Yellow
yy Homozygous recessive	Green

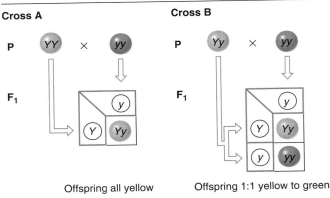

YY genotype, all the offspring of the testcross will show the dominant yellow phenotype. But if the dominant parent of unknown genotype is a heterozygous hybrid (*Yy*), 1/2 of the progeny are expected to be yellow peas, and the other half green. In this way, the testcross establishes the genotype behind a dominant phenotype, resolving any uncertainty.

As we mentioned earlier, Mendel deliberately simplified the problem of heredity, focusing on traits that come in only two forms. He was able to replicate his basic monohybrid findings with corn, beans, and four-o'clocks (plants with tubular, white or bright red flowers). As it turns out, his concept of the gene and his law of segregation can be generalized to almost all sexually reproducing organisms.

> The results of a testcross, in which an individual showing the dominant phenotype is crossed with an individual showing the recessive phenotype, indicate whether the individual with the dominant phenotype is a homozygote or a heterozygote.

Dihybrid crosses reveal the law of independent assortment

Having determined from monohybrid crosses that genes are inherited according to the law of segregation, Mendel turned his attention to the simultaneous inheritance of two or more apparently unrelated traits in peas. He asked how two pairs of alleles would segregate in a **dihybrid** individual, that is, in a plant that is heterozygous for two genes at the same time.

To construct such a dihybrid, Mendel mated true-breeding plants grown from yellow round peas (*YY RR*) with true-breeding plants grown from green wrinkled peas (*yy rr*). From this cross he obtained a dihybrid F_1 generation (*Yy Rr*) showing only the two dominant phenotypes, yellow and round (**Fig. 2.15**). He then allowed these F_1 dihybrids to self-fertilize to produce the F_2 generation. Mendel could not predict the outcome of this mating. Would all the F_2 progeny be **parental types** that looked like either the original yellow round parent or the green wrinkled parent? Or would some new combinations of phenotypes occur that were not seen in the parental lines, such as yellow wrinkled or green round peas? New phenotypic combinations like these are called **recombinant types.** When Mendel counted the F_2 generation of one experiment, he found 315 yellow round peas, 101 yellow wrinkled, 108 green round, and 32 green wrinkled. There were, in fact, yellow wrinkled and green round recombinant phenotypes, providing evidence that some shuffling of the alleles of different genes had taken place.

Figure 2.15 A dihybrid cross produces parental types and recombinant types. In this dihybrid cross, pure-breeding parents (P) produce a genetically uniform generation of F_1 dihybrids. Self-pollination or cross-pollination of the F_1 plants yields the characteristic F_2 phenotypic ratio of 9:3:3:1.

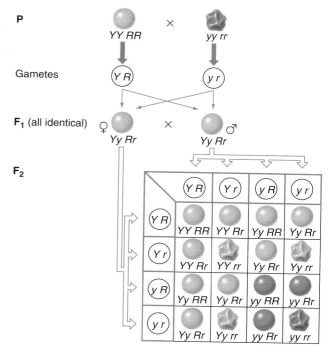

Type	Genotype		Phenotype	Number	Phenotypic Ratio
Parental	*Y– R–*		yellow round	315	9/16
Recombinant	*yy R–*		green round	108	3/16
Recombinant	*Y– rr*		yellow wrinkled	101	3/16
Parental	*yy rr*		green wrinkled	32	1/16

Ratio of yellow (dominant) to green (recessive) = 12:4 or 3:1
Ratio of round (dominant) to wrinkled (recessive) = 12:4 or 3:1

The law of independent assortment

From the observed ratios, Mendel inferred the biological mechanism of that shuffling—the **independent assortment** of gene pairs during gamete formation. Because the genes for pea color and for pea shape assort independently, the allele for pea shape in a *Y* carrying gamete could with equal likelihood be either *R* or *r*. Thus, the presence of a particular allele of one gene, say, the dominant *Y* for pea color, provides no information whatsoever about the allele of the second gene. Each dihybrid of the F_1 generation can therefore make four kinds of gametes: *Y R, Y r, y R,* and *y r.* In a large number of gametes, the four kinds will appear in an almost perfect ratio of 1:1:1:1, or put another way, roughly 1/4 of the eggs and 1/4 of the pollen will contain each of the four possible combinations of alleles. That "the different kinds of germinal cells [eggs or pollen] of a hybrid are produced on the average in equal numbers" was yet another one of Mendel's incisive insights.

At fertilization then, in a mating of dihybrids, 4 different kinds of eggs can combine with any 1 of 4 different kinds of pollen, producing a total of 16 possible zygotes. Once again, a Punnett square is a convenient way to visualize the process. If you look at the square in Fig. 2.15, you will see that some of the 16 potential allelic combinations are identical. In fact, there are only nine different genotypes—*YY RR, YY Rr, Yy RR, Yy Rr, yy RR, yy Rr, YY rr, Yy rr,* and *yy rr*—because the source of the alleles (egg or pollen) does not make any difference. If you look at the combinations of traits determined by the nine genotypes, you will see only four phenotypes—yellow round, yellow wrinkled, green round, and green wrinkled—in a ratio of 9:3:3:1. If, however, you look at just pea color or just pea shape, you can see that each trait is inherited in the 3:1 ratio predicted by Mendel's law of segregation. In the Punnett square, there are 12 yellow for every 4 green and 12 round for every 4 wrinkled. In other words, the ratio of each dominant trait (yellow or round) to its antagonistic recessive trait (green or wrinkled) is 12:4, or 3:1. This means that the inheritance of the gene for pea color is unaffected by the inheritance of the gene for pea shape, and vice versa.

The preceding analysis became the basis of Mendel's second general genetic principle, the **law of independent assortment:** *During gamete formation, different pairs of alleles segregate independently of each other* (**Fig. 2.16**). The independence of their segregation and the subsequent

random union of gametes at fertilization determine the phenotypes observed. Using the product rule for assessing the probability of independent events, you can see mathematically how the 9:3:3:1 phenotypic ratio observed in a dihybrid cross derives from two separate 3:1 phenotypic ratios. If the two sets of alleles assort independently, the yellow-to-green ratio in the F_2 generation will be $3/4 : 1/4$, and likewise, the round-to-wrinkled ratio will be $3/4 : 1/4$. To find the probability that two independent events such as yellow and round will occur simultaneously in the same plant, you multiply as follows:

Probability of yellow round $= 3/4 \times 3/4 = 9/16$

Probability of yellow wrinkled $= 3/4 \times 1/4 = 3/16$

Probability of green round $= 1/4 \times 3/4 = 3/16$

Probability of green wrinkled $= 1/4 \times 1/4 = 1/16$

Thus, in a population of F_2 plants, there will be a 9:3:3:1 phenotypic ratio of yellow round to yellow wrinkled to green round to green wrinkled.

Branched-line diagrams

A convenient way to keep track of the probabilities of each potential outcome in a genetic cross is to construct a **branched-line diagram (Fig. 2.17)**, which shows all the possibilities for each gene in a sequence of columns. In Fig. 2.17, the first column shows the two possible pea color phenotypes; and the second column demonstrates that each pea color can occur with either of two pea shapes. Again, the 9:3:3:1 ratio of phenotypes is apparent.

Testcrosses with dihybrids

An understanding of dihybrid crosses has many applications. Suppose, for example, that you work for a wholesale nursery, and your assignment is to grow pure-breeding plants guaranteed to produce yellow round peas. How would you proceed? One answer would be to plant the peas

Figure 2.16 The law of independent assortment. In a dihybrid cross, each pair of alleles assorts independently during gamete formation. In the gametes, *Y* is equally likely to be found with *R* or *r* (that is, *Y R* = *Y r*); the same is true for *y* (that is, *y R* = *y r*). As a result, all four possible types of gametes (*Y R, Y r, y R,* and *y r*) are produced in equal frequency among a large population.

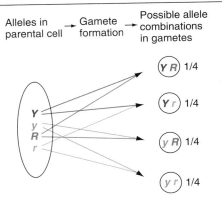

Alleles in parental cell → Gamete formation → Possible allele combinations in gametes

Y
y
R
r

Y R 1/4
Y r 1/4
y R 1/4
y r 1/4

Figure 2.17 Following crosses with branched-line diagrams. A branched-line diagram, which uses a series of columns to track every gene in a cross, provides an organized overview of all possible outcomes. This branched-line diagram of a dihybrid cross generates the same phenotypic ratios as the Punnett square in Fig. 2.15, showing that the two methods are equivalent.

Gene 1	Gene 2	Phenotypes
3/4 yellow	3/4 round	9/16 yellow round
	1/4 wrinkled	3/16 yellow wrinkled
1/4 green	3/4 round	3/16 green round
	1/4 wrinkled	1/16 green wrinkled

Figure 2.18 Testcrosses on dihybrids. Testcrosses involving two pairs of independently assorting alleles yield different, predictable results depending on the tested individual's genotype for the two genes in question.

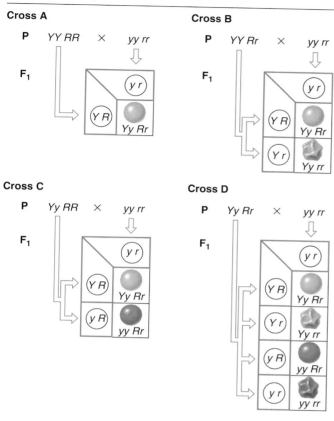

Geneticists use Mendel's laws to calculate probabilities and make predictions

Mendel performed several sets of dihybrid crosses and also carried out **multihybrid crosses:** matings between the F_1 progeny of true-breeding parents that differed in three or more unrelated traits. In all of these experiments, he observed numbers and ratios very close to what he expected on the basis of his two general biological principles: the alleles of a gene segregate during the formation of egg or pollen, and the alleles of different genes assort independently of each other. Mendel's laws of inheritance, in conjunction with the mathematical rules of probability, provide geneticists with powerful tools for predicting and interpreting the results of genetic crosses. But as with all tools, they have their limitations. We examine here both the power and the limitations of Mendelian analysis.

First, the power: Using simple Mendelian analysis, it is possible to make accurate predictions about the offspring of extremely complex crosses. Suppose you want to predict the occurrence of one specific genotype in a cross involving several independently assorting genes. For example, if hybrids that are heterozygous for four traits are allowed to self-fertilize—*Aa Bb Cc Dd* × *Aa Bb Cc Dd*—what proportion of their progeny will have the genotype *AA bb Cc Dd*? You could set up a Punnett square to answer the question. Because for each trait there are two different alleles, the number of different eggs or sperm is found by raising 2 to the power of the number of differing traits (2^n, where n is the number of traits). By this calculation, each hybrid parent in this cross with 4 traits would make $2^4 = 16$ different kinds of gametes. The Punnett square depicting such a cross would thus contain 256 boxes (16×16). This may be fine if you live in a monastery with a bit of time on your hands, but not if you're taking a 1-hour exam. It would be much simpler to analyze the problem by breaking down the multihybrid cross into four independently assorting monohybrid crosses. Remember that the genotypic ratios of each monohybrid cross are 1 homozygote for the dominant allele, to 2 heterozygotes, to 1 homozygote for the recessive allele = $1/4 : 2/4 : 1/4$. Thus, you can find the probability of *AA bb Cc Dd* by multiplying the probability of each independent event: *AA* (1/4 of the progeny produced by *Aa* × *Aa*); *bb* (1/4); *Cc* (2/4); *Dd* (2/4):

$$1/4 \times 1/4 \times 2/4 \times 2/4 = 4/256 = 1/64$$

The Punnett square approach would provide the same answer, but it would require much more time.

If instead of a specific genotype, you want to predict the probability of a certain phenotype, you can again use the product rule as long as you know the phenotypic ratios produced by each pair of alleles in the cross. For

produced from a dihybrid cross that have the desired yellow round phenotype. Only one out of nine of such progeny—those grown from peas with a *YY RR* genotype—will be appropriate for your uses. To find these plants, you could subject each yellow round candidate to a testcross for genotype with a green wrinkled (*yy rr*) plant, as illustrated in **Fig. 2.18.** If the testcross yields all yellow round offspring (testcross A), you can sell your test plant, because you know it is homozygous for both pea color and pea shape. If your testcross yields 1/2 yellow round and 1/2 yellow wrinkled (testcross B), or 1/2 yellow round and 1/2 green round (testcross C), you know that the candidate plant in question is genetically homozygous for one trait and heterozygous for the other and must therefore be discarded. Finally, if the testcross yields 1/4 yellow round, 1/4 yellow wrinkled, 1/4 green round, and 1/4 green wrinkled (testcross D), you know that the plant is a heterozygote for both the pea color and the pea shape genes.

> The law of independent assortment states that the alleles of genes for different traits segregate independently of each other during gamete formation.

example, if in the multihybrid cross of Aa Bb Cc Dd $\times$ Aa Bb Cc Dd, you want to know how many offspring will show the dominant A trait (genotype AA or Aa = 1/4 + 2/4, or 3/4), the recessive b trait (genotype bb = 1/4), the dominant C trait (genotype CC or Cc = 3/4), and the dominant D trait (genotype DD or Dd = 3/4), you simply multiply

$$3/4 \times 1/4 \times 3/4 \times 3/4 = 27/256$$

In this way, the rules of probability make it possible to predict the outcome of very complex crosses.

You can see from these examples that particular problems in genetics are amenable to particular modes of analysis. As a rule of thumb, Punnett squares are excellent for visualizing simple crosses involving a few genes, but they become unwieldy in the dissection of more complicated matings. Direct calculations of probabilities, such as those in the two preceding problems, are useful when you want to know the chances of one or a few outcomes of complex crosses. If, however, you want to know all the outcomes of a multihybrid cross, a branched-line diagram is the best way to go as it will keep track of the possibilities in an organized fashion.

Now, the limitations of Mendelian analysis: Like Mendel, if you were to breed pea plants or corn or any other organism, you would most likely observe some deviation from the ratios you expected in each generation. What can account for such variation? One element is chance, as witnessed in the common coin toss experiment. With each throw, the probability of the coin coming up heads is equal to the likelihood it will come up tails. But if you toss a coin 10 times, you may get 30% (3) heads and 70% (7) tails, or vice versa. If you toss it 100 times, you are more likely to get a result closer to the expected 50% heads and 50% tails. The larger the number of trials, the lower the probability that chance significantly skews the data. This is one reason Mendel worked with large numbers of pea plants. Mendel's laws, in fact, have great predictive power for populations of organisms, but they do not tell us what will happen in any one individual. With a garden full of self-fertilizing monohybrid pea plants, for example, you can expect that 3/4 of the F_2 progeny will show the dominant phenotype and 1/4 the recessive, but you cannot predict the phenotype of any particular F_2 plant. In Chapter 5, we discuss mathematical methods for assessing whether the chance variation observed in a sample of individuals within a population is compatible with a genetic hypothesis.

> Branched-line diagrams or direct calculations of probabilities are often more efficient methods than Punnett squares for the analysis of genetic crosses involving two or more genes.

Mendel's work was unappreciated before 1900

Mendel's insights into the workings of heredity were a breakthrough of monumental proportions. By counting and analyzing data from hundreds of pea plant crosses, he inferred the existence of genes—independent units that determine the observable patterns of inheritance for particular traits. His work explained the reappearance of "hidden" traits, disproved the idea of blended inheritance, and showed that mother and father make an equal genetic contribution to the next generation. The model of heredity that he formulated was so specific that he could test predictions based on it by observation and experiment.

With the exception of Abbot Napp, none of Mendel's contemporaries appreciated the importance of his research. Mendel did not teach at a prestigious university and was not well known outside Brno. Even in Brno, members of the Natural Science Society were disappointed when he presented "Experiments on Plant Hybrids" to them. They wanted to view and discuss intriguing mutants and lovely flowers, so they did not appreciate his numerical analyses. Mendel, it seems, was far ahead of his time. Sadly, despite written requests from Mendel that others try to replicate his studies, no one repeated his experiments. Several citations of his paper between 1866 and 1900 referred to his expertise as a plant breeder but made no mention of his laws. Moreover, at the time Mendel presented his work, no one had yet seen the structures within cells, the *chromosomes,* that actually carry the genes. That would happen only in the next few decades (as described in Chapter 4). If scientists had been able to see these structures, they might have more readily accepted Mendel's ideas, because the chromosomes are actual physical structures that behave exactly as Mendel predicted.

Mendel's work might have had an important influence on early debates about evolution if it had been more widely appreciated. Charles Darwin (1809–1882), who was unfamiliar with Mendel's work, was plagued in his later years by criticism that his explanations for the persistence of variation in organisms were insufficient. Darwin considered such variation a cornerstone of his theory of evolution, maintaining that natural selection would favor particular variants in a given population in a given environment. If the selected combinations of variant traits were passed on to subsequent generations, this transmission of variation would propel evolution. He could not, however, say how that transmission might occur. Had Darwin been aware of Mendel's ideas, he might not have been backed into such an uncomfortable corner.

TOOLS OF GENETICS

Plants as Living Chemical Factories

For millenia, farmers used selective breeding to obtain crop plants or domestic animals with desired phenotypic characteristics, such as hardiness, improved yields, or better taste. Then, beginning in the early twentieth century, breeders were able to apply Mendel's laws to the inheritance of many traits and to make probability-based predictions about the outcomes of crosses. Even with the application of these basic rules of genetics, however, plant and animal breeders cannot always achieve their goals. Desired phenotypes often result from complex interactions involving many genes whose cumulative effects are difficult to predict. Geneticists are also limited by the availability of useful alleles, because most mutations generating new alleles of genes occur extremely rarely.

Beginning in the 1980s, a revolution in genetics took place that made it possible to overcome these limitations. Scientists developed techniques that allowed them to study and then manipulate DNA, the molecule of which genes are made. You will learn about these methods later in this book. These new tools of genetic engineering allow researchers to remove a specific gene from an organism, change the gene in virtually any way they desire, and even move a gene from one organism to an individual of a different species.

Genetic engineering has two major advantages over selective breeding programs. First, genetic engineering is extremely efficient in that researchers can specifically target a gene they think might have an interesting effect on phenotype. Second, investigators can now use their imaginations to make new alleles of genes (or even new genes!) that could otherwise never be found.

One of the most exciting potential applications of these new tools is the genetic engineering of plants to convert them into factories that inexpensively make useful biomolecules such as pharmaceutical drugs or vaccines. Consider, for example, potato plants containing a foreign gene (a *transgene*) from the hepatitis B virus that specifies a protein found on the viral surface. If the potatoes could use this gene to make a large amount of the viral protein, then people who ate these potatoes might develop an immune response to that protein. The immune response would protect them from infection by hepatitis B; in other words, such potatoes would act as an "edible vaccine"

against the virus. Edible vaccines can be grown in a field rather than made in a laboratory; they do not require refrigeration; and they can be administered orally, instead of being injected by medical personnel. The basic idea of an edible vaccine appears to be feasible: Volunteers eating such genetically engineered potatoes have mounted an immune response against hepatitis B, but many technical difficulties remain. For example, the immune response in different people has been quite variable. In addition, cooking the potatoes destroys the vaccine, and few volunteers have been eager to eat sizeable helpings of raw potatoes.

Plants genetically engineered in other ways have already had a huge economic impact. Crop plants such as corn and cotton have been genetically engineered to express the gene for a protein called Bt. This protein, made naturally by the bacterium *Bacillus thuringiensis,* is lethal to insect larvae that ingest it but not to other animals. If an insect pest such as a corn borer eats part of a corn plant making the Bt protein, the corn borer will die. In this sense, the engineered corn manufactures its own insecticide, reducing the need for costly chemical pesticides that may damage the environment. This approach has already shown itself to be very successful: Approximately one-third of all corn currently grown in the United States contains *Bt* transgenes.

Despite its promise, many people are uncomfortable with the concept of genetically modified (GM) crops. Some critics, for example, have raised concerns about this technology's potential negative effects on human health, agricultural communities (particularly in developing countries), and the environment. Researchers who are developing GM crops respond that prior to the advent of genetic engineering, plant breeders altered crops in astonishing ways simply by mating various plants together, and that the occasional exchange of genetic information between different species has occurred naturally throughout evolution.

In the Genetics and Society box on p. 304 of Chapter 9, we describe one way to evaluate GM crops such as Bt corn. This method balances potential benefits against dangers that are calculated relative to risks associated with traditional agricultural products long accepted by society.

For 34 years, Mendel's laws lay dormant—untested, unconfirmed, and unapplied. Then in 1900, 16 years after Mendel's death, Carl Correns, Hugo de Vries, and Erich von Tschermak independently rediscovered and acknowledged his work (**Fig. 2.19**). The scientific community had finally caught up with Mendel. Within a decade, investigators had coined many of the modern terms we have been using: phenotype, genotype, homozygote, heterozygote, gene, and genetics, the label given

to the twentieth-century science of heredity. Mendel's paper provided the new discipline's foundation. His principles and analytic techniques endure today, guiding geneticists and evolutionary biologists in their studies of genetic variation. The Tools of Genetics box on this page explains how modern-day "genetic engineers" apply Mendel's laws to help them artificially manipulate genes and genomes in new ways not achieved by natural evolution on earth.

Figure 2.19 The science of genetics begins with the rediscovery of Mendel. Working independently near the beginning of the twentieth century, Correns, de Vries, and von Tschermak each came to the same conclusions as those Mendel summarized in his laws.

(a) Gregor Mendel

(b) Carl Correns

(c) Hugo de Vries

(d) Erich von Tschermak

2.3 Mendelian Inheritance in Humans

Although many human traits clearly run in families, most do not show a simple Mendelian pattern of inheritance. Suppose, for example, that you have brown eyes, but both your parents' eyes appear to be blue. Because blue is normally considered recessive to brown, does this mean that you are adopted or that your father isn't really your father? Not necessarily, because eye color is influenced by more than one gene.

Like eye color, most common and obvious human phenotypes arise from the interaction of many genes.

In contrast, single-gene traits in people usually involve an abnormality that is disabling or life-threatening. Examples are the progressive mental retardation and other neurological damage of Huntington disease and the clogged lungs and potential respiratory failure of cystic fibrosis. A defective allele of a single gene gives rise to Huntington disease; defective alleles of a different gene are responsible for cystic fibrosis. There were roughly 4300 such single-gene traits known in humans in 2009, and the number continues to grow as new studies confirm the genetic basis of more traits. **Table 2.1** lists some of the most common single-gene traits in humans.

TABLE 2.1	Some of the Most Common Single-Gene Traits in Humans	
Disease	**Effect**	**Incidence of Disease**
Caused by a Recessive Allele		
Thalassemia (chromosome 16 or 11)	Reduced amounts of hemoglobin; anemia, bone and spleen enlargement	1/10 in parts of Italy
Sickle-cell anemia (chromosome 11)	Abnormal hemoglobin; sickle-shaped red cells, anemia, blocked circulation; increased resistance to malaria	1/625 African-Americans
Cystic fibrosis (chromosome 7)	Defective cell membrane protein; excessive mucus production; digestive and respiratory failure	1/2000 Caucasians
Tay-Sachs disease (chromosome 15)	Missing enzyme; buildup of fatty deposit in brain; buildup disrupts mental development	1/3000 Eastern European Jews
Phenylketonuria (PKU) (chromosome 12)	Missing enzyme; mental deficiency	1/10,000 Caucasians
Caused by a Dominant Allele		
Hypercholesterolemia (chromosome 19)	Missing protein that removes cholesterol from the blood; heart attack by age 50	1/122 French Canadians
Huntington disease (chromosome 4)	Progressive mental and neurological damage; neurologic disorders by ages 40–70	1/25,000 Caucasians

Pedigrees aid the study of hereditary traits in human families

Determining a genetic defect's pattern of transmission is not always an easy task because people make slippery genetic subjects. Their generation time is long, and the families they produce are relatively small, which makes statistical analysis difficult. They do not base their choice of mates on purely genetic considerations. There are thus no pure-breeding lines and no controlled matings. And there is rarely a true F_2 generation (like the one in which Mendel observed the 3:1 ratios from which he derived his rules) because brothers and sisters almost never mate.

Geneticists circumvent these difficulties by working with a large number of families or with several generations of a very large family. This allows them to study the large numbers of genetically related individuals needed to establish the inheritance patterns of specific traits. A family history, known as a **pedigree,** is an orderly diagram of a family's relevant genetic features, extending back to at least both sets of grandparents and preferably through as many more generations as possible. From systematic pedigree analysis in the light of Mendel's laws, geneticists can tell if a trait is determined by alternative alleles of a single gene and whether a single-gene trait is dominant or recessive. Because Mendel's principles are so simple and straightforward, a little logic can go a long way in explaining how traits are inherited in humans.

Figure 2.20 shows how to interpret a family pedigree diagram. Squares (□) represent males, circles (○) are females, diamonds (◇) indicate that the sex is unspecified; family members affected by the trait in question are indicated by a filled-in symbol (for example, ■). A single horizontal line connecting a male and a female (□—○) represents a mating, a double connecting line (□═○) designates a **consanguineous mating,** that is, a mating between relatives, and a horizontal line above a series of symbols (○ □ ○) indicates the children of the same parents (a *sibship*) arranged and numbered from left to right in order of

Figure 2.20 Symbols used in pedigree analysis. In the simple pedigree at the bottom, I.1 is the father, I.2 is the mother, and II.1 and II.2 are their sons. The father and the first son are both affected by the disease trait.

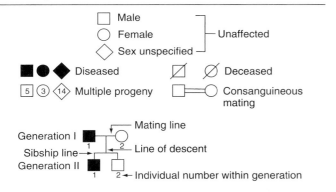

their birth. Roman numerals to the left or right of the diagram indicate the generations.

To reach a conclusion about the mode of inheritance of a family trait, human geneticists must use a pedigree that supplies sufficient information. For example, they could not determine whether the allele causing the disease depicted at the bottom of Fig. 2.20 is dominant or recessive solely on the basis of the simple pedigree shown. The data are consistent with both possibilities. If the trait is dominant, then the father and the affected son are heterozygotes, while the mother and the unaffected son are homozygotes for the recessive normal allele. If instead the trait is recessive, the father and affected son are homozygotes for the recessive disease-causing allele, while the mother and the unaffected son are heterozygotes.

Several kinds of additional information could help resolve this uncertainty. Human geneticists would particularly want to know the frequency at which the trait in question is found in the population from which the family came. If the trait is rare in the population, then the allele giving rise to the trait should also be rare, and the most likely hypothesis would require that the fewest genetically unrelated people carry the allele. Only the father in Fig. 2.20 would need to have a dominant disease-causing allele, but both parents would need to carry a recessive disease-causing allele (the father two copies and the mother one). However, even the information that the trait is rare does not allow us to draw the firm conclusion that it is inherited in a dominant fashion. The pedigree in the figure is so limited that we cannot be sure the two parents are themselves unrelated. As we discuss later in more detail, related parents might have both received a rare recessive allele from their common ancestor. This example illustrates why human geneticists try to collect family histories that cover several generations.

We now look at more extensive pedigrees for the dominant trait of Huntington disease and for the recessive condition of cystic fibrosis. The patterns by which these traits appear in the pedigrees provide important clues that can indicate modes of inheritance and allow geneticists to assign genotypes to family members.

A vertical pattern of inheritance indicates a rare dominant trait

Huntington disease is named for George Huntington, the New York physician who first described its course. This illness usually shows up in middle age and slowly destroys its victims both mentally and physically. Symptoms include intellectual deterioration, severe depression, and jerky, irregular movements, all caused by the progressive death of nerve cells. If one parent develops the symptoms, his or her children have a 50% probability of suffering from the disease, provided they live to adulthood. Because symptoms are not present at birth and manifest themselves only

GENETICS AND SOCIETY

Developing Guidelines for Genetic Screening

In the early 1970s, the United States launched a national screening program for carriers of sickle-cell anemia, a recessive genetic disease that afflicts roughly 1 in 600 African-Americans. The disease is caused by a particular allele, called $Hb\beta^S$, of the β-globin gene; the dominant normal allele is $Hb\beta^A$. The protein determined by the β-globin gene is one component of the oxygen-carrying hemoglobin molecule. $Hb\beta^S$ $Hb\beta^S$ homozygotes have a decrease in oxygen supply, tire easily, and often develop heart failure from stress on the circulatory system.

The national screening program for sickle-cell anemia was based on a simple test of hemoglobin mobility: normal and "sickling" hemoglobins move at different rates in a gel. People who participated in the screening program could use the test results to make informed reproductive decisions. A healthy man, for example, who learned he was a carrier (that is, that he was a $Hb\beta^S$ $Hb\beta^A$ heterozygote), would not have to worry about having an affected child if his mate was a noncarrier. If, however, they were both carriers, they could choose either not to conceive or to conceive in spite of the 25% risk of bearing an afflicted child.

In the 1980s, newly developed techniques allowing direct prenatal detection of the fetal genotype provided additional options. Depending on their beliefs, a couple could decide to continue a pregnancy only if the fetus was not a homozygote for the $Hb\beta^S$ allele, or knowing that their child would have sickle-cell anemia, they could learn how to deal with the symptoms of the condition.

The original sickle-cell screening program, based on detection of the abnormal hemoglobin protein, was not an unqualified success, largely because of insufficient educational follow-through. Many who learned they were carriers mistakenly thought they had the disease. Moreover, because employers and insurance companies obtained access to the information, some $Hb\beta^S$ $Hb\beta^A$ heterozygotes were denied jobs or health insurance for no acceptable reason. Problems of public relations and education thus made a reliable screening test into a source of dissent and alienation.

Today, at-risk families may be screened for a growing number of genetic disorders, thanks to the ability to evaluate genotypes directly. The need to establish guidelines for genetic screening thus becomes more and more pressing. Several related questions reveal the complexity of the issue.

1. *Why carry out genetic screening at all?* The first reason for screening is to obtain information that will benefit individuals. For example, if you learn at an early age that you have a genetic predisposition to heart disease, you can change your lifestyle if necessary to include more exercise and a low-fat diet, thereby improving your chances of staying healthy. You can also use the results from genetic screening to make informed reproductive decisions that reduce the probability of having children affected by a genetic disease. In Brooklyn, New York, for example, a high incidence of a fatal neurodegenerative syndrome known as Tay-Sachs disease was found among a community of Hasidic Jews of Eastern European descent. In this traditional, Old World community, marriages are arranged by rabbis or matchmakers. With confidential access to test results, a rabbi could counsel against marriages between two carriers.

   The second reason for genetic screening, which often conflicts with the first, is to benefit groups within society. Insurance companies and employers, for example, would like to be able to find out who is at risk for various genetic conditions.

2. *Should screening be required or optional?* This is partly a societal decision because the public treasury bears a large part of the cost of caring for the sufferers of genetic diseases. But it is also a personal decision. For most inherited diseases, no cures currently exist. Because the psychological burden of anticipating a fatal late-onset disease for which there is no treatment can be devastating, some people

---

later in life, Huntington disease is known as a **late-onset** genetic condition.

How would you proceed in assigning genotypes to the individuals in the Huntington disease pedigree depicted in **Fig. 2.21**? First, you would need to find out if the disease-producing allele is dominant or recessive. Several clues suggest that Huntington disease is transmitted by a dominant allele of a single gene. Everyone who develops the disease has at least one parent who shows the trait, and in several generations, approximately half of the offspring are affected. The pattern of affected individuals is thus vertical: If you trace back through the ancestors of any affected individual, you would see at least one affected person in each generation, giving a continuous line of family members with the disease. When a disease is rare in the population as a whole, a vertical pattern is strong evidence that a dominant allele causes the trait; the alternative would require that many unrelated people

Figure 2.21 Huntington disease: A rare dominant trait.
All individuals represented by filled-in symbols are heterozygotes (except I-1, who could have been homozygous for the dominant *HD* disease allele); all individuals represented by open symbols are homozygotes for the recessive *HD⁺* normal allele. Among the 14 children of the consanguineous mating, DNA testing shows that some are *HD HD*, some are *HD HD⁺*, and some are *HD⁺ HD⁺*. The diamond designation masks personal details to protect confidentiality.

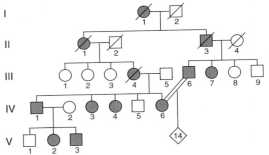

might decide not to be tested. Others may object to testing for religious reasons, or because of confidentiality concerns. On the other hand, timely information about the presence of an abnormal allele that causes a condition for which therapy is available can save lives and reduce suffering. Timely information may also affect childbearing decisions and thereby reduce the incidence of a disease in the population.

3. *If a screening program is established, who should be tested?* The answer depends on what the test is trying to accomplish as well as on its expense. Ultimately, the cost of a procedure must be weighed against the usefulness of the data it provides. In the United States, only one-tenth as many African-Americans as Caucasians are affected by cystic fibrosis, and Asians almost never have the disease. Should all racial groups be tested or only Caucasians? Because of the expense, DNA testing for cystic fibrosis and other relatively rare genetic diseases has not yet been carried out on large populations. Rather it has been reserved for couples or individuals whose family history puts them at risk.

4. *Should private employers and insurance companies be allowed to test their clients and employees?* Some employers advocate genetic screening to reduce the incidence of occupational disease, arguing that they can use data from genetic tests to make sure employees are not assigned to environments that might cause them harm. People with sickle-cell disease, for example, may be at increased risk for a life-threatening episode of severe sickling if exposed to carbon monoxide or trace amounts of cyanide. Critics of this position say that screening violates workers' rights, including the right to privacy, and increases racial and ethnic discrimination in the workplace. Many critics also oppose informing insurance companies of the results of genetic screening, as these companies may deny coverage to people with inherited medical problems or just the possibility of developing such problems. In 2008, President George W. Bush signed into law the Genetic Information Non-discrimination Act, which prohibits insurance companies and employers in the United States from discriminating (through reduced insurance coverage or adverse employment decisions) on the basis of information derived from genetic tests.

A recent high-profile case illustrates some of these issues. The Chicago Bulls, before signing a contract with the basketball player Eddy Curry, wanted him to take a DNA test to find out if he had a genetic predisposition for hypertrophic cardiomyopathy (a potentially fatal condition). The Bulls requested this test because Curry had suffered from episodes of heart arrythmia. Curry refused, citing privacy issues and stating that the test would not be in his or his family's best interest. After a battery of health exams—but not the DNA test—Curry was deemed fit to play, but he was traded to another team and eventually signed a six-year, $56 million contract with the New York Knicks.

5. *Finally, how should people be educated about the meaning of test results?* In one small-community screening program, people identified as carriers of the recessive, life-threatening blood disorder known as β-thalassemia were ostracized; as a result, carriers ended up marrying one another. This only made medical matters worse as it greatly increased the chances that their children would be born with two copies of the defective allele and thus the disease. By contrast, in Ferrara, Italy, where 30 new cases of β-thalassemia had been reported every year, extensive screening was so successfully combined with intensive education that the 1980s passed with no more than a few new cases of the disease.

Given all of these considerations, what kind of guidelines would you like to see established to ensure that genetic screening reaches the right people at the right time, and that information gained from such screening is used for the right purposes?

---

carry a rare recessive allele. (A recessive trait that is extremely common might also show up in every generation; we examine this possibility in Problem 34 at the end of this chapter.)

In tracking a dominant allele through a pedigree, you can view every mating between an affected and an unaffected partner as analogous to a testcross. If some of the offspring do not have Huntington's, you know the parent showing the trait is a heterozygote. You can check your genotype assignments against the answers in the caption to Fig. 2.21.

No effective treatment yet exists for Huntington disease, and because of its late onset, there was until the 1980s no way for children of a Huntington's parent to know before middle age—usually until well after their own childbearing years—whether they carried the Huntington disease allele (*HD*). Children of Huntington's parents have a 50% probability of inheriting *HD* and, before they are diagnosed, a 25% probability of passing the defective allele on to one of their children. In the mid-1980s, with new knowledge of the gene, molecular geneticists developed a DNA test that determines whether an individual carries the *HD* allele. Because of the lack of effective treatment for the disease, some young adults whose parents died of Huntington's prefer not to be tested so that they will not prematurely learn their own fate. However, other at-risk individuals employ the test for the *HD* allele to guide their decisions about having children. If someone whose parent had Huntington disease does not have *HD*, he or she has no chance of developing the disease or of transmitting it to offspring. If the test shows the presence of *HD*, the at-risk person and his or her partner might chose to conceive a child, obtain a prenatal diagnosis of the fetus, and then, depending on their beliefs, elect an abortion if the fetus is affected. The Genetics and Society box "Developing Guidelines for Genetic Screening" on the two previous pages discusses significant social and ethical issues raised by information obtained from family pedigrees and molecular tests.

> If an individual is affected by a rare dominant trait, the trait should also affect at least one of that person's parents, one of that person's grandparents, and so on.

A horizontal pattern of inheritance indicates a rare recessive trait

Unlike Huntington disease, most confirmed single-gene traits in humans are recessive. This is because, with the exception of late-onset traits, deleterious dominant traits are unlikely to be transmitted to the next generation. For example, if people affected with Huntington disease died by the age of 10, the trait would disappear from the population. In contrast, individuals can carry one allele for a recessive trait without ever being affected by any symptoms. **Figure 2.22** shows three pedigrees for cystic fibrosis (CF), the most commonly inherited recessive disease among Caucasian children in the United States. A double dose of the recessive *CF* allele causes a fatal disorder in which the lungs, pancreas, and other organs become clogged with a thick, viscous mucus that can interfere with breathing and digestion. One in every 2000 white Americans is born with cystic fibrosis, and only 10% of them survive into their 30s.

Figure 2.22 Cystic fibrosis: A recessive condition. In **(a)**, the two affected individuals (VI-4 and VII-1) are *CF CF*; that is, homozygotes for the recessive disease allele. Their unaffected parents must be carriers, so V-1, V-2, VI-1, and VI-2 must all be *CF CF⁺*. Individuals II-2, II-3, III-2, III-4, IV-2, and IV-4 are probably also carriers. We cannot determine which of the founders (I-1 or I-2) was a carrier, so we designate their genotypes as *CF⁺–*. Because the *CF* allele is relatively rare, it is likely that II-1, II-4, III-1, III-3, IV-1, and IV-3 are *CF⁺CF⁺* homozygotes. The genotype of the remaining unaffected people (VI-3, VI-5, and VII-2) is uncertain (*CF⁺–*). (**b** and **c**) These two families demonstrate horizontal patterns of inheritance. Without further information, the unaffected children in each pedigree must be regarded as having a *CF⁺–* genotype.

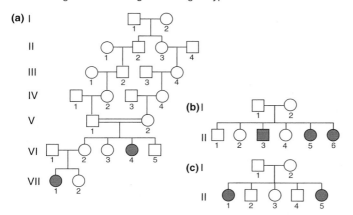

There are two salient features of the CF pedigrees. First, the family pattern of people showing the trait is often horizontal: The parents, grandparents, and great-grandparents of children born with CF do not themselves manifest the disease, while several brothers and sisters in a single generation may. A horizontal pedigree pattern is a strong indication that the trait is recessive. The unaffected parents are heterozygous **carriers:** They bear a dominant normal allele that masks the effects of the recessive abnormal one. An estimated 12 million Americans are carriers of the recessive *CF* allele. **Table 2.2** summarizes some of the clues found in pedigrees that can help you decide whether a trait is caused by a dominant or a recessive allele.

The second salient feature of the CF pedigrees is that many of the couples who produce afflicted children are blood relatives; that is, their mating is consanguineous (as indicated by the double line). In Fig. 2.22a, the consanguineous mating in generation V is between third cousins. Of course, children with cystic fibrosis can also have unrelated carrier parents, but because relatives share genes, their offspring have a much greater than average chance of receiving two copies of a rare allele. Whether or not they are related, carrier parents are both heterozygotes. Thus among their offspring, the proportion of unaffected to affected children is expected to be 3:1. To look at it another way, the chances are that one out of four children of two heterozygous carriers will be homozygous CF sufferers.

You can gauge your understanding of this inheritance pattern by assigning a genotype to each person in Fig. 2.22 and then checking your answers against the caption. Note that for several individuals, such as the generation I individuals in part (a) of the figure, it is

TABLE 2.2	How to Recognize Dominant and Recessive Traits in Pedigrees

Dominant Traits

1. Affected children always have at least one affected parent.

2. As a result, dominant traits show a *vertical pattern* of inheritance: the trait shows up in every generation.

3. Two affected parents can produce unaffected children, if both parents are heterozygotes.

Recessive Traits

1. Affected individuals can be the children of two unaffected carriers, particularly as a result of consanguineous matings.

2. All the children of two affected parents should be affected.

3. *Rare* recessive traits show a *horizontal pattern* of inheritance: the trait first appears among several members of one generation and is not seen in earlier generations.

4. Recessive traits may show a vertical pattern of inheritance if the trait is extremely common in the population.

impossible to assign a full genotype. We know that one of these people must be the carrier who supplied the original *CF* allele, but we do not know if it was the male or the female. As with an ambiguous dominant phenotype in peas, the unknown second allele is indicated by a dash.

In Fig. 2.22a, a mating between the unrelated carriers VI-1 and VI-2 produced a child with cystic fibrosis. How likely is such a marriage between unrelated carriers for a recessive genetic condition? The answer depends on the gene in question and the particular population into which a person is born. As Table 2.1 on p. 30 shows, the incidence of genetic diseases (and thus the frequency of their carriers) varies markedly among populations. Such variation reflects the distinct genetic histories of different groups. The area of genetics that analyzes differences among groups of individuals is called *population genetics*, a subject we cover in detail in Chapter 19. Notice that in

Fig. 2.22a, several unrelated, unaffected people, such as II-1 and II-4, married into the family under consideration. Although it is highly probable that these individuals are homozygotes for the normal allele of the gene (CF^+CF^+), there is a small chance (whose magnitude depends on the population) that any one of them could be a carrier of the disease.

Genetic researchers identified the cystic fibrosis gene in 1989, but they are still in the process of developing a gene therapy that would ameliorate the disease's debilitating symptoms (review the Fast Forward box "Genes Encode Proteins" on pp. 20–21).

If an individual is affected by a rare recessive trait, it is likely that none of that person's ancestors displayed the same trait. In many cases, the affected individual is the product of a consanguineous mating.

Connections

Mendel answered the three basic questions about heredity as follows: To "What is inherited?" he replied, "alleles of genes." To "How is it inherited?" he responded, "according to the principles of segregation and independent assortment." And to "What is the role of chance in heredity?" he said, "for each individual, inheritance is determined by chance, but within a population, this chance operates in a context of strictly defined probabilities."

Within a decade of the 1900 rediscovery of Mendel's work, numerous breeding studies had shown that Mendel's laws hold true not only for seven pairs of antagonistic characteristics in peas, but for an enormous diversity of traits in a wide variety of sexually reproducing plant and animal species, including four-o'clock flowers, beans, corn, wheat, fruit flies, chickens, mice, horses, and humans. Some of these same breeding studies, however, raised a challenge to the new genetics. For certain traits

in certain species, the studies uncovered unanticipated phenotypic ratios, or the results included F_1 and F_2 progeny with novel phenotypes that resembled those of neither pure-breeding parent.

These phenomena could not be explained by Mendel's hypothesis that for each gene, two alternative alleles, one completely dominant, the other recessive, determine a single trait. We now know that most common traits, including skin color, eye color, and height in humans, are determined by interactions between two or more genes. We also know that within a given population, more than two alleles may be present for some of those genes. Chapter 3 shows how the genetic analysis of such complex traits, that is, traits produced by complex interactions between genes and between genes and the environment, extended rather than contradicted Mendel's laws of inheritance.

ESSENTIAL CONCEPTS

1. Discrete units called genes control the appearance of inherited traits.

2. Genes come in alternative forms called alleles that are responsible for the expression of different forms of a trait.

3. Body cells of sexually reproducing organisms carry two copies of each gene. When the two copies of a gene are the same allele, the individual is

   homozygous for that gene. When the two copies of a gene are different alleles, the individual is heterozygous for that gene.

4. The genotype is a description of the allelic combination of the two copies of a gene present in an individual. The phenotype is the observable form of the trait that the individual expresses.

5. A cross between two parental lines (P) that are pure-breeding for alternative alleles of a gene will produce a first filial (F_1) generation of hybrids that are heterozygous. The phenotype expressed by these hybrids is determined by the dominant allele of the pair, and this phenotype is the same as that expressed by individuals homozygous for the dominant allele. The phenotype associated with the recessive allele will reappear only in the F_2 generation in individuals homozygous for this allele. In crosses between F_1 heterozygotes, the dominant and recessive phenotypes will appear in the F_2 generation in a ratio of 3:1.

6. The two copies of each gene segregate during the formation of gametes. As a result, each egg and each sperm or pollen grain contains only one copy, and thus, only one allele, of each gene. Male and female gametes unite at random at fertilization. Mendel described this process as the law of segregation.

7. The segregation of alleles of any one gene is independent of the segregation of the alleles of other genes. Mendel described this process as the law of independent assortment. According to this law, crosses between Aa Bb F_1 dihybrids will generate F_2 progeny with a phenotypic ratio of 9 (A– B–) : 3 (A– bb) : 3 (aa B–) : 1 (aa bb).

On Our Website | www.mhhe.com/hartwell4

Annotated Suggested Readings and Links to Other Websites

- More about Mendel and the early history of genetics
- More on the practice of human genetics
- An online database of human genetic diseases (OMIM)

Specialized Topics

- The binomial expansion: application of an advanced statistical method to genetics
- Conditional probabilities (Bayesian analysis): application of another advanced statistical method to genetic analysis

Solved Problems

Solving Genetics Problems

The best way to evaluate and increase your understanding of the material in the chapter is to apply your knowledge in solving genetics problems. Genetics word problems are like puzzles. Take them in slowly—don't be overwhelmed by the whole problem. Identify useful facts given in the problem, and use the facts to deduce additional information. Use genetic principles and logic to work toward the solutions. The more problems you do, the easier they become. In doing problems, you will not only solidify your understanding of genetic concepts, but you will also develop basic analytical skills that are applicable in many disciplines.

Solving genetics problems requires more than simply plugging numbers into formulas. Each problem is unique and requires thoughtful evaluation of the information given and the question being asked. The following are general guidelines you can follow in approaching these word problems:

a. Read through the problem once to get some sense of the concepts involved.

b. Go back through the problem, noting all the information supplied to you. For example, genotypes or phenotypes of offspring or parents may be given to you or implied in the problem. Represent the known information in a symbolic format—assign symbols for alleles; use these symbols to indicate genotypes; make a diagram of the crosses including genotypes and phenotypes given or implied. Be sure that you do not assign different letters of the alphabet to two alleles of the same gene, as this can cause confusion. Also, be careful to discriminate clearly between the upper- and lowercases of letters, such as $C(c)$ or $S(s)$.

c. Now, reassess the question and work toward the solution using the information given. Make sure you answer the question being asked!

d. When you finish the problem, check to see that the answer makes sense. You can often check solutions by working backwards; that is, see if you can reconstruct the data from your answer.

e. After you have completed a question and checked your answer, spend a minute to think about which major concepts were involved in the solution. This is a critical step for improving your understanding of genetics.

For each chapter, the logic involved in solving two or three types of problems is described in detail.

I. In cats, white patches are caused by the dominant allele P, while pp individuals are solid-colored. Short hair is caused by a dominant allele S, while ss cats have long hair. A long-haired cat with patches whose mother was solid-colored and short-haired mates with a short-haired, solid-colored cat whose mother was long-haired and solid-colored. What kinds of kittens can arise from this mating, and in what proportions?

Answer

The solution to this problem requires an understanding of dominance/recessiveness, gamete formation, and the independent assortment of alleles of two genes in a cross.

First make a representation of the known information:

Mothers:	solid, short-haired		solid, long-haired
Cross:	cat 1		cat 2
	patches, long-haired	×	solid, short-haired

What genotypes can you assign? Any cat showing a recessive phenotype must be homozygous for the recessive allele. Therefore the long-haired cats are ss; solid cats are pp. Cat 1 is long-haired, so it must be homozygous for the recessive allele (ss). This cat has the dominant phenotype of patches and could be either PP or Pp, but because the mother was pp and could only contribute a p allele in her gametes, the cat must be Pp. Cat 1's full genotype is $Pp\ ss$. Similarly, cat 2 is solid-colored, so it must be homozygous for the recessive allele (pp). Because this cat is short-haired, it could have either the SS or Ss genotype. Its mother was long-haired (ss) and could only contribute an s allele in her gamete, so cat 2 must be heterozygous Ss. The full genotype is $pp\ Ss$.

The cross is therefore between a $Pp\ ss$ (cat 1) and a $pp\ Ss$ (cat 2). To determine the types of kittens, first establish the types of gametes that can be produced by each cat and then set up a Punnett square to determine the genotypes of the offspring. Cat 1 ($Pp\ ss$) produces Ps and ps gametes in equal proportions. Cat 2 ($pp\ Ss$) produces pS and ps gametes in equal proportions. *Four types of kittens can result from this mating with equal probability:* Pp Ss *(patches, short-haired),* Pp ss *(patches, long-haired),* pp Ss *(solid, short-haired), and* pp ss *(solid, long-haired).*

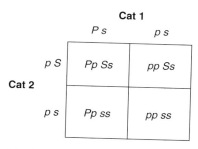

You could also work through this problem using the product rule of probability instead of a Punnett square. The principles are the same: gametes produced in equal amounts by either parent are combined at random.

Cat 1 gamete		Cat 2 gamete		Progeny
1/2 $P\ s$	×	1/2 $p\ S$	→	1/4 $Pp\ Ss$ patches, short-haired
1/2 $P\ s$	×	1/2 $p\ s$	→	1/4 $Pp\ ss$ patches, long-haired
1/2 $p\ s$	×	1/2 $p\ S$	→	1/4 $pp\ Ss$ solid-colored, short-haired
1/2 $p\ s$	×	1/2 $p\ s$	→	1/4 $pp\ ss$ solid-colored, long-haired

II. In tomatoes, red fruit is dominant to yellow fruit, and purple stems are dominant to green stems. The progeny from one mating consisted of 305 red fruit, purple stem plants; 328 red fruit, green stem plants; 110 yellow fruit, purple stem plants; and 97 yellow fruit, green stem plants. What were the genotypes of the parents in this cross?

Answer

This problem requires an understanding of independent assortment in a dihybrid cross as well as the ratios predicted from monohybrid crosses.

Designate the alleles:

R = red, r = yellow

P = purple stems, p = green stems

In genetics problems, the ratios of offspring can indicate the genotype of parents. You will usually need to total the number of progeny and approximate the ratio of offspring in each of the different classes. For this problem, in which the inheritance of two traits is given, consider each trait independently. For red fruit, there are 305 + 328 = 633 red-fruited plants out of a total of 840 plants. This value (633/840) is close to 3/4. About 1/4 of the plants have yellow fruit (110 + 97 = 207/840). From Mendel's work, you know that a 3:1 phenotypic ratio results from crosses between plants that are hybrid (heterozygous) for one gene. Therefore, the genotype for fruit color of each parent must have been Rr.

For stem color, 305 + 110 or 415/840 plants had purple stems. About half had purple stems, and the other half (328 + 97) had green stems. A 1:1 phenotypic ratio occurs when a heterozygote is mated to a homozygous recessive (as in a testcross). The parents' genotypes must have been Pp and pp for stem color.

The complete genotype of the parent plants in this cross was Rr Pp × Rr pp.

III. Tay-Sachs is a recessive lethal disease in which there is neurological deterioration early in life. This disease is rare in the population overall but is found at relatively high frequency in Ashkenazi Jews from Central Europe. A woman whose maternal uncle had the disease is trying to determine the probability that she and her husband could have an affected child. Her father does not come from a high-risk population. Her husband's sister died of the disease at an early age.
   a. Draw the pedigree of the individuals described. Include the genotypes where possible.
   b. Determine the probability that the couple's first child will be affected.

Answer

This problem requires an understanding of dominance/recessiveness and probability. Designate the alleles:

T = normal allele; *t* = Tay-Sachs allele

The genotypes of the two affected individuals, the woman's uncle (II-1) and the husband's sister (III-3) are *tt*. Because the uncle was affected, his parents must

have been heterozygous. There was a 1/4 chance that these parents had a homozygous recessive (affected) child, a 2/4 chance that they had a heterozygous child (carrier), and a 1/4 chance they had a homozygous dominant (unaffected) child. However, you have been told that the woman's mother (II-2) is unaffected, so the mother could only have had a heterozygous or a homozygous dominant genotype. Consider the probability that these two genotypes will occur. If you were looking at a Punnett square, there would be only three combinations of alleles possible for the normal mother. Two of these are heterozygous combinations and one is homozygous dominant. There is a 2/3 chance (2 out of the 3 possible cases) that the mother was a carrier. The father was not from a high-risk population, so we can assume that he is homozygous dominant. There is a 2/3 chance that the wife's mother was heterozygous and if so, a 1/2 chance that the wife inherited a recessive allele from her mother. Because both conditions are necessary for inheritance of a recessive allele, the individual probabilities are multiplied, and the probability that the wife (III-1) is heterozygous is 2/3 × 1/2.

The husband (III-2) has a sister who died from the disease; therefore, his parents must have been heterozygous. The probability that he is a carrier is 2/3 (using the same rationale as for II-2). The probability that the man and woman are both carriers is 2/3 × 1/2 × 2/3. Because there is a 1/4 probability that a particular child of two carriers will be affected, *the overall probability that the first child of this couple (III-1 and III-2) will be affected is 2/3 × 1/2 × 2/3 × 1/4 = 4/72, or 1/18.*

Problems

Interactive Web Exercise

The National Center for Biotechnology Information (NCBI) at the National Institutes of Health maintains several databases that are a treasure trove for geneticists. One of these databases is Online Mendelian Inheritance in Man (OMIM), which catalogs information about inherited conditions in humans and the genes involved in these syndromes. Our website at www.mhhe.com/hartwell4 contains a brief exercise to introduce you to the use of this database; once at the website, go to Chapter 2 and click on "Interactive Web Exercise."

Vocabulary

1. For each of the terms in the left column, choose the best matching phrase in the right column.

   a. phenotype

   b. alleles

   c. independent assortment

   d. gametes

   e. gene

   f. segregation

   g. heterozygote

   h. dominant

   i. F$_1$

   j. testcross

   k. genotype

   l. recessive

   m. dihybrid cross

   n. homozygote

   1. having two identical alleles of a given gene
   2. the allele expressed in the phenotype of the heterozygote
   3. alternate forms of a gene
   4. observable characteristic
   5. a cross between individuals both heterozygous for two genes
   6. alleles of one gene separate into gametes randomly with respect to alleles of other genes
   7. reproductive cells containing only one copy of each gene
   8. the allele that does not contribute to the phenotype of the heterozygote
   9. the cross of an individual of ambiguous genotype with a homozygous recessive individual
   10. an individual with two different alleles of a gene
   11. the heritable entity that determines a characteristic
   12. the alleles an individual has
   13. the separation of the two alleles of a gene into different gametes
   14. offspring of the P generation

Section 2.1

2. During the millennia in which selective breeding was practiced, why did breeders fail to uncover the principle that traits are governed by discrete units of inheritance (that is, by genes)?

3. Describe the characteristics of the garden pea that made it a good organism for Mendel's analysis of the basic principles of inheritance. Evaluate how easy or difficult it would be to make a similar study of inheritance in humans by considering the same attributes you described for the pea.

Section 2.2

4. An albino corn snake is crossed with a normal-colored corn snake. The offspring are all normal-colored. When these first generation progeny snakes are crossed among themselves, they produce 32 normal-colored snakes and 10 albino snakes.
   a. Which of these phenotypes is controlled by the dominant allele?
   b. In these snakes, albino color is determined by a recessive allele *a,* and normal pigmentation is determined by the *A* allele. A normal-colored female snake is involved in a testcross. This cross produces 10 normal-colored and 11 albino offspring. What are the genotypes of the parents and the offspring?

5. Two short-haired cats mate and produce six short-haired and two long-haired kittens. What does this information suggest about how hair length is inherited?

6. Piebald spotting is a condition found in humans in which there are patches of skin that lack pigmentation. The condition results from the inability of pigment-producing cells to migrate properly during development. Two adults with piebald spotting have one child who has this trait and a second child with normal skin pigmentation.
   a. Is the piebald spotting trait dominant or recessive? What information led you to this answer?
   b. What are the genotypes of the parents?

7. As a *Drosophila* research geneticist, you keep stocks of flies of specific genotypes. You have a fly that has normal wings (dominant phenotype). Flies with short wings are homozygous for a recessive allele of the wing-length gene. You need to know if this fly with normal wings is pure-breeding or heterozygous for the wing-length trait. What cross would you do to determine the genotype, and what results would you expect for each possible genotype?

8. A mutant cucumber plant has flowers that fail to open when mature. Crosses can be done with this plant by manually opening and pollinating the flowers with pollen from another plant. When closed × open crosses were done, all the F$_1$ progeny were open. The F$_2$ plants were 145 open and 59 closed. A cross of closed × F$_1$ gave 81 open and 77 closed. How is the closed trait inherited? What evidence led you to your conclusion?

9. In a particular population of mice, certain individuals display a phenotype called "short tail," which is inherited as a dominant trait. Some individuals display a recessive trait called "dilute," which affects coat color. Which of these traits would be easier to eliminate from the population by selective breeding? Why?

10. In humans, a dimple in the chin is a dominant characteristic.
   a. A man who does not have a chin dimple has children with a woman with a chin dimple whose mother lacked the dimple. What proportion of their children would be expected to have a chin dimple?
   b. A man with a chin dimple and a woman who lacks the dimple produce a child who lacks a dimple. What is the man's genotype?
   c. A man with a chin dimple and a nondimpled woman produce eight children, all having the chin dimple. Can you be certain of the man's genotype? Why or why not? What genotype is more likely, and why?

11. Among native Americans, two types of earwax (cerumen) are seen, dry and sticky. A geneticist studied the inheritance of this trait by observing the types of offspring produced by different kinds of matings. He observed the following numbers:

Parents	Number of mating pairs	Offspring Sticky	Dry
Sticky × sticky	10	32	6
Sticky × dry	8	21	9
Dry × dry	12	0	42

   a. How is earwax type inherited?
   b. Why are there no 3:1 or 1:1 ratios in the data shown in the chart?

12. Imagine you have just purchased a black stallion of unknown genotype. You mate him to a red mare, and she delivers twin foals, one red and one black. Can you tell from these results how color is inherited, assuming that alternative alleles of a single gene are involved? What crosses could you do to work this out?

13. If you roll a die (singular of dice), what is the probability you will roll: (a) a 6? (b) an even number? (c) a number divisible by 3? (d) If you roll a pair of dice, what is the probability that you will roll two 6s? (e) an even number on one and an odd number on the other? (f) matching numbers? (g) two numbers both over 4?

14. In a standard deck of playing cards, there are four suits (red suits = hearts and diamonds, black suits = spades and clubs). Each suit has thirteen cards: Ace (A), 2, 3, 4, 5, 6, 7, 8, 9, 10, and the face cards Jack (J), Queen (Q), and King (K). In a single draw, what is the probability that you will draw a face card? A red card? A red face card?

15. How many genetically different eggs could be formed by women with the following genotypes?
    a. *Aa bb CC DD*
    b. *AA Bb Cc dd*
    c. *Aa Bb cc Dd*
    d. *Aa Bb Cc Dd*

16. What is the probability of producing a child that will phenotypically resemble either one of the two parents in the following four crosses? How many phenotypically different kinds of progeny could potentially result from each of the four crosses?
    a. *Aa Bb Cc Dd* × *aa bb cc dd*
    b. *aa bb cc dd* × *AA BB CC DD*
    c. *Aa Bb Cc Dd* × *Aa Bb Cc Dd*
    d. *aa bb cc dd* × *aa bb cc dd*

17. A mouse sperm of genotype *a B C D E* fertilizes an egg of genotype *a b c D e*. What are all the possibilities for the genotypes of (a) the zygote and (b) a sperm or egg of the baby mouse that develops from this fertilization?

18. Galactosemia is a recessive human disease that is treatable by restricting lactose and glucose in the diet. Susan Smithers and her husband are both heterozygous for the galactosemia gene.
    a. Susan is pregnant with twins. If she has fraternal (nonidentical) twins, what is the probability both of the twins will be girls who have galactosemia?
    b. If the twins are identical, what is the probability that both will be girls and have galactosemia?

    For parts *c–g,* assume that none of the children is a twin.

    c. If Susan and her husband have four children, what is the probability that none of the four will have galactosemia?
    d. If the couple has four children, what is the probability that at least one child will have galactosemia?
    e. If the couple has four children, what is the probability that the first two will have galactosemia and the second two will not?
    f. If the couple has three children, what is the probability that two of the children will have galactosemia and one will not, regardless of order?
    g. If the couple has four children with galactosemia, what is the probability that their next child will have galactosemia?

19. Albinism is a condition in which pigmentation is lacking. In humans, the result is white hair, nonpigmented skin, and pink eyes. The trait in humans is caused by a recessive allele. Two normal parents have an albino child. What are the parents' genotypes? What is the probability that the next child will be albino?

20. A cross between two pea plants, both of which grew from yellow round seeds, gave the following numbers of seeds: 156 yellow round and 54 yellow wrinkled. What are the genotypes of the parent plants? (Yellow and round are dominant traits.)

21. A third-grader decided to breed guinea pigs for her school science project. She went to a pet store and bought a male with smooth black fur and a female with rough white fur. She wanted to study the inheritance of those features and was sorry to see that the first litter of eight contained only rough black animals. To her disappointment, the second litter from those same parents contained seven rough black animals. Soon the first litter had begun to produce F_2 offspring, and they showed a variety of coat types. Before long, the child had 125 F_2 guinea pigs. Eight of them had smooth white coats, 25 had smooth black coats, 23 were rough and white, and 69 were rough and black.
    a. How are the coat color and texture characteristics inherited? What evidence supports your conclusions?
    b. What phenotypes and proportions of offspring should the girl expect if she mates one of the smooth white F_2 females to an F_1 male?

22. The self-fertilization of an F_1 pea plant produced from a parent plant homozygous for yellow and wrinkled seeds and a parent homozygous for green and round seeds resulted in a pod containing seven F_2 peas. (Yellow and round are dominant.) What is the probability that all seven peas in the pod are yellow and round?

23. The achoo syndrome (sneezing in response to bright light) and trembling chin (triggered by anxiety) are both dominant traits in humans.
    a. What is the probability that the first child of parents who are heterozygous for both the achoo gene and trembling chin will have achoo syndrome but lack the trembling chin?
    b. What is the probability that the first child will not have achoo syndrome or trembling chin?

24. A pea plant from a pure-breeding strain that is tall, has green pods, and has purple flowers that are terminal is crossed to a plant from a pure-breeding strain that is dwarf, has yellow pods, and has white flowers that are axial. The F_1 plants are all tall and have purple axial flowers as well as green pods.
    a. What phenotypes do you expect to see in the F_2?
    b. What phenotypes and ratios would you predict in the progeny from crossing an F_1 plant to the dwarf parent?

25. The following chart shows the results of different matings between jimsonweed plants that had either purple or white flowers and spiny or smooth pods. Determine the dominant allele for the two traits and indicate the genotypes of the parents for each of the crosses.

Parents	Offspring			
	Purple Spiny	White Spiny	Purple Smooth	White Smooth
a. purple spiny × purple spiny	94	32	28	11
b. purple spiny × purple smooth	40	0	38	0
c. purple spiny × white spiny	34	30	0	0
d. purple spiny × white spiny	89	92	31	27
e. purple smooth × purple smooth	0	0	36	11
f. white spiny × white spiny	0	45	0	16

26. A pea plant heterozygous for plant height, pod shape, and flower color was selfed. The progeny consisted of 272 tall, inflated pods, purple flowers; 92 tall, inflated, white flowers; 88 tall, flat pods, purple; 93 dwarf, inflated, purple; 35 tall, flat, white; 31 dwarf, inflated, white; 29 dwarf, flat, purple; 11 dwarf, flat, white. Which alleles are dominant in this cross?

27. In the fruit fly *Drosophila melanogaster,* the following genes and mutations are known:

Wingsize: recessive allele for tiny wings *t;* dominant allele for normal wings *T.*

Eye shape: recessive allele for narrow eyes *n;* dominant allele for normal (oval) eyes *N.*

For each of the following crosses, give the genotypes of each of the parents.

Male		Female		
Wings	Eyes	Wings	Eyes	Offspring
1 tiny	oval	× tiny	oval	78 tiny wings, oval eyes
				24 tiny wings, narrow eyes
2 normal	narrow	× tiny	oval	45 normal wings, oval eyes
				40 normal wings, narrow eyes
				38 tiny wings, oval eyes
				44 tiny wings, narrow eyes
3 normal	narrow	× normal	oval	35 normal wings, oval eyes
				29 normal wings, narrow eyes
				10 tiny wings, oval eyes
				11 tiny wings, narrow eyes
4 normal	narrow	× normal	oval	62 normal wings, oval eyes
				19 tiny wings, oval eyes

28. Based on the information you discovered in Problem 27 above, answer the following:
   a. A female fruit fly with genotype *Tt nn* is mated to a male of genotype *Tt Nn*. What is the probability that any one of their offspring will have normal phenotypes for both characters?
   b. What phenotypes would you expect among the offspring of this cross? If you obtained 200 progeny, how many of each phenotypic class would you expect?

Section 2.3

29. For each of the following human pedigrees, indicate whether the inheritance pattern is recessive or dominant. What feature(s) of the pedigree did you use to determine the inheritance? Give the genotypes of affected individuals and of individuals who carry the disease allele.

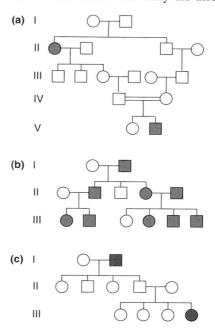

30. Consider the pedigree that follows for cutis laxa, a connective tissue disorder in which the skin hangs in loose folds.
   a. Assuming complete penetrance and that the trait is rare, what is the apparent mode of inheritance?
   b. What is the probability that individual II-2 is a carrier?
   c. What is the probability that individual II-3 is a carrier?
   d. What is the probability that individual III-1 is affected by the disease?

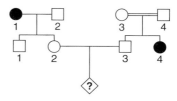

31. A young couple went to see a genetic counselor because each had a sibling affected with cystic fibrosis. (Cystic fibrosis is a recessive disease, and neither member of the couple nor any of their four parents is affected.)
   a. What is the probability that the female of this couple is a carrier?
   b. What are the chances that their child will be affected with cystic fibrosis?
   c. What is the probability that their child will be a carrier of the cystic fibrosis mutation?

32. Huntington disease is a rare fatal, degenerative neurological disease in which individuals start to show symptoms, on average, in their 40s. It is caused by a dominant allele. Joe, a man in his 20s, just learned that his father has Huntington disease.
  a. What is the probability that Joe will also develop the disease?
  b. Joe and his new wife have been eager to start a family. What is the probability that their first child will eventually develop the disease?

33. Is the disease shown in the following pedigree dominant or recessive? Why? Based on this limited pedigree, do you think the disease allele is rare or common in the population? Why?

34. Figure 2.21 on p. 32 shows the inheritance of Huntington disease in a family from a small village near Lake Maracaibo in Venezuela. The village was founded by a small number of immigrants, and generations of their descendents have remained concentrated in this isolated location. The allele for Huntington disease has remained unusually prevalent there.
  a. Why could you not conclude definitively that the disease is the result of a dominant or a recessive allele solely by looking at this pedigree?
  b. Is there any information you could glean from the family's history that might imply the disease is due to a dominant rather than a recessive allele?

35. The common grandfather of two first cousins has hereditary hemochromatosis, a recessive condition causing an abnormal buildup of iron in the body. Neither of the cousins has the disease nor do any of their relatives.
  a. If the first cousins mated with each other and had a child, what is the chance that the child would have hemochromatosis? Assume that the unrelated, unaffected parents of the cousins are not carriers.
  b. How would your calculation change if you knew that 1 out of every 10 unaffected people in the population (including the unrelated parents of these cousins) was a carrier for hemochromatosis?

36. People with nail-patella syndrome have poorly developed or absent kneecaps and nails. Individuals with alkaptonuria have arthritis as well as urine that darkens when exposed to air. Both nail-patella syndrome and alkaptonuria are rare phenotypes. In the following pedigree, vertical red lines indicate individuals with nail-patella syndrome, while horizontal green lines denote individuals with alkaptonuria.
  a. What are the most likely modes of inheritance of nail-patella syndrome and alkaptonuria? What genotypes can you ascribe to each of the individuals in the pedigree for both of these phenotypes?
  b. In a mating between IV-2 and IV-5, what is the chance that the child produced would have both nail-patella syndrome and alkaptonuria? Nail-patella syndrome alone? Alkaptonuria alone? Neither defect?

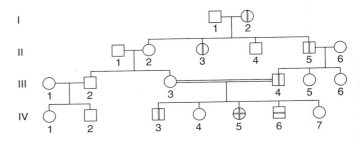

37. Midphalangeal hair (hair on top of the middle segment of the fingers) is a common phenotype caused by a dominant allele M. Homozygotes for the recessive allele (mm) lack hair on the middle segment of their fingers. Among 1000 families in which both parents had midphalangeal hair, 1853 children showed the trait while 209 children did not. Explain this result.

Extensions to Mendel's Laws

Unlike the pea traits that Mendel examined, most human characteristics do not fall neatly into just two opposing phenotypic categories. These complex traits, such as skin and hair color, height, athletic ability and many others, seem to defy Mendelian analysis. The same can be said of traits expressed by many of the world's food crops; their size, shape, succulence, and nutrient content vary over a wide range of values.

Lentils (*Lens culinaris*) provide a graphic illustration of this variation. Lentils, a type of legume, are grown in many parts of the world as a rich source of both protein and carbohydrate. The mature plants set fruit in the form of diminutive pods that contain two small seeds. These seeds can be ground into meal or used in soups, salads, and stews. Lentils come in an intriguing array of colors and patterns (**Fig. 3.1**), and commercial growers always seek to produce combinations to suit the cuisines of different cultures. But crosses between pure-breeding lines of lentils result in some startling surprises. A cross between pure-breeding tan and pure-breeding gray parents, for example, yields an all-brown F_1 generation. When these hybrids self-pollinate, the F_2 plants produce not only tan, gray, and brown lentils, but also green.

In this array of green, brown, and red lentils, some of the seeds have speckled patterns, while others are clear.

Beginning with the first decade of the twentieth century, geneticists subjected many kinds of plants and animals to controlled breeding tests, using Mendel's 3:1 phenotypic ratio as a guideline. If the traits under analysis behaved as predicted by Mendel's laws, then they were assumed to be determined by a single gene with alternative dominant and recessive alleles. Many traits, however, did not behave in this way. For some, no definitive dominance and recessiveness could be observed, or more than two alleles could be found in a particular cross. Other traits turned out to be **multifactorial,** that is, determined by two or more genes, or by the interaction of genes with the environment. The seed coat color of lentils is a multifactorial trait.

Because such traits arise from an intricate network of interactions, they do not necessarily generate straightforward Mendelian phenotypic ratios. Nonetheless, simple extensions of Mendel's hypotheses can clarify the relationship between genotype and phenotype, allowing explanation of the observed deviations without challenging Mendel's basic laws.

CHAPTER OUTLINE

- 3.1 Extensions to Mendel for Single-Gene Inheritance
- 3.2 Extensions to Mendel for Multifactorial Inheritance

Figure 3.1 Some phenotypic variation poses a challenge to Mendelian analysis. Lentils show complex speckling patterns that are controlled by a gene that has more than two alleles.

One general theme stands out from these breeding studies: To make sense of the enormous phenotypic variation of the living world, geneticists usually try to limit the number of variables under investigation at any one time. Mendel did this by using pure-breeding, inbred strains of peas that differed from each other by one or a few traits, so that the action of single genes could be detected. Similarly, twentieth-century geneticists used inbred populations of fruit flies, mice, and other experimental organisms to study specific traits. Of course, geneticists cannot approach people in this way. Human populations are typically far from inbred, and researchers cannot ethically perform breeding experiments on people. As a result, the genetic basis of much human variation remained a mystery. The advent of molecular biology in the 1970s provided new tools that geneticists now use to unravel the genetics of complex human traits as described later in Chapters 9–11.

3.1 Extensions to Mendel for Single-Gene Inheritance

William Bateson, an early interpreter and defender of Mendel, who coined the terms "genetics," "allelomorph" (later shortened to "allele"), "homozygote," and "heterozygote," entreated the audience at a 1908 lecture: "Treasure your exceptions! . . . Keep them always uncovered and in sight. Exceptions are like the rough brickwork of a growing building which tells that there is more to come and shows where the next construction is to be." Consistent exceptions to simple Mendelian ratios revealed unexpected patterns of single-gene inheritance. By distilling the significance of these patterns, Bateson and other early geneticists extended the scope of Mendelian analysis and obtained a deeper understanding of the relationship between genotype and phenotype. We now look at the major extensions to Mendelian analysis elucidated over the last century.

Dominance is not always complete

A consistent working definition of dominance and recessiveness depends on the F_1 hybrids that arise from a mating between two pure-breeding lines. If a hybrid is identical to one parent for the trait under consideration, the allele carried by that parent is deemed dominant to the allele carried by the parent whose trait is not expressed in the hybrid. If, for example, a mating between a pure-breeding white line and a pure-breeding blue line produces F_1 hybrids that are white, the white allele of the

gene for color is dominant to the blue allele. If the F_1 hybrids are blue, the blue allele is dominant to the white one (**Fig. 3.2**).

Mendel described and relied on complete dominance in sorting out his ratios and laws, but it is not the only kind of dominance he observed. Figure 3.2 diagrams two situations in which neither allele of a gene is completely dominant. As the figure shows, crosses between true-breeding strains can produce hybrids with phenotypes that differ from both parents. We now explain how these phenotypes arise.

Incomplete dominance: The F_1 hybrid resembles neither pure-breeding parent

A cross between pure late-blooming and pure early-blooming pea plants results in an F_1 generation that blooms in between the two extremes. This is just one of many examples of **incomplete dominance,** in which the hybrid does not resemble either pure-breeding parent. F_1 hybrids that differ from both parents often express a phenotype that is intermediate between those of the pure-breeding parents. Thus, with incomplete dominance, neither parental allele is dominant or recessive to the other; both contribute to the F_1 phenotype. Mendel observed plants that bloomed midway between two extremes when he cultivated various types of pure-breeding peas for his hybridization studies, but he did not pursue the implications. Blooming time was not one of the seven characteristics he chose to analyze in detail, almost certainly because in peas, the time of bloom was not as clear-cut as seed shape or flower color.

Figure 3.2 Different dominance relationships. The phenotype of the heterozygote defines the dominance relationship between two alleles of the same gene (here, A^1 and A^2). Dominance is complete when the hybrid resembles one of the two pure-breeding parents. Dominance is incomplete when the hybrid resembles neither parent; its novel phenotype is usually intermediate. Codominance occurs when the hybrid shows the traits from both pure-breeding parents.

Type of Dominance	A^1/A^1	A^2/A^2	A^1/A^2 hybrids	
Complete				A^1 is dominant to A^2 A^2 is recessive to A^1
Complete				A^2 is dominant to A^1 A^1 is recessive to A^2
Incomplete				A^1 and A^2 are incompletely dominant relative to each other
Codominant				A^1 and A^2 are codominant relative to each other

Figure 3.3 Pink flowers are the result of incomplete dominance. (a) Color differences in these snapdragons reflect the activity of one pair of alleles. **(b)** The F$_1$ hybrids from a cross of pure-breeding red and white strains of snapdragons have pink blossoms. Flower colors in the F$_2$ appear in the ratio of 1 red : 2 pink : 1 white. This ratio signifies that the alleles of a single gene determine these three colors.

(a) *Antirrhinum majus* (snapdragons)

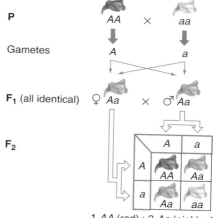

(b) A Punnett square for incomplete dominance

1 *AA* (red) : 2 *Aa* (pink) : 1 *aa* (white)

In many plant species, flower color serves as a striking example of incomplete dominance. With the tubular flowers of four-o'clocks or the floret clusters of snapdragons, for instance, a cross between pure-breeding red-flowered parents and pure-breeding white yields hybrids with pink blossoms, as if a painter had mixed red and white pigments to get pink (**Fig. 3.3a**). If allowed to self-pollinate, the F$_1$ pink-blooming plants produce F$_2$ progeny bearing red, pink, and white flowers in a ratio of 1:2:1 (**Fig. 3.3b**). This is the familiar *genotypic* ratio of an ordinary single-gene F$_1$ self-cross. What is new is that because the heterozygotes look unlike either homozygote, the *phenotypic* ratios are an exact reflection of the genotypic ratios.

The modern biochemical explanation for this type of incomplete dominance is that each allele of the gene under analysis specifies an alternative form of a protein molecule with an enzymatic role in pigment production. If the "white" allele does not give rise to a functional enzyme, no pigment appears. Thus, in snapdragons and four-o'clocks, two "red" alleles per cell produce a double dose of a red-producing enzyme, which generates enough pigment to make the flowers look fully red. In the heterozygote, one copy of the "red" allele per cell results in only enough pigment to make the flowers look pink. In the homozygote for the "white" allele, where there is no functional enzyme and thus no red pigment, the flowers appear white.

Codominance: The F₁ hybrid exhibits traits of both parents

A cross between pure-breeding spotted lentils and pure-breeding dotted lentils produces heterozygotes that are both spotted and dotted (**Fig. 3.4a**). These F₁ hybrids illustrate a second significant departure from complete dominance. They look like both parents, which means that neither the "spotted" nor the "dotted" allele is dominant or recessive to the other. Because both traits show up equally in the heterozygote's phenotype, the alleles are termed **codominant**. Self-pollination of the spotted/dotted F₁ generation generates F₂ progeny in the ratio of 1 spotted : 2 spotted/dotted : 1 dotted. The Mendelian 1:2:1 ratio among these F₂ progeny establishes that the spotted and dotted traits are determined by alternative alleles of a single gene. Once again, because the heterozygotes can be distinguished from both homozygotes, the phenotypic and genotypic ratios coincide.

In humans, some of the complex membrane-anchored molecules that distinguish different types of red blood cells exhibit codominance. For example, one gene (I) with alleles I^A and I^B controls the presence of a sugar polymer that protrudes from the red blood cell membrane. The alternative alleles each encode a slightly different form of an enzyme that causes production of a slightly different form of the complex sugar. In heterozygous individuals, the red blood cells carry both the I^A-determined and the I^B-determined sugars on their surface, whereas the cells of homozygous individuals display the products of either I^A or I^B alone (**Fig. 3.4b**). As this example illustrates, when both alleles produce a functional gene product, they are usually codominant for phenotypes analyzed at the molecular level.

Figure 3.2 on p. 45 summarizes the differences between complete dominance, incomplete dominance, and codominance for phenotypes reflected in color variations. Determinations of dominance relationships depend on what phenotype appears in the F₁ generation. With complete dominance, F₁ progeny look like one of the true-breeding parents. Complete dominance, as we saw in Chapter 2, results in a 3:1 ratio of phenotypes in the F₂. With incomplete dominance, hybrids resemble neither of the parents and thus display neither pure-breeding trait. With codominance, the phenotypes of both pure-breeding lines show up simultaneously in the F₁ hybrid. Both incomplete dominance and codominance yield 1:2:1 F₂ ratios.

Figure 3.4 In codominance, F₁ hybrids display the traits of both parents. (a) A cross between pure-breeding spotted lentils and pure-breeding dotted lentils produces heterozygotes that are both spotted and dotted. Each genotype has its own corresponding phenotype, so the F₂ ratio is 1:2:1. **(b)** The I^A and I^B blood group alleles are codominant because the red blood cells of an $I^A I^B$ heterozygote have both kinds of sugars at their surface.

(a) Codominant lentil coat patterns

1 $C^S C^S$ (spotted) : 2 $C^S C^D$ (spotted/dotted) : 1 $C^D C^D$ (dotted)

(b) Codominant blood group alleles

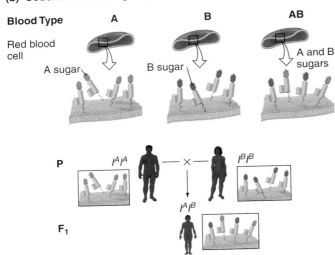

Mendel's law of segregation still holds

The dominance relations of a gene's alleles do not affect the alleles' transmission. Whether two alternative alleles of a single gene show complete dominance, incomplete dominance, or codominance depends on the kinds of proteins determined by the alleles and the biochemical function of those proteins in the cell. These same phenotypic dominance relations, however, have no bearing on the segregation of the alleles during gamete formation.

As Mendel proposed, cells still carry two copies of each gene, and these copies—a pair of either similar or dissimilar alleles—segregate during gamete formation. Fertilization then restores two alleles to each cell without reference to whether the alleles are the same or different. Variations in dominance relations thus do not detract from Mendel's laws of segregation. Rather, they reflect differences in the way gene products control the production of phenotypes, adding a level of complexity to the tasks of interpreting the visible results of gene transmission and inferring genotype from phenotype.

> In cases of incomplete dominance or codominance, mating of F_1 hybrids produces an F_2 generation with a 1:2:1 phenotypic ratio. The reason is that heterozygotes have a phenotype different from that of either homozygote.

A gene may have more than two alleles

Mendel analyzed "either-or" traits controlled by genes with two alternative alleles, but for many traits, there are more than two alternatives. Here, we look at three such traits: human ABO blood types, lentil seed coat patterns, and human histocompatibility antigens.

ABO blood types

If a person with blood type A mates with a person with blood type B, it is possible in some cases for the couple to have a child that is neither A nor B nor AB, but a fourth blood type called O. The reason? The gene for the ABO blood types has three alleles: I^A, I^B, and i (**Fig. 3.5a**). Allele I^A gives rise to blood type A by specifying an enzyme that adds sugar A, I^B results in blood type B by specifying an enzyme that adds sugar B; i does not produce a functional sugar-adding enzyme. Alleles I^A and I^B are both dominant to i, and blood type O is therefore a result of homozygosity for allele i.

Note in Fig. 3.5a that the A phenotype can arise from two genotypes, $I^A I^A$ or $I^A i$. The same is true for the B blood type, which can be produced by $I^B I^B$ or $I^B i$. But a combination of the two alleles $I^A I^B$ generates blood type AB.

We can draw several conclusions from these observations. First, as already stated, a given gene may have more than two alleles, or **multiple alleles;** in our example, the series of alleles is denoted I^A, I^B, i.

Second, although the ABO blood group gene has three alleles, each person carries only two of the alternatives—$I^A I^A$, $I^B I^B$, $I^A I^B$, $I^A i$, $I^B i$, or ii. There are thus six possible ABO genotypes. Because each individual carries no more than two alleles for each gene, no matter how many alleles there are in a series, Mendel's law of segregation remains intact, because in a sexually reproducing organism, the two alleles of a gene separate during gamete formation.

Third, an allele is not inherently dominant or recessive; its dominance or recessiveness is always relative to a second allele. In other words, dominance relations are unique to a pair of alleles. In our example, I^A is completely dominant to i, but it is codominant with I^B. Given these dominance relations, the six genotypes possible with I^A, I^B, and i generate four different phenotypes:

Figure 3.5 ABO blood types are determined by three alleles of one gene. (a) Six genotypes produce the four blood group phenotypes. (b) Blood serum contains antibodies against foreign red blood cell molecules. (c) If a recipient's serum has antibodies against the sugars on a donor's red blood cells, the blood types of recipient and donor are incompatible and coagulation of red blood cells will occur during transfusions. In this table, a plus (+) indicates compatibility, and a minus (−) indicates incompatibility. Antibodies in the donor's blood usually do not cause problems because the amount of transfused antibody is small.

(a)

Genotypes	Corresponding Phenotypes: Type(s) of Molecule on Cell
$I^A I^A$ $I^A i$	A
$I^B I^B$ $I^B i$	B
$I^A I^B$	AB
ii	O

(b)

Blood Type	Antibodies in Serum
A	Antibodies against B
B	Antibodies against A
AB	No antibodies against A or B
O	Antibodies against A and B

(c)

Blood Type of Recipient	Donor Blood Type (Red Cells)			
	A	B	AB	O
A	+	−	−	+
B	−	+	−	+
AB	+	+	+	+
O	−	−	−	+

blood groups A, B, AB, and O. With this background, you can understand how a type A and a type B parent could produce a type O child: The parents must be $I^A i$ and $I^B i$ heterozygotes, and the child receives an i allele from each parent.

An understanding of the genetics of the ABO system has had profound medical and legal repercussions. Matching ABO blood types is a prerequisite of successful blood transfusions, because people make antibodies to foreign blood cell molecules. A person whose cells carry only A molecules, for example, produces anti-B antibodies; B people manufacture anti-A antibodies; AB individuals make neither type of antibody; and O individuals produce both anti-A and anti-B antibodies (**Fig. 3.5b**). These antibodies cause coagulation of cells displaying the foreign molecules (**Fig. 3.5c**). As a result, people with blood type O have historically been known as universal donors because their red blood cells carry no surface molecules that will stimulate an antibody attack. In contrast, people with blood type AB are considered universal recipients, because they make neither anti-A nor anti-B antibodies, which, if present, would target the surface molecules of incoming blood cells.

Information about ABO blood types can also be used as legal evidence in court, to exclude the possibility of paternity or criminal guilt. In a paternity suit, for example, if the mother is type A and her child is type B, logic dictates that the I^B allele must have come from the father, whose genotype may be $I^A I^B$, $I^B I^B$, or $I^B i$. In 1944, the actress Joan Barry (phenotype A) sued Charlie Chaplin (phenotype O) for support of a child (phenotype B) whom she claimed he fathered. The scientific evidence indicated that Chaplin could not have been the father, since he was apparently ii and did not carry an I^B allele. This evidence was admissible in court, but the jury was not convinced, and Chaplin had to pay. Today, the molecular genotyping of DNA (*DNA fingerprinting,* see Chapter 11) provides a powerful tool to help establish paternity, guilt, or innocence, but juries still often find it difficult to evaluate such evidence.

Lentil seed coat patterns

Lentils offer another example of multiple alleles. A gene for seed coat pattern has five alleles: spotted, dotted, clear (pattern absent), and two types of marbled. Reciprocal crosses between pairs of pure-breeding lines of all patterns (marbled-1 × marbled-2, marbled-1 × spotted, marbled-2 × spotted, and so forth) have clarified the dominance relations of all possible pairs of the alleles to reveal a **dominance series** in which alleles are listed in order from most dominant to most recessive. For example, crosses of marbled-1 with marbled-2, or of marbled-1 with spotted or dotted or clear, produce the marbled-1 phenotype in the F_1 generation and a ratio of three marbled-1 to one of any of the other phenotypes in the F_2. This indicates that the marbled-1 allele is completely dominant to each of the other four alleles.

Analogous crosses with the remaining four phenotypes reveal the dominance series shown in **Fig. 3.6.** Recall that dominance relations are meaningful only when comparing two alleles; an allele, such as marbled-2, can be recessive to a second allele (marbled-1) but dominant to a third and fourth (dotted and clear). The fact that all tested pairings of lentil seed coat pattern alleles yielded a 3:1 ratio in the F_2 generation (except for spotted × dotted, which yielded the 1:2:1 phenotypic ratio reflective of codominance) indicates that these lentil seed coat patterns are determined by different alleles of the same gene.

Histocompatibility in humans

In some multiple allelic series, each allele is codominant with every other allele, and every distinct genotype therefore produces a distinct phenotype. This happens particularly with traits defined at the molecular level. An extreme example is the group of three major genes that encode a

Figure 3.6 How to establish the dominance relations between multiple alleles. Pure-breeding lentils with different seed coat patterns are crossed in pairs, and the F_1 progeny are self-fertilized to produce an F_2 generation. The 3:1 or 1:2:1 F_2 monohybrid ratios from all of these crosses indicate that different alleles of a single gene determine all the traits. The phenotypes of the F_1 hybrids establish the dominance relationships (*bottom*). Spotted and dotted alleles are codominant, but each is recessive to the marbled alleles and is dominant to clear.

Dominance series: marbled-1 > marbled-2 > spotted = dotted > clear

family of related cell surface molecules in humans and other mammals known as **histocompatibility antigens.** Carried by all of the body's cells except the red blood cells and sperm, histocompatibility antigens play a critical role in facilitating a proper immune response that destroys intruders (viral or bacterial, for example) while leaving the body's own tissues intact. Because each of the three major histocompatibility genes (called *HLA-A, HLA-B,* and *HLA-C* in humans) has between 20 and 100 alleles, the number of possible allelic combinations creates a powerful potential for the phenotypic variation of cell surface molecules. Other than identical (that is, *monozygotic*) twins, no two people are likely to carry the same array of cell surface molecules.

> Within a population, a gene may have multiple alleles, but any one individual can have at most two of these alleles. Considered in pairs, the alleles can exhibit a variety of dominance relationships.

Mutations are the source of new alleles

How do the multiple alleles of an allelic series arise? The answer is that chance alterations of the genetic material, known as **mutations,** arise spontaneously in nature. Once they occur in gamete-producing cells, they are faithfully inherited. Mutations that have phenotypic consequences can be counted, and such counting reveals that they occur at low frequency. The frequency of gametes carrying a mutation in a particular gene varies anywhere from 1 in 10,000 to 1 in 1,000,000. This range exists because different genes have different mutation rates.

Mutations make it possible to follow gene transmission. If, for example, a mutation specifies an alteration in an enzyme that normally produces yellow so that it now makes green, the new phenotype (green) will make it possible to recognize the new mutant allele. In fact, it takes at least two alleles, that is, some form of variation, to "see" the transmission of a gene. Thus, in segregation studies, geneticists can analyze only genes with variants; they have no way of following a gene that comes in only one form. If all peas were yellow, Mendel would not have been able to decipher the transmission patterns of the gene for the seed color trait. We discuss mutations in greater detail in Chapter 7.

Allele frequencies and monomorphic genes

Because each organism carries two copies of every gene, you can calculate the number of copies of a gene in a given population by multiplying the number of individuals by 2. Each allele of the gene accounts for a percentage of the total number of gene copies, and that percentage is known as the **allele frequency.** The most common allele in a population is usually called the **wild-type allele,** often designated by a superscript plus sign ($^+$). A rare allele in the same population is considered a **mutant allele.** (A mutation is a newly arisen mutant allele.)

In mice, for example, one of the main genes determining coat color is the *agouti* gene. The wild-type allele (*A*) produces fur with each hair having yellow and black bands that blend together from a distance to give the appearance of dark gray, or agouti. Researchers have identified in the laboratory 14 distinguishable mutant alleles for the *agouti* gene. One of these (*a^t*) is recessive

Figure 3.7 **The mouse *agouti* gene: One wild-type allele, many mutant alleles. (a)** Black-backed, yellow-bellied (*top left*); black (*top right*); and agouti (*bottom*) mice. **(b)** Genotypes and corresponding phenotypes for alleles of the *agouti* gene. **(c)** Crosses between pure-breeding lines reveal a dominance series. Interbreeding of the F₁ hybrids (not shown) yields 3:1 phenotypic ratios of F₂ progeny, indicating that *A, a^t*, and *a* are in fact alleles of one gene.

(a) *Mus musculus* **(house mouse) coat colors**

(b) **Alleles of the *agouti* gene**

Genotype	Phenotype
A–	agouti
a^t a^t	black/yellow
aa	black
a^t a	black/yellow

(c) **Evidence for a dominance series**

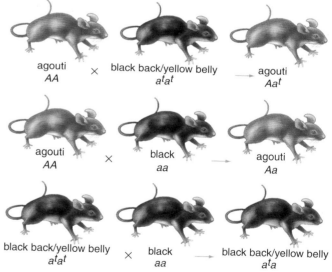

agouti *AA* × black back/yellow belly *a^t a^t* → agouti *Aa^t*

agouti *AA* × black *aa* → agouti *Aa*

black back/yellow belly *a^t a^t* × black *aa* → black back/yellow belly *a^t a*

Dominance series: $A > a^t > a$

to the wild type and gives rise to a black coat on the back and a yellow coat on the belly; another (*a*) is also recessive to *A* and produces a pure black coat (**Fig. 3.7**). In nature, wild-type agoutis (*AA*) survive to reproduce, while very few black-backed or pure black mutants (*a^t a^t* or *aa*) do so because their dark coat makes it hard for them to evade the eyes of predators. As a result, *A* is present at a frequency of much more than 99% and is thus the only wild-type allele in mice for the *agouti* gene. A gene with only one common, wild-type allele is **monomorphic.**

Allele frequencies and polymorphic genes

In contrast, some genes have more than one common allele, which makes them **polymorphic.** For example, in the ABO blood type system, all three alleles—I^A, I^B, and i—have appreciable frequencies in most human populations. Although all three of these alleles can be considered to be wild-type, geneticists instead usually refer to the high-frequency alleles of a polymorphic gene as *common variants*.

A rather unusual mechanism leading to the proliferation of many different alleles occurs in the mating systems of wild species of tomatoes and petunias. Evolution of an "incompatibility" gene whose alleles determine acceptance or rejection of pollen has allowed these plants to prevent self-fertilization and promote outbreeding. In this form of incompatibility, a plant cannot accept pollen carrying an allele identical to either of its own incompatibility alleles. If, for example, pollen carrying allele S_1 of the incompatibility gene lands on the stigma of a plant that also carries S_1 as one of its incompatibility alleles, a pollen tube will not grow (**Fig. 3.8**). Every plant is thus heterozygous for the incompatibility

Figure 3.8 Plant incompatibility systems prevent self-fertilization and thus promote outbreeding and allele proliferation. A pollen grain carrying a self-incompatibility allele that is identical to either of the two alleles carried by a potential female parent cannot grow a pollen tube; as a result, fertilization cannot take place.

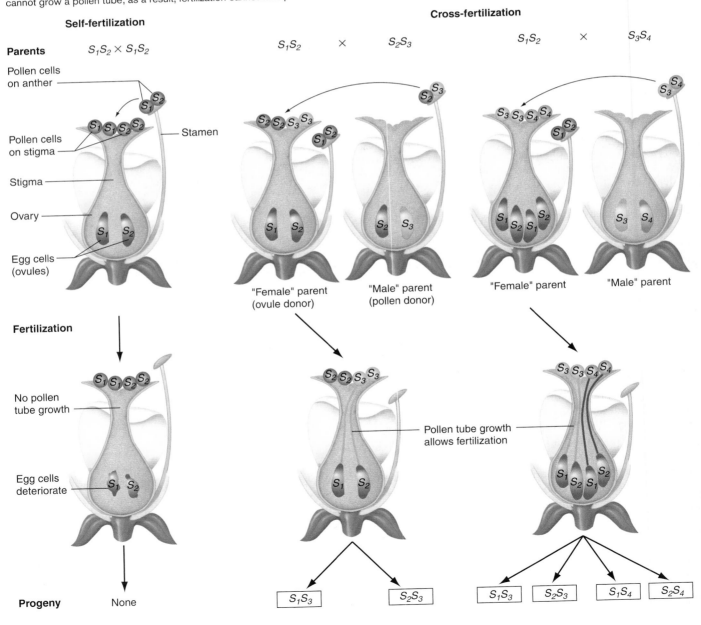

gene, since the pollen grain and female reproductive organs needed to form the plant cannot share alleles. Plants carrying rare alleles (that have arisen relatively recently by mutation and are not present in many other plants) will be able to send pollen to and receive pollen from most of the other plants in their population. In some species with this type of mating system, geneticists have detected as many as 92 alleles for the incompatibility gene. Because the incompatibility mechanism encourages the proliferation of new mutants, this is an extreme case of multiple alleles, not seen with most genes.

> Genes and alleles can be classified according to allele frequencies. A monomorphic gene has a single common allele referred to as the wild-type allele; a polymorphic gene has several common variants. Rare or newly arisen alleles of any gene are mutant alleles.

One gene may contribute to several characteristics

Mendel derived his laws from studies in which one gene determined one trait; but, always the careful observer, he himself noted possible departures. In listing the traits selected for his pea experiments, he remarked that specific seed coat colors are always associated with specific flower colors.

The phenomenon of a single gene determining a number of distinct and seemingly unrelated characteristics is known as **pleiotropy.** Because geneticists now know that each gene determines a specific protein and that each protein can have a cascade of effects on an organism, we can understand how pleiotropy arises. Among the aboriginal Maori people of New Zealand, for example, many of the men develop respiratory problems and are also sterile. Researchers have found that the fault lies with the recessive allele of a single gene. The gene's normal dominant allele specifies a protein necessary for the action of cilia and flagella, both of which are hairlike structures extending from the surfaces of some cells. In men who are homozygous for the recessive allele, cilia that normally clear the airways fail to work effectively, and flagella that normally propel sperm fail to do their job. Thus, one gene determines a protein that indirectly affects both respiratory function and reproduction. Because most proteins act in a variety of tissues and influence multiple biochemical processes, mutations in almost any gene may have pleiotropic effects.

Recessive lethal alleles

A significant variation of pleiotropy occurs in alleles that not only produce a visible phenotype but also affect viability. Mendel assumed that all genotypes are equally viable—that is, they have the same likelihood of survival. If this were not true and a large percentage of, say, homozygotes for a particular allele died before germination or birth, you

would not be able to count them after birth, and this would alter the 1:2:1 genotypic ratios and the 3:1 phenotypic ratios predicted for the F_2 generation.

Consider the inheritance of coat color in mice. As mentioned earlier, wild-type agouti (AA) animals have black and yellow striped hairs that appear dark gray to the eye. One of the 14 mutant alleles of the *agouti* gene gives rise to mice with a much lighter, almost yellow color. When inbred AA mice are mated to yellow mice, one always observes a 1:1 ratio of the two coat colors among the offspring (**Fig. 3.9a**). From this result, we can draw three conclusions: (1) All yellow mice must carry the *agouti* allele even though they do not express it; (2) yellow is therefore dominant to agouti; and (3) all yellow mice are heterozygotes.

Note again that dominance and recessiveness are defined in the context of each pair of alleles. Even though, as previously mentioned, agouti (A) is dominant to the a^t and a mutations for black coat color, it can still be recessive to the yellow coat color allele. If we designate the allele for yellow as A^y, the yellow mice in the preceding cross are A^yA heterozygotes, and the agoutis, AA homozygotes.

Figure 3.9 A^y: **A recessive lethal allele that also produces a dominant coat color phenotype. (a)** A cross between inbred agouti mice and yellow mice yields a 1:1 ratio of yellow to agouti progeny. The yellow mice are therefore A^yA heterozygotes, and for the trait of coat color, A^y (for yellow) is dominant to A (for agouti). **(b)** Yellow mice do not breed true. In a yellow × yellow cross, the 2:1 ratio of yellow to agouti progeny indicates that the A^y allele is a recessive lethal.

(a) All yellow mice are heterozygotes.

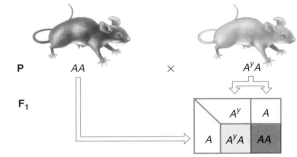

(b) Two copies of A^y cause lethality.

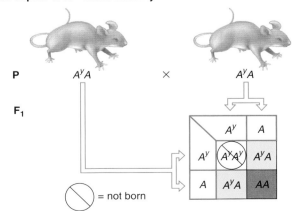

So far, no surprises. But a mating of yellow to yellow produces a skewed phenotypic ratio of two yellow mice to one agouti (**Fig. 3.9b**). Among these progeny, matings between agouti mice show that the agoutis are all pure-breeding and therefore *AA* homozygotes as expected. There are, however, no pure-breeding yellow mice among the progeny. When the yellow mice are mated to each other, they unfailingly produce 2/3 yellow and 1/3 agouti offspring, a ratio of 2:1, so they must therefore be heterozygotes. In short, one can never obtain pure-breeding yellow mice.

How can we explain this phenomenon? The Punnett square in Fig. 3.9b suggests an answer. Two copies of the A^y allele prove fatal to the animal carrying them, whereas one copy of the allele produces a yellow coat. This means that the A^y allele affects two different traits: It is dominant to *A* in the determination of coat color, but it is recessive to *A* in the production of lethality. An allele, such as A^y, that negatively affects the survival of a homozygote is known as a **recessive lethal allele.** Note that the same two alleles (A^y and *A*) can display different dominance relationships when looked at from the point of view of different phenotypes; we return later to this important point.

Because the A^y allele is dominant for yellow coat color, it is easy to detect carriers of this particular recessive lethal allele in mice, but such is not the case for the vast majority of recessive lethal mutations that do not simultaneously show a visible dominant phenotype for some other trait. Lethal mutations can arise in many different genes, and as a result, most animals, including humans, carry some recessive lethal mutations. Such mutations usually remain "silent," except in rare cases of homozygosity, which in people are often caused by consanguineous matings (that is, matings between close relatives). If a mutation produces an allele that prevents production of a crucial molecule, homozygous individuals would not make any of the vital molecule and would not survive. Heterozygotes, by contrast, with only one copy of the deleterious mutation and one wild-type allele, would be able to produce 50% of the wild-type amount of the normal molecule; this is usually sufficient to sustain normal cellular processes such that life goes on.

Delayed lethality

In the preceding discussion, we have described recessive alleles that result in the death of homozygotes prenatally, *in utero.* With some mutations, however, homozygotes may survive beyond birth and die later from the deleterious consequences of the genetic defect. An example is seen in human infants with Tay-Sachs disease. The seemingly normal newborns remain healthy for five to six months but then develop blindness, paralysis, mental retardation, and other symptoms of a deteriorating nervous system; the disease usually proves fatal by the age of six. Tay-Sachs disease results from the absence of an active lysosomal enzyme called hexosaminidase A, leading to the accumulation of a toxic waste product inside nerve cells. The approximate incidence of Tay-Sachs among live births is 1/35,000 worldwide, but it is 1/3000 among Jewish people of Eastern European descent. Reliable tests that detect carriers, in combination with genetic counseling and educational programs, have all but eliminated the disease in the United States.

Recessive alleles causing prenatal or early childhood lethality can only be passed on to subsequent generations by heterozygous carriers, because affected homozygotes die before they can mate. However, for late-onset diseases causing death in adults, homozygous patients can pass on the lethal allele before they become debilitated. An example is provided by the degenerative disease Friedreich ataxia: Some homozygotes first display symptoms of ataxia (loss of muscle coordination) at age 30–35 and die about five years later from heart failure.

Dominant alleles causing late-onset lethality can also be transmitted to subsequent generations; Figure 2.21 on p. 32 illustrates this for the inheritance of Huntington disease. By contrast, if the lethality caused by a dominant allele occurs instead during fetal development or early childhood, the allele will not be passed on, so all dominant early lethal mutant alleles must be new mutations.

Table 3.1 summarizes Mendel's basic assumptions about dominance, the number and viability of one gene's alleles, and the effects of each gene on phenotype, and then

TABLE 3.1	For Traits Determined by One Gene: Extensions to Mendel's Analysis Explain Alterations of the 3:1 Monohybrid Ratio		
What Mendel Described	**Extension**	**Extension's Effect on Heterozygous Phenotype**	**Extension's Effect on Ratios Resulting from an F₁ × F₁ Cross**
Complete dominance	Incomplete dominance Codominance	Unlike either homozygote	Phenotypes coincide with genotypes in a ratio of 1:2:1
Two alleles	Multiple alleles	Multiplicity of phenotypes	A series of 3:1 ratios
All alleles are equally viable	Recessive lethal alleles	No effect	2:1 instead of 3:1
One gene determines one trait	Pleiotropy: one gene influences several traits	Several traits affected in different ways, depending on dominance relations	Different ratios, depending on dominance relations for each affected trait

compares these assumptions with the extensions contributed by his twentieth-century successors. Through carefully controlled monohybrid crosses, these later geneticists analyzed the transmission patterns of the alleles of single genes, challenging and then confirming the law of segregation.

> A mutant allele can disrupt many biochemical processes; as a result, mutations often have pleiotropic effects that can include lethality at various times in an organism's life cycle.

A comprehensive example: Sickle-cell disease illustrates many extensions to Mendel's analysis

Sickle-cell disease is the result of a faulty hemoglobin molecule. Hemoglobin is composed of two types of polypeptide chains, alpha (α) globin and beta (β) globin, each specified by a different gene: $Hb\alpha$ for α globin and $Hb\beta$ for β globin. Normal red blood cells are packed full of millions upon millions of hemoglobin molecules, each of which picks up oxygen in the lungs and transports it to all the body's tissues.

Multiple alleles

The β-globin gene has a normal wild-type allele ($Hb\beta^A$) that gives rise to fully functional β globin, as well as close to 400 mutant alleles that have been identified so far. Some of these mutant alleles result in the production of hemoglobin that carries oxygen only inefficiently. Other mutant alleles prevent the production of β globin, causing a hemolytic (blood-destroying) disease called β-thalassemia. Here, we discuss the most common mutant allele of the β-globin gene, $Hb\beta^S$, which specifies an abnormal polypeptide that causes sickling of red blood cells (**Fig. 3.10a**).

Pleiotropy

The $Hb\beta^S$ allele of the β-globin gene affects more than one trait (**Fig. 3.10b**). Hemoglobin molecules in the red blood cells of homozygous $Hb\beta^S$ $Hb\beta^S$ individuals undergo an aberrant transformation after releasing their oxygen. Instead of remaining soluble in the cytoplasm, they aggregate to form long fibers that deform the red blood cell from a normal biconcave disk to a sickle shape (see Fig. 3.10a). The deformed cells clog the small blood vessels, reducing oxygen flow to the tissues and giving rise to muscle cramps, shortness of breath, and fatigue. The sickled cells are also very fragile and easily broken.

Figure 3.10 **Pleiotropy of sickle-cell anemia: Dominance relations vary with the phenotype under consideration.** **(a)** A normal red blood cell (*top*) is easy to distinguish from the sickled cell in the scanning electron micrograph at the *bottom*. **(b)** Different levels of analysis identify various phenotypes. Dominance relationships between the $Hb\beta^S$ and $Hb\beta^A$ alleles of the $Hb\beta$ gene vary with the phenotype and sometimes even change with the environment.

(a)   (b)

Consumption of fragmented cells by phagocytic white blood cells leads to a low red blood cell count, a condition called anemia.

On the positive side, $Hb\beta^S Hb\beta^S$ homozygotes are resistant to malaria, because the organism that causes the disease, *Plasmodium falciparum,* can multiply rapidly in normal red blood cells, but cannot do so in cells that sickle. Infection by *P. falciparum* causes sickle-shaped cells to break down before the malaria organism has a chance to multiply.

Recessive lethality

People who are homozygous for the recessive $Hb\beta^S$ allele often develop heart failure because of stress on the circulatory system. Many sickle-cell sufferers die in childhood, adolescence, or early adulthood.

Different dominance relations

Comparisons of heterozygous carriers of the sickle-cell allele—individuals whose cells contain one $Hb\beta^A$ and one $Hb\beta^S$ allele—with homozygous $Hb\beta^A Hb\beta^A$ (normal) and homozygous $Hb\beta^S Hb\beta^S$ (diseased) individuals make it possible to distinguish different dominance relations for different phenotypic aspects of sickle-cell anemia (Fig. 3.10b).

At the molecular level—the production of β globin—both alleles are expressed such that $Hb\beta^A$ and $Hb\beta^S$ are *codominant*. At the cellular level, in their effect on red blood cell shape, the $Hb\beta^A$ and $Hb\beta^S$ alleles show *incomplete dominance*. Although under normal oxygen conditions, the great majority of a heterozygote's red blood cells have the normal biconcave shape, when oxygen levels drop, sickling occurs in some cells. All $Hb\beta^A Hb\beta^S$ cells, however, are resistant to malaria because like the $Hb\beta^S Hb\beta^S$ cells described previously, they break down before the malarial organism has a chance to reproduce. Thus for the trait of resistance to malaria, the $Hb\beta^S$ allele is *dominant* to the $Hb\beta^A$ allele. But luckily for the heterozygote, for the phenotypes of anemia or death, $Hb\beta^S$ is *recessive* to $Hb\beta^A$. A corollary of this observation is that in its effect on general health under normal environmental conditions and its effect on red blood cell count, the $Hb\beta^A$ allele is *dominant* to $Hb\beta^S$.

Thus, for the β-globin gene, as for other genes, dominance and recessiveness are not an inherent quality of alleles in isolation; rather, they are specific to each pair of alleles and to the level of physiology at which the phenotype is examined. When discussing dominance relationships, it is therefore essential to define the particular phenotype under analysis.

In the 1940s, the incomplete dominance of the $Hb\beta^A$ and $Hb\beta^S$ alleles in determining red blood cell shape had significant repercussions for certain soldiers who fought in World War II. Aboard transport planes flying troops across the Pacific, several heterozygous carriers suffered sickling crises similar to those usually seen in $Hb\beta^S Hb\beta^S$ homozygotes. The reason was that heterozygous red blood cells of a carrier produce both normal and abnormal hemoglobin molecules. At sea level, these molecules together deliver sufficient oxygen, although less than the normal amount, to the body's tissues, but with a decrease in the amount of oxygen available at the high-flying altitudes, the hemoglobin picks up less oxygen, the rate of red blood cell sickling increases, and symptoms of the disease occur.

The complicated dominance relationships between the $Hb\beta^S$ and $Hb\beta^A$ alleles also help explain the puzzling observation that the normally deleterious allele $Hb\beta^S$ is widespread in certain populations. In areas where malaria is endemic, heterozygotes are better able to survive and pass on their genes than are either type of homozygote. $Hb\beta^S Hb\beta^S$ individuals often die of sickle-cell disease, while those with the genotype $Hb\beta^A Hb\beta^A$ often die of malaria. Heterozygotes, however, are relatively immune to both conditions, so high frequencies of both alleles persist in tropical environments where malaria is found. We explore this phenomenon in more quantitative detail in Chapter 19 on population genetics.

New therapies have improved the medical condition of many $Hb\beta^S Hb\beta^S$ individuals, but these treatments have significant shortcomings; as a result, sickle-cell disease remains a major health problem. The Fast Forward box "Gene Therapy for Sickle-Cell Disease in Mice" on the following page describes recent success in using genetic engineering to counteract red blood cell sickling in mice whose genomes carry human $Hb\beta^S$ alleles. Researchers hope that similar types of "gene therapies" will one day lead to a cure for sickle-cell disease in humans.

3.2 Extensions to Mendel for Multifactorial Inheritance

Although some traits are indeed determined by allelic variations of a single gene, the vast majority of common traits in all organisms are *multifactorial,* arising from the action of two or more genes, or from interactions between genes and the environment. In genetics, the term *environment* has an unusually broad meaning that encompasses all aspects of the outside world an organism comes into contact with. These include temperature, diet, and exercise as well as the uterine environment before birth.

In this section, we examine how geneticists again used breeding experiments and the guidelines of Mendelian ratios to analyze the complex network of interactions that give rise to multifactorial traits.

Two genes can interact to determine one trait

Two genes can interact in several ways to determine a single trait, such as the color of a flower, a seed coat, a chicken's feathers, or a dog's fur, and each type of interaction

FAST FORWARD

Gene Therapy for Sickle-Cell Disease in Mice

The most widespread inherited blood disorder in the United States is sickle-cell disease, which affects approximately 80,000 Americans. It is caused, as you have seen, by homozygosity for the $Hb\beta^S$ allele of the gene that specifies the β-globin constituent of hemoglobin. Because heterozygotes for this allele are partially protected from malaria, $Hb\beta^S$ is fairly common in people of African, Indian, Mediterranean, and Middle Eastern descent; 1 in 13 African-Americans is a carrier of the sickle-cell allele. Before the 1980s, most people with sickle-cell disease died during child-hood. However, advances in medical care have improved the out-look for many of these patients so that about half of them now live beyond the age of 50.

The main therapies in use today include treatment with the drug hydroxyurea, which stimulates the production of other kinds of hemoglobin; and bone marrow transplantation, which replaces the patient's red-blood-cell-forming hematopoietic stem cells with those of a healthy donor. Unfortunately, these treatments are not ideal. Hydroxyurea has toxic side effects, and bone marrow transplantation can be carried out successfully only with a donor whose tissues are perfectly matched with the patient's. As a result, medical researchers are exploring an alternative: the pos-sibility of developing gene therapy for sickle-cell disease in humans.

In 2001 a research team from Harvard Medical School announced the successful use of gene therapy to treat mice that had been genetically engineered to have sickling red blood cells. These transgenic mice (called SAD mice) express an allelic form of the human $Hb\beta$ gene, closely related to $Hb\beta^S$.

The research team began by removing bone marrow from the SAD mice and isolating the hematopoietic stem cells from the marrow. They next used genetic engineering to add an antisickling transgene to these stem cells. The transgene was a synthetically mutated allele of the human $Hb\beta$ gene; it encoded a special β-globin protein designed to prevent sickling in red blood cells that also contain $Hb\beta^S$. When the genetically modified stem cells were transplanted back into the SAD mice, healthy, nonsickling red blood cells were produced. The new genetically modified transgene thus counteracted the effects of the Hb^S allele and prevented sickling, as predicted.

For human gene therapy, adding a transgene to hematopoi-etic stem cells derived from the sickle-cell patient would in theory mean no threat of tissue rejection when these engineered stem cells are transplanted back into the patient. However, research-ers must overcome several potential problems. First, the method is not guaranteed to work in humans because SAD mice do not exhibit all aspects of sickle-cell disease in humans. Another dif-ficulty is how to make sure the therapeutic gene gets into enough target cells to make a difference. The Harvard group resolved this issue in mice by using a modified version of the HIV virus causing AIDS (*A*cquired *I*mmune *D*eficiency *S*yndrome) to transport the genetically engineered antisickling transgene into the stem cells. It has not been proven that virus-treated cells will be safe when reintroduced into the human body. Finally, successful gene ther-apy of this type requires that all the hematopoietic stem cells without the transgene must be removed. The Harvard research-ers did this by destroying the bone marrow in the SAD mice with large doses of X-rays before putting the transgene-containing stem cells back into the mice. However, such a treatment in humans would be extremely toxic. Despite these potential com-plications, the successful application of gene therapy to a mouse model for sickle-cell disease suggests an exciting pathway for future clinical research.

produces its own signature of phenotypic ratios. In many of the following examples showing how two genes interact to affect one trait, we use big *A* and little *a* to represent alter-native alleles of the first gene and big *B* and little *b* for those of the second gene.

Novel phenotypes resulting from gene interactions

In the chapter opening, we described a mating of tan and gray lentils that produced a uniformly brown F$_1$ genera-tion and then an F$_2$ generation containing lentils with brown, tan, gray, and green seed coats. An understand-ing of how this can happen emerges from experimental results demonstrating that the ratio of the four F$_2$ colors is 9 brown: 3 tan: 3 gray: 1 green (**Fig. 3.11a**). Recall from Chapter 2 that this is the same ratio Mendel observed in his analysis of the F$_2$ generations from dihybrid crosses following two independently assorting genes. In Mendel's studies, each of the four classes consisted of plants that

expressed a combination of two unrelated traits. With len-tils, however, we are looking at a single trait—seed coat color. The simplest explanation for the parallel ratios is that a combination of genotypes at two independently assorting genes interacts to produce the phenotype of seed coat color in lentils.

Results obtained from self-crosses with the various types of F$_2$ lentil plants support this explanation. Self-crosses of F$_2$ green individuals show that they are pure-breeding, producing an F$_3$ generation that is entirely green. Tan individuals generate either all tan offspring, or a mixture of tan offspring and green offspring. Grays similarly produce either all gray, or gray and green. Self-crosses of brown F$_2$ individuals can have four possible outcomes: all brown, brown plus tan, brown plus gray, or all four colors (**Fig. 3.11b**). The two-gene hypothesis explains why there is

- only one green genotype: pure-breeding *aa bb,* but
- two types of tans: pure-breeding *AA bb* as well as tan- and green-producing *Aa bb,* and

Figure 3.11 How two genes interact to produce seed colors in lentils. (a) In a cross of pure-breeding tan and gray lentils, all the F₁ hybrids are brown, but four different phenotypes appear among the F₂ progeny. The 9:3:3:1 ratio of F₂ phenotypes suggests that seed coat color is determined by two independently assorting genes. **(b)** Expected results of selfing individual F₂ plants of the indicated phenotypes to produce an F₃ generation, if seed coat color results from the interaction of two genes. The third column shows the proportion of the F₂ population that would be expected to produce the observed F₃ phenotypes. **(c)** Other two-generation crosses involving pure-breeding parental lines also support the two-gene hypothesis. In this table, the F₁ hybrid generation has been omitted.

(a) A dihybrid cross with lentil coat colors

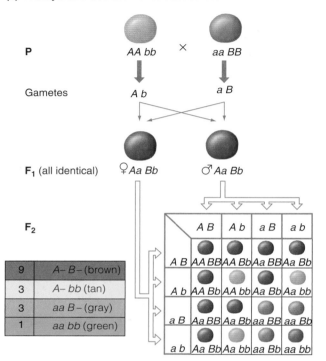

(b) Self-pollination of the F₂ to produce an F₃

Phenotypes of F₂ Individual	Observed F₃ Phenotypes	Expected Proportion of F₂ Population*
Green	Green	1/16
Tan	Tan	1/16
Tan	Tan, green	2/16
Gray	Gray, green	2/16
Gray	Gray	1/16
Brown	Brown	1/16
Brown	Brown, tan	2/16
Brown	Brown, gray	2/16
Brown	Brown, gray, tan, green	4/16

*This 1:1:2:2:1:1:2:2:4 F₂ genotypic ratio corresponds to a 9 brown:3 tan:3 gray:1 green F₂ phenotypic ratio.

(c) Sorting out the dominance relations by select crosses

Seed Coat Color of Parents	F₂ Phenotypes and Frequencies	Ratio
Tan × green	231 tan, 85 green	3:1
Gray × green	2586 gray, 867 green	3:1
Brown × gray	964 brown, 312 gray	3:1
Brown × tan	255 brown, 76 tan	3:1
Brown × green	57 brown, 18 gray, 13 tan, 4 green	9:3:3:1

- two types of grays: pure-breeding *aa BB* and gray- and green-producing *aa Bb,* yet
- four types of browns: true-breeding *AA BB,* brown- and tan-producing *AA Bb,* brown- and gray-producing *Aa BB,* and *Aa Bb* dihybrids that give rise to plants producing lentils of all four colors.

In short, for the two genes that determine seed coat color, both dominant alleles must be present to yield brown (*A– B–*); the dominant allele of one gene produces tan (*A– bb*); the dominant allele of the other specifies gray (*aa B–*); and the complete absence of dominant alleles (that is, the double recessive) yields green (*aa bb*). Thus, the four color phenotypes arise from four **genotypic classes,** with each class defined in terms of the presence or absence of the dominant alleles of two genes: (1) both present (*A– B–*), (2) one present (*A– bb*), (3) the other present (*aa B–*), and (4) neither present (*aa bb*). Note that the *A–* notation means that the second allele of this gene can be either *A* or *a,* while *B–* denotes a second allele of either *B* or *b.* Note also that only with a two-gene system in which the dominance and recessiveness of alleles at both genes is complete can the nine different genotypes of the F₂ generation be categorized into the four genotypic

classes described. With incomplete dominance or codominance, the F₂ genotypes could not be grouped together in this simple way, as they would give rise to more than four phenotypes.

Further crosses between plants carrying lentils of different colors confirmed the two-gene hypothesis (**Fig. 3.11c**). Thus, the 9:3:3:1 phenotypic ratio of brown to tan to gray to green in an F₂ descended from pure-breeding tan and pure-breeding gray lentils tells us not only that two genes assorting independently interact to produce the seed coat color, but also that each genotypic class (*A– B–, A– bb, aa B–,* and *aa bb*) determines a particular phenotype.

Complementary gene action

In some two-gene interactions, the four F₂ genotypic classes produce fewer than four observable phenotypes, because some of the phenotypes include two or more genotypic classes. For example, in the first decade of the twentieth century, William Bateson conducted a cross between two lines of pure-breeding white-flowered sweet peas (**Fig. 3.12**). Quite unexpectedly, all of the F₁ progeny were purple. Self-pollination of these novel hybrids produced a ratio

Figure 3.12 Complementary gene action generates color in sweet peas. (a) White and purple sweet pea flowers. **(b)** The 9:7 ratio of purple to white F_2 plants indicates that at least one dominant allele for each gene is necessary for the development of purple color.

(a) *Lathyrus odoratus* **(sweet peas)**

(b) A dihybrid cross involving complementary gene action

of 9 purple : 7 white in the F_2 generation. The explanation? Two genes work in tandem to produce purple sweet-pea flowers, and a dominant allele of both genes must be present to produce that color.

A simple biochemical hypothesis for this type of **complementary gene action** is shown in **Fig. 3.13.** Because it takes two enzymes catalyzing two separate biochemical reactions to change a colorless precursor into a colorful pigment, only the *A– B–* genotypic class, which produces active forms of both required enzymes, can generate colored flowers. The other three genotypic classes (*A– bb, aa B–,* and *aa bb*) become grouped together with respect to phenotype because they do not specify functional forms of one or the other requisite enzyme and thus give rise to no color, which is the same as white. It is easy to see how the "7" part of the 9:7 ratio encompasses the 3:3:1 of the 9:3:3:1 ratio of two genes in action. The 9:7 ratio is the phenotypic signature of this type of complementary gene interaction in which the dominant alleles of two genes acting together (*A– B–*) produce color or some other trait, while the other three genotypic classes (*A– bb, aa B–,* and *aa bb*) do not (see Fig. 3.12b).

Epistasis

In some gene interactions, the four Mendelian genotypic classes produce fewer than four observable phenotypes because one gene masks the phenotypic effects of another. An example is seen in the sleek, short-haired coat of Labrador retrievers, which can be black, chocolate brown,

Figure 3.13 A possible biochemical explanation for complementary gene action in the generation of sweet pea color. Enzymes specified by the dominant alleles of two genes are both necessary to produce pigment. The recessive alleles of both genes specify inactive enzymes. In *aa* homozygotes, no intermediate precursor 2 is created, so even if enzyme B is available, it cannot create purple pigment.

Figure 3.14 Recessive epistasis: Coat color in Labrador retrievers and a rare human blood type. (a) Golden Labrador retrievers are homozygous for the recessive *e* allele, which masks the effects of the *B* or *b* alleles of a second coat color gene. In *E–* dogs, a *B–* genotype produces black and a *bb* genotype produces brown. **(b)** Homozygosity for the *h* Bombay allele is epistatic to the *I* gene determining ABO blood types. *hh* individuals fail to produce substance H, which is needed for the addition of A or B sugars at the surface of red blood cells.

(a) A dihybrid cross showing recessive epistasis

(b) Molecular basis of the Bombay phenotype

or golden yellow. (These phenotypes may be viewed in Fig. 2.3 on p. 14) Which color shows up depends on the allelic combinations of two independently assorting coat color genes (**Fig. 3.14a**). The dominant *B* allele of the first gene determines black, while the recessive *bb* homozygote is brown. With the second gene, the dominant *E* allele has no visible effect on black or brown coat color, but a double dose of the recessive allele (*ee*) hides the effect of any combination of the black or brown alleles to yield gold. A gene interaction in which the effects of an allele at one gene hide the effects of alleles at another gene is known as **epistasis;** the allele that is doing the masking (in this case, the *e* allele of the *E* gene) is **epistatic** to the gene that is being masked (the *hypostatic gene*). In this example, where homozygosity for a recessive *e* allele of the second gene is required to hide the effects of another gene, the masking phenomenon is called **recessive epistasis** (because the allele causing the epistasis is recessive), and the recessive *ee* homozygote is considered epistatic to any allelic combination at the first gene.

Recessive Epistasis Let's look at the phenomenon in greater detail. Crosses between pure-breeding black retrievers (*BB EE*) and one type of pure-breeding golden retriever (*bb ee*) create an F_1 generation of dihybrid black retrievers (*Bb Ee*). Crosses between these F_1 dihybrids produce an F_2 generation with nine black dogs (*B– E–*) for every three

brown (*bb E–*) and four gold (*– – ee*) (Fig. 3.14a). Note that there are only three phenotypic classes because the two genotypic classes without a dominant *E* allele—the three *B– ee* and the one *bb ee*—combine to produce golden phenotypes. The telltale ratio of recessive epistasis in the F_2 generation is thus 9:3:4, with the 4 representing a combination of 3 (*B– ee*) + 1 (*bb ee*). Because the *ee* genotype completely masks the influence of the other gene for coat color, you cannot tell by looking at a golden Labrador what its genotype is for the black or brown (*B* or *b*) gene.

An understanding of recessive epistasis made it possible to resolve an intriguing puzzle in human genetics. In rare instances, two parents who appear to have blood type O, and thus genotype *ii*, produce a child who is either blood type A (genotype $I^A i$) or blood type B (genotype $I^B i$). This phenomenon occurs because an extremely rare trait, called the Bombay phenotype after its discovery in Bombay, India, superficially resembles blood type O. As **Fig. 3.14b** shows, the Bombay phenotype actually arises from homozygosity for a mutant recessive allele (*hh*) of a second gene that masks the effects of any ABO alleles that might be present.

Here's how it works at the molecular level. In the construction of the red blood cell surface molecules that determine blood type, type A individuals make an enzyme that adds polysaccharide A onto a base consisting of a sugar polymer known as substance H; type B individuals make an altered form of the enzyme that

Figure 3.15 Dominant epistasis produces telltale phenotypic ratios of 12:3:1 or 13:3. (a) In summer squash, the dominant *B* allele causes white color and is sufficient to mask the effects of any combination of *A* and *a* alleles. As a result, yellow (*A–*) or green (*aa*) color is expressed only in *bb* individuals. **(b)** In the F₂ generation resulting from a dihybrid cross between white leghorn and white wyandotte chickens, the ratio of white birds to birds with color is 13:3. This is because at least one copy of *A* and the absence of *B* is needed to produce color.

adds polysaccharide B onto the base; and type O individuals make neither A-adding nor B-adding enzyme and thus have an exposed substance H in the membranes of their red blood cells. All people of A, B, or O phenotype carry at least one dominant wild-type *H* allele for the second gene and thus produce some substance H. In contrast, the rare Bombay-phenotype individuals, with genotype *hh* for the second gene, do not make substance H at all, so even if they make an enzyme that would add A or B to this polysaccharide base, they have nothing to add it onto; as a result, they appear to be type O. For this reason, homozygosity for the recessive *h* allele of the H-substance gene masks the effects of the *ABO* gene, making the *hh* genotype epistatic to any combination of I^A, I^B, and *i* alleles.

A person who carries I^A, I^B, or both I^A and I^B but is also an *hh* homozygote for the H-substance gene may appear to be type O, but he or she will be able to pass along an I^A or I^B allele in sperm or egg. The offspring receiving, let's say, an I^A allele for the ABO gene and a recessive *h* allele for the H-substance gene from its mother plus an *i* allele and a dominant *H* allele from its father would have blood type A (genotype $I^A i$, *Hh*), even though neither of its parents is phenotype A or AB.

Dominant Epistasis Epistasis can also be caused by a dominant allele. In summer squash, two genes influence the color of the fruit (**Fig. 3.15a**). With one gene, the dominant allele (*A–*) determines yellow, while homozygotes for the recessive allele (*aa*) are green. A second gene's dominant allele (*B–*) produces white, while *bb* fruit may be either yellow or green, depending on the genotype of the first gene. In the interaction between these two genes, the presence of *B* hides the effects of either *A–* or *aa*, producing white fruit, and *B–* is thus epistatic to any genotype of the *Aa* gene. The recessive *b* allele has no effect on fruit color determined by the *Aa* gene. Epistasis in which the dominant allele of one gene hides the effects of another gene is called **dominant epistasis.** In a cross between white F₁ dihybrids (*Aa Bb*), the F₂ phenotypic ratio is 12 white : 3 yellow : 1 green (Fig. 3.15a). The "12" includes two genotypic classes: 9 *A– B–* and 3 *aa B–*. Another way of looking at this same phenomenon is that dominant epistasis restores the 3:1 ratio for the dominant epistatic phenotype (12 white) versus all other phenotypes (4 green plus yellow).

A variation of this ratio is seen in the feather color of certain chickens (**Fig. 3.15b**). White leghorns have a doubly dominant *AA BB* genotype for feather color; white wyandottes are homozygous recessive for both

TABLE 3.2	Summary of Discussed Gene Interactions					
		F₂ Genotypic Ratios from an F₁ Dihybrid Cross				**F₂ Pheno-**
Gene Interaction	**Example**	**A– B–**	**A– bb**	**aa B–**	**aa bb**	**typic Ratio**
None: Four distinct F₂ phenotypes	Lentil: seed coat color (see Fig. 3.11a)	9	3	3	1	**9:3:3:1**
Complementary: One dominant allele of each of two genes is necessary to produce phenotype	Sweet pea: flower color (see Fig. 3.12b)	9	3	3	1	**9:7**
Recessive epistasis: Homozygous recessive of one gene masks both alleles of another gene	Retriever coat color (see Fig. 3.14a)	9	3	3	1	**9:3:4**
Dominant epistasis I: Dominant allele of one gene hides effects of both alleles of another gene	Summer squash: color (see Fig. 3.15a)	9	3	3	1	**12:3:1**
Dominant epistasis II: Dominant allele of one gene hides effects of dominant allele of another gene	Chicken: feather color (see Fig. 3.15b)	9	3	3	1	**13:3**

genes (*aa bb*). A cross between these two pure-breeding white strains produces an all-white dihybrid (*Aa Bb*) F₁ generation, but birds with color in their feathers appear in the F₂, and the ratio of white to colored is 13:3 (Fig. 3.15b). We can explain this ratio by assuming a kind of dominant epistasis in which *B* is epistatic to *A;* the *A* allele (in the absence of *B*) produces color; and the *a, B,* and *b* alleles produce no color. The interaction is characterized by a 13:3 ratio because the 9 *A– B–,* 3 *aa B–,* and 1 *aa bb* genotypic classes combine to produce only one phenotype: white.

So far we have seen that when two independently assorting genes interact to determine a trait, the 9:3:3:1 ratio of the four Mendelian genotypic classes in the F₂ generation can produce a variety of phenotypic ratios, depending on the nature of the gene interactions. The result may be four, three, or two phenotypes, composed of different combinations of the four genotypic classes. **Table 3.2** summarizes some of the possibilities, correlating the phenotypic ratios with the genetic phenomena they reflect.

Heterogeneous traits and the complementation test

Close to 50 different genes have mutant alleles that can cause deafness in humans. Many genes generate the developmental pathway that brings about hearing, and a loss of function in any part of the pathway, for instance, in one small bone of the middle ear, can result in deafness. In other words, it takes a dominant wild-type allele at each of these 50 genes to produce normal hearing. Thus, deafness is a **heterogeneous trait:** A mutation at any one of a number of genes can give rise to the same phenotype.

It is not always possible to determine which of many different genes has mutated in a person who expresses a heterogeneous mutant phenotype. In the case of deafness, for example, it is usually not possible to discover whether a particular nonhearing man and a particular nonhearing woman carry mutations at the same gene, unless they have children together. If they have only children who can hear, the parents most likely carry mutations at two different genes, and the children carry one normal, wild-type allele at both of those genes (**Fig. 3.16a**). By contrast, if all of their children are deaf, it is likely that both parents are homozygous for a mutation in the same gene, and all of their children are also homozygous for this same mutation (**Fig. 3.16b**).

This method of discovering whether a particular phenotype arises from mutations in the same or separate genes is a naturally occurring version of an experimental genetic tool called the **complementation test.** Simply put, when what appears to be an identical *recessive* phenotype arises in two separate breeding lines, geneticists want to know whether mutations at the same gene are responsible for the phenotype in both lines. They answer this question by setting up a mating between affected individuals from the two lines. If offspring receiving the two mutations—one from each parent—express the wild-type phenotype, complementation has occurred. The observation of complementation means that the original mutations affected two different genes, and for both genes, the normal allele from one parent can provide what the mutant allele of the same gene from the other parent cannot. Figure 3.16a illustrates one example of this phenomenon in humans. By contrast, if offspring receiving two recessive mutant alleles—again, one from each parent—express the mutant phenotype, complementation does not occur because the two mutations independently alter the same gene

Figure 3.16 Genetic heterogeneity in humans: Mutations in many genes can cause deafness. (a) Two deaf parents can have hearing offspring. This situation is an example of genetic complementation; it occurs if the nonhearing parents are homozygous for recessive mutations in different genes. **(b)** Two deaf parents may produce all deaf children. In such cases, complementation does not occur because both parents carry mutations in the same gene.

(Fig. 3.16b). Thus, the occurrence of complementation reveals genetic heterogeneity. Note that complementation tests cannot be used if either of the mutations is dominant to the wild type. Chapter 7 includes an in-depth discussion of complementation tests and their uses.

To summarize, several variations on the theme of multifactorial traits can be identified:

(1) genes can interact to generate novel phenotypes,
(2) the dominant alleles of two interacting genes can both be necessary for the production of a particular phenotype,
(3) one gene's alleles can mask the effects of alleles at another gene, and
(4) mutant alleles at one of two or more different genes can result in the same phenotype.

In examining each of these categories, for the sake of simplicity, we have looked at examples in which one allele of each gene in a pair showed complete dominance over the other. But for any type of gene interaction, the alleles of one or both genes may exhibit incomplete dominance or codominance, and these possibilities increase the potential for phenotypic diversity. For example, **Fig. 3.17** shows how incomplete dominance at both genes in a dihybrid cross generates additional phenotypic variation.

Although the possibilities for variation are manifold, none of the observed departures from Mendelian phenotypic ratios contradicts Mendel's genetic laws of segregation and independent assortment. The alleles of each gene still segregate as he proposed. Interactions between the alleles of many genes simply make it harder to unravel the complex relation of genotype to phenotype.

Figure 3.17 With incomplete dominance, the interaction of two genes can produce nine different phenotypes for a single trait. In this example, two genes produce purple pigments. Alleles A and a of the first gene exhibit incomplete dominance, as do alleles B and b of the second gene. The two alleles of each gene can generate three different phenotypes, so double heterozygotes can produce nine (3×3) different colors in a ratio of 1:2:2:1:4:1:2:2:1.

1	AA BB	purple shade 9
2	AA Bb	purple shade 8
2	Aa BB	purple shade 7
1	AA bb	purple shade 6
4	Aa Bb	purple shade 5
1	aa BB	purple shade 4
2	Aa bb	purple shade 3
2	aa Bb	purple shade 2
1	aa bb	purple shade 1 (white)

F₂ phenotypic ratios of 9:3:3:1 or its derivatives indicate the combined action of two independently assorting genes. For heterogeneous traits caused by recessive alleles of two or more genes, a mating between affected individuals acts as a complementation test, revealing whether they carry mutations in the same gene or in different genes.

Breeding studies help decide how a trait is inherited

How do geneticists know whether a particular trait is caused by the alleles of one gene or by two genes interacting in one of a number of possible ways? Breeding tests can usually resolve the issue. Phenotypic ratios diagnostic of a particular mode of inheritance (for instance, the 9:7 or 13:3

ratios indicating that two genes are interacting) can provide the first clues and suggest hypotheses. Further breeding studies can then show which hypothesis is correct. We have seen, for example, that yellow coat color in mice is determined by a dominant allele of the *agouti* gene, which also acts as a recessive lethal. We now look at two other mouse genes for coat color. Because we have already designated alleles of the *agouti* gene as *Aa*, we use *Bb* and *Cc* to designate the alleles of these additional genes.

A mating of one strain of pure-breeding white albino mice with pure-breeding brown results in black hybrids; and a cross between the black F₁ hybrids produces 90 black, 30 brown, and 40 albino offspring. What is the genetic constitution of these phenotypes? We could assume that we are seeing the 9:3:4 ratio of recessive epistasis and hypothesize that two genes, one epistatic to the other, interact to produce the three mouse phenotypes (**Fig. 3.18a**). But how do we know if this hypothesis is

Figure 3.18 Specific breeding tests can help decide between hypotheses. Either of two hypotheses could explain the results of a cross-tracking coat color in mice. **(a)** In one hypothesis, two genes interact with recessive epistasis to produce a 9:3:4 ratio. **(b)** In the other hypothesis, a single gene with incomplete dominance between the alleles generates the observed results. One way to decide between these models is to cross each of several albino F₂ mice with true-breeding brown mice. The two-gene model predicts several different outcomes depending on the − − *cc* albino's genotype at the *B* gene. The one-gene model predicts that all progeny of all the crosses will be black.

(a) Hypothesis 1 (two genes with recessive epistasis)

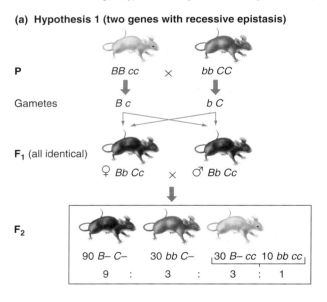

(b) Hypothesis 2 (one gene with incomplete dominance)

correct? We might also explain the data—160 progeny in a ratio of 90:30:40—by the activity of one gene (**Fig. 3.18b**). According to this one-gene hypothesis, albinos would be homozygotes for one allele (*bb*), brown mice would be homozygotes for a second allele (*BB*), and black mice would be heterozygotes (*Bb*) that have their own "intermediate" phenotype because *B* shows incomplete dominance over *b*. Under this system, a mating of black (*Bb*) to black (*Bb*) would be expected to produce 1 *BB* brown : 2 *Bb* black : 1 *bb* albino, or 40 brown : 80 black : 40 albino. Is it possible that the 30 brown, 90 black, and 40 albino mice actually counted were obtained from the inheritance of a single gene? Intuitively, the answer is yes: the ratios 40:80:40 and 30:90:40 do not seem that different. We know that if we flip a coin 100 times, it doesn't always come up 50 heads : 50 tails; sometimes it's 60:40 just by chance. So, how can we decide between the two-gene versus the one-gene model?

The answer is that we can use other types of crosses to verify or refute the hypotheses. For instance, if the one-gene hypothesis were correct, a mating of pure white F$_2$ albinos with pure-breeding brown mice similar to those of the parental generation would produce all black heterozygotes (brown [*BB*] × albino [*bb*] = all black [*Bb*]) (Fig. 3.18b). But if the two-gene hypothesis is correct, with recessive mutations at an albino gene (called *C*) epistatic to all expression from the *B* gene, different matings of pure-breeding brown (*bb CC*) with the F$_2$ albinos (– – *cc*) will give different results—all progeny are black; half are black and half brown; all are brown—depending on the albino's genotype at the *B* gene (see Fig. 3.18a). In fact, when the experiment is actually performed, the diversity of results confirms the two-gene hypothesis. The comprehensive example on pp. 68–69 outlines additional details of the interactions of the three mouse genes for coat color.

With humans, pedigree analysis replaces breeding experiments

Breeding experiments cannot be applied to humans, for obvious ethical reasons. But a careful examination of as many family pedigrees as possible can help elucidate the genetic basis of a particular condition.

In a form of albinism known as ocular-cutaneous albinism (OCA), for example, people with the inherited condition have little or no pigment in their skin, hair, and eyes (**Fig. 3.19a**). The horizontal inheritance pattern seen in **Fig. 3.19b** suggests that OCA is determined by the recessive allele of one gene, with albino family members being homozygotes for that allele. But a 1952 paper on albinism reported a family in which two albino parents produced three normally pigmented

Figure 3.19 Family pedigrees help unravel the genetic basis of ocular-cutaneous albinism (OCA). **(a)** An albino Nigerian girl and her sister celebrating the conclusion of the All Africa games. **(b)** A pedigree following the inheritance of OCA in an inbred family indicates that the trait is recessive. **(c)** A family in which two albino parents have nonalbino children demonstrates that homozygosity for a recessive allele of either of two genes can cause OCA.

(a) Ocular-cutaneous albinism (OCA)

(b) OCA is recessive

(c) Complementation for albinism

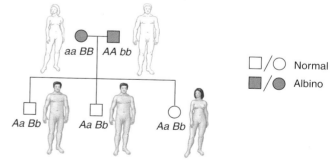

children (**Fig. 3.19c**). How would you explain this phenomenon?

The answer is that albinism is another example of heterogeneity: Mutant alleles at any one of several different genes can cause the condition. The reported mating was, in effect, an inadvertent complementation test, which showed that one parent was homozygous for an OCA-causing mutation in gene *A*, while the other parent was homozygous for an OCA-causing mutation in a different gene, *B* (compare with Fig. 3.16 on p. 61).

The same genotype does not always produce the same phenotype

In our discussion of gene interactions so far, we have looked at examples in which a genotype reliably fashions a particular phenotype. But this is not always what happens. Sometimes a genotype is not expressed at all; that is, even though the genotype is present, the expected phenotype does not appear. Other times, the trait caused by a genotype is expressed to varying degrees or in a variety of ways in different individuals. Factors that alter the phenotypic expression of genotype include modifier genes, the environment (in the broadest sense, as defined earlier), and chance.

Penetrance and expressivity

Retinoblastoma, the most malignant form of eye cancer, arises from a dominant mutation of one gene, but only 75% of people who carry the mutant allele develop the disease. Geneticists use the term **penetrance** to describe how many members of a population with a particular genotype show the expected phenotype. Penetrance can be *complete* (100%), as in the traits that Mendel studied, or *incomplete,* as in retinoblastoma (see the Genetics and Society box "Disease Prevention Versus the Right to Privacy" on p. 67 for another example of incomplete penetrance). For retinoblastoma, the penetrance is 75%.

In some people with retinoblastoma, only one eye is affected, while in other individuals with the phenotype, both eyes are diseased. **Expressivity** refers to the degree or intensity with which a particular genotype is expressed in a phenotype. Expressivity can be *variable,* as in retinoblastoma (one or both eyes affected), or *unvarying,* as in pea color. As we will see, the incomplete penetrance and variable expressivity of retinoblastoma are the result of chance, but in other cases, it is modifier genes and/or the environment that causes such variations in the appearance of phenotype.

Modifier genes

Not all genes that influence the appearance of a trait contribute equally to the phenotype. Major genes have a large influence, while **modifier genes** have a more subtle, secondary effect. Modifier genes alter the phenotypes produced by the alleles of other genes. There is no formal distinction between major and modifier genes. Rather, there is a continuum between the two, and the cutoff is arbitrary.

Modifier genes influence the length of a mouse's tail. The mutant *T* allele of the tail-length gene causes a shortening of the normally long wild-type tail. But not all mice carrying the *T* mutation have the same length tail. A comparison of several inbred lines points to modifier genes as the cause of this variable expressivity. In one inbred line, mice carrying the *T* mutation have tails that are approximately 75% as long as normal tails; in another inbred line, the tails are 50% normal length; and in a third line, the tails are only 10% as long as wild-type tails. Because all members of each inbred line grow the same length tail, no matter what the environment (for example, diet, cage temperature, or bedding), geneticists conclude it is genes and not the environment or chance that determines the length of a mutant mouse's tail. Different inbred lines most likely carry different alleles of the modifier genes that determine exactly how short the tail will be when the *T* mutation is present.

Environmental effects on phenotype

Temperature is one element of the environment that can have a visible effect on phenotype. For example, temperature influences the unique coat color pattern of Siamese cats (**Fig. 3.20**). These domestic felines are homozygous for one of the multiple alleles of a gene that encodes an enzyme catalyzing the production of the dark pigment melanin. The form of the enzyme generated by the variant *"Siamese"* allele does not function at the cat's normal body temperature. It becomes active only at the lower temperatures found in the cat's extremities, where it promotes the production of melanin, which darkens the animal's ears, nose, paws, and tail. The enzyme is thus *temperature sensitive.* Under the normal environmental conditions in temperate climates, the Siamese phenotype does not vary much in expressivity from one cat to another, but one can imagine the expression of a very different phenotype—no dark extremities—in equatorial deserts, where the ambient temperature is at or above normal body temperature.

Temperature can also affect survivability. In one type of experimentally bred fruit fly (*Drosophila melanogaster*), some individuals develop and multiply normally at temperatures between 18°C and 29°C; but if the thermometer climbs beyond that cutoff for a short time, they become reversibly paralyzed, and if the temperature remains high for more than a few hours, they die. These insects carry a temperature-sensitive allele of the *shibire* gene, which encodes a protein essential for nerve cell transmission. This type of allele is known as a **conditional lethal** because it is lethal only under certain conditions. The range of temperatures under which the insects remain viable are **permissive conditions;** the lethal temperatures above that are **restrictive conditions.** Thus, at one temperature, the allele gives rise to a phenotype that is indistinguishable from the wild type, while at another temperature, the same allele generates a mutant phenotype (in this case, lethality). Flies with the wild-type *shibire* allele are viable even at the higher temperatures. The fact that some mutations are lethal only under certain conditions clearly illustrates that the environment can affect the penetrance of a phenotype.

Figure 3.20 In Siamese cats, temperature affects coat color. (a) A Siamese cat. **(b)** Melanin is produced only in the cooler extremities. This is because Siamese cats are homozygous for a mutation that renders an enzyme involved in melanin synthesis temperature sensitive. The mutant enzyme is active at lower temperatures but inactive at higher temperatures.

(a)

(b)

Even in genetically normal individuals, exposure to chemicals or other environmental agents can have phenotypic consequences that are similar to those caused by mutant alleles of specific genes. A change in phenotype arising in such a way is known as a **phenocopy.** By definition, phenocopies are not heritable because they do not result from a change in a gene. In humans, ingestion of the sedative thalidomide by pregnant women in the early 1960s produced a phenocopy of a rare dominant trait called *phocomelia.* By disrupting limb development in otherwise normal fetuses, the drug mimicked the effect of the phocomelia-causing mutation. When this became evident, thalidomide was withdrawn from the market.

Some types of environmental change may have a positive effect on an organism's survivability, as in the following example, where a straightforward application of medical science artificially reduces the penetrance of a mutant phenotype. Children born with the recessive trait known as phenylketonuria, or PKU, will develop a range of neurological problems, including convulsive seizures and mental retardation, unless they are put on a special diet. Homozygosity for the mutant PKU allele eliminates the activity of a gene encoding the enzyme phenylalanine hydroxylase. This enzyme normally converts the amino acid phenylalanine to the amino acid tyrosine. Absence of the enzyme causes a buildup of phenylalanine, and this buildup results in neurological problems. Today, a reliable blood test can detect the condition in newborns. Once a baby with PKU is identified, a protective diet that excludes phenylalanine is prescribed; the diet must also provide enough calories to prevent the infant's body from breaking down its own proteins,

thereby releasing the damaging amino acid from within. Such dietary therapy—a simple change in the environment—now enables many PKU infants to develop into healthy adults.

Finally, two of the top killer diseases in the United States—cardiovascular disease and lung cancer—also illustrate how the environment can alter phenotype by influencing both expressivity and penetrance. People may inherit a propensity to heart disease, but the environmental factors of diet and exercise contribute to the occurrence (penetrance) and seriousness (expressivity) of their condition. Similarly, some people are born genetically prone to lung cancer, but whether or not they develop the disease (penetrance) is strongly determined by whether they choose to smoke.

Thus, various aspects of an organism's environment, including temperature, diet, and exercise, interact with its genotype to generate the functional phenotype, the ultimate combination of traits that determines what a plant or animal looks like and how it behaves.

The effects of random events on penetrance and expressivity

Whether a carrier of the retinoblastoma mutation described earlier develops the phenotype, and whether the disease affects one or both eyes, depend on additional genetic events that occur at random. To produce retinoblastoma, these events must alter the second allele of the gene in specific body cells. Examples of random events that can trigger the onset of the disease include cosmic rays (to which humans are constantly exposed) that alter the genetic material in retinal cells or mistakes made during cell division in the retina. Chance events provide the second "hit"—a mutation in the second copy of the retinoblastoma gene—necessary to turn a normal retinal cell into a cancerous one. The phenotype of retinoblastoma thus results from a specific heritable mutation in a specific gene, but the incomplete penetrance and variable expressivity of the disease depend on random genetic events that affect the other allele in certain cells.

By contributing to incomplete penetrance and variable expressivity, modifier genes, the environment, and chance give rise to phenotypic variation. Unlike dominant epistasis or recessive lethality, however, the probability of penetrance and the level of expressivity cannot be derived from the original Mendelian principles of segregation and independent assortment; they are determined empirically by observation and counting.

> Because modifier genes, the environment, and chance events can affect phenotypes, the relationship of a particular genotype and its corresponding phenotype is not always absolute: An allele's penetrance can be incomplete, and its expressivity can be variable.

Mendelian principles can also explain continuous variation

In Mendel's experiments, height in pea plants was determined by two segregating alleles of one gene (in the wild, it is determined by many genes, but in Mendel's inbred populations, the alleles of all but one of these genes were invariant). The phenotypes that resulted from these alternative alleles were clear-cut, either short or tall, and pea plant height was therefore known as a **discontinuous trait.** In contrast, because people do not produce inbred populations, height in humans is determined by segregating alleles of many different genes whose interaction with each other and the environment produces continuous variation in the phenotype; height in humans is thus an example of a **continuous trait.** Within human populations, individual heights vary over a range of values that when charted on a graph produce a bell curve (**Fig. 3.21a**). In fact, many human traits, including height, weight, and skin color, show continuous variation, rather than the clear-cut alternatives analyzed by Mendel.

Continuous traits often appear to blend and "unblend." Think for a moment of skin color. Children of marriages between people of African and Northern European descent, for example, often seem to be a blend of their parents' skin colors. Progeny of these F$_1$ individuals produce offspring displaying a wide range of skin pigmentation; a few may be as light as the original Northern European parent, a few as dark as the original African parent, but most will fall in a range between the two

Figure 3.21 Continuous traits in humans. (a) Women runners at the start of a 5th Avenue mile race in New York City demonstrate that height is a trait showing continuous variation. **(b)** The skin color of most F$_1$ offspring is usually between the parental extremes, while the F$_2$ generation exhibits a broader distribution of continuous variation.

(a)

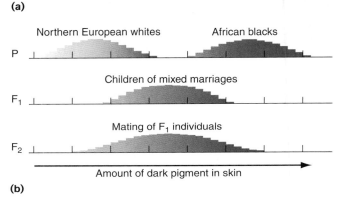

(b)

(**Fig. 3.21b**). For such reasons, early human geneticists were slow to accept Mendelian analysis. Because they were working with outbred populations, they found very few examples of "either-or" Mendelian traits in normal, healthy people.

By 1930, however, studies of corn and tobacco conclusively demonstrated that it is possible to provide a Mendelian explanation of continuous variation by simply increasing the number of genes contributing to a phenotype. The more genes, the more phenotypic classes, and the more classes, the more the variation appears continuous.

As a hypothetical example, consider a series of genes (*A, B, C, . . .*) all affecting the height of pole beans. For each gene, there are two alleles, a *"0"* allele that contributes nothing to height and a *"1"* allele that increases the height of a plant by one unit. All alleles exhibit incomplete dominance relative to alternative alleles at the same gene. The phenotypes determined by all these genes are additive. What would be the result of a two-generation cross between pure-breeding plants carrying only *0* alleles at each height gene and

GENETICS AND SOCIETY

Disease Prevention Versus the Right to Privacy

In one of the most extensive human pedigrees ever assembled, a team of researchers traced a familial pattern of blindness back through five centuries of related individuals to its origin in a couple who died in a small town in northwestern France in 1495. More than 30,000 French men and women alive today descended from that one fifteenth-century couple, and within this direct lineage reside close to half of all reported French cases of hereditary juvenile glaucoma. The massive genealogic tree for the trait (when posted on the office wall, it was over 100 feet long) showed that the genetic defect follows a simple Mendelian pattern of transmission determined by the dominant allele of a single gene (**Fig. A**). The pedigree also showed that the dominant genetic defect displays incomplete penetrance: Not all people receiving the dominant allele become blind; these sighted carriers may unknowingly pass the blindness-causing dominant allele to their children.

Unfortunately, people do not know they have the disease until their vision starts to deteriorate. By that time, their optic fibers have sustained irreversible damage, and blindness is all but inevitable. Surprisingly, the existence of medical therapies that make it possible to arrest the nerve deterioration created a quandary in the late 1980s. Because treatment, to be effective, has to begin before symptoms of impending blindness show up, information in the pedigree could have helped doctors pinpoint people who are at risk, even if neither of their parents is blind. The researchers who compiled the massive family history therefore wanted to give physicians the names of at-risk individuals living in their area, so that doctors could monitor certain patients and recommend treatment if needed. However, a long-standing French law protecting personal privacy forbids public circulation of the names in genetic pedigrees. The French government agency interpreting this law maintained that if the names in the glaucoma pedigree were made public, potential carriers of the disease might suffer discrimination in hiring or insurance.

France thus faced a serious ethical dilemma: On the one hand, giving out names could save perhaps thousands of people from blindness; on the other hand, laws designed to protect personal privacy precluded the dissemination of specific names. The solution adopted by the French government at the time was a massive educational program to alert the general public to the problem so that concerned families could seek medical advice. This approach addressed the legal issues but was only partially helpful in dealing with the medical problem, because many affected individuals escaped detection.

Figure A A pedigree showing the transmission of juvenile glaucoma. A small part of the genealogic tree: The vertical transmission pattern over seven generations shows that a dominant allele of a single gene causes juvenile glaucoma. The lack of glaucoma in V-2 followed by its reappearance in VI-2 reveals that the trait is incompletely penetrant. As a result, sighted heterozygotes may unknowingly pass the condition on to their children.

By 1997, molecular geneticists had identified the gene whose dominant mutant allele causes juvenile glaucoma. This gene specifies a protein called myocilin whose normal function in the eye is at present unknown. The mutant allele encodes a form of myocilin that folds incorrectly and then accumulates abnormally in the tiny canals through which eye fluid normally drains into the bloodstream. Misfolded myocilin blocks the outflow of excess vitreous humor, and the resulting increased pressure within the eye (glaucoma) eventually damages the optic nerve, leading to blindness.

Knowledge of the specific disease-causing mutations in the *myocilin* gene has more recently led to the development of diagnostic tests based on the direct analysis of genotype. (We describe methods for direct genotype analysis in Chapters 9 and 11.) These DNA-based tests can not only identify individuals at risk, but they can also improve disease management. Detection of the mutant allele before the optic nerve is permanently damaged allows for timely treatment. If these tests become sufficiently inexpensive in the future, they could resolve France's ethical dilemma. Doctors could routinely administer the tests to all newborns and immediately identify nearly all potentially affected children; private information in a pedigree would thus not be needed.

---

pure-breeding plants carrying only *1* alleles at each height gene? If only one gene were responsible for height, and if environmental effects could be discounted, the F$_2$ population would be distributed among three classes: homozygous A^0A^0 plants with 0 height (they lie prostrate on the ground); heterozygous A^0A^1 plants with a height of 1; and homozygous A^1A^1 plants with a height of 2 (**Fig. 3.22a** on p. 68). This distribution of heights

over three phenotypic classes does not make a continuous curve. But for two genes, there will be five phenotypic classes in the F$_2$ generation (**Fig. 3.22b**); for three genes, seven classes (**Fig. 3.22c**); and for four genes, nine classes (not shown).

The distributions produced by three and four genes thus begin to approach continuous variation, and if we add a small contribution from environmental variation,

Figure 3.22 A Mendelian explanation of continuous variation. The more genes or alleles, the more possible phenotypic classes, and the greater the similarity to continuous variation. In these examples, several pairs of incompletely dominant alleles have additive effects. Percentages shown at the *bottom* denote frequencies of each genotype expressed as fractions of the total population.

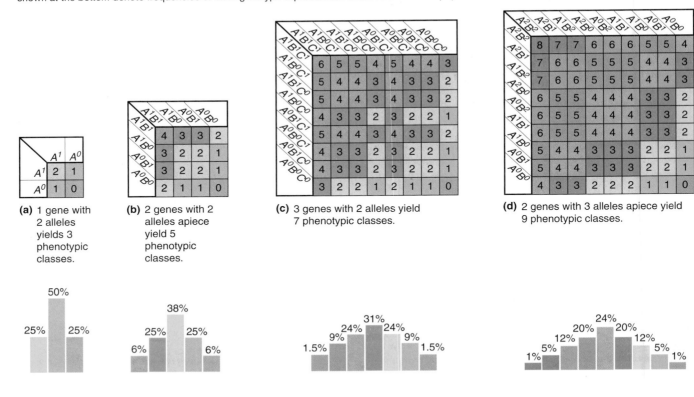

(a) 1 gene with 2 alleles yields 3 phenotypic classes.

(b) 2 genes with 2 alleles apiece yield 5 phenotypic classes.

(c) 3 genes with 2 alleles yield 7 phenotypic classes.

(d) 2 genes with 3 alleles apiece yield 9 phenotypic classes.

a smoother curve will appear. After all, we would expect bean plants to grow better in good soil, with ample sunlight and water. The environmental component effectively converts the stepped bar graph to a continuous curve by producing some variation in expressivity within each genotypic class. Moreover, additional variation might arise from more than two alleles at some genes (Fig. 3.22d), unequal contribution to the phenotype by the various genes involved (review Fig. 3.17 on p. 61), interactions with modifier genes, and chance. Thus, from what we now know about the relation between genotype and phenotype, it is possible to see how just a handful of genes that behave according to known Mendelian principles can easily generate continuous variation.

Continuous traits (also called **quantitative traits**) vary over a range of values and can usually be measured: the length of a tobacco flower in millimeters, the amount of milk produced by a cow per day in liters, or the height of a person in meters. Continuous traits are usually **polygenic**—controlled by multiple genes—and show the additive effects of a large number of alleles, which creates an enormous potential for variation within a population. Differences in the environments encountered by different individuals contribute even more variation. We discuss

the analysis and distribution of multifactorial traits in Chapter 19 on population genetics.

> The action of a handful of genes, combined with environmental effects, can produce an enormous range of phenotypic variation for a particular trait.

A comprehensive example: Mouse coat color is determined by multiple alleles of several genes

Most field mice are a dark gray (agouti), but mice bred for specific mutations in the laboratory can be gray, tan, yellow, brown, black, or various combinations thereof. Here we look at the alleles of three of the genes that make such variation possible. This review underscores how allelic interactions of just a handful of genes can produce an astonishing diversity of phenotypes.

Gene 1: Agouti or other color patterns

The *agouti* gene determines the distribution of color on each hair, and it has multiple alleles. The wild-type allele *A* specifies bands of yellow and black that give the agouti appearance; A^y gets rid of the black and thus produces solid yellow; a gets rid of the yellow and thus produces solid black; and a^t specifies black on the animal's back and yellow on the belly. The dominance series for this set of *agouti* gene alleles is $A^y > A > a^t > a$. However, although A^y is dominant to all other alleles for coat color, it is recessive to all the others for lethality: A^yA^y homozygotes die before birth, while A^yA, A^ya^t, or A^ya heterozygotes survive.

Gene 2: Black or brown

A second gene specifies whether the dark color of each hair is black or brown. This gene has two alleles: B is dominant and designates black; b is recessive and generates brown. Because the A^y allele at the *agouti* gene completely eliminates the dark band of each hair, it acts in a dominant epistatic manner to the B gene. With all other *agouti* alleles, however, it is possible to distinguish the effects of the two different B alleles on phenotype. The $A– B–$ genotype gives rise to the wild-type agouti having black with yellow hairs. The $A– bb$ genotype generates a color referred to as cinnamon (with hairs having stripes of brown and yellow); $aa\ bb$ is all brown; and $a^ta^t\ bb$ is brown on the animal's back and yellow on the belly. A cross between two F_1 hybrid animals of genotype $A^ya\ Bb$ would yield an F_2 generation with yellow ($A^ya – –$), black ($aa\ B–$), and brown ($aa\ bb$) animals in a ratio of 8:3:1. This ratio reflects the dominant epistasis

of A^y and the loss of a class of four (A^yA^y – –) due to prenatal lethality.

Gene 3: Albino or pigmented

Like other mammals, mice have a third gene influencing coat color. A recessive allele (c) abolishes the function of the enzyme that leads to the formation of the dark pigment melanin, making this allele epistatic to all other coat color genes. As a result, cc homozygotes are pure white, while $C–$ mice are agouti, black, brown, yellow, or yellow and black (or other colors and patterns), depending on what alleles they carry at the A and B genes, as well as at some 50 other genes known to play a role in determining the coat color of mice. Adding to the complex color potential are other alleles that geneticists have uncovered for the albino gene; these cause only a partial inactivation of the melanin-producing enzyme and thus have a partial epistatic effect on phenotype.

This comprehensive example of coat color in mice gives some idea of the potential for variation from just a few genes, some with multiple alleles. Amazingly, this is just the tip of the iceberg. When you realize that both mice and humans carry roughly 25,000 genes, the number of interactions that connect the various alleles of these genes in the expression of phenotype is in the millions, if not the billions. The potential for variation and diversity among individuals is staggering indeed.

Connections

Part of Mendel's genius was to look at the genetic basis of variation through a very narrow window, focusing his first glimpse of the mechanisms of inheritance on simple yet fundamental phenomena. Mendel worked on just a handful of traits in inbred populations of one species. For each trait, he manipulated one gene with one completely dominant and one recessive allele that determined two distinguishable, or discontinuous, phenotypes. Both the dominant and recessive alleles showed complete penetrance and negligible differences of expressivity.

In the first few decades of the twentieth century, many questioned the general applicability of Mendelian analysis, for it seemed to shed little light on the complex inheritance patterns of most plant and animal traits or on the mechanisms producing continuous variation. Simple embellishments, however, clarified the genetic basis of continuous variation and provided explanations for other apparent exceptions to Mendelian analysis. These embellishments included the ideas that dominance need not be complete; that one gene can have multiple alleles; that one gene can determine more than one trait; that several

genes can contribute to the same trait; and that the expression of genes can be affected in a variety of ways by other genes, the environment, and chance. Each embellishment extends the range of Mendelian analysis and deepens our understanding of the genetic basis of variation. And no matter how broad the view, Mendel's basic conclusions, embodied in his first law of segregation, remain valid.

But what about Mendel's second law that genes assort independently? As it turns out, its application is not as universal as that of the law of segregation. Many genes do assort independently, but some do not; rather, they appear to be linked and transmitted together from generation to generation. An understanding of this fact emerged from studies that located Mendel's hereditary units, the genes, in specific cellular organelles, the chromosomes. In describing how researchers deduced that genes travel with chromosomes, Chapter 4 establishes the physical basis of inheritance, including the segregation of alleles, and clarifies why some genes assort independently while others do not.

ESSENTIAL CONCEPTS

1. The F_1 phenotype defines the dominance relationship between each pair of alleles. One allele is not always completely dominant or completely recessive to another. With incomplete dominance, the F_1 hybrid phenotype resembles neither parent. With codominance, the F_1 hybrid phenotype includes aspects derived from both parents. Many allele pairs are codominant at the level of protein production.

2. In pleiotropy, one gene contributes to multiple traits. For such a gene, the dominance relation between any two alleles can vary according to the particular phenotype under consideration.

3. A single gene may have any number of alleles, each of which can cause the appearance of different phenotypes. New alleles arise by mutation. Common alleles in a population are considered wild types; rare alleles are mutants. When two or more common alleles exist for a gene, the gene is polymorphic; a gene with only one wild-type allele is monomorphic.

4. Two or more genes may interact in several ways to affect the production of a single trait. These interactions may be understood by observing characteristic deviations from traditional Mendelian phenotypic ratios (review Table 3.2).

5. In epistasis, the action of an allele at one gene can hide traits normally caused by the expression of alleles at another gene. In complementary gene action, dominant alleles of two or more genes are required to generate a trait. In heterogeneity, mutant alleles at any one of two or more genes are sufficient to elicit a phenotype. The complementation test can reveal whether a particular phenotype seen in two individuals arises from mutations in the same or separate genes.

6. In many cases, the route from genotype to phenotype can be modified by the environment, chance, or other genes. A phenotype shows incomplete penetrance when it is expressed in fewer than 100% of individuals with the same genotype. A phenotype shows variable expressivity when it is expressed at a quantitatively different level among individuals with the same genotype.

7. A continuous trait can have any value of expression between two extremes. Most traits of this type are polygenic, that is, determined by the interactions of multiple genes.

On Our Website   www.mhhe.com/hartwell4

Annotated Suggested Readings and Links to Other Websites

- Additional historical examples of complications in Mendelian analysis
- Recently discovered interesting genetic systems

Specialized Topics

- Use of chi-square analysis to test the likelihood that the experimental outcomes of a cross can be explained by a particular hypothesis for the mode of inheritance. (This is a different use of chi-square analysis than the one we present in Chapter 5, where we introduce the technique as a way to determine whether two genes are linked to each other.)

Solved Problems

I. Imagine you purchased an albino mouse (genotype cc) in a pet store. The c allele is epistatic to other coat color genes. How would you go about determining the genotype of this mouse at the brown locus? (In pigmented mice, BB and Bb are black, bb is brown.)

Answer

This problem requires an understanding of gene interactions, specifically epistasis. You have been placed in the role of experimenter and need to design crosses that will answer the question. To determine the alleles of the B gene present, you need to eliminate the blocking action of the *cc* genotype. Because only the recessive *c* allele is epistatic, when a *C* allele is present, no epistasis will occur. To introduce a *C* allele during the mating, the test mouse you mate to your albino can have the genotype *CC* or *Cc*. (If the mouse is *Cc*, half of the progeny will be albino and will not contribute useful information, but the nonalbinos from this cross would be informative.) What alleles of the *B* gene should the test mouse carry? To make this decision, work through the expected results using each of the possible genotypes.

Test mouse genotype		Albino mouse	Expected progeny
BB	×	*BB*	all black
	×	*Bb*	all black
	×	*bb*	all black
Bb	×	*BB*	all black
	×	*Bb*	3/4 black, 1/4 brown
	×	*bb*	1/2 black, 1/2 brown
bb	×	*BB*	all black
	×	*Bb*	1/2 black, 1/2 brown
	×	*bb*	all brown

From these hypothetical crosses, you can see that a test mouse with either the *Bb* or *bb* genotype would yield distinct outcomes for each of the three possible albino mouse genotypes. However, a *bb* test mouse would be more useful and less ambiguous. First, it is easier to identify a mouse with the *bb* genotype because a brown mouse must have this homozygous recessive genotype. Second, the results are completely different for each of the three possible genotypes when you use the *bb* test mouse. (In contrast, a *Bb* test mouse would yield both black and brown progeny whether the albino mouse was *Bb* or *bb*; the only distinguishing feature is the ratio.) *To determine the full genotype of the albino mouse, you should cross it to a brown mouse (which could be* CC bb *or* Cc bb).

II. In a particular kind of wildflower, the wild-type flower color is deep purple, and the plants are true-breeding. In one true-breeding mutant stock, the flowers have a reduced pigmentation, resulting in a lavender color. In a different true-breeding mutant stock, the flowers have no pigmentation and are thus white. When a lavender-flowered plant from the first mutant stock was crossed to a white-flowered plant from the second mutant stock, all the F_1 plants had purple flowers. The F_1 plants were then allowed to self-fertilize to produce an F_2 generation. The 277 F_2 plants were 157 purple : 71 white : 49 lavender. Explain how flower color is inherited. Is this trait controlled by the alleles of a single gene? What kinds of progeny would be produced if lavender F_2 plants were allowed to self-fertilize?

Answer

Are there any modes of single-gene inheritance compatible with the data? The observations that the F_1 plants look different from either of their parents and that the F_2 generation is composed of plants with three different phenotypes exclude complete dominance. The ratio of the three phenotypes in the F_2 plants has some resemblance to the 1:2:1 ratio expected from codominance or incomplete dominance, but the results would then imply that purple plants must be heterozygotes. This conflicts with the information provided that purple plants are true-breeding.

Consider now the possibility that two genes are involved. From a cross between plants heterozygous for two genes (*W* and *P*), the F_2 generation would contain a 9:3:3:1 ratio of the genotypes *W– P–*, *W– pp*, *ww P–*, and *ww pp* (where the dash indicates that the allele could be either a dominant or a recessive form). Are there any combinations of the 9:3:3:1 ratio that would be close to that seen in the F_2 generation in this example? The numbers seem close to a 9:4:3 ratio. What hypothesis would support combining two of the classes (3 + 1)? If *w* is epistatic to the *P* gene, then the *ww P–* and *ww pp* genotypic classes would have the same white phenotype. With this explanation, 1/3 of the F_2 lavender plants would be *WW pp*, and the remaining 2/3 would be *Ww pp*. Upon self-fertilization, *WW pp* plants would produce only lavender (*WW pp*) progeny, while *Ww pp* plants would produce a 3:1 ratio of lavender (*W– pp*) and white (*ww pp*) progeny.

III. Huntington disease (HD) is a rare dominant condition in humans that results in a slow but inexorable deterioration of the nervous system. HD shows what might be called "age-dependent penetrance," which is to say that the probability that a person with the HD genotype will express the phenotype varies with age. Assume that 50% of those inheriting the *HD* allele will express the symptoms by age 40. Susan is a 35-year-old woman whose father has HD. She currently shows no symptoms. What is the probability that Susan will show symptoms in five years?

Answer

This problem involves probability and penetrance. Two conditions are necessary for Susan to show symptoms of the disease. There is a 1/2 (50%) chance that she inherited the mutant allele from her father and a 1/2 (50%) chance that she will express the phenotype by age 40. Because these are independent events, *the probability is the product of the individual probabilities, or 1/4.*

Problems

Interactive Web Exercise

PubMed is a database maintained by the National Center for Biotechnology Information (NCBI) that provides synopses of, and in many cases direct access to, published biomedical journal articles. This database is invaluable to genetics researchers, as well as all biologists and physicians. Our website at www.mhhe.com/hartwell4 contains a brief exercise introducing you to the resources at PubMed; once at the website, go to Chapter 3 and click on "Interactive Web Exercise."

Vocabulary

1. For each of the terms in the left column, choose the best matching phrase in the right column.

a. epistasis	1. one gene affecting more than one phenotype
b. modifier gene	2. the alleles of one gene mask the effects of alleles of another gene
c. conditional lethal	3. both parental phenotypes are expressed in the F_1 hybrids
d. permissive condition	4. a heritable change in a gene
e. reduced penetrance	5. cell surface molecules that are involved in the immune system and are highly variable
f. multifactorial trait	6. genes whose alleles alter phenotypes produced by the action of other genes
g. incomplete dominance	7. less than 100% of the individuals possessing a particular genotype express it in their phenotype
h. codominance	8. environmental conditions that allow conditional lethals to live
i. histocompatibility antigens	9. a trait produced by the interaction of alleles of at least two genes or from interactions between gene and environment
j. mutation	10. individuals with the same genotype have related phenotypes that vary in intensity
k. pleiotropy	11. a genotype that is lethal in some situations (for example, high temperature) but viable in others
l. variable expressivity	12. the heterozygote resembles neither homozygote

Section 3.1

2. In four-o'clocks, the allele for red flowers is incompletely dominant over the allele for white flowers, so heterozygotes have pink flowers. What ratios of flower colors would you expect among the offspring of the following crosses: (a) pink × pink, (b) white × pink, (c) red × red, (d) red × pink, (e) white × white, and (f) red × white? If you specifically wanted to produce pink flowers, which of these crosses would be most efficient?

3. A cross between two plants that both have yellow flowers produces 80 offspring plants, of which 38 have yellow flowers, 22 have red flowers, and 20 have white flowers. If one assumes that this variation in color is due to inheritance at a single locus, what is the genotype associated with each flower color, and how can you describe the inheritance of flower color?

4. In the fruit fly *Drosophila melanogaster,* very dark (ebony) body color is determined by the *e* allele. The e^+ allele produces the normal wild-type, honey-colored body. In heterozygotes for the two alleles, a dark marking called the trident can be seen on the thorax, but otherwise the body is honey-colored. The e^+ allele is thus considered to be incompletely dominant to the *e* allele.
   a. When female e^+e^+ flies are crossed to male e^+e flies, what is the probability that progeny will have the dark trident marking?
   b. Animals with the trident marking mate among themselves. Of 300 progeny, how many would be expected to have a trident, how many ebony bodies, and how many honey-colored bodies?

5. A wild legume with white flowers and long pods is crossed to one with purple flowers and short pods. The F_1 offspring are allowed to self-fertilize, and the F_2 generation has 301 long purple, 99 short purple, 612 long pink, 195 short pink, 295 long white, and 98 short white. How are these traits being inherited?

6. In radishes, color and shape are each controlled by a single locus with two incompletely dominant alleles. Color may be red (*RR*), purple (*Rr*), or white (*rr*) and shape can be long (*LL*), oval (*Ll*), or round (*ll*). What phenotypic classes and proportions would you expect among the offspring of a cross between two plants heterozygous at both loci?

7. Familial hypercholesterolemia (FH) is an inherited trait in humans that results in higher than normal serum cholesterol levels (measured in milligrams of cholesterol per deciliter of blood [mg/dl]). People with serum cholesterol levels that are roughly twice normal have a 25 times higher frequency of heart attacks than unaffected individuals. People with serum cholesterol levels three or more times higher than normal have severely blocked arteries and almost always die before they reach the age of 20

The pedigrees below show the occurrence of FH in four Japanese families:

a. What is the most likely mode of inheritance of FH based on this data? Are there any individuals in any of these pedigrees who do not fit your hypothesis? What special conditions might account for such individuals?

b. Why do individuals in the same phenotypic class (unfilled, yellow, or red symbols) show such variation in their levels of serum cholesterol?

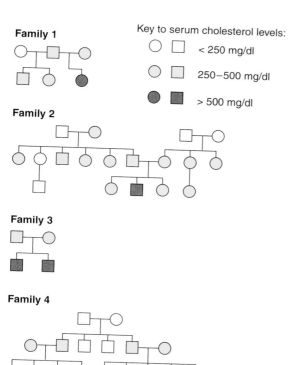

Family 1

Key to serum cholesterol levels:

○ □ < 250 mg/dl

○ □ 250–500 mg/dl

● ■ > 500 mg/dl

Family 2

Family 3

Family 4

8. Describe briefly:

a. The genotype of a person who has sickle-cell anemia.

b. The genotype of a person with a normal phenotype who has a child with sickle-cell anemia.

c. The *total* number of different alleles of the β-globin gene that could be carried by five children with the same mother and father.

9. Assuming no involvement of the Bombay phenotype:

a. If a girl has blood type O, what could be the genotypes and corresponding phenotypes of her parents?

b. If a girl has blood type B and her mother has blood type A, what genotype(s) and corresponding phenotype(s) could the other parent have?

c. If a girl has blood type AB and her mother is also AB, what are the genotype(s) and corresponding phenotype(s) of any male who could *not* be the girl's father?

10. There are several genes in humans in addition to the *ABO* gene that give rise to recognizable antigens on the surface of red blood cells. The *MN* and *Rh* genes are two examples. The *Rh* locus can contain either a positive or negative allele, with positive being dominant to negative. *M* and *N* are codominant alleles of the *MN* gene. The following chart shows several mothers and their children. For each mother–child pair, choose the father of the child from among the males in the right column, assuming one child per male.

	Mother	Child	Males
a.	O M Rh pos	B MN Rh neg	O M Rh neg
b.	B MN Rh neg	O N Rh neg	A M Rh pos
c.	O M Rh pos	A M Rh neg	O MN Rh pos
d.	AB N Rh neg	B MN Rh neg	B MN Rh pos

11. Alleles of the gene that determines seed coat patterns in lentils can be organized in a dominance series: marbled > spotted = dotted (codominant alleles) > clear. A lentil plant homozygous for the marbled seed coat pattern allele was crossed to one homozygous for the spotted pattern allele. In another cross, a homozygous dotted lentil plant was crossed to one homozygous for clear. An F_1 plant from the first cross was then mated to an F_1 plant from the second cross.

a. What phenotypes in what proportions are expected from this mating between the two F_1 types?

b. What are the expected phenotypes of the F_1 plants from the two original parental crosses?

12. In clover plants, the pattern on the leaves is determined by a single gene with multiple alleles that are related in a dominance series. Seven different alleles of this gene are known; an allele that determines the absence of a pattern is recessive to the other six alleles, each of which produces a different pattern. All heterozygous combinations of alleles show complete dominance.

a. How many different kinds of leaf patterns (including the absence of a pattern) are possible in a population of clover plants in which all seven alleles are represented?

b. What is the largest number of different genotypes that could be associated with any one phenotype? Is there any phenotype that could be represented by only a single genotype?

c. In a particular field, you find that the large majority of clover plants lack a pattern on their leaves, even though you can identify a few plants representative of all possible pattern types. Explain this finding.

13. In a population of rabbits, you find three different coat color phenotypes: chinchilla (C), himalaya (H), and albino (A). To understand the inheritance of coat colors, you cross individual rabbits with each other and note the results in the following table.

Cross number	Parental phenotypes	Phenotypes of progeny
1	H × H	3/4 H : 1/4 A
2	H × A	1/2 H : 1/2 A
3	C × C	3/4 C : 1/4 H
4	C × H	all C
5	C × C	3/4 C : 1/4 A
6	H × A	all H
7	C × A	1/2 C : 1/2 A
8	A × A	all A
9	C × H	1/2 C : 1/2 H
10	C × H	1/2 C : 1/4 H : 1/4 A

a. What can you conclude about the inheritance of coat color in this population of rabbits?

b. Ascribe genotypes to the parents in each of the 10 crosses.

c. What kinds of progeny would you expect, and in what proportions, if you crossed the chinchilla parents in crosses #9 and #10?

14. Some plant species have an incompatibility system different from that shown in Fig. 3.8. In this alternate kind of incompatibility, a mating cannot produce viable seeds if the male parent shares an incompatibility allele with the female parent. (Just as with the kind of incompatibility system shown in Fig. 3.8, this system ensures that all plants are heterozygous for the incompatibility gene.) Five plants were isolated from a wild population of a species with this alternate type of incompatiblity. The results of matings between each pair of plants are given here (− means no seeds were produced; + means seeds were produced). How many different alleles of the incompatibility gene are present in this group of five plants? What are the genotypes of the five plants?

	1	2	3	4	5
1	−	−	−	+	−
2		−	+	+	+
3			−	+	−
4				−	−
5					−

15. Fruit flies with one allele for curly wings (Cy) and one allele for normal wings (Cy^+) have curly wings. When two curly-winged flies were crossed, 203 curly-winged and 98 normal-winged flies were obtained. In fact, all crosses between curly-winged flies produce nearly the same curly : normal ratio among the progeny.

a. What is the approximate phenotypic ratio in these offspring?

b. Suggest an explanation for these data.

c. If a curly-winged fly was mated to a normal-winged fly, how many flies of each type would you expect among 180 total offspring?

16. Spherocytosis is an inherited blood disease in which the erythrocytes (red blood cells) are spherical instead of biconcave. This condition is inherited in a dominant fashion, with Sph^- dominant to Sph^+. In people with spherocytosis, the spleen "reads" the spherical red blood cells as defective, and it removes them from the bloodstream, leading to anemia. The spleen in different people removes the spherical erythrocytes with different efficiencies. Some people with spherical erythrocytes suffer severe anemia and some mild anemia, yet others have spleens that function so poorly there are no symptoms of anemia at all. When 2400 people with the genotype Sph^- Sph^+ were examined, it was found that 2250 had anemia of varying severity, but 150 had no symptoms.

a. Does this description of people with spherocytosis represent incomplete penetrance, variable expressivity, or both? Explain your answer. Can you derive any values from the numerical data to measure penetrance or expressivity?

b. Suggest a treatment for spherocytosis and describe how the incomplete penetrance and/or variable expressivity of the condition might affect this treatment.

17. In a species of tropical fish, a colorful orange and black variety called montezuma occurs. When two montezumas, are crossed, 2/3 of the progeny are montezuma, and 1/3 are the wild-type, dark grayish green color. Montezuma is a single-gene trait, and montezuma fish are never true-breeding.

a. Explain the inheritance pattern seen here and show how your explanation accounts for the phenotypic ratios given.

b. In this same species, the morphology of the dorsal fin is altered from normal to ruffled by homozygosity for a recessive allele designated f. What progeny would you expect to obtain, and in what proportions, from the cross of a montezuma fish homozygous for normal fins to a green, ruffled fish?

c. What phenotypic ratios of progeny would be expected from the crossing of two of the montezuma progeny from part b?

18. You have come into contact with two unrelated patients who express what you think is a rare phenotype—a dark spot on the bottom of the foot. According to a medical source, this phenotype is seen in 1 in every 100,000 people in the population. The two patients give their family histories to you, and you generate the pedigrees that follow.

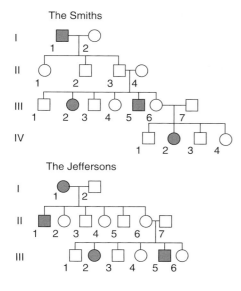

The Smiths

The Jeffersons

a. Given that this trait is rare, do you think the inheritance is dominant or recessive? Are there any special conditions that appear to apply to the inheritance?

b. Which nonexpressing members of these families must carry the mutant allele?

c. If this trait is instead quite common in the population, what alternative explanation would you propose for the inheritance?

d. Based on this new explanation (part *c*), which non-expressing members of these families must have the genotype normally causing the trait?

19. Polycystic kidney disease is a dominant trait that causes the growth of numerous cysts in the kidneys. The condition eventually leads to kidney failure. A child with polycystic kidney disease is born to a couple, neither of whom shows the disease. What possibilities might explain this outcome?

Section 3.2

20. A rooster with a particular comb morphology called walnut was crossed to a hen with a type of comb morphology known as single. The F_1 progeny all had walnut combs. When F_1 males and females were crossed to each other, 93 walnut and 11 single combs were seen among the F_2 progeny, but there were also 29 birds with a new kind of comb called rose and 32 birds with another new comb type called pea.

a. Explain how comb morphology is inherited.

b. What progeny would result from crossing a homozygous rose-combed hen with a homozygous pea-combed rooster? What phenotypes and ratios would be seen in the F_2 progeny?

c. A particular walnut rooster was crossed to a pea hen, and the progeny consisted of 12 walnut, 11 pea, 3 rose, and 4 single chickens. What are the likely genotypes of the parents?

d. A different walnut rooster was crossed to a rose hen, and all the progeny were walnut. What are the possible genotypes of the parents?

21. A black mare was crossed to a chestnut stallion and produced a bay son and a bay daughter. The two offspring were mated to each other several times, and they produced offspring of four different coat colors: black, bay, chestnut, and liver. Crossing a liver grandson back to the black mare gave a black foal, and crossing a liver granddaughter back to the chestnut stallion gave a chestnut foal. Explain how coat color is being inherited in these horses.

22. Filled-in symbols in the pedigree that follows designate individuals suffering from deafness.

a. Study the pedigree and explain how deafness is being inherited.

b. What is the genotype of the individuals in generation V? Why are they not affected?

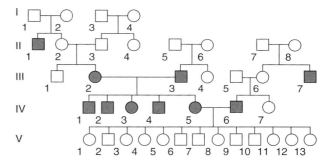

23. You do a cross between two true-breeding strains of zucchini. One has green fruit and the other has yellow fruit. The F_1 plants are all green, but when these are crossed, the F_2 plants consist of 9 green : 7 yellow.

a. Explain this result. What were the genotypes of the two parental strains?

b. Indicate the phenotypes, with frequencies, of the progeny of a testcross of the F_1 plants.

24. Two true-breeding white strains of the plant *Illegitimati noncarborundum* were mated, and the F_1 progeny were all white. When the F_1 plants were allowed to self-fertilize, 126 white-flowered and 33 purple-flowered F_2 plants grew.

a. How could you describe inheritance of flower color? Describe how specific alleles influence each other and therefore affect phenotype.

b. A white F_2 plant is allowed to self-fertilize. Of the progeny, 3/4 are white-flowered, and 1/4 are purple-flowered. What is the genotype of the white F_2 plant?

c. A purple F_2 plant is allowed to self-fertilize. Of the progeny, 3/4 are purple-flowered, and 1/4 are white-flowered. What is the genotype of the purple F_2 plant?

d. Two white F_2 plants are crossed with each other. Of the progeny, 1/2 are purple-flowered, and 1/2 are white-flowered. What are the genotypes of the two white F_2 plants?

25. Explain the difference between epistasis and dominance. How many loci are involved in each case?

26. As you will learn in later chapters, duplication of genes is an important evolutionary mechanism. As a result, many cases are known in which a species has two or more nearly identical genes.

a. Suppose there are two genes, *A* and *B*, that specify production of the same enzyme. An abnormal phenotype results only if an individual does not make any of that enzyme. What ratio of normal versus abnormal progeny would result from a mating between two parents of genotype *Aa Bb,* where *A* and *B* represent alleles that specify production of the enzyme, while *a* and *b* are alleles that do not?

b. Suppose now that there are three genes specifying production of this enzyme, and again that a single functional allele is sufficient for a wild-type phenotype. What ratio of normal versus abnormal progeny would result from a mating between two triply heterozygous parents?

27. "Secretors" (genotypes *SS* and *Ss*) secrete their A and B blood group antigens into their saliva and other body fluids, while "nonsecretors" (*ss*) do not. What would be the apparent phenotypic blood group proportions among the offspring of an $I^A I^B Ss$ woman and an $I^A I^A Ss$ man if typing was done using saliva?

28. Normally, wild violets have yellow petals with dark brown markings and erect stems. Imagine you discover a plant with white petals, no markings, and prostrate stems. What experiment could you perform to determine whether the non-wild-type phenotypes are due to several different mutant genes or to the pleiotropic effects of alleles at a single locus? Explain how your experiment would settle the question.

29. The following table shows the responses of blood samples from the individuals in the pedigree to anti-A and anti-B sera. A "+" in the anti-A row indicates that the red blood cells of that individual were clumped by anti-A serum and therefore the individual made A antigens, and a "−" indicates no clumping. The same notation is used to describe the test for the B antigens.

a. Deduce the blood type of each individual from the data in the table.

b. Assign genotypes for the blood groups as accurately as you can from these data, explaining the pattern of inheritance shown in the pedigree. Assume that all genetic relationships are as presented in the pedigree (that is, there are no cases of false paternity).

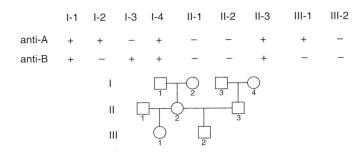

	I-1	I-2	I-3	I-4	II-1	II-2	II-3	III-1	III-2
anti-A	+	+	−	+	−	−	+	+	−
anti-B	+	−	+	+	−	−	+	−	−

30. Three different pure-breeding strains of corn that produce ears with white kernels were crossed to each other. In each case, the F_1 plants were all red, while both red and white kernels were observed in the F_2 generation in a 9:7 ratio. These results are tabulated here.

	F_1	F_2
white-1 × white-2	red	9 red : 7 white
white-1 × white-3	red	9 red : 7 white
white-2 × white-3	red	9 red : 7 white

a. How many genes are involved in determining kernel color in these three strains?

b. Define your symbols and show the genotypes for the pure-breeding strains white-1, white-2, and white-3.

c. Diagram the cross between white-1 and white-2, showing the genotypes and phenotypes of the F_1 and F_2 progeny. Explain the observed 9:7 ratio.

31. In mice, the A^y allele of the *agouti* gene is a recessive lethal allele, but it is dominant for yellow coat color. What phenotypes and ratios of offspring would you expect from the cross of a mouse heterozygous at the agouti locus (genotype $A^y A$) and also at the albino locus (*Cc*) to an albino mouse (*cc*) heterozygous at the agouti locus ($A^y A$)?

32. A student whose hobby was fishing pulled a very unusual carp out of Cayuga Lake: It had no scales on its body. She decided to investigate whether this strange nude phenotype had a genetic basis. She therefore obtained some inbred carp that were pure-breeding for the wild-type scale phenotype (body covered with scales in a regular pattern) and crossed them with her nude fish. To her surprise, the F_1 progeny consisted of wild-type fish and fish with a single linear row of scales on each side in a 1:1 ratio.

a. Can a single gene with two alleles account for this result? Why or why not?

b. To follow up on the first cross, the student allowed the linear fish from the F_1 generation to mate with each other. The progeny of this cross consisted of fish with four phenotypes: linear, wild type, nude, and scattered (the latter had a few scales scattered irregularly on the body). The ratio of these phenotypes was 6:3:2:1, respectively. How many genes appear to be involved in determining these phenotypes?

c. In parallel, the student allowed the phenotypically wild-type fish from the F_1 generation to mate with each other and observed, among their progeny, wild-type and scattered carp in a ratio of 3:1. How many genes with how many alleles appear to determine the difference between wild-type and scattered carp?

d. The student confirmed the conclusions of part *c* by crossing those scattered carp with her pure-breeding wild-type stock. Diagram the genotypes and phenotypes of the parental, F_1, and F_2 generations for this cross and indicate the ratios observed.

e. The student attempted to generate a true-breeding nude stock of fish by inbreeding. However, she found that this was impossible. Every time she crossed two nude fish, she found nude and scattered fish in the progeny, in a 2:1 ratio. (The scattered fish from these crosses bred true.) Diagram the phenotypes and genotypes of this gene in a nude × nude cross and explain the altered Mendelian ratio.

f. The student now felt she could explain all of her results. Diagram the genotypes in the linear × linear cross performed by the student (in part *b*). Show the genotypes of the four phenotypes observed among the progeny and explain the 6:3:2:1 ratio.

33. You picked up two mice (one female and one male) that had escaped from experimental cages in the animal facility. One mouse is yellow in color, and the other is brown agouti. You know that this mouse colony has animals with different alleles at only three coat color genes: the agouti or nonagouti or yellow alleles of the *A* gene, the black or brown allele of the *B* gene, and the albino or nonalbino alleles of the *C* gene. However, you don't know which alleles of these genes are actually present in each of the animals that you've captured. To determine the genotypes, you breed them together. The first litter has only three pups. One is albino, one is brown (nonagouti), and the third is black agouti.

a. What alleles of the *A, B,* and *C* genes are present in the two mice you caught?

b. After raising several litters from these two parents, you have many offspring. How many different coat color phenotypes (in total) do you expect to see expressed in the population of offspring? What are the phenotypes and corresponding genotypes?

34. Figure 3.17 on p. 61 and Fig. 3.22b on p. 68 both show traits that are determined by two genes, each of which has two incompletely dominant alleles. But in Fig. 3.17 the gene interaction produces nine different phenotypes, while the situation depicted in Fig. 3.22b shows only five possible phenotypic classes. How can you explain this difference in the amount of phenotypic variation?

35. Three genes in fruit flies affect a particular trait, and one dominant allele of *each* gene is necessary to get a wild-type phenotype.

a. What phenotypic ratios would you predict among the progeny if you crossed triply heterozygous flies?

b. You cross a particular wild-type male in succession with three tester strains. In the cross with one tester strain (*AA bb cc*), only 1/4 of the progeny are wild type. In the crosses involving the other two tester strains (*aa BB cc* and *aa bb CC*), half of the progeny are wild type. What is the genotype of the wild-type male?

36. The garden flower *Salpiglossis sinuata* ("painted tongue") comes in many different colors. Several crosses are made between true-breeding parental strains to produce F_1 plants, which are in turn self-fertilized to produce F_2 progeny.

Parents	F_1 phenotypes	F_2 phenotypes
red × blue	all red	102 red, 33 blue
lavender × blue	all lavender	149 lavender, 51 blue
lavender × red	all bronze	84 bronze, 43 red, 41 lavender
red × yellow	all red	133 red, 58 yellow, 43 blue
yellow × blue	all lavender	183 lavender, 81 yellow, 59 blue

a. State a hypothesis explaining the inheritance of flower color in painted tongues.

b. Assign genotypes to the parents, F_1 progeny, and F_2 progeny for all five crosses.

c. In a cross between true-breeding yellow and true-breeding lavender plants, all of the F_1 progeny are bronze. If you used these F_1 plants to produce an F_2 generation, what phenotypes in what ratios would you expect? Are there any genotypes that might produce a phenotype that you cannot predict from earlier experiments, and if so, how might this alter the phenotypic ratios among the F_2 progeny?

37. In foxgloves, there are three different petal phenotypes: white with red spots (WR), dark red (DR), and light red (LR). There are actually two different kinds of true-breeding WR strains (WR-1 and WR-2) that can be distinguished by two-generation intercrosses with true-breeding DR and LR strains:

	Parental	F_1	F_2		
			WR	**LR**	**DR**
1	WR-1 × LR	all WR	480	39	119
2	WR-1 × DR	all WR	99	0	32
3	DR × LR	all DR	0	43	132
4	WR-2 × LR	all WR	193	64	0
5	WR-2 × DR	all WR	286	24	74

a. What can you conclude about the inheritance of the petal phenotypes in foxgloves?

b. Ascribe genotypes to the four true-breeding parental strains (WR-1, WR-2, DR, and LR).

c. A WR plant from the F_2 generation of cross #1 is now crossed with an LR plant. Of 500 total progeny from this cross, there were 253 WR, 124 DR, and 123 LR plants. What are the genotypes of the parents in this WR × LR mating?

38. In a culture of fruit flies, matings between any two flies with hairy wings (wings abnormally containing additional small hairs along their edges) always produce both hairy-winged and normal-winged flies in a 2:1 ratio. You now take hairy-winged flies from this culture and cross them with four types of normal-winged flies; the results for each cross are shown in the following table. Assuming that there are only two possible alleles of the hairy-winged gene (one for hairy wings and one for normal wings), what can you say about the genotypes of the four types of normal-winged flies?

Type of normal-winged flies	Progeny obtained from cross with hairy-winged flies	
	Fraction with normal wings	Fraction with hairy wings
1	1/2	1/2
2	1	0
3	3/4	1/4
4	2/3	1/3

39. A married man and woman, both of whom are deaf, carry some recessive mutant alleles in three different "hearing genes": *d1* is recessive to *D1*, *d2* is recessive to *D2*, and *d3* is recessive to *D3*. Homozygosity for a mutant allele at any one of these three genes causes deafness. In addition, homozygosity for any two of the three genes together in the same genome will cause prenatal lethality (and spontaneous abortion) with a penetrance of 25%. Furthermore, homozygosity for the mutant alleles of all three genes will cause prenatal lethality with a penetrance of 75%. If the genotypes of the mother and father are as indicated here, what is the likelihood that a live-born child will be deaf?

Mother: *D1 d1, D2 d2, d3 d3*
Father: *d1 d1, D2 d2, D3 d3*

The Chromosome Theory of Inheritance

Each of these three human chromosomes carries hundreds to thousands of genes.

In the spherical, membrane-bounded nuclei of plant and animal cells prepared for viewing under the microscope, chromosomes appear as brightly colored, threadlike bodies. The nuclei of normal human cells carry 23 pairs of chromosomes for a total of 46. There are noticeable differences in size and shape among the 23 pairs, but within each pair, the two chromosomes appear to match exactly. (The only exceptions are the male's sex chromosomes, designated X and Y, which constitute an unmatched pair.)

Down syndrome was the first human genetic disorder attributable not to a gene mutation but to an abnormal number of chromosomes. Children born with Down syndrome have 47 chromosomes in each cell nucleus because they carry three, instead of the normal pair, of a very small chromosome referred to as number 21. The aberrant genotype, known as trisomy 21, gives rise to an abnormal phenotype, including a wide skull that is flatter than normal at the back, an unusually large tongue, learning disabilities caused by the abnormal development of the hippocampus and other parts of the brain, and a propensity to respiratory infections as well as heart disorders, rapid aging, and leukemia (**Fig. 4.1**).

How can one extra copy of a chromosome that is itself of normal size and shape cause such wide-ranging phenotypic effects? The answer has two parts. First and foremost, chromosomes are the cellular structures responsible for transmitting genetic information. In this chapter, we describe how geneticists concluded that chromosomes are the carriers of genes, an idea that became known as the **chromosome theory of inheritance.** The second part of the answer is that proper development depends not just on what type of genetic material is present but also on how much of it there is. Thus the mechanisms governing gene transmission during cell division must vigilantly maintain each cell's chromosome number.

Proof that genes are located on chromosomes comes from both breeding experiments and the microscopic examination of cells. As you will see, the behavior of chromosomes during one type of nuclear division called *meiosis* accounts for the segregation and independent assortment of genes proposed by Mendel. Meiosis figures prominently in the process by which most sexually reproducing organisms generate the gametes—eggs or sperm—that at fertilization unite to form the first cell of the next generation. This first cell is the fertilized egg, or *zygote.* The zygote then undergoes a second kind of nuclear division, known as *mitosis,* which continues to occur during the millions of cell divisions that propel development from a single

CHAPTER OUTLINE

- 4.1 Chromosomes: The Carriers of Genes
- 4.2 Mitosis: Cell Division That Preserves Chromosome Number
- 4.3 Meiosis: Cell Divisions That Halve Chromosome Number
- 4.4 Gametogenesis
- 4.5 Validation of the Chromosome Theory

Figure 4.1 Down syndrome: One extra chromosome 21 has widespread phenotypic consequences. Trisomy 21 usually causes changes in physical appearance as well as in the potential for learning. Many children with Down syndrome, such as the fifth grader at the center of the photograph, are able to participate fully in regular activities.

cell to a complex multicellular organism. Mitosis provides each of the many cells in an individual with the same number and types of chromosomes.

The precise chromosome-parceling mechanisms of meiosis and mitosis are crucial to the normal functioning of an organism. When the machinery does not function properly, errors in chromosome distribution can have dire repercussions on the individual's health and survival. Down syndrome, for example, is the result of a failure of chromosome segregation during meiosis. The meiotic error gives rise to an egg or sperm carrying an extra chromosome 21, which if incorporated in the zygote at fertilization, is passed on via mitosis to every cell of the developing embryo. Trisomy—three copies of a chromosome instead of two—can occur with other chromosomes as well, but in nearly all of these cases, the condition is prenatally lethal and results in a miscarriage.

Two themes emerge in our discussion of meiosis and mitosis. First, direct microscopic observations of chromosomes during gamete formation led early twentieth-century investigators to recognize that *chromosome movements parallel the behavior of Mendel's genes, so chromosomes are likely to carry the genetic material.* This chromosome theory of inheritance was proposed in 1902 and was confirmed in the following 15 years through elegant experiments performed mainly on the fruit fly *Drosophila melanogaster.* Second, the chromosome theory transformed the concept of a gene from an abstract particle to a physical reality—part of a chromosome that could be seen and manipulated.

4.1 Chromosomes: The Carriers of Genes

One of the first questions asked at the birth of an infant—is it a boy or a girl?—acknowledges that male and female are mutually exclusive characteristics like the yellow versus green of Mendel's peas. What's more, among humans and most other sexually reproducing species, a roughly 1:1 ratio exists between the two genders. Both males and females produce cells specialized for reproduction—sperm or eggs—that serve as a physical link to the next generation. In bridging the gap between generations, these gametes must each contribute half of the genetic material for making a normal, healthy son or daughter. Whatever part of the gamete carries this material, its structure and function must be able to account for the either-or aspect of sex determination as well as the generally observed 1:1 ratio of males to females. These two features of sex determination were among the earliest clues to the cellular basis of heredity.

Genes reside in the nucleus

The nature of the specific link between sex and reproduction remained a mystery until Anton van Leeuwenhoek, one of the earliest and most astute of microscopists, discovered in 1667 that semen contains spermatozoa

(literally "sperm animals"). He imagined that these microscopic creatures might enter the egg and somehow achieve fertilization, but it was not possible to confirm this hypothesis for another 200 years. Then, during a 20-year period starting in 1854 (about the same time Gregor Mendel was beginning his pea experiments), microscopists studying fertilization in frogs and sea urchins observed the union of male and female gametes and recorded the details of the process in a series of drawings. These drawings, as well as later micrographs (photographs taken through a microscope), clearly show that egg and sperm nuclei are the only elements contributed equally by maternal and paternal gametes. This observation implies that something in the nucleus contains the hereditary material. In humans, the nuclei of the gametes are less than 2 millionth of a meter in diameter. It is indeed remarkable that the genetic link between generations is packaged within such an exceedingly small space.

Genes reside in chromosomes

Further investigations, some dependent on technical innovations in microscopy, suggested that yet smaller, discrete structures within the nucleus are the repository of genetic information. In the 1880s, for example, a newly discovered combination of organic and inorganic dyes revealed the existence of the long, brightly staining, threadlike bodies within the nucleus that we call **chromosomes** (literally "colored bodies"). It was now possible to follow the movement of chromosomes during different kinds of cell division.

In embryonic cells, the chromosomal threads split lengthwise in two just before cell division, and each of the two newly forming daughter cells receives one-half of every split thread. The kind of nuclear division followed by cell division that results in two daughter cells containing the same number and type of chromosomes as the original parent cell is called **mitosis** (from the Greek *mitos* meaning "thread" and -*osis* meaning "formation" or "increase").

In the cells that give rise to male and female gametes, the chromosomes composing each pair become segregated, so that the resulting gametes receive only one chromosome from each chromosome pair. The kind of nuclear division that generates egg or sperm cells containing half the number of chromosomes found in other cells within the same organism is called **meiosis** (from the Greek word for "diminution").

Fertilization: The union of haploid gametes to produce diploid zygotes

In the first decade of the twentieth century, cytologists—scientists who use the microscope to study cell structure—showed that the chromosomes in a fertilized egg actually consist of two matching sets, one contributed by the maternal gamete, the other by the paternal gamete. The corresponding maternal and paternal chromosomes appear alike in size and shape, forming pairs (with one exception—the *sex chromosomes*—which we discuss in a later section).

Gametes and other cells that carry only a single set of chromosomes are called **haploid** (from the Greek word for "single"). Zygotes and other cells carrying two matching sets are **diploid** (from the Greek word for "double"). The number of chromosomes in a normal haploid cell is designated by the shorthand symbol *n;* the number of chromosomes in a normal diploid cell is then *2n.* **Figure 4.2** shows diploid cells as well as the haploid gametes that arise from them in *Drosophila,* where $2n = 8$ and $n = 4$. In humans, $2n = 46$; $n = 23$.

You can see how the halving of chromosome number during meiosis and gamete formation, followed by the union of two gametes' chromosomes at fertilization, normally allows a constant *2n* number of chromosomes to be maintained from generation to generation in all individuals of a species. The chromosomes of every pair must segregate from each other during meiosis so that the haploid gametes will each have one complete set of chromosomes. After fertilization forms the zygote, the process of mitosis then ensures that all the cells of the developing individual have identical diploid chromosome sets.

Microscopic studies suggested that the nuclei of egg and sperm contribute equally to the offspring by providing a single set of *n* chromosomes. The zygote formed by the union of haploid gametes is diploid (2*n*).

Species variations in the number and shape of chromosomes

Scientists analyze the chromosomal makeup of a cell when the chromosomes are most visible—at a specific moment in the cell cycle of growth and division, just before the nucleus divides. At this point, known as *metaphase* (described in detail later), individual chromosomes have duplicated and condensed from thin threads into compact rodlike structures. Each chromosome now consists of two identical halves known as **sister chromatids** attached to each other at a specific location called the **centromere** (**Fig. 4.3**). In **metacentric** chromosomes, the centromere is more or less in the middle; in **acrocentric** chromosomes, the centromere is very close to one end. Modern high-resolution microscopy has failed to find any chromosomes in which the centromere is exactly at one end. As a result, the sister chromatids of all chromosomes

Figure 4.2 Diploid versus haploid: 2*n* versus *n*. Most body cells are diploid: They carry a maternal and paternal copy of each chromosome. Meiosis generates haploid gametes with only one copy of each chromosome. In *Drosophila,* diploid cells have eight chromosomes ($2n = 8$), while gametes have four chromosomes ($n = 4$). Note that the chromosomes in this diagram are pictured before their replication. The X and Y chromosomes determine the sex of the individual.

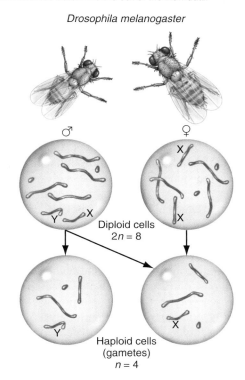

Drosophila melanogaster

Diploid cells
$2n = 8$

Haploid cells
(gametes)
$n = 4$

Figure 4.3 Metaphase chromosomes can be classified by centromere position. Before cell division, each chromosome replicates into two sister chromatids connected at a centromere. In highly condensed metaphase chromosomes, the centromere can appear near the middle (a metacentric chromosome), very near an end (an acrocentric chromosome), or anywhere in between. In a diploid cell, one homologous chromosome in each pair is from the mother and the other from the father.

actually have two "arms" separated by a centromere, even if one of the arms is very short.

Cells in metaphase can be fixed and stained with one of several dyes that highlight the chromosomes and accentuate the centromeres. The dyes also produce characteristic banding patterns made up of lighter and darker regions. Chromosomes that match in size, shape, and banding are called **homologous chromosomes,** or **homologs.** The two homologs of each pair contain the same set of genes, although for some of those genes, they may carry different alleles. The differences between alleles occur at the molecular level and don't show up in the microscope.

Figure 4.3 introduces a system of notation employed throughout this book, using color to indicate degrees of relatedness between chromosomes. Thus, sister chromatids, which are identical duplicates, appear in the same shade of the same color. Homologous chromosomes, which carry the same genes but may vary in the identity of particular alleles, are pictured in different shades (light or dark) of the same color. *Nonhomologous chromosomes,* which carry completely unrelated sets of genetic information, appear in different colors.

To study the chromosomes of a single organism, geneticists arrange micrographs of the stained chromosomes in homologous pairs of decreasing size to produce a **karyotype.** Karyotype assembly can now be speeded and automated by computerized image analysis. **Figure 4.4** shows the karyotype of a human male, with 46 chromosomes arranged in 22 matching pairs of chromosomes and one nonmatching pair. The 44 chromosomes in matching

Figure 4.4 Karyotype of a human male. Photos of metaphase human chromosomes are paired and arranged in order of decreasing size. In a normal human male karyotype, there are 22 pairs of autosomes, as well as an X and a Y ($2n = 46$). Homologous chromosomes share the same characteristic pattern of dark and light bands.

pairs are known as **autosomes.** The two unmatched chromosomes in this male karyotype are called *sex chromosomes,* because they determine the sex of the individual. (We discuss sex chromosomes in more detail in subsequent sections.)

Modern methods of DNA analysis can reveal differences between the maternally and paternally derived chromosomes of a homologous pair, and can thus track the origin of the extra chromosome 21 that causes Down syndrome in individual patients. In 80% of cases, the third chromosome 21 comes from the egg; in 20%, from the sperm. The Genetics and Society box on the next page describes how physicians use karyotype analysis and a technique called *amniocentesis* to diagnose Down syndrome prenatally, roughly three months after a fetus is conceived.

Through thousands of karyotypes on normal individuals, cytologists have verified that the cells of each species carry a distinctive diploid number of chromosomes. Among three species of fruit flies, for example, *Drosophila melanogaster* carries 8 chromosomes in 4 pairs, *Drosophila obscura* carries 10 (5 pairs), and *Drosophila virilis,* 12 (6 pairs). Mendel's peas contain 14 chromosomes (7 pairs) in each diploid cell, macaroni wheat has 28 (14 pairs), giant sequoia trees 22 (11 pairs), goldfish 94 (47 pairs), dogs 78 (39 pairs), and people 46 (23 pairs). Differences in the size, shape, and number of chromosomes reflect differences in the assembled genetic material that determines what each species looks like and how it functions. As these figures show, the number of chromosomes does not always correlate with the size or complexity of the organism.

Karyotyping, the analysis of stained images of all the chromosomes in a cell, reveals that different species have different numbers and shapes of chromosomes.

GENETICS AND SOCIETY

Prenatal Genetic Diagnosis

With new technologies for observing chromosomes and the DNA in genes, modern geneticists can define an individual's genotype directly. They can use this information to predict aspects of the individual's phenotype, even before these traits manifest themselves. Doctors can even use this basic strategy to diagnose, before birth, whether or not a baby will be born with a genetic condition.

The first prerequisite for prenatal diagnosis is to obtain fetal cells whose DNA and chromosomes can be analyzed for genotype. The most frequently used method for acquiring these cells is **amniocentesis (Fig. A)**. To carry out this procedure, a doctor inserts a needle through a pregnant woman's abdominal wall into the amniotic sac in which the fetus is growing; this procedure is performed about 16 weeks after the woman's last menstrual period. By using ultrasound imaging to guide the location of the needle, the physician can minimize the chance of injuring the fetus. The doctor then withdraws some of the amniotic fluid, in which the fetus is suspended, back through the needle into a syringe. This fluid contains living cells called *amniocytes* that were shed by the fetus. When placed in a culture medium, these fetal cells undergo several rounds of mitosis and increase in number. Once enough fetal cells are available, clinicians look at the chromosomes and genes in those cells. In later chapters, we describe techniques that allow the direct examination of the DNA constituting particular disease genes.

Amniocentesis also allows the diagnosis of Down syndrome through the analysis of chromosomes by karyotyping. Because the risk of Down syndrome increases rapidly with the age of the mother, more than half the pregnant women in North America who are over the age of 35 currently undergo amniocentesis. Although the goal of this karyotyping is usually to learn whether the fetus is trisomic for chromosome 21, many other abnormalities in chromosome number or shape may show up when the karyotype is examined.

The availability of amniocentesis and other techniques of prenatal diagnosis is intimately entwined with the personal and societal issue of abortion. The large majority of amniocentesis procedures are performed with the understanding that a fetus whose genotype indicates a genetic disorder, such as Down syndrome, will be aborted. Some prospective parents who are opposed to abortion still elect to undergo amniocentesis so that they can better prepare for an affected child, but this is rare.

The ethical and political aspects of the abortion debate influence many of the practical questions underlying prenatal diagnosis. For example, parents must decide which genetic conditions

Figure A Obtaining fetal cells by amniocentesis. A physician guides insertion of the needle into the amniotic sac using ultrasound imaging and extracts amniotic fluid containing fetal cells into the syringe.

would be sufficiently severe that they would be willing to abort the fetus. They must also assess the risk that amniocentesis might harm the fetus. The normal risk of miscarriage at 16 weeks of gestation is about 2–3%; amniocentesis increases that risk by about 0.5% (about 1 in 200 procedures). From the economic point of view, society must decide who should pay for prenatal diagnosis procedures. In the United States, almost all private insurance companies and most state Medicaid programs cover at least some of the approximately $1500 cost of amniocentesis.

In current practice, the risks and costs of prenatal testing generally restrict amniocentesis to women over age 35 or to mothers whose fetuses are at high risk for a testable genetic condition because of family history. The personal and societal equations determining the frequency of prenatal testing may, however, need to be overhauled in the not-to-distant future because of technological advances that will simplify the procedures and thereby minimize the costs and risks. As one example, clinicians may soon be able to take advantage of new methods currently under evaluation to purify the very small number of fetal cells that find their way into the mother's bloodstream during pregnancy. Collecting these cells from the mother's blood would be much less invasive and expensive than amniocentesis and would pose no risk to the fetus, yet their karyotype analysis would be just as accurate.

Sex chromosomes

Walter S. Sutton, a young American graduate student at Columbia University in the first decade of the twentieth century, was one of the earliest cytologists to realize that particular chromosomes carry the information for determining sex. In one study, he obtained cells from the testes of the great lubber grasshopper (*Brachystola magna;* **Fig. 4.5**)

and followed them through the meiotic divisions that produce sperm. He observed that prior to meiosis, precursor cells within the testes of a great lubber grasshopper contain a total of 24 chromosomes. Of these, 22 are found in 11 matched pairs and are thus autosomes. The remaining 2 chromosomes are unmatched. He called the larger of these the X chromosome and the smaller the Y chromosome.

Figure 4.5 The great lubber grasshopper. In this mating pair, the smaller male is astride the female.

Figure 4.6 How the X and Y chromosomes determine sex in humans. (a) This colorized micrograph shows the human X chromosome on the *left* and the human Y on the *right*. **(b)** Children can receive only an X chromosome from their mother, but they can inherit either an X or a Y from their father.

(a)

(b)

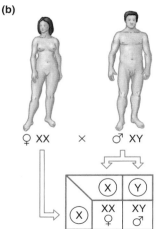

After meiosis, the sperm produced within these testes are of two equally prevalent types: one-half have a set of 11 autosomes plus an X chromosome, while the other half have a set of 11 autosomes plus a Y. By comparison, all of the eggs produced by females of the species carry an 11-plus-X set of chromosomes like the set found in the first class of sperm. When a sperm with an X chromosome fertilizes an egg, an XX female grasshopper results; when a Y-containing sperm fuses with an egg, an XY male develops. Sutton concluded that the X and Y chromosomes determine sex.

Several researchers studying other organisms soon verified that in many sexually reproducing species, two distinct chromosomes—known as the **sex chromosomes**—provide the basis of sex determination. One sex carries two copies of the same chromosome (a matching pair), while the other sex has one of each type of sex chromosome (an unmatched pair). The cells of normal human females, for example, contain 23 pairs of chromosomes. The two chromosomes of each pair, including the sex-determining X chromosomes, appear to be identical in size and shape. In males, however, there is one unmatched pair of chromosomes: the larger of these is the X; the smaller, the Y (Fig. 4.4 and **Fig. 4.6a**). Apart from this difference in sex chromosomes, the two sexes are not distinguishable at any other pair of chromosomes. Thus, geneticists can designate women as XX and men as XY and represent sexual reproduction as a simple cross between XX and XY.

If sex is an inherited trait determined by a pair of sex chromosomes that separate to different cells during gamete formation, then an XX × XY cross could account for both the mutual exclusion of genders and the near 1:1 ratio of males to females, which are hallmark features of sex determination (**Fig. 4.6b**). And if chromosomes carry information defining the two contrasting sex phenotypes, we can easily infer that chromosomes also carry genetic information specifying other characteristics as well.

Species variations in sex determination

You have just seen that humans and other mammals have a pair of sex chromosomes that are identical in the XX female but different in the XY male. Several studies have shown that in humans, it is the presence or absence of the Y that actually makes the difference; that is, any person carrying a Y chromosome will look like a male. For example, rare humans with two X and one Y chromosomes (XXY) are males displaying certain abnormalities collectively called *Klinefelter syndrome*. Klinefelter males are typically tall, thin, and sterile, and they sometimes show mental retardation. That these individuals are males shows that two X chromosomes are insufficient for female development in the presence of a Y. In contrast, humans carrying an X and no second sex chromosome (XO) are females with *Turner syndrome*. Turner females are usually sterile, lack secondary sexual characteristics such as pubic hair, are of short stature, and have folds of skin between their necks and shoulders (webbed necks). Even though these

TABLE 4.1	Sex Determination in Fruit Flies and Humans						
Complement of Sex Chromosomes							
	XXX	**XX**	**XXY**	**XO**	**XY**	**XYY**	**OY**
Drosophila	Dies	Normal female	Normal female	Sterile male	Normal male	Normal male	Dies
Humans	Nearly normal female	Normal female	Klinefelter male (sterile); tall, thin	Turner female (sterile); webbed neck	Normal male	Normal or nearly normal male	Dies

Humans can tolerate extra X chromosomes (e.g., XXX) better than can *Drosophila*. Complete absence of an X chromosome is lethal to both fruit flies and humans. Additional Y chromosomes have little effect in either species.

individuals have only one X chromosome, they develop as females because they have no Y chromosome.

Other species show variations on this XX versus XY chromosomal strategy of sex determination. In fruit flies, for example, although normal females are XX and normal males XY (see Fig. 4.2), it is ultimately the ratio of X chromosomes to autosomes (and not the presence or absence of the Y) that determines sex. In female *Drosophila,* the ratio is 1:1 (there are two X chromosomes and two copies of each autosome); in males, the ratio is 1:2 (there is one X chromosome but two copies of each autosome). Curiously, a rarely observed abnormal intermediate ratio of 2:3 produces intersex flies that display both male and female characteristics. Although the Y chromosome in *Drosophila* does not determine whether a fly looks like a male, it is necessary for male fertility; XO flies are thus sterile males. **Table 4.1** compares how humans and *Drosophila* respond to unusual complements of sex chromosomes. Differences between the two species arise in part because the genes they carry on their sex chromosomes are not identical and in part because the strategies they use to deal with the presence of additional sex chromosomes are not the same. The molecular mechanisms of sex determination in *Drosophila* are covered in detail in Chapter 16.

The XX = female / XY = male strategy of sex determination is by no means universal. In some species of moths, for example, the females are XX, but the males are XO. In *C. elegans* (one species of nematode), males are similarly XO, but XX individuals are not females; they are instead self-fertilizing hermaphrodites that produce both eggs and sperm. In birds and butterflies, males have the matching sex chromosomes, while females have an unmatched set; in such species, geneticists represent the sex chromosomes as ZZ in the male and ZW in the female. The gender having two different sex chromosomes is termed the **heterogametic sex** because it gives rise to two different types of gametes. These gametes would contain either X or Y in the case of male humans, and either Z or W in the case of female birds. Yet other variations include the complicated sex-determination mechanisms of bees and wasps, in which females are diploid and males haploid, and the systems of certain fish, in which sex is determined by changes in the environment, such as fluctuations in

temperature. **Table 4.2** summarizes some of the astonishing variety in the ways that different species have solved the problem of assigning gender to individuals.

In spite of these many differences between species, early researchers concluded that chromosomes can carry the genetic information specifying sexual identity—and probably many other characteristics as well. Sutton and other early adherents of the chromosome theory realized that the perpetuation of life itself therefore depends on the proper distribution of chromosomes during cell division. In the next sections, you will see that the behavior of chromosomes during mitosis and meiosis is exactly that expected of cellular structures carrying genes.

In many species, the sex of an individual correlates with a particular pair of chromosomes termed the sex chromosomes. The segregation of the sex chromosomes during gamete formation and their random reunion at fertilization explains the 1:1 ratio of the two sexes.

TABLE 4.2	Mechanisms of Sex Determination	
	♀	♂
Humans and Drosophila	XX	XY
Moths and C. elegans	XX (hermaphrodites in *C. elegans*)	XO
Birds and Butterflies	ZW	ZZ
Bees and Wasps	Diploid	Haploid
Lizards and Alligators	Cool temperature	Warm temperature
Tortoises and Turtles	Warm temperature	Cool temperature
Anemone Fish	Older adults	Young adults

In the species highlighted in *purple*, sex is determined by sex chromosomes. The species highlighted in *green* have identical chromosomes in the two sexes, and sex is determined instead by environmental or other factors. Anemone fish (bottom row) undergo a sex change from male to female as they age.

4.2 Mitosis: Cell Division That Preserves Chromosome Number

The fertilized human egg is a single diploid cell that preserves its genetic identity unchanged through more than 100 generations of cells as it divides again and again to produce a full-term infant ready to be born. As the newborn infant develops into a toddler, a teenager, and an adult, yet more cell divisions fuel continued growth and maturation. Mitosis, the nuclear division that apportions chromosomes in equal fashion to two daughter cells, is the cellular mechanism that preserves genetic information through all these generations of cells. In this section, we take a close look at how the nuclear division of mitosis fits into the overall scheme of cell growth and division.

If you were to peer through a microscope and follow the history of one cell through time, you would see that for much of your observation, the chromosomes resemble a mass of extremely fine tangled string—called **chromatin**—surrounded by the **nuclear envelope.** Each convoluted thread of chromatin is composed mainly of DNA (which carries the genetic information) and protein (which serves as a scaffold for packaging and managing that information, as described in Chapter 12). You would also be able to distinguish one or two darker areas of chromatin called *nucleoli* (singular, **nucleolus,** literally "small nucleus"); nucleoli play a key role in the manufacture of ribosomes, organelles that function in protein synthesis. During the period between cell divisions, the chromatin-laden nucleus houses a great deal of invisible activity necessary for the growth and survival of the cell. One particularly important part of this activity is the accurate duplication of all the chromosomal material.

With continued vigilance, you would observe a dramatic change in the nuclear landscape during one very short period in the cell's life history: The chromatin condenses into discrete threads, and then each chromosome compacts even further into the twin rods clamped together at the centromere that can be identified in karyotype analysis (review Fig. 4.3 on p. 82). Each rod in a duo is called a **chromatid;** as described earlier, it is an exact duplicate of the other sister chromatid to which it is connected. Continued observation would reveal the doubled chromosomes beginning to jostle around inside the cell, eventually lining up at the cell's midplane. At this point, the sister chromatids comprising each chromosome separate to opposite poles of the now elongating cell, where they become identical sets of chromosomes. Each of the two identical sets eventually ends up enclosed in a separate nucleus in a separate cell. The two cells, known as *daughter cells,* are thus genetically identical.

The repeating pattern of cell growth (an increase in size) followed by division (the splitting of one cell into two) is called the **cell cycle (Fig. 4.7).** Only a small part

Figure 4.7 The cell cycle: An alternation between interphase and mitosis. (a) Chromosomes replicate to form sister chromatids during synthesis (S phase); the sister chromatids segregate to daughter cells during mitosis (M phase). The gaps between the S and M phases, during which most cell growth takes place, are called the G_1 and G_2 phases. In multicellular organisms, some terminally differentiated cells stop dividing and arrest in a "G_0" stage. **(b)** Interphase consists of the G_1, S, and G_2 phases together.

(a) The cell cycle

(b) Chromosomes replicate during S phase

of the cell cycle is spent in division (or **M phase**); the period between divisions is called **interphase.**

During interphase, cells grow and replicate their chromosomes

Interphase consists of three parts: gap 1 **(G_1),** synthesis **(S),** and gap 2 **(G_2)** (Fig. 4.7). G_1 lasts from the birth of a new cell to the onset of chromosome replication; for the genetic material, it is a period when the chromosomes are neither duplicating nor dividing. During this time, the cell achieves most of its growth by using the information from its genes to make and assemble the materials it needs to function normally. G_1 varies in length more than any other phase of the cell cycle. In rapidly dividing cells of the human embryo, for example, G_1 is as short as a few hours. In contrast, mature brain cells become arrested in a resting form of G_1 known as **G_0** and do not normally divide again during a person's lifetime.

Synthesis (S) is the time when the cell duplicates its genetic material by synthesizing DNA. During duplication, each chromosome doubles to produce identical sister chromatids that will become visible when the chromosomes condense at the beginning of mitosis. The two sister chromatids remain joined to each other at the centromere. (Note that this joined structure is considered a single chromosome as long as the connection between sister chromatids is maintained.) The replication of chromosomes during S phase is critical; the genetic material must be copied exactly so that both daughter cells receive identical sets of chromosomes.

Gap 2 (G_2) is the interval between chromosome duplication and the beginning of mitosis. During this time, the cell may grow (usually less than during G_1); it also synthesizes proteins that are essential to the subsequent steps of mitosis itself.

In addition, during interphase an array of fine microtubules crucial for many interphase processes becomes visible outside the nucleus. The microtubules radiate out into the cytoplasm from a single organizing center known as the **centrosome,** usually located near the nuclear envelope. In animal cells, the discernible core of each centrosome is a pair of small, darkly staining bodies called **centrioles** (**Fig. 4.8a**); the microtubule-organizing center of plants does not contain centrioles. During the S and G_2 stages of interphase, the centrosomes replicate, producing two centrosomes that remain in extremely close proximity.

During mitosis, sister chromatids separate and two daughter nuclei form

Although the rigorously choreographed events of nuclear and cellular division occur as a dynamic and continuous process, scientists traditionally analyze the process in separate stages marked by visible cytological events. The artist's sketches in Fig. 4.8 illustrate these stages in the nematode *Ascaris,* whose diploid cells contain only four chromosomes (two pairs of homologous chromosomes).

Prophase: Chromosomes condense (Fig. 4.8a)

During all of interphase, the cell nucleus remains intact, and the chromosomes are indistinguishable aggregates of chromatin. At **prophase** (from the Greek *pro-* meaning "before"), the gradual emergence, or **condensation,** of individual chromosomes from the undifferentiated mass of chromatin marks the beginning of mitosis. Each condensing chromosome has already been duplicated during interphase and thus consists of sister chromatids attached at the centromere. At this stage in *Ascaris* cells, there are therefore four chromosomes with a total of eight chromatids.

The progressive appearance of an array of individual chromosomes is a truly impressive event: Interphase DNA molecules as long as 3–4 cm condense into discrete chromosomes whose length is measured in microns (millionths of a meter). This is equivalent to compacting a 200 m length of thin string (as long as two football fields) into a cylinder 8 mm long and 1 mm wide.

Another visible change in chromatin also takes place during prophase: The darkly staining nucleoli begin to break down and disappear. As a result, the manufacture of ribosomes ceases, providing one indication that general cellular metabolism shuts down so that the cell can focus its energy on chromosome movements and cellular division.

Several important processes that characterize prophase occur outside the nucleus in the cytoplasm. The centrosomes, which replicated during interphase, now move apart and become clearly distinguishable as two separate entities in the light microscope. At the same time, the interphase scaffolding of long, stable microtubules disappears and is replaced by a set of dynamic microtubules that rapidly grow from and shrink back toward their centrosomal organizing centers. The centrosomes continue to move apart, migrating around the nuclear envelope toward opposite ends of the nucleus, apparently propelled by forces exerted between interdigitated microtubules extending from both centrosomes.

Prometaphase: The spindle forms (Fig. 4.8b)

Prometaphase ("before middle stage") begins with the breakdown of the nuclear envelope, which allows microtubules extending from the two centrosomes to invade the nucleus. Chromosomes attach to these microtubules through the **kinetochore,** a structure in the centromere region of each chromatid that is specialized for conveyance. Each kinetochore contains proteins that act as molecular motors, enabling the chromosome to slide along the microtubule. When the kinetochore of a chromatid originally contacts a microtubule at prometaphase, the kinetochore-based motor moves the entire chromosome toward the centrosome from which that microtubule radiates. Microtubules growing from the two centrosomes randomly capture chromosomes by the kinetochore of one of the two sister chromatids. As a result, it is sometimes possible to observe groups of chromosomes congregating in the vicinity of each centrosome. In this early part of prometaphase, for each chromosome, one chromatid's kinetochore is attached to a microtubule, but the sister chromatid's kinetochore remains unattached.

During prometaphase, three different types of microtubule fibers together form the **mitotic spindle;** all of these microtubules originate from the centrosomes, which function as the two "poles" of the spindle apparatus. Microtubules that extend between a centrosome and the kinetochore of a chromatid are called **kinetochore microtubules,** or *centromeric fibers.* Microtubules from each centrosome that are directed toward the middle of the cell are **polar microtubules;** polar microtubules originating in opposite centrosomes interdigitate near the

Figure 4.8 Mitosis maintains the chromosome number of the parent cell nucleus in the two daughter nuclei. In the photomicrographs of newt lung cells at the left, chromosomes are stained *blue* and microtubules appear either *green* or *yellow*.

In animal cells

Centriole

Microtubules
Centrosome
Centromere
Chromosome
Sister chromatids
Nuclear envelope

(a) Prophase: (1) Chromosomes condense and become visible; (2) centrosomes move apart toward opposite poles and generate new microtubules; (3) nucleoli begin to disappear.

Astral microtubules
Kinetochore
Kinetochore microtubules
Polar microtubules

(b) Prometaphase: (1) Nuclear envelope breaks down; (2) microtubules from the centrosomes invade the nucleus; (3) sister chromatids attach to microtubules from opposite centrosomes.

Metaphase plate

(c) Metaphase: Chromosomes align on the metaphase plate with sister chromatids facing opposite poles.

Separating sister chromatids

(d) Anaphase: (1) Centromeres divide; (2) the now separated sister chromatids move to opposite poles.

Re-forming nuclear envelope
Nucleoli reappear
Chromatin

(e) Telophase: (1) Nuclear membranes and nucleoli re-form; (2) spindle fibers disappear; (3) chromosomes uncoil and become a tangle of chromatin.

(f) Cytokinesis: The cytoplasm divides, splitting the elongated parent cell into two daughter cells with identical nuclei.

cell's equator. Finally, there are short **astral microtubules** that extend out from the centrosome toward the cell's periphery.

Near the end of prometaphase, the kinetochore of each chromosome's previously unattached sister chromatid now associates with microtubules extending from the opposite centrosome. This event orients each chromosome such that one sister chromatid faces one pole of the cell, and the other, the opposite pole. Experimental manipulation has shown that if both kinetochores become attached to microtubules from the same pole, the configuration is unstable; one of the kinetochores will repeatedly detach from the spindle until it associates with microtubules from the other pole. The attachment of sister chromatids to opposite spindle poles is the only stable arrangement.

Metaphase: Chromosomes align at the cell's equator (Fig. 4.8c)

During **metaphase** ("middle stage"), the connection of sister chromatids to opposite spindle poles sets in motion a series of jostling movements that cause the chromosomes to move toward an imaginary equator halfway between the two poles. The imaginary midline is called the **metaphase plate.** When the chromosomes are aligned along it, the forces pulling and pushing them toward or away from each pole are in a balanced equilibrium. As a result, any movement away from the metaphase plate is rapidly compensated by tension that restores the chromosome to its position equidistant between the poles.

> The essence of mitosis is the arrangement of chromosomes at metaphase. The kinetochores of sister chromatids are connected to fibers from opposite spindle poles, but the sister chromatids remain held together by their connection at the centromere.

Anaphase: Sister chromatids move to opposite spindle poles (Fig. 4.8d)

The nearly simultaneous severing of the centromeric connection between the sister chromatids of all chromosomes indicates that **anaphase** (from the Greek *ana-* meaning "up" as in "up toward the poles") is underway. The separation of sister chromatids allows each chromatid to be pulled toward the spindle pole to which it is connected by its kinetochore microtubules; as the chromatid moves toward the pole, its kinetochore microtubules shorten. Because the arms of the chromatids lag behind the kinetochores, metacentric chromatids have a characteristic V shape during anaphase. The connection of sister chromatids to microtubules emanating from opposite spindle poles means that the genetic information migrating toward one pole is exactly the same as its counterpart moving toward the opposite pole.

Telophase: Identical sets of chromosomes are enclosed in two nuclei (Fig. 4.8e)

The final transformation of chromosomes and the nucleus during mitosis happens at **telophase** (from the Greek *telo-* meaning "end"). Telophase is like a rewind of prophase. The spindle fibers begin to disperse; a nuclear envelope forms around the group of chromatids at each pole; and one or more nucleoli reappears. The former chromatids now function as independent chromosomes, which decondense (uncoil) and dissolve into a tangled mass of chromatin. Mitosis, the division of one nucleus into two identical nuclei, is over.

Cytokinesis: The cytoplasm divides (Fig. 4.8f)

In the final stage of cell division, the daughter nuclei emerging at the end of telophase are packaged into two separate daughter cells. This final stage of division is called **cytokinesis** (literally "cell movement"). During cytokinesis, the elongated parent cell separates into two smaller independent daughter cells with identical nuclei. Cytokinesis usually begins during anaphase, but it is not completed until after telophase.

The mechanism by which cells accomplish cytokinesis differs in animals and plants. In animal cells, cytoplasmic division depends on a **contractile ring** that pinches the cell into two approximately equal halves, similar to the way the pulling of a string closes the opening of a bag of marbles (**Fig. 4.9a**). Intriguingly, some types of molecules that form the contractile ring also participate in the mechanism

Figure 4.9 Cytokinesis: The cytoplasm divides, producing two daughter cells. (a) In this dividing frog zygote, the contractile ring at the cell's periphery has contracted to form a cleavage furrow that will eventually pinch the cell in two. **(b)** In this dividing onion root cell, a cell plate that began forming near the equator of the cell expands to the periphery, separating the two daughter cells.

(a) Cytokinesis in an animal cell

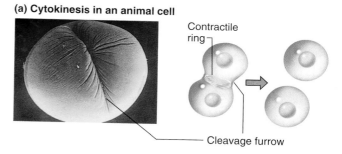

Contractile ring

Cleavage furrow

(b) Cytokinesis in a plant cell

Cell plate

responsible for muscle contraction. In plants, whose cells are surrounded by a rigid cell wall, a membrane-enclosed disk, known as the **cell plate,** forms inside the cell near the equator and then grows rapidly outward, thereby dividing the cell in two (**Fig. 4.9b**).

During cytokinesis, a large number of important organelles and other cellular components, including ribosomes, mitochondria, membranous structures such as Golgi bodies, and (in plants) chloroplasts, must be parcelled out to the emerging daughter cells. The mechanism accomplishing this task does not appear to predetermine which organelle is destined for which daughter cell. Instead, because most cells contain many copies of these cytoplasmic structures, each new cell is bound to receive at least a few representatives of each component. This original complement of structures is enough to sustain the cell until synthetic activity can repopulate the cytoplasm with organelles.

Sometimes cytoplasmic division does not immediately follow nuclear division, and the result is a cell containing more than one nucleus. An animal cell with two or more nuclei is known as a **syncytium.** The early embryos of fruit flies are multinucleated syncytia (**Fig. 4.10**), as are the precursors of spermatozoa in humans and many other animals. A multinucleate plant tissue is called a **coenocyte;** coconut milk is a nutrient-rich food composed of coenocytes.

After mitosis plus cytokinesis, the sister chromatids of every chromosome are separated into two daughter cells. As a result, these two cells are genetically identical to each other and to the original parental cell.

Figure 4.10 If cytokinesis does not follow mitosis, one cell may contain many nuclei. In fertilized *Drosophila* eggs, 13 rounds of mitosis take place without cytokinesis. The result is a single-celled syncytial embryo that contains several thousand nuclei. The photograph shows part of an embryo in which the nuclei are all dividing; chromosomes are in *red,* and spindle fibers are in *green.* Nuclei at the *upper left* are in metaphase, while nuclei toward the *bottom right* are progressively later in anaphase. Membranes eventually grow around these nuclei, dividing the embryo into cells.

Regulatory checkpoints ensure correct chromosome separation

The cell cycle is a complex sequence of precisely coordinated events. In higher organisms, a cell's "decision" to divide depends on both intrinsic factors, such as conditions within the cell that register a sufficient size for division; and signals from the environment, such as hormonal cues or contacts with neighboring cells that encourage or restrain division. Once a cell has initiated events leading to division, usually during the G_1 period of interphase, everything else follows like clockwork. A number of **checkpoints**—moments at which the cell evaluates the results of previous steps—allow the sequential coordination of cell-cycle events. Consequently, under normal circumstances, the chromosomes replicate before they condense, and the doubled chromosomes separate to opposite poles only after correct metaphase alignment of sister chromatids ensures equal distribution to the daughter nuclei (**Fig. 4.11**).

In one illustration of the molecular basis of checkpoints, even a single kinetochore that has not attached to

Figure 4.11 Checkpoints help regulate the cell cycle. Cellular checkpoints (*red wedges*) ensure that important events in the cell cycle occur in the proper sequence. At each checkpoint, the cell determines whether prior events have been completed before it can proceed to the next step of the cell cycle. (For simplicity, we show only two chromosomes per cell.)

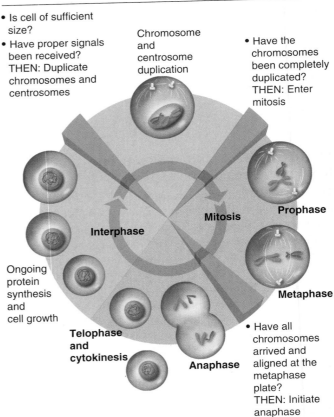

- Is cell of sufficient size?
- Have proper signals been received? THEN: Duplicate chromosomes and centrosomes

Chromosome and centrosome duplication

- Have the chromosomes been completely duplicated? THEN: Enter mitosis

Mitosis

Prophase

Interphase

Metaphase

Ongoing protein synthesis and cell growth

Telophase and cytokinesis

Anaphase

- Have all chromosomes arrived and aligned at the metaphase plate? THEN: Initiate anaphase

FAST FORWARD

How Gene Mutations Cause Errors in Mitosis

During each cell cycle, the chromosomes participate in a tightly patterned choreography that proceeds through sequential steps, synchronized in both time and space. Through their dynamic dance, the chromosomes convey a complete set of genes to each of two newly forming daughter cells. Not surprisingly, some of the genes they carry encode proteins that direct them through the dance.

A variety of proteins, some assembled into structures such as centrosomes and microtubule fibers, make up the molecular machinery that helps coordinate the orderly progression of events in mitosis. Because a particular gene specifies each protein, we might predict that mutant alleles generating defects in particular proteins could disrupt the dance. Cells homozygous for a mutant allele might be unable to complete chromosome duplication, mitosis, or cytokinesis because of a missing or nonfunctional component. Experiments on organisms as disparate as yeast and fruit flies have borne out this prediction. Here we describe the effects of a mutation in one of the many *Drosophila* genes critical for proper chromosome segregation.

Although most mistakes in mitosis are eventually lethal to a multicellular organism, some mutant cells may manage to divide early in development. When prepared for viewing under the microscope, these cells actually allow us to see the effects of defective mitosis. To understand these effects, we first present part of a normal mitosis as a basis for comparison. **Figure A** (*left panel*) shows the eight condensed metaphase chromosomes of a wild-type male fruit fly (*Drosophila melanogaster*): two pairs of large metacentric autosomes with the centromere in the center, a pair of dotlike autosomes that are so small it is not possible to see the centromere region, an acrocentric X chromosome with the centromere very close to one end, and a metacentric Y chromosome. Because most of the Y chromosome consists of a special form of chromatin known as heterochromatin, the two Y sister chromatids remain so tightly connected that they often appear as one.

Figure B (*left panel*) shows the results of aberrant mitosis in an animal homozygous for a mutation in a gene called *zw10* that encodes a component of the chromosomal kinetochores. The mutation disrupted mitotic chromosome segregation during early development, producing cells with the wrong number of chromosomes. The problem in chromosome segregation probably occurred during anaphase of the previous cell division.

Figure A (*right panel*) shows a normal anaphase separation leading to the wild-type chromosome complement. Figure B (*right panel*) portrays an aberrant anaphase separation in a *zw10* mutant animal that could lead to an abnormal chromosome complement similar to that depicted in the left panel of the same figure; you can see that many more chromatids are migrating to one spindle pole than to the other.

The smooth unfolding of each cell cycle depends on a diverse array of proteins. Particular genes specify each of the proteins active in mitosis and cytokinesis, and each protein makes a contribution to the coordinated events of the cell cycle. As a result, a mutation in any of a number of genes can disrupt the meticulously choreographed mechanisms of cell division.

Figure A Metaphase and anaphase chromosomes in a wild-type male fruit fly.

Figure B Metaphase and anaphase chromosomes in a mutant fly. These cells are from a *Drosophila* male homozygous for a mutation in the *zw10* gene. The mutant metaphase cell (*left*) contains extra chromosomes as compared with the wild-type metaphase cell in Fig. A. In the mutant anaphase cell (*right*), more chromatids are moving toward one spindle pole than toward the other.

spindle fibers generates a molecular signal that prevents the sister chromatids of all chromosomes from separating at their centromeres. This signal makes the beginning of anaphase dependent on the prior proper alignment of all the chromosomes at metaphase. As a result of multiple cell-cycle checkpoints, each daughter cell reliably receives the right number of chromosomes.

Breakdown of the mitotic machinery can produce division mistakes that have crucial consequences for the cell. Improper chromosome segregation, for example, can cause serious malfunction or even the death of daughter cells. As the Fast Forward box "How Gene Mutations Cause Errors in Mitosis" explains, gene mutations that disrupt mitotic structures, such as the spindle, kinetochores, or centrosomes are one source of improper segregation. Other problems occur in cells where the normal restraints on cell division, such as checkpoints, have broken down. Such cells may divide uncontrollably, leading to a tumor. We present the details of cell-cycle regulation, checkpoint controls, and cancer formation in Chapter 17.

4.3 Meiosis: Cell Divisions That Halve Chromosome Number

During the many rounds of cell division within an embryo, most cells either grow and divide via the mitotic cell cycle just described, or they stop growing and become arrested in G_0. These mitotically dividing and G_0-arrested cells are the so-called **somatic cells** whose descendants continue to make up the vast majority of each organism's tissues throughout the lifetime of the individual. Early in the embryonic development of animals, however, a group of cells is set aside for a different fate. These are the **germ cells:** cells destined for a specialized role in the production of gametes. Germ cells arise later in plants, during floral development instead of during embryogenesis. The germ cells become incorporated in the reproductive organs—ovaries and testes in animals; ovaries and anthers in flowering plants—where they ultimately undergo meiosis, the special two-part cell division that produces gametes (eggs and sperm or pollen) containing half the number of chromosomes as other body cells.

The union of haploid gametes at fertilization yields diploid offspring that carry the combined genetic heritage of two parents. Sexual reproduction therefore requires the alternation of haploid and diploid generations. If gametes were diploid rather than haploid, the number of chromosomes would double in each successive generation such that in humans, for example, the children would have 92 chromosomes per cell, the grandchildren 184, and so on. Meiosis prevents this lethal, exponential accumulation of chromosomes.

In meiosis, the chromosomes replicate once but the nucleus divides twice

Unlike mitosis, meiosis consists of two successive nuclear divisions, logically named **division I of meiosis** and **division II of meiosis,** or simply **meiosis I** and **meiosis II.** With each round, the cell passes through a prophase, metaphase, anaphase, and telophase followed by cytokinesis. In meiosis I, the parent nucleus divides to form two daughter nuclei; in meiosis II, each of the two daughter nuclei divides, resulting in four nuclei (**Fig. 4.12**). These four nuclei—the final products of meiosis—become partitioned in four separate daughter cells because cytokinesis occurs after both rounds of division. The chromosomes

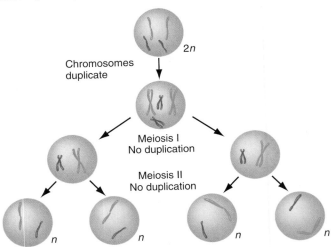

Figure 4.12 An overview of meiosis: The chromosomes replicate once, while the nuclei divide twice. In this figure, all four chromatids of each chromosome pair are shown in the same shade of the same color. Note that the chromosomes duplicate before meiosis I, but they do not duplicate between meiosis I and meiosis II.

duplicate at the start of meiosis I, but they do not duplicate in meiosis II, which explains why the gametes contain half the number of chromosomes found in other body cells. A close look at each round of meiotic division reveals the mechanisms by which each gamete comes to receive one full haploid set of chromosomes.

During meiosis I, homologs pair, exchange parts, and then segregate

The events of meiosis I are unique among nuclear divisions (**Fig. 4.13**, meiosis I, pp. 94–95). The process begins with the replication of chromosomes, after which each one consists of two sister chromatids. A key to understanding meiosis I is the observation that the centromeres joining these chromatids remain intact throughout the entire division, rather than splitting as in mitosis.

As the division proceeds, homologous chromosomes align across the cellular equator to form a coupling that ensures proper chromosome segregation to separate nuclei. Moreover, during the time homologous chromosomes face each other across the equator, the maternal and paternal chromosomes of each homologous pair may exchange parts, creating new combinations of alleles at different genes along the chromosomes. Afterward, the two homologous chromosomes, each still consisting of two sister chromatids connected at a single, unsplit centromere, are pulled to opposite poles of the spindle. As a result, it is homologous chromosomes (rather than sister chromatids as in mitosis) that segregate into different daughter cells at the conclusion of the first meiotic division. With this overview in mind, let us take a closer look at the specific events of meiosis I, bearing in mind that we analyze a dynamic, flowing sequence of cellular events by breaking it down somewhat arbitrarily into the easily pictured, traditional phases.

Prophase I: Homologs condense and pair, and crossing-over occurs

Among the critical events of **prophase I** are the condensation of chromatin, the pairing of homologous chromosomes, and the reciprocal exchange of genetic information between these paired homologs. Figure 4.13 shows a generalized view of prophase I; however, research suggests that the exact sequence of events may vary in different species. These complicated processes can take many days, months, or even years to complete. For example, in the female germ cells of several species, including humans, meiosis is suspended at prophase I until ovulation (as discussed further in section 4.4).

Leptotene (from the Greek for "thin" and "delicate") is the first definable substage of prophase I, the time when the long, thin chromosomes begin to thicken (see **Fig. 4.14a** on p. 96 for a more detailed view). Each chromosome has already duplicated prior to prophase I (as in mitosis) and thus consists of two sister chromatids affixed at a centromere. At this point, however, these sister chromatids are so tightly bound together that they are not yet visible as separate entities.

Zygotene (from the Greek for "conjugation") begins as each chromosome seeks out its homologous partner and the matching chromosomes become zipped together in a process known as **synapsis**. The "zipper" itself is an elaborate protein structure called the **synaptonemal complex** that aligns the homologs with remarkable precision, juxtaposing the corresponding genetic regions of the chromosome pair (**Fig. 4.14b**).

Pachytene (from the Greek for "thick" or "fat") begins at the completion of synapsis when homologous chromosomes are united along their length. Each synapsed chromosome pair is known as a **bivalent** (because it encompasses two chromosomes), or a **tetrad** (because it contains four chromatids). On one side of the bivalent is a maternally derived chromosome, on the other side a paternally derived one. Because X and Y chromosomes are not identical, they do not synapse completely; there is, however, a small region of similarity (or "homology") between the X and the Y chromosomes that allows for a limited amount of pairing.

During pachytene, structures called **recombination nodules** begin to appear along the synaptonemal complex, and an exchange of parts between nonsister (that is, between maternal and paternal) chromatids occurs at these nodules (see **Fig. 4.14c** for details). Such an exchange is known as **crossing-over**; it results in the **recombination** of genetic material. As a result of crossing-over, chromatids may no longer be of purely maternal or paternal origin; however, no genetic information is gained or lost, so all chromatids retain their original size.

Diplotene (from the Greek for "twofold" or "double") is signaled by the gradual dissolution of the synaptonemal zipper complex and a slight separation of regions of the homologous chromosomes (see **Fig. 4.14d**). The aligned homologous chromosomes of each bivalent nonetheless remain very tightly merged at intervals along their length called **chiasmata** (singular, *chiasma*), which represent the sites where crossing-over occurred.

Diakinesis (from the Greek for "double movement") is accompanied by further condensation of the chromatids. Because of this chromatid thickening and shortening, it can now clearly be seen that each tetrad consists of four separate chromatids, or viewed in another way, that the two homologous chromosomes of a bivalent are each composed of two sister chromatids held together at a centromere (see **Fig. 4.14e**). Nonsister chromatids that have undergone crossing-over remain closely associated at chiasmata. The end of diakinesis is analogous to the prometaphase of mitosis: The nuclear envelope breaks down, and the microtubules of the spindle apparatus begin to form.

> During prophase I, homologous chromosomes pair, and recombination occurs between nonsister chromatids of the paired homologs.

Metaphase I: Paired homologs attach to spindle fibers from opposite poles

During mitosis, each sister chromatid has a kinetochore that becomes attached to microtubules emanating from opposite spindle poles. During meiosis I, the situation is different. The kinetochores of sister chromatids fuse, so that each chromosome contains only a single functional kinetochore. The result of this fusion is that sister chromatids remain together throughout meiosis I because no oppositely directed forces exist that can pull the chromatids apart. Instead, during **metaphase I** (Fig. 4.13, meiosis I), it is the kinetochores of homologous chromosomes that attach to microtubules from opposite spindle poles. As a result, in chromosomes aligned at the metaphase plate, the kinetochores of maternally and paternally derived chromosomes face opposite spindle poles, positioning the homologs to move in opposite directions. Because each bivalent's alignment and hookup is independent of that of every other bivalent, the chromosomes facing each pole are a random mix of maternal and paternal origin.

> The essence of the first meiotic division is the arrangement of chromosomes at metaphase I. The kinetochores of homologous chromosomes are connected to fibers from opposite spindle poles. The homologs are held together by chiasmata.

FEATURE FIGURE 4.13

Meiosis: One Diploid Cell Produces Four Haploid Cells

Meiosis I: A reductional division

Prophase I: Leptotene
1. Chromosomes thicken and become visible, but the chromatids remain invisible.
2. Centrosomes begin to move toward opposite poles.

Prophase I: Zygotene
1. Homologous chromosomes enter *synapsis.*
2. The *synaptonemal complex* forms.

Prophase I: Pachytene
1. Synapsis is complete.
2. *Crossing-over*, genetic exchange between nonsister chromatids of a homologous pair, occurs.

Metaphase I
1. Tetrads line up along the *metaphase plate.*
2. Each chromosome of a homologous pair attaches to fibers from opposite poles.
3. Sister chromatids attach to fibers from the same pole.

Anaphase I
1. The centromere does not divide.
2. The chiasmata migrate off chromatid ends.
3. Homologous chromosomes move to opposite poles.

Meiosis II: An equational division

Prophase II
1. Chromosomes condense.
2. Centrioles move toward the poles.
3. The nuclear envelope breaks down at the end of prophase II (not shown).

Metaphase II
1. Chromosomes align at the metaphase plate.
2. Sister chromatids attach to spindle fibers from opposite poles.

Anaphase II
1. Centromeres divide, and sister chromatids move to opposite poles.

Prophase I: Diplotene
1. Synaptonemal complex dissolves.
2. A *tetrad* of four chromatids is visible.
3. Crossover points appear as *chiasmata*, holding nonsister chromatids together.
4. Meiotic arrest occurs at this time in many species.

Prophase I: Diakinesis
1. Chromatids thicken and shorten.
2. At the end of prophase I, the nuclear membrane (not shown earlier) breaks down, and the spindle begins to form.

Telophase I
1. The nuclear envelope re-forms.
2. Resultant cells have half the number of chromosomes, each consisting of two sister chromatids.

Interkinesis
1. This is similar to interphase with one important exception: *No chromosomal duplication takes place.*
2. In some species, the chromosomes decondense; in others, they do not.

Telophase II
1. Chromosomes begin to uncoil.
2. Nuclear envelopes and nucleoli (not shown) re-form.

Cytokinesis
1. The cytoplasm divides, forming four new haploid cells.

Figure 4.13 To aid visualization of the chromosomes, the figure is simplified in two ways: (1) The nuclear envelope is not shown during prophase of either meiotic division. (2) The chromosomes are shown as fully condensed at zygotene; in reality, full condensation is not achieved until diakinesis.

Figure 4.14 Prophase I of meiosis at very high magnification.

(a) Leptotene: Threadlike chromosomes begin to condense and thicken, becoming visible as discrete structures. Although the chromosomes have duplicated, the sister chromatids of each chromosome are not yet visible in the microscope.

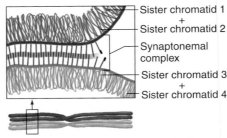

(b) Zygotene: Chromosomes are clearly visible and begin pairing with homologous chromosomes along the synaptonemal complex to form a bivalent, or tetrad.

(c) Pachytene: Full synapsis of homologs. Recombination nodules appear along the synaptonemal complex.

(d) Diplotene: Bivalent appears to pull apart slightly but remains connected at crossover sites, called chiasmata.

(e) Diakinesis: Further condensation of chromatids. Nonsister chromatids that have exchanged parts by crossing-over remain closely associated at chiasmata.

Anaphase I: Homologs move to opposite spindle poles

At the onset of **anaphase I,** the chiasmata joining homologous chromosomes dissolve, which allows the maternal and paternal homologs to begin to move toward opposite spindle poles (see Fig. 4.13, meiosis I). Note that in the first meiotic division, the centromeres do not divide as they do in mitosis. Thus, from each homologous pair, one chromosome consisting of two sister chromatids joined at their centromere segregates to each spindle pole.

Recombination through crossing-over plays an important role in the proper segregation of homologous chromosomes during the first meiotic division. The chiasmata, in holding homologs together, ensure that their kinetochores remain attached to opposite spindle poles throughout metaphase. When recombination does not occur within a bivalent, mistakes in hookup and conveyance may cause homologous chromosomes to move to the same pole, instead of segregating to opposite poles. In some organisms, however, proper segregation of nonrecombinant chromosomes nonetheless occurs through other pairing processes. Investigators do not yet completely understand the nature of these processes and are currently evaluating several models to explain them.

Telophase I: Nuclear envelopes re-form

The telophase of the first meiotic division, or **telophase I,** takes place when nuclear membranes begin to form around the chromosomes that have moved to the poles. Each of the incipient daughter nuclei contains one-half the number of chromosomes in the original parent nucleus, but each chromosome consists of two sister chromatids joined at the centromere (see Fig. 4.13, meiosis I). Because the number of chromosomes is reduced to one-half the normal diploid number, meiosis I is often called a **reductional division.**

In most species, cytokinesis follows telophase I, with daughter nuclei becoming enclosed in separate daughter cells. A short interphase then ensues. During this time, the chromosomes usually decondense, in which case they must recondense during the prophase of the subsequent second meiotic division. In some cases, however, the chromosomes simply stay condensed. Most importantly, there is no S phase during the interphase between meiosis I and meiosis II; that is, the chromosomes do not replicate during meiotic interphase. The relatively brief interphase between meiosis I and meiosis II is known as **interkinesis.**

During meiosis II, sister chromatids separate to produce haploid gametes

The second meiotic division (meiosis II) proceeds in a fashion very similar to that of mitosis, but because the number of chromosomes in each dividing nucleus has already been reduced by half, the resulting daughter cells are haploid. The same process occurs in each of the two daughter cells generated by meiosis I, producing four haploid cells at the end of this second meiotic round (see Fig. 4.13, meiosis II).

Prophase II: The chromosomes condense

If the chromosomes decondensed during the preceding interphase, they recondense during **prophase II.** At the end of prophase II, the nuclear envelope breaks down, and the spindle apparatus re-forms.

Metaphase II: Chromosomes align at the metaphase plate

The kinetochores of sister chromatids attach to microtubule fibers emanating from opposite poles of the spindle apparatus, just as in mitotic metaphase. There are nonetheless two significant features of **metaphase II** that distinguish it from mitosis. First, the number of chromosomes is one-half that in mitotic metaphase of the same species. Second, in most chromosomes, the two sister chromatids are no longer strictly identical because of the recombination through crossing-over that occurred during meiosis I. The sister chromatids still contain the same genes, but they may carry different combinations of alleles.

Anaphase II: Sister chromatids move to opposite spindle poles

Just as in mitosis, severing of the centromeric connection between sister chromatids allows them to move toward opposite spindle poles during **anaphase II.**

Telophase II: Nuclear membranes re-form, and cytokinesis follows

Membranes form around each of four daughter nuclei in **telophase II,** and cytokinesis places each nucleus in a separate cell. The result is four haploid gametes. Note that at the end of meiosis II, each daughter cell (that is, each gamete) has the same number of chromosomes as the parental cell present at the beginning of this division. For this reason, meiosis II is termed an **equational division.**

> Meiosis consists of two rounds of cell division. The first is a reductional division during which homologs segregate, producing haploid daughter cells. The second is an equational division during which sister chromatids are separated.

Mistakes in meiosis produce defective gametes

Segregational errors during either meiotic division can lead to aberrations, such as trisomies, in the next generation. If, for example, the homologs of a chromosome pair do not segregate during meiosis I (a mistake known as **nondisjunction**), they may travel together to the same pole and eventually become part of the same gamete. Such an error may at fertilization result in any one of a large variety of possible trisomies. Most autosomal trisomies, as we already mentioned, are lethal *in utero;* one exception is trisomy 21, the genetic basis of Down syndrome. Like trisomy 21, extra sex chromosomes may also be nonlethal but cause a variety of mental and physical abnormalities, such as those seen in Klinefelter syndrome (see Table 4.1 on p. 85).

In contrast to rare mistakes in the segregation of one pair of chromosomes, some hybrid animals carry nonhomologous chromosomes that can never pair up and segregate properly. **Figure 4.15** shows the two dissimilar sets of

Figure 4.15 Hybrid sterility: When chromosomes cannot pair during meiosis I, they segregate improperly. The mating of a male donkey (*Equus asinus; green*) and a female horse (*Equus caballus; peach color*) produces a mule with 63 chromosomes. In this karyotype of a female mule, the first 13 donkey and horse chromosomes are homologous and pictured in pairs. Starting at chromosome 14, the donkey and horse chromosomes are too dissimilar to pair with each other during meiosis I.

chromosomes carried by the diploid cells of a mule. The set inherited from the donkey father contains 31 chromosomes, while the set from the horse mother has 32 chromosomes. Viable gametes cannot form in these animals, so mules are sterile.

Meiosis contributes to genetic diversity

The wider the assortment of different gene combinations among members of a species, the greater the chance that at least some individuals will carry combinations of alleles that allow survival in a changing environment. Two aspects of meiosis contribute to genetic diversity in a population. First, because only chance governs which paternal or maternal homologs migrate to the two poles during the first meiotic division, different gametes carry a different mix of maternal and paternal chromosomes. **Figure 4.16a** shows how two different patterns of homolog migration produce four different mixes of parental chromosomes in the gametes. The amount of potential variation generated by this random independent assortment increases with the number of chromosomes. In *Ascaris,* for example, where $n = 2$ (the chromosome complement shown in Fig. 4.16a), the random assortment of homologs could produce only 2^2, or 4 types of gametes. In a human being, however, where $n = 23$, this same mechanism alone could generate 2^{23}, or more than 8 million genetically different kinds of gametes.

A second feature of meiosis, the reshuffling of genetic information through crossing-over during prophase I, ensures an even greater amount of genetic diversity in gametes. Because crossing-over recombines maternally and paternally derived genes, each chromosome in each different gamete could consist of different combinations of maternal and paternal information (**Fig. 4.16b**).

Of course, sexual reproduction adds yet another means of producing genetic diversity. At fertilization, any one of a vast number of genetically diverse sperm can fertilize an egg with its own distinctive genetic constitution. It is thus not very surprising that, with the exception of identical twins, the 6 billion people in the world are all genetically unique.

> Genetic diversity is ensured by the independent assortment of nonhomologous chromosomes and the recombination of homologous chromosomes during meiosis, as well as by the random union of genetically distinct sperm and eggs.

Mitosis and meiosis: A comparison

Mitosis occurs in all types of eukaryotic cells (that is, cells with a membrane-bounded nucleus) and is a conservative

Figure 4.16 How meiosis contributes to genetic diversity.
(a) The variation resulting from the independent assortment of nonhomologous chromosomes increases with the number of chromosomes in the genome. **(b)** Crossing-over between homologous chromosomes ensures that each gamete is unique.

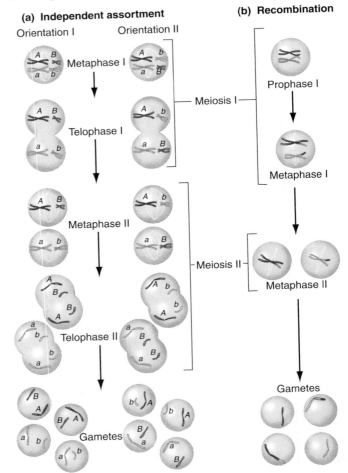

mechanism that preserves the genetic status quo. Mitosis followed by cytokinesis produces growth by increasing the number of cells. It also promotes the continual replacement of roots, stems, and leaves in plants and the regeneration of blood cells, intestinal tissues, and skin in animals.

Meiosis, on the other hand, occurs only in sexually reproducing organisms, in just a few specialized germ cells within the reproductive organs that produce haploid gametes. It is not a conservative mechanism; rather, the extensive combinatorial changes arising from meiosis are one source of the genetic variation that fuels evolution. **Table 4.3** illustrates the significant contrasts between the two mechanisms of cell division.

TABLE 4.3   Comparing Mitosis and Meiosis

Mitosis

Occurs in somatic cells
Haploid and diploid cells can undergo mitosis
One round of division

Mitosis is preceded by S phase (chromosome duplication).

Homologous chromosomes do not pair.

Genetic exchange between homologous chromosomes is very rare.

Sister chromatids attach to spindle fibers from opposite poles during metaphase.

The centromere splits at the beginning of anaphase.

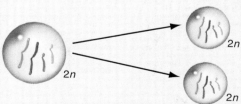

$2n$

$2n$

$2n$

Mitosis produces two new daughter cells, identical to each other and the original cell. Mitosis is thus genetically conservative.

Meiosis

Occurs in germ cells as part of the sexual cycle
Two rounds of division, meiosis I and meiosis II
Only diploid cells undergo meiosis

Meiosis I   Meiosis II

G_1 S G_2

Interkinesis   Gamete formation

Chromosomes duplicate prior to meiosis I but not before meiosis II.

During prophase of meiosis I, homologous chromosomes pair (synapse) along their length.

Crossing-over occurs between homologous chromosomes during prophase of meiosis I.

Homologous chromosomes (not sister chromatids) attach to spindle fibers from opposite poles during metaphase I.

The centromere does not split during meiosis I.

Sister chromatids attach to spindle fibers from opposite poles during metaphase II.

The centromere splits at the beginning of anaphase II.

Meiosis I   Meiosis II

$2n$

n

n

n

n

Meiosis produces four haploid cells, one (egg) or all (sperm) of which can become gametes. None of these is identical to each other or to the original cell, because meiosis results in combinatorial change.

4.4 Gametogenesis

In all sexually reproducing animals, the embryonic germ cells (collectively known as the **germ line**) undergo a series of mitotic divisions that yield a collection of specialized diploid cells, which subsequently divide by meiosis to produce haploid cells. As with other biological processes, many variations on this general pattern have been observed. In some species, the haploid cells resulting from meiosis are the gametes themselves, while in other species, those cells must undergo a specific plan of differentiation to fulfill that function. Moreover, in certain organisms, the four haploid products of a single meiosis do not all become gametes. Gamete formation, or **gametogenesis,** thus gives rise to haploid gametes marked not only by the events of meiosis per se but also by cellular events that precede and follow meiosis. Here we illustrate gametogenesis with a description of egg and sperm formation in humans. The details of gamete

formation in several other organisms appear throughout the book in discussions of specific experimental studies; they also appear in the Genetic Portraits on our website (www.mhhe.com/hartwell4).

Oogenesis in humans produces one ovum from each primary oocyte

The end product of egg formation in humans is a large, nutrient-rich ovum whose stored resources can sustain the early embryo. The process, known as **oogenesis (Fig. 4.17)**, begins when diploid germ cells in the ovary, called **oogonia** (singular, *oogonium*), multiply rapidly by mitosis and produce a large number of **primary oocytes,** which then undergo meiosis.

For each primary oocyte, meiosis I results in the formation of two daughter cells that differ in size, so this division is asymmetric. The larger of these cells, the

Figure 4.17 In humans, egg formation begins in the fetal ovaries and arrests during the prophase of meiosis I. Fetal ovaries contain about 500,000 primary oocytes arrested in the diplotene substage of meiosis I. If the egg released during a menstrual cycle is fertilized, meiosis is completed. Only one of the three (rarely, four) cells produced by meiosis serves as the functional gamete, or ovum.

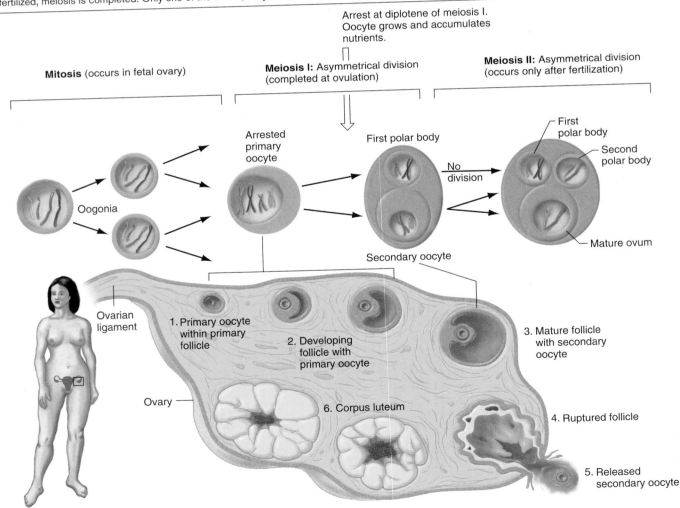

secondary oocyte, receives over 95% of the cytoplasm. The other small sister cell is known as the first **polar body.** During meiosis II, the secondary oocyte undergoes another asymmetrical division to produce a large haploid **ovum** and a small, haploid second polar body. The first polar body usually arrests its development and does not undergo the second meiotic division. However, in a small proportion of cases the first polar body does divide, producing two haploid polar bodies. The two (or rarely, three) small polar bodies apparently serve no function and disintegrate, leaving one large haploid ovum as the functional gamete. Thus, only one of the three (or rarely, four) products of a single meiosis serves as a female gamete. A normal human ovum carries 22 autosomes and an X sex chromosome.

Oogenesis begins in the fetus. By six months after conception, the fetal ovaries are fully formed and contain about half a million primary oocytes arrested in the diplotene substage of prophase I. These cells, with their homologous chromosomes locked in synapsis, are the only oocytes the female will produce, so a girl is born with all the oocytes she will ever possess. From the onset of puberty, at about age 12, until menopause, some 35–40 years later, most women release one primary oocyte each month (from alternate ovaries), amounting to roughly 480 oocytes released during the reproductive years. The remaining primary oocytes disintegrate during menopause.

At ovulation, a released oocyte completes meiosis I and proceeds as far as the metaphase of meiosis II. If the oocyte is then fertilized, that is, penetrated by a sperm nucleus, it quickly completes meiosis II. The nuclei of the sperm and ovum then fuse to form the diploid nucleus of the zygote, and the zygote divides by mitosis to produce a functional embryo. In contrast, unfertilized oocytes exit the body during the menses stage of the menstrual cycle.

The long interval before completion of meiosis in oocytes released by women in their 30s, 40s, and 50s may contribute to the observed correlation between maternal age and meiotic segregational errors, including those that produce trisomies. Women in their mid-20s, for example, run a very small risk of trisomy 21; only 0.05% of children born to women of this age have Down syndrome. During the later childbearing years, however, the risk rapidly rises; at age 35, it is 0.9% of live births, and at age 45, it is 3%. You would not expect this age-related increase in risk if meiosis were completed before the mother's birth.

Spermatogenesis in humans produces four sperm from each primary spermatocyte

The production of sperm, or **spermatogenesis (Fig. 4.18)**, begins in the male testes in germ cells known as **spermatogonia.** Mitotic divisions of the spermatogonia

produce many diploid cells, the **primary spermatocytes.** Unlike primary oocytes, primary spermatocytes undergo a symmetrical meiosis I, producing two **secondary spermatocytes,** each of which undergoes a symmetrical meiosis II. At the conclusion of meiosis, each original primary spermatocyte thus yields four equivalent haploid **spermatids.** These spermatids then mature by developing a characteristic whiplike tail and by concentrating all their chromosomal material in a head, thereby becoming functional **sperm.** A human sperm, much smaller than the ovum it will fertilize, contains 22 autosomes and *either* an X *or* a Y sex chromosome.

The timing of sperm production differs radically from that of egg formation. The meiotic divisions allowing conversion of primary spermatocytes to spermatids begin only at puberty, but meiosis then continues throughout a man's life. The entire process of spermatogenesis takes about 48–60 days: 16–20 for meiosis I, 16–20 for meiosis II, and 16–20 for the maturation of spermatids into fully functional sperm. Within each testis after puberty, millions of sperm are always in production, and a single ejaculate can contain up to 300 million. Over a lifetime, a man can produce billions of sperm, almost equally divided between those bearing an X and those bearing a Y chromosome.

Gametogenesis involves mitotic divisions of specialized germ-line cells that then undergo meiotic divisions to produce gametes. In human females, oocytes undergo asymmetrical meiosis to produce a large ovum and two or three nonfunctional polar bodies. In human males, spermatocytes undergo symmetrical meiosis to produce four sperm.

4.5 Validation of the Chromosome Theory

So far, we have presented two circumstantial lines of evidence in support of the chromosome theory of inheritance. First, the phenotype of sexual identity is associated with the inheritance of particular chromosomes. Second, the events of mitosis, meiosis, and gametogenesis ensure a constant number of chromosomes in the somatic cells of all members of a species over time; one would expect the genetic material to exhibit this kind of stability even in organisms with very different modes of reproduction. Final acceptance of the chromosome theory depended on researchers going beyond the circumstantial evidence to a rigorous demonstration of two key points: (1) that the inheritance of genes corresponds with the inheritance of chromosomes in every detail, and (2) that the transmission of particular chromosomes coincides with the transmission of specific traits other than sex determination.

Figure 4.18 Human sperm form continuously in the testes after puberty. Spermatogonia are located near the exterior of seminiferous tubules in a human testis. Once they divide to produce the primary spermatocytes, the subsequent stages of spermatogenesis—meiotic divisions in the spermatocytes and maturation of spermatids into sperm—occur successively closer to the middle of the tubule. Mature sperm are released into the central lumen of the tubule for ejaculation.

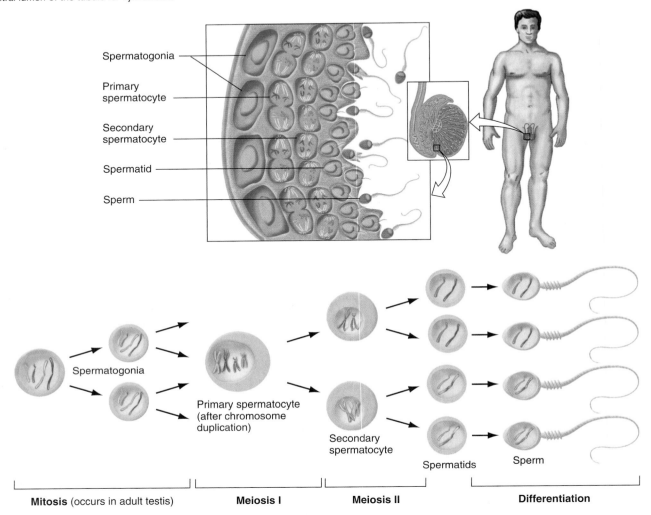

Mendel's laws correlate with chromosome behavior during meiosis

Walter Sutton first outlined the chromosome theory of inheritance in 1902–1903, building on the theoretical ideas and experimental results of Theodor Boveri in Germany, E. B. Wilson in New York, and others. In a 1902 paper, Sutton speculated that "the association of paternal and maternal chromosomes in pairs and their subsequent separation during the reducing division [that is, meiosis I] . . . may constitute the physical basis of the Mendelian law of heredity." In 1903, he suggested that chromosomes carry Mendel's hereditary units for the following reasons:

1. Every cell contains two copies of each kind of chromosome, and there are two copies of each kind of gene.

2. The chromosome complement, like Mendel's genes, appears unchanged as it is transmitted from parents to offspring through generations.

3. During meiosis, homologous chromosomes pair and then separate to different gametes, just as the alternative alleles of each gene segregate to different gametes.

4. Maternal and paternal copies of each chromosome pair move to opposite spindle poles without regard to the assortment of any other homologous chromosome pair, just as the alternative alleles of unrelated genes assort independently.

5. At fertilization, an egg's set of chromosomes unites with a randomly encountered sperm's set of chromosomes, just as alleles obtained from one parent unite at random with those from the other parent.

6. In all cells derived from the fertilized egg, one-half of the chromosomes and one-half of the genes are of maternal origin, the other half of paternal origin.

The two parts of **Table 4.4** show the intimate relationship between the chromosome theory of inheritance and Mendel's laws of segregation and independent assortment. If Mendel's genes for pea shape and pea color are assigned to different (that is, nonhomologous) chromosomes, the behavior of chromosomes can be seen to parallel the behavior of genes. Walter Sutton's observation of these parallels led him to propose that chromosomes and genes are physically connected in some manner. Meiosis ensures that each gamete will contain only a single chromatid of a bivalent and thus only a single allele of any gene on that chromatid (Table 4.4a). The independent behavior of two bivalents during meiosis means that the genes carried on different chromosomes will assort into gametes independently (Table 4.4b).

From a review of Fig. 4.16 (on p. 98), which follows two different chromosome pairs through the process of meiosis, you might wonder whether crossing-over abolishes the clear correspondence between Mendel's laws and the movement of chromosomes. The answer is no. Each chromatid of a homologous chromosome pair contains only one copy of a given gene, and only one chromatid from each pair of homologs is incorporated into each gamete. Because alternative alleles remain on different chromatids even after crossing-over has occurred, alternative alleles still segregate to different gametes as demanded by Mendel's first law. And because the orientation of nonhomologous chromosomes is completely random with respect to each other during both meiotic divisions, the genes on different chromosomes assort independently even if crossing-over occurs, as demanded by Mendel's second law.

Specific traits are transmitted with specific chromosomes

The fate of a theory depends on whether its predictions can be validated. Because genes determine traits, the prediction that chromosomes carry genes could be tested by breeding experiments that would show whether transmission of a specific chromosome coincides with transmission of a specific trait. Cytologists knew that one pair of chromosomes, the sex chromosomes, determines whether an individual is male or female. Would similar correlations exist for other traits?

A gene determining eye color on the Drosophila X chromosome

Thomas Hunt Morgan, an American experimental biologist with training in embryology, headed the research group whose findings eventually established a firm experimental base for the chromosome theory. Morgan chose to work with the fruit fly *Drosophila melanogaster* because it is extremely prolific and has a very short generation time, taking only 12 days to develop from a fertilized egg into a mature adult capable of producing hundreds of offspring. Morgan fed his flies mashed bananas and housed them in empty milk bottles capped with wads of cotton.

In 1910, a white-eyed male appeared among a large group of flies with brick-red eyes. A mutation had apparently altered a gene determining eye color, changing it from the normal wild-type allele specifying red to a new allele that produced white. When Morgan allowed the white-eyed male to mate with its red-eyed sisters, all the flies of the F_1 generation had red eyes; the red allele was clearly dominant to the white (**Fig. 4.19,** cross A).

Establishing a pattern of nomenclature for *Drosophila* geneticists, Morgan named the gene identified by the abnormal white eye color, the *white* gene, for the mutation that revealed its existence. The normal wild-type allele of the *white* gene, abbreviated w^+, is for brick-red eyes, while the counterpart mutant w allele results in white eye color. The superscript $+$ signifies the wild type. By writing the gene name and abbreviation in lowercase, Morgan symbolized that the mutant w allele is recessive to the wild-type w^+. (If a mutation results in a dominant non-wild-type phenotype, the first letter of the gene name or of its abbreviation is capitalized; thus the mutation known as *Bar* eyes is dominant to the wild-type *Bar*$^+$ allele. See the *Guidelines for Gene Nomenclature* on p. 731, directly following Chapter 21.)

Morgan then crossed the red-eyed males of the F_1 generation with their red-eyed sisters (Fig. 4.19, cross B) and obtained an F_2 generation with the predicted 3:1 ratio of red to white eyes. But there was something askew in the pattern: Among the red-eyed offspring, there were two females for every one male, and all the white-eyed offspring were males. This result was surprisingly different from the equal transmission to both sexes of the Mendelian traits discussed in Chapters 2 and 3. In these fruit flies, the ratio of various phenotypes was not the same in male and female progeny.

By mating F_2 red-eyed females with their white-eyed brothers (Fig. 4.19, cross C), Morgan obtained some females with white eyes, which then allowed him to mate a white-eyed female with a red-eyed wild-type male (Fig. 4.19, cross D). The result was exclusively red-eyed daughters and white-eyed sons. The pattern seen in cross D is known as **crisscross inheritance** because the males inherit their eye color from their mothers, while the daughters inherit their eye color from their fathers. Note in Fig. 4.19 that the results of the reciprocal crosses red female × white male (cross A) and white female × red male (cross D) are not identical, again in contrast with Mendel's findings.

TABLE 4.4   How the Chromosome Theory of Inheritance Explains Mendel's Laws

(a) The Law of Segregation

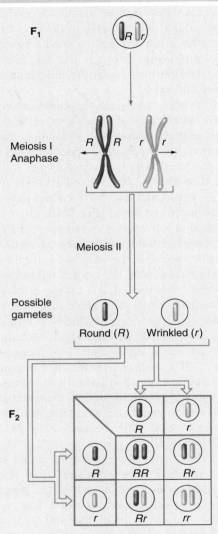

(b) The Law of Independent Assortment

In an F₁ hybrid plant, the allele for round-seeded peas (*R*) is found on one chromosome, and the allele for wrinkled peas (*r*) is on the homologous chromosome. The pairing between the two homologous chromosomes during prophase through metaphase of meiosis I makes sure that the homologs will separate to opposite spindle poles during anaphase I. At the end of meiosis II, two types of gametes have been produced: half have *R*, and half have *r*, but no gametes have both alleles. Thus, the separation of homologous chromosomes at meiosis I corresponds to the segregation of alleles. As the Punnett square shows, fertilization of 50% *R* and 50% *r* eggs with the same proportion of *R* and *r* pollen leads to Mendel's 3:1 ratio in the F₂ generation.

One pair of homologous chromosomes carries the gene for seed texture (alleles *R* and *r*). A second pair of homologous chromosomes carries the gene for seed color (alleles *Y* and *y*). Each homologous pair aligns at random at the metaphase plate during meiosis I, independently of the other homologous pair. Thus, two equally likely configurations are possible for the migration of any two chromosome pairs toward the poles during anaphase I. As a result, a dihybrid individual will generate four equally likely types of gametes with regard to the two traits in question. As the Punnett square affirms, this independent assortment of traits carried by nonhomologous chromosomes produces Mendel's 9:3:3:1 ratio.

Figure 4.19 A *Drosophila* eye color gene is located on the X chromosome. X-linkage explains the inheritance of alleles of the *white* gene in this series of crosses performed by Thomas Hunt Morgan. The progeny of Crosses A, B, and C outlined with green dotted boxes are those used as the parents in the next cross of the series.

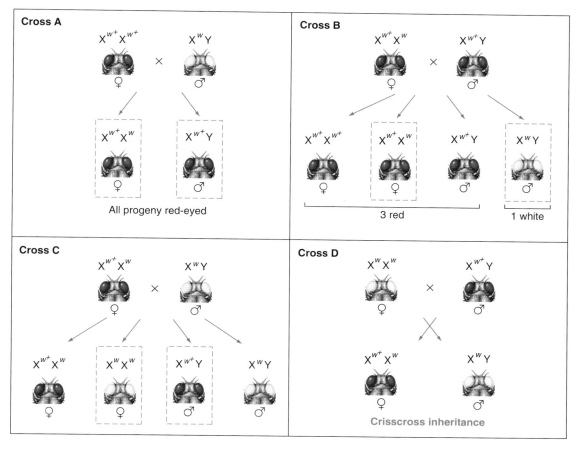

From the data, Morgan reasoned that the *white* gene for eye color is **X linked,** that is, carried by the X chromosome. (Note that while symbols for genes and alleles are italicized, symbols for chromosomes are not.) The Y chromosome carries no allele of this gene for eye color. Males, therefore, have only one copy of the gene, which they inherit from their mother along with their only X chromosome; their Y chromosome must come from their father. Thus, males are **hemizygous** for this eye color gene, because their diploid cells have half the number of alleles carried by the female on her two X chromosomes.

If the single *white* gene on the X chromosome of a male is the wild-type w^+ allele, he will have red eyes and a genotype that can be written $X^{w^+}Y$. (Here we designate the chromosome [X or Y] together with the allele it carries, to emphasize that certain genes are X linked.) In contrast to an $X^{w^+}Y$ male, a hemizygous X^wY male would have a phenotype of white eyes. Females with two X chromosomes can be one of three genotypes: $X^w X^w$ (white-eyed), $X^w X^{w^+}$ (red-eyed because w^+ is dominant to w), or $X^{w^+} X^{w^+}$ (red-eyed).

As shown in Fig. 4.19, Morgan's assumption that the gene for eye color is X linked explains the results of his breeding experiments. Crisscross inheritance, for example, occurs because the only X chromosome in sons of a white-eyed mother ($X^w X^w$) must carry the w allele, so the sons will be white-eyed. In contrast, because daughters of a red-eyed ($X^{w^+}Y$) father must receive a w^+-bearing X chromosome from their father, they will have red eyes.

Through a series of crosses, T. H. Morgan demonstrated that the inheritance of a gene controlling eye color in *Drosophila* was best explained by the hypothesis that this gene lies on the X chromosome.

Support for the chromosome theory from the analysis of nondisjunction

Although Morgan's work strongly supported the hypothesis that the gene for eye color lies on the X chromosome, he himself continued to question the validity of the chromosome theory until Calvin Bridges, one of his top students, found another key piece of evidence. Bridges repeated the cross Morgan had performed between white-eyed females and red-eyed males, but this time he did the experiment on a larger scale. As expected, the progeny of this cross consisted mostly of red-eyed females and white-eyed males. However, about 1 in every 2000 males had red eyes, and about the same small fraction of females had white eyes.

Bridges hypothesized that these exceptions arose through rare events in which the X chromosomes fail to separate during meiosis in females. He called such failures in chromosome segregation *nondisjunction*. As **Fig. 4.20a** shows, nondisjunction would result in some eggs with two X chromosomes and others with none. Fertilization of these chromosomally abnormal eggs could produce four types of zygotes: XXY (with two X chromosomes from the egg and a Y from the sperm), XXX (with two Xs from the egg and one X from the sperm), XO (with the lone sex chromosome from the sperm and no sex chromosome from the egg), and OY (with the only sex chromosome again coming from the sperm). When Bridges examined the sex chromosomes

of the rare white-eyed females produced in his large-scale cross, he found that they were indeed XXY individuals who must have received two X chromosomes and with them two *w* alleles from their white-eyed $X^w X$ mothers. The exceptional red-eyed males emerging from the cross were XO; their eye color showed that they must have obtained their sole sex chromosome from their $X^{w+} Y$ fathers. In this study, transmission of the *white* gene alleles followed the predicted behavior of X chromosomes during rare meiotic mistakes, indicating that the X chromosome carries the gene for eye color. These results also suggested that zygotes with the two other abnormal sex chromosome karyotypes expected from nondisjunction in females (XXX and OY) die during embryonic development and thus produce no progeny.

Because XXY white-eyed females have three sex chromosomes rather than the normal two, Bridges reasoned they would produce four kinds of eggs: XY and X, or XX and Y (**Fig. 4.20b**). You can visualize the formation of these four kinds of eggs by imagining that when the three chromosomes pair and disjoin during meiosis, two chromosomes must go to one pole and one

Figure 4.20 Nondisjunction: Rare mistakes in meiosis help confirm the chromosome theory. (a) Rare events of nondisjunction in an XX female produce XX and O eggs. The results of normal disjunction in the female are not shown. XO males are sterile because the missing Y chromosome is needed for male fertility in *Drosophila*. **(b)** In an XXY female, the three sex chromosomes can pair and segregate in two ways, producing progeny with unusual sex chromosome complements.

chromosome to the other. With this kind of segregation, only two results are possible: Either one X and the Y go to one pole and the second X to the other (yielding XY and X gametes), or the two Xs go to one pole and the Y to the other (yielding XX and Y gametes). The first of these two scenarios occurs more often because it comes about when the two similar X chromosomes pair with each other, ensuring that they will go to opposite poles during the first meiotic division. The second, less likely possibility happens only if the two X chromosomes fail to pair with each other.

Bridges next predicted that fertilization of these four kinds of eggs by normal sperm would generate an array of sex chromosome karyotypes associated with specific eye color phenotypes in the progeny. Bridges verified all his predictions when he analyzed the eye color and sex chromosomes of a large number of offspring. For instance, he showed cytologically that all of the white-eyed females emerging from the cross in Fig. 4.20b had two X chromosomes and one Y chromosome, while one-half of the white-eyed males had a single X chromosome and two Y chromosomes. Bridges' painstaking observations provided compelling evidence that specific genes do in fact reside on specific chromosomes.

X- and Y-linked traits in humans

A person unable to tell red from green would find it nearly impossible to distinguish the rose, scarlet, and magenta in the flowers of a garden bouquet from the delicately variegated greens in their foliage, or to complete a complex electrical circuit by fastening red-clad metallic wires to red ones and green to green. Such a person has most likely inherited some form of red-green colorblindness, a recessive condition that runs in families and affects mostly males. Among Caucasians in North America and Europe, 8% of men but only 0.44% of women have this vision defect. **Figure 4.21** suggests to readers with normal color vision what people with red-green colorblindness actually see.

In 1911, E. B. Wilson, a contributor to the chromosome theory of inheritance, combined familiarity with studies of colorblindness and recent knowledge of sex determination by the X and Y chromosomes to make the first assignment of a human gene to a particular chromosome. The gene for red-green colorblindness, he said, lies on the X because the condition usually passes from a maternal grandfather through an unaffected carrier mother to roughly 50% of the grandsons.

Several years after Wilson made this gene assignment, pedigree analysis established that various forms of hemophilia, or "bleeders disease" (in which the blood fails to clot properly), also result from mutations on the X chromosome that give rise to a relatively rare, recessive trait. In this context, rare means "infrequent in the population." The family histories under review, including

Figure 4.21 Red-green colorblindness is an X-linked recessive trait in humans. How the world looks to a person with either normal color vision (*top*) or a kind of red-green colorblindness known as deuteranopia (*bottom*).

one following the descendants of Queen Victoria of England (**Fig. 4.22a**), showed that relatively rare X-linked traits appear more often in males than in females and often skip generations. The clues that suggest X-linked recessive inheritance in a pedigree are summarized in **Table 4.5**.

Unlike colorblindness and hemophilia, some—although very few—of the known rare mutations on the X chromosome are dominant to the wild-type allele. With such dominant X-linked mutations, more females than males show the aberrant phenotype. This is because all the daughters of an affected male but none of the sons will have the condition, while one-half the sons and one-half the daughters of an affected female will receive the dominant allele and therefore show the phenotype (see Table 4.5). Vitamin D–resistant rickets, or hypophosphatemia, is an example of an X-linked dominant trait. **Figure 4.22b** presents the pedigree of a family affected by this disease.

Theoretically, phenotypes caused by mutations on the Y chromosome should also be identifiable by pedigree

Figure 4.22 X-linked traits may be recessive or dominant.
(a) Pedigree showing inheritance of the recessive X-linked trait hemophilia in Queen Victoria's family. **(b)** Pedigree showing the inheritance of the dominant X-linked trait hypophosphatemia, commonly referred to as vitamin D–resistant rickets.

(a) X-linked recessive: Hemophilia

(b) X-linked dominant: Hypophosphatemia

TABLE 4.5	Pedigree Patterns Suggesting Sex-Linked Inheritance

X-Linked Recessive Trait

1. The trait appears in more males than females since a female must receive two copies of the rare defective allele to display the phenotype, whereas a hemizygous male with only one copy will show it.

2. The mutation will never pass from father to son because sons receive only a Y chromosome from their father.

3. An affected male passes the X-linked mutation to all his daughters, who are thus unaffected carriers. One-half of the sons of these carrier females will inherit the defective allele and thus the trait.

4. The trait often skips a generation as the mutation passes from grandfather through a carrier daughter to grandson.

5. The trait can appear in successive generations when a sister of an affected male is a carrier. If she is, one-half her sons will be affected.

6. With the rare affected female, all her sons will be affected and all her daughters will be carriers.

X-Linked Dominant Trait

1. More females than males show the aberrant trait.

2. The trait is seen in every generation because it is dominant.

3. All the daughters but none of the sons of an affected male will be affected. This criterion is the most useful for distinguishing an X-linked dominant trait from an autosomal dominant trait.

4. One-half the sons and one-half the daughters of an affected female will be affected.

Y-Linked Trait

1. The trait is seen only in males.

2. All male descendants of an affected man will exhibit the trait.

3. Not only do females not exhibit the trait, they also cannot transmit it.

analysis. Such traits would pass from an affected father to all of his sons, and from them to all future male descendants. Females would neither exhibit nor transmit a Y-linked phenotype (see Table 4.5). However, besides the determination of maleness itself, as well as a contribution to sperm formation and thus male fertility, no clear-cut Y-linked visible traits have turned up. The paucity of known Y-linked traits in humans reflects the fact that the small Y chromosome contains very few genes. Indeed, one would expect the Y chromosome to have only a limited effect on phenotype because normal XX females do perfectly well without it.

Autosomal genes and sexual dimorphism

Not all genes that produce sexual dimorphism (differences in the two sexes) reside on the X or Y chromosomes. Some autosomal genes govern traits that appear in one sex but not the other, or traits that are expressed differently in the two sexes.

Sex-limited traits affect a structure or process that is found in one sex but not the other. Mutations in genes for sex-limited traits can influence only the phenotype of the sex that expresses those structures or processes. A curious example of a sex-limited trait occurs in *Drosophila* males homozygous for an autosomal recessive mutation known as *stuck,* which affects the ability

of mutant males to retract their penis and release the claspers by which they hold on to female genitalia during copulation. The mutant males have difficulty separating from females after mating. In extreme cases, both individuals die, forever caught in their embrace. Because females lack penises and claspers, homozygous *stuck* mutant females can mate normally.

Sex-influenced traits show up in both sexes, but expression of such traits may differ between the two sexes because of hormonal differences. Pattern baldness, a condition in which hair is lost prematurely from the top of the head but not from the sides (**Fig. 4.23**), is a sex-influenced trait in humans. Although pattern baldness is a complex trait that can be affected by many genes, an autosomal gene appears to play an important role in certain families.

Figure 4.23 Male pattern baldness, a sex-influenced trait. (a) John Adams (1735–1862), second president of the United States, at about age 60. **(b)** John Quincy Adams (1767–1848), son of John Adams and the sixth president of the United States, at about the same age. The father-to-son transmission suggests that the form of male pattern baldness in the Adams family is likely determined by an allele of an autosomal gene.

(a)   (b)

Men in these families who are heterozygous for the balding allele lose their hair while still in their 20s, whereas heterozygous women do not show any significant hair loss. In contrast, homozygotes in both sexes become bald (though the onset of baldness in homozygous women is usually much later in life than in homozygous men). This sex-influenced trait is thus dominant in men, recessive in women.

The chromosome theory integrates many aspects of gene behavior

Mendel had assumed that genes are located in cells. The chromosome theory assigned the genes to a specific structure within cells and explained alternative alleles as physically matching parts of homologous chromosomes. In so doing, the theory provided an explanation of Mendel's laws. The mechanism of meiosis ensures that the matching parts of homologous chromosomes will segregate to different gametes (except in rare instances of nondisjunction), accounting for the segregation of alleles predicted by Mendel's first law. Because each homologous chromosome pair aligns independently of all others at meiosis I, genes carried on different chromosomes will assort independently, as predicted by Mendel's second law.

The chromosome theory is also able to explain the creation of new alleles through mutation, a spontaneous change in a particular gene (that is, in a particular part of a chromosome). If a mutation occurs in the germ line, it can be transmitted to subsequent generations.

Finally, through mitotic cell division in the embryo and after birth, each cell in a multicellular organism receives the same chromosomes—and thus the same maternal and paternal alleles of each gene—as the zygote received from the egg and sperm at fertilization. In this way, an individual's genome—the chromosomes and genes he or she carries—remains constant throughout life.

The idea that genes reside on chromosomes was verified by experiments involving sex-linked genes in *Drosophila* and by the analysis of pedigrees showing X-linked patterns of inheritance in humans. The chromosome theory provides a physical basis for understanding Mendel's laws.

Connections

T. H. Morgan and his students, collectively known as the *Drosophila* group, acknowledged that Mendelian genetics could exist independently of chromosomes. "Why then, we are often asked, do you drag in the chromosomes? Our answer is that because the chromosomes furnish exactly the kind of mechanism that Mendelian laws call for, and since there is an ever-increasing body of information that points clearly to the chromosomes as the bearers of the Mendelian factors, it would be folly to close one's eyes to so patent a relation. Moreover, as biologists, we are interested in heredity not primarily as a mathematical formulation, but rather as a problem concerning the cell, the egg, and the sperm."

The *Drosophila* group went on to find several X-linked mutations in addition to white eyes. One made the body yellow instead of brown, another shortened the wings, yet another made bent instead of straight body bristles. These findings raised several compelling questions. First, if the genes for all of these traits are physically linked together on the X chromosome, does this linkage affect their ability to assort independently, and if so, how? Second, does each gene have an exact chromosomal address, and if so, does this specific location in any way affect its transmission? In Chapter 5 we describe how the *Drosophila* group and others analyzed the transmission patterns of genes on the same chromosome in terms of known chromosome movements during meiosis, and then used the information obtained to localize genes at specific chromosomal positions.

ESSENTIAL CONCEPTS

1. Chromosomes are cellular structures specialized for the storage and transmission of genetic material. Genes are located on chromosomes and travel with them during cell division and gamete formation.

2. In sexually reproducing organisms, somatic cells carry a precise number of homologous pairs of chromosomes, which is characteristic of the species. One chromosome of each pair is of maternal origin; the other, paternal.

3. Mitosis underlies the growth and development of the individual. Through mitosis, diploid cells produce identical diploid progeny cells. During mitosis, the sister chromatids of every chromosome separate to each of two daughter cells. Before the next cell division, the chromosomes again duplicate to form sister chromatids.

4. During the first division of meiosis, homologous chromosomes in germ cells segregate from each other. As a result, each gamete receives one member of each matching pair, as predicted by Mendel's first law.

5. Also during the first meiotic division, the independent alignment of each pair of homologous chromosomes at the cellular midplane results in the independent assortment of genes carried on different chromosomes, as predicted by Mendel's second law.

6. Crossing-over and the independent alignment of homologs during the first meiotic division generate diversity.

7. The second meiotic division generates gametes with a haploid number of chromosomes (n).

8. Fertilization—the union of egg and sperm—restores the diploid number of chromosomes ($2n$) to the zygote.

9. The discovery of sex linkage, by which specific genes could be assigned to the X chromosome, provided important support for the chromosome theory of inheritance. Later, the analysis of rare mistakes in meiotic chromosome segregation (nondisjunction) yielded more detailed proof that specific genes are carried on specific chromosomes.

On Our Website   www.mhhe.com/hartwell4

Annotated Suggested Readings and Links to Other Websites

- More on the history of the chromosome theory of inheritance
- Mechanisms of sex determination in various organisms

- Recent research into the biochemical mechanisms underlying mitosis and meiosis
- Further examples of sex-linked inheritance in humans

Specialized Topics

- Chromosome behavior during mitosis and meiosis

Solved Problems

I. In humans, chromosome 16 sometimes has a heavily stained area in the long arm near the centromere. This feature can be seen through the microscope but has no effect on the phenotype of the person carrying it. When such a "blob" exists on a particular copy of chromosome 16, it is a constant feature of that chromosome and is inherited. A couple conceived a child, but the fetus had multiple abnormalities and was miscarried. When the chromosomes of the fetus were studied, it was discovered that it was trisomic for chromosome 16, and that two of the three chromosome 16s had large blobs. Both chromosome 16 homologs in the mother lacked blobs, but the father was heterozygous for blobs. Which parent experienced nondisjunction, and in which meiotic division did it occur?

Answer

This problem requires an understanding of nondisjunction during meiosis. When individual chromosomes contain some distinguishing feature that allows one homolog to be distinguished from another, it is possible to follow the path of the two homologs through meiosis. In this case, because the fetus had two chromosome 16s with the blob, we can conclude that the extra chromosome came from the father (the only parent with a blobbed chromosome). In which meiotic division did the nondisjunction occur? When nondisjunction occurs during meiosis I, homologs fail to segregate to opposite poles. If this occurred in the father, the chromosome with the blob and the normal chromosome 16 would segregate into the same cell (a secondary spermatocyte). After meiosis II, the gametes resulting from this cell would carry both types of chromosomes. If such sperm fertilized a normal egg, the zygote would have two copies of the normal chromosome 16 and one of the chromosome with a blob. On the other hand, if nondisjunction occurred during meiosis II in the father in a secondary spermatocyte containing the blobbed chromosome 16, sperm with two copies of the blob-marked chromosome would be produced. After fertilization with a normal egg, the result would be a zygote of the type seen in this spontaneous abortion. *Therefore, the nondisjunction occurred in meiosis II in the father.*

II. (a) What sex ratio would you expect among the offspring of a cross between a normal male mouse and a female mouse heterozygous for a recessive X-linked lethal gene? (b) What would be the expected sex ratio among the offspring of a cross between a normal hen and a rooster heterozygous for a recessive Z-linked lethal allele?

Answer

This problem deals with sex-linked inheritance and sex determination.

a. Mice have a sex determination system of XX = female and XY = male. A normal male mouse (X^RY) × a heterozygous female mouse (X^RX^r) would result in X^RX^R, X^RX^r, X^RY, and X^rY mice. The X^rY mice would die, so there would be a 2:1 ratio of females to males.

b. The sex determination system in birds is ZZ = male and ZW = female. A normal hen (Z^RW) × a heterozygous rooster (Z^RZ^r) would result in Z^RZ^R, Z^RZ^r, Z^RW, and Z^rW chickens. Because the Z^rW offspring do not live, the ratio of females to males would be 1:2.

III. A woman with normal color vision whose father was color-blind mates with a man with normal color vision.

a. What do you expect to see among their offspring?

b. What would you expect if it was the normal man's father who was color-blind?

Answer

This problem involves sex-linked inheritance.

a. The woman's father has a genotype of $X^{cb}Y$. Because the woman had to inherit an X from her father, she must have an X^{cb} chromosome, but because she has normal color vision, her other X chromosome must be X^{CB}. The man she mates with has normal color vision and therefore has an $X^{CB}Y$ genotype. Their children could with equal probability be $X^{CB}X^{CB}$ (normal female), $X^{CB}X^{cb}$ (carrier female), $X^{CB}Y$ (normal male), or $X^{cb}Y$ (color-blind male).

b. If the man with normal color vision had a color-blind father, the X^{cb} chromosome would not have been passed on to him, because a male does not inherit an X chromosome from his father. The man has the genotype $X^{CB}Y$ and cannot pass on the color-blind allele.

Problems

Vocabulary

1. Choose the best matching phrase in the right column for each of the terms in the left column.

a. meiosis	1. X and Y	g. synapsis	7. haploid germ cells that unite at fertilization
b. gametes	2. chromosomes that do not differ between the sexes	h. sex chromosomes	8. an animal cell containing more than one nucleus
c. karyotype	3. one of the two identical halves of a replicated chromosome	i. cytokinesis	9. pairing of homologous chromosomes
d. mitosis	4. microtubule organizing centers at the spindle poles	j. anaphase	10. one diploid cell gives rise to two diploid cells
e. interphase	5. cells in the testes that undergo meiosis	k. chromatid	11. the array of chromosomes in a given cell
f. syncytium	6. division of the cytoplasm	l. autosomes	12. the part of the cell cycle during which the chromosomes are not visible
		m. centromere	13. one diploid cell gives rise to four haploid cells

n. centrosomes

o. polar body

p. spermatocytes

14. cell produced by meiosis that does not become a gamete

15. the time during mitosis when sister chromatids separate

16. connection between sister chromatids

Section 4.1

2. Humans have 46 chromosomes in each somatic cell.
   a. How many chromosomes does a child receive from its father?
   b. How many autosomes and how many sex chromosomes are present in each somatic cell?
   c. How many chromosomes are present in a human ovum?
   d. How many sex chromosomes are present in a human ovum?

3. The figure that follows shows the metaphase chromosomes of a male of a particular species. These chromosomes are prepared as they would be for a karyotype, but they have not yet been ordered in pairs of decreasing size.
   a. How many centromeres are shown?
   b. How many chromosomes are shown?
   c. How many chromatids are shown?
   d. How many pairs of homologous chromosomes are shown?
   e. How many chromosomes on the figure are metacentric? Acrocentric?
   f. What is the likely mode of sex determination in this species? What would you predict to be different about the karyotype of a female in this species?

Section 4.2

4. One oak tree cell with 14 chromosomes undergoes mitosis. How many daughter cells are formed, and what is the chromosome number in each cell?

5. Indicate which of the cells numbered i–v matches each of the following stages of mitosis:
   a. anaphase
   b. prophase

c. metaphase
d. G_2
e. telophase/cytokinesis

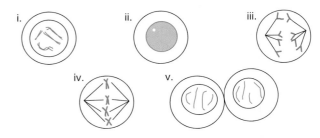

6. a. What are the four major stages of the cell cycle?
   b. Which stages are included in interphase?
   c. What events distinguish G_1, S, and G_2?

7. Answer the questions that follow for each stage of the cell cycle (G_1, S, G_2, prophase, metaphase, anaphase, telophase). If necessary, use an arrow to indicate a change that occurs during a particular cell cycle stage (for example, 1 → 2 or yes → no).
   a. How many chromatids comprise each chromosome during this stage?
   b. Is the nucleolus present?
   c. Is the mitotic spindle organized?
   d. Is the nuclear membrane present?

8. Is there any reason that mitosis could not occur in a cell whose genome is haploid?

Section 4.3

9. One oak tree cell with 14 chromosomes undergoes meiosis. How many cells will result from this process, and what is the chromosome number in each cell?

10. Which type(s) of cell division (mitosis, meiosis I, meiosis II) reduce(s) the chromosome number by half? Which type(s) of cell division can be classified as reductional? Which type(s) of cell division can be classified as equational?

11. Complete the following statements using as many of the following terms as are appropriate: mitosis, meiosis I (first meiotic division), meiosis II (second meiotic division), and none (not mitosis nor meiosis I nor meiosis II).
    a. The spindle apparatus is present in cells undergoing _____.
    b. Chromosome replication occurs just prior to _____.
    c. The cells resulting from _____ in a haploid cell have a ploidy of n.

d. The cells resulting from _____ in a diploid cell have a ploidy of *n*.

e. Homologous chromosome pairing regularly occurs during _____.

f. Nonhomologous chromosome pairing regularly occurs during _____.

g. Physical recombination leading to the production of recombinant progeny classes occurs during _____.

h. Centromere division occurs during _____.

i. Nonsister chromatids are found in the same cell during _____.

12. The five cells shown in figures a–e below are all from the same individual. For each cell, indicate whether it is in mitosis, meiosis I, or meiosis II. What stage of cell division is represented in each case? What is *n* in this organism?

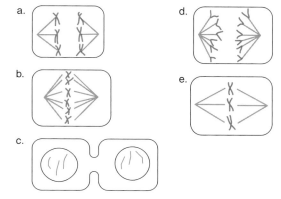

13. One of the first microscopic observations of chromosomes in cell division was published in 1905 by Nettie Stevens. Because it was hard to reproduce photographs at the time, she recorded these observations as *camera lucida* sketches. One such drawing, of a completely normal cell division in the mealworm *Tenebrio molitor,* is shown here. The techniques of the time were relatively unsophisticated by today's standards, and they did not allow her to resolve chromosomal structures that must have been present.

a. Describe in as much detail as possible the kind of cell division and the stage of division depicted in the drawing.

b. What chromosomal structure(s) cannot be resolved in the drawing?

c. How many chromosomes are present in normal *Tenebrio molitor* gametes?

14. A person is simultaneously heterozygous for two autosomal genetic traits. One is a recessive condition for albinism (alleles *A* and *a*); this albinism gene is found near the centromere on the long arm of an acrocentric autosome. The other trait is the dominantly inherited Huntington disease (alleles *HD* and HD^+). The Huntington gene is located near the telomere of one of the arms of a metacentric autosome. Draw all copies of the two relevant chromosomes in this person as they would appear during metaphase of (a) mitosis, (b) meiosis I, and (c) meiosis II. In each figure, label the location on every chromatid of the alleles for these two genes, assuming that no recombination takes place.

15. Assuming (i) that the two chromosomes in a homologous pair carry different alleles of some genes, and (ii) that no crossing-over takes place, how many genetically different offspring could any one human couple potentially produce? Which of these two assumptions (i or ii) is more realistic?

16. In the moss *Polytrichum commune,* the haploid chromosome number is 7. A haploid male gamete fuses with a haploid female gamete to form a diploid cell that divides and develops into the multicellular sporophyte. Cells of the sporophyte then undergo meiosis to produce haploid cells called spores. What is the probability that an individual spore will contain a set of chromosomes all of which came from the male gamete? Assume no recombination.

17. Is there any reason that meiosis could not occur in an organism whose genome is always haploid?

18. Sister chromatids are held together through metaphase of mitosis by complexes of *cohesin* proteins that form rubber band–like rings bundling the two sister chromatids. Cohesin rings are found both at centromeres and at many locations scattered along the length of the chromosomes. The rings are destroyed by protease enzymes at the beginning of anaphase, allowing the sister chromatids to separate.

a. Cohesin complexes between sister chromatids are also responsible for keeping homologous chromosomes together until anaphase of meiosis I. With this point in mind, which of the two diagrams that follow (i or ii) properly represents the arrangement of chromatids during prophase through metaphase of meiosis I? Explain.

b. What does your answer to part (a) allow you to infer about the nature of cohesin complexes at the centromere versus those along the chromosome arms? Suggest a molecular hypothesis to explain your inference.

i   ii

Section 4.4

19. In humans,
   a. How many sperm develop from 100 primary spermatocytes?
   b. How many sperm develop from 100 secondary spermatocytes?
   c. How many sperm develop from 100 spermatids?
   d. How many ova develop from 100 primary oocytes?
   e. How many ova develop from 100 secondary oocytes?
   f. How many ova develop from 100 polar bodies?

20. Somatic cells of chimpanzees contain 48 chromosomes.
   How many chromatids and chromosomes are present at (a) anaphase of mitosis, (b) anaphase I of meiosis, (c) anaphase II of meiosis, (d) G_1 prior to mitosis, (e) G_2 prior to mitosis, (f) G_1 prior to meiosis I, and (g) prophase of meiosis I?
   How many chromatids or chromosomes are present in (h) an oogonial cell prior to S phase, (i) a spermatid, (j) a primary oocyte arrested prior to ovulation, (k) a secondary oocyte arrested prior to fertilization, (l) a second polar body, and (m) a chimpanzee sperm?

21. In a certain strain of turkeys, unfertilized eggs sometimes develop parthenogenetically to produce diploid offspring. (Females have ZW and males have ZZ sex chromosomes. Assume that WW cells are inviable.) What distribution of sexes would you expect to see among the parthenogenetic offspring according to each of the following models for how parthenogenesis occurs?
   a. The eggs develop without ever going through meiosis.
   b. The eggs go all the way through meiosis and then duplicate their chromosomes to become diploid.
   c. The eggs go through meiosis I, and the chromatids separate to create diploidy.
   d. The egg goes all the way through meiosis and then fuses at random with one of its three polar bodies (this assumes the first polar body goes through meiosis II).

22. Female mammals, including women, sometimes develop benign tumors called "ovarian teratomas" or "dermoid cysts" in their ovaries. Such a tumor begins when a primary oocyte escapes from its prophase I arrest and finishes meiosis I within the ovary. (Normally meiosis I does not finish until the primary oocyte is expelled from the ovary upon ovulation.) The secondary oocyte then develops as if it were an embryo, and it implants and develops within the follicle. Development is disorganized, however, and results in a tumor containing a wide variety of differentiated tissues, including teeth, hair, bone, muscle, nerve, and many others. If a dermoid cyst forms in a woman whose genotype is *Aa,* what are the possible genotypes of the cyst?

Section 4.5

23. A system of sex determination known as haplodiploidy is found in honeybees. Females are diploid, and males (drones) are haploid. Male offspring result from the development of unfertilized eggs. Sperm are produced by mitosis in males and fertilize eggs in the females. Ivory eye is a recessive characteristic in honeybees; wild-type eyes are brown.
   a. What progeny would result from an ivory-eyed queen and a brown-eyed drone? Give both genotype and phenotype for progeny produced from fertilized and nonfertilized eggs.
   b. What would result from crossing a daughter from the mating in part *a* with a brown-eyed drone?

24. Imagine you have two pure-breeding lines of canaries, one with yellow feathers and the other with brown feathers. In crosses between these two strains, yellow female × brown male gives only brown sons and daughters, while brown female × yellow male gives only brown sons and yellow daughters. Propose a hypothesis to explain these results.

25. Barred feather pattern is a Z-linked dominant trait in chickens. What offspring would you expect from (a) the cross of a barred hen to a nonbarred rooster? (b) the cross of an F_1 rooster from part (a) to one of his sisters?

26. Each of the four pedigrees that follow represents a human family within which a genetic disease is segregating. Affected individuals are indicated by filled-in symbols. One of the diseases is transmitted as an autosomal recessive condition, one as an X-linked recessive, one as an autosomal dominant, and one as an X-linked dominant. Assume all four traits are rare in the population.
   a. Indicate which pedigree represents which mode of inheritance, and explain how you know.
   b. For each pedigree, how would you advise the parents of the chance that their child (indicated by the hexagon shape) will have the condition?

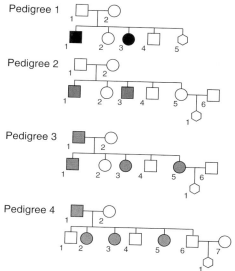

Pedigree 1

Pedigree 2

Pedigree 3

Pedigree 4

27. In a vial of *Drosophila,* a research student noticed several female flies (but no male flies) with "bag" wings each consisting of a large, liquid-filled blister instead of the usual smooth wing blade. When bag-winged females were crossed with wild-type males, 1/3 of the progeny were bag-winged females, 1/3 were normal-winged females, and 1/3 were normal-winged males. Explain these results.

28. Duchenne muscular dystrophy (DMD) is caused by a relatively rare X-linked recessive allele. It results in progressive muscular wasting and usually leads to death before age 20.

a. What is the probability that the first son of a woman whose brother is affected will be affected?

b. What is the probability that the second son of a woman whose brother is affected will be affected, if her first son was affected?

c. What is the probability that a child of an unaffected man whose brother is affected will be affected?

d. An affected man mates with his unaffected first cousin; there is otherwise no history of DMD in this family. If the mothers of this man and his mate were sisters, what is the probability that the couple's first child will be an affected boy? An affected girl? An unaffected child?

e. If two of the parents of the couple in part (d) were brother and sister, what is the probability that the couple's first child will be an affected boy? An affected girl? An unaffected child?

29. The following is a pedigree of a family in which a rare form of colorblindness is found (filled-in symbols). Indicate as much as you can about the genotypes of all the individuals in the pedigree.

30. In 1995, doctors reported a Chinese family in which retinitis pigmentosa (progressive degeneration of the retina leading to blindness) affected only males. All six sons of affected males were affected, but all of the five daughters of affected males (and all of the children of these daughters) were unaffected.

a. What is the likelihood that this form of retinitis pigmentosa is due to an autosomal mutation showing complete dominance?

b. What other possibilities could explain the inheritance of retinitis pigmentosa in this family? Which of these possibilities do you think is most likely?

31. The pedigree that follows indicates the occurrence of albinism in a group of Hopi Indians, among whom the trait is unusually frequent. Assume that the trait is fully penetrant (all individuals with a genotype that could give rise to albinism will display this condition).

a. Is albinism in this population caused by a recessive or a dominant allele?

b. Is the gene sex-linked or autosomal?

What are the genotypes of the following individuals?

c. individual I-1

d. individual I-8

e. individual I-9

f. individual II-6

g. individual II-8

h. individual III-4

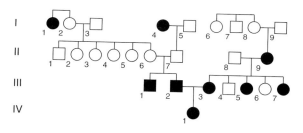

32. When Calvin Bridges observed a large number of offspring from a cross of white-eyed female *Drosophila* to red-eyed males, he observed very rare white-eyed females and red-eyed males among the offspring. He was able to show that these exceptions resulted from nondisjunction, such that the white-eyed females had received two Xs from the egg and a Y from the sperm, while the red-eyed males had received no sex chromosome from the egg and an X from the sperm. What progeny would have arisen from these same kinds of nondisjunctional events if they had occurred in the male parent? What would their eye colors have been?

33. In *Drosophila,* a cross was made between a yellow-bodied male with vestigial (not fully developed) wings and a wild-type female (brown body). The F_1 generation consisted of wild-type males and wild-type females. F_1 males and females were crossed, and the F_2 progeny consisted of 16 yellow-bodied males with vestigial wings, 48 yellow-bodied males with normal wings, 15 males with brown bodies and vestigial wings, 49 wild-type males, 31 brown-bodied females with vestigial wings, and 97 wild-type females. Explain the inheritance of the two genes in question based on these results.

34. Consider the following pedigrees from human families containing a male with Klinefelter syndrome (a set of abnormalities seen in XXY individuals; indicated with shaded boxes). In each, *A* and *B* refer to codominant alleles of the X-linked *G6PD* gene. The *phenotypes* of each individual (A, B, or AB) are shown on the pedigree. Indicate if nondisjunction occurred in the mother or father of the son with Klinefelter syndrome for each of the three examples. Can you tell if the nondisjunction was in the first or second meiotic division?

35. The pedigree at the bottom of the page shows five generations of a family that exhibits congenital hypertrichosis, a rare condition in which affected individuals are born with unusually abundant amounts of hair on their faces and upper bodies. The two small black dots in the pedigree indicate miscarriages.
   a. What can you conclude about the inheritance of hypertrichosis in this family, assuming complete penetrance of the trait?
   b. On what basis can you exclude other modes of inheritance?
   c. With how many fathers did III-2 and III-9 have children?

36. In *Drosophila,* the autosomal recessive *brown* eye color mutation displays interactions with both the X-linked recessive *vermilion* mutation and the autosomal recessive *scarlet* mutation. Flies homozygous for *brown* and simultaneously hemizygous or homozygous for *vermilion* have white eyes. Flies simultaneously homozygous for both the *brown* and *scarlet* mutations also have white eyes. Predict the F_1 and F_2 progeny of crossing the following true-breeding parents:
   a. vermilion females × brown males
   b. brown females × vermilion males
   c. scarlet females × brown males
   d. brown females × scarlet males

37. Several different antigens can be detected in blood tests. The following four traits were tested for each individual shown:

ABO type	(I^A and I^B codominant, i recessive)
Rh type	(Rh^+ dominant to Rh^-)
MN type	(M and N codominant)
$Xg^{(a)}$ type	($Xg^{(a+)}$ dominant to $Xg^{(a-)}$)

All of these blood type genes are autosomal, except for $Xg^{(a)}$, which is X linked.

Mother	AB	Rh^-	MN	$Xg^{(a+)}$
Daughter	A	Rh^+	MN	$Xg^{(a-)}$
Alleged father 1	AB	Rh^+	M	$Xg^{(a+)}$
Alleged father 2	A	Rh^-	N	$Xg^{(a-)}$
Alleged father 3	B	Rh^+	N	$Xg^{(a-)}$
Alleged father 4	O	Rh^-	MN	$Xg^{(a-)}$

   a. Which, if any, of the alleged fathers could be the real father?
   b. Would your answer to part *a* change if the daughter had Turner syndrome (the abnormal phenotype seen in XO individuals)? If so, how?

38. In 1919, Calvin Bridges began studying an X-linked recessive mutation causing eosin-colored eyes in *Drosophila*. Within an otherwise true-breeding culture of eosin-eyed flies, he noticed rare variants that had much lighter cream-colored eyes. By intercrossing these variants, he was able to make a true-breeding cream-eyed stock. Bridges now crossed males from

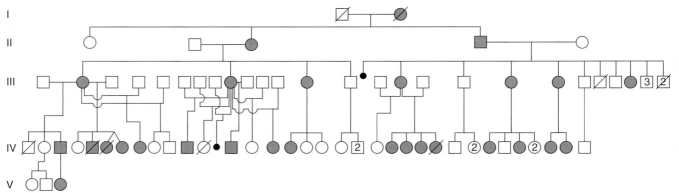

this cream-eyed stock with true-breeding wild-type females. All the F_1 progeny had red (wild-type) eyes. When F_1 flies were intercrossed, the F_2 progeny were 104 females with red eyes, 52 males with red eyes, 44 males with eosin eyes, and 14 males with cream eyes. Assume this represents an 8:4:3:1 ratio.

a. Formulate a hypothesis to explain the F_1 and F_2 results, assigning phenotypes to all possible genotypes.

b. What do you predict in the F_1 and F_2 generations if the parental cross is between true-breeding eosin-eyed males and true-breeding cream-eyed females?

c. What do you predict in the F_1 and F_2 generations if the parental cross is between true-breeding eosin-eyed females and true-breeding cream-eyed males?

39. As we learned in this chapter, the *white* mutation of *Drosophila* studied by Thomas Hunt Morgan is X linked and recessive to wild type. When true-breeding white-eyed males carrying this mutation were crossed with true-breeding purple-eyed females, all the F_1 progeny had wild-type (red) eyes. When the F_1 progeny were intercrossed, the F_2 progeny emerged in the ratio 3/8 wild-type females: 1/4 white-eyed males: 3/16 wild-type males: 1/8 purple-eyed females: 1/16 purple-eyed males.

a. Formulate a hypothesis to explain the inheritance of these eye colors.

b. Predict the F_1 and F_2 progeny if the parental cross was reversed (that is, if the parental cross was between true-breeding white-eyed females and true-breeding purple-eyed males).

40. The ancestry of a white female tiger bred in a city zoo is depicted in the pedigree following part (e) of this problem. White tigers are indicated with unshaded symbols. (As you can see, there was considerable inbreeding in this lineage. For example, the white tiger Mohan was mated with his daughter.) In answering the following questions, assume that "white" is determined by allelic differences at a single gene and that the trait is fully penetrant. Explain your answers by citing the relevant information in the pedigree.

a. Could white coat color be caused by a Y-linked allele?

b. Could white coat color be caused by a dominant X-linked allele?

c. Could white coat color be caused by a dominant autosomal allele?

d. Could white coat color be caused by a recessive X-linked allele?

e. Could white coat color be caused by a recessive autosomal allele?

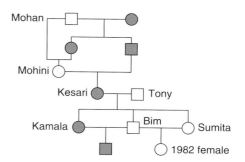

41. The pedigree at the bottom of the page shows the inheritance of various types of cancer in a particular family. Molecular analyses (described in subsequent chapters) indicate that with one exception, the cancers occurring in the patients in this pedigree are associated with a rare mutation in a gene called *BRCA2*.

a. Which individual is the exceptional cancer patient whose disease is not associated with a *BRCA2* mutation?

b. Is the *BRCA2* mutation dominant or recessive to the normal *BRCA2* allele in terms of its cancer-causing effects?

c. Is the *BRCA2* gene likely to reside on the X chromosome, the Y chromosome, or an autosome? How definitive is your assignment of the chromosome carrying *BRCA2*?

d. Is the penetrance of the cancer phenotype complete or incomplete?

e. Is the expressivity of the cancer phenotype unvarying or variable?

f. Are any of the cancer phenotypes associated with the *BRCA2* mutation sex-limited or sex-influenced?

g. How can you explain the absence of individuals diagnosed with cancer in generations I and II?

Linkage, Recombination, and the Mapping of Genes on Chromosomes

Maps illustrate the spatial relationships of objects, such as the locations of subway stations along subway lines. Genetic maps portray the positions of genes along chromosomes.

In 1928, doctors completed a four-generation pedigree tracing two known X-linked traits: red-green colorblindness and hemophilia A (the more serious X-linked form of "bleeders disease"). The maternal grandfather of the family exhibited both traits, which means that his single X chromosome carried mutant alleles of the two corresponding genes. As expected, neither colorblindness nor hemophilia showed up in his sons and daughters, but two grandsons and one great-grandson inherited both of the X-linked conditions (**Fig. 5.1a**). The fact that none of the descendants manifested one of the traits without the other suggests that the mutant alleles did not assort independently during meiosis. Instead they traveled together in the gametes forming one generation and then into the gametes forming the next generation, producing grandsons and great-grandsons with an X chromosome specifying both colorblindness and hemophilia. Genes that travel together more often than not exhibit **genetic linkage.**

In contrast, another pedigree following colorblindness and the slightly different B form of hemophilia, which also arises from a mutation on the X chromosome, revealed a different inheritance pattern. A grandfather with hemophilia B and colorblindness had four grandsons, but only one of them exhibited both conditions. In this family, the genes for colorblindness and hemophilia appeared to assort independently, producing in the male progeny all four possible combinations of the two traits—normal vision and normal blood clotting, colorblindness and hemophilia, colorblindness and normal clotting, and normal vision and hemophilia—in approximately equal frequencies (**Fig. 5.1b**). Thus, even though the mutant alleles of the two genes were on the same X chromosome in the grandfather, they had to separate to give rise to grandsons III-2 and III-3. This separation of genes on the same chromosome is the result of **recombination,** the occurrence in progeny of new gene combinations not seen in previous generations. (Note that *recombinant progeny* can result in either of two ways: from the recombination of genes on the same chromosome during gamete formation, discussed in this chapter, or from the independent assortment of genes on nonhomologous chromosomes, previously described in Chapter 4.)

Two important themes emerge as we follow the transmission of genes linked on the same chromosome. The first is that the farther apart two genes are, the greater is the probability of separation through recombination. Extrapolating from this general rule, you can see that the gene for hemophilia A must be very close to the gene

CHAPTER OUTLINE

- 5.1 Gene Linkage and Recombination
- 5.2 The Chi-Square Test and Linkage Analysis
- 5.3 Recombination: A Result of Crossing-Over During Meiosis
- 5.4 Mapping: Locating Genes Along a Chromosome
- 5.5 Tetrad Analysis in Fungi
- 5.6 Mitotic Recombination and Genetic Mosaics

Figure 5.1 Pedigrees indicate that colorblindness and two forms of hemophilia are X-linked traits. (a) Transmission of red-green colorblindness and hemophilia A. The traits travel together through the pedigree, indicating their genetic linkage. **(b)** Transmission of red-green colorblindness and hemophilia B. Even though both genes are X linked, the mutant alleles are inherited together in only one of four grandsons in generation III. These two pedigrees indicate that the gene for colorblindness is close to the hemophilia A gene but far away from the hemophilia B gene.

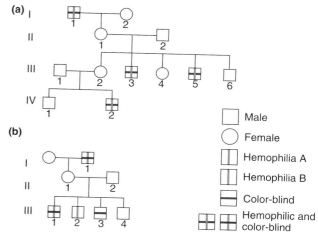

for red-green colorblindness, because, as Fig. 5.1a shows, the two rarely separate. By comparison, the gene for hemophilia B must lie far away from the colorblindness gene, because, as Fig. 5.1b indicates, new combinations of alleles of the two genes occur quite often. A second crucial theme arising from these considerations is that geneticists can use data about how often genes separate during transmission to map the genes' relative locations on a chromosome. Such mapping is a key to sorting out and tracking down the components of complex genetic networks; it is also crucial to geneticists' ability to isolate and characterize genes at the molecular level.

5.1 Gene Linkage and Recombination

If people have roughly 20,000 genes but only 23 pairs of chromosomes, most human chromosomes must carry hundreds, if not thousands, of genes. This is certainly true of the human X chromosome: In 2005, a group of bioinformatics specialists reported that they found 739 protein-encoding genes on this chromosome. This number is likely to grow, at least slightly, as geneticists develop new techniques to analyze the X chromosome's DNA sequence. Moreover, this number does not account for the many genes that do not encode proteins. Recognition that many genes reside on each chromosome raises an important question. If genes on *different* chromosomes assort independently because nonhomologous chromosomes align independently on the spindle during meiosis I, how do genes on the *same* chromosome assort?

Some genes on the same chromosome do not assort independently

We begin our analysis with X-linked *Drosophila* genes because they were the first to be assigned to a specific chromosome. As we outline various crosses, remember that females carry two X chromosomes, and thus two alleles for each X-linked gene. Males, in contrast, have only a single X chromosome (from the female parent), and thus only a single allele for each of these genes.

We look first at two X-linked genes that determine a fruit fly's eye color and body color. These two genes are said to be **syntenic** because they are located on the same chromosome. The *white* gene was previously introduced in Chapter 4; you will recall that the dominant wild-type allele w^+ specifies red eyes, while the recessive mutant allele w confers white eyes. The alleles of the *yellow* body color gene are y^+ (the dominant wild-type allele for brown bodies) and y (the recessive mutant allele for yellow bodies). To avoid confusion, note that lowercase y and y^+ refer to alleles of the *yellow* gene, while capital Y refers to the Y chromosome (which does not carry genes for either eye or body color). You should also pay attention to the slash symbol (/), which is used to separate genes found on chromosomes of a pair (either the X and Y chromosomes as in this case, or a pair of X chromosomes or homologous autosomes). Thus $w\ y\ /\ Y$ represents the genotype of a male with an X chromosome bearing w and y, as well as a Y chromosome; phenotypically this male has white eyes and a yellow body.

Detecting linkage by analyzing the gametes produced by a dihybrid

In a cross between a female with mutant white eyes and a wild-type brown body ($w\ y^+/w\ y^+$) and a male with wild-type red eyes and a mutant yellow body ($w^+\ y$/Y), the F$_1$ offspring are evenly divided between brown-bodied females with normal red eyes ($w\ y^+$/$w^+\ y$) and brown-bodied males with mutant white eyes ($w\ y^+$/Y) (**Fig. 5.2**). Note that the male progeny look like their mother because their phenotype directly reflects the genotype of the single X chromosome they received from her. The same is not true for the F$_1$ females, who received w and y^+ on the X from their mother and $w^+\ y$ on the X from their father. These F$_1$ females are thus dihybrids: With two alleles for each X-linked gene, one derived from each parent, the dominance relations of each pair of alleles determine the female phenotype.

Now comes the significant cross for answering our question about the assortment of genes on the same chromosome. If these two *Drosophila* genes for eye and body color assort independently, as predicted by Mendel's second law, the dihybrid F$_1$ females should make four kinds of gametes, with four different combinations of genes on the X chromosome—$w\ y^+$, $w^+\ y$, $w^+\ y^+$, and $w\ y$. These four types of gametes should occur with equal frequency, that is, in a ratio of 1:1:1:1. If it happens this way, approximately half of the gametes will be of the two **parental types,** carrying either the $w\ y^+$ allele combination seen in the original female of the P generation or the $w^+ y$ allele combination seen in the original male of the P generation. The remaining half of the gametes will be of two **recombinant types,** in which reshuffling has produced either $w^+ y^+$ or $w\ y$ allele combinations not seen in the P generation parents of the F$_1$ females.

We can see whether the 1:1:1:1 ratio of the four kinds of gametes actually materializes by counting the different types of male progeny in the F$_2$ generation, as these sons receive their only X-linked genes from their maternal gamete. The bottom part of Fig. 5.2 depicts the results of a breeding study that produced 9026 F$_2$ males. The relative numbers of the four X-linked gene combinations passed on by the dihybrid F$_1$ females' gametes reflect a significant departure from the 1:1:1:1 ratio expected of independent assortment. By far, the largest numbers of gametes carry the parental combinations $w\ y^+$ and $w^+ y$. Of the total 9026 male flies counted, 8897, or almost 99%, had these genotypes. In contrast, the new combinations $w^+ y^+$ and $w\ y$ made up little more than 1% of the total.

We can explain why the two genes fail to assort independently in one of two ways. Either the $w\ y^+$ and $w^+\ y$ combinations are preferred because of some intrinsic chemical affinity between these particular alleles, or it is the parental combination of alleles the F$_1$ female receives from one or the other of her P generation parents that shows up most frequently.

Figure 5.2 When genes are linked, parental combinations outnumber recombinant types. Doubly heterozygous $w\ y^+$/$w^+\ y$ F$_1$ females produce four types of male offspring. Sons that look like the father ($w^+\ y$ / Y) or mother ($w\ y^+$ / Y) of the F$_1$ females are parental types. Other sons ($w^+ y^+$ / Y or $w\ y$ / Y) are recombinant types. For these closely linked genes, many more parental types are produced than recombinant types.

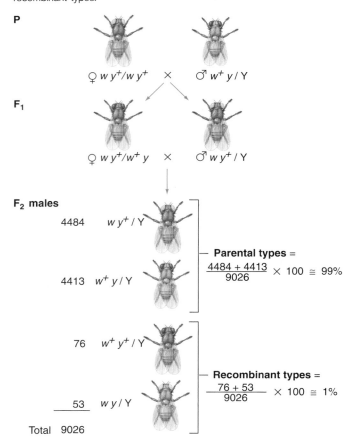

P

♀ $w\ y^+$/$w\ y^+$ × ♂ $w^+\ y$ / Y

F$_1$

♀ $w\ y^+$/$w^+\ y$ × ♂ $w\ y^+$ / Y

F$_2$ males

4484 $w\ y^+$ / Y

4413 $w^+\ y$ / Y

Parental types =
$$\frac{4484 + 4413}{9026} \times 100 \cong 99\%$$

76   $w^+ y^+$ / Y

53   $w\ y$ / Y

Recombinant types =
$$\frac{76 + 53}{9026} \times 100 \cong 1\%$$

Total   9026

Linkage: A preponderance of parental classes of gametes

A second set of crosses involving the same genes but with a different arrangement of alleles explains why the dihybrid F$_1$ females do not produce a 1:1:1:1 ratio of the four possible types of gametes (see Cross Series B in **Fig. 5.3**). In this second set of crosses, the original parental generation consists of red-eyed, brown-bodied females ($w^+\ y^+$/$w^+\ y^+$) and white-eyed, yellow-bodied males ($w\ y$/Y), and the resultant F$_1$ females are all $w^+\ y^+$/$w\ y$ dihybrids. To find out what kinds and ratios of gametes these F$_1$ females produce, we need to look at the telltale F$_2$ males.

This time, as Cross B in Fig. 5.3 shows, $w^+\ y$/Y and $w\ y^+$/Y are the recombinants that account for little more than 1% of the total, while $w\ y$/Y and $w^+\ y^+$/Y are the parental combinations, which again add up to almost 99%. You can see that there is no preferred association of w^+ and y or of y^+ and w in this cross. Instead, a comparison of the two experiments with these particular X chromosome genes demonstrates that the observed

Figure 5.3 Designations of "parental" and "recombinant" relate to past history. Figure 5.2 has been redrawn here as **Cross Series A** for easier comparison with **Cross Series B,** in which the dihybrid F₁ females received different allelic combinations of the *white* and *yellow* genes. Note that the parental and recombinant classes in the two cross series are the opposite of each other. The percentages of recombinant and parental types are nonetheless similar in both experiments, showing that the frequency of recombination is independent of the arrangement of alleles.

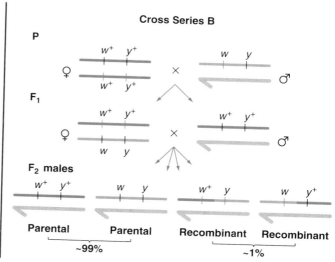

frequencies of the various types of progeny depend on how the arrangement of alleles in the F₁ females originated. We have redrawn Fig. 5.2 as Cross Series A in Fig. 5.3 so that you can make this comparison more directly. Note that in both experiments, it is the **parental classes**—the combinations originally present in the P generation—that show up most frequently in the F₂ generation. The reshuffled **recombinant classes** occur less frequently. It is important to appreciate that the designation of "parental" and "recombinant" gametes or progeny of a doubly heterozygous F₁ female is operational, that is, determined by the particular set of alleles she receives from each of her parents.

When genes assort independently, the numbers of parental and recombinant F₂ progeny are equal, because a doubly heterozygous F₁ individual produces an equal number of all four types of gametes. By comparison, two genes are considered **linked** when the number of F₂ progeny with parental genotypes exceeds the number of F₂ progeny with recombinant genotypes. Instead of assorting independently, the genes behave as if they are connected to each other much of the time. The genes for eye and body color that reside on the X chromosome in *Drosophila* are an extreme illustration of the linkage concept. The two genes are so tightly coupled that the parental combinations of alleles—w^+ y and w y^+ (in Cross Series A of Fig. 5.3) or w^+ y^+ and w y (in Cross Series B)—are reshuffled to form recombinants in only 1 out of every 100 gametes formed. In other words, the two parental allele combinations of these tightly linked genes are inherited together 99 times out of 100.

Gene-pair-specific variation in the degree of linkage

Linkage is not always this tight. In *Drosophila*, a mutation for miniature wings (*m*) is also found on the X chromosome. A cross of red-eyed females with normal wings (w^+ m^+/w^+ m^+) and white-eyed males with miniature wings (w $m/$Y) yields an F₁ generation containing all red-eyed, normal-winged flies. The genotype of the dihybrid F₁ females is w^+ m^+/w m. Of the F₂ males, 67.2% are parental types (w^+ m^+ and w m), while the remaining 32.8% are recombinants (w m^+ and w^+ m).

This preponderance of parental combinations among the F₂ genotypes reveals that the two genes are linked: The parental combinations of alleles travel together more often than not. But compared to the 99% linkage between the *w* and *y* genes for eye color and body color, the linkage of *w* to *m* is not that tight. The parental combinations for color and wing size are reshuffled in roughly 33 (instead of 1) out of every 100 gametes.

Autosomal traits can also exhibit linkage

Linked autosomal genes are not inherited according to the 9:3:3:1 Mendelian ratio expected for two independently assorting genes. Early twentieth-century geneticists were puzzled by the many experimentally observed departures from this ratio, which they could not explain in terms of the gene interactions discussed in Chapter 3.

They found it difficult to interpret these unexpected results because although they knew that individuals receive two copies of each autosomal gene, one from each parent, it was hard to trace which alleles came from which parent. However, by setting up testcrosses in which one parent was homozygous for the recessive alleles of both genes, they were able to analyze the gene combinations received from the gametes of the other, doubly heterozygous parent.

Fruit flies, for example, carry an autosomal gene for body color (in addition to the X-linked y gene); the wild type is once again brown, but a recessive mutation in this gene gives rise to black (b). A second gene on the same autosome helps determine the shape of a fruit fly's wing, with the wild type having straight edges and a recessive mutation (c) producing curves. **Figure 5.4** depicts a cross between black-bodied females with straight wings ($b\ c^+ /\ b\ c^+$) and brown-bodied males with curved wings ($b^+\ c /\ b^+\ c$). All the F_1 progeny are double heterozygotes ($b\ c^+ /\ b^+\ c$) that are phenotypically wild type. In a testcross of the F_1 females with $b\ c / b\ c$ males, all of the offspring receive the recessive b and c alleles from their father. The phenotypes of the offspring thus indicate the kinds of gametes received from the mother. For example, a black fly with normal wings would be genotype $b\ c^+ / b\ c$; because we know it received the $b\ c$ combination from its father, it must have received $b\ c^+$ from its mother. As Fig. 5.4 shows, roughly 77% of the testcross progeny in one experiment received parental gene combinations (that is, allelic combinations transmitted into the F_1 females by the gametes of each of her parents), while the remaining 23% were recombinants. Because the parental classes outnumbered the recombinant classes, we can conclude that the autosomal genes for black body and curved wings are linked.

> Linkage between two genes can be detected in the proportion of gametes that a doubly heterozygous individual produces. If the numbers of parental-type and recombinant-type gametes are equal, then the two genes are assorting independently. If the parental-type gametes exceed the recombinant form, then the genes are linked.

5.2 The Chi-Square Test and Linkage Analysis

How do you know from a particular experiment whether two genes assort independently or are genetically linked? At first glance, this question should pose no problem. Discriminating between the two possibilities involves straightforward calculations based on assumptions well supported by observations. For independently assorting genes, a dihybrid F_1 female produces four types of gametes in equal numbers, so one-half of the F_2 progeny are of the parental classes and the other half of the recombinant classes. In contrast, for linked genes, the two types of parental classes by definition always outnumber the two types of recombinant classes in the F_2 generation.

The problem is that because real-world genetic transmission is based on chance events, in a particular study even unlinked, independently assorting genes can produce deviations from the 1:1:1:1 ratio, just as in 10 tosses of a coin, you may easily get 6 heads and 4 tails (rather than the predicted 5 and 5). Thus, if a breeding experiment analyzing the transmission of two genes shows a deviation from the equal ratios of parentals and recombinants expected of independent assortment, can we necessarily conclude the two genes are linked? Is it instead possible that the results represent a statistically acceptable chance fluctuation from the mean values expected of unlinked genes that assort independently? Such questions become more pressing in cases where linkage is not all that tight, so that even though the genes are linked, the percentage of recombinant classes approaches 50%.

Figure 5.4 Autosomal genes can also exhibit linkage.
A testcross shows that the recombination frequency for the body color (b) and wing shape (c) pair of *Drosophila* genes is 23%. Because parentals outnumber recombinants, the b and c genes are genetically linked and must be on the same autosome.

P	$♀\ b\ c^+ / b\ c^+\ \times\ ♂\ b^+\ c / b^+\ c$

F$_1$ (all identical) $b\ c^+ / b^+\ c$

Testcross $♀\ b\ c^+ / b^+\ c\ \times\ ♂\ b\ c / b\ c$

Testcross
progeny   2934 $b\ c^+ / b\ c$ ⎤ Parental $= \dfrac{2934 + 2768}{7419} \times 100 = 77\%$
          2768 $b^+\ c / b\ c$ ⎦ classes

          871 $b\ c / b\ c$ ⎤ Recombinant $= \dfrac{871 + 846}{7419} \times 100 = 23\%$
          846 $b^+\ c^+ / b\ c$ ⎦ classes

Total 7419

The chi-square test evaluates the significance of differences between predicted and observed values

To answer these kinds of questions, statisticians have devised a quantitative measure of the likelihood that an experimentally observed deviation from the predictions of a particular hypothesis could have occurred solely by chance. This measure of the "goodness of fit" between observed and predicted results is a probability test known as the **chi-square test.** The test is designed to account for the fact that the size of an experimental population (the "sample size") is an important component of statistical significance. To appreciate the role of sample size, let's return to the proverbial coin toss before examining the details of the chi-square test.

In 10 tosses of a coin, an outcome of 6 heads (60%) and 4 tails (40%) is not unexpected because of the effects of chance. However, with 1000 tosses of the coin, a result of 600 heads (60%) and 400 tails (40%) would intuitively be highly unlikely. In the first case, a change in the results of one coin toss would alter the expected 5:5 ratio to the observed 6:4 ratio. In the second case, 100 tosses would have to change from tails to heads to generate the stated deviation from the predicted 500:500 ratio. Chance events could reasonably, and even likely, cause 1 deviation from the predicted number, but not 100.

Two important concepts emerge from this simple example. First, a comparison of percentages or ratios alone will never allow you to determine whether or not *observed* data are significantly different from *predicted* values. Second, the absolute numbers obtained are important because they reflect the size of the experiment. The larger the sample size, the closer the observed percentages can be expected to match the values predicted by the experimental hypothesis, *if the hypothesis is correct*. The chi-square test is therefore always calculated with numbers—actual data—and not percentages or proportions.

The chi-square test cannot prove a hypothesis, but it can allow researchers to reject a hypothesis. For this reason, a critical prerequisite of the chi-square test is the framing of a **null hypothesis:** a model that might possibly be refuted by the test and that leads to clear-cut numerical predictions. Although contemporary geneticists use the chi-square test to interpret many kinds of genetic experiments, they use it most often to discover whether data obtained from breeding experiments provide evidence for or against the hypothesis that two genes are linked. But the problem with the general hypothesis that "genes *A* and *B* are linked" is that there is no precise prediction of what to expect in terms of breeding data. The reason is that the frequency of recombinations, as we have seen, varies with each linked gene pair.

In contrast, the alternative hypothesis "that genes *A* and *B* are *not* linked" gives rise to a precise prediction: that alleles at different genes will assort independently and produce 50% parental and 50% recombinant progeny. So, whenever a geneticist wants to determine whether two genes are linked, he or she actually tests whether the observed data are consistent with the null hypothesis of no linkage. If the chi-square test shows that the observed data differ significantly from those expected with independent assortment—that is, they differ enough not to be reasonably attributable to chance alone—then the researcher can reject the null hypothesis of no linkage and accept the alternative of linkage between the two genes.

The Tools of Genetics box on p. 124 presents the general protocol of the chi-square test. The final result of the calculations is the determination of the numerical probability—the *p* value—that a particular set of observed experimental results represents a chance deviation from the values predicted by a particular hypothesis. If the probability is high, it is likely that the hypothesis being tested explains the data, and the observed deviation from expected results is considered *insignificant*. If the probability is very low, the observed deviation from expected results becomes *significant*. When this happens, it is unlikely that the hypothesis under consideration explains the data, and the hypothesis can be rejected.

Applying the chi-square test to linkage analysis: An example

Figure 5.5 depicts two sets of data obtained from testcross experiments asking whether genes *A* and *B* are linked. We first apply the chi-square analysis to data accumulated in the first experiment. The total number of offspring is 50, of which 31 (that is, 17 + 14) are observed to be parental types and 19 (8 + 11) recombinant types. Dividing 50 by 2, you get 25, the number of parental or recombinant offspring expected according to the null hypothesis of independent assortment (which predicts that parentals = recombinants).

Now, considering first the parental types alone, you square the observed deviation from the expected value, and divide the result by the expected value. After doing the same for the recombinant types, you add the two quotients to obtain the value of chi square.

$$\chi^2 = \frac{(31 - 25)^2}{25} + \frac{(19 - 25)^2}{25} = 1.44 + 1.44 = 2.88$$

Figure 5.5 Applying the chi-square test to see if genes *A* and *B* are linked. The null hypothesis is that the two genes are unlinked. For Experiment 1, $p > 0.05$, so it is not possible to reject the null hypothesis. For Experiment 2, with a data set twice the size, $p < 0.05$. Based on this latter result, most geneticists would reject the null hypothesis and conclude with greater than 95% confidence that the genes are linked.

Progeny	Experiment 1		Experiment 2	
A B	17		34	
a b	14		28	
A b	8		16	
a B	11		22	
Total	50		100	
Class	**Observed / Expected**		**Observed / Expected**	
Parentals	31	25	62	50
Recombinants	19	25	38	50

TOOLS OF GENETICS

The Chi-Square Test

The general protocol for using the chi-square test and evaluating its results can be stated in a series of steps. Two preparatory steps precede the actual chi-square calculation.

1. Use the data obtained from a breeding experiment to answer the following questions:
   a. What is the *total number* of offspring (events) analyzed?
   b. How many different *classes* of offspring (events) are there?
   c. In each class, what is the *number* of offspring (events) *observed*?
2. Calculate how many offspring (events) would be expected for each class if the null hypothesis (here, no linkage) were correct: Multiply the percentage predicted by the null hypothesis (here, 50% parentals and 50% recombinants) by the total number of offspring. You are now ready for the chi-square calculation.
3. To calculate chi square, begin with one class of offspring. Subtract the expected number from the observed number to obtain the deviation from the predicted value for the class. Square the result, and divide this value by the expected number.

   Do this for all classes and then sum the individual results. The final result is the chi-square (χ^2) value. This step is summarized by the equation

   $$\chi^2 = \Sigma \frac{(Number\ observed - Number\ expected)^2}{Number\ expected}$$

   where Σ means "sum of all classes."

4. Next, you consider the **degrees of freedom (df).** The df is a measure of the number of independently varying parameters in the experiment (see text). The value of degrees of freedom is one less than the number of classes. Thus, if N is the number of classes, then the degrees of freedom (df) $= N - 1$. If there are 4 classes, then there are 3 df.
5. Use the chi-square value together with the df to determine a **p value:** the probability that a deviation from the predicted numbers at least as large as that observed in the experiment would occur by chance. Although the p value is arrived at through a numerical analysis, geneticists routinely determine the value by a quick search through a table of critical χ^2 values for different degrees of freedom, such as **Table 5.1.**
6. Evaluate the significance of the p value. You can think of the p value as the probability that the null hypothesis is true. A value greater than 0.05 indicates that in more than 1 in 20 (or more than 5%) repetitions of an experiment of the same size, the observed deviation from predicted values could have been obtained by chance, even if the null hypothesis is actually true; the data are therefore *not significant* for rejecting the null hypothesis. Statisticians have arbitrarily selected the 0.05 p value as the boundary between accepting and rejecting the null hypothesis. A p value of less than 0.05 means that you can consider the deviation to be *significant*, and you can reject the null hypothesis.

TABLE 5.1	Critical Chi-Square Values					
	p Values					
	Cannot Reject the Null Hypothesis				**Null Hypothesis Rejected**	
Degrees of Freedom	0.99	0.90	0.50	0.10	0.05	0.01	0.001
	χ^2 Values					
1	—	0.02	0.45	2.71	3.84	6.64	10.83
2	0.02	0.21	1.39	4.61	5.99	9.21	13.82
3	0.11	0.58	2.37	6.25	7.81	11.35	16.27
4	0.30	1.06	3.36	7.78	9.49	13.28	18.47
5	0.55	1.61	4.35	9.24	11.07	15.09	20.52

Note: χ^2 values that lie in the *yellow* region of this table allow you to reject the null hypothesis with $> 95\%$ confidence, and for recombination experiments, to postulate linkage.

You next determine the **degrees of freedom (df)** for this experiment. Degrees of freedom is a mathematical concept that takes into consideration the number of independently varying parameters. For example, if the offspring in an experiment fall into four classes, and you know the total number of offspring as well as the numbers present in three of the classes, then you can directly calculate the number present in the fourth class. Therefore, the df with four classes is one less than the number of classes, or three. Because with two classes (parentals and recombinants), the number of degrees of freedom is 1, you scan the chi-square table (see Table 5.1 on p. 124) for $\chi^2 = 2.88$ and df = 1. You find by extrapolation that the corresponding p value is greater than 0.05 (roughly 0.09). From this p value you can conclude that it is not possible to reject the null hypothesis on the basis of this experiment, which means that this data set is not sufficient to demonstrate linkage between A and B.

If you use the same strategy to calculate a p value for the data observed in the second experiment, where there are a total of 100 offspring and thus an expected number of 50 parentals and 50 recombinants, you get

$$\chi^2 = \frac{(62 - 50)^2}{50} + \frac{(38 - 50)^2}{50} = 2.88 + 2.88 = 5.76$$

The number of degrees of freedom (df) remains 1, so Table 5.1 arrives at a p value greater than 0.01 but less than 0.05. In this case, you can consider the difference between the observed and expected values to be significant. As a result, you can reject the null hypothesis of independent assortment and conclude it is likely that genes A and B are linked.

Statisticians have arbitrarily selected a p value of 0.05 as the boundary between significance and nonsignificance. Values lower than this indicate there would be less than 5 chances in 100 of obtaining the same results by random sampling if the null hypothesis were true. A p value of less than 0.05 thus suggests that the data shows major deviations from predicted values significant enough to reject the null hypothesis with greater than 95% confidence. More conservative scientists often set the boundary of significance at $p = 0.01$, and they would therefore reject the null hypothesis only if their confidence was greater than 99%.

In contrast, p values greater than 0.01 or 0.05 do not necessarily mean that two genes are unlinked; it may mean only that the sample size is not large enough to provide an answer. With more data, the p value normally rises if the null hypothesis of no linkage is correct and falls if there is, in fact, linkage.

Note that in Fig. 5.5 all of the numbers in the second set of data are simply double the numbers in the first set, with the percentages remaining the same. Thus, just by doubling the sample size from 50 to 100 individuals, it was possible to go from no significant difference to a significant difference between the observed and the

expected values. In other words, the larger the sample size, the less the likelihood that a certain percentage deviation from expected results happened simply by chance. Bearing this in mind, you can see that it is not appropriate to use the chi-square test when analyzing very small samples of less than 10. This creates a problem for human geneticists, because human families produce only a small number of children. To achieve a reasonable sample size for linkage studies in humans, scientists must instead pool data from a large number of family pedigrees.

The chi-square test *does not* prove linkage or its absence. What it *does* do is provide a quantitative measure of the likelihood that the data from an experiment can be explained by a particular hypothesis. The chi-square analysis is thus a general statistical test for significance; it can be used with many different experimental designs and with hypotheses other than the absence of linkage. As long as it is possible to propose a null hypothesis that leads to a predicted set of values for a defined set of data classes, you can readily determine whether or not the observed data are consistent with the hypothesis.

When experiments lead to rejection of a null hypothesis, you may need to confirm an alternative. For instance, if you are testing whether two opposing traits result from the segregation of two alleles of a single gene, you would expect a testcross between an F_1 heterozygote and a recessive homozygote to produce a 1:1 ratio of the two traits in the offspring. If instead, you observe a ratio of 6:4 and the chi-square test produces a p value of 0.009, you can reject the null hypothesis. But you are still left with the question of what the absence of a 1:1 ratio means. There are actually two alternatives: (1) Individuals with the two possible genotypes are not equally viable, *or* (2) more than one gene encodes the trait. The chi-square test cannot tell you which possibility is correct, and you would have to study the matter further. The problems at the end of this chapter illustrate several applications of the chi-square test pertinent to genetics.

Geneticists use the chi-square test to evaluate the probability that differences between predicted results and observed results are due to random sampling error. For linkage analysis, p values of less than 0.05 allow rejection of the null hypothesis that the two genes are unlinked.

5.3 Recombination: A Result of Crossing-Over During Meiosis

It is easy to understand how genes that are physically connected on the same chromosome can be transmitted together and thus show genetic linkage. It is not as obvious why all linked genes always show some recombination in a sample population of sufficient size. Do the chromosomes participate in a physical process that gives rise to the reshuffling of linked genes that we call recombination? The answer to this question is of more than passing interest as it provides a basis for gauging relative distances between pairs of genes on a chromosome.

In 1909, the Belgian cytologist Frans Janssens described structures he had observed in the light microscope during prophase of the first meiotic division. He called these structures *chiasmata;* as described in Chapter 4, they seemed to represent regions in which nonsister chromatids of homologous chromosomes cross over each other (review Fig. 4.14 on p. 96). Making inferences from a combination of genetic and cytological data, Thomas Hunt Morgan suggested that the chiasmata observed through the light microscope were sites of chromosome breakage and exchange resulting in genetic recombination.

Reciprocal exchanges between homologs are the physical basis of recombination

Morgan's idea that the physical breaking and rejoining of chromosomes during meiosis was the basis of genetic recombination seemed reasonable. But although Janssens's chiasmata could be interpreted as signs of the process, before 1930 no one had produced visible evidence that crossing-over between homologous chromosomes actu-

ally occurs. The identification of **physical markers,** or cytologically visible abnormalities that make it possible to keep track of specific chromosome parts from one generation to the next, enabled researchers to turn the logical deductions about recombination into facts derived from experimental evidence. In 1931, Harriet Creighton and Barbara McClintock, who studied corn, and Curt Stern, who worked with *Drosophila,* published the results of experiments showing that genetic recombination indeed depends on the reciprocal exchange of parts between maternal and paternal chromosomes. Stern, for example bred female flies with two different X chromosomes, each containing a distinct physical marker near one of the ends These same females were also doubly heterozygous for two X-linked **genetic markers**—genes that could serve as points of reference in determining whether particular progeny were the result of recombination.

Figure 5.6 diagrams the chromosomes of these heterozygous females. One X chromosome carried mutations producing carnation eyes (a dark ruby color, abbreviated *car*) that were kidney-shaped (*Bar*); in addition this chromosome was marked physically by a visible discontinuity, which resulted when the end of the X chromosome was broken off and attached to an autosome. The other X chromosome had wild-type alleles (+) for both the *car* and the *Bar* genes, and its physical

Figure 5.6 Evidence that recombination results from reciprocal exchanges between homologous chromosomes. Genetic recombination between the *car* and *Bar* genes on the *Drosophila* X chromosome is accompanied by the exchange of physical markers observable in the microscope. Note that this depiction of crossing-over is a simplification, as genetic recombination actually occurs after each chromosome has replicated into sister chromatids. Note also that the piece of the X chromosome to the right of the discontinuity is actually attached to an autosome.

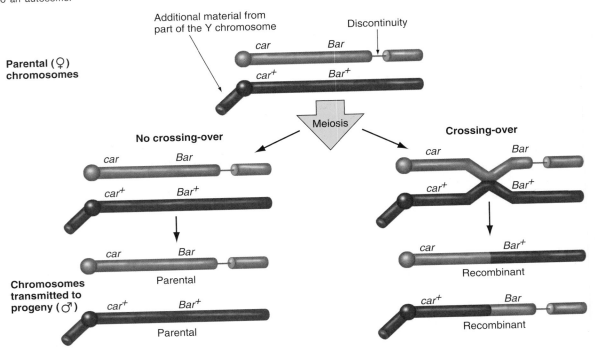

marker consisted of part of the Y chromosome that had become connected to the X-chromosome centromere.

Figure 5.6 illustrates how the chromosomes in these *car Bar / car⁺ Bar⁺* females were transmitted to male progeny. According to the experimental results, all sons showing a phenotype determined by one or the other parental combination of genes (either *car Bar* or *car⁺ Bar⁺*) had an X chromosome that was structurally indistinguishable from one of the original X chromosomes in the mother. In recombinant sons, however, such as those that manifested carnation eye color and normal eye shape (*car Bar⁺ / Y*), an identifiable exchange of the abnormal features marking the ends of the homologous X chromosomes accompanied the recombination of genes. The evidence thus tied an instance of phenotypic recombination to the crossing-over of particular genes located in specifically marked parts of particular chromosomes. This experiment elegantly demonstrated that genetic recombination is associated with the actual reciprocal exchange of segments between homologous chromosomes during meiosis.

Chiasmata mark the sites of recombination

Figure 5.7 outlines what is currently known about the steps of recombination as they appear in chromosomes viewed through the light microscope. Although this low-resolution view may not represent certain details of recombination with complete accuracy, it nonetheless provides a useful frame of reference. In Fig. 5.7a, the two homologs of each chromosome pair have already replicated, so there are now two pairs of sister chromatids or a total of four chromatids within each bivalent. In Fig. 5.7b, the synaptonemal complex zips together homologous chromosome pairs along their length. The synaptonemal zipper aligns homologous regions of all four chromatids such that allelic DNA sequences are physically near each other (see Fig. 4.14b on p. 96 for a detailed depiction). This proximity facilitates crossing-over between homologous sequences; as we will see in Chapter 6, the biochemical mechanism of recombination requires a close interaction of DNAs on homologous chromosomes that have identical, or nearly identical, nucleotide sequences.

In Fig. 5.7c, the synaptonemal complex begins to disassemble. Although at least some steps of the recombination process occurred while the chromatids were zipped in synapsis, it is only now that the recombination event becomes apparent. As the zipper dissolves, homologous chromosomes remain attached at chiasmata, the actual sites of crossing-over. Visible in the light microscope, chiasmata indicate where chromatid sections have switched from one molecule to another. In Fig. 5.7d, during anaphase I, as the two homologs separate, starting at their centromeres, the ends of the two recombined

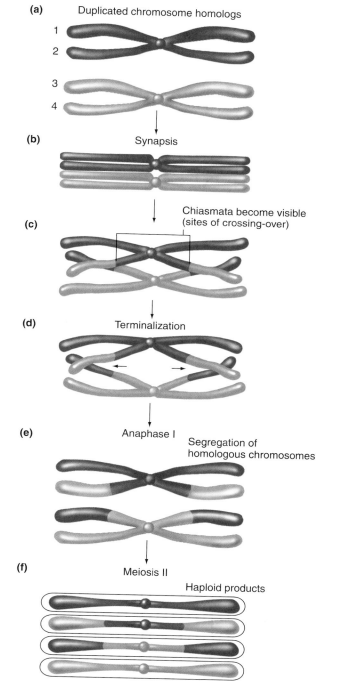

Figure 5.7 Recombination through the light microscope.
(a) A pair of duplicated homologous chromosomes very early in prophase of meiosis I. **(b)** During leptotene and zygotene of prophase I, the synaptonemal complex helps align corresponding regions of homologous chromosomes, allowing recombination. **(c)** As the synaptonemal complex disassembles during diplotene, homologous chromosomes remain attached at chiasmata. **(d)** and **(e)** The chiasmata terminalize (move toward the chromosome ends), allowing the recombined chromosomes to separate during anaphase and telophase. **(f)** The result of the process is recombinant gametes.

(a)   Duplicated chromosome homologs

1
2
3
4

(b)   Synapsis

Chiasmata become visible
(sites of crossing-over)

(c)

(d)   Terminalization

(e)   Anaphase I

Segregation of homologous chromosomes

(f)   Meiosis II

Haploid products

chromatids pull free of their respective sister chromatids, and the chiasmata shift from their original positions toward a chromosome end, or telomere. This movement of chiasmata is known as **terminalization.** When the chiasmata reach the telomeres, the homologous chromosomes can separate from each other (Fig. 5.7e). Meiosis continues and eventually produces four haploid cells that contain one chromatid—now a chromosome—apiece (Fig. 5.7f). Homologous chromosomes have exchanged parts.

Recombination can also take place apart from meiosis. As explained near the end of this chapter, recombination sometimes, though rarely, occurs during mitosis. It also occurs with the circular chromosomes of prokaryotic organisms and cellular organelles such as mitochondria and chloroplasts, which do not undergo meiosis and do not form chiasmata (see Chapter 14).

Recombination frequencies reflect the distances between two genes

Thomas Hunt Morgan's belief that chiasmata represent sites of physical crossing-over between chromosomes and that such crossing-over may result in recombination, led him to the following logical deduction: Different gene pairs exhibit different linkage rates because genes are arranged in a line along a chromosome. The closer together two genes are on the chromosome, the less their chance of being separated by an event that cuts and recombines the line of genes. To look at it another way, if we assume for the moment that chiasmata can form anywhere along a chromosome with equal likelihood, then the probability of a crossover occurring between two genes increases with the distance separating them. If this is so, the frequency of genetic recombination also must increase with the distance between genes. To illustrate the point, imagine pinning to a wall 10 inches of ribbon with a line of tiny black dots along its length and then repeatedly throwing a dart to see where you will cut the ribbon. You would find that practically every throw of the dart separates a dot at one end of the ribbon from a dot at the other end, while few if any throws separate any two particular dots positioned right next to each other.

Alfred H. Sturtevant, one of Morgan's students, took this idea one step further. He proposed that the percentage of total progeny that were recombinant types, the **recombination frequency (RF),** could be used as a gauge of the physical distance separating any two genes on the same chromosome. Sturtevant arbitrarily defined one RF percentage point as the unit of measure along a chromosome; later, another geneticist named the unit a **centimorgan (cM)** after T. H. Morgan. Mappers often refer to a centimorgan as a **map unit (m.u.).** Although the two terms are interchangeable, researchers prefer

Figure 5.8 Recombination frequencies are the basis of genetic maps. (a) 1.1% of the gametes produced by a female doubly heterozygous for the genes w and y are recombinant. The recombination frequency (RF) is thus 1.1%, and the genes are approximately 1.1 map units (m.u.) or 1.1 centimorgans (cM) apart. **(b)** The distance between the w and m genes is longer: 32.8 m.u. (or 32.8 cM).

one or the other, depending on their experimental organism. *Drosophila* geneticists, for example, use map units while human geneticists use centimorgans. In Sturtevant's system, 1% RF = 1 cM = 1 m.u. A review of the two pairs of X-linked *Drosophila* genes we analyzed earlier shows how his proposal works. Because the X-linked genes for eye color (w) and body color (y) recombine in 1.1% of F_2 progeny, they are 1.1 m.u. apart (**Fig. 5.8a**). In contrast, the X-linked genes for eye color (w) and wing size (m) have a recombination frequency of 32.8 and are therefore 32.8 m.u. apart (**Fig. 5.8b**).

As a unit of measure, the map unit is simply an index of recombination probabilities assumed to reflect distances between genes. According to this index, the y and w genes are much closer together than the m and w genes. Geneticists have used this logic to map thousands of genetic markers to the chromosomes of *Drosophila,* building recombination maps step-by-step with closely linked markers. And as we see next, they have learned that genes very far apart on the same chromosome may appear unlinked, even though their recombination distances relative to closely linked intervening markers confirm that the genes are indeed on the same chromosome.

Recombination frequencies between two genes never exceed 50%

If the definition of linkage is that the proportion of recombinant classes is less than that of parental classes, a recombination frequency of less than 50% indicates linkage. But what can we conclude about the relative location of genes if there are roughly equal numbers of parental and recombinant progeny? And does it ever happen that recombinants are in the majority?

We already know one situation that can give rise to a recombination frequency of 50%. Genes located on different (that is, nonhomologous) chromosomes will obey Mendel's law of independent assortment because the two chromosomes can line up on the spindle during meiosis in either of two equally likely configurations (review Fig. 4.16a on p. 98). A dihybrid for these two genes wil thus produce all four possible types of gametes (*AB*, *Ab*, *aB*, and *ab*) with approximately equal frequency. Importantly, experiments have established that genes located very far apart on the same chromosome also show recombination frequencies of approximately 50%.

Researchers have never observed statistically significant recombination frequencies between two genes greater than 50%, which means that in any cross following two genes, recombinant types are never in the majority. As we explain in more detail later in the chapter, this upper limit of 50% on the recombination frequency between two genes results from two aspects of chromosome behavior during meiosis I. First, multiple crossovers can occur between two genes if they are far apart on the same chromosome, and second, recombination takes place after the chromosomes have replicated into sister chromatids.

For now, simply note that recombination frequencies near 50% suggest either that two genes are on different chromosomes or that they lie far apart on the same chromosome. The only way to tell whether the two genes are syntenic (that is, on the same chromosome) is through a series of matings showing definite linkage with other genes that lie between them. In short, even though crosses between two genes lying very far apart on a chromosome may show no linkage at all (because recombinant and parental classes are equal), you can demonstrate they are on the same chromosome if you can tie each of the widely separated genes to one or more common intermediaries. **Table 5.2** summarizes the relationship between the relative locations of two genes and the presence or absence of linkage as measured by recombination frequencies.

Recombination results from crossing-over of homologs during meiosis I. If two syntenic genes are close together, little chance exists for crossing-over, so the recombination frequency is low. As the distance between syntenic genes increases, the RF increases to a maximum of 50%. Thus, genes far enough apart on a single chromosome assort independently, just as do genes on nonhomologous chromosomes.

5.4 Mapping: Locating Genes Along a Chromosome

Maps are images of the relative positions of objects in space. Whether depicting the floor plan of New York's Metropolitan Museum of Art, the layout of the Roman Forum, or the location of cities served by the railways of Europe, maps turn measurements into patterns of spatial relationships that add a new level of meaning to the original data of distances. Maps that assign genes to locations on particular chromosomes called *loci* (singular **locus**) are no exception. By transforming genetic data into spatial arrangements, maps sharpen our ability to predict the inheritance patterns of specific traits.

We have seen that recombination frequency (RF) is a measure of the distance separating two genes along a chromosome. We now examine how data from many crosses following two and three genes at a time can be compiled and compared to generate accurate, comprehensive gene/chromosome maps.

Comparisons of two-point crosses establish relative gene positions

In his senior undergraduate thesis, Morgan's student A. H. Sturtevant asked whether data obtained from a large number of two-point crosses (crosses tracing two genes at a time) would support the idea that genes form a definite linear series along a chromosome. Sturtevant began by looking at X-linked genes in *Drosophila*. **Figure 5.9a** lists his recombination data for several two-point crosses. Recall that the distance between two

Figure 5.9 Mapping genes by comparisons of two-point crosses. (a) Sturtevant's data for the distances between pairs of X-linked genes in *Drosophila*. **(b)** Because the distance between *y* and *m* is greater than the distance between *w* and *m*, the order of genes must be *y-w-m*. **(c)** and **(d)** Maps for five genes on the *Drosophila* X chromosome. The left-to-right orientation is arbitrary. Note that the numerical position of the *r* gene depends on how it is calculated. The best genetic maps are obtained by summing many small intervening distances as in (d).

TABLE 5.2	Properties of Linked Versus Unlinked Genes

Linked Genes

Parentals > recombinants (RF < 50%)

Linked genes must be syntenic and sufficiently close together on the same chromosome so that they do not assort independently.

Unlinked Genes

Parentals = recombinants (RF = 50%)

Occurs either when genes are on different chromosomes or when they are sufficiently far apart on the same chromosome.

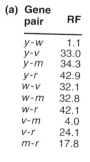

(a) Gene pair	RF
y-w	1.1
y-v	33.0
y-m	34.3
y-r	42.9
w-v	32.1
w-m	32.8
w-r	42.1
v-m	4.0
v-r	24.1
m-r	17.8

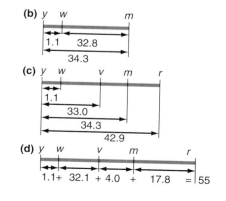

genes that yields 1% recombinant progeny—an RF of 1%—is 1 m.u.

As an example of Sturtevant's reasoning, consider the three genes *w, y,* and *m.* If these genes are arranged in a line (instead of a more complicated branched structure, for example), then one of them must be in the middle, flanked on either side by the other two. The greatest genetic distance should separate the two genes on the outside, and this value should roughly equal the sum of the distances separating the middle gene from each outside gene. The data Sturtevant obtained are consistent with this idea, implying that *w* lies between *y* and *m* (**Fig. 5.9b**). Note that the left-to-right orientation of this map was selected at random; the map in Fig. 5.9b would be equally correct if it portrayed *y* on the right and *m* on the left.

By following exactly the same procedure for each set of three genes, Sturtevant established a self-consistent order for all the genes he investigated on *Drosophila*'s X chromosome (**Fig. 5.9c;** once again, the left-to-right arrangement is an arbitrary choice). By checking the data for every combination of three genes, you can assure yourself that this ordering makes sense. The fact that the recombination data yield a simple linear map of gene position supports the idea that genes reside in a unique linear order along a chromosome.

Limitations of two-point crosses

Though of great importance, the pairwise mapping of genes has several shortcomings that limit its usefulness. First, in crosses involving only two genes at a time, it may be difficult to determine gene order if some gene pairs lie very close together. For example, in mapping *y, w,* and *m,* 34.3 m.u. separate the outside genes *y* and *m,* while nearly as great a distance (32.8 m.u.) separates the middle *w* from the outside *m* (Fig. 5.9b). Before being able to conclude with any confidence that *y* and *m* are truly farther apart, that is, that the small difference between the values of 34.3 and 32.8 is not the result of sampling error, you would have to examine a very large number of flies and subject the data to a statistical test, such as the chi-square test.

A second problem with Sturtevant's mapping procedure is that the actual distances in his map do not always add up, even approximately. As an example, suppose that the locus of the *y* gene at the far left of the map is regarded as position 0 (Fig. 5.9c). The *w* gene would then lie near position 1, and *m* would be located in the vicinity of 34 m.u. But what about the *r* gene, named for a mutation that produces rudimentary (very small) wings? Based solely on its distance from *y,* as inferred from the *y* ↔ *r* data in Fig. 5.9a, we would place it at position 42.9 (Fig. 5.9c). However, if we calculate its position as the sum of all intervening distances inferred from the data in Fig. 5.9a, that is, as the sum of *y* ↔ *w* plus *w* ↔ *v* plus *v* ↔ *m* plus *m* ↔ *r,* the locus of *r* becomes 1.1 + 32.1 + 4.0 + 17.8 = 55.0 (**Fig. 5.9d**). What can explain this

difference, and which of these two values is closer to the truth? Three-point crosses help provide some of the answers.

Three-point crosses provide faster and more accurate mapping

The simultaneous analysis of three markers makes it possible to obtain enough information to position the three genes in relation to each other from just one set of crosses. To describe this procedure, we look at three genes linked on one of *Drosophila*'s autosomes.

A homozygous female with mutations for vestigial wings (*vg*), black body (*b*), and purple eye color (*pr*) was mated to a wild-type male (**Fig. 5.10a**). All the triply heterozygous F₁ progeny, both male and female, had normal phenotypes for the three characteristics, indicating that the mutations are autosomal recessive. In a testcross of the F₁ females with males having vestigial wings, black body, and purple eyes, the progeny were of eight different phenotypes reflecting eight different genotypes. The order in which the genes in each phenotypic class are listed in Fig. 5.10a is completely arbitrary. Thus, instead

Figure 5.10 Analyzing the results of a three-point cross. (a) Results from a three-point testcross of F₁ females simultaneously heterozygous for *vg, b,* and *pr.* (b) The gene in the middle must be *pr* because the longest distance is between the other two genes: *vg* and *b.* The most accurate map distances are calculated by summing shorter intervening distances, so 18.7 m.u. is a more accurate estimate of the genetic distance between *vg* and *b* than 17.7 m.u.

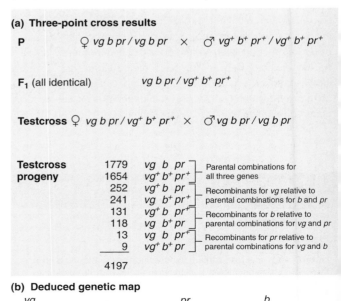

(a) Three-point cross results

| P | ♀ *vg b pr / vg b pr* × ♂ *vg⁺ b⁺ pr⁺ / vg⁺ b⁺ pr⁺* |

F₁ (all identical) *vg b pr / vg⁺ b⁺ pr⁺*

Testcross ♀ *vg b pr / vg⁺ b⁺ pr⁺* × ♂ *vg b pr / vg b pr*

Testcross progeny			
1779	*vg b pr*	⎤	Parental combinations for all three genes
1654	*vg⁺ b⁺ pr⁺*	⎦	
252	*vg⁺ b pr*	⎤	Recombinants for *vg* relative to parental combinations for *b* and *pr*
241	*vg b⁺ pr⁺*	⎦	
131	*vg⁺ b pr⁺*	⎤	Recombinants for *b* relative to parental combinations for *vg* and *pr*
118	*vg b⁺ pr*	⎦	
13	*vg b pr⁺*	⎤	Recombinants for *pr* relative to parental combinations for *vg* and *b*
9	*vg⁺ b⁺ pr*	⎦	
4197			

(b) Deduced genetic map

vg ———————— *pr* ———— *b*

| 12.3 m.u. | 6.4 m.u. | = 18.7 m.u |
| 17.7 m.u. | | |

of vg b pr, one could write b vg pr or vg pr b to indicate the same genotype. Remember that at the outset we do not know the gene order; deducing it is the goal of the mapping study.

In analyzing the data, we look at two genes at a time (recall that the recombination frequency is always a function of a pair of genes). For the pair vg and b, the parental combinations are vg b and vg^+b^+; the nonparental recombinants are vg b^+ and vg^+b. To determine whether a particular class of progeny is parental or recombinant for vg and b, we do not care whether the flies are pr or pr^+. Thus, to the nearest tenth of a map unit, the $vg \leftrightarrow b$ distance, calculated as the percentage of recombinants in the total number of progeny, is

$$\frac{252 + 241 + 131 + 118}{4197} \times 100$$

$$= 17.7 \text{ m.u. } (vg \leftrightarrow b \text{ distance})$$

Similarly, because recombinants for the vg–pr gene pair are vg pr^+ and vg^+ pr, the interval between these two genes is

$$\frac{252 + 241 + 13 + 9}{4197} \times 100$$

$$= 12.3 \text{ m.u. } (vg \leftrightarrow pr \text{ distance})$$

while the distance separating the b–pr pair is

$$\frac{131 + 118 + 13 + 9}{4197} \times 100$$

$$= 6.4 \text{ m.u. } (b \leftrightarrow pr \text{ distance})$$

These recombination frequencies show that vg and b are separated by the largest distance (17.7 m.u., as compared with 12.3 and 6.4) and must therefore be the outside genes, flanking pr in the middle (**Fig. 5.10b**). But as with the X-linked y and r genes analyzed by Sturtevant, the distance separating the outside vg and b genes (17.7) does not equal the sum of the two intervening distances (12.3 + 6.4 = 18.7). In the next section, we learn that the reason for this discrepancy is the rare occurrence of double crossovers.

Correction for double crossovers

Figure 5.11 depicts the homologous autosomes of the F_1 females that are heterozygous for the three genes vg, pr, and b. A close examination of the chromosomes reveals the kinds of crossovers that must have occurred to generate the classes and numbers of progeny observed. In this and subsequent figures, the chromosomes depicted are in late prophase/early metaphase of meiosis I, when there are

Figure 5.11 Inferring the location of a crossover event. Once you establish the order of genes involved in a three-point cross, it is easy to determine which crossover events gave rise to particular recombinant gametes. Note that double crossovers are needed to generate gametes in which the gene in the middle has recombined relative to the parental combinations for the genes at the ends.

four chromatids for each pair of homologous chromosomes. As we have suggested previously and demonstrate more rigorously later, prophase I is the stage at which recombination takes place. Note that we call the space between *vg* and *pr* "region 1" and the space between *pr* and *b* "region 2."

Recall that the progeny from the testcross performed earlier fall into eight groups (review Fig. 5.10). Flies in the two largest groups carry the same configurations of genes as did their grandparents of the P generation: *vg b pr* and *vg⁺ b⁺ pr⁺*; they thus represent the parental classes (Fig. 5.11a). The next two groups—*vg⁺ b pr* and *vg b⁺ pr⁺*—are composed of recombinants that must be the reciprocal products of a crossover in region 1 between *vg* and *pr* (Fig. 5.11b). Similarly the two groups containing *vg⁺ b pr⁺* and *vg b⁺ pr* flies must have resulted from recombination in region 2 between *pr* and *b* (Fig. 5.11c).

But what about the two smallest groups made up of rare *vg b pr⁺* and *vg⁺ b⁺ pr* recombinants? What kinds of chromosome exchange could account for them? Most likely, they result from two different crossover events occurring simultaneously, one in region 1, the other in region 2 (Fig. 5.11d). The gametes produced by such double crossovers still have the parental configuration for the outside genes *vg* and *b*, even though not one but two exchanges must have occurred.

Because of the existence of double crossovers, the *vg ↔ b* distance of 17.7 m.u. calculated in the previous section does not reflect all of the recombination events producing the gametes that gave rise to the observed progeny. To correct for this oversight, it is necessary to adjust the recombination frequency by adding the double crossovers twice, because each individual in the double crossover groups is the result of two exchanges between *vg* and *b*. The corrected distance is

$$\frac{252 + 241 + 131 + 118 + 13 + 13 + 9 + 9}{4197} \times 100$$

$$= 18.7 \text{ m.u.}$$

This value makes sense because you have accounted for all of the crossovers that occur in region 1 as well as all of the crossovers in region 2. As a result, the corrected value of 18.7 m.u. for the distance between *vg* and *b* is now exactly the same as the sum of the distances between *vg* and *pr* (region 1) and between *pr* and *b* (region 2).

As previously discussed, when Sturtevant originally mapped several X-linked genes in *Drosophila* by two-point crosses, the locus of the rudimentary wings (*r*) gene was ambiguous. A two-point cross involving *y* and *r* gave a recombination frequency of 42.9, but the sum of all the intervening distances was 55.0 (review Fig. 5.9 on p. 129). This discrepancy occurred because the two-point cross ignored double crossovers that might have occurred in the large interval between the *y* and *r* genes. The data summing

the smaller intervening distances accounted for at least some of these double crossovers by catching recombinations of gene pairs between *y* and *r*. Moreover, each smaller distance is less likely to encompass a double crossover than a larger distance, so each number for a smaller distance is inherently more accurate.

Note that even a three-point cross like the one for *vg*, *pr*, and *b* ignores the possibility of two recombination events taking place in, say, region 1. For greatest accuracy, it is always best to construct a map using many genes separated by relatively short distances.

Interference: Fewer double crossovers than expected

In a three-point cross following three linked genes, of the eight possible genotypic classes, the two parental classes contain the largest number of progeny, while the two double recombinant classes, resulting from double crossovers, are always the smallest (see Fig. 5.10). We can understand why double-crossover progeny are the rarest by looking at the probability of their occurrence. If an exchange in region 1 of a chromosome does not affect the probability of an exchange in region 2, the probability that both will occur simultaneously is the product of the separate probabilities (recall the product rule in Chapter p. 23). For example, if progeny resulting from recombination in region 1 alone account for 10% of the total progeny (that is, if region 1 is 10 m.u.) and progeny resulting from recombination in region 2 alone account for 20%, then the probability of a double crossover (one event region 1, the second in region 2) is 0.10 × 0.20 = 0.0 or 2%. This makes sense because the likelihood of two rare events occurring simultaneously is even less than that of either rare event occurring alone.

If there are eight classes of progeny in a three-point cross, the two classes containing the fewest progeny must have arisen from double crossovers. The numerical frequencies of observed double crossovers, however, almost never coincide with expectations derived from the product rule. Let's look at the actual numbers from the cross we have been discussing. The probability of a single crossover between *vg* and *pr* is 0.123 (corresponding 12.3 m.u.), and the probability of a single crossover between *pr* and *b* is 0.064 (6.4 m.u.). The product these probabilities is

$$0.123 \times 0.064 = 0.0079 = 0.79\%$$

But the observed proportion of double crossovers Fig. 5.10) was

$$\frac{13 + 9}{4197} \times 100 = 0.52\%$$

The fact that the number of observed double crossovers is less than the number expected if the two exchanges independent events suggests that the occurrence of crossover reduces the likelihood that another crossover will occur in an adjacent part of the chromosome. This phenomenon—of crossovers not occurring independently—is called **chromosomal interference.**

Interference may exist to ensure that every pair of homologous chromosomes undergoes at least one crossover event. It is critical that every pair of homologous chromosomes sustain one or more crossover events because such events help the chromosomes orient properly at the metaphase plate during the first meiotic division. Indeed, homologous chromosome pairs without crossovers often segregate improperly. If only a limited number of crossovers can occur during each meiosis and interference lowers the number of crossovers on large chromosomes, then the remaining possible crossovers are more likely to occur on small chromosomes. This increases the probability that at least one crossover will take place on every homologous pair. Though the molecular mechanism underlying interference is not yet clear, recent experiments suggest that interference is mediated by the synaptonemal complex.

Interference is not uniform and may vary even for different regions of the same chromosome. Investigators can obtain a quantitative measure of the amount of interference in different chromosomal intervals by first calculating a **coefficient of coincidence,** defined as the ratio between the actual frequency of double crossovers observed in an experiment and the number of double crossovers expected on the basis of independent probabilities.

$$\text{Coefficient of coincidence} = \frac{\text{frequency observed}}{\text{frequency expected}}$$

For the three-point cross involving vg, pr, and b, the coefficient of coincidence is

$$\frac{0.52}{0.79} = 0.66$$

The definition of interference itself is

$$\text{Interference} = 1 - \text{coefficient of coincidence}$$

In this case, it is

$$1 - 0.66 = 0.34$$

To understand the meaning of interference, it is helpful to contrast what happens when there is no interference with what happens when it is complete. If interference is 0, the frequency of observed double crossovers equals expectations, and crossovers in adjacent regions of a chromosome occur independently of each other. If interference is complete (that is, if interference = 1), no double crossovers occur in the experimental progeny because one exchange effectively prevents another. As an example, in a particular three-point cross in mice, the recombination frequency for the pair of genes on the left (region 1) is 20, and for the pair of genes on the right (region 2), it is

also 20. Without interference, the expected rate of double crossovers in this chromosomal interval is

$$0.20 \times 0.20 = 0.04, \text{ or } 4\%$$

but when investigators observed 1000 progeny of this cross, they found 0 double recombinants instead of the expected 40.

A method to determine the gene in the middle

The smallest of the eight possible classes of progeny in a three-point cross are the two that contain double recombinants generated by double crossovers. It is possible to use the composition of alleles in these double crossover classes to determine which of the three genes lies in the middle, even without calculating any recombination frequencies. Consider again the progeny of a three-point testcross looking at the vg, pr, and b genes. The F_1 females are $vg\ pr\ b\,/\,vg^+\ pr^+\ b^+$. As Fig. 5.11d demonstrated, testcross progeny resulting from double crossovers in the trihybrid females of the F_1 generation received gametes from their mothers carrying the allelic combinations vg $pr^+\ b$ and $vg^+\ pr\ b^+$. In these individuals, the alleles of the vg and b genes retain their parental associations ($vg\ b$ and $vg^+\ b^+$), while the pr gene has recombined with respect to both the other genes ($pr\ b^+$ and $pr^+\ b$; $vg\ pr^+$ and $vg^+\ pr$). The same is true in all three-point crosses: In those gametes formed by double crossovers, the gene whose alleles have recombined relative to the parental configurations of the other two genes must be the one in the middle.

> Genetic maps of genes along chromosomes can be approximated using data from two-point crosses. Three-point crosses yield more accurate maps because they allow correction for double crossovers as well as estimates of interference (fewer double crossovers than expected). The most accurate maps are constructed with many closely linked genetic markers.

Three-point crosses: A comprehensive example

The technique of looking at double recombinants to discover which gene has recombined with respect to both other genes allows immediate clarification of gene order even in otherwise difficult cases. Consider the three X-linked genes y, w, and m that Sturtevant located in his original mapping experiment (see Fig. 5.9 on p. 129). Because the distance between y and m (34.3 m.u.) appeared slightly larger than the distance separating w and m (32.8 m.u.), he concluded that w was the gene in the middle. But because of the small difference between the two numbers, his conclusion was subject to questions of statistical significance. If, however, we look at a

Figure 5.12 How three-point crosses verify Sturtevant's map. The parental classes correspond to the two X chromosomes in the F₁ female. The genotype of the double recombinant classes shows that w must be the gene in the middle.

$$\female\ w^+\,w\,y^+\,y\,m^+\,m\ \times\ \male\ X/Y$$

Before data analysis, you do not know the gene order or allele combination on each chromosome.

Male progeny		
	2278 $w^+\,y^+\,m$ /Y	Parental class
	2157 $w\,y\,m^+$ /Y	(noncrossover)
	1203 $w\,y\,m$ /Y	Crossover in region 2
	1092 $w^+\,y^+\,m^+$ /Y	(between w and m)
	49 $w^+\,y\,m$ /Y	Crossover in region 1
	41 $w\,y^+\,m^+$ /Y	(between y and w)
	2 $w^+\,y\,m^+$ /Y	Double
	1 $w\,y^+\,m$ /Y	crossovers
	6823	

After data analysis, you can conclude that the gene order and allele combinations on the X chromosomes of the F₁ females were $y\,w\,m^+\,/\,y^+\,w^+\,m$.

three-point cross following y, w, and m, these questions disappear.

Figure 5.12 tabulates the classes and numbers of male progeny arising from females heterozygous for the y, w, and m genes. Because these male progeny receive their only X chromosome from their mothers, their phenotypes directly indicate the gametes produced by the heterozygous females. In each row of the figure's table, the genes appear in an arbitrary order that does not presuppose knowledge of the actual map. As you can see, the two classes of progeny listed at the top of the table outnumber the remaining six classes, which indicates that all three genes are linked to each other. Moreover, these largest groups, which are the parental classes, show that the two X chromosomes of the heterozygous females were $w^+\,y^+\,m$ and $w\,y\,m^+$.

Among the male progeny in Fig. 5.12, the two smallest classes, representing the double crossovers, have X chromosomes carrying $w^+\,y\,m^+$ and $w\,y^+\,m$ combinations, in which the w alleles are recombined relative to those of y and m. The w gene must therefore lie between y and m, verifying Sturtevant's original assessment.

To complete a map based on the $w\ y\ m$ three-point cross, you can calculate the interval between y and w (region 1)

$$\frac{49 + 41 + 1 + 2}{6823} \times 100 = 1.3 \text{ m.u.}$$

as well as the interval between w and m (region 2)

$$\frac{1203 + 1092 + 2 + 1}{6823} \times 100 = 33.7 \text{ m.u.}$$

The genetic distance separating y and m is the sum of

$$1.3 + 33.7 = 35.0 \text{ m.u.}$$

Note that you could also calculate the dista between y and m directly by including double crosso twice, to account for the total number of recombina events detected between these two genes.

$$\begin{aligned} RF = (1203 + 1092 + 49 + 41 + 2 + 2 \\ + 1 + 1)/6823 \times 100 = 35.0 \text{ m.u.} \end{aligned}$$

This method yields the same value as the sum of the intervening distances (region 1 + region 2).

Further calculations show that interference is siderable in this portion of the *Drosophila* X chro some, at least as inferred from the set of data tabul in Fig. 5.12. The percentage of observed double rec binants was

$$3/6823 = 0.00044, \text{ or } 0.044\%$$

(rounding to the nearest thousandth of a percent), w the percentage of double recombinants expected the basis of independent probabilities by the law of product is

$$0.013 \times 0.337 = 0.0044, \text{ or } 0.44\%$$

Thus, the coefficient of coincidence is

$$0.044/0.44 = 0.1$$

and the interference is

$$1 - 0.1 = 0.9$$

Do genetic maps correlate with physical reality?

Many types of experiments presented later in this clearly show that the *order of genes* revealed by rec bination mapping corresponds to the order of t same genes along the DNA molecule of a chromose In contrast, the *actual physical distances betv genes*—that is, the amount of DNA separating the does not always show a direct correspondence to ge map distances.

The relationship between recombination frequ and physical distance along a chromosome is not sin One complicating factor is the existence of double, t and even more crossovers. When genes are separate 1 m.u. or less, double crossovers are not significant bec the probability of their occurring is so small (0.0 $0.01 = 0.0001$). But for genes separated by 20, 3 40 m.u., the probability of double crossovers skewing data takes on greater significance. A second confoun factor is the 50% limit on the recombination frequ observable in a cross. This limit reduces the precisic RF as a measure of chromosomal distances. No m how far apart two genes are on a long chromosome, will never recombine more than 50% of the time. Yet a third problem is that recombination is not uniform even over the length of a single chromosome: Certain "hotspots" are favored sites of recombination, while other areas—often in the vicinity of centromeres—are "recombination deserts" in which few crossovers ever take place.

Ever since Morgan, Sturtevant, and others began mapping, geneticists have generated mathematical equations called **mapping functions** to compensate for the inaccuracies inherent in relating recombination frequencies to physical distances. These equations generally make large corrections for RF values of widely separated genes, while barely changing the map distances separating genes that lie close together. This reflects the fact that multiple recombination events and the 50% limit on recombination do not confound the calculation of distances between closely linked genes. However, the corrections for large distances are at best imprecise, because mapping functions are based on simplifying assumptions (such as no interference) that are only rarely justified. Thus, the best way to create an accurate map is still by summing many smaller intervals, locating widely separated genes through linkage to common intermediaries. Maps are subject to continual refinement as more and more newly discovered genes are included.

Rates of recombination may differ from species to species. We know this because recent elucidation of the complete DNA sequences of several organisms' genomes has allowed investigators to compare the actual physical distances between genes (in base pairs of DNA) with genetic map distances. They found that in humans, a map unit corresponds on average to about 1 million base pairs. In yeast, however, where the rate of recombination per length of DNA is much higher than in humans, one map unit is approximately 2500 base pairs. Thus, although map units are useful for estimating distances between the genes of an organism, 1% RF can reflect very different expanses of DNA in different organisms.

Recombination rates sometimes vary even between the two sexes of a single species. *Drosophila* provides an extreme example: No recombination occurs during meiosis in males. If you review the examples already discussed in this chapter, you will discover that they all measure recombination among the progeny of doubly heterozygous *Drosophila* females. Problem 19 at the end of this chapter shows how geneticists can exploit the absence of recombination in *Drosophila* males to establish rapidly that genes far apart on the same chromosome are indeed syntenic.

Multiple-factor crosses help establish linkage groups

Genes chained together by linkage relationships are known collectively as a **linkage group.** When enough genes have been assigned to a particular chromosome, the terms *chromosome* and *linkage group* become synonymous. If you

can demonstrate that gene *A* is linked to gene *B*, *B* to *C*, *C* to *D*, and *D* to *E*, you can conclude that all of these genes are syntenic. When the genetic map of a genome becomes so dense that it is possible to show that any gene on a chromosome is linked to another gene on the same chromosome, the number of linkage groups equals the number of pairs of homologous chromosomes in the species. Humans have 23 linkage groups, mice have 20, and fruit flies have 4 (**Fig. 5.13**).

The total genetic distance along a chromosome, which is obtained by adding many short distances between genes, may be much more than 50 m.u. For example, the two long *Drosophila* autosomes are both slightly more than 100 m.u. in length (Fig. 5.13), while the longest human chromosome is approximately 270 m.u. Recall, however, that even with the longest chromosomes, *pairwise* crosses between genes located at the two ends will not produce more than 50% recombinant progeny.

Linkage mapping has practical applications of great importance. For example, the Fast Forward box "Gene Mapping May Lead to a Cure for Cystic Fibrosis" on p. 137 describes how researchers used linkage information to locate the gene for this important human hereditary disease.

> When sufficient genes have been mapped, all the genes on a single chromosome will form a single linkage group. The order of the genes determined by mapping corresponds to their actual sequence along the chromosome; however, the map distance between the genes is not simply correlated with the actual physical distance along the chromosome's DNA.

5.5 Tetrad Analysis in Fungi

With *Drosophila*, mice, peas, people, and other diploid organisms, each individual represents only one of the four potential gametes generated by each parent in a single meiotic event. Thus, until now, our presentation of linkage, recombination, and mapping has depended on inferences derived from examining the phenotypes of diploid progeny resulting from random unions of random products of meiosis. For such diploid organisms, we do not know which, if any, of the parents' other progeny arose from gametes created in the same meiosis. Because of this limitation, the analysis of random products of meiosis in diploid organisms must be based on statistical samplings of large populations.

In contrast, various species of fungi provide a unique opportunity for genetic analysis because they house all four haploid products of each meiosis in a sac called an **ascus** (plural, *asci*). These haploid cells, or **ascospores** (also known as *haplospores*), can germinate and survive as viable haploid individuals that grow and perpetuate themselves by mitosis. The phenotype of such haploid fungi is a direct representation of their genotype, without complications of

Figure 5.13 *Drosophila melanogaster* **has four linkage groups.** A genetic map of the fruit fly, showing the position of many genes affecting body morphology, including those used as examples in this chapter (*highlighted in bold*). Because so many *Drosophila* genes have been mapped, each of the four chromosomes can be represented as a single linkage group.

dominance. **Figure 5.14** illustrates the life cycles of two fungal species that preserve their meiotic products in a sac. One, the normally unicellular baker's yeast (*Saccharomyces cerevisiae*), is sold in supermarkets and contributes to the texture, shape, and flavor of bread; it generates four ascospores with each meiosis. The other, *Neurospora crassa,* is a bread mold that renders the bread on which it grows inedible; it too generates four ascospores with each meiosis, but at the completion of meiosis, each of the four haploid ascospores immediately divides once by mitosis to yield four pairs, for a total of eight haploid cells. The two cells in each pair of *Neurospora* ascospores have the same genotype, because they arose from mitosis.

Haploid cells of both yeast and *Neurospora* normally reproduce vegetatively (that is, asexually) by mitosis. However, sexual reproduction is possible because the haploid cells come in two mating types, and cells of opposite mating types can fuse to form a diploid zygote (Fig. 5.14).

In baker's yeast, these diploid cells are stable and ca reproduce through successive mitotic cycles. Stress, suc as that caused by a scarcity or lack of essential nutrient induces the diploid cells of yeast to enter meiosis. In brea mold, the diploid zygote instead immediately undergoe meiosis, so the diploid state is only transient.

Mutations in haploid yeast and mold affect man different traits, including the appearance of the cel and their ability to grow under particular conditions. Fo instance, yeast cells with the *his4* mutation are unabl to grow in the absence of the amino acid histidine, whil yeast with the *trp1* mutation cannot grow without a external source of the amino acid tryptophan. Geneticis who specialize in the study of yeast have devised a sy tem of representing genes that is slightly different fro the ones for *Drosophila* and mice. They use capital le ters (*HIS4*) to designate dominant alleles and lowercas letters (*his4*) to represent recessives. For most of th

▶▶ FAST FORWARD

Gene Mapping May Lead to a Cure for Cystic Fibrosis

For 40 years after the symptoms of cystic fibrosis were first described in 1938, no molecular clue—no visible chromosomal abnormality transmitted with the disease, no identifiable protein defect carried by affected individuals—suggested the genetic cause of the disorder. As a result, there was no effective treatment for the 1 in 2000 Caucasian Americans born with the disease, most of whom died before they were 30. In the 1980s, however, geneticists were able to combine recently invented techniques for looking directly at DNA with maps constructed by linkage analysis to pinpoint a precise chromosomal position, or locus, for the cystic fibrosis gene.

The mappers of the cystic fibrosis gene faced an overwhelming task. They were searching for a gene that encoded an unknown protein, a gene that had not yet even been assigned to a chromosome. It could lie anywhere among the 23 pairs of chromosomes in a human cell. Imagine looking for a close friend you lost track of years ago, who might now be anywhere in the world. You would first have to find ways to narrow the search to a particular continent (the equivalent of a specific chromosome in the gene mappers' search); then to a country (the long or short arm of the chromosome); next to the state or province, county, city, or town, and street (all increasingly narrow bands of the chromosome); and finally, to a house address (the locus itself). Here, we briefly summarize how researchers applied some of these steps in mapping the cystic fibrosis gene.

- A review of many family pedigrees containing first-cousin marriages confirmed that cystic fibrosis is most likely determined by a single gene (CF). Investigators collected white blood cells from 47 families with two or more affected children, obtaining genetic data from 106 patients, 94 parents, and 44 unaffected siblings.
- They next tried to discover if any other trait is reliably transmitted with cystic fibrosis. Analyses of the easily obtainable serum enzyme paroxonase showed that its gene (PON) is indeed linked to CF. At first, this knowledge was not that helpful, because PON had not yet been assigned to a chromosome.
- Then, in the early 1980s, geneticists developed a large series of DNA markers, based on new techniques that enabled them to recognize variations in the genetic material. A **DNA marker** is a piece of DNA of known size, representing a specific locus, that comes in identifiable variations. These allelic variations segregate according to Mendel's laws, which means it is possible to follow their transmission as you would any gene's. Chapter 11 explains the discovery and use of DNA markers in greater detail; for now, it is only important to know that they exist and can be identified.

By 1986, linkage analyses of hundreds of DNA markers had shown that one marker, known as D7S15, is linked with both PON and CF. Researchers computed recombination frequencies and found that the distance from the DNA marker to CF was 15 cM; from the DNA marker to PON, 5 cM; and from PON to CF, 10 cM. They concluded that the order of the three loci was

Figure A How molecular markers helped locate the gene for cystic fibrosis (CF).

D7S15-PON-CF (**Fig. A**). Because CF could lie 15 cM in either of two directions from the DNA marker, the area under investigation was approximately 30 cM. And because the human genome consists of roughly 3000 cM, this step of linkage analysis narrowed the search to 1% of the human genome.

- Next, the DNA marker D7S15 was localized to the long arm of chromosome 7, which meant that the gene for cystic fibrosis also resides in that chromosome arm. Researchers had now placed the CF gene in a certain country on a particular genetic continent.
- Finally, investigators discovered linkage with several other markers on the long arm of chromosome 7, called J3.11, βTR, and met. Two of the markers turned out to be separated from CF by a distance of only 1 cM. It now became possible to place CF in band 31 of chromosome 7's long arm (band 7q31, Fig. A). For families with at least one child who has cystic fibrosis, geneticists using DNA analyses of these closely linked markers could now identify carriers of an abnormal copy of the CF gene with substantial confidence.

By 1989, researchers had used this mapping information to identify and clone the CF gene on the basis of its location. And by 1992, they had shown it encodes a cell membrane protein that regulates the flow of chloride ions into and out of cells (review the Fast Forward box "Genes Encode Proteins" in Chapter 2). This knowledge has become the basis of new therapies to open up ion flow, as well as gene therapies to introduce normal copies of the CF gene into the cells of CF patients. Although only in the early stages of development, such gene therapy holds out hope of an eventual cure for cystic fibrosis.

Figure 5.14 The life cycles of the yeast *Saccharomyces cerevisiae* and the bread mold *Neurospora crassa*. Both *S. cerevisiae* and *N. crassa* have two mating types that can fuse to form diploid cells that undergo meiosis. **(a)** Yeast cells can grow vegetatively either as haploids or diploids. The products of meiosis in a diploid cell are four haploid ascospores that are arranged randomly in unordered yeast asci. **(b)** The diploid state in *Neurospora* exists only for a short period. Meiosis in *Neurospora* is followed by mitosis, to give eight haploid ascospores in the ascus. The ordered arrangement of spores in *Neurospora* asci reflects the geometry of the meiotic and mitotic spindles. The photographs showing a budding (mitotically dividing) yeast cell and a yeast tetrad in part (a) are at much higher magnification than the photograph displaying *Neurospora* asci in part (b).

east genes we will discuss, the wild-type alleles are dominant and may be represented by the alternative shorthand "+", while the symbol for the recessive alleles remains the lowercase abbreviation (his4). Remember, however, that dominance or recessiveness is relevant only for diploid yeast cells, not for haploid cells that carry only one allele.

An ascus contains all four products of a single meiosis

After meiosis, the assemblage of four ascospores (or four pairs of ascospores) in a single ascus is called a **tetrad.** Note that this is a second meaning for the term *tetrad*. In Chapter 4, a tetrad was the four homologous chromatids—two in each chromosome of a bivalent—synapsed during the prophase and metaphase of meiosis I. Here, it is the four products of a single meiosis held together in a sac. Because the four chromatids of a bivalent give rise to the four products of meiosis, the two meanings of tetrad refer to almost the same things. In yeast, each tetrad is **unordered;** that is, the four meiotic products, known as spores, are arranged at random within the ascus. In *Neurospora crassa*, each tetrad is **ordered,** with the four pairs, or eight haplospores, arranged in a line.

To analyze both unordered and ordered tetrads, researchers can release the spores of each ascus, induce the haploid cells to germinate under appropriate conditions, and then analyze the genetic makeup of the resulting haploid cultures. The data they collect in this way enable them to identify the four products of a single meiosis and compare them with the four products of many other distinct meioses. Ordered tetrads offer another possibility. With the aid of a dissecting microscope, investigators can recover the ascospores in the order in which they occur within the ascus and thereby obtain additional information that is useful for mapping. We look first at the analysis of randomly arranged spores, using the unordered tetrads of yeast as an example. We then describe the additional information that can be gleaned from the microanalysis of ordered tetrads, using *Neurospora* as our model organism.

Tetrads can be characterized as parental ditypes (PDs), nonparental ditypes (NPDs), or tetratypes (Ts)

What kinds of tetrads arise when diploid yeast cells heterozygous for two genes on different chromosomes are induced to undergo meiosis? Consider a mating between a haploid strain of yeast of mating type *a*, carrying the *his4* mutation and the wild-type allele of the *TRP1* gene, and a strain of the opposite mating type that has the genotype *HIS4 trp1*. The resulting *a/α*

diploid cells are *his4/HIS4; trp1/TRP1,* as shown in **Fig. 5.15a.** (In genetic nomenclature, a semicolon [;] is usually employed to separate genes on nonhomologous chromosomes.) When conditions promote meiosis, the two unlinked genes will assort independently to produce equal frequencies of two different kinds of tetrads. In one kind, all the spores are parental in that the genotype of each spore is the same as one of the parents: *his4 TRP1* or *HIS4 trp1* (**Fig. 5.15b**). A tetrad that contains four parental class haploid cells is known as a **parental ditype (PD).** Note that *di-,* meaning two, indicates there are two possible parental combinations of alleles; the PD tetrad contains two of each combination. The second kind of tetrad, arising from the equally likely alternative distribution of chromosomes during meiosis, contains four recombinant spores: two *his4 trp1* and two *HIS4 TRP1* (**Fig. 5.15c**). This kind of tetrad is termed a **nonparental ditype (NPD),** because the two parental classes have recombined to form two reciprocal nonparental combinations of alleles.

A third kind of tetrad also appears when *his4/HIS4; trp1/TRP1* cells undergo meiosis. Called a **tetratype (T)** from the Greek word for "four," it carries four kinds of haploid cells: two different parental class spores (one *his4 TRP1* and one *HIS4 trp1*) and two different recombinants (one *his4 trp1* and one *HIS4 TRP1*). Tetratypes result from a crossover between one of the two genes and the centromere of the chromosome on which it is located (**Fig. 5.15d**).

Figure 5.15e displays the data from one experiment. Bear in mind that the column headings of PD, NPD, and T refer to tetrads (the group of four cells produced in meiosis) and not to individual haploid cells. Because the spores released from a yeast ascus are not arranged in any particular order, the order in which the spores are listed does not matter. The classification of a tetrad as PD, NPD, or T is based solely on the number of parental and recombinant spores found in the ascus.

When PDs equal NPDs, the two genes are unlinked

A cross following two unlinked genes must give equal numbers of individual parental and recombinant spores. This is simply another way of stating Mendel's second law of independent assortment, which predicts a 50% recombination frequency in such cases. Because T tetrads, regardless of their number, contain two recombinant and two nonrecombinant spores and because all four spores in PD tetrads are parental, the only way 50% of the total progeny spores could be recombinant (as demanded by independent assortment) is if the number of NPDs (with four recombinant spores apiece) is the same as the number of PDs. For this reason, if PD = NPD (as in Fig. 5.15e), the two genes must be unlinked, either because they reside

Figure 5.15 How meiosis can generate three kinds of tetrads when two genes are on different chromosomes. (a) Parental cross. (b) and (c) In the absence of recombination, the two equally likely alternative arrangements of two pairs of chromosomes yield either PD or NPD tetrads. T tetrads are made only if either gene recombines with respect to its corresponding centromere, as in (d). Numerical data in (e) show that the number of PD tetrads ≈ the number of NPD tetrads when the two genes are unlinked.

Figure 5.16 When genes are linked, PDs exceed NPDs.

P	arg3 ura2 (a-mating type)	×	ARG3 URA2 (α-mating type)

Diploid cell   arg3 ura2 / ARG3 URA2

Meiosis

Products of meiosis	**PD**	**NPD**	**T**
	arg3 ura2 arg3 ura2 ARG3 URA2 ARG3 URA2	arg3 URA2 arg3 URA2 ARG3 ura2 ARG3 ura2	arg3 ura2 arg3 URA2 ARG3 ura2 ARG3 URA2
Number of tetrads	127	3	70

on different chromosomes or because they lie very far apart on the same chromosome.

When PDs greatly outnumber NPDs, the two genes are linked

The genetic definition of linkage is the emergence of more parental types than recombinants among the progeny of a doubly heterozygous parent. In the preceding section, we saw that tetratypes always contribute an equal number of parental and recombinant spores. Thus, with tetrads, linkage exists only when PD >> NPD; that is, when the number of PD tetrads (carrying only parental-type spores) substantially exceeds the number of NPD tetrads (containing only recombinants). By analyzing an actual cross involving linked genes, we can see how this follows from the events occurring during meiosis.

A haploid yeast strain containing the *arg3* and *ura2* mutations was mated to a wild-type *ARG3 URA2* haploid strain (**Fig. 5.16**). When the resultant *a*/α diploid was induced to sporulate (that is, undergo meiosis), the 200 tetrads produced had the distribution shown in Fig. 5.16. As you can see, the 127 PD tetrads far outnumber the 3 NPD tetrads, suggesting that the two genes are linked.

Figure 5.17 shows how we can explain the particular kinds of tetrads observed in terms of the various types of crossovers that could occur between the linked genes. If no crossing-over occurs between the two genes, the resulting tetrad must be PD; Because none of the four chromatids participates in an exchange, all of the products are of parental configuration (Fig. 5.17a). A single crossover between *ARG3* and *URA2* will generate a tetratype, containing four genetically different spores (Fig. 5.17b). But what about double crossovers? There are actually four different possibilities, depending on which chromatids participate, and each of the four should occur with equal frequency. A double crossover involving only two chromatids (that is, one where both crossovers affect the same two chromatids) produces only parental-type progeny,

Figure 5.17 How crossovers between linked genes generate different tetrads. **(a)** PDs arise when there is no crossing-over. **(b)** Single crossovers between the two genes yield tetratypes. **(c)** to **(f)** Double crossovers between linked genes can generate PD, T, or NPD tetrads, depending on which chromatids participate in the crossovers.

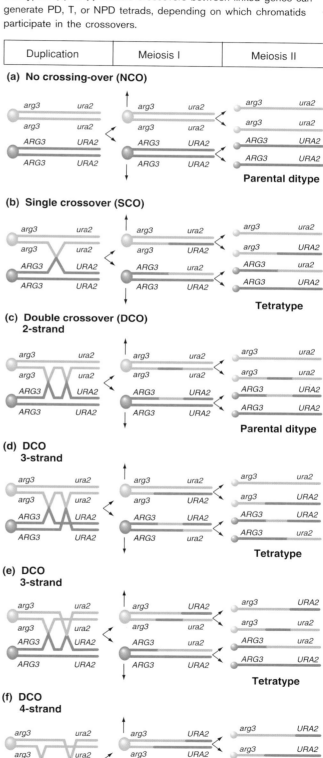

Duplication	Meiosis I	Meiosis II

(a) No crossing-over (NCO)

Parental ditype

(b) Single crossover (SCO)

Tetratype

(c) Double crossover (DCO) 2-strand

Parental ditype

(d) DCO 3-strand

Tetratype

(e) DCO 3-strand

Tetratype

(f) DCO 4-strand

Nonparental ditype

generating a PD tetrad (Fig. 5.17c). Three-strand double crossovers can occur in the two ways depicted in Fig. 5.17d and e; either way, a tetratype results. Finally, if all four strands take part in the two crossovers (one crossover involves two strands and the other crossover, the other two strands), all four progeny spores will be recombinant, and the resulting tetrad is NPD (Fig. 5.17f). Therefore, if two genes are linked, the only way to generate an NPD tetrad is through a four-strand double exchange. Meioses with crossovers generating such a specific kind of double recombination must be a lot rarer than no crossing-over or single crossovers, which produce PD and T tetrads, respectively. This explains why, if two genes are linked, PD must greatly exceed NPD.

> In certain fungi, all four products of a single meiosis are contained together in one ascus (tetrad). The asci produced by a diploid yeast cell heterozygous for two genes can be characterized by the fraction of the four ascospores that are recombinants. Tetrads are either PD (0/4 recombinants), NPD (4/4), or T (2/4). The two genes are unlinked if PD = NPD; the two genes are linked if PD >> NPD.

How to calculate recombinant frequencies in tetrad analysis

Because we know that all of the spores in an NPD tetrad are recombinant and half of the four spores in a tetratype are recombinant, we can say that

$$RF = \frac{NPD + 1/2T}{Total\ tetrads} \times 100$$

For the *ARG3 URA2* example in Fig. 5.16,

$$RF = \frac{3 + (1/2)(70)}{200} \times 100 = 19\ m.u.$$

It is reassuring that this formula gives exactly the same result as calculating the RF as the percentage of individual recombinant spores. For example, the 200 tetrads analyzed in this experiment contain 800 (that is, 200 × 4) individual spores; each NPD ascus holds 4 recombinant ascospores, and each T tetrad contains 2 recombinants. Thus,

$$RF = \frac{(4 \times 3) + (2 \times 70)}{800} \times 100 = 19\ m.u.$$

The formula used here for calculating the RF is very accurate for genes separated by small distances, but it is less reliable for more distant genes because it does not account for all types of double crossovers. Problem 39 at the end of this chapter will allow you to derive an alternative equation that yeast geneticists often use to measure large distances more accurately.

Tetrad analysis deepens our understanding of meiosis

The fact than an ascus contains all four products of a single meiosis allows geneticists to infer basic information about the timing and mechanism of meiosis from the observed results of tetrad analysis.

Evidence that recombination takes place at the four-strand stage

Both T and NPD tetrads contain recombinant spores, and when tetrad analysis reveals linked genes, the T tetrads always outnumber the NPDs, as in the example we have been discussing. This makes sense, because all single and some double crossovers yield tetratypes, while only 1/4 of the rare double crossovers produce NPDs.

The very low number of NPDs establishes that recombination occurs after the chromosomes have replicated, when there are four chromatids for each pair of homologs. If recombination took place before chromosome duplication, every single crossover event would yield four recombinant chromatids and generate an NPD tetrad (**Fig. 5.18**). A model assuming that recombination occurs when there are two rather than four chromatids per pair of homologous chromosomes would thus not allow the generation of T tetrads. Even if Ts could rarely be produced by some mechanism other than meiotic recombination (for example, errors like nondisjunction), the two-strand model would predict more NPD than T tetrads. However, experimental observations show just the opposite; Ts are always more numerous than NPDs (see Figs. 5.15e and 5.16).

The fact that recombination takes place after the chromosomes have replicated explains the 50% limit on recombination for genes on the same chromosome. Single crossovers between two genes generate T tetrads containing two out of four spores that are recombinant. Thus,

Figure 5.18 A disproven model: Recombination before chromosome replication. If recombination occurred before the chromosomes duplicated and if two genes were linked, most tetrads containing recombinant spores would be NPDs instead of Ts. Actual results show that the opposite is true.

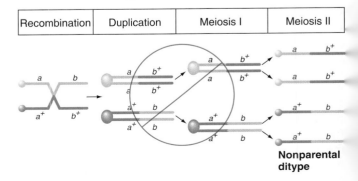

Recombination	Duplication	Meiosis I	Meiosis II

Nonparental ditype

ven if one crossover occurred between two such genes
n every meiosis, the observed recombination frequency
vould be 50%. The four kinds of double crossovers
ield either

- PD tetrads with 0/4 recombinants (Fig. 5.17c),
- T tetrads with 2/4 recombinants (Fig. 5.17d),
- Other T tetrads also with 2/4 recombinants (Fig. 5.17e), or
- NPD tetrads with 4/4 recombinants (Fig. 5.17f).

Because these four kinds of double crossovers almost
lways occur with equal frequency, no more than 50% of
he progeny resulting from double (or, in fact, triple or
nore) crossovers can be recombinant.

Evidence that recombination is usually reciprocal

Suppose you are following linked genes *A* and *B* in a
ross between *A B* and *a b* strains of yeast. If the recom-
ination that occurs during meiosis is reciprocal, every
etrad with recombinant progeny should contain equal
umbers of both classes of recombinants. Observations
ave in general confirmed this prediction: Every T tetrad
arries one *A b* and one *a B* spore, while every NPD
etrad contains two of each type of recombinant. We can
us conclude that meiotic recombination is almost always
eciprocal, generating two homologous chromosomes that
re inverted images of each other.

There are, however, exceptions. Very rarely, a par-
cular cross produces tetrads containing unequal num-
ers of reciprocal classes, and such tetrads cannot be
lassified as PD, NPD, or T. In these exceptional tetrads,
e two input alleles of one of the genes, instead of seg-
egating at a ratio of 2*A* : 2*a*, produce ratios of 1*A* : 3*a*
r 3*A* : 1*a*, or even 0*A* : 4*a* or 4*A* : 0*a* (**Fig. 5.19**). In
ese same tetrads, markers such as *B/b* and *C/c* that
ank the *A* or *a* allele on the same chromosome still
egregate 2*B* : 2*b* and 2*C* : 2*c*. Moreover, careful pheno-
pic and genetic tests show that even when alleles do
ot segregate 2:2, only the original two input alleles
ccur in the progeny. Thus, recombination, no matter
hat ratios it generates, does not create new alleles.
eneticists believe that the unusual non-2:2 segregation
tios observed in rare instances result from molecular
vents at the site of recombination. We discuss these
vents at the molecular level in Chapter 6. For now, it
simply necessary to know that the unusual ratios exist
ut are quite rare.

Tetrad analysis has confirmed two essential characteristics
of recombination: (1) Crossing-over occurs at the four-strand
stage of meiosis, after the chromosomes have duplicated, and
(2) recombination is usually reciprocal, with rare exceptions.

**Figure 5.19 In rare tetrads, the two alleles of a gene
do not segregate 2:2.** Researchers sporulated a *HIS4* / *his4*
diploid yeast strain and dissected the four haploid spores from three
different tetrads. They then plated these spores on petri plates
containing medium without histidine. Each row on the petri plate
presents the four spores of a single tetrad. The top two rows show
the normal 2:2 segregation of the two alleles of a single gene: two of
the spores are *HIS4* and form colonies, whereas the other two spores
are *his4* and cannot grow into colonies. The bottom row displays a
rare tetrad with an unusual segregation of 3 *HIS4* : 1 *his4*.

2:2

2:2

3:1

Ordered tetrads help locate genes in relation to the centromere

Analyses of ordered tetrads, such as those produced by
the bread mold *Neurospora crassa,* allow you to map the
centromere of a chromosome relative to other genetic
markers, information that you cannot normally obtain
from unordered yeast tetrads. As described earlier, immediately after specialized haploid *Neurospora* cells of different mating types fuse at fertilization, the diploid zygote
undergoes meiosis within the confines of a narrow ascus
(review Fig. 5.14b on p. 138). At the completion of meiosis, each of the four haploid meiotic products divides once
by mitosis, yielding an **octad** of eight haploid ascospores.
Dissection of the ascus at this point allows one to determine the phenotype of each of the eight haploid cells.

The cross-sectional diameter of the ascus is so small
that cells cannot slip past each other. Moreover, during
each division after fertilization, the microtubule fibers of
the spindle extend outward from the centrosomes parallel to the long axis of the ascus. These facts have two
important repercussions. First, when each of the four
products of meiosis divides once by mitosis, the two
genetically identical cells that result lie adjacent to each
other (**Fig. 5.20**). Because of this feature, starting from
either end of the ascus, you can count the octad of
ascospores as four cell pairs and analyze it as a tetrad.
Second, from the precise positioning of the four ascospore
pairs within the ascus, you can infer the arrangement
of the four chromatids of each homologous chromosome
pair during the two meiotic divisions.

Figure 5.20 How ordered tetrads form. Spindles form parallel to the long axis of the growing *Neurospora* ascus, and the cells cannot slide around each other. The order of ascospores thus reflects meiotic spindle geometry. After meiosis, each haploid cell undergoes mitosis, producing an eight-cell ascus (an octad). The octad consists of four pairs of cells; the two cells of each pair are genetically identical.

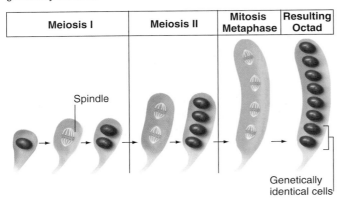

To understand the genetic consequences of the geometry of the ascospores, it is helpful to consider what kinds of tetrads you would expect from the segregation of two alleles of a single gene. (In the following discussion, you will see that *Neurospora* geneticists denote alleles with

symbols similar to those used for *Drosophila*, as detailed in the nomenclature guide on p. 731 of the Appendix. The mutant *white-spore* allele (*ws*) alters ascospore color from wild-type black to white. In the absence of recombination, the two alleles (*ws*$^+$ and *ws*) separate from each other at the first meiotic division because the centromeres to which they are attached separate at that stage. The second meiotic division and subsequent mitosis create asci in which the top four ascospores are of one genotype (for instance *ws*$^+$) and the bottom four of the other (*ws*). Whether the top four are *ws*$^+$ and the bottom four *ws*, or vice versa depends on the random metaphase I orientation of the homologs that carry the gene relative to the long axis of the developing ascus.

The segregation of two alleles of a single gene at the first meiotic division is thus indicated by an ascus in which an imaginary line drawn between the fourth and the fifth ascospores of the octad cleanly separates haploid products bearing the two alleles. Such an ascus displays a **first-division segregation pattern** (**Fig. 5.21a**).

Suppose now that during meiosis I, a crossover occurs in a heterozygote between the *white-spore* gene and the centromere of the chromosome on which it travels. As **Fig. 5.21b** illustrates, this can lead to four equally possible ascospore arrangements, each one depending on a particular orientation of the four chromatids during the two meiotic divisions. In all four cases, both *ws*$^+$ and *ws* spores

Figure 5.21 Two segregation patterns in ordered asci. (a) In the absence of a crossover between a gene and its centromere, the two alleles of a gene will separate at the first meiotic division. The result is a first-division segregation pattern in which each allele appears in spores located on only one side of an imaginary line through the middle of the ascus. **(b)** A crossover between a gene and its centromere produces a second-division segregation pattern in which both alleles appear on the same side of the middle line.

are found on both sides of the imaginary line drawn between ascospores 4 and 5, because cells with only one kind of allele do not arise until the end of the second meiotic division. Octads carrying this configuration of spores display a **second-division segregation pattern.**

Because second-division segregation patterns result from meioses in which there has been a crossover between a gene and its centromere, the relative number of asci with this pattern can be used to determine the gene ↔ centromere distance. In an ascus showing second-division segregation, one-half of the ascospores are derived from chromatids that have exchanged parts, while the remaining half arise from chromatids that have not participated in crossovers leading to recombination. To calculate the distance between a gene and its centromere, you therefore simply divide the percentage of second-division segregation octads by 2. Geneticists use information about the location of centromeres to make more accurate genetic maps as well as to study the structure and function of centromeres.

Because meiosis in *Neurospora* occurs in a narrow ascus, the octet ascospores are generated in predictable sequence. Analysis of an ordered ascus allows researchers to deduce whether in that particular meiosis, a crossover took place between a gene and the centromere of the chromosome carrying that gene. This information can be used to calculate gene-to-centromere distances.

Tetrad analysis: A numerical example

In one experiment, a thr^+arg^+ wild-type strain of *Neurospora* was crossed with a *thr arg* double mutant. The *thr* mutants cannot grow in the absence of the amino acid threonine, while *arg* mutants cannot grow without a source of the amino acid arginine; cells carrying the wild-type alleles of both genes can grow in medium that contains neither amino acid. From this cross, 105 octads, considered here as tetrads, were obtained. These tetrads were classified in seven different groups—A, B, C, D, E, F, and G—as shown in **Fig. 5.22a.** For each of the two genes, we can now find the distance between the gene and the centromere of the chromosome on which it is located.

To do this for the *thr* gene, we count the number of tetrads with a second-division segregation pattern for that gene. Drawing an imaginary line through the middle of the tetrads, we see that those in groups B, D, E, and G are the result of second-division segregations for *thr,* while the remainder show first-division patterns. The centromere ↔ *thr* distance is thus

Percentage of second-division patterns =

$$\frac{(1/2)(16 + 2 + 2 + 1)}{105} \times 100 = 10 \text{ m.u.}$$

Figure 5.22 Genetic mapping by ordered-tetrad analysis: An example. (a) In ordered-tetrad analysis, tetrad classes are defined not only as PD, NPD, or T but also according to whether they show a first- or second-division segregation pattern. Each entry in this table represents a pair of adjacent, identical spores in the actual *Neurospora* octad. Red dots indicate the middle of the asci. **(b)** Genetic map derived from the data in part (a). Ordered-tetrad analysis allows determination of the centromere's position as well as distances between genes.

(a) A *Neurospora* cross

Tetrad group	A	B	C	D	E	F	G
Segregation pattern	thr arg	thr arg	thr arg	thr arg$^+$	thr arg$^+$	thr arg$^+$	thr arg
	thr arg	thr$^+$arg	thr arg$^+$	thr$^+$arg	thr$^+$arg	thr arg$^+$	thr$^+$arg$^+$
	thr$^+$arg$^+$	thr$^+$arg$^+$	thr$^+$arg	thr$^+$arg$^+$	thr$^+$arg	thr$^+$arg	thr$^+$arg$^+$
	thr$^+$arg$^+$	thr arg$^+$	thr$^+$arg$^+$	thr arg	thr arg$^+$	thr$^+$arg	thr arg
Total in group	72	16	11	2	2	1	1

(b) Corresponding genetic map

arg ← 16.7 m.u. → thr
7.6 m.u.   10 m.u.

Similarly, the second-division tetrads for the *arg* gene are in groups C, D, E, and G, so the distance between *arg* and its centromere is

$$\frac{(1/2)(11 + 2 + 2 + 1)}{105} \times 100 = 7.6 \text{ m.u.}$$

To ascertain whether the *thr* and *arg* genes are linked, we need to evaluate the seven tetrad groups in a different way, looking at the combinations of alleles for the two genes to see if the tetrads in that group are PD, NPD, or T. We can then ask whether PD >> NPD. Referring again to Fig. 5.22a, we find that groups A and G are PD, because all the ascospores show parental combinations, while groups E and F, with four recombinant spores, are NPD. PD is thus $72 + 1 = 73$, while NPD is $1 + 2 = 3$. From these data, we can conclude that the two genes are linked.

What is the map distance between *thr* and *arg?* For this calculation, we need to find the numbers of T and NPD tetrads. Tetratypes are found in groups B, C, and D, and we already know that groups E and F carry NPDs. Using the same formula for map distances as the one previously used for yeast,

$$RF = \frac{NPD + 1/2T}{\text{Total tetrads}} \times 100$$

we get

$$RF = \frac{3 + (1/2)(16 + 11 + 2)}{105} \times 100 = 16.7 \text{ m.u.}$$

TABLE 5.3	Rules for Tetrad Analysis

For Ordered and Unordered Tetrads

Considering genes two at a time, assign tetrads as PD, NPD, or T.

If PD >> NPD, the two genes are genetically linked.

If PD = NPD, the two genes are genetically independent (unlinked).

The map distance between two genes if they are genetically linked

$$= \frac{NDP + (1/2)T}{Total\ tetrads} \times 100$$

For Ordered Tetrads Only

The map distance between a gene and its centromere

$$= \frac{(1/2) \times (\#\ of\ tetrads\ showing\ second\text{-}division\ segregation\ for\ this\ gene)}{Total\ tetrads} \times 100$$

Because the distance between *thr* and *arg* is larger than that separating either gene from the centromere, the centromere must lie between *thr* and *arg*, yielding the map in **Fig. 5.22b.** The distance between the two genes calculated by the formula above (16.7 m.u.) is smaller than the sum of the two gene ↔ centromere distances (10.0 + 7.6 = 17.6 m.u.) because the formula does not account for all of the double crossovers. As always, calculating map positions for more genes with shorter distances between them produces the most accurate picture.

Table 5.3 summarizes the procedures for mapping genes in fungi producing ordered and unordered tetrads.

5.6 Mitotic Recombination and Genetic Mosaics

The recombination of genetic material is a critical feature of meiosis. It is thus not surprising that eukaryotic organisms express a variety of enzymes (described in Chapter 6) that specifically initiate meiotic recombination. Recombination can also occur during mitosis. Unlike what happens in meiosis, however, mitotic crossovers are initiated by mistakes in chromosome replication or by chance exposures to radiation that break DNA molecules, rather than by a well-defined cellular program. As a result, mitotic recombination is a rare event, occurring no more frequently than once in a million somatic cell divisions. Nonetheless, the growth of a colony of yeast cells or the development of a complex multicellular organism involves so many cell divisions that geneticists can routinely detect these rare mitotic events.

"Twin spots" indicate mosaicism caused by mitotic recombination

In 1936, the *Drosophila* geneticist Curt Stern originally inferred the existence of mitotic recombination from observations of "twin spots" in a few fruit flies. **Twin spots** are adjacent islands of tissue that differ both from each other and from the tissue surrounding them. The distinctive patches arise from homozygous cells with a recessive phenotype growing amid a generally heterozygous cell population displaying the dominant phenotype. In *Drosophila,* the *yellow* (*y*) mutation changes body color from normal brown to yellow, while the *singed bristles* (*sn*) mutation causes body bristles to be short and curled rather than long and straight. Both of these genes are on the X chromosome.

In his experiments, Stern examined *Drosophila* females of genotype $y\ sn^+ / y^+\ sn$. These double heterozygotes were generally wild type in appearance, but Stern noticed that some flies carried patches of yellow body color, others had small areas of singed bristles, and still others displayed twin spots: adjacent patches of yellow cells and cells with singed bristles (**Fig. 5.23**). He assumed that mistakes in the mitotic divisions accompanying fly development could have led to these **mosaic** animals containing tissues of different genotypes. Individual yellow or singed patches could arise from chromosome loss or by mitotic nondisjunction. These errors in mitosis would yield XO cells containing only *y* (but not y^+) or *sn* (but not sn^+) alleles; such cells would show one of the recessive phenotypes.

The twin spots must have a different origin. Stern reasoned that they represented the reciprocal products of mitotic crossing-over between the *sn* gene and the centromere. The mechanism is as follows. During mitosis in a diploid cell, after chromosome duplication, homologous chromosomes occasionally—very occasionally—pair up with each other. While the chromosomes are paired,

Figure 5.23 Twin spots: A form of genetic mosaicism. In a *y sn+ / y+sn Drosophila* female, most of the body is wild type, but aberrant patches showing either yellow color or singed bristles sometimes occur. In some cases, yellow and singed patches are adjacent to each other, a configuration known as *twin spots.*

Single yellow spot	Twin spot	Single singed spot

Figure 5.24 Mitotic crossing-over. (a) In a y sn⁺ / y⁺sn *Drosophila* female, a mitotic crossover between the centromere and *sn* can produce two daughter cells, one homozygous for *y* and the other homozygous for *sn,* that can develop into adjacent aberrant patches (twin spots). This outcome depends on a particular distribution of chromatids at anaphase (*top*). If the chromatids are arranged in the equally likely opposite orientation, only phenotypically normal cells will result (*bottom*). **(b)** Crossovers between *sn* and *y* can generate single yellow patches. However, a single mitotic crossover in these females cannot produce a single singed spot if the *sn* gene is closer to the centromere than the *y* gene.

nonsister chromatids (that is, one chromatid from each of the two homologous chromosomes) can exchange parts by crossing-over. The pairing is transient, and the homologous chromosomes soon resume their independent positions on the mitotic metaphase plate. There, the two chromosomes can line up relative to each other in either of two ways (**Fig. 5.24a**). One of these orientations would yield two daughter cells that remain heterozygous for both genes and thus be indistinguishable from the surrounding wild-type cells. The other orientation, however, will generate two homozygous daughter cells, one y sn⁺/y sn⁺, the other y⁺sn/y⁺sn. Because the two daughter cells would lie next to each other, subsequent mitotic divisions would produce adjacent patches of *y* and *sn* tissue (that

is, twin spots). Note that if crossing-over occurs between *sn* and *y,* single spots of yellow tissue can form, but a reciprocal singed spot cannot be generated in this fashion (**Fig. 5.24b**).

Sectored yeast colonies can arise from mitotic recombination

Diploid yeast cells that are heterozygous for one or more genes exhibit mitotic recombination in the form of **sectors:** portions of a growing colony that have a different genotype than the remainder of the colony. If a diploid yeast cell of genotype *ADE2 / ade2* is placed on a petri

GENETICS AND SOCIETY

Mitotic Recombination and Cancer Formation

In humans, some tumors, such as those found in retinoblastoma, may arise as a result of mitotic recombination. Recall from the discussion of penetrance and expressivity in Chapter 3 that retinoblastoma is the most malignant form of eye cancer. The retinoblastoma gene (RB) resides on chromosome 13, where the normal wild-type allele (RB^+) encodes a protein that regulates retinal growth and differentiation. Cells in the eye need at least one copy of the normal wild-type allele to maintain control over cell division. The normal, wild-type RB^+ allele is thus known as a tumor-suppressor gene.

People with a genetic predisposition to retinoblastoma are born with only one functional copy of the normal RB^+ allele; their second chromosome 13 carries either a nonfunctional RB^- allele or no RB gene at all. If a mutagen (such as radiation) or a mistake in gene replication or segregation destroys or removes the single remaining normal copy of the gene in a retinal cell in either eye, a retinoblastoma tumor will develop at that site. In one study of people with a genetic predisposition to retinoblastoma, cells taken from eye tumors were RB^- homozygotes, while white blood cells from the same people were RB^+/RB^- heterozygotes. As **Fig. A** shows, mitotic recombination between the RB gene and the centromere of the chromosome carrying the gene provides one mechanism by which a cell in an RB^+/RB^- individual could become RB^-/RB^-. Once a homozygous RB^- cell is generated, it will divide uncontrollably, leading to tumor formation.

Only 40% of retinoblastoma cases follow the preceding scenario. The other 60% occur in people who are born with two normal copies of the RB gene. In such people, it takes two mutational events to cause the cancer. The first of these must convert an RB^+ allele to RB^-, while the second could be a mitotic recombination producing daughter cells that become cancerous because they are homozygous for the newly mutant, nonfunctional allele.

Interestingly, the role of mitotic recombination in the formation of retinoblastoma helps explain the incomplete penetrance and variable expressivity of the disease. People born as RB^+/RB^- heterozygotes may or may not develop the condition (incomplete penetrance). If, as usually happens, they do, they may have it in one or both eyes (variable expressivity). It all depends on whether and in what cells of the body mitotic recombination (or some other "homozygosing" event that affects chromosome 13) occurs.

Figure A How mitotic crossing-over can contribute to cancer. Mitotic recombination during retinal growth in an RB^-/RB^+ heterozygote may produce an RB^-/RB^- daughter cell that lacks a functional retinoblastoma gene and thus divides out of control. The crossover must occur between the RB gene and its centromere. Only the arrangement of chromatids yielding this result is shown.

Transient Pairing of Homologous Chromosomes 13 During Mitosis	Mitotic Metaphase	Daughter Cells

plate, its mitotic descendents will grow into a colony. Usually, such colonies will appear white because the dominant wild-type *ADE2* allele specifies that color. However, many colonies will contain red sectors of diploid *ade2 / ade2* cells, which arose as a result of mitotic recombination events between the *ADE2* gene and its centromere (**Fig. 5.25**). (Homozygous *ADE2 / ADE2* cells will also be produced by the same event, but they cannot be distinguished from heterozygotes because both types of cells are white.) The size of the red sectors indicates when mitotic recombination took place. If they are large, it happened early in the growth of the colony, giving the resulting daughter cells a long time to proliferate; if they are small, the recombination happened later.

Figure 5.25 Mitotic recombination during the growth of diploid yeast colonies can create sectors. Arrows point to large, red *ade2 / ade2* sectors formed from *ADE2 / ade2* heterozygotes.

Mitotic recombination is significant both as an experimental tool and because of the phenotypic consequences of particular mitotic crossovers. Problem 44 at the end of this chapter illustrates how geneticists use mitotic recombination to obtain information for mapping genes relative to each other and to the centromere. Mitotic crossing-over has also been of great value in the study of development because it can generate animals in which different cells have different genotypes (see Chapter 18). Finally, as the Genetics and Society box "Mitotic Recombination and Cancer Formation" explains, mitotic recombination can have major repercussions for human health.

Crossing-over can occur in rare instances during mitosis, so that a diploid heterozygous cell can produce diploid homozygous daughter cells. The consequences of mitotic recombination include genetic mosaicism in multicellular organisms and sectoring during the growth of yeast colonies.

Connections

Medical geneticists have used their understanding of linkage, recombination, and mapping to make sense of the pedigrees presented at the beginning of this chapter (see Fig. 5.1 on p. 119). The X-linked gene for red-green colorblindness must lie very close to the gene for hemophilia A because the two are tightly coupled. In fact, the genetic distance between the two genes is only 3 m.u. The sample size in Fig. 5.1a was so small that none of the individuals in the pedigree were recombinant types. In contrast, even though hemophilia B is also on the X chromosome, it lies far enough away from the red-green colorblindness locus that the two genes recombine relatively freely. The colorblindness and hemophilia B genes may appear to be genetically unlinked in a small sample (as in Fig. 5.1b), but the actual recombination distance separating the two genes is about 36 m.u. Pedigrees pointing to two different forms of hemophilia, one very closely linked to colorblindness, the other almost not linked at all, provided one of several indications that hemophilia is determined by more than one gene (Fig. 5.26).

Refining the human chromosome map poses a continuous challenge for medical geneticists. The newfound potential for finding and fitting more and more DNA markers into the map (review the Fast Forward box in this chapter) enormously improves the ability to identify genes that cause disease, as discussed in Chapter 11.

Linkage and recombination are universal among lifeforms and must therefore confer important advantages to living organisms. Geneticists believe that linkage provides the potential for transmitting favorable combinations of genes intact to successive generations, while recombination produces great flexibility in generating new combinations of alleles. Some new combinations may help a species adapt to changing environmental conditions, whereas the inheritance of successfully tested combinations can preserve what has worked in the past.

Thus far, this book has examined how genes and chromosomes are transmitted. As important and useful as this knowledge is, it tells us very little about the structure and mode of action of the genetic material. In the next section (Chapters 6–8), we carry our analysis to the level of DNA, the actual molecule of heredity. In Chapter 6, we look at DNA structure and learn how the DNA molecule carries genetic information. In Chapter 7, we describe how geneticists defined the gene as a localized region of DNA containing many nucleotides that together encode the information to make a protein. In Chapter 8, we examine how the cellular machinery interprets the genetic information in genes to produce the multitude of phenotypes that make up an organism.

Figure 5.26 A genetic map of part of the human X chromosome.

Hunter syndrome
Hemophilia B

Fragile X syndrome

Hemophilia A

G6PD deficiency: Favism
Drug-sensitive anemia
Chronic hemolytic anemia

Colorblindness (several forms)
Dyskeratosis congenita
Deafness with stapes fixation
TKCR syndrome

Adrenoleukodystrophy
Adrenomyeloneuropathy

Emery muscular dystrophy
SED tarda
Spastic paraplegia, X-linked

ESSENTIAL CONCEPTS

1. Gene pairs that are close together on the same chromosome are genetically linked because they are transmitted together more often than not. The hallmark of linkage is that the number of parental types is greater than the number of recombinant types among the progeny of double heterozygotes.

2. The recombination frequencies of pairs of genes indicate how often two genes are transmitted together. For linked genes, the recombination frequency is less than 50%.

3. Gene pairs that assort independently exhibit a recombination frequency of 50%, because the number of parental types equals the number of recombinants. Genes may assort independently either because they are on different chromosomes or because they are far apart on the same chromosome.

4. Statistical analysis helps determine whether or not two genes assort independently. The probability value (p) calculated by the chi-square test measures the likelihood that a particular set of data supports the null hypothesis of independent assortment, or no linkage. The lower the p value, the less likely is the null hypothesis, and the more likely the linkage. The chi-square test can also be used to determine how well the outcomes of crosses fit other genetic hypotheses (see www. mhhe.com/hartwell4: Chapter 3 for examples).

5. The greater the physical distance between linked genes, the higher the recombination frequency. However, recombination frequencies become more and more inaccurate as the distance between genes increases.

6. Recombination occurs because chromatids of homologous chromosomes exchange parts (that is, cross over) during the prophase of meiosis I, after the chromosomes have replicated.

7. Genetic maps are a visual representation of relative recombination frequencies. The greater the density of genes on the map (and thus the smaller the distance between the genes), the more accurate and useful the map becomes in predicting inheritance.

8. Organisms that retain all the products of one meiosis within an ascus reveal the relation between genetic recombination and the segregation of chromosomes during the two meiotic divisions. Organisms like *Neurospora* that produce ordered octads make it possible to locate a chromosome's centromere on the genetic map.

9. In diploid organisms heterozygous for two alleles of a gene, rare mitotic recombination between the gene and its centromere can produce genetic mosaics in which some cells are homozygous for one allele or the other.

On Our Website | www.mhhe.com/hartwell4

Annotated Suggested Readings and Links to Other Websites

- The early history of genetic mapping
- Construction of a linkage map of the human genome
- New ideas about the significance of chromosomal interference
- Using mitotic recombination to trace cells during development

Specialized Topics

- The derivation and use of mapping functions
- Determining the linkage of human genes using likelihood ratios and LOD scores.

Solved Problems

I. The *Xg* locus on the human X chromosome has two alleles, a^+ and a. The a^+ allele causes the presence of the Xg surface antigen on red blood cells, while the recessive a allele does not allow antigen to appear. The

Xg locus is 10 m.u. from the *Sts* locus. The *Sts* allele produces normal activity of the enzyme steroid sulfatase, while the recessive *sts* allele results in the lack of steroid sulfatase activity and the disease ichthyosis (scaly skin)

A man with ichthyosis and no Xg antigen has a normal daughter with Xg antigen, who is expecting a child.

a. If the child is a son, what is the probability he will lack antigen and have ichthyosis?

b. What is the probability that a son would have both the antigen and ichthyosis?

c. If the child is a son with ichthyosis, what is the probability he will have Xg antigen?

Answer

a. This problem requires an understanding of how linkage affects the proportions of gametes. First designate the genotype of the individual in which recombination during meiosis affects the transmission of alleles: in this problem, the daughter. The X chromosome she inherited from her father (who had icthyosis and no Xg antigen) must be *sts a.* (No recombination could have separated the genes during meiosis in her father since he has only one X chromosome.) Because the daughter is normal and has the Xg antigen, her other X chromosome (inherited from her mother) must contain the *Sts* and *a*+ alleles. Her X chromosomes can be diagrammed as:

Because the *Sts* and *Xg* loci are 10 m.u. apart on the chromosome, there is a 10% recombination frequency. Ninety percent of the gametes will be parental: *sts a* or *Sts a*+ (45% of each type) and 10% will be recombinant: *sts a*+ or *Sts a* (5% of each type). The phenotype of a son directly reflects the genotype of the X chromosome from his mother. *Therefore, the probability that he will lack the Xg antigen and have icthyosis (genotype: sts a/Y) is 45/100.*

b. *The probability that he will have the antigen and ichthyosis (genotype: sts a*+*/Y) is 5/100.*

c. There are two classes of gametes containing the ichthyosis allele: *sts a* (45%) and *sts a*+ (5%). If the total number of gametes is 100, then 50 will have the *sts* allele. Of those gametes, 5 (or 10%) will have the *a*+ allele. *Therefore there is a 1/10 probability that a son with the sts allele will have the Xg antigen.*

II. *Drosophila* females of wild-type appearance but heterozygous for three autosomal genes are mated with males showing three autosomal recessive traits: glassy eyes, coal-colored bodies, and striped thoraxes. One thousand (1000) progeny of this cross are distributed in the following phenotypic classes:

Wild type	27
Striped thorax	11
Coal body	484
Glassy eyes, coal body	8
Glassy eyes, striped thorax	441
Glassy eyes, coal body, striped thorax	29

a. Draw a genetic map based on this data.

b. Show the arrangement of alleles on the two homologous chromosomes in the parent females.

c. Normal-appearing males containing the same chromosomes as the parent females in the preceding cross are mated with females showing glassy eyes, coal-colored bodies, and striped thoraxes. Of 1000 progeny produced, indicate the numbers of the various phenotypic classes you would expect.

Answer

A logical, methodical way to approach a three-point cross is described here.

a. Designate the alleles:

t^+ = wild-type thorax t = striped thorax
g^+ = wild-type eyes g = glassy eyes
c^+ = wild-type body c = coal-colored body

In solving a three-point cross, designate the types of events that gave rise to each group of individuals and the genotypes of the gametes obtained from their mother. (The paternal gametes contain only the recessive alleles of these genes [*t g c*]. They do not change the phenotype and can be ignored.)

Progeny	Number	Type of event	Genotype
1. wild type	27	single crossover	t^+ g^+ c^+
2. striped thorax	11	single crossover	t g^+ c^+
3. coal body	484	parental	t^+ g^+ c
4. glassy eyes, coal body	8	single crossover	t^+ g c
5. glassy eyes, striped thorax	441	parental	t g c^+
6. glassy eyes, coal body, striped thorax	29	single crossover	t g c

Picking out the parental classes is easy. If all the other classes are rare, the two most abundant categories are those gene combinations that have not undergone recombination. Then there should be two sets of two phenotypes that correspond to a single crossover event between the first and second genes, or between the second and third genes. Finally, there should be a pair of classes containing small numbers that result from double crossovers. In this example, there are no flies in the double crossover classes, which would have been in the two missing phenotypic combinations: glassy eyes, coal body, and striped thorax.

Look at the most abundant classes to determine which alleles were on each chromosome in the female heterozygous parent. One parental class had the phenotype of coal body (484 flies), so one chromosome in the female must have contained the t^+, g^+, and c alleles. (Notice that we cannot yet say in what order these alleles are located on the chromosome.) The other parental class was glassy eyes and striped thorax, corresponding to a chromosome with the t, g, and c^+ alleles.

To determine the order of the genes, compare the t^+ g c^+ double crossover class (not seen in the data) with the most similar parental class (t g c^+). The alleles of g and c retain their parental associations (g c^+), while the t gene has recombined with respect to both other genes in the double recombinant class. Thus, the t gene is between g and c.

In order to complete the map, calculate the recombination frequencies between the center gene and each of the genes on the ends. For g and t, the nonparental combinations of alleles are in classes 2 and 4, so RF = (11 + 8)/1000 = 19/1000, or 1.9%. For t and c, classes 1 and 6 are nonparental, so RF = (27 + 29)/1000 = 56/1000, or 5.6%.

The genetic map is

```
c⁺                                        t⁺        g⁺
|————————————————————————————————————|————————|
          5.6 m.u.                      1.9 m.u.
```

b. The alleles on each chromosome were already determined (c, g^+, t^+ and c^+, g, t). Now that the order of loci has also been determined, the arrangement of the alleles can be indicated.

```
   c          t⁺        g⁺
————————————————————————————

   c⁺          t         g
```

c. Males of the same genotype as the starting female (c t^+ g^+/c^+ t g) could produce only two types of gametes: parental types c t^+ g^+ and c^+ t g because there is no recombination in male *Drosophila*. The progeny expected from the mating with a homozygous recessive female are thus 500 coal body and 500 glassy eyed, striped thorax flies.

III. The following asci were obtained in *Neurospora* when a wild-type strain (ad^+ leu^+) was crossed to a double mutant strain that cannot grow in the absence of adenine or leucine (ad^- leu^-). Only one member of each spore pair produced by the final mitosis is shown, because the two cells in a pair have the same genotype. Total asci = 120.

Spore pair	Ascus type				
1–2	ad^+ leu^+	ad^+ leu^-	ad^+ leu^+	ad^+ leu^-	ad^- leu^+
3–4	ad^+ leu^+	ad^+ leu^-	ad^+ leu^-	ad^- leu^+	ad^+ leu^+
5–6	ad^- leu^-	ad^- leu^+	ad^- leu^+	ad^- leu^-	ad^- leu^-
7–8	ad^- leu^-	ad^- leu^+	ad^- leu^-	ad^+ leu^+	ad^+ leu^-
# of asci	30	30	40	2	18

a. What genetic event causes the alleles of two genes to segregate to different cells at the second meiotic division, and when does this event occur?

b. Provide the best possible map for the two genes and their centromere(s).

Answer

This problem requires an understanding of tetrad analysis and the process (meiosis) that produces the patterns seen in ordered asci.

a. *A crossover between a gene and its centromere causes the segregation of alleles at the second meiotic division. The crossover event occurs during prophase of meiosis I.*

b. Using ordered tetrads you can determine whether two genes are linked, the distance between two genes, and the distance between each gene and its centromere. First designate the five classes of asci shown. The first class is a parental ditype (spores contain the same combinations of alleles as their parents); the second is a nonparental ditype; the last three are tetratypes. Next determine if these genes are linked. The number of PD = number of NPD, so the genes are not linked. When genes are unlinked, the tetratype asci are generated by a crossing-over event between a gene and its centromere. Looking at the *leu* gene, there is a second-division segregation pattern of that gene in the third and fourth asci types. Therefore, the percent of second-division segregation is

$$\frac{40 + 2}{120} \times 100 = 35\%$$

Because only half of the chromatids in the meioses that generated these tetratype asci were involved in the crossover, the map distance between *leu* and its centromere is 35/2, or 17.5 m.u. Asci of the fourth and fifth types show a second-division segregation pattern for the *ad* gene

$$\frac{2 + 18}{120} \times 100 = 16.6\%$$

Dividing 16.6% by 2 gives the recombination frequency and map distance of 8.3 m.u. *The map of these two genes is the following:*

Problems

Vocabulary

1. Choose the phrase from the right column that best fits the term in the left column.

a. recombination	1. a statistical method for testing the fit between observed and expected results
b. linkage	2. an ascus containing spores of four different genotypes
c. chi-square test	3. one crossover along a chromosome makes a second nearby crossover less likely
d. chiasma	4. when two loci recombine in less than 50% of gametes
e. tetratype	5. the relative chromosomal location of a gene
f. locus	6. the ratio of observed double crossovers to expected double crossovers
g. coefficient of coincidence	7. individual composed of cells with different genotypes
h. interference	8. formation of new genetic combinations by exchange of parts between homologs
i. parental ditype	9. when the two alleles of a gene are segregated into different cells at the first meiotic division
j. ascospores	10. an ascus containing only two nonrecombinant kinds of spores
k. first-division segregation	11. structure formed at the spot where crossing-over occurs between homologs
l. mosaic	12. fungal spores contained in a sac

Section 5.1

2. a. A *Drosophila* male from a true-breeding stock with scabrous eyes was mated with a female from a true-breeding stock with javelin bristles. Both scabrous eyes and javelin bristles are autosomal traits. The F_1 progeny all had normal eyes and bristles. F_1 females from this cross were mated with males with both scabrous eyes and javelin bristles. Write all the possible phenotypic classes of the progeny that could be produced from the cross of the F_1 females with the scabrous, javelin males, and indicate for each class whether it is a recombinant or parental type.

   b. The cross above yielded the following progeny: 77 scabrous eyes and normal bristles; 76 wild type (normal eyes and bristles); 74 normal eyes and javelin bristles; and 73 scabrous eyes and javelin bristles. Are the genes governing these traits likely to be linked, or do they instead assort independently? Why?

   c. Suppose you mated the F_1 females from the cross in part (a) to wild-type males. Why would this cross fail to inform you whether the two genes are linked?

   d. Suppose you mated females from the true-breeding stock with javelin bristles to males with scabrous eyes and javelin bristles. Why would this cross fail to inform you whether the two genes are linked?

3. With modern molecular methods it is now possible to examine variants in DNA sequence from a very small amount of tissue like a hair follicle or even a single sperm. You can consider these variants to be "alleles" of a particular site on a chromosome (a "locus"; "loci" in plural). For example, AAAAAAA, AAACAAA, AAAGAAA, and AAATAAA at the same location (call it B) on homologous autosomes in different sperm might be called alleles *1, 2, 3,* and *4* of locus B (B_1, B_2, etc.). John's genotype for two loci B and D is B_1B_3 and D_1D_3. John's father was B_1B_2 and D_1D_4, while his mother was B_3B_3 and D_2D_3.

   a. What is (are) the genotype(s) of the parental type sperm John could produce?

   b. What is (are) the genotype(s) of the recombinant type sperm John could produce?

   c. In a sample of 100 sperm, 51 of John's sperm were found to be B_1 and D_1, while the remaining 49 sperm were B_3D_3. Can you conclude whether the *B* and *D* loci are linked, or whether they instead assort independently?

Section 5.2

4. Do the data that Mendel obtained fit his hypotheses? For example, Mendel obtained 315 yellow round, 101 yellow wrinkled, 108 green round, and 32 green wrinkled seeds from the selfing of *Yy Rr* individuals (a total of 556). His hypotheses of segregation and independent assortment predict a 9:3:3:1 ratio in this case. Use the chi-square test to determine whether Mendel's data are significantly different from what he predicted. (The chi-square test did not exist in Mendel's day, so he was not able to test his own data for goodness of fit to his hypotheses.)

5. Two genes control color in corn snakes as follows:

   O– B– snakes are brown, *O– bb* are orange, *oo B–* are black, and *oo bb* are albino. An orange snake was mated to a black snake, and a large number of F_1 progeny were obtained, all of which were brown. When the F_1 snakes were mated to one another, they produced 100 brown offspring, 25 orange, 22 black, and 13 albino.

a. What are the genotypes of the F_1 snakes?

b. What proportions of the different colors would have been expected among the F_2 snakes if the two loci assort independently?

c. Do the observed results differ significantly from what was expected, assuming independent assortment is occurring?

d. What is the probability that differences this great between observed and expected values would happen by chance?

6. A mouse from a true-breeding population with normal gait was crossed to a mouse displaying an odd gait called "dancing." The F_1 animals all showed normal gait.

a. If dancing is caused by homozygosity for the recessive allele of a single gene, what proportion of the F_2 mice should be dancers?

b. If mice must be homozygous for recessive alleles of both of two different genes to have the dancing phenotype, what proportion of the F_2 should be dancers if the two genes are unlinked?

c. When the F_2 mice were obtained, 42 normal and 8 dancers were seen. Use the chi-square test to determine if these results better fit the one-gene model from part *a* or the two-gene model from part *b*.

7. Figure 5.5 on p. 123 applied the chi-square method to test linkage between two genes by asking whether the observed numbers of parental and recombinant classes differed significantly from the expectation of independent assortment that parentals = recombinants. Another possible way to analyze the results from these same experiments is to ask whether the observed frequencies of the four genotypic classes (*A B, a b, A b,* and *a B*) can be explained by a null hypothesis predicting that they should appear in a 1:1:1:1 ratio. In order to consider the relative advantages and disadvantages of analyzing the data in these two different ways answer the following:

a. What is the null hypothesis in each case?

b. Which is a more sensitive test of linkage? (Analyze the data in Fig. 5.5 by the second method.)

c. How would both methods respond to a situation in which one allele of one of the genes causes reduced viability?

Section 5.3

8. In *Drosophila,* males from a true-breeding stock with raspberry-colored eyes were mated to females from a true-breeding stock with sable-colored bodies. In the F_1 generation, all the females had wild-type eye and body color, while all the males had wild-type eye color but sable-colored bodies. When F_1 males and females were mated, the F_2 generation was composed of 216 females with wild-type eyes and bodies, 223 females with wild-type eyes and sable bodies, 191 males with wild-type eyes and sable bodies, 188 males with raspberry eyes and wild-type bodies, 23 males with wild-type eyes and bodies, and 27 males with raspberry eyes and sable bodies. Explain these results by diagramming the crosses, and calculate any relevant map distances.

9. In mice, the dominant allele *Gs* of the X-linked gene *Greasy* produces shiny fur, while the recessive wild-type Gs^+ allele determines normal fur. The dominant allele *Bhd* of the X-linked *Broadhead* gene causes skeletal abnormalities including broad heads and snouts, while the recessive wild-type Bhd^+ allele yields normal skeletons. Female mice heterozygous for the two alleles of both genes were mated with wild-type males. Among 100 male progeny of this cross, 49 had shiny fur, 48 had skeletal abnormalities, 2 had shiny fur and skeletal abnormalities, and 1 was wild type.

a. Diagram the cross described, and calculate the distance between the two genes.

b. What would have been the results if you had counted 100 female progeny of the cross?

10. *CC DD* and *cc dd* individuals were crossed to each other, and the F_1 generation was backcrossed to the *cc dd* parent. 903 *Cc Dd,* 897 *cc dd,* 98 *Cc dd,* and 102 *cc Dd* offspring resulted.

a. How far apart are the *c* and *d* loci?

b. What progeny and in what frequencies would you expect to result from testcrossing the F_1 generation from a *CC dd × cc DD* cross to *cc dd?*

11. If the *a* and *b* loci are 20 m.u. apart in humans and an *A B / a b* woman mates with an *a b / a b* man, what is the probability that their first child will be *A b / a b?*

12. In a particular human family, John and his mother both have brachydactyly (a rare autosomal dominant causing short fingers). John's father has Huntington disease (another rare autosomal dominant). John's wife is phenotypically normal and is pregnant. Two-thirds of people who inherit the Huntington (*HD*) allele show symptoms by age 50, and John is 50 and has no symptoms. Brachydactyly is 90% penetrant.

a. What are the genotypes of John's parents?

b. What are the possible genotypes for John?

c. What is the probability the child will express both brachydactyly and Huntington disease by age 50 if the two genes are unlinked?

d. If these two loci are 20 m.u. apart, how will it change your answer to part *c?*

13. In mice, the autosomal locus coding for the β-globin chain of hemoglobin is 1 m.u. from the albino locus. Assume for the moment that the same is true in humans. The disease sickle-cell anemia is the result of homozygosity for a particular mutation in the β-globin gene.

   a. A son is born to an albino man and a woman with sickle-cell anemia. What kinds of gametes will the son form, and in what proportions?

   b. A daughter is born to a normal man and a woman who has both albinism and sickle-cell anemia. What kinds of gametes will the daughter form, and in what proportions?

   c. If the son in part *a* grows up and marries the daughter in part *b,* what is the probability that a child of theirs will be an albino with sickle-cell anemia?

14. In corn, the allele *A* allows the deposition of anthocyanin (blue) pigment in the kernels (seeds), while *aa* plants have yellow kernels. At a second gene, *W–* produces smooth kernels, while *ww* kernels are wrinkled. A plant with blue smooth kernels was crossed to a plant with yellow wrinkled kernels. The progeny consisted of 1447 blue smooth, 169 blue wrinkled, 186 yellow smooth, and 1510 yellow wrinkled.

   a. Are the *a* and *w* loci linked? If so, how far apart are they?

   b. What was the genotype of the blue smooth parent? Include the chromosome arrangement of alleles.

   c. If a plant grown from a blue wrinkled progeny seed is crossed to a plant grown from a yellow smooth F$_1$ seed, what kinds of kernels would be expected, and in what proportions?

15. Albino rabbits (lacking pigment) are homozygous for the recessive *c* allele (*C* allows pigment formation). Rabbits homozygous for the recessive *b* allele make brown pigment, while those with at least one copy of *B* make black pigment. True-breeding brown rabbits were crossed to albinos, which were *BB*. F$_1$ rabbits, which were all black, were crossed to the double recessive (*bb cc*). The progeny obtained were 34 black, 66 brown, and 100 albino.

   a. What phenotypic proportions would have been expected if the *b* and *c* loci were unlinked?

   b. How far apart are the two loci?

16. Write the number of *different kinds* of phenotypes, excluding gender, you would see among a large number of progeny from an F$_1$ mating between individuals of identical genotype that are heterozygous for one or two genes (that is, *Aa* or *Aa Bb*) as indicated. No gene interactions means that the phenotype determined by one gene is not influenced by the genotype of the other gene.

   a. One gene; *A* completely dominant to *a*.

   b. One gene; *A* and *a* codominant.

   c. One gene; *A* incompletely dominant to *a*.

   d. Two unlinked genes; no gene interactions; *A* completely dominant to *a,* and *B* completely dominant to *b*.

   e. Two genes, 10 m.u. apart; no gene interactions; *A* completely dominant to *a,* and *B* completely dominant to *b*.

   f. Two unlinked genes; no gene interactions; *A* and *a* codominant, and *B* incompletely dominant to *b*.

   g. Two genes, 10 m.u. apart; *A* completely dominant to *a,* and *B* completely dominant to *b;* and with recessive epistasis between the genes.

   h. Two unlinked duplicated genes (that is, *A* and *B* perform the same function); *A* and *B* completely dominant to *a* and *b*, respectively.

   i. Two genes, 0 m.u. apart; no gene interactions; *A* completely dominant to *a,* and *B* completely dominant to *b*. (There are two possible answers.)

17. If the *a* and *b* loci are 40 cM apart and an *AA BB* individual and an *aa bb* individual mate:

   a. What gametes will the F$_1$ individuals produce, and in what proportions? What phenotypic classes in what proportions are expected in the F$_2$ generation (assuming complete dominance for both genes)?

   b. If the original cross was *AA bb* × *aa BB*, what gametic proportions would emerge from the F$_1$? What would be the result in the F$_2$ generation?

18. A DNA variant has been found linked to a rare autosomal dominant disease in humans and can thus be used as a marker to follow inheritance of the disease allele. In an informative family (in which one parent is heterozygous for both the disease allele and the DNA marker in a known chromosomal arrangement of alleles, and his or her mate does not have the same alleles of the DNA variant), the reliability of such a marker as a predictor of the disease in a fetus is related to the map distance between the DNA marker and the gene causing the disease. Imagine that a man affected with the disease (genotype *Dd*) is heterozygous for the *V^1* and *V^2* forms of the DNA variant, with form *V^1* on the same chromosome as the *D* allele and form *V^2* on the same chromosome as *d*. His wife is *V^{3}V^3 dd*, where *V^3* is another allele of the DNA marker. Typing of the fetus by amniocentesis reveals that the fetus has the *V^2* and *V^3* variants of the DNA marker. How likely is it that the fetus has inherited the disease allele *D* if the distance between the *D* locus and the marker locus is (a) 0 m.u., (b) 1 m.u., (c) 5 m.u., (d) 10 m.u., (e) 50 m.u.?

Section 5.4

19. In *Drosophila*, the recessive *dp* allele of the *dumpy* gene produces short, curved wings, while the recessive allele *bw* of the *brown* gene causes brown eyes.

In a testcross using females heterozygous for both of these genes, the following results were obtained:

wild-type wings, wild-type eyes	178
wild-type wings, brown eyes	185
dumpy wings, wild-type eyes	172
dumpy wings, brown eyes	181

In a testcross using males heterozygous for both of these genes, a different set of results was obtained:

wild-type wings, wild-type eyes	247
dumpy wings, brown eyes	242

a. What can you conclude from the first testcross?
b. What can you conclude from the second testcross?
c. How can you reconcile the data shown in parts *a* and *b?* Can you exploit the difference between these two sets of data to devise a general test for synteny in *Drosophila?*
d. The genetic distance between *dumpy* and *brown* is 91.5 m.u. How could this value be measured?

20. Cinnabar eyes (*cn*) and reduced bristles (*rd*) are autosomal recessive characters in *Drosophila.* A homozygous wild-type female was crossed to a reduced, cinnabar male, and the F_1 males were then crossed to the F_1 females to obtain the F_2. Of the 400 F_2 offspring obtained, 292 were wild type, 9 were cinnabar, 7 were reduced, and 92 were reduced, cinnabar. Explain these results and estimate the distance between the *cn* and *rd* loci.

21. Map distances were determined for four different genes (*MAT, HIS4, THR4,* and *LEU2*) on chromosome III of the yeast *Saccharomyces cerevisiae:*

$HIS4 \leftrightarrow MAT$	37 cM
$THR4 \leftrightarrow LEU2$	35 cM
$LEU2 \leftrightarrow HIS4$	23 cM
$MAT \leftrightarrow LEU2$	16 cM
$MAT \leftrightarrow THR4$	16 cM

What is the order of genes on the chromosome?

22. From a series of two-point crosses, the following map distances were obtained for the syntenic genes *A, B, C, D,* and *E* in peas:

$B \leftrightarrow C$	23 m.u.
$A \leftrightarrow C$	15 m.u.
$C \leftrightarrow D$	14 m.u.
$A \leftrightarrow B$	12 m.u.
$B \leftrightarrow D$	11 m.u.
$A \leftrightarrow D$	1 m.u.

Chi-square analysis cannot reject the null hypothesis of no linkage for gene *E* with any of the other four genes.

a. Draw a cross scheme that would allow you to determine the $B \leftrightarrow C$ map distance.

b. Diagram the best genetic map that can be assembled from this dataset.
c. Explain any inconsistencies or unknown features in your map.
d. What additional experiments would allow you to resolve these inconsistencies or ambiguities?

23. In *Drosophila,* the recessive allele *mb* of one gene causes missing bristles, the recessive allele *e* of a second gene causes ebony body color, and the recessive allele *k* of a third gene causes kidney-shaped eyes. (Dominant wild-type alleles of all three genes are indicated with a + superscript.) The three different P generation crosses in the table that follows were conducted, and then the resultant F_1 females from each cross were testcrossed to males that were homozygous for the recessive alleles of both genes in question. The phenotypes of the testcross offspring are tabulated as follows. Determine the best genetic map explaining all the data.

Parental cross	Testcross offspring of F_1 females	
$mb^+\ mb^+,\ e^+\ e^+ \times$	normal bristles, normal body	117
$mb\ mb,\ e\ e$	normal bristles, ebony body	11
	missing bristles, normal body	15
	missing bristles, ebony body	107
$k^+\ k^+,\ e\ e \times k\ k,\ e^+\ e^+$	normal eyes, normal body	11
	normal eyes, ebony body	150
	kidney eyes, normal body	144
	kidney eyes, ebony body	7
$mb^+\ mb^+,\ k^+\ k^+ \times$	normal bristles, normal eyes	203
$mb\ mb,\ k\ k$	normal bristles, kidney eyes	11
	missing bristles, normal eyes	15
	missing bristles, kidney eyes	193

24. In the tubular flowers of foxgloves, wild-type coloration is red while a mutation called *white* produces white flowers. Another mutation, called *peloria,* causes the flowers at the apex of the stem to be huge. Yet another mutation, called *dwarf,* affects stem length. You cross a white-flowered plant (otherwise phenotypically wild type) to a plant that is dwarf and peloria but has wild-type red flower color. All of the F_1 plants are tall with white, normal-sized flowers. You cross an F_1 plant back to the dwarf and peloria parent, and you see the 543 progeny shown in the chart. (Only mutant traits are noted.)

dwarf, peloria	172
white	162
dwarf, peloria, white	56
wild type	48
dwarf, white	51
peloria	43
dwarf	6
peloria, white	5

a. Which alleles are dominant?

b. What were the genotypes of the parents in the original cross?

c. Draw a map showing the linkage relationships of these three loci.

d. Is there interference? If so, calculate the coefficient of coincidence and the interference value.

5. In *Drosophila,* three autosomal genes have the following map:

a. Provide the data, in terms of the expected number of flies in the following phenotypic classes, when $a^+ b^+ c^+/a\, b\, c$ females are crossed to $a\, b\, c/a\, b\, c$ males. Assume 1000 flies were counted and that there is no interference in this region.

a^+	b^+	c^+
a	b	c
a^+	b	c
a	b^+	c^+
a^+	b^+	c
a	b	c^+
a^+	b	c^+
a	b^+	c

b. If the cross were reversed, such that $a^+ b^+ c^+/a\, b\, c$ males are crossed to $a\, b\, c/a\, b\, c$ females, how many flies would you expect in the same phenotypic classes?

6. A snapdragon with pink petals, black anthers, and long stems was allowed to self-fertilize. From the resulting seeds, 650 adult plants were obtained. The phenotypes of these offspring are listed here.

78	red	long	tan
26	red	short	tan
44	red	long	black
15	red	short	black
39	pink	long	tan
13	pink	short	tan
204	pink	long	black
68	pink	short	black
5	white	long	tan
2	white	short	tan
117	white	long	black
39	white	short	black

a. Using *P* for one allele and *p* for the other, indicate how flower color is inherited.

b. What numbers of red : pink : white would have been expected among these 650 plants?

c. How are anther color and stem length inherited?

d. What was the genotype of the original plant?

e. Do any of the three genes show independent assortment?

f. For any genes that are linked, indicate the arrangements of the alleles on the homologous chromosomes in the original snapdragon, and estimate the distance between the genes.

27. Male *Drosophila* expressing the recessive mutations *sc* (scute), *ec* (echinus), *cv* (crossveinless), and *b* (black) were crossed to phenotypically wild-type females, and the 3288 progeny listed were obtained. (Only mutant traits are noted.)

653	black, scute, echinus, crossveinless
670	scute, echinus, crossveinless
675	wild type
655	black
71	black, scute
73	scute
73	black, echinus, crossveinless
74	echinus, crossveinless
87	black, scute, echinus
84	scute, echinus
86	black, crossveinless
83	crossveinless
1	black, scute, crossveinless
1	scute, crossveinless
1	black, echinus
1	echinus

a. Diagram the genotype of the female parent.

b. Map these loci.

c. Is there evidence of interference? Justify your answer with numbers.

28. *Drosophila* females heterozygous for each of three recessive autosome mutations with independent phenotypic effects (thread antennae [*th*], hairy body [*h*], and scarlet eyes [*st*]) were testcrossed to males showing all three mutant phenotypes. The 1000 progeny of this testcross were

thread, hairy, scarlet	432
wild type	429
thread, hairy	37
thread, scarlet	35
hairy	34
scarlet	33

a. Show the arrangement of alleles on the relevant chromosomes in the triply heterozygous females.

b. Draw the best genetic map that explains these data.

c. Calculate any relevant interference values.

29. A true-breeding strain of Virginia tobacco has dominant alleles determining leaf morphology (*M*), leaf color (*C*), and leaf size (*S*). A Carolina strain is homozygous for the recessive alleles of these three genes. These genes are found on the same chromosome as follows:

An F$_1$ hybrid between the two strains is now backcrossed to the Carolina strain. Assuming no interference:

a. What proportion of the backcross progeny will resemble the Virginia strain for all three traits?

b. What proportion of the backcross progeny will resemble the Carolina strain for all three traits?

c. What proportion of the backcross progeny will have the leaf morphology and leaf size of the Virginia strain but the leaf color of the Carolina strain?

d. What proportion of the backcross progeny will have the leaf morphology and leaf color of the Virginia strain but the leaf size of the Carolina strain?

30. a. In *Drosophila*, crosses between F$_1$ heterozygotes of the form *A b / a B* always yield the same ratio of phenotypes in the F$_2$ progeny regardless of the distance between the two genes (assuming complete dominance for both autosomal genes). What is this ratio? Would this also be the case if the F$_1$ heterozygotes were *A B / a b?*

b. If you intercrossed F$_1$ heterozygotes of the form *A b / a B* in mice, the phenotypic ratio among the F$_2$ progeny would vary with the map distance between the two genes. Is there a simple way to estimate the map distance based on the frequencies of the F$_2$ phenotypes, assuming rates of recombination are equal in males and females? Could you estimate map distances in the same way if the mouse F$_1$ heterozygotes were *A B / a b?*

31. The following list of four *Drosophila* mutations indicates the symbol for the mutation, the name of the gene, and the mutant phenotype:

Allele symbol	Gene name	Mutant phenotype
dwp	*dwarp*	small body, warped wings
rmp	*rumpled*	deranged bristles
pld	*pallid*	pale wings
rv	*raven*	dark eyes and bodies

You perform the following crosses with the indicated results:

Cross #1: dwarp, rumpled females × pallid, raven males
→ dwarp, rumpled males and wild-type females

Cross #2: pallid, raven females × dwarp, rumpled males
→ pallid, raven males and wild-type females

F$_1$ females from cross #1 were crossed to males from a true-breeding *dwarp rumpled pallid raven* stock. The 1000 progeny obtained were as follows:

pallid	3
pallid, raven	428
pallid, raven, rumpled	48
pallid, rumpled	23
dwarp, raven	22
dwarp, raven, rumpled	2
dwarp, rumpled	427
dwarp	47

Indicate the best map for these four genes, including all relevant data. Calculate interference values when appropriate.

Section 5.5

32. A cross was performed between one haploid strain of yeast with the genotype *a f g* and another haploid strain with the genotype α *f$^+$ g$^+$* (*a* and α are mating types). The resulting diploid was sporulated, and a random sample of 101 of the resulting haploid spores was analyzed. The following genotypic frequencies were seen:

α	*f$^+$*	*g$^+$*	31
a	*f*	*g*	29
a	*f*	*g$^+$*	14
α	*f$^+$*	*g*	13
a	*f$^+$*	*g*	6
α	*f*	*g$^+$*	6
a	*f$^+$*	*g$^+$*	1
α	*f*	*g*	1

a. Map the loci involved in the cross.

b. Assuming all three genes are on the same chromosome arm, is it possible that a particular ascus could contain an α *f g* spore but not an *a f$^+$ g$^+$* spore? If so, draw a meiosis that could generate such an ascus.

33. *Neurospora* of genotype *a + c* are crossed with *Neurospora* of genotype *+ b +*. The following tetrads are obtained (note that the genotype of the four spore pairs in an ascus are listed, rather than listing all eight spores):

a + c	*a b c*	*+ + c*	*+ b c*	*a b +*	*a + c*
a + c	*a b c*	*a + c*	*a b c*	*a b +*	*a b c*
+ b +	*+ + +*	*+ b +*	*+ + +*	*+ + c*	*+ + +*
+ b +	*+ + +*	*a b +*	*a + +*	*+ + c*	*+ b +*
137	141	26	25	2	3

a. In how many cells has meiosis occurred to yield these data?

b. Give the best genetic map to explain these results. Indicate all relevant genetic distances, both between genes and between each gene and its respective centromere.

c. Diagram a meiosis that could give rise to one of the three tetrads in the class at the far right in the list.

34. Two crosses were made in *Neurospora* involving the mating type locus and either the *ad* or *p* genes. In both cases, the mating type locus (*A* or *a*) was one of the loci whose segregation was scored. One cross was *ad A* × *ad*⁺ *a* (cross a), and the other was *p A* × *p*⁺ *a* (cross b). From cross a, 10 parental ditype, 9 nonparental ditype, and 1 tetratype asci were seen. From cross b, the results were 24 parental ditype, 3 nonparental ditype, and 27 tetratype asci.

a. What are the linkage relationships between the mating type locus and the other two loci?

b. Although these two crosses were performed in *Neurospora,* you cannot use the data given to calculate centromere-to-gene distances for any of these genes. Why not?

35. A cross was performed between a yeast strain that requires methionine and lysine for growth (*met*⁻ *lys*⁻) and another yeast strain, which is *met*⁺ *lys*⁺. One hundred asci were dissected, and colonies were grown from the four spores in each ascus. Cells from these colonies were tested for their ability to grow on petri plates containing either minimal medium (min), min + lysine (lys), min + methionine (met), or min + lys + met. The asci could be divided into two groups based on this analysis:

> Group 1: In 89 asci, cells from two of the four spore colonies could grow on all four kinds of media, while the other two spore colonies could grow only on min + lys + met.

> Group 2: In 11 asci, cells from one of the four spore colonies could grow on all four kinds of petri plates. Cells from a second one of the four spore colonies could grow only on min + lys plates and on min + lys + met plates. Cells from a third of the four spore colonies could only grow on min + met plates and on min + lys + met. Cells from the remaining colony could only grow on min + lys + met.

a. What are the genotypes of each of the spores within the two groups of asci?

b. Are the *lys* and *met* genes linked? If so, what is the map distance between them?

c. If you could extend this analysis to many more asci, you would eventually find some asci with a different pattern. For these asci, describe the phenotypes of the four spores. List these phenotypes as the ability of dissected spores to form colonies on the four kinds of petri plates.

36. The *a, b,* and *c* loci are all on different chromosomes in yeast. When *a b*⁺ yeast were crossed to *a*⁺ *b* yeast and the resultant tetrads analyzed, it was found that

the number of nonparental ditype tetrads was equal to the number of parental ditypes, but there were no tetratype asci at all. On the other hand, many tetratype asci were seen in the tetrads formed after *a c*⁺ was crossed with *a*⁺ *c,* and after *b c*⁺ was crossed with *b*⁺ *c.* Explain these results.

37. Indicate the percentage of tetrads that would have 0, 1, 2, 3, or 4 viable spores after *Saccharomyces cerevisiae a / α* diploids of the following genotypes are sporulated:

a. A true-breeding wild-type strain (with no mutations in any gene essential for viability).

b. A strain heterozygous for a null (completely inactivating) mutation in a single essential gene.

For the remaining parts of this problem, consider crosses between yeast strains of the form *a* × *b,* where *a* and *b* are both temperature-sensitive mutations in different essential genes. The cross is conducted under permissive (low-temperature) conditions. Indicate the percentage of tetrads that would have 0, 1, 2, 3, or 4 viable spores subsequently measured under restrictive (high-temperature) conditions.

c. *a* and *b* are unlinked, and both are 0 m.u. from their respective centromeres.

d. *a* and *b* are unlinked; *a* is 0 m.u. from its centromere, while *b* is 10 m.u. from its centromere.

e. *a* and *b* are 0 m.u. apart.

f. *a* and *b* are 10 m.u. apart. Assume all crossovers between *a* and *b* are SCOs (single crossovers).

g. In part (*f*), if a four-strand DCO (double crossover) occurred between *a* and *b,* how many of the spores in the resulting tetrad would be viable at high temperature?

38. Two genes are located on the same chromosome as follows:

A haploid cross of the form *C D* × *c d* is made.

a. What proportions of PD, NPD, and T tetrads would you expect if this cross was made between strains of *Saccharomyces cerevisiae* and the interference in this region = 1?

b. If the interference in this region = 0?

c. What kinds of tetrads, and in what proportions, would you expect if this cross was made between strains of *Neurospora crassa* and the interference in this region = 1? (Consider not only whether a tetrad is PD, NPD, or T but also whether the tetrad shows first or second division segregation for each gene.)

d. If the interference in this region = 0?

39. A yeast strain that cannot grow in the absence of the amino acid histidine (*his⁻*) is mated with a yeast strain that cannot grow in the absence of the amino acid lysine (*lys⁻*). Among the 400 unordered tetrads resulting from this mating, 233 were PD, 11 were NPD, and 156 were T.

a. What types of spores are in the PD, NPD, and T tetrads?

b. What is the distance in map units between the *his* and *lys* genes?

c. Assuming that none of these tetrads was caused by more than two crossovers between the genes, how can you estimate the number of meioses that generated these 400 tetrads in which zero, one, or two crossovers took place?

d. Based on your answer to part *c*, what is the mean number of crossovers per meiosis in the region between the two genes?

e. The equation RF = 100 × (NPD + 1/2T) / total tetrads accounts for some, but not all, double crossovers between two genes. Which double crossovers are missed? Can you extrapolate from your answer to part *d* to obtain a more accurate equation for calculating map distances between two genes from the results of tetrad analysis?

f. Using your corrected equation from part *e*, what is a more accurate measurement of the distance in map units between the *his* and *lys* genes?

40. A research group has selected three independent *trp⁻* haploid strains of *Neurospora*, each of which cannot grow in the absence of the amino acid tryptophan. They first mated these three strains with a wild-type strain of opposite mating type, and then they analyzed the resultant octads. For all three matings, two of the four spore pairs in every octad could grow on minimal medium (that is, in the absence of tryptophan), while the other two spore pairs were unable to grow on this minimal medium.

a. What can you conclude from this result?

In the matings of mutant strains 1 and 2 with wild type, one of the two topmost pairs in some octads had spores that could grow on minimal medium while the other of the two topmost pairs in the same octads had spores that could not grow on minimal medium. In the mating of mutant strain 3 with wild type, either all the spores in the two topmost pairs could grow on minimal medium or all could not grow on minimal medium.

b. What can you conclude from this result?

The researchers next prepared two separate cultures of each mutant strain; one of these cultures was of mating type *A* and the other of mating type *a*. They mated these strains in pairwise fashion, dissected the resultant octads, and determined how many of the individual spores could grow on minimal medium. The results are shown here.

Mating	% of octads with *x* number of spores viable on minimal medium				
	x = 0	2	4	6	8
1 × 2	78	22	0	0	0
1 × 3	46	6	48	0	0
2 × 3	42	16	42	0	0

c. For each of the three matings in the table, how many of the 100 octads are PD? NPD? T?

d. Draw a genetic map explaining all of the preceding data. Assume that the sample sizes are sufficiently small that none of the octads are the result of double crossovers.

e. Although this problem describes crosses in *Neurospora*, it does not help in this particular case to present the matings in the table as ordered octads. Why not?

f. Why in this particular problem can you obtain gene ↔ centromere distances from the crosses in the table, even though the data are not presented as ordered octads?

Section 5.6

41. A single yeast cell placed on a solid agar will divide mitotically to produce a colony of about 10⁷ cells. A haploid yeast cell that has a mutation in the *ade2* gene will produce a red colony; an *ade2⁺* colony will be white. Some of the colonies formed from diploid yeast cells with a genotype of *ade2⁺*/*ade2⁻* will contain sectors of red within a white colony.

a. How would you explain these sectors?

b. Although the white colonies are roughly the same size, the red sectors within some of the white colonies vary markedly in size. Why? Do you expect the majority of the red sectors to be relatively large or relatively small?

42. A diploid strain of yeast has a wild-type phenotype but the following genotype:

a, *b*, *c*, *d*, and *e* all represent recessive alleles that yield a visible phenotype, and *leth* represents a recessive lethal mutation. All genes are on the same chromosome, and *a* is very tightly linked to its centromere (indicated by a small circle). Which of the following phenotypes could be found in sectors resulting from mitotic recombination in this cell? (1) *a*; (2) *b*; (3) *c*; (4) *d*; (5) *e*; (6) *b e*; (7) *c d*; (8) *c d e*; (9) *d e*; (10) *a b*. Assume that double mitotic crossovers are too rare to be observed.

43. In *Drosophila,* the *yellow* (*y*) gene is near the end of the acrocentric X chromosome, while the *singed* (*sn*) gene is located near the middle of the X chromosome. On the wings of female flies of genotype $y\ sn / y^+\ sn^+$, you can very rarely find patches of yellow tissue within which a small subset of cells also have singed bristles.

a. How can you explain this phenomenon?

b. Would you find similar patches on the wings of females having the genotype $y^+\ sn / y\ sn^+$?

44. Neurofibromas are tumors of the skin that can arise when a skin cell that is originally $NF1^+ / NF1^-$ loses the $NF1^+$ allele. This wild-type allele encodes a functional tumor suppressor protein, while the $NF1^-$ allele encodes a nonfunctional protein.

A patient of genotype $NF1^+ / NF1^-$ has 20 independent tumors in different areas of the skin. Samples are taken of normal, noncancerous cells from this patient, as well as of cells from each of the 20 tumors. Extracts of these samples are analyzed by a technique called gel electrophoresis that can detect variant forms of four different proteins (A, B, C, and D) all encoded by genes that lie on the same autosome as *NF1*. Each protein has a slow (S) and a fast (F) form that are encoded by different alleles (for example, A^S and A^F). In the extract of normal tissue, slow and fast variants of all four proteins are found. In the extracts of the tumors, 12 had only the fast variants of proteins A and D but both the fast and slow variants of proteins B and C; 6 had only the fast variant of protein A but both the fast and slow variants of proteins B, C, and D; and the remaining 2 tumor extracts had only the fast variant of protein A, only the slow variant of protein B, the fast and slow variants of protein C, and only the fast variant of protein D.

a. What kind of genetic event described in this chapter could cause all 20 tumors, assuming that all the tumors are produced by the same mechanism?

b. Draw a genetic map describing these data, assuming that this small sample represents all the types of tumors that could be formed by the same mechanism in this patient. Show which alleles of which genes lie on the two homologous chromosomes. Indicate all relative distances that can be estimated.

c. Another mechanism that can lead to neurofibromas in this patient is a mitotic error producing cells with 45 rather than the normal 46 chromosomes. How can this mechanism cause tumors? How do you know, just from the results described, that none of these 20 tumors is formed by such mitotic errors?

d. Can you think of any other type of error that could produce the results described?

Anatomy and Function of a Gene: Dissection Through Mutation

A scale played on a piano keyboard and a gene on a chromosome are both a series of simple, linear elements (keys or nucleotide pairs) that produce information. A wrong note or an altered nucleotide pair calls attention to the structure of the musical scale or the gene.

Human chromosome 3 consists of approximately 220 million base pairs and carries 1000–2000 genes (**Fig. 7.1**). Somewhere on the long arm of the chromosome resides the gene for rhodopsin, a light-sensitive protein active in the rod cells of our retinas. The rhodopsin gene determines perception of low-intensity light. People who carry the normal, wild-type allele of the gene see well in a dimly lit room and on the road at night. One simple change—a mutation—in the rhodopsin gene, however, diminishes light perception just enough to lead to night blindness. Other alterations in the gene cause the destruction of rod cells, resulting in total blindness. Medical researchers have so far identified more than 30 mutations in the rhodopsin gene that affect vision in different ways.

The case of the rhodopsin gene illustrates some very basic questions. Which of the 220 million base pairs on chromosome 3 make up the rhodopsin gene? How are the base pairs that comprise this gene arranged along the chromosome? How can a single gene sustain so many mutations that lead to such divergent phenotypic effects? In this chapter, we describe the ingenious experiments performed by geneticists during the 1950s and 1960s as they examined the relationships among mutations, genes, chromosomes, and phenotypes in an effort to understand, at the molecular level, what genes are and how they function.

We can recognize three main themes from the elegant work of these investigators. The first is that mutations are heritable changes in base sequence that affect phenotype. The second is that physically, a gene is usually a specific protein-encoding segment of DNA in a discrete region of a chromosome. (We now know that some genes encode various kinds of RNA that do not get translated into protein.) Third, a gene is not simply a bead on a string, changeable only as a whole and only in one way, as some had believed. Rather, genes are divisible, and each gene's subunits—the individual nucleotide pairs of DNA—can mutate independently and can recombine with each other.

Knowledge of what genes are and how they work deepens our understanding of Mendelian genetics by providing a biochemical explanation for how genotype influences phenotype. One mutation in the rhodopsin gene, for example, causes

CHAPTER OUTLINE

- 7.1 Mutations: Primary Tools of Genetic Analysis
- 7.2 What Mutations Tell Us About Gene Structure
- 7.3 What Mutations Tell Us About Gene Function
- 7.4 A Comprehensive Example: Mutations That Affect Vision

Figure 7.1 The DNA of each human chromosome contains hundreds to thousands of genes. The DNA of this human chromosome has been spread out and magnified 50,000×. No topological signs reveal where along the DNA the genes reside. The darker, chromosome-shaped structure in the middle is a scaffold of proteins to which the DNA is attached.

the substitution of one particular amino acid for another in the construction o the rhodopsin protein. This single substitution changes the three-dimensiona structure of rhodopsin and thus the protein's ability to absorb photons, ult mately altering a person's ability to perceive light.

7.1 Mutations: Primary Tools of Genetic Analysis

We saw in Chapter 3 that genes with one common allele are *monomorphic,* while genes with several common alleles in natural populations are *polymorphic.* The term **wild-type allele** has a clear definition for monomorphic genes, where the allele found on the large majority of chromosomes in the population under consideration is wild-type. In the case of polymorphic genes, the definition is less straightforward. Some geneticists consider all alleles with a frequency of greater than 1% to be wild-type, while others describe the many alleles present at appreciable frequencies in the population as *common variants* and reserve "wild-type allele" for use only in connection with monomorphic genes.

Mutations are heritable changes in DNA base sequences

A mutation that changes a wild-type allele of a gene (regardless of the definition) to a different allele is called a **forward mutation.** The resulting novel mutant allele can be either recessive or dominant to the original wild type. Geneticists often diagram forward mutations as $A^+ \rightarrow a$ when the mutation is recessive and as $b^+ \rightarrow B$ when the mutation is dominant. Mutations can also cause a novel mutant allele to revert back to wild type ($a \rightarrow A^+$, or $B \rightarrow b^+$) in a process known as **reverse mutation,** or **reversion.** In this chapter, we designate wild-type alleles, whether recessive or dominant, with a plus sign ($+$).

Mendel originally defined genes by the visible phenotypic effects—yellow or green, round or wrinkled—of their alternative alleles. In fact, the only way he knew that genes existed at all was because alternative alleles for seven particular pea genes had arisen through for-

ward mutations. Close to a century later, knowledge DNA structure clarified that such mutations are heritab changes in DNA base sequence. DNA thus carries th potential for genetic change in the same place it carrie genetic information—the sequence of its bases.

Mutations may be classified by how they change DNA

A **substitution** occurs when a base at a certain positio in one strand of the DNA molecule is replaced by one the other three bases (**Fig. 7.2a**); after DNA replication, new base pair will appear in the daughter double heli Substitutions can be subdivided into *transitions,* in whic one purine (A or G) replaces the other purine, or or pyrimidine (C or T) replaces the other; and *transversion* in which a purine changes to a pyrimidine, or vice vers

Other types of mutations produce more complicate rearrangements of DNA sequence. A **deletion** occurs whe a block of one or more nucleotide pairs is lost from a DN molecule; an **insertion** is just the reverse—the addition one or more nucleotide pairs (**Figs. 7.2b** and **c**). Deletio and insertions can be as small as a single base pair as large as megabases (that is, millions of base pair Researchers can see the larger changes under the micr scope when they observe chromosomes in the context a karyotype, such as that shown in Fig. 4.4 on p. 82.

More complex mutations include **inversions,** 18 rotations of a segment of the DNA molecule (**Fig. 7.2** and **reciprocal translocations,** in which parts of two no homologous chromosomes change places (**Fig. 7.2** Large-scale DNA rearrangements, including megaba deletions and insertions as well as inversions and transl cations, cause major genetic reorganizations that ca change either the order of genes along a chromosome the number of chromosomes in an organism. We discu

Figure 7.2 Mutations classified by their effect on DNA.

Starting sequence

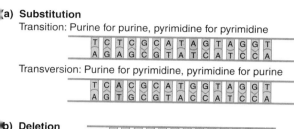

Type of mutation and effect on base sequence

(a) Substitution

Transition: Purine for purine, pyrimidine for pyrimidine

Transversion: Purine for pyrimidine, pyrimidine for purine

(b) Deletion

(c) Insertion

(d) Inversion

(e) Reciprocal translocation

these **chromosomal rearrangements,** which affect many genes at a time, in Chapter 13. In this chapter, we focus on mutations that alter only one gene at a time.

Only a small fraction of the mutations in a genome actually alter the nucleotide sequences of genes in a way that affects gene function. By changing one allele to another, these mutations modify the structure or amount of a gene's protein product, and the modification in protein structure or amount influences phenotype. All other mutations either alter genes in a way that does not affect their function or change the DNA between genes. We discuss mutations

without observable phenotypic consequences in Chapter 11; such mutations are very useful for mapping genes and tracking differences between individuals. In the remainder of this chapter, we focus on those mutations that have an impact on gene function and thereby influence phenotype.

> Mutations—heritable changes in DNA base sequences—include substitutions, deletions, insertions, inversions, and translocations.

Spontaneous mutations occur at a very low rate

Mutations that modify gene function happen so infrequently that geneticists must examine a very large number of individuals from a formerly homogeneous population to detect the new phenotypes that reflect these mutations. In one ongoing study, dedicated investigators have monitored the coat colors of millions of specially bred mice and discovered that on average, a given gene mutates to a recessive allele in roughly 11 out of every 1 million gametes (**Fig. 7.3**). Studies of several other organisms have yielded similar results: an average spontaneous rate of $2-12 \times 10^{-6}$ mutations per gene per gamete.

Figure 7.3 Rates of spontaneous mutation. (a) Mutant mouse coat colors: albino (*left*), brown (*right*). **(b)** Mutation rates from wild type to recessive mutant alleles for five coat color genes. Mice from highly inbred wild-type strains were mated with homozygotes for recessive coat color alleles. Progeny with mutant coat colors indicated the presence of recessive mutations in gametes produced by the inbred mice.

(a)

(b)

Locus[a]	Number of gametes tested	Number of mutations	Mutation rate ($\times 10^{-6}$)
a^- (albino)	67,395	3	44.5
b^- (brown)	919,699	3	3.3
c^- (nonagouti)	150,391	5	33.2
d^- (dilute)	839,447	10	11.9
ln^- (leaden)	243,444	4	16.4
	2,220,376	25	11.2 (average)

[a] Mutation is from wild type to the recessive allele shown.

Looking at the mutation rate from a different perspective, you could ask how many mutations there might be in the genes of an individual. To find out, you would simply multiply the rate of $2-12 \times 10^{-6}$ mutations per gene times 30,000, a generous current estimate of the number of genes in the human genome, to obtain an answer of between $0.06-0.36$ mutations per haploid genome. This very rough calculation would mean that, on average, 1 new mutation affecting phenotype could arise in every 4–20 human gametes.

Different genes, different mutation rates

Although the average mutation rate per gene is $2-12 \times 10^{-6}$, this number masks considerable variation in the mutation rates for different genes. Experiments with many organisms show that mutation rates range from less than 10^{-9} to more than 10^{-3} per gene per gamete. Variation in the mutation rate of different genes within the same organism reflects differences in gene size (larger genes are larger targets that sustain more mutations) as well as differences in the susceptibility of particular genes to the various mechanisms that cause mutations (described later in this chapter).

Estimates of the average mutation rates in bacteria range from 10^{-8} to 10^{-7} mutations per gene per cell division. Although the units here are slightly different than those used for multicellular eukaryotes (because bacteria do not produce gametes), the average rate of mutation in gamete-producing eukaryotes still appears to be considerably higher than that in bacteria. The main reason is that numerous cell divisions take place between the formation of a zygote and meiosis, so mutations that appear in a gamete may have actually occurred many cell generations before the gamete formed. In other words, there are more chances for mutations to accumulate. Some scientists speculate that the diploid genomes of multicellular organisms allow them to tolerate relatively high rates of mutation in their gametes because a zygote would have to receive recessive mutations in the same gene from both gametes for any deleterious effects to occur. In contrast, a bacterium would be affected by just a single mutation that disrupted its only copy of the gene.

Gene function: Easy to disrupt, hard to restore

In the mouse coat color study, when researchers allowed brother and sister mice homozygous for a recessive mutant allele of one of the five mutant coat color genes to mate with each other, they could estimate the rate of reversion by examining the F_1 offspring. Any progeny expressing the dominant wild-type phenotype for a particular coat color, of necessity, carried a gene that had sustained a reverse mutation. Calculations based on observations of several million F_1 progeny revealed a reverse mutation rate ranging from $0-2.5 \times 10^{-6}$ per gene per gamete; the rate of reversion varied somewhat from gene to gene. In this study, then, the rate of reversion was significantly lower than the rate of forward mutation, most likely because there are many ways to disrupt gene function, but there are only a few ways to restore function once it has been disrupted. The conclusion that the rate of reversion is significantly lower than the rate of forward mutation holds true for most types of mutation. In one extreme example, deletions of more than a few nucleotide pairs can never revert, because DNA information that has disappeared from the genome cannot spontaneously reappear.

Although estimates of mutation rates are extremely rough, they nonetheless support three general conclusions: (1) Mutations affecting phenotype occur very rarely; (2) different genes mutate at different rates; and (3) the rate of forward mutation (a disruption of gene function) is almost always higher than the rate of reversion.

Spontaneous mutations arise from many kinds of random events

Because spontaneous mutations affecting a gene occur so infrequently, it is very difficult to study the events that produce them. To overcome this problem, researchers turned to bacteria as the experimental organisms of choice. It is easy to grow many millions of individuals and then rapidly search through enormous populations to find the few that carry a novel mutation. In one study, investigators spread wild-type bacteria on the surface of agar containing sufficient nutrients for growth as well as a large amount of a bacteria-killing substance, such as an antibiotic or a bacteriophage. Although most of the bacterial cells died, a few showed resistance to the bactericidal substance and continued to grow and divide. The descendants of a single resistant bacterium, produced by many rounds of binary fission, formed a mound of genetically identical cells called a **colony.**

The few bactericide-resistant colonies that appeared presented a puzzle. Had the cells in the colonies somehow altered their internal biochemistry to produce a life-saving response to the antibiotic or bacteriophage? Or did they carry heritable mutations conferring resistance to the bactericide? And if they did carry mutations, did those mutations arise by chance from random spontaneous events that take place continuously, even in the absence of a bactericidal substance, or did they only arise in response to environmental signals (in this case, the addition of the bactericide)?

The fluctuation test

In 1943, Salvador Luria and Max Delbrück devised an experiment to examine the origin of bacterial resistance (**Fig. 7.4**). According to their reasoning, if bacteriophage-resistant colonies arise in direct response to infection

Figure 7.4 The Luria-Delbrück fluctuation experiment. (a) Hypothesis 1: If resistance arises only after exposure to a bactericide, all bacterial cultures of equal size should produce roughly the same number of resistant colonies. Hypothesis 2: If random mutations conferring resistance arise before exposure to bactericide, the number of resistant colonies in different cultures should vary (fluctuate) widely. **(b)** Actual results showing large fluctuations suggest that mutations in bacteria occur as spontaneous mistakes independent of exposure to a selective agent.

(a) Two hypotheses for the origin of bactericide resistance

(b) Fluctuation test results

Time of exposure to selective agent

bacteriophages, separate suspensions of bacteria containing equal numbers of cells will generate similar, small numbers of resistant colonies when spread in separate petri plates on nutrient agar suffused with phages. By contrast, if resistance arises from mutations that occur spontaneously even when the phages are not present, then different liquid cultures, when spread on separate petri plates, will generate very different numbers of resistant colonies. The reason is that the mutation conferring resistance can, in theory, arise at any time during the growth of the culture. If it happens early, the cell in which it occurs will produce many mutant progeny prior to petri plating; if it happens later, there will be far fewer mutant progeny when the time for plating arrives. After plating, these numerical differences will show up as fluctuations in the numbers of resistant colonies growing in the different petri plates.

The results of this **fluctuation test** were clear: Most plates supported zero to a few resistant colonies, but a few harbored hundreds of resistant colonies. From this observation of a substantial fluctuation in the number of resistant colonies in different petri plates, Luria and Delbrück concluded that bacterial resistance arises from mutations that exist before exposure to bacteriophage. After exposure, however, the bactericide in the petri plate becomes a selective agent that kills off nonresistant cells, allowing only the preexisting resistant ones to survive.

Figure 7.5 illustrates how researchers used another technique, known as *replica plating,* to demonstrate even more directly that the mutations conferring bacterial resistance occur before the cells encounter the bactericide that selects for their resistance.

These key experiments showed that bacterial resistance to phages and other bactericides is the result of mutations, and these mutations do not arise in particular genes as a directed response to environmental change. Instead, mutations occur spontaneously as a result of random processes that can happen at any time and hit the genome at any place. Once such random changes occur, however, they usually remain stable. If the resistant mutants of the Luria-Delbrück experiment, for example, were grown for many generations in medium that did not contain bacteriophages, they would nevertheless remain resistant to this bactericidal virus.

We now describe some of the many kinds of random events that cause mutations; later, we discuss how cells cope with the damage.

Luria and Delbrück's fluctuation test showed that mutations in bacteria conferring resistance to bacteriophages occur prior to exposure to the phages and are caused by random, spontaneous events.

Figure 7.5 Replica plating verifies that bacterial resistance is the result of preexisting mutations. (a) Pressing a *master plate* onto a velvet surface transfers some cells from each bacterial colony onto the velvet. Pressing a *replica plate* onto the velvet then transfers some cells from each colony onto the replica plate. Investigators track which colonies on the master plate are able to grow on the replica plate (here, only penicillin-resistant ones). **(b)** Colonies on a master plate without penicillin are sequentially transferred to three replica plates with penicillin. Resistant colonies grow in the same positions on all three replicas, showing that some colonies on the master plate had multiple resistant cells before exposure to the antibiotic.

(a) The replica plating technique

1. Invert master plate; pressing against velvet surface leaves an imprint of colonies. Save plate.

2. Invert second plate (replica plate); pressing against velvet surface picks up colony imprint.

Master plate
No penicillin in medium

Penicillin in medium

3. Incubate plate.

Velvet

Replica plate

S = penicillin-sensitive bacteria
R = penicillin-resistant bacteria

4. Only penicillin-resistant colonies grow. Compare with position of colonies on original plate.

(b) Mutations occur prior to penicillin exposure

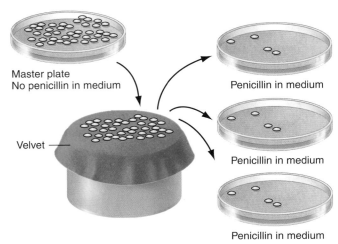

10^7 colonies of penicillin-sensitive bacteria

Make three replica plates. Incubate to allow penicillin-resistant colonies to grow.

Master plate
No penicillin in medium

Penicillin in medium

Velvet

Penicillin in medium

Penicillin in medium

Penicillin-resistant colonies grow in the same position on all three plates.

Natural processes that alter DNA

Chemical and physical assaults on DNA are quite frequen[t]. Geneticists estimate, for example, that the hydrolysis of [a] purine base, A or G, from the deoxyribose-phosphat[e] backbone occurs 1000 times an hour in every human cel[l]. This kind of DNA alteration is called **depurinatio[n]** (**Fig. 7.6a**). Because the resulting *apurinic site* cann[ot] specify a complementary base, the DNA replication pr[o]cess sometimes introduces a random base opposite th[e] apurinic site, causing a mutation in the newly synthesize[d] complementary strand three-quarters of the time.

Another naturally occurring process that may modif[y] DNA's information content is **deamination:** the removal [of] an amino ($-NH_2$) group. Deamination can change cytosin[e] to uracil (U), the nitrogenous base found in RNA but not i[n] DNA. Because U pairs with A rather than G, deaminatio[n] followed by replication may alter a C–G base pair to a T–[A] pair in future generations of DNA molecules (**Fig. 7.6b**[)]; such a C–G to T–A change is a transition mutation.

Other assaults include naturally occurring radiation suc[h] as cosmic rays and X-rays, which break the sugar-phospha[te] backbone (**Fig. 7.6c**); ultraviolet light, which causes adjace[nt] thymine residues to become chemically linked into thymine[-] thymine dimers (**Fig. 7.6d**); and oxidative damage to any [of] the four bases (**Fig. 7.6e**). All of these changes alter th[e] information content of the DNA molecule.

Mistakes during DNA replication

If the cellular machinery for some reason incorporates a[n] incorrect base during replication, for instance, a C opp[o]site an A instead of the expected T, then during the ne[xt] replication cycle, one of the daughter DNAs will hav[e] the normal A–T base pair, while the other will have [a] mutant G–C. Careful measurements of the fidelity of re[p]lication *in vivo,* in both bacteria and human cells, sho[w] that such errors are exceedingly rare, occurring less th[an] once in every 10^9 base pairs. That is equivalent to typi[ng] this entire book 1000 times while making only one typi[ng] error. Considering the complexities of helix unwindin[g,] base pairing, and polymerization, this level of accuracy [is] amazing. How do cells achieve it?

The replication machinery minimizes errors throug[h] successive stages of correction. In the test tube, DNA pol[y]merases replicate DNA with an error rate of about o[ne] mistake in every 10^6 bases copied. This rate is about 100[0-] fold worse than that achieved by the cell. Even so, it [is] impressively low and is only attained because polymera[se] molecules provide, along with their polymerization fun[c]tion, a proofreading/editing function in the form of [a] nuclease that is activated whenever the polymerase mak[es] a mistake. This nuclease portion of the polymerase mol[e]cule, called the *3'-to-5' exonuclease,* recognizes a mi[s]paired base and excises it, allowing the polymerase to co[py] the nucleotide correctly on the next try (**Fig. 7.7**). With[out] its nuclease portion, DNA polymerase would have an er[ror]

Figure 7.6 How natural processes can change the information stored in DNA. (a) In depurination, the hydrolysis of A or G bases leaves a DNA strand with an unspecified base. **(b)** In deamination, the removal of an amino group from C initiates a process that causes a transition after DNA replication. **(c)** X-rays break the sugar-phosphate backbone and thereby split a DNA molecule into smaller pieces, which may be spliced back together improperly. **(d)** Ultraviolet (UV) radiation causes adjacent Ts to form dimers, which can disrupt the readout of genetic information. **(e)** Irradiation causes the formation of *free radicals* (such as oxygen molecules with an unpaired electron) that can alter individual bases. Here, the pairing of the altered base GO with A creates a transversion that changes a G–C base pair to T–A.

(a) Depurination

(b) Deamination

(c) X-rays break the DNA backbone

(d) UV light produces thymine dimers

(e) Oxidation

rate of one mistake in every 10^4 bases copied, so its editing function improves the fidelity of replication 100-fold. DNA polymerase *in vivo* is part of a replication system including many other proteins that collectively improve on the error rate another 10-fold, bringing it to within about 100-fold of the fidelity attained by the cell.

The 100-fold higher accuracy of the cell depends on a backup system called *methyl-directed mismatch repair* that notices and corrects residual errors in the newly replicated DNA. We present the details of this repair system later in the chapter when we describe the various ways in which cells attempt to correct mutations once they occur.

Unequal crossing-over and transposable elements

Some mutations arise from events other than chemical and physical assaults or replication errors. Erroneous recombination is one such mechanism. For example, in **unequal crossing-over,** two closely related DNA sequences that are located in different places on two homologous chromosomes can pair with each other during meiosis. If recombination takes place between the mispaired sequences, one homologous chromosome ends up with a duplication (a kind of insertion), while the other homolog sustains a

Figure 7.7 DNA polymerase's proofreading function. If DNA polymerase mistakenly adds an incorrect nucleotide at the 3′-end of the strand it is synthesizing, the enzyme's 3′-to-5′ exonuclease activity removes this nucleotide, giving the enzyme a second chance to add the correct nucleotide.

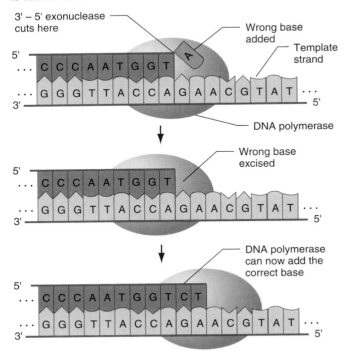

deletion. As **Fig. 7.8a** shows, some forms of red-green colorblindness arise from deletions and duplications in the genes that enable us to perceive red and green wavelengths of light; these reciprocal informational changes are the result of unequal crossing-over.

Another notable mechanism for altering DNA sequence involves the units of DNA known as **transposable elements (TEs).** TEs are DNA segments several hundred to several thousand base pairs long that move (or "transpose" or "jump") from place to place in the genome. If a TE jumps into a gene, it can disrupt the gene's function and cause a mutation. Certain TEs frequently insert themselves into particular genes and not others; this is one reason that mutation rates vary from gene to gene. Although some TEs move by making a copy that becomes inserted into a different chromosomal location while the initial version stays put, other TE types actually leave their original position when they move (**Fig. 7.8b**). Mutations caused by TEs that transpose by this second mechanism are exceptions to the general rule that the rate of reversion is lower than the rate of forward mutation. This is because TE transposition can occur relatively frequently, and when it is accompanied by excision of the TE, the original sequence and function of the gene are restored. Chapter 13 discusses additional genetic consequences of TE behavior.

Unstable trinucleotide repeats

In 1992, a group of molecular geneticists discovered an unusual and completely unexpected type of mutation in humans: the excessive amplification of a CGG base triple

Figure 7.8 How unequal crossing-over and the movement of transposable elements (TEs) change DNA's information content. (a) If two nearby regions contain a similar DNA sequence, the two homologous chromosomes may pair out of register during meiosis and produce gametes with either a deletion or a reciprocal duplication. Colorblindness in humans can result from unequal crossing-over between the nearby and highly similar genes for red and green photoreceptors. **(b)** TEs move around the genome. Some TEs copy themselves before moving, while others are excised from their original positions during transposition. Insertion of a TE into a gene often has phenotypic consequences.

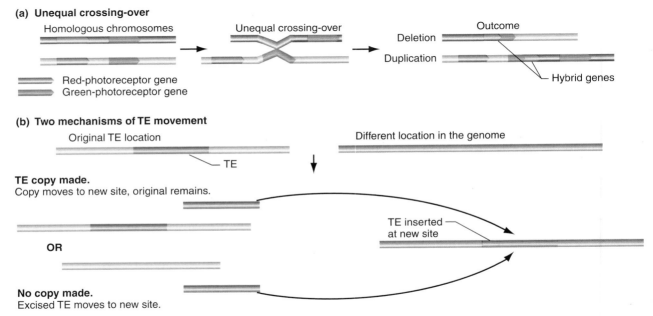

normally repeated only a few to 50 times in succession. f, for example, a normal allele of a gene carries 5 con-ecutive repetitions of the base triplet CGG (that is, CGGCGGCGGCGGCGG on one strand), an abnormal llele resulting from mutation could carry 200 repeats in row. Further investigations revealed that repeats of sev-ral trinucleotides—CAG, CTG, and GAA, in addition to CGG—can be unstable such that the number of repeats ften increases or decreases in different cells of a single ndividual. Instability can also occur during the produc-on of gametes, resulting in changes in repeat number rom one generation to the next. The expansion and con-action of trinucleotide repeats has now been found not nly in humans but in many other species as well.

The rules governing trinucleotide repeat instability ppear to be quite complicated, but one general feature is nat the larger the number of repeats at a particular loca-on, the higher the probability that expansion and con-action will occur. Usually, tracts with less than 30–50 epetitions of a triplet change in size only infrequently, nd the mutations that do occur cause only small varia-ons in the repeat number. Larger tracts involving hun-reds of repeats change in size more frequently, and they lso exhibit more variation in the number of repetitions.

Researchers have not yet determined the precise mech-nism of triplet repeat amplification. One possibility is that egions with long trinucleotide repeats form unusual DNA ructures that are hard to replicate because they force the opying machinery to slip off, then hop back on, slip off, nen hop back on. Such stopping and starting may produce replication "stutter" that causes synthesis of the same trip-t to repeat over and over again, expanding the number of

copies. This type of mechanism could conversely shrink the size of the trinucleotide repeat tract if, after slipping off, the replication machinery restarts copying at a repeat farther down the template sequence. Whatever the cause, mutations of long trinucleotide stretches occur quite often, suggesting that the enzymes for excision or mismatch repair are not very efficient at restoring the original number of repeats.

The expansion of trinucleotide repeats is at the root of *fragile X syndrome,* one of the most common forms of human mental retardation, as well as Huntington disease and many other disorders of the nervous system. The Genetics and Society box "Unstable Trinucleotide Repeats and Fragile X Syndrome" on pp. 208–209 discusses the fascinating medical implications of this phenomenon.

> Many naturally occurring mechanisms can generate sponta-neous mutations. These include chemical or radiation assaults that modify DNA bases or break DNA chains, mistakes dur-ing DNA replication or recombination, the movement of transposable elements, and the expansion or contraction of unstable trinucleotide repeats.

Mutagens induce mutations

Mutations make genetic analysis possible, but most muta-tions appear spontaneously at such a low rate that research-ers have looked for controlled ways to increase their occurrence. H. J. Muller, an original member of Thomas Hunt Morgan's *Drosophila* group, first showed that expo-sure to a dose of X-rays higher than the naturally occurring level increases the mutation rate in fruit flies (**Fig. 7.9**).

igure 7.9 Exposure to X-rays increases the mutation rate in *Drosophila*. F₁ females are constructed that have an irradiated aternal X chromosome (*red line*), and a *Bar*-marked "balancer" maternal X chromosome (*wavy blue line*). These two chromosomes cannot combine because the balancer chromosome has multiple inversions (as explained in Chapter 13). Single F₁ females, each with a single X-ray-posed X chromosome from their father, are then individually mated with wild-type males. If the paternal X chromosome in any one F₁ female has X-ray-induced recessive lethal mutation (*m*), she can produce only Bar-eyed sons (*left*). If the X chromosome has no such mutation, this F₁ nale will produce both Bar-eyed and non-Bar-eyed sons (*right*).

GENETICS AND SOCIETY

Unstable Trinucleotide Repeats and Fragile X Syndrome

Expansions of the base triplet CGG cause a heritable disorder known as *fragile X syndrome*. Adults affected by this syndrome manifest several physical anomalies, including an unusually large head, long face, large ears, and in men, large testicles. They also exhibit moderate to severe mental retardation. Fragile X syndrome has been found in men and women of all races and ethnic backgrounds. The fragile X mutation is, in fact, a leading genetic cause of mental retardation worldwide, second only to the trisomy 21 that results in Down syndrome.

Specially prepared karyotypes of cells from people with fragile X symptoms reveal a slightly constricted, so-called fragile site near the tip of the long arm of the X chromosome (**Fig. A**). The long tracts of CGG trinucleotides, which make up the fragile X mutation, apparently produce a localized constricted region that can even break off in some karyotype preparations. Geneticists named the fragile X disorder for this specific pinpoint of fragility more than 20 years before they identified the mutation that gives rise to it.

The gene in which the fragile X mutation occurs is called *FMR-1* (for fragile-X-associated mental retardation). Near one end of the gene, different people carry a different number of repeats of the sequence CGG, and geneticists now have the molecular tools to quantify these differences. Normal alleles contain 5–54 of these triplet repeats, while the *FMR-1* gene in people with fragile X syndrome contains 200–4000 repeats (**Fig. B.1**). The rest of the gene's base sequence is the same in both normal and abnormal alleles.

The triplet repeat mutation that underlies fragile X syndrome has a surprising transmission feature. Alleles with a full-blown mutation are foreshadowed by *premutation alleles* that carry an intermediate number of repeats—more than 50 but fewer than 200 (**Fig. B.1**). Premutation alleles do not themselves generate fragile X symptoms in most carriers, but they show significant instability and

Figure A A karyotype reveals a fragile X chromosome. The fragile X site is seen on the bottom of both chromatids of the X chromosome at the *right*.

thus forecast the risk of genetic disease in a carrier's progeny. The greater the number of repeats in a premutation allele, the higher the risk of disease in that person's children. For example, if a woman carries a premutation allele with 60 CGG repeats, 17% of her offspring run the risk of exhibiting fragile X syndrome. If she carries a premutation allele with 90 repeats, close to 50% of her offspring will show symptoms. Interestingly, the expansion of *FMR-1* premutation alleles has some as-yet-unexplained relation to the

---

Muller exposed male *Drosophila* to increasingly large doses of X-rays and then mated these males with females that had one X chromosome containing an easy-to-recognize dominant mutation causing Bar eyes. This X chromosome (called a *balancer*) also carried chromosomal rearrangements known as inversions that prevented it from crossing-over with other X chromosomes. (Chapter 13 explains the details of this phenomenon.) Some of the F₁ daughters of this mating were heterozygotes carrying a mutagenized X from their father and a *Bar*-marked X from their mother. If X-rays induced a recessive lethal mutation anywhere on the paternally derived X chromosome, then these F₁ females would be unable to produce non-Bar-eyed sons. Thus, simply by noting the presence or absence of non-Bar-eyed sons, Muller could establish whether a mutation had occurred in any of the more than 1000 genes on the X chromosome that are essential to *Drosophila* viability. He concluded that the greater the X-ray dose, the greater the frequency of recessive lethal mutations.

Any physical or chemical agent that raises the frequency of mutations above the spontaneous rate is called a **mutagen.** Researchers use many different mutagens to produce mutations for study. With the Watson-Crick model of DNA structure as a guide, they can understand the action of most mutagens at the molecular level. The X-rays used by Muller to induce mutations on the X chromosome, for example, can break the sugar-phosphate backbones of DNA strands, sometimes at the same position on the two strands of the double helix. Multiple double-strand breaks produce DNA fragmentation, and the improper stitching back together of the fragments can cause inversions, deletions, or other rearrangements (see Fig. 7.6c).

Another molecular mechanism of mutagenesis involves mutagens known as **base analogs,** which are so similar in chemical structure to the normal nitrogenous bases that the replication machinery can incorporate them into DNA (**Fig. 7.10a,** p. 210). Because a base analog may have pairing properties different from those of the base it replaces, it can

Figure B Amplification of CGG triplet repeats correlates with the fragile X syndrome. (1) *FMR-1* genes in unaffected people generally have fewer than 50 CGG repeats. Unstable premutation alleles have between 50 and 200 repeats. Disease-causing alleles have more than 200 CGG repeats. **(2)** A fragile X pedigree showing the number of CGG repeats in each chromosome. Fragile X patients are almost always the progeny of mothers with premutation alleles.

(1) Effect of (CGG) repeat number

$(CGG)_{<50}$
Wild-type alleles

$(CGG)_{50-200}$
Premutation alleles

$(CGG)_{>200}$
Disease-causing alleles

(2) A fragile X pedigree

22/29   82   29/80

22/83   22/90   ~500

>200   >200

☐ Unaffected
▨ Affected
▨ Heterozygous or hemizygous for premutation allele

parental origin of the repeats. Whereas most male carriers transmit their *FMR-1* allele with only a small change in the number of repeats, many women with premutation alleles bear children with 250–4000 CGG repeats in their *FMR-1* gene (**Fig. B.2**). One possible explanation is that whatever conditions generate fragile X mutations occur most readily during oogenesis.

The CGG trinucleotide repeat expansion underlying fragile X syndrome has interesting implications for genetic counseling. Thousands of possible alleles of the *FMR-1* gene exist, ranging from the smallest normal allele isolated to date, with 5 triplet repeats, to the largest abnormal allele so far isolated, with roughly 4000 repeats. The relation between genotype and phenotype is clear at both ends of the triplet-repeat spectrum: Individuals whose alleles contain less than 55 repeats are normal, while people with an allele carrying more than 200 repeats are almost always moderately to severely retarded. With an intermediate number of repeats, however, expression of the mental retardation phenotype is highly variable, depending to an unknown degree on chance, the environment, and modifier genes.

This range of variable expressivity leads to an ethical dilemma: Where should medical geneticists draw the line in their assessment of risk? Prospective parents with a family history of mental retardation may consult with a counselor to determine their options. The counselor would first test the parents for fragile X premutation alleles. If the couple is expecting a child, the counselor would also want to analyze the fetal cells directly by amniocentesis, to determine whether the fetus carries an expanded number of CGG repeats in its *FMR-1* gene. If the results indicate the presence of an allele in the middle range of triplet repeats, the counselor will have to acknowledge the unpredictability of outcomes. The prospective parents' difficult decision of whether or not to continue the pregnancy will then rest on the very shaky ground of an inconclusive, overall evaluation of risk.

cause base substitutions on the complementary strand synthesized in the next round of DNA replication. Other chemical mutagens generate substitutions by directly altering a base's chemical structure and properties (**Fig. 7.10b**). Again, the effects of these changes become fixed in the genome when the altered base causes incorporation of an incorrect complementary base during a subsequent round of replication.

Yet another class of chemical mutagens consists of compounds known as **intercalators**: flat, planar molecules that can sandwich themselves between successive base pairs and disrupt the machinery for replication, recombination, or repair (**Fig. 7.10c**). The disruption may eventually generate deletions or insertions of a single base pair.

Scientists use mutagens such as X-rays, base analogs, and intercalators to increase the frequency of mutation as an aid to genetic research.

DNA repair mechanisms minimize mutations

Natural environments expose genomes to many kinds of chemicals or radiation that can alter DNA sequences; furthermore, the side effects of normal DNA metabolism within cells, such as inaccuracies in DNA replication or the movement of TEs, can also be mutagenic. Cells have evolved a variety of enzymatic systems that locate and repair damaged DNA and thereby dramatically diminish the high potential for mutation. The combination of these repair systems must be extremely efficient, because the rates of spontaneous mutation observed for almost all genes are very low.

Reversal of DNA base alterations

If methyl or ethyl groups were mistakenly added to guanine (as in Fig. 10.7b), *alkyltransferase* enzymes can remove them so as to recreate the original base. Other enzymes remedy other base structure alterations. For example, the

Figure 7.10 How mutagens alter DNA. (a) Base analogs incorporated into DNA may pair aberrantly, allowing the addition of incorrect nucleotides to the opposite strand during replication. **(b)** Some mutagens alter the structure of bases such that they pair inappropriately in the next round of replication. **(c)** Intercalating agents are roughly the same size and shape as a base pair of the double helix. Their incorporation into DNA produces insertions or deletions of single base pairs.

Type of Mutagen	Chemical Action of Mutagen
(a) Replace a base: Base analogs have a chemical structure almost identical to that of a DNA base.	5-Bromouracil: almost identical to thymine. Normally pairs with A; in transient state, pairs with G.
(b) Alter base structure and properties: *Hydroxylating agents:* add a hydroxyl (–OH) group	Hydroxylamine adds –OH to cytosine; with the –OH, hydroxylated C now pairs with A instead of G.
Alkylating agents: add ethyl (–CH₂–CH₃) or methyl (–CH₃) groups	Ethylmethane sulfonate adds an ethyl group to guanine or thymine. Modified G pairs with T above, and modified T pairs with G (not shown).
Deaminating agents: remove amine (–NH₂) groups	Nitrous acid modifies cytosine to uracil, which pairs with A instead of G; modifies adenine to hypoxanthine, a base that pairs with C instead of T.
(c) Insert between bases: Intercalating agents	Proflavin intercalates into the double helix. This disrupts DNA metabolism, eventually resulting in deletion or addition of a base pair.

(Continued

Figure 7.10 How mutagens alter DNA. (*Continued*)

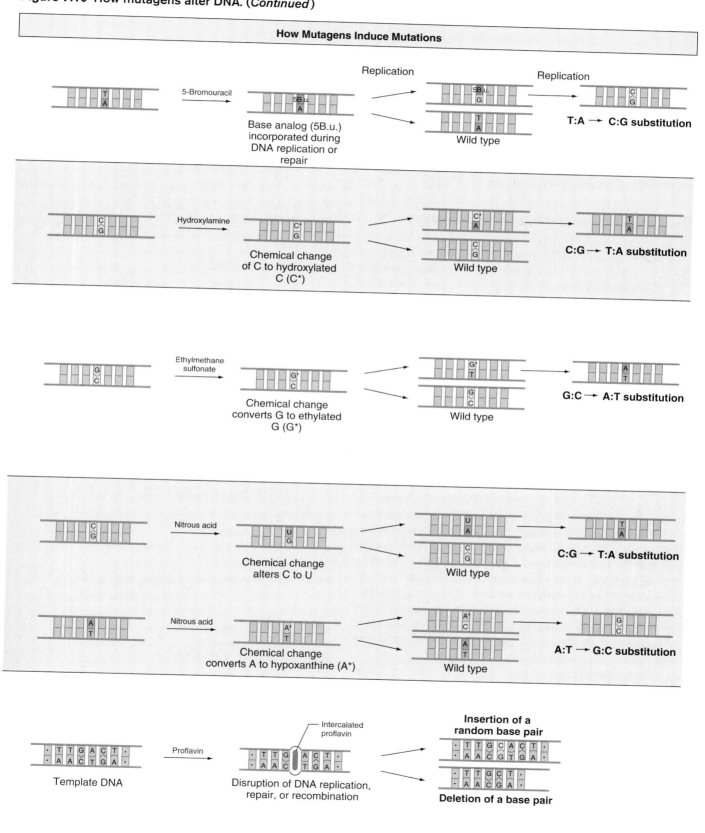

How Mutagens Induce Mutations

enzyme *photolyase* recognizes the thymine–thymine dimers produced by exposure to ultraviolet light (review Fig. 7.6d) and reverses the damage by splitting the chemical linkage between the thymines.

Interestingly, the photolyase enzyme works only in the presence of visible light. In carrying out its DNA repair tasks, it associates with a small molecule called a *chromophore* that absorbs light in the visible range of the spectrum; the enzyme then uses the energy captured by the chromophore to split thymine–thymine dimers. Because it does not function in the dark, the photolyase mechanism is called *light repair,* or *photorepair.*

Removal of damaged bases or nucleotides

Many repair systems use the general strategy of *homology-dependent repair* in which they first remove a small region from the DNA strand that contains the altered nucleotide, and then use the other strand as a template to resynthesize the removed region. This strategy makes use of one of the great advantages of the double-helical structure: If one strand sustains damage, cells can use complementary base pairing with the undamaged strand to re-create the original sequence.

Base excision repair is one homology-dependent mechanism. In this type of repair, enzymes called *DNA glycosylases* cleave an altered nitrogenous base from the sugar of its nucleotide, releasing the base and creating an apurinic or apyrimidinic (AP) site in the DNA chain (**Fig. 7.11**). Different glycosylase enzymes cleave specific damaged bases. Base excision repair is particularly important in the removal of uracil from DNA (recall that uracil often results from the natural deamination of cytosine; review Fig. 7.6b). In this repair process, after the enzyme *uracil-DNA glycosylase* has removed uracil from its sugar, leaving an AP site, the enzyme *AP endonuclease* makes a nick in the DNA backbone at the AP site. Other enzymes (known as *DNA exonucleases*) attack the nick and remove nucleotides from its vicinity to create a gap in the previously damaged strand. DNA polymerase fills in the gap by copying the undamaged strand, restoring the original nucleotide in the process. Finally, DNA ligase seals up the backbone of the newly repaired DNA strand.

Nucleotide excision repair (**Fig. 7.12**) removes alterations that base excision cannot repair because the cell lacks a DNA glycosylase that recognizes the problem base. Nucleotide excision repair depends on enzyme complexes containing more than one protein molecule. In *E. coli,* these complexes are made of two out of three possible proteins: UvrA, UvrB, and UvrC. One of the complexes (UvrA + UvrB) patrols the DNA for irregularities, detecting lesions that disrupt Watson-Crick base pairing and thus distort the double helix (such as thymine–thymine dimers that have not been corrected by photorepair). A second complex (UvrB + UvrC) cuts the damaged strand in two places that

Figure 7.11 Base excision repair removes damaged bases. Glycosylase enzymes remove aberrant bases [like uracil (*red*), formed by the deamination of cytosine], leaving an AP site. AP endonuclease cuts the sugar-phosphate backbone, creating a nick. Exonucleases extend the nick into a gap, which is filled in with the correct information (*green*) by DNA polymerase. DNA ligase reseals the corrected strand.

1. Deaminated DNA with uracil

2. Glycosylase removes uracil, leaving an AP site.

3. AP endonuclease cuts backbone to make a nick at the AP site.

4. DNA exonucleases remove nucleotides near the nick, creating a gap.

5. DNA polymerase synthesizes new DNA to fill in the gap.

6. DNA ligase seals the nick.

flank the damage. This double-cutting excises a short region of the damaged strand and leaves a gap that will be filled in by DNA polymerase and sealed with DNA ligase.

Correction of DNA replication errors

DNA polymerase is remarkably accurate in copying DNA, but the DNA replication system still makes about 100 times more mistakes than most cells can tolerate. A backup repair system called **methyl-directed mismatch repair** corrects almost all of these errors (**Fig. 7.13**). Because mismatch repair is active only *after* DNA replication, this system needs to solve a difficult problem. Suppose that a G–C pair

Figure 7.12 Nucleotide excision repair corrects damaged nucleotides. A complex of the UvrA and UvrB proteins (*not shown*) scans DNA for distortions caused by DNA damage, such as thymine–thymine dimers. At the damaged site, UvrA dissociates from UvrB, allowing UvrB (*red*) to associate with UvrC (*blue*). These enzymes nick the DNA exactly 4 nucleotides to one side of the damage and 7 nucleotides to the other side, releasing a small fragment of single-stranded DNA. DNA polymerases then resynthesize the missing information (*green*), and DNA ligase reseals the now-corrected strand.

1. Exposure to UV light

2. Thymine dimer forms.

3. UvrB and C endonucleases nick strand containing dimer.

4. Damaged fragment is released from DNA.

5. DNA polymerase fills in the gap with new DNA (*green*).

6. DNA ligase seals the repaired strand.

Figure 7.13 In bacteria, methyl-directed mismatch repair corrects mistakes in replication. Parental strands are in *light blue* and newly synthesized strands are *purple*. The MutS protein is *green,* MutL is *dark blue,* and MutH is *yellow.* See text for details.

(a) Parental strands are marked with methyl groups.

(b) MutS and MutL recognize mismatch in replicated DNA.

(c) MutL recruits MutH to GATC; MutH makes a nick (*short arrow*) in strand opposite methyl tag.

(d) DNA exonucleases (*not shown*) excise DNA from unmethylated new strand.

(e) Repair and methylation of newly synthesized DNA strand

has been copied to produce two daughter molecules, one of which has the correct G–C base pair, the other an incorrect G–T. The mismatch repair system can easily recognize the incorrectly matched G–T base pair because the improper base pairing distorts the double helix, resulting in abnormal bulges and hollows. But how does the system know whether to correct the pair to a G–C or to an A–T?

Bacteria solve this problem by placing a distinguishing mark on the parental DNA strands at specific places: everywhere the sequence GATC occurs, the enzyme *adenine methylase* puts a methyl group on the A (Fig. 7.13a). Shortly after replication, the old template strand bears the methyl mark, while the new daughter strand—which contains the wrong nucleotide—is as yet unmarked (Fig. 7.13b). A pair of proteins in *E. coli,* called MutL and MutS, detect and bind to the mismatched nucleotides. MutL and MutS direct another protein, MutH, to nick the newly synthesized strand of DNA at a position across from the nearest methylated GATC; MutH can discriminate the newly synthesized strand because its GATC is *not* methylated (Fig. 7.13c). DNA exonucleases then remove all the nucleotides between the nick and a position just beyond the mismatch, leaving a gap on the new, unmethylated strand (Fig. 7.13d). DNA polymerase can now resynthesize the information using the old, methylated strand as a template, and DNA ligase then seals up the repaired strand.

With the completion of replication and repair, enzymes mark the new strand with methyl groups so that its parental origin will be evident in the next round of replication (Fig. 7.13e).

Eukaryotic cells also have a mismatch correction system, but we do not yet know how this system distinguishes templates from newly replicated strands. Unlike prokaryotes, GATCs in eukaryotes are not tagged with methyl groups, and eukaryotes do not seem to have a protein closely related to MutH. One potentially interesting clue is that the MutS and MutL proteins in eukaryotes associate with DNA replication factors; perhaps these interactions might help MutS and MutL identify the strand to be repaired.

> Cells contain many enzymatic systems to repair DNA. The most accurate systems take advantage of complementary base pairing, using the undamaged strand as a template to correct the damaged DNA strand. Some examples are base or nucleotide excision repair systems, and mismatch repair systems.

Error-prone repair systems: A last resort

The repair systems just described are very accurate in repairing DNA damage because they are able to replace damaged nucleotides with a complementary copy of the undamaged strand. However, cells sometimes become exposed to levels or types of mutagens that they cannot handle with these high-fidelity repair systems. Strong doses of UV light, for example, might make more thymine–thymine dimers than the cell can fix. Any unrepaired damage has severe consequences for cell division: The DNA polymerases normally used in replication will stall at such lesions, so the cells cannot proliferate. Although these cells can initiate emergency responses that may allow them to survive and divide despite the stalling, their ability to proceed in such circumstances comes at the expense of introducing new mutations into the genome.

One type of emergency repair in bacteria, called the **SOS system** (after the Morse code distress signal), relies on error-prone (or "sloppy") DNA polymerases. These sloppy DNA polymerases are not available for normal DNA replication; they are produced only in the presence of DNA damage. The damage-induced, error-prone DNA polymerases are attracted to replication forks that have become stalled at sites of unrepaired, damaged nucleotides. There they add random nucleotides to the strand being synthesized opposite the damaged bases. The SOS polymerase enzymes thus allow the cell with damaged DNA to divide into two daughter cells, but because the sloppy polymerases restore the proper nucleotide only 1/4 of the time, the genomes of these daughter cells carry new mutations. In bacteria, the mutagenic effect of many mutagens either depends on, or is enhanced by, the SOS system.

Figure 7.14 Repair of double-strand breaks by nonhomologous end-joining. The proteins KU70, KU80, and PK$_{CS}$ bind to DNA ends and bring them together. Other proteins (*not shown*) trim the ends so as to remove any single-stranded regions, and then ligate the two ends together. This mechanism may result in the deletion of nucleotides and is thus potentially mutagenic.

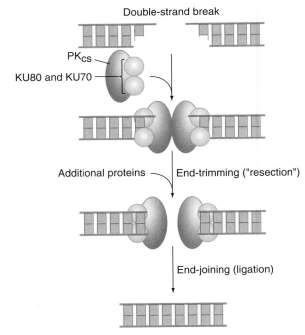

Double-strand break

PK$_{CS}$

KU80 and KU70

Additional proteins — End-trimming ("resection")

End-joining (ligation)

Another kind of emergency repair system deals with a particularly dangerous kind of DNA lesion: *double-strand breaks,* in which both strands of the double helix are broken at nearby sites (**Fig. 7.14**). Recall from Chapter 6 that double-strand breaks occur as the first step in meiotic recombination. We do not consider this type of double-strand break here because the mechanism of recombination repairs them with high fidelity and efficiency using complementary base pairing (review Fig. 6.24 on pp. 190–193). However, double-strand breaks can also result from exposure to high-energy radiation such as X-rays (Fig. 7.6c) or highly reactive oxygen molecules. If left unrepaired, these breaks can lead to a variety of potentially lethal chromosome aberrations, such as large deletions, inversions, or translocations.

Cells can restitch the ends formed by such double-strand breaks using a mechanism called **nonhomologous end-joining,** which relies on a group of three proteins that bind to the strand ends and bring them close together (Fig. 7.14). After binding, these proteins recruit other proteins that cut back (or "resect") any overhanging nucleotides on the ends that do not have a complementary nucleotide to pair with, and then join the two ends together. Because of the resection step, nonhomologous end-joining can result in the loss of DNA and is thus error prone. Evidently, the mutagenic effects of nonhomologous end-joining are less deleterious to the cell than genomic injuries caused by unrepaired double-strand breaks.

Error-prone DNA repair systems, such as the SOS system and nonhomologous end-joining, do not utilize complementary base pairing. Cells use these systems only as a last resort.

Health consequences of mutations in genes encoding DNA repair proteins

Although differences of detail exist between the DNA repair systems of various organisms, DNA repair mechanisms appear in some form in virtually all species. For example, humans have six proteins with amino acid compositions that are about 25% identical with that of the *E. coli* mismatch repair protein MutS. DNA repair systems are thus very old and must have evolved soon after life emerged roughly 3.5 billion years ago. Some scientists believe DNA repair became essential when plants first started to deposit oxygen into the atmosphere, because oxygen favors the formation of free radicals that can damage DNA.

The many known human hereditary diseases associated with the defective repair of DNA damage reveal how crucial these mechanisms are for survival. In one example, the cells of patients with *Xeroderma pigmentosum* lack the ability to conduct nucleotide excision repair; these people are homozygous for mutations in one of seven genes encoding enzymes that normally function in this repair system. As a result, the thymine–thymine dimers caused by ultraviolet light cannot be removed efficiently. Unless these people avoid all exposure to sunlight, their skin cells begin to accumulate mutations that eventually lead to skin cancer (**Fig. 7.15**). In another example, researchers have recently learned that hereditary forms of colorectal cancer in humans are associated with mutations in human genes that are closely related to the *E. coli* genes encoding the mismatch-repair proteins MutS and MutL. Chapter 17 discusses the fascinating connections between DNA repair and cancer in more detail.

Mutations in genes encoding DNA repair proteins can allow other mutations to accumulate throughout the genome, often leading toward cancer.

Mutations have consequences for species evolution as well as individual survival

"The capacity to blunder slightly is the real marvel of DNA. Without this special attribute, we would still be anaerobic bacteria and there would be no music." In these two sentences, the eminent medical scientist and self-appointed "biology watcher" Lewis Thomas acknowledges that changes in DNA are behind the phenotypic variations that are the raw material on which natural selection has acted for billions of years to drive evolution. The wide-ranging variation in the genetic makeup of the human population—and other populations as well—is, in fact, the result of a balance between: (1) the continuous introduction of new mutations; (2) the loss of deleterious mutations because of the selective disadvantage they impose on the individuals that carry them; and (3) the increase in frequency of rare mutations that either provide a selective advantage to the individuals carrying them or that spread through a population by other means.

In sexually reproducing multicellular organisms, only germline mutations that can be passed on to the next generation play a role in evolution. Nevertheless, mutations in somatic cells can still have an impact on the well-being and survival of individuals. Somatic mutations in genes that help regulate the cell cycle may, for example, lead to cancer. The U.S. Food and Drug Administration tries to identify potential cancer-causing agents (known as carcinogens) by using the **Ames test** to screen for chemicals that cause mutations in bacterial cells (**Fig. 7.16**). This test asks whether a particular chemical can induce histidine$^+$ (*his$^+$*) revertants of a special histidine$^-$ (*his$^-$*) mutant strain of the bacterium *Salmonella typhimurium*. The *his$^+$* revertants can synthesize all the histidine they need from simple compounds in their environment; whereas the original *his$^-$* mutants cannot make histidine, so they can survive only if histidine is supplied.

The advantage of the Ames test is that only revertants can grow on petri plates that do not contain histidine, so it is possible to examine large numbers of cells from an originally *his$^-$* culture to find the rare *his$^+$* revertants induced by the chemical in question. To increase the sensitivity of mutation detection, the *his$^-$* strain used in the Ames test system contains a second mutation that inactivates the nucleotide excision repair system and

Figure 7.15 Skin lesions in a xeroderma pigmentosum patient. This heritable disease is caused by the lack of a critical enzyme in the nucleotide excision repair system.

Figure 7.16 The Ames test identifies potential carcinogens. A compound to be tested is mixed with cells of a *his⁻* strain of *Salmonella typhimurium* and with a solution of rat liver enzymes (which can sometimes convert a harmless compound into a mutagen). Only *his⁺* revertants grow on a petri plate without histidine. If this plate (*left*) has more *his⁺* revertants than a control plate (also without histidine), containing unexposed cells (*right*), the compound is considered mutagenic and a potential carcinogen. The rare revertants on the control plate represent the spontaneous rate of mutation.

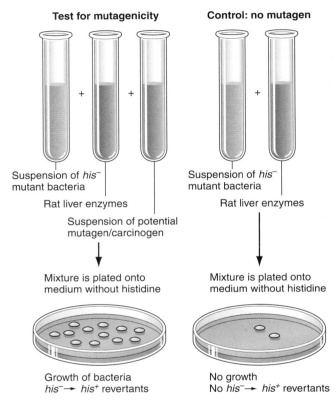

Test for mutagenicity | Control: no mutagen

Suspension of *his⁻* mutant bacteria

Rat liver enzymes

Suspension of potential mutagen/carcinogen

Suspension of *his⁻* mutant bacteria

Rat liver enzymes

Mixture is plated onto medium without histidine

Mixture is plated onto medium without histidine

Growth of bacteria
his⁻ → *his⁺* revertants

No growth
No *his⁻* → *his⁺* revertants

thereby prevents the ready repair of mutations caused by the potential mutagen, and a third mutation causing defects in the cell wall that allows tested chemicals easier access to the cell interior.

Because most agents that cause mutations in bacteria should also damage the DNA of higher eukaryotic organisms, any mutagen that increases the rate of mutation in bacteria might be expected to cause cancer in people and other mammals. Mammals, however, have complicated metabolic processes capable of inactivating hazardous chemicals. Other biochemical events in mammals can create a mutagenic substance from nonhazardous chemicals. To simulate the action of mammalian metabolism, toxicologists often add a solution of rat liver enzymes to the chemical under analysis by the Ames test (Fig. 7.16). Because this simulation is not perfect, Food and Drug Administration agents ultimately assess whether bacterial mutagens identified by the Ames test can cause cancer in rodents by including the agents in test animals' diets.

Mutations are the ultimate source of variation within and between species. Although some mutations confer a selective advantage, most are deleterious. DNA repair systems help keep mutations to a low level that balances organisms' need to evolve with their need to avoid damage to their genomes.

7.2 What Mutations Tell Us About Gene Structure

The science of genetics depends absolutely on mutations because we can track genes in crosses only through the phenotypic effects of their mutant variants. In the 1950s and 1960s, scientists realized they could also use mutations to learn how DNA sequences along a chromosome constitute individual genes. These investigators wanted to collect a large series of mutations in a single gene and analyze how these mutations are arranged with respect to each other. For this approach to be successful, they had to establish that various mutations were, in fact, in the same gene. This was not a trivial exercise, as illustrated by the following situation.

Early *Drosophila* geneticists identified a large number of X-linked recessive mutations affecting the normally red wild-type eye color (**Fig. 7.17**). The first of these to be discovered produced the famous white eyes studied by Morgan's group. Other mutations caused a whole palette of hues to appear in the eyes: darkened shades such as garnet and ruby; bright colors such as vermilion, cherry, and coral; and lighter pigmentations known as apricot, buff, and carnation. This wide variety of eye color phenotypes posed a puzzle: Were the mutations that caused them multiple alleles of a single gene, or did they affect more than one gene?

Complementation testing reveals whether two mutations are in a single gene or in different genes

Researchers commonly define a gene as a functional unit that directs the appearance of a molecular product that, in turn, contributes to a particular phenotype. They can use this definition to determine whether two mutations are in the same gene or in different genes. If two homologous chromosomes in an individual each carrie a mutation recessive to wild type, a normal phenotype will result if the mutations are in different genes. The normal phenotype occurs because almost all recessive mutations disrupt a gene's function (as will be explained in Chapter 8). The dominant wild-type alleles on each of the two homologs can make up for, or **complement**

Figure 7.17 *Drosophila* **eye color mutations produce a variety of phenotypes.** Flies carrying different X-linked eye color mutations. From the *left:* ruby, white, and apricot; a wild-type eye is at the *far right*.

the defect in the other chromosome by generating enough of both gene products to yield a normal phenotype (**Fig. 7.18a,** *left*).

In contrast, if the recessive mutations on the two homologous chromosomes are in the same gene, no wild-type allele of that gene exists in the individual and neither mutated copy of the gene will be able to perform the normal function. As a result, no complementation will occur and no normal gene product will be made, so a mutant phenotype will appear (Fig. 7.18a, *right*). Ironically, a collection of mutations that do *not* complement each other is known as a **complementation group.** Geneticists often use "complementation group" as a synonym for "gene" because the mutations in a complementation group all affect the same unit of function, and thus, the same gene.

A simple test based on the idea of a gene as a unit of function can determine whether or not two mutations are alleles of the same gene. You simply examine the phenotype of a heterozygous individual in which one homolog of a particular chromosome carries one of the recessive mutations and the other homolog carries the other recessive mutation. If the phenotype is wild type, the mutations cannot be in the same gene. This technique is known as **complementation testing.** For example, because a female *Drosophila* heterozygous for garnet and ruby (*garnet ruby⁺ / garnet⁺ ruby*) has wild-type brick-red eyes, it is possible to conclude that the mutations causing garnet and ruby colors complement each other and are therefore in different genes.

Complementation testing has, in fact, shown that garnet, ruby, vermilion, and carnation pigmentation are governed by separate genes. But chromosomes carrying mutations yielding white, cherry, coral, apricot, and buff phenotypes fail to complement each other. These mutations therefore make up different alleles of a single gene. *Drosophila* geneticists named this gene the *white*, or *w*, gene after the first mutation observed; they designate the

wild-type allele as w^+ and the various mutations as w^l (the original white-eyed mutation discovered by T. H. Morgan, often simply designated as w), w^{cherry}, w^{coral}, $w^{apricot}$, and w^{buff}. As an example, the eyes of a w^l / $w^{apricot}$ female are a dilute apricot color; because the phenotype of this heterozygote is not wild type, the two mutations are allelic. **Figure 7.18b** illustrates how researchers collate data from many complementation tests in a **complementation table.** Such a table helps visualize the relationships among a large group of mutants.

In *Drosophila*, mutations in the *w* gene map very close together in the same region of the X chromosome, while mutations in other eye color genes lie elsewhere on the chromosome (**Fig. 7.18c**). This result suggests that genes are not disjointed entities with parts spread out from one end of a chromosome to another; each gene, in fact, occupies only a relatively small, discrete area of a chromosome. Studies defining genes at the molecular level have shown that most genes consist of 1000–20,000 contiguous base pairs (bp). In humans, among the shortest genes are the roughly 500-bp-long genes that govern the production of histone proteins, while the longest gene so far identified is the Duchenne muscular dystrophy (*DMD*) gene, which has a length of more than 2 million nucleotide pairs. All known human genes fall somewhere between these extremes. To put these figures in perspective, an average human chromosome is approximately 130 million base pairs in length.

The complementation test looks at the phenotype of individuals simultaneously heterozygous for two different recessive mutations. A mutant phenotype indicates that the mutations fail to complement each other, that is, they are in the same gene (complementation group). A wild-type phenotype indicates the mutations complement each other, and thus are in different genes.

Figure 7.18 Complementation testing of *Drosophila* eye color mutations. (a) A heterozygote has one mutation (m₁) on one chromosome and a different mutation (m₂) on its homolog. If the mutations are in different genes, the heterozygote will be wild type; the mutations complement each other (*left*). If both mutations affect the same gene, the phenotype will be mutant; the mutations do not complement each other (*right*). Complementation testing makes sense only when both mutations are recessive to wild type. **(b)** This complementation table reveals five complementation groups (five different genes) for eye color. A "+" indicates mutant combinations with wild type eye color; these mutations complement and are thus in different genes. Several mutations fail to complement (−) and are thus alleles of one gene, *white*. **(c)** Recombination mapping shows that mutations in different genes are often far apart, while different mutations in the same gene are very close together.

(a) Complementation testing

(b) A complementation table: X-linked eye color mutations in *Drosophila*

Mutation	white	garnet	ruby	vermilion	cherry	coral	apricot	buff	carnation
white	−	+	+	+	−	−	−	−	+
garnet		−	+	+	+	+	+	+	+
ruby			−	+	+	+	+	+	+
vermilion				−	+	+	+	+	+
cherry					−	−	−	−	+
coral						−	−	−	+
apricot							−	−	+
buff								−	+
carnation									−

(c) Genetic map: X-linked eye color mutations in *Drosophila*

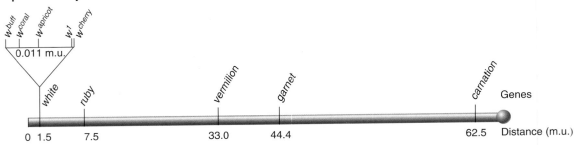

A gene is a set of nucleotide pairs that can mutate independently and recombine with each other

Although complementation testing makes it possible to distinguish mutations in different genes from mutations in the same gene, it does not clarify how the structure of a gene can accommodate different mutations and how these different mutations can alter phenotype in different ways. Does each mutation change the whole gene at a single stroke in a particular way, or does it change only a specific part of a gene, while other mutations alter other parts?

In the late 1950s, the American geneticist Seymour Benzer used recombination analysis to show that two different mutations that did not complement each other and were therefore known to be in the same gene can in fact change different parts of that gene. He reasoned that if recombination can occur not only between genes but within a gene as well, crossovers between homologous chromosomes carrying different mutations known to be in the same gene could in theory generate a wild type allele (**Fig. 7.19**). Because mutations affecting a single gene are likely to lie very close together, it is necessary to examine a very large number of progeny to see even one crossover event between them. The resolution of the experimental system must thus be extremely high, allowing rapid detection of rare genetic events. For his experimental organism, Benzer chose bacteriophage T4, a DNA virus that infects *Escherichia coli* cells.

Figure 7.19 How recombination within a gene could generate a wild-type allele. Suppose a gene, indicated by the region between brackets, is composed of many sites that can mutate independently. Recombination between mutations m₁ and m₂ at different sites in the same gene produces a wild-type allele and a reciprocal allele containing both mutations.

Original chromosomes	Recombination event	Resultant chromosomes

(**Fig. 7.20a**). Because each T4 phage that infects a bacterium generates 100–1000 phage progeny in less than an hour, Benzer could easily produce enough rare recombinants for his analysis (Fig. 7.20a.1 and 2). Moreover, by exploiting a peculiarity of certain T4 mutations, he devised conditions that allowed only recombinant phages, and not parental phages, to proliferate.

The experimental system: *rII⁻* mutations of bacteriophage T4

Even though bacteriophages are too small to be seen without the aid of an electron microscope, a simple technique makes it possible to detect their presence with the unaided eye (Fig. 7.20a.3). To do this, researchers mix a population of bacteriophage particles with a much larger number of bacteria and then pour this mixture onto a petri plate, where the cells are immobilized in a nutrient agar. If a single phage infects a single bacterial cell somewhere on this so-called **lawn** of bacteria, the cell produces and releases progeny viral particles that diffuse away to infect adjacent bacteria, which, in turn, produce and release yet more phage progeny. With each release of virus particles, the bacterial host cell dies. Thus, several cycles of phage infection, replication, and release produce a circular cleared area in the plate, called a **plaque,** devoid of living bacterial cells. The rest of the petri plate surface is covered by an opalescent lawn of living bacteria.

Most plaques contain from 1 million to 10 million viral progeny of the single bacteriophage that originally infected a cell in that position on the petri plate. Sequential dilution of phage-containing solutions makes it possible to measure the number of phages in a particular plaque and arrive at a countable number of viral particles (Fig. 7.20a.4).

When Benzer first looked for genetic traits associated with bacteriophage T4, he found mutants that, when added to a lawn of *E. coli* B strain bacteria, produced larger plaques with sharper, more clearly rounded edges than those produced by the wild-type bacteriophage (**Fig. 7.20b**). Because these changes in plaque morphology seemed to result from the abnormally rapid lysis of the host bacteria, Benzer named the mutations *r* for "rapid lysis." Many *r* mutations map to a region of the T4 chromosome known as the *rII* region; these are called *rII⁻* mutations.

An additional property of *rII⁻* mutations makes them ideal for the genetic **fine structure mapping** (the mapping of mutations within a gene) undertaken by Benzer. Wild-type *rII⁺* bacteriophages form plaques of normal shape and size on cells of both the *E. coli* B strain and a strain known as *E. coli* K(λ). The *rII⁻* mutants, however, have an altered host range: They cannot form plaques with *E. coli* K(λ) cells, although as we have seen, they produce large, unusually distinct plaques with *E. coli* B cells (Fig. 7.20b). The reason that *rII⁻* mutants are unable to infect cells of the K(λ) strain was not clear to Benzer, but this property allowed him to develop an extremely simple and effective test for *rII⁺* gene function.

The *rII* region has two genes

Before he could check whether two mutations in the same gene could recombine, Benzer had to be sure he was really looking at two mutations in a single gene. To verify this, he performed customized complementation tests tailored to two significant characteristics of bacteriophage T4: They are haploid (that is, each phage carries a single T4 chromosome), and they can replicate only in a host bacterium. Because T4 phages are haploid, Benzer needed to ensure that two T4 chromosomes entered the same bacterial cell in order to test for complementation between the mutations. In his complementation tests, he simultaneously infected *E. coli* K(λ) cells with two types of T4 chromosomes—one carried one *rII⁻* mutation, the other carried a different *rII⁻* mutation—and then looked for cell lysis (**Fig. 7.20c**). To ensure that the two kinds of phages would infect almost every bacterial cell, he added many more phages of each type than there were bacteria. If the two *rII⁻* mutations were in different genes, each of the mutant T4 chromosomes would supply one wild-type *rII⁺* gene function, making up for the lack of that function in the other chromosome and resulting in lysis. On the other hand, if the two *rII⁻* mutations were in the same gene, no plaques would appear, because neither mutant chromosome would be able to supply the missing function.

Benzer had to satisfy one final experimental requirement: For the complementation test to be meaningful, he had to make sure that the two *rII⁻* mutations were each recessive to wild type and did not interact with each other to produce an *rII⁻* phenotype dominant to wild type. He checked these points by a control experiment in which he placed the two *rII⁻* mutations on the same chromosome and then simultaneously infected *E. coli* K(λ) with these

How Benzer Analyzed the *rII* Genes of Bacteriophage T4

(a.1)

Head
Tail
Tail fibers
100 nm

Viral chromosome
Sheath
Tail fibers

(a.2)
1. Phage injects its DNA into host cell.
Host chromosome
2. Phage proteins synthesized; DNA replicated. Host chromosome degraded.
3. Assembly of phages within host cell
4. Lysis of host cell

(a.3)

(a.4)
Pipette out
0.01 ml   0.01 ml   0.1 ml
0.1 ml
Add plating bacteria
1 ml   1 ml   1 ml   1 ml
Concentrated solution of bacteriophages
Tubes containing medium without phage
25 plaques

(a) Working with bacteriophage T4

1. Bacteriophage T4 (at a magnification of approximately 100,000×) and in an artist's rendering. The viral chromosome is contained within a protein head. Other proteinaceous parts of the phage particle include the tail fibers, which help the phage attach to host cells, and the sheath, a conduit for injecting the phage chromosome into the host cell.

2. The lytic cycle of bacteriophage T4. A single phage particle infects a host cell; the phage DNA replicates and directs the synthesis of viral protein components using the machinery of the host cell; the new DNA and protein components assemble into new bacteriophage particles. Eventual lysis of the host cell releases up to 1000 progeny bacteriophages into the environment.

3. Clear plaques of bacteriophages in a lawn of bacterial cells. A mixture of bacteriophages and a large number of bacteria are poured onto the agar surface of a petri plate. Uninfected bacterial cells grow, producing an opalescent lawn. A bacterial cell infected by even a single bacteriophage will lyse and release progeny bacteriophages, which can infect adjacent bacteria. Several cycles of infection result in a plaque: a circular cleared area containing millions of bacteriophages genetically identical to the one that originally infected the bacterial cell.

4. Counting bacteriophages by serial dilution. A small sample of a concentrated solution of bacteriophages is transferred to a test tube containing fresh medium, and a small sample of this dilution is transferred to another tube of fresh medium. Successive repeats of this process increase the degree of dilution. A sample of the final dilution, when mixed with bacteria and poured on the agar of a petri plate, yields a countable number of plaques from which it is possible to extrapolate back and calculate the number of bacteriophage particles in the starting solution. The original 1 ml of solution in this illustration contained roughly 2.5×10^7 bacteriophages.

(b) Phenotypic properties of *rII⁻* mutants of bacteriophage T4

1. *rII⁻* mutants, when plated on *E. coli* B cells, produce plaques that are larger and more distinct (with sharper edges) than plaques formed by *rII⁺* wild-type phage.

2. *rII⁻* mutants are particularly useful for looking at rare recombination events because they have an altered host range. In contrast to *rII⁺* wild-type phages, *rII⁻* mutants cannot form plaques in lawns of *E. coli* strain K(λ) host bacteria.

(b.1)

rII⁺
rII⁻
rII⁺

(b.2)

T4 strain	E. coli strain	
	B	K(λ)
rII⁻	Large, distinct	No plaques
rII⁺	Small, fuzzy	Small, fuzzy

(c.1) Complementation test

(*trans* configuration)

━━ Gene *rIIA*   ━━ Gene *rIIB*

(c.2) Control

(*cis* configuration)

Mixed infection

rII⁻ mut. 1   *rII⁻* mut. 2

E. coli K(λ)

m₁
m₂

rIIA   *rIIB*
nonfunctional   functional

No complementation
- no cell lysis
- no phage progeny

m₁
m₂

rIIA   *rIIB*
functional   functional

Complementation
- cell lysis
- phage progeny

rII⁻ mut.1+2   *rII⁺*

E. coli K(λ)

m₁ m₂

If mutations
are recessive,
cell lysis.

If mutations
are dominant,
no cell lysis.

(c) A customized complementation test between *rII⁻* mutants of bacteriophage T4

1. *E. coli* K(λ) cells are simultaneously infected with an excess of two different *rII⁻* mutants (m₁ and m₂). Inside the cell, the two mutations will be in *trans*; that is, they lie on different chromosomes. If the two mutations are in the same gene, they will affect the same function and cannot complement each other, so no progeny phages will be produced. If the two mutations are in different genes (*rIIA* and *rIIB*), they will complement each other, leading to progeny phage production and cell lysis.

2. An important control for this complementation test is the simultaneous infection of *E. coli* K(λ) bacteria with a wild-type T4 strain and a T4 strain containing both m₁ and m₂. Inside the infected cells, the two mutations will be in *cis*; that is, they lie on the same chromosome. Release of phage progeny shows that both mutations are recessive to wild type and that there is no interaction between the mutations that prevents the cells from producing progeny phages. Complementation tests are meaningful only if the two mutations tested are both recessive to wild type.

(d.1) Recombination test

rIIA₁   *rIIA₂*

rIIA₁   *rIIA₂*

E. coli B

Recombination

rIIA₁ *rIIA₂*

rII⁺   *rIIA₁* + *rIIA₂*
progeny wild type double mutant

Forms plaques   No plaques
on *E. coli* K(λ) on *E. coli* K(λ)

(d.2) Control

rIIA₁   *rIIA₂*

E. coli B   *E. coli* B

rIIA₁   *rIIA₂*

No plaques on
E. coli K(λ)

(d) Detecting recombination between two mutations in the same gene

1. *E. coli* B cells are simultaneously infected with a large excess of two different *rIIA⁻* mutants (*rIIA₁* and *rIIA₂*). If no recombination between the two *rIIA⁻* mutations takes place, progeny phages will carry either of the original mutations and will be phenotypically *rII⁻*. If recombination between the two mutations occurs, one of the products will be an *rII⁺* recombinant, while the reciprocal product will be a double mutant chromosome containing both *rIIA₁* and *rIIA₂*. When the phage progeny subsequently infect *E. coli* K(λ) bacteria, only *rII⁺* recombinants will be able to form plaques.

2. As a control, *E. coli* B cells are infected with a large amount of only one kind of mutant (*rIIA₁* or *rIIA₂*). The only *rII⁺* phages that can result are revertants of either mutation. This control experiment shows that such revertants are extremely rare and can be ignored among the *rII⁺* progeny made in the recombination experiment at the *left*. Even if the two *rIIA⁻* mutations are in adjacent base pairs, the number of *rII⁺* recombinants obtained is more than 100 times higher than the number of *rII⁺* revertants the cells infected by a single mutant could produce.

double rII^- mutants and with wild-type phages (Fig. 7.20c). If the mutations were recessive and did not interact with each other, the cells would lyse, in which case the complementation test would be interpretable.

The significant distinction between the actual complementation test and the control experiment is in the placement of the two rII^- mutations. In the complementation test, one rII^- mutation is on one chromosome, while the other rII^- mutation is on the other chromosome; two mutations arranged in this way are said to be in the *trans* configuration. In the control experiment, the two mutations are on the same chromosome, in the so-called *cis* configuration. The complete test, including the complementation test and the control experiment, is known as a *cis-trans* test. Benzer called any complementation group identified by the cis-trans test a **cistron,** and some geneticists still use the term "cistron" as a synonym for "gene."

Tests of many different pairs of rII^- mutations showed that they fall into two complementation groups: the genes *rIIA* and *rIIB*. With this knowledge, Benzer could look for two mutations in the same gene and then see if they ever recombine to produce wild-type progeny.

Recombination between different mutations in a single gene

When Benzer infected *E. coli* B strain bacteria with a mixture of phages carrying different mutations in the same gene ($rIIA_1$ and $rIIA_2$, for example), he did observe the appearance of rII^+ progeny (**Fig. 7.20d**). He knew these wild-type progeny resulted from recombination and not from reverse mutations because the frequencies of the rII^+ phage particles he observed were much higher than the frequencies of rII^+ revertants seen among progeny produced by infecting B strain bacteria with either mutant alone. On the basis of these observations, he drew three conclusions about gene structure: (1) A gene consists of different parts that can each mutate; (2) recombination between different mutable sites in the same gene can generate a normal, wild-type allele; and (3) a gene performs its normal function only if all of its components are wild type. From what we now know about the molecular structure of DNA, this all makes perfect sense.

> Different nucleotide pairs within a gene are independently mutable, and recombination can occur between nucleotide pairs within a gene as well as between genes.

A gene is a discrete linear set of nucleotide pairs

How are the multiple nucleotide pairs that make up a gene arranged—in a continuous row or dispersed in precise patterns around the genome? And do the various muta-tions that affect gene function alter many different nucleotides or only a small subset within each gene?

To answer these questions about the arrangement of nucleotides in a gene, Benzer eventually obtained thousands of spontaneous and mutagen-induced rII^- mutations that he mapped with respect to each other. To map the location of a thousand mutants through comparisons of all possible two-point crosses, he would have had to set up a million ($10^3 \times 10^3$) matings. But by taking advantage of deletion mutations, he could obtain the same information with far fewer crosses.

Using deletions to map mutations

Deletions, as you learned earlier, are mutations that remove contiguous nucleotide pairs along a DNA molecule. In crosses between bacteriophages carrying a mutation and bacteriophages carrying deletions of the corresponding region, no wild-type recombinant progeny can arise, because neither chromosome carries the proper information at the location of the mutation. However, if the mutation lies outside the region deleted from the homologous chromosome, wild-type progeny can appear (**Fig. 7.21a**). This is true whether the mutation is a **point mutation,** that is, a mutation of one nucleotide, or is itself a deletion. Crosses between any uncharacterized mutation and a known deletion thus immediately reveal whether the mutation resides in the region deleted from the other phage chromosome, providing a rapid way to find the general location of a mutation. Using a series of overlapping deletions, Benzer divided the *rII* region into a series of intervals. He could then assign any point mutation to an interval by observing whether it recombined to give rII^+ progeny when crossed with the series of deletions (**Fig. 7.21b**).

Benzer mapped 1612 spontaneous point mutations and several deletions in the *rII* locus of bacteriophage T4 through recombination analysis. He first used recombination to determine the relationship between the deletions. He next found the approximate location of individual point mutations by observing which deletions could recombine with each mutant to yield wild-type progeny. He then performed recombination tests between all point mutations known to lie in the same small region of the chromosome. These results produced a map of the "fine structure" of the region (**Fig. 7.21c**).

From the observation that the number of mutable sites in the *rII* region is very close to the number of nucleotides estimated to be in this region, Benzer inferred that a mutation can arise from the change of a single nucleotide and that recombination can occur between adjacent nucleotide pairs. From the observation that mutations within the *rII* region form a self-consistent, linear recombination map, he concluded that a gene is composed of a continuous linear sequence of nucleotide pairs within the DNA. And from observations that the positions of mutations in the

Figure 7.21 Fine structure mapping of the bacteriophage T4 *rll* genes. (a) A phage cross between a point mutation and a deletion removing the DNA at the position of the mutation cannot yield wild-type recombinants. The same is true if two different deletion mutations overlap each other. **(b)** Large deletions divide the *rll* locus into regions; finer deletions divide each region into subsections. Point mutations, such as 271 (in red at bottom), map to region 3 if they do not recombine with deletions PT1, PB242, or A105 but do recombine with deletion 638 (*top*). Point mutations can be mapped to subsections of region 3 using other deletions (*middle*). Recombination tests map point mutations in the same subregion (*bottom*). Point mutations 201 and 155 cannot recombine to yield wild-type recombinants because they affect the same nucleotide pair. **(c)** Benzer's fine structure map. Hot spots are locations with many independent mutations that cannot recombine with each other.

(a) Using deletions for rapid mapping

Point mutation within deletion limits

Point mutation outside deletion limits

Overlapping deletions

Nonoverlapping deletions

Cannot produce wild-type progeny by recombination

Produce wild-type progeny by recombination

(c) Fine structure of the *rll* region

Each box represents an independent occurrence of a mutation at this site.

Many mutations at a site create a "hot spot."

B cistron | *A* cistron

(b) Portion of the *rllA* deletion map at increasing resolutions

PT1

PB242

A105

Region missing in deletion

638

Regions

1   2   3   4

PT8

164

H88

PB82

Subsections

A   B   C   D   E

201 155

271   279   240

Point mutations

0.15   0.055   0.12

Map units

Fine structure of subsection

---

rIIA gene did not overlap those of the *rIIB* gene, he inferred that the nucleotide sequences composing those two genes are separate and distinct. A *gene* is thus a linear set of nucleotide pairs, located within a discrete region of a chromosome, that serves as a unit of function.

"Hot spots" of mutation

Some sites within a gene spontaneously mutate more frequently than others and as a result are known as **hot spots** (Fig. 7.21c). The existence of hot spots suggests that certain nucleotides can be altered more readily than others. Treatment with mutagens also turns up hot spots, but because mutagens have specificities for particular nucleotides, the highly mutable sites that turn up with various mutagens are often at different positions in a gene than the hot spots resulting from spontaneous mutation.

Nucleotides are chemically the same whether they lie within a gene or in the DNA between genes, and as Benzer's experiments show, the molecular machinery responsible for mutation and recombination does not discriminate between those nucleotides that are *intragenic* (within a gene) and those that are *intergenic* (between genes). The main distinction between DNA within and DNA outside a gene is that the array of nucleotides composing a gene has evolved a function that determines phenotype. Next, we describe how geneticists discovered what that function is.

> The mechanisms governing mutation and recombination do not discriminate between nucleotide pairs within or outside of genes; however, the nucleotide pairs within a gene together comprise a unit of function that contributes to phenotype.

7.3 What Mutations Tell Us About Gene Function

Mendel's experiments established that an individual gene can control a visible characteristic, but his laws do not explain how genes actually govern the appearance of traits. Investigators working in the first half of the twentieth century carefully studied the biochemical changes caused by mutations in an effort to understand the genotype–phenotype connection.

In one of the first of these studies, conducted in 1902, the British physician Dr. Archibald Garrod showed that a human genetic disorder known as *alkaptonuria* is determined by the recessive allele of an autosomal gene. Garrod analyzed family pedigrees and performed biochemical analyses on family members with and without the trait. The urine of people with alkaptonuria turns black on exposure to air. Garrod found that a substance known as homogentisic acid, which blackens upon contact with oxygen, accumulates in the urine of alkaptonuria patients. Alkaptonuriacs excrete all of the homogentisic acid they ingest, while people without the condition excrete no homogentisic acid in their urine even after ingesting the substance.

From these observations, Garrod concluded that people with alkaptonuria are incapable of metabolizing homogentisic acid to the breakdown products generated by normal individuals (**Fig. 7.22**). Because many biochemical reactions within the cells of organisms are catalyzed by enzymes, Garrod hypothesized that lack of the enzyme that breaks down homogentisic acid is the cause of alkaptonuria. In the absence of this enzyme, the acid accumulates and causes the urine to turn black on contact with oxygen. He called this condition an "inborn error of metabolism."

Garrod studied several other inborn errors of metabolism and suggested that all arose from mutations that prevented a particular gene from producing an enzyme

Figure 7.22 Alkaptonuria: An inborn error of metabolism. The biochemical pathway in humans that degrades phenylalanine and tyrosine via homogentisic acid (HA). In alkaptonuria patients, the enzyme HA hydroxylase is not functional so it does not catalyze the conversion of HA to maleylacetoacetic acid. As a result, HA, which oxidizes to a black compound, accumulates in the urine.

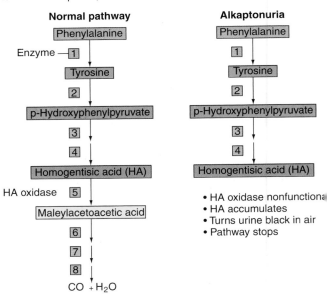

required for a specific biochemical reaction. In today's terminology, the wild-type allele of the gene would allow production of functional enzyme (in the case of alkaptonuria, the enzyme is homogentisic acid oxidase) whereas the mutant allele would not. Because the single wild-type allele in heterozygotes generates sufficient enzyme to prevent accumulation of homogentisic acid and thus the condition of alkaptonuria, the mutant allele is recessive.

A gene contains the information for producing a specific enzyme: The one gene, one enzyme hypothesis

In the 1940s, George Beadle and Edward Tatum carried out a series of experiments on the bread mold *Neurospora crassa* (whose life cycle was described in Chapter 5) that demonstrated a direct relation between genes and the enzymes that catalyze specific biochemical reactions. Their strategy was simple. They first isolated a number of mutations that disrupted synthesis of the amino acid arginine, a compound needed for *Neurospora* growth. They next hypothesized that different mutations blocked different steps in a particular **biochemical pathway:** the ordered series of reactions that allows *Neurospora* to obtain simple molecules from the environment and convert them step-by-step into successively more complicated molecules culminating in arginine.

Figure 7.23 Experimental support for the "one gene, one enzyme" hypothesis. (a) Beadle and Tatum mated an X-ray-mutagenized strain of *Neurospora* with another strain, and they isolated haploid ascospores that grew on complete medium. Cultures that failed to grow on minimal medium were nutritional mutants. Nutritional mutants that could grow on minimal medium plus arginine were *arg⁻* auxotrophs. **(b)** The ability of wild-type and mutant strains to grow on minimal medium supplemented with intermediates in the arginine pathway. **(c)** Each of the four *ARG* genes encodes an enzyme needed to convert one intermediate to the next in the pathway.

(a) Isolation of arginine auxotrophs

X-rays

Asci

Mutagenized conidia

Wild type

Crossed with opposite wild type

Fruiting bodies

Ascospores dissected and transferred; one to each culture tube

Tubes of complete medium inoculated with single ascospores

Complete medium

Germination, production of conidia

Conidia from each culture tested on minimal medium.

Minimal medium

No growth = nutritional mutant

Conidia from cultures that fail to grow on minimal medium are tested on minimal medium supplemented with individual amino acids.

Glycine Leucine Arginine Valine Tyrosine Proline Glutamic acid Asparagine Serine Cysteine

Addition of arginine restores growth, reveals arginine auxotroph.

(b) Growth response if nutrient is added to minimal medium

| Mutant strain | Nothing | Supplements | | | |
		Ornithine	Citrulline	Arginino-succinate	Arginine
Wildtype: *Arg⁺*	+	+	+	+	+
Arg-E⁻	−	+	+	+	+
Arg-F⁻	−	−	+	+	+
Arg-G⁻	−	−	−	+	+
Arg-H⁻	−	−	−	−	+

(c) Inferred biochemical pathway

Genes:

ARG-E   ARG-F   ARG-G   ARG-H

Enzymes:

Acetylornithinase   Ornithine transcarbamylase   Argininosuccinate synthetase   Argininosuccinate lyase

Reactions:

N-Acetylornithine ⟶ Ornithine ⟶ Citrulline ⟶ Argininosuccinate ⟶ Arginine

Carbamyl phosphate   Aspartate

Experimental evidence for "one gene, one enzyme"

Figure 7.23a illustrates the experiments Beadle and Tatum performed to test their hypothesis. They first obtained a set of mutagen-induced mutations that prevented *Neurospora* from synthesizing arginine. Cells with any one of these mutations were unable to make arginine and could therefore grow on a minimal medium containing salt and sugar only if it had been supplemented with arginine. A nutritional mutant microorganism that requires supplementation with substances not needed by wild-type strains is known as an **auxotroph.** The cells just mentioned were arginine auxotrophs. (In contrast, a cell that does not require addition of a substance is a **prototroph** for that factor. In a more general meaning, *prototroph* refers to a wild-type cell that can grow on minimal medium alone.) Recombination analyses located the auxotrophic arginine-blocking

mutations in four distinct regions of the genome, and complementation tests showed that each of the four regions correlated with a different complementation group. On the basis of these results, Beadle and Tatum concluded that at least four genes support the biochemical pathway for arginine synthesis. They named the four genes *ARG-E, ARG-F, ARG-G,* and *ARG-H.*

They next asked whether any of the mutant *Neurospora* strains could grow in minimal medium supplemented with any of three known intermediates (ornithine, citrulline, and arginosuccinate) in the biochemical pathway leading to arginine, instead of with arginine itself. This test would identify *Neurospora* mutants able to convert the intermediate compound into arginine. Beadle and Tatum compiled a table describing which arginine auxotrophic mutants were able to grow on minimal medium supplemented with each of the intermediates (**Fig. 7.23b**).

Interpretation of results: Genes encode enzymes

On the basis of these results, Beadle and Tatum proposed a model of how *Neurospora* cells synthesize arginine (**Fig.7.23c**). In the linear progression of biochemical reactions by which a cell constructs arginine from the constituents of minimal medium, each intermediate is both the product of one step and the substrate for the next. Each reaction in the precisely ordered sequence is catalyzed by a specific enzyme, and the presence of each enzyme depends on one of the four *ARG* genes. A mutation in one gene blocks the pathway at a particular step because the cell lacks the corresponding enzyme and thus cannot make arginine on its own. Supplementing the medium with any intermediate that occurs beyond the blocked reaction restores growth because the organism has all the enzymes required to convert the intermediate to arginine. Supplementation with an intermediate that occurs before the missing enzyme does not work because the cell is unable to convert the intermediate into arginine.

Each mutation abolishes the cell's ability to make an enzyme capable of catalyzing a certain reaction. By inference, then, each gene controls the synthesis or activity of an enzyme, or as stated by Beadle and Tatum: one gene, one enzyme. Of course, the gene and the enzyme are not the same thing; rather, the sequence of nucleotides in a gene contains information that somehow encodes the structure of an enzyme molecule.

Although the analysis of the arginine pathway studied by Beadle and Tatum was straightforward, studies of biochemical pathways are not always so easy to interpret. Some biochemical pathways are not linear progressions of stepwise reactions. For example, a branching pathway occurs if different enzymes act on the same intermediate to convert it into two different end products. If the cell requires both of these end products for growth, a mutation in a gene encoding any of the enzymes required to synthesize the intermediate would make the cell dependent on supplementation with both end products. A second possibility is that a cell might employ either of two independent, parallel pathways to synthesize a needed end product. In such a case, a mutation in a gene encoding an enzyme in one of the pathways would be without effect. Only a cell with mutations affecting both pathways would display an aberrant phenotype.

Even with nonlinear progressions such as these, careful genetic analysis can reveal the nature of the biochemical pathway on the basis of Beadle and Tatum's insight that genes encode proteins.

> Beadle and Tatum found that mutations in a single complementation group (that is, a single gene) disrupted one particular enzymatic step of a known biochemical pathway, while mutations in other genes disrupted other steps. They concluded that each gene specifies a different enzyme ("one gene, one enzyme").

Genes specify the identity and order of amino acids in polypeptide chains

Although the one gene, one enzyme hypothesis was a critical advance in understanding how genes influence phenotype, it is an oversimplification. Not all genes govern the construction of enzymes active in biochemical pathways. Enzymes are only one class of the molecules known as proteins, and cells contain many other kinds of proteins. Among the other types are proteins that provide shape and rigidity to a cell, proteins that transport molecules in and out of cells, proteins that help fold DNA into chromosomes, and proteins that act as hormonal messengers. Genes direct the synthesis of all proteins, enzymes and nonenzymes alike. Moreover, as we see next, genes actually determine the construction of polypeptides, and because some proteins are composed of more than one type of polypeptide, more than one gene determines the construction of such proteins.

Proteins: Linear polymers of amino acids linked by peptide bonds

To review the basics, proteins are polymers composed of building blocks known as **amino acids.** Cells use mainly 20 different amino acids to synthesize the proteins they need. All of these amino acids have certain basic features, encapsulated by the formula NH_2–CHR–COOH (**Fig. 7.24a**). The –COOH component, also known as *carboxylic acid,* is, as the name implies, acidic; the –NH_2 component, also known as an *amino group,* is basic. The R refers to side chains that distinguish each of the 20 amino acids (**Fig. 7.24b**). An R group can be as simple as a hydrogen atom (in the amino acid glycine) or as complex as a benzene ring (in phenylalanine). Some side chains are relatively neutral and nonreactive, others are acidic, and still others are basic.

During protein synthesis, a cell's protein-building machinery links amino acids by constructing covalent **peptide bonds** that join the –COOH group of one amino acid to the –NH_2 group of the next (**Fig. 7.24c**). A pair of amino acids connected in this fashion is a **dipeptide;** several amino acids linked together constitute an **oligopeptide.** The amino acid chains that make up proteins contain hundreds to thousands of amino acids joined by peptide bonds and are known as **polypeptides.** Proteins are thus linear polymers of amino acids. Like the chains of nucleotides in DNA, polypeptides have a chemical polarity. One end of a polypeptide is called the **N terminus** because it contains a free amino group that is not connected to any other amino acid. The other end of the polypeptide chain is the **C terminus,** because it contains a free carboxylic acid group.

Mutations can alter amino acid sequences

Each protein is composed of a unique sequence of amino acids. The chemical properties that enable structural proteins to give a cell its shape, or enzymes to catalyze specific reactions are a direct consequence of the identity, number, and linear order of amino acids in the protein.

a) Generic amino acid structure

Amino (–NH₂) group

CHR group

Carboxyl (–COOH) group

c) Peptide bond formation

H₂O

H₂O

terminus   Peptide bonds   C terminus

(b) Amino acids with nonpolar R groups

Amino acids with uncharged polar R groups

Amino acids with basic R groups

Amino acids with acidic R groups

Figure 7.24 Proteins are chains of amino acids linked by peptide bonds. (a) Amino acids contain a basic amino group (–NH₂), an acidic carboxylic acid group (–COOH), and a ⟩CHR moiety, where R stands for one of the 20 different side chains. **(b)** Amino acids commonly found in proteins, arranged according to the properties of their R groups. **(c)** One molecule of water is lost when a covalent amide linkage (a peptide bond) is formed between the –COOH of one amino acid and the –NH₂ of the next amino acid. Polypeptides such as the tripeptide shown here have polarity; they extend from an N terminus (with a free amino group) to a C terminus (with a free carboxylic acid group).

If genes encode proteins, then at least some mutations could be changes in a gene that alter the proper sequence of amino acids in the protein encoded by that gene. In the mid-1950s, Vernon Ingram began to establish what kinds of changes particular mutations cause in the corresponding protein. Using recently developed techniques for determining the sequence of amino acids in a protein, he compared the amino acid sequence of the normal adult form of hemoglobin (HbA) with that of hemoglobin in the bloodstream of people homozygous for the mutation that causes sickle-cell anemia (HbS). Remarkably, he found only a single amino acid difference between the wild-type and mutant proteins (**Fig. 7.25a**). Hemoglobin consists of two types of polypeptides: a so-called α (alpha) chain and a β (beta) chain. The sixth amino acid from the N terminus of the β chain was glutamic acid in normal individuals but valine in sickle-cell patients.

Ingram thus established that a mutation substituting one amino acid for another had the power to change the structure and function of hemoglobin and thereby alter the phenotype from normal to sickle-cell anemia (**Fig. 7.25b**). We now know that the glutamic acid–to-valine change affects the solubility of hemoglobin within the red blood cell. At low concentrations of oxygen, the less soluble sickle-cell form of hemoglobin aggregates into long chains that deform the red blood cell (Fig. 7.25a).

Because people suffering from a variety of inherited anemias also have defective hemoglobin molecules, Ingram and other geneticists were able to determine how a large number of different mutations affect the amino acid sequence of hemoglobin (**Fig. 7.25c**). Most of the altered hemoglobins have a change in only one amino acid. In various patients with anemia, the alteration is generally in different amino acids, but occasionally, two independent mutations result in different substitutions for the same amino acid. Geneticists use the term **missense mutation** to describe a genetic alteration that causes the substitution of one amino acid for another.

> Proteins are polymers of amino acids linked by peptide bonds; protein chains are polar because they have chemically distinct N and C termini. Some mutations in genes can change the identify of a single amino acid in a protein; such amino acid substitutions can disrupt the protein's function.

Figure 7.25 The molecular basis of sickle-cell and other anemias. (a) Substitution of glutamic acid with valine at the sixth amino acid from the N terminus affects the three-dimensional structure of the β chain of hemoglobin. Hemoglobins incorporating the mutant β chain form aggregates that cause red blood cells to sickle. **(b)** Red blood cell sickling has many phenotypic effects. **(c)** Other mutations in the β-chain gene also cause anemias.

(a) From mutation to phenotype

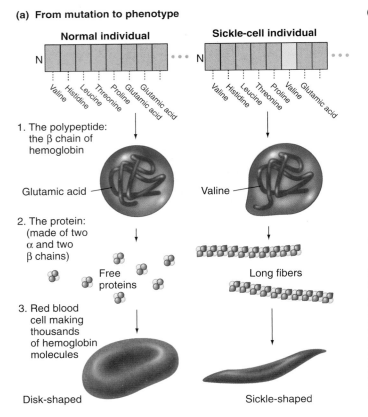

(b) Sickle-cell anemia is pleiotropic

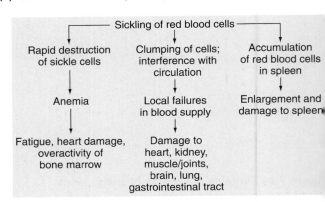

(c) β-chain substitutions/variants

| | Amino-acid position | | | | | | | | | |
	1	2	3 ···	6	7 ···	26 ···	63 ···	67···125···14‹
Normal (HbA)	Val	His	Leu	Glu	Glu	Glu	His	Val	Glu	Hi‹
HbS	Val	His	Leu	Val	Glu	Glu	His	Val	Glu	Hi‹
HbC	Val	His	Leu	Lys	Glu	Glu	His	Val	Glu	Hi‹
HbG San Jose	Val	His	Leu	Glu	Gly	Glu	His	Val	Glu	Hi‹
HbE	Val	His	Leu	Glu	Glu	Lys	His	Val	Glu	Hi‹
HbM Saskatoon	Val	His	Leu	Glu	Glu	Glu	Tyr	Val	Glu	Hi‹
Hb Zurich	Val	His	Leu	Glu	Glu	Glu	Arg	Val	Glu	H‹
HbM Milwaukee 1	Val	His	Leu	Glu	Glu	Glu	His	Glu	Glu	H‹
HbDβ Punjab	Val	His	Leu	Glu	Glu	Glu	His	Val	Gln	H‹

Primary, secondary, and tertiary protein structures

Despite the uniform nature of protein construction—a line of amino acids joined by peptide bonds—each type of polypeptide folds into a unique three-dimensional shape. The linear sequence of amino acids within a polypeptide is its **primary structure.** Each unique primary structure places constraints on how a chain can arrange itself in three-dimensional space. Because the R groups distinguishing the 20 amino acids have dissimilar chemical properties, some amino acids form hydrogen bonds or electrostatic bonds when brought into proximity with other amino acids. Nonpolar amino acids, for example, may become associated with each other by interactions that "hide" them from water in localized hydrophobic regions. As another example, two cysteine amino acids can form covalent disulfide bridges (–S–S–) through the oxidation of their –SH groups.

All of these interactions (**Fig. 7.26a**) help stabilize the polypeptide in a specific three-dimensional conformation. The primary structure (**Fig. 7.26b**) determines three-dimensional shape by generating localized regions with a characteristic geometry known as **secondary structure** (**Fig. 7.26c**). Primary structure is also responsible for

other folds and twists that together with the secondary structure produce the ultimate three-dimensional **tertiary structure** of the entire polypeptide (**Fig. 7.26d**). Normal tertiary structure—the way a long chain of amino acids naturally folds in three-dimensional space under physiological conditions—is known as a polypeptide's *native configuration.* Various forces, including hydrogen bonds, electrostatic bonds, hydrophobic interactions, and disulfide bridges, help stabilize the native configuration.

It is worth repeating that primary structure—the sequence of amino acids in a polypeptide—directly determines secondary and tertiary structures. The information required for the chain to fold into its native configuration is inherent in its linear sequence of amino acids. In one example of this principle, many proteins unfold, or become **denatured,** when exposed to urea and mercaptoethanol or to increasing heat or pH. These treatments disrupt the interactions that normally stabilize the secondary and tertiary structures. When conditions return to normal, many proteins spontaneously refold into their native configuration without help from other agents. No other information beyond the primary structure is needed to achieve the proper three-dimensional shape of such proteins.

Figure 7.26 Levels of polypeptide structure. (a) Covalent and noncovalent interactions determine the structure of a polypeptide. **(b)** A polypeptide's primary (1°) structure is its amino acid sequence. **(c)** Localized regions form secondary (2°) structures such as α helices and β-pleated sheets. **(d)** The tertiary (3°) structure is the complete three-dimensional arrangement of a polypeptide. In this portrait of myoglobin, the iron-containing heme group, which carries oxygen, is *red,* while the polypeptide itself is *green.*

(a) Interactions determining polypeptide structure

COVALENT

Peptide   Disulfide

NONCOVALENT

Hydrogen

Nonpolar

Ionic

(b) 1° structure

One amino acid

terminus   C terminus

(c) 2° structures

α helix

β-pleated sheets

(d) 3° structure

Myoglobin

Quaternary structure: Multimeric proteins

Certain proteins, such as the rhodopsin that promotes black-and-white vision, consist of a single polypeptide. Many others, however, such as the lens crystallin protein, which provides rigidity and transparency to the lenses of our eyes, or the hemoglobin molecule described earlier, are composed of two or more polypeptide chains that associate in a specific way (**Fig. 7.27a and b**). The individual polypeptides in an aggregate are known as *subunits*, and the complex of subunits is often referred to as a *multimer*. The three-dimensional configuration of subunits in a multimer is a complex protein's **quaternary structure.**

The same forces that stabilize the native form of a polypeptide (that is, hydrogen bonds, electrostatic bonds, hydrophobic interactions, and disulfide bridges) also contribute to the maintenance of quaternary structure. As Fig. 7.27a shows, in some multimers, the two or more interacting subunits are identical polypeptides. These identical chains are encoded by one gene. In other multimers, by contrast, more than one kind of polypeptide makes up the protein (Fig. 7.27b). The different polypeptides in these multimers are encoded by different genes.

Alterations in just one kind of subunit, caused by a mutation in a single gene, can affect the function of a multimer. The adult hemoglobin molecule, for example, consists of two α and two β subunits, with each type of subunit determined by a different gene—one for the α chain and one for the β chain. A mutation in the *Hbβ* gene resulting in an amino acid switch at position 6 in the β chain causes sickle-cell anemia. Similarly, if several multimeric proteins share a common subunit, a single mutation in the gene encoding that subunit may affect all the

Figure 7.27 Multimeric proteins. (a) β2 lens crystallin contains two copies of one kind of subunit; the two subunits are the product of a single gene. The peptide backbones of the two subunits are shown in different shades of *purple*. **(b)** Hemoglobin is composed of two different kinds of subunits, each encoded by a different gene. **(c)** Three distinct protein receptors for the immune-system molecules called interleukins (ILs; *purple*). All contain a common gamma (γ) chain (*yellow*), plus other receptor-specific polypeptides (*green*). A mutant γ chain blocks the function of all three receptors, leading to XSCID. **(d)** One α-tubulin and one β-tubulin polypeptide associate to form a tubulin dimer. Many tubulin dimers form a single microtubule. The mitotic spindle is an assembly of many microtubules.

(a) A multimer with identical subunits

β2 lens crystallin

Two identical subunits

β2 lens crystallin gene

(b) A multimer with nonidentical subunits

Hemoglobin

Two α subunits   Two β subunits

Hb α gene   *Hb β gene*

(c) One polypeptide in different proteins

IL-4 Receptor   IL-2 Receptor   IL-7 Receptor

IL-4   IL-2   IL-2Rα   IL-7

IL-4R   γ   IL-2Rβ   γ   IL-7R   γ

γ   Gamma-chain subunit

Defective gamma chain → XSCID

(d) Microtubules: large assemblies of subunits

— α tubulin — β tubulin   Tubulin dimer

Assembly of microtubules: mitotic metaphase

Microtubule

Chromosomes aligned on spindle apparatus

Disassembly of microtubules: mitotic telophase

Spindle apparatus breaks down

roteins simultaneously. An example is an X-linked muta-on in mice and humans that incapacitates several differ-nt proteins all known as interleukin (IL) receptors. Because all of these receptors are essential to the normal unction of immune-system cells that fight infection and gen-rate immunity, this one mutation causes the life-threatening ondition known as X-linked severe combined immune eficiency (XSCID; **Fig. 7.27c**).

The polypeptides of complex proteins can assemble into extremely large structures capable of changing with the needs of the cell. For example, the microtubules that make up the spindle during mitosis are gigantic assem-lages of mainly two polypeptides: α tubulin and β tubu-n (**Fig. 7.27d**). The cell can organize these subunits into ery long hollow tubes that grow or shrink as needed at ifferent stages of the cell cycle.

ne gene, one polypeptide

ecause more than one gene governs the production of me multimeric proteins and because not all proteins are zymes, the "one gene, one enzyme" hypothesis is not oad enough to define gene function. A more accurate atement is "one gene, one polypeptide": Each gene gov-ns the construction of a particular polypeptide. As you ill see in Chapter 8, even this reformulation does not ncompass the function of all genes, as a few genes in all ganisms do not determine the construction of proteins; stead, they encode RNAs that are not translated into lypeptides.

Beadle and Tatum's experiments were based on the ncept that if each gene encodes a different polypeptide d if each polypeptide plays a specific role in the devel-ment, physiology, or behavior of an organism, then a utation in the gene will block a biological process (like ginine synthesis in *Neurospora*) in a characteristic way. her scientists soon realized they could use this approach study virtually any interesting problem in biology. In e Fast Forward box "Using Mutagenesis to Look at ological Processes" on the following page, we describe w one biologist found a large group of mutations that srupted the assembly of bacteriophage T4 particles. By refully studying the phenotypes caused by these muta-ns, he inferred the complex pathway that produces an tire bacteriophage.

Knowledge about the connection between genes and lypeptides enabled geneticists to analyze how different tations in a single gene can produce different pheno-es. If each amino acid has a specific effect on the ee-dimensional structure of a protein, then changing ino acids at different positions in a polypeptide chain alter protein function in different ways. For example, st enzymes have an active site that carries out the enzy-tic task, while other parts of the protein support the pe and position of that site. Mutations that change the ntity of amino acids at the active site may have more

serious consequences than those affecting amino acids outside the active site. Some kinds of amino acid substitu-tions, such as replacement of an amino acid having a basic side chain with an amino acid having an acidic side chain, would be more likely to compromise protein function than would substitutions that retain the chemical characteristics of the original amino acid.

Some mutations do not affect the amino acid compo-sition of a protein but still generate an abnormal pheno-type. As discussed in the following chapter, such mutations change the amount of normal polypeptide produced by dis-rupting the biochemical processes responsible for decoding a gene into a polypeptide.

> Most (but not all) genes specify the amino acid sequence of a polypeptide; a protein is comprised of one or more poly-peptides. The primary amino acid sequences of the consti-tuent polypeptides determine a protein's three-dimensional structure and thus its function.

7.4 A Comprehensive Example: Mutations That Affect Vision

Researchers first described anomalies of color perception in humans close to 200 years ago. Since that time, they have discovered a large number of mutations that modify human vision. By examining the phenotype associated with each mutation and then looking directly at the DNA alter-ations inherited with the mutation, they have learned a great deal about the genes influencing human visual perception and the function of the proteins they encode.

Using human subjects for vision studies has several advantages. First, people can recognize and describe vari-ations in the way they see, from trivial differences in what the color red looks like, to not seeing any difference between red and green, to not seeing any color at all. Second, the highly developed science of psychophysics provides sensitive, noninvasive tests for accurately defin-ing and comparing phenotypes. One diagnostic test, for example, is based on the fact that people perceive each color as a mixture of three different wavelengths of light—red, green, and blue—and the human visual system can adjust ratios of red, green, and blue light of different intensities to match an arbitrarily chosen fourth wave-length such as yellow. The mixture of wavelengths does not combine to form the fourth wavelength; it just appears that way to the eye. A person with normal vision, for instance, will select a well-defined proportion of red and green lights to match a particular yellow, but a person who can't tell red from green will permit any proportion of these two color lights to make the same match. Finally, because inherited variations in the visual system rarely

Using Mutagenesis to Look at Biological Processes

Geneticists can use mutations to dissect complicated biological processes into their protein components. To determine the specific, dedicated role of each protein, they introduce mutations into the genes encoding the protein. The mutations knock out, or delete, functional protein either by preventing protein production altogether or by altering it such that the resulting protein is nonfunctional. The researchers then observe what happens when the cell or organism attempts to perform the biological process without the deleted protein.

In the 1960s, Robert Edgar set out to delineate the function of the proteins determined by all the genes in the T4 bacteriophage genome. After a single viral particle infects an *E. coli* bacterium, the host cell stops producing bacterial proteins and becomes a factory for making only viral proteins. Thirty minutes after infection, the bacterial cell lyses, releasing 100 new viral particles. The head of each particle carries a DNA genome 200,000 base pairs in length that encodes at least 120 genes.

Edgar's experimental design was to obtain many different mutant bacteriophages, each containing a mutation that inactivates one of the genes essential for viral reproduction. By analyzing what went wrong with each type of mutant during the infective cycle, he would learn something about the function of each of the proteins produced by the T4 genome.

There was just one barrier to implementing this plan. A mutation that prevents viral reproduction by definition makes the virus unable to reproduce and therefore unavailable for experimental study. The solution to this dilemma came with the discovery of *conditional lethal mutants:* viruses, microbes, or other organisms carrying mutations that are lethal to the organism under one condition but not another. One type of conditional lethal mutant used by Edgar was temperature sensitive; that is, the mutant T4 phage could reproduce only at low temperatures. The mutations causing temperature sensitivity changed one amino acid in a polypeptide such that the protein was stable and functional at a low temperature but became unstable and nonfunctional at a higher temperature. Temperature-sensitive mutations can occur in almost any gene. Edgar isolated thousands of conditional lethal bacteriophage T4 mutants, and using complementation studies, he discovered that they fall into 65 complementation groups. These complementation groups defined 65 genes whose function is required for bacteriophage replication.

Edgar next studied the consequences of infecting bacterial cells under *restrictive conditions*, that is, under conditions in which the mutant protein could not function. For the temperature-sensitive mutants, the restrictive condition was high temperature. He found that mutations in 17 genes prevented viral DNA replication and concluded that these 17 genes contribute to that process. Mutations in most of the other 48 genes did not impede viral DNA replication but were necessary for the construction of complete viral particles.

Electron microscopy showed that mutations in these 48 genes caused the accumulation of partially constructed viral particles. Edgar used the incomplete particles to plot the path of viral assembly. As **Fig. A** illustrates, three subassembly lines—one for the tail, one for the head, and one for the tail fibers—come together during the assembly of the viral product. Once the heads are completed and filled with DNA, they attach to the tails, after which attachment of the fibers completes particle construction. It would have been very difficult to discern this trilateral assembly pathway by any means other than mutagenesis-driven genetic dissection.

Between 1990 and 1995, molecular geneticists determined the complete DNA sequence of the T4 genome, and then using the genetic code dictionary (described in Chapter 8), translated that sequence into coding regions for proteins. In addition to the 65 genes identified by Edgar, another 55 genes became evident from the sequence. Edgar did not find these genes because they are not essential to viral reproduction under the conditions used in the laboratory. The previously unidentified genes most likely play important roles in the T4 life cycle outside the laboratory, perhaps when the virus infects hosts other than the *E. coli* strain normally used in the laboratory, or when the virus grows under different environmental conditions and is competing with other viruses.

Figure A Steps in the assembly of bacteriophage T4.

Robert Edgar determined what kinds of phage structures formed in bacterial cells infected with mutant T4 phage at restrictive temperatures. As an example, a cell infected with a phage carrying a temperature-sensitive mutation in gene 63 filled up with normal-looking phage that lacked tail fibers, and with normal-looking tail fibers. Edgar concluded that gene 63 encodes a protein that allows tail fibers to attach to otherwise completely assembled phage particles.

affect an individual's life span or ability to reproduce, mutations generating many of the new alleles that change visual perception remain in a population over time.

Cells of the retina carry light-sensitive proteins

People perceive light through neurons in the retina at the back of the eye (**Fig. 7.28a**). These neurons are of two types: rods and cones. The rods, which make up 95% of all light-receiving neurons, are stimulated by weak light over a range of wavelengths. At higher light intensities, the rods become saturated and no longer send meaningful information to the brain. This is when the cones take over, processing wavelengths of bright light that enable us to see color.

The cones come in three forms—one specializes in the reception of red light, a second in the reception of green, and a third in the reception of blue. For each photoreceptor cell, the act of reception consists of absorbing photons from light of a particular wavelength, transducing information about the number and energy of those photons to electrical signals, and transmitting the signals via the optic nerve to the brain.

Four related proteins with different light sensitivities

The protein that receives photons and triggers the processing of information in rod cells is **rhodopsin.** It consists of a single polypeptide chain containing 348 amino acids that snakes back and forth across the cell membrane (**Fig. 7.28b**). One lysine within the chain associates with retinal, a carotenoid pigment molecule that actually absorbs photons. The amino acids in the vicinity of the retinal constitute rhodopsin's active site; by positioning the retinal in a particular way, they determine its response to light. Each rod cell contains approximately 100 million molecules of rhodopsin in its specialized membrane. As you learned at the beginning of this chapter, the gene governing the production of rhodopsin is on chromosome 3.

The protein that receives and initiates the processing of photons in the blue cones is a relative of rhodopsin, also consisting of a single polypeptide chain containing 348 amino acids and also encompassing one molecule of retinal. Slightly less than half of the 348 amino acids in the blue-receiving protein are the same as those found in rhodopsin; the rest are different and account for the specialized light-receiving ability of the protein (Fig. 7.28b). The gene for the blue protein is on chromosome 7.

Similarly related to rhodopsin are the red- and green-receiving proteins in the red and green cones. These are also single polypeptides associated with retinal and embedded in the cell membrane, although they are both slightly larger at 364 amino acids in length (Fig. 7.28b). Like the blue protein, the red and green proteins differ from

Figure 7.28 The cellular and molecular basis of vision.
(a) Rod and cone cells in the retina carry membrane-bound photoreceptors. **(b)** The photoreceptor in rod cells is rhodopsin. The blue, green, and red receptor proteins in cone cells are related to rhodopsin. **(c)** One red photoreceptor gene and one to three green photoreceptor genes are clustered on the X chromosome. **(d)** The genes for rhodopsin and the three color receptors probably evolved from a primordial photoreceptor gene through three gene duplication events followed by divergence of the duplicated copies.

(a) Photoreceptor-containing cells

(b) Photoreceptor proteins

(c) Red/green pigment genes
X chromosomes from normal individuals:

(d) Evolution of visual pigment genes

rhodopsin in nearly half of their amino acids; they differ from each other in only four amino acids out of every hundred. Even these small differences, however, are sufficient to differentiate the light sensitivities of the two types of cones and confer on them distinct spectral sensitivities. The genes for the red and green proteins both reside on the X chromosome in a tandem head-to-tail arrangement. Most individuals have one red gene and one to three green genes on their X chromosomes (**Fig. 7.28c**).

Evolution of the rhodopsin gene family

The similarity in structure and function between the four rhodopsin proteins suggests that the genes encoding these polypeptides arose by duplication of an original photoreceptor gene and then divergence through the accumulation of many mutations. Many of the mutations that promoted the ability to see color must have provided selective advantages to their bearers over the course of evolution. The red and green genes are the most similar, differing by less than five nucleotides out of every hundred. This suggests they diverged from each other only in the relatively recent evolutionary past. The less pronounced amino acid similarity of the red or green proteins with the blue protein, and the even lower relatedness between rhodopsin and any color photoreceptor, reflect earlier duplication and divergence events (**Fig. 7.28d**).

> Duplication and divergence (through mutation) of an ancestral rhodopsin-like gene have produced four specialized genes encoding rhodopsin and the blue, red, and green photoreceptor proteins.

How mutations in the rhodopsin gene family affect the way we see

Mutations in the genes encoding rhodopsin and the three color photoreceptor proteins can alter vision through many different mechanisms. These mutations range from point mutations that change the identity of a single amino acid in a single protein to larger aberrations resulting from unequal crossing-over that can increase or decrease the number of photoreceptor genes.

Mutations in the rhodopsin gene

At least 29 different single nucleotide substitutions in the rhodopsin gene cause an autosomal dominant vision disorder known as *retinitis pigmentosa* that begins with an early loss of rod function, followed by a slow progressive degeneration of the peripheral retina. **Figure 7.29a** shows the location of the amino acids affected by these mutations. These amino acid changes result in abnormal rhodopsin proteins that either do not fold properly or, once folded, are unstable. Although normal rhodopsin is an essential structural element of rod cell membranes, these nonfunctional

mutant proteins are retained in the body of the cell, where they remain unavailable for insertion into the membrane. Rod cells that cannot incorporate enough rhodopsin into their membranes eventually die. Depending on how many rod cells die, partial or complete blindness ensues.

Other mutations in the rhodopsin gene cause the far less serious condition of night blindness (Fig. 7.29a). These mutations change the protein's amino acid sequence so that the threshold of stimulation required to trigger the vision cascade increases. With the changes, very dim light is no longer enough to initiate vision.

Mutations in the cone-cell pigment genes

Vision problems caused by mutations in the cone-cell pigment genes are less severe than those caused by similar defects in the rod cells' rhodopsin genes. Most likely, this difference occurs because the rods make up 95% of a person's light-receiving neurons, while the cones comprise only about 5%. Some mutations in the blue gene on chromosome 7 cause *tritanopia,* a defect in the ability to discriminate between colors that differ only in the amount of blue light.

Figure 7.29 How mutations modulate light and color perception. (a) Amino acid substitutions (*black dots*) that disrupt rhodopsin's three-dimensional structure result in retinitis pigmentosa. Other substitutions diminishing rhodopsin's sensitivity to light cause night blindness. **(b)** Substitutions in the blue pigment can produce tritanopia (blue colorblindness). **(c)** Red colorblindness can result from particular mutations that destabilize the red photoreceptor. **(d)** Unequal crossing-over between the red and green genes can change gene number and create genes encoding hybrid photoreceptor proteins.

(a) Retinitis pigmentosa

Rhodopsin

Night blindness

Ala292⇒Gly

Gly90⇒Asp

Rhodopsin

(b) Tritanopia

Pro264⇒Ser

Gly79⇒Arg

Blue photoreceptor

(c) Red colorblindness

Cys203⇒Arg

Red photoreceptor

(d) Unequal crossing-over

Figure 7.30 How the world looks to a person with tritano-pia. Compare with Fig. 4.21 on p. 107.

they contain (**Figs. 7.29b** and **7.30**). Mutations in the red gene on the X chromosome can modify or abolish red protein function and as a result, the red cone cells' sensitivity to light. For example, a change at position 203 in the red-receiving protein from cysteine to arginine disrupts one of the disulfide bonds required to support the protein's tertiary structure (see **Fig. 7.29c**). Without that bond, the protein cannot stably maintain its native configuration, and a person with the mutation has red colorblindness.

Unequal crossing-over between the red and green genes

People with normal color vision have a single red gene; some of these normal individuals also have a single adjacent green gene, while others have two or even three green genes. The red and green genes are 96% identical in DNA sequence; the different green genes, 99.9% identical. The proximity and high degree of homology make these genes unusually prone to unequal crossing-over. A variety of unequal recombination events produce DNA containing no red gene, no green gene, various combinations of green genes, or hybrid red-green genes (see **Fig. 7.29d**). These different DNA combinations account for the large majority of the known aberrations in red-green color perception, with the remaining abnormalities stemming from point mutations, as described earlier. Because the accurate perception of red and green depends on the differing ratios of red and green light processed, people with no red or no green gene perceive red and green as the same color (see Fig. 4.21 on p. 107).

> We see the way we do in part because four genes direct the production of four photoreceptor polypeptides in the rod and cone cells of the retina. Mutations that alter those polypeptides or their amounts change our perception of light or color.

Connections

Careful studies of mutations showed that genes are linear arrays of mutable elements that direct the assembly of amino acids in a polypeptide. The mutable elements are the nucleotide building blocks of DNA.

Biologists call the parallel between the sequence of nucleotides in a gene and the order of amino acids in a polypeptide **colinearity**. In Chapter 8, we explain how colinearity arises from base pairing, a genetic code, specific enzymes, and macromolecular assemblies like ribosomes that guide the flow of information from DNA through RNA to protein.

ESSENTIAL CONCEPTS

1. Mutations are alterations in the nucleotide sequence of the DNA molecule that occur by chance and modify the genome at random. Mutations in single-celled organisms or in the germ line of multicelluar organisms can be transmitted from generation to generation when DNA replicates.

2. Mutations that affect phenotype occur naturally at a very low rate. Forward mutations usually occur more often than reversions.

3. The agents of spontaneously occurring mutations include chemical hydrolysis, radiation, and mistakes during DNA replication.

4. Mutagens raise the frequency of mutation above the spontaneous rate. The Ames test screens for mutagenic chemicals.

5. Cells have evolved a number of enzyme systems that repair DNA and thus minimize mutations.

6. Mutations are the raw material of evolution. Although some mutations may confer a selective advantage, most are harmful. Somatic mutations can cause cancer and other illnesses in individuals.

7. Mutations within a single gene usually fail to complement each other. The concept of a complementation group thus defines the gene as a unit of function. A gene is composed of a linear sequence of nucleotide pairs in a discrete, localized region of a chromosome. Recombination can occur within a gene, and even between adjacent nucleotide pairs.

8. The function of most genes is to specify the linear sequence of amino acids in a particular polypeptide

(one gene, one polypeptide). The sequence determines the polypeptide's three-dimensional structure, which, in turn, determines its function. Mutations can alter amino acid sequence and thus change protein function in many ways.

9. Each protein consists of one, two, or more polypeptides. Proteins composed of two or more different subunits are encoded by two or more genes.

10. The rhodopsin gene family provides an example of how the processes of gene duplication followed by gene divergence mutation can lead to evolution of functional refinements, such as the emergence of accurate systems for color vision.

On Our Website   www.mhhe.com/hartwell4

Annotated Suggested Readings and Links to Other Websites

- Historical monographs on the nature of mutation, the action of mutagens, DNA repair systems, fine-structure mapping, the "one gene, one polypeptide" hypothesis, and the genetics of human color vision.
- Interesting recent research articles about whether mutations are truly introduced at random, how TEs and trinucleotide repeats affect genomic stability and human health, and examples of the use of genetics to analyze complicated biological processes.

Specialized Topics

- Complications in the interpretation of complementation analysis: a document explaining rare exceptions to the rule that mutations in the same gene are unable to complement each other, as well as other rare cases in which mutations in different genes can fail to complement each other.

Solved Problems

I. Mutations can often be reverted to wild type by treatment with mutagens. The type of mutagen that will reverse a mutation gives us information about the nature of the original mutation. The mutagen EMS almost exclusively causes transitions; proflavin is an intercalating agent that causes insertion or deletion of a base; ultraviolet (UV) light causes single-base substitutions. Cultures of several *E. coli* met^- mutants were treated with three mutagens separately and spread onto a plate lacking methionine to look for revertants. (In the chart, − indicates that no colonies grew, and + indicates that some met^+ revertant colonies grew.)

Mutant number	Mutagen treatment		
	EMS	Proflavin	UV light
1	+	−	+
2	−	+	−
3	−	−	−
4	−	−	+

a. Given the results, what can you say about the nature of the original mutation in each of the strains?

b. Experimental controls are designed to eliminate possible explanations for the results, thereby ensuring that data are interpretable. In the experiment described, we scored the presence or absence of colonies. How do we know if colonies that appear on plates are mutagen-induced revertants? What else could they be? What control would enable us to be confident of our revertant analysis?

Answer

To answer this question, you need to understand the concepts of mutation and reversion.

a. Mutation 1 is reverted by the mutagen that causes transitions, *so mutation 1 must have been a transition.* Consistent with this conclusion is the fact the UV light can also revert the mutation and the intercalating agent proflavin does not cause reversion. *Mutation 2 is reverted by proflavin and therefore must be either an insertion or deletion of a base.* The other two mutagens do not revert mutation 2. Mutation 3 is not reverted by any of these mutagenic agents. It is therefore not a single-base substitution, a single-base insertion, or a single-base deletion. *Mutation 3 could be a deletion of several bases or an inversion.* Mutation 4 is reverted by UV light, so it is a single-base change, but it is not a transition, since EMS did not revert the mutation. *Mutation 4 must a transversion.*

b. *The colonies on the plates could arise by spontaneous reversion of the mutation.* Spontaneous reversion should occur with lower frequency than mutagen-induced reversion. The important control here is to *spread each mutant culture without any mutagen treatment onto selective media to assess the level of spontaneous reversion.*

II. Imagine that 10 independently isolated recessive lethal mutations (l^1, l^2, l^3, etc.) map to chromosome 7 in mice. You perform complementation testing by mating all pairwise combinations of heterozygotes bearing these lethal mutations, and you score the absence of complementation by examining pregnant females for dead fetuses. A + in the chart means that the two lethals complemented, and dead embryos were not found. A − indicates that dead embryos were found, at the rate of about one in four conceptions. (The crosses between heterozygous mice would be expected to yield the homozygous recessive showing the lethal phenotype in 1/4 of the embryos.) The lethal mutation in the parental heterozygotes for each cross are listed across the top and down the left side of the chart (that is, l^1 indicates a heterozygote in which one chromosome bears the l^1 mutation and the homologous chromosome is wild type).

	l^1	l^2	l^3	l^4	l^5	l^6	l^7	l^8	l^9	l^{10}
l^1	−	+	+	+	+	−	−	+	+	+
l^2		−	+	+	+	+	+	+	+	+
l^3			−	−	−	+	+	−	−	+
l^4				−	−	+	+	−	−	+
l^5					−	+	+	−	−	+
l^6						−	−	+	+	+
l^7							−	+	+	+
l^8								−	−	+
l^9									−	+
l^{10}										−

How many genes do the 10 lethal mutations represent? What are the complementation groups?

Answer

This problem involves the application of the complementation concept to a set of data. There are two ways to analyze these results. You can focus on the mutations that do complement each other, conclude that they are in different genes, and begin to create a list of mutations in separate genes. Alternatively, you can focus on mutations that do not complement each other and therefore are alleles of the same genes. The latter approach is more efficient when several mutations are involved. For example, l^1 does not complement l^6 and l^7. These three alleles are in one complementation group. l^2 does not complement l^{10}; they are in a second complementation group. l^3 does

not complement l^4, l^5, l^8, or l^9, so they form a third complementation group. *There are three complementation groups.* (Note also that for each mutant, the cross between individuals carrying the same alleles resulted in no complementation, because the homozygous recessive lethal was generated.) *The three complementation groups consist of (1) l^1, l^6, l^7; (2) l^2, l^{10}; and (3) l^3, l^4, l^5, l^8, l^9.*

III. W, X, and Y are the intermediates (in that order) in a biochemical pathway whose product is Z. Z^- mutants are found in five different complementation groups. *Z1* mutants will grow on Y or Z but not W or X. *Z2* mutants will grow on X, Y, or Z. *Z3* mutants will only grow on Z. *Z4* mutants will grow on Y or Z. Finally, *Z5* mutants will grow on W, X, Y, or Z.
   a. Order the five complementation groups in terms of the steps they block.
   b. What does this genetic information reveal about the nature of the enzyme that carries out the conversion of X to Y?

Answer

This problem requires that you understand complementation and the connection between genes and enzymes in a biochemical pathway.
   a. A biochemical pathway represents an ordered set of reactions that must occur to produce a product. This problem gives the order of intermediates in a pathway for producing product Z. The lack of any enzyme along the way will cause the phenotype of Z^-, but the block can occur at different places along the pathway. If the mutant grows when given an intermediate compound, the enzymatic (and hence gene) defect must be before production of that intermediate compound. The *Z1* mutants that grow on Y or Z (but not on W or X) must have a defect in the enzyme that produces Y. *Z2* mutants have a defect prior to X; *Z3* mutants have a defect prior to Z; *Z4* mutants have a defect prior to Y: *Z5* have a defect prior to W. *The five complementation groups can be placed in order of activity within the biochemical pathway as follows:*

$$\xrightarrow{Z5} W \xrightarrow{Z2} X \xrightarrow{Z1,\ Z4} Y \xrightarrow{Z3} Z$$

   b. Mutants *Z1* and *Z4* affect the same step, but because they are in different complementation groups, we know they are in different genes. *Mutations Z1 and Z4 are probably in genes that encode subunits of a multisubunit enzyme that carries out the conversion of X to Y.* Alternatively, there could be a currently unknown additional intermediate step between X and Y.

Problems

Vocabulary

1. The following is a list of mutational changes. For each of the specific mutations described, indicate which of the terms in the right-hand column applies, either as a description of the mutation or as a possible cause. More than one term from the right column can apply to each statement in the left column.

1. an A–T base pair in the wild-type gene is changed to a G–C pair
2. an A–T base pair is changed to a T–A pair
3. the sequence AAGCTTATCG is changed to AAGCTATCG
4. the sequence AAGCTTATCG is changed to AAGCTTTATCG
5. the sequence AACGTTATCG is changed to AATGTTATCG
6. the sequence AACGTCACACACACATCG is changed to AACGTCACACATCG
7. the gene map in a given chromosome arm is changed from *bog-rad-fox1-fox2-try-duf* (where *fox1* and *fox2* are highly homologous, recently diverged genes) to *bog-rad-fox1-fox3-fox2-try-duf* (where *fox3* is a new gene with one end similar to *fox1* and the other similar to *fox2*)
8. the gene map in a chromosome is changed from *bog-rad-fox1-fox2-try-duf* to *bog-rad-fox2-fox1-try-duf*
9. the gene map in a given chromosome is changed from *bog-rad-fox1-fox2-try-duf* to *bog-rad-fox1-mel-qui-txu-sqm*

a. transition
b. base substitution
c. transversion
d. inversion
e. translocation
f. deletion
g. insertion
h. deamination
i. X-ray irradiation
j. intercalator
k. unequal crossing-over

Section 7.1

2. What explanations can account for the pedigree of the very rare trait shown below? Be as specific as possible. How might you be able to distinguish between these explanations?

3. The DNA sequence of a gene from three independently isolated mutants is given here. Using this information, what is the sequence of the wild-type gene in this region?

```
mutant 1    ACCGTAATCGACTGGTAAACTTTGCGCG
mutant 2    ACCGTAGTCGACCGGTAAACTTTGCGCG
mutant 3    ACCGTAGTCGACTGGTTAACTTTGCGCG
```

4. Among mammals, measurements of the rate of generation of autosomal recessive mutations have been made almost exclusively in mice, while many measurements of the rate of generation of dominant mutations have been made both in mice and in humans. Why do you think there has been this difference?

5. Over a period of several years, a large hospital kept track of the number of births of babies displaying the trait achondroplasia. Achondroplasia is a very rare autosomal dominant condition resulting in dwarfism with abnormal body proportions. After 120,000 births, it was noted that there had been 27 babies born with achondroplasia. One physician was interested in determining how many of these dwarf babies result from new mutations and whether the apparent mutation rate in his area was higher than normal. He looked up the families of the 27 dwarf births and discovered that 4 of the dwarf babies had a dwarf parent. What is the apparent mutation rate of the achondroplasia gene in this population? Is it unusually high or low?

6. Suppose you wanted to study genes controlling the structure of bacterial cell surfaces. You decide to start by isolating bacterial mutants that are resistant to infection by a bacteriophage that binds to the cell surface. The selection procedure is simple: Spread cells from a culture of sensitive bacteria on a petri plate, expose them to a high concentration of phages, and pick the bacterial colonies that grow. To set up the selection you could (1) spread cells from a single liquid culture of sensitive bacteria on many different plates and pick every resistant colony *or* (2) start many different cultures, each grown from a single colony of sensitive bacteria, spread one plate from each culture, and then pick a single mutant from each plate. Which method would ensure that you are isolating many independent mutations?

7. In a genetics lab, Kim and Maria infected a sample from an *E. coli* culture with a particular virulent bacteriophage. They noticed that most of the cells were lysed, but a few survived. The survival rate in their sample was about 1×10^{-4}. Kim was sure the bacteriophage induced the resistance in the cells, while Maria thought that resistant mutants probably already existed in the sample of cells they used. Earlier, for a different experiment, they had spread a dilute suspension of *E. coli* onto solid medium in a large petri dish, and, after seeing that about 10^5 colonies were growing up, they had replica-plated that plate onto three other plates. Kim and Maria decided to use these plates to test their theories. They pipette a suspension of the bacteriophage onto each of the three replica plates. What should they see if Kim is right? What should they see if Maria is right?

8. The pedigree below shows the inheritance of a completely penetrant, dominant trait called amelogenesis imperfecta that affects the structure and integrity of the teeth. DNA analysis of blood obtained from affected individuals III-1 and III-2 shows the presence of the same mutation in one of the two copies of an autosomal gene called *ENAM* that is not seen in DNA from the blood of any of the parents in generation II. Explain this result, citing Fig. 4.18 on p. 102 and Fig. 7.4 on p. 203. Do you think this type of inheritance pattern is rare or common?

9. A wild-type male *Drosophila* was exposed to a large dose of X-rays and was then mated to an unirradiated female, one of whose X chromosomes carried both a dominant mutation for the trait *Bar* eyes and several inversions. Many F$_1$ females from this mating were recovered who had the *Bar*, multiply inverted X chromosome from their mother, and an irradiated X chromosome from their fathers. (The inversions ensure that viable offspring of these F$_1$ females will not have recombinant X chromosomes, as explained in Chapter 13.) After mating to normal males, most F$_1$ females produced *Bar* and wild-type sons in equal proportions. There were three exceptional F$_1$ females, however. Female A produced as many sons as daughters, but half of the sons had *Bar* eyes, and the other half had white eyes. Female B produced half as many sons as daughters, and all of the sons had *Bar* eyes. Female C produced 75% as many sons as daughters. Of these sons, 2/3 had *Bar* eyes, and 1/3 had wild-type eyes. Explain the results obtained with each exceptional F$_1$ female.

10. A wild-type *Drosophila* female was mated to a wild-type male that had been exposed to X-rays. One of the F$_1$ females was then mated with a male that had the following recessive markers on the X chromosome: *yellow* body (*y*), *crossveinless* wings (*cv*), *cut* wings (*ct*), *singed* bristles (*sn*), and *miniature* wings (*m*). These markers are known to map in the order *y−cv−ct−sn−m*. The progeny of this second mating were unusual in two respects. First, there were twice as many females as males. Second, while all of the males were wild type in phenotype, 1/2 of the females were wild type, and the other 1/2 exhibited the *ct* and *sn* phenotypes.

a. What did the X-rays do to the irradiated male?

b. Draw the X-chromosome pair present in a progeny female fly produced by the second mating that was phenotypically *ct* and *sn*.

c. If the *ct* and *sn* female fly whose chromosomes were drawn in part *b* was then crossed to a wild-type male, what phenotypic classes would you expect to find among the progeny males?

11. In the experiment shown in Fig. 7.9 on p. 207, H. J. Muller first performed a control in which the P generation males were not exposed to X-rays. He found that 99.7% of the individual F$_1$ Bar-eyed females produced some male progeny with Bar eyes and some with wild-type (non-Bar) eyes, but 0.3% of these females produced male progeny that were all wild type.

a. If the average spontaneous mutation rate for *Drosophila* genes is 3.5×10^{-6} mutations/gene/gamete, how many genes on the X chromosome can be mutated to produce a recessive lethal allele?

b. As of the year 2010, analysis of the *Drosophila* genome had revealed a total of 2283 genes on the X chromosome. Assuming the X chromosome is typical of the genome, what is the fraction of genes in the fly genome that is essential to survival?

c. Muller now exposed male flies to a specific high dosage of X-rays and found that 12% of F$_1$ Bar-eyed females produced male progeny that were all wild type. What does this new information say?

12. Figure 7.10 on pp. 210–211 shows examples of base substitutions induced by the mutagens 5-bromouracil, hydroxylamine, ethylmethane sulfonate, and nitrous acid. Which of these mutagens cause transitions, and which cause transversions?

13. So-called *two-way mutagens* can induce both a particular mutation and (when added subsequently to cells whose chromosomes carry this mutation) a reversion of the mutation that restores the original DNA sequence. In contrast, *one-way mutagens* can induce mutations but not exact reversions of these mutations. Based on Fig. 7.10 (pp. 210–211), which of the following mutagens can be classified as one-way and which as two-way?

a. 5-bromouracil

b. hydroxylamine

c. ethylmethane sulfonate

d. nitrous acid

e. proflavin

14. In 1967, J. B. Jenkins treated wild-type male *Drosophila* with the mutagen ethylmethane sulfonate (EMS) and mated them with females homozygous for a recessive mutation called *dumpy* that causes shortened wings. He found some F$_1$ progeny with two wild-type wings, some with two short wings, and some with one short wing and one wild-type wing. When he mated single F$_1$ flies with two short wings to *dumpy* homozygotes, he surprisingly found that only about 1/3 of these matings produced any short-winged progeny.

a. Explain these results in light of the mechanism of action of EMS shown in Fig. 7.10 on pp. 210–211.

b. Should the short-winged progeny of the second cross have one or two short wings? Why?

15. Aflatoxin B_1 is a highly mutagenic and carcinogenic compound produced by certain fungi that infect crops such as peanuts. Aflatoxin is a large, bulky molecule that chemically bonds to the base guanine to form the aflatoxin-guanine "adduct" that is pictured below. (In the figure, the aflatoxin is *orange,* and the guanine base is *purple.*) This adduct distorts the DNA double helix and blocks replication.

a. What type(s) of DNA repair system is (are) most likely to be involved in repairing the damage caused by exposure of DNA to aflatoxin B_1?

b. Recent evidence suggests that the adduct of guanine and aflatoxin B_1 can attack the bond that connects it to deoxyribose; this liberates the adduced base, forming an apurinic site. How does this new information change your answer to part *a*?

Aflatoxin-guanine adduct

16. When a particular mutagen identified by the Ames test is injected into mice, it causes the appearance of many tumors, showing that this substance is carcinogenic. When cells from these tumors are injected into other mice not exposed to the mutagen, almost all of the new mice develop tumors. However, when mice carrying mutagen-induced tumors are mated to unexposed mice, virtually all of the progeny are tumor free. Why can the tumor be transferred horizontally (by injecting cells) but not vertically (from one generation to the next)?

17. When the *his*⁻ *Salmonella* strain used in the Ames test is exposed to substance X, no *his*⁺ revertants are seen. If, however, rat liver supernatant is added to the cells along with substance X, revertants do occur. Is substance X a potential carcinogen for human cells? Explain.

Section 7.2

18. Imagine that you caught a female albino mouse in your kitchen and decided to keep it for a pet. A few months later, while vacationing in Guam, you caught a male albino mouse and decided to take it home for some interesting genetic experiments. You wonder whether the two mice are both albino due to mutations in the same gene. What could you do to find out the answer to this question? Assume that both mutations are recessive.

19. Plant breeders studying genes influencing leaf shape in the plant *Arabidopsis thaliana* identified six independent recessive mutations that resulted in plants that had unusual leaves with serrated rather than smooth edges. The investigators started to perform complementation tests with these mutants, but some of the tests could not be completed because of an accident in the greenhouse. The results of the complementation tests that could be finished are shown in the table that follows.

	1	2	3	4	5	6
1	–	+	–		+	
2		–				–
3			–	–		
4				–		
5					–	+
6						–

a. Exactly what experiment was done to fill in individual boxes in the table with a + or a − ? What does + represent? What does − represent? Why are some boxes in the table filled in *green?*

b. Assuming no complications, what do you expect for the results of the complementation tests that were not performed? That is, complete the table above by placing a + or a − in each of the blank boxes.

c. How many genes are represented among this collection of mutants? Which mutations are in which genes?

20. In humans, albinism is normally inherited in an autosomal recessive fashion. Figure 3.19c on p. 63 shows a pedigree in which two albino parents have several children, none of whom is an albino.

a. Interpret this pedigree in terms of a complementation test.

b. It is very rare to find examples of human pedigrees such as Fig. 3.19c that could be interpreted as complementation test. This is because most genetic conditions in humans are rare, so it is highly unlikely that unrelated people with the same condition would mate. In the absence of complementation testing, what kinds of experiments could be done to determine whether a particular human disease phenotype can be caused by mutations at more than one gene?

c. Complementation testing requires that the two mutations to be tested both be recessive to wild type. Suppose that two dominant mutations cause similar phenotypes. How could you establish whether the mutations affected the same gene or different genes?

21. a. Seymour Benzer's fine structure analysis of the *rII* region of bacteriophage T4 depended in large part on deletion analysis as shown in Fig. 7.21 on p. 223. But to perform such deletion analysis, Benzer had to know which *rII⁻* bacteriophage strains were deletions and which were point mutations. How do you think he was able to distinguish *rII⁻* deletions from point mutations?

b. Benzer concluded that recombination can occur between adjacent nucleotide pairs, even within the same gene. How was he able to make this statement? At the time, Benzer had two relevant pieces of information: (i) the total length in μm of the bacteriophage T4 chromosome (measured in the electron microscope) and (ii) many mutations in many bacteriophage T4 genes, including *rIIA* and *rIIB*.

c. Figure 7.21c on p. 223 shows Benzer's fine structure map of point mutations in the *rII* region. A key feature of this map is the existence of "hot spots," which Benzer interpreted as nucleotide pairs that were particularly susceptible to mutation. How could Benzer say that all the independent mutations in a hot spot were due to mutations of the same nucleotide pair?

22. a. You have a test tube containing 5 ml of a solution of bacteriophage, and you would like to estimate the number of bacteriophage in the tube. Assuming the tube actually contains a total of 15 billion bacteriophage, design a serial dilution experiment that would allow you to estimate this number. Ideally, the final plaque-containing plates you count should contain more than 10 and less than 1000 plaques.

b. When you count bacteriophage by the serial dilution method as in part *a*, you are assuming a *plating efficiency* of 100%; that is, the number of plaques on the petri plate exactly represents the number of bacteriophage you mixed with the plating bacteria. Is there any way to test the possibility that only a certain percentage of bacteriophage particles are able to form plaques (so that the plating efficiency would be less than 100%)? Conversely, why is it fair to assume that any plaques are initiated by one rather than multiple bacteriophage particles?

23. You found five T4 *rII⁻* mutants that will not grow on *E. coli* K(λ). You mixed together all possible combinations of two mutants (as indicated in the following chart), added the mixtures to *E. coli* K(λ), and scored for the ability of the mixtures to grow and make plaques (indicated as a + in the chart).

	1	2	3	4	5
1	−	+	+	−	+
2		−	−	+	−
3			−	+	−
4				−	+
5					−

a. How many genes were identified by this analysis?

b. Which mutants belong to the same complementation groups?

24. The *rosy (ry)* gene of *Drosophila* encodes an enzyme called xanthine dehydrogenase. Flies homozygous for *ry* mutations exhibit a rosy eye color. Heterozygous females were made that had ry^{41} *Sb* on one homolog and *Ly* ry^{564} on the other homolog, where ry^{41} and ry^{564} are two independently isolated alleles of *ry*. *Ly* (*Lyra* [narrow] wings) and *Sb* (*Stubble* [short] bristles) are dominant markers to the left and right of *ry*, respectively. These females are now mated to males homozygous for ry^{41}. Out of 100,000 progeny, 8 have wild-type eyes, *Lyra* wings, and *Stubble* bristles, while the remainder have rosy eyes.

a. What is the order of these two *ry* mutations relative to the flanking genes *Ly* and *Sb?*

b. What is the genetic distance separating ry^{41} and $ry^{564}?$

25. Nine *rII⁻* mutants of bacteriophage T4 were used in pairwise infections of *E. coli* K(λ) hosts. Six of the mutations in these phages are point mutations; the other three are deletions. The ability of the doubly infected cells to produce progeny phages in large numbers is scored in the following chart.

	1	2	3	4	5	6	7	8	9
1	−	−	+	+	−	−	−	+	+
2		−	+	+	−	−	−	+	+
3			−	−	+	−	+	−	−
4				−	+	−	+	−	−
5					−	−	−	+	+
6						−	−	−	−
7							−	+	+
8								−	−
9									−

The same nine mutants were then used in pairwise infections of *E. coli* B hosts. The production of progeny phage that can subsequently lyse *E. coli* K(λ) hosts is now scored. In the table, 0 means the progeny do not produce any plaques on *E. coli* K(λ) cells; − means that only a very few progeny phages produce plaques; and + means that many progeny produce plaques (more than 10 times as many as in the − cases).

	1	2	3	4	5	6	7	8	9
1	−	+	+	+	+	−	−	+	+
2		−	+	+	+	+	−	+	+
3			0	−	+	0	+	+	−
4				−	+	−	+	+	+
5					−	+	−	+	+
6						0	0	−	+
7							0	+	+
8								−	+
9									−

a. Which of the mutants are the three deletions? What criteria did you use to reach your conclusion?

b. If you know that mutation 9 is in the *rIIB* gene, draw the best genetic map possible to explain the data, including the positions of all point mutations and the extent of the three deletions.

c. There should be one uncertainty remaining in your answer to part *b*. How could you resolve this uncertainty?

26. In a haploid yeast strain, eight recessive mutations were found that resulted in a requirement for the amino acid lysine. All the mutations were found to revert at a frequency of about 1×10^{-6}, except mutations 5 and 6, which did not revert. Matings were made between *a* and α cells carrying these mutations. The ability of the resultant diploid strains to grow on minimal medium in the absence of lysine is shown in the following chart (+ means growth and − means no growth.)

	1	2	3	4	5	6	7	8
1	−	+	+	+	+	−	+	−
2	+	−	+	+	+	+	+	+
3	+	+	−	−	−	−	−	+
4	+	+	−	−	−	−	−	+
5	+	+	−	−	−	−	−	+
6	−	+	−	−	−	−	−	−
7	+	+	−	−	−	−	−	+
8	−	+	+	+	+	−	+	−

a. How many complementation groups were revealed by these data? Which point mutations are found within which complementation groups?

The same diploid strains are now induced to undergo sporulation. The vast majority of resultant spores are auxotrophic; that is, they cannot form colonies when plated on minimal medium minus lysine. However, particular diploids can produce rare spores that do form colonies when plated on minimal medium minus lysine (prototrophic spores). The following table shows whether (+) or not (−) any prototrophic spores are formed upon sporulation of the various diploid cells.

	1	2	3	4	5	6	7	8
1	−	+	+	+	+	−	+	+
2	+	−	+	+	+	+	+	+
3	+	+	−	+	−	+	+	+
4	+	+	+	−	−	−	+	+
5	+	+	−	−	−	−	+	+
6	−	+	+	−	−	−	+	+
7	+	+	+	+	+	+	−	+
8	+	+	+	+	+	+	+	−

b. When prototrophic spores occur during sporulation of the diploids just discussed, what ratio of auxotrophic to prototrophic spores would you generally expect to see in any tetrad containing such a prototrophic spore? Explain the ratio you expect.

c. Using the data from all parts of this question, draw the best map of the eight lysine mutations under study. Show the extent of any deletions involved, and indicate the boundaries of the various complementation groups.

Section 7.3

27. The pathway for arginine biosynthesis in *Neurospora crassa* involves several enzymes that produce a series of intermediates.

$$argE \qquad argF \qquad argG \qquad argH$$
N-acetylornithine → ornithine → citrulline → argininosuccinate → arginine

a. If you did a cross between $argE^-$ and $argH^-$ *Neurospora* strains, what would be the distribution of Arg$^+$ and Arg$^-$ spores within parental ditype and nonparental ditype asci? Give the spore types in the order in which they would appear in the ascus.

b. For each of the spores in your answer to part *a*, what nutrients could you supply in the media to get spore growth?

28. In corn snakes, the wild-type color is brown. One autosomal recessive mutation causes the snake to be orange, and another causes the snake to be black. An orange snake was crossed to a black one, and the F$_1$ offspring were all brown. Assume that all relevant genes are unlinked.

a. Indicate what phenotypes and ratios you would expect in the F$_2$ generation of this cross if there is one pigment pathway, with orange and black being different intermediates on the way to brown.

b. Indicate what phenotypes and ratios you would expect in the F$_2$ generation if orange pigment is a product of one pathway, black pigment is the product of another pathway, and brown is the effect of mixing the two pigments in the skin of the snake.

29. In a certain species of flowering plants with a diploid genome, four enzymes are involved in the generation of flower color. The genes encoding these four enzymes are on different chromosomes. The biochemical pathway involved is as follows; the figure shows that either of two different enzymes is sufficient to convert a blue pigment into a purple pigment.

$$\text{white} \rightarrow \text{green} \rightarrow \text{blue} \underset{\rightarrow}{\overset{\rightarrow}{}} \text{purple}$$

A true-breeding green-flowered plant is mated with a true-breeding blue-flowered plant. All of the plants in the resultant F$_1$ generation have purple flowers. F$_1$ plants are allowed to self-fertilize, yielding an F$_2$ generation. Show genotypes for P, F$_1$, and F$_2$ plants, and indicate which genes specify which biochemical step.

Determine the fraction of F_2 plants with the following phenotypes: white flowers, green flowers, blue flowers, and purple flowers. Assume the green-flowered parent is mutant in only a single step of the pathway.

30. The intermediates A, B, C, D, E, and F all occur in the same biochemical pathway. G is the product of the pathway, and mutants 1 through 7 are all G^-, meaning that they cannot produce substance G. The following table shows which intermediates will promote growth in each of the mutants. Arrange the intermediates in order of their occurrence in the pathway, and indicate the step in the pathway at which each mutant strain is blocked. A + in the table indicates that the strain will grow if given that substance, an O means lack of growth.

| Mutant | Supplements | | | | | | |
	A	B	C	D	E	F	G
1	+	+	+	+	+	O	+
2	O	O	O	O	O	O	+
3	O	+	+	O	+	O	+
4	O	+	O	O	+	O	+
5	+	+	+	O	+	O	+
6	+	+	+	+	+	+	+
7	O	O	O	O	+	O	+

31. In each of the following cross schemes, two true-breeding plant strains are crossed to make F_1 plants, all of which have purple flowers. The F_1 plants are then self-fertilized to produce F_2 progeny as shown here.

Cross	Parents	F_1	F_2
1	blue × white	all purple	9 purple: 4 white: 3 blue
2	white × white	all purple	9 purple: 7 white
3	red × blue	all purple	9 purple: 3 red: 3 blue: 1 white
4	purple × purple	all purple	15 purple: 1 white

a. For each cross, explain the inheritance of flower color.

b. For each cross, show a possible biochemical pathway that could explain the data.

c. Which of these crosses is compatible with an underlying biochemical pathway involving only a single step that is catalyzed by an enzyme with two dissimilar subunits, both of which are required for enzyme activity?

d. For each of the four crosses, what would you expect in the F_1 and F_2 generations if all relevant genes were tightly linked?

32. The pathways for the biosynthesis of the amino acids glutamine (Gln) and proline (Pro) involve one or more common intermediates. Auxotrophic yeast mutants numbered 1–7 are isolated that require either glutamine or proline or both amino acids for their growth,

as shown in the following table (+ means growth; − no growth). These mutants are also tested for their ability to grow on the intermediates A–E. What is the order of these intermediates in the glutamine and proline pathways, and at which point in the pathway is each mutant blocked?

Mutant	A	B	C	D	E	Gln	Pro	Gln + Pro
1	+	−	−	−	+	−	+	+
2	−	−	−	−	−	−	+	+
3	−	−	+	−	−	−	−	+
4	−	−	−	−	−	+	−	+
5	−	−	+	+	−	−	−	+
6	+	−	−	−	−	−	+	+
7	−	+	−	−	−	+	−	+

33. The following noncomplementing *E. coli* mutants were tested for growth on four known precursors of thymine, A–D.

| Mutant | Precursor/product | | | | |
	A	B	C	D	Thymine
9	+	−	+	−	+
10	−	−	+	−	+
14	+	+	+	−	+
18	+	+	+	+	+
21	−	−	−	−	+

a. Show a simple linear biosynthetic pathway of the four precursors and the end product, thymine. Indicate which step is blocked by each of the five mutations.

b. What precursor would accumulate in the following double mutants: 9 and 10? 10 and 14?

34. In 1952, an article in the *British Medical Journal* reported interesting differences in the behavior of blood plasma obtained from several individuals who suffered from X-linked recessive hemophilia. When mixed together, the cell-free blood plasma from certain combinations of individuals could form clots in the test tube. For example, the following table shows whether (+) or not (−) clots could form in various combinations of plasma from four individuals with hemophilia:

1 and 1	−		2 and 3	+
1 and 2	−		2 and 4	+
1 and 3	+		3 and 3	−
1 and 4	+		3 and 4	−
2 and 2	−		4 and 4	−

What do these data tell you about the inheritance of hemophilia in these individuals? Do these data allow you to exclude any models for the biochemical pathway governing blood clotting?

35. Mutations in an autosomal gene in humans cause a form of hemophilia called von Willebrand disease (vWD). This gene specifies a blood plasma protein cleverly called von Willebrand factor (vWF). vWF stabilizes factor VIII, a blood plasma protein specified by the wild-type hemophilia A gene. Factor VIII is needed to form blood clots. Thus, factor VIII is rapidly destroyed in the absence of vWF.

Which of the following might successfully be employed in the treatment of bleeding episodes in hemophiliac patients? Would the treatments work immediately or only after some delay needed for protein synthesis? Would the treatments have only a short-term or a prolonged effect? Assume that all mutations are null (that is, the mutations result in the complete absence of the protein encoded by the gene) and that the plasma is cell-free.

a. transfusion of plasma from normal blood into a vWD patient
b. transfusion of plasma from a vWD patient into a different vWD patient
c. transfusion of plasma from a hemophilia A patient into a vWD patient
d. transfusion of plasma from normal blood into a hemophilia A patient
e. transfusion of plasma from a vWD patient into a hemophilia A patient
f. transfusion of plasma from a hemophilia A patient into a different hemophilia A patient
g. injection of purified vWF into a vWD patient
h. injection of purified vWF into a hemophilia A patient
i. injection of purified factor VIII into a vWD patient
j. injection of purified factor VIII into a hemophilia A patient

36. Antibodies were made that recognize six proteins that are part of a complex inside the *Caenorhabditis elegans* one-cell embryo. The mother produces proteins that are believed to assemble stepwise into a structure in the egg, beginning at the embryo's inner surface. The antibodies were used to detect the protein location in embryos produced by mutant mothers (who are homozygous recessive for the gene[s] encoding each protein). The *C. elegans* mothers are self-fertilizing hermaphrodites so no wild-type copy of a gene will be introduced during fertilization. In the following table, * means the protein was present and at the embryo surface, − means that the protein was not present, and + means that the protein was present but not at the embryo surface. Assume all mutations prevent production of the corresponding protein.

Mutant in gene for protein	Protein production and location					
	A	B	C	D	E	F
A	−	+	*	+	*	+
B	*	−	*	*	*	*
C	*	+	−	+	*	+
D	*	+	*	−	*	+
E	+	+	+	+	−	+
F	*	+	*	*	*	−

Complete the following figure, which shows the construction of the hypothetical protein complex, by writing the letter of the proper protein in each circle. The two proteins marked with arrowheads can assemble into the complex independently of each other, but both are needed for the addition of subsequent proteins to the complex.

Outside

Embryo surface

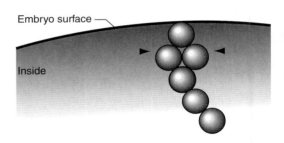

Inside

37. Adult hemoglobin is a multimeric protein with four polypeptides, two of which are α globin and two of which are β globin.

a. How many genes are needed to define the structure of the hemoglobin protein?
b. If a person is heterozygous for wild-type alleles and alleles that would yield amino acid substitution variants for both α globin and β globin, how many different kinds of hemoglobin protein would be found in the person's red blood cells and in what proportion? Assume all alleles are expressed at the same level.

38. This problem refers to Fig. A in the Fast Forward box on p. 232. For each part that follows, describe what structures Robert Edgar would have seen in the electron microscope if he examined extracts of *E. coli* cells infected with the indicated temperature-sensitive mutant strains of bacteriophage T4 under restrictive conditions.

a. A strain with a mutation in gene 19
b. A strain with a mutation in gene 16
c. Simultaneous infection with two mutant strains, one in gene 13 and the other in gene 14. The polypeptide

produced by genes 13 and 14 associate with each other to form a multimeric protein that governs one step of phage head assembly (see Fig. A on p. 232).

   d. A strain whose genome contains mutations in both genes 15 and 35

Section 7.4

39. In addition to the predominant adult hemoglobin, HbA, which contains two α-globin chains and two β-globin chains ($\alpha_2\beta_2$), there is a minor hemoglobin, HbA$_2$, composed of two α and two δ chains ($\alpha_2\delta_2$). The β- and δ-globin genes are arranged in tandem and are highly homologous. Draw the chromosomes that would result from an event of unequal crossing-over between the β and δ genes.

40. Most mammals, including "New World" primates such as marmosets (a kind of monkey), are *dichromats*: they have only two kinds of rhodopsin-related color receptors. "Old World" primates such as humans and gorillas are *trichromats* with three kinds of color receptors. Primates diverged from other mammals roughly 65 million years ago (Myr), while Old World and New World primates diverged from each other roughly 35 Myr.

   a. Using this information, define on Fig. 7.28d (see p. 233) the time span of any events that can be dated.

   b. Some New World monkeys have an autosomal color receptor gene and a single X-linked color receptor gene. The X-linked gene has three alleles, each of which encodes a photoreceptor that responds to light of a different wavelength (all three wavelengths are different from that recognized by the autosomal color receptor). How is color vision inherited in these monkeys?

   c. About 95% of all light-receiving neurons in humans and other mammals are rod cells containing rhodopsin, a pigment that responds to low-level light of many wavelengths. The remaining 5% of light-receiving neurons are cone cells with pigments that respond to light of specific wavelengths of high intensity. What does this suggest about the lifestyle of the earliest mammals?

Gene Expression: The Flow of Information from DNA to RNA to Protein

A dedicated effort to determine the complete nucleotide sequence of the haploid genome in a variety of organisms has been underway since 1990. This massive endeavor has been more successful than many scientists thought possible. By 2001, the DNA sequence in the genomes of more than 20 different species, including the bacterium *Escherichia coli,* the yeast *Saccharomyces cerevisiae,* the fruit fly *Drosophila melanogaster,* the nematode *Caenorhabditis elegans,* the plant *Arabidopsis thaliana,* and humans (*Homo sapiens*), had already been deciphered. With this sequence information in hand, geneticists can consult the genetic code—the cipher equating nucleotide sequence with amino acid sequence—to decide what parts of a genome are likely to be genes. They can also identify genes through matches with nucleotide sequences already known to encode proteins in other organisms. As a result, modern geneticists can discover the number and amino acid sequences of all the polypeptides that determine phenotype. Knowledge of DNA sequence thus opens up powerful new possibilities for understanding an organism's growth and development at the molecular level.

The ability of an aminoacyl-tRNA synthetase (red) to recognize a particular tRNA (blue) and couple it to its corresponding amino acid (not shown) is central to the molecular machinery that converts the language of nucleic acids into the language of proteins.

CHAPTER OUTLINE

- 8.1 The Genetic Code
- 8.2 Transcription: From DNA to RNA
- 8.3 Translation: From mRNA to Protein
- 8.4 Differences in Gene Expression Between Prokaryotes and Eukaryotes
- 8.5 A Comprehensive Example: Computerized Analysis of Gene Expression in *C. elegans*
- 8.6 The Effect of Mutations on Gene Expression and Gene Function

Later in this chapter, you'll see how studies of *Caenorhabditis elegans* illustrate the insights possible from the complete sequence of genomic DNA. *C. elegans* is a tiny roundworm that lives in soils throughout the world (**Fig. 8.1**). The entire sequence of its relatively small genome (100 million base pairs in six chromosomes) was determined in 1998. Interestingly, roughly 15% of the ≈20,000 genes in *C. elegans* genes encode molecules that play some role in **gene expression:** the process by which cells convert DNA sequence information to RNA and then decode the RNA information to the amino acid sequence of a polypeptide (**Fig. 8.2**).

In this chapter, we describe the cellular mechanisms that carry out gene expression. As intricate as some of the details may appear, the general scheme of gene expression is elegant and straightforward: *Within each cell, genetic information flows from DNA to RNA to protein.* This statement was set forth as the "Central Dogma" of molecular biology by Francis Crick in 1957. As Crick explained, "Once 'information' has passed into protein, it cannot get out again."

The Central Dogma maintains that genetic information flows in two distinct stages (Fig. 8.2). If you think of genes as instructions written in the language of nucleic acids, the cellular machinery first transcribes the instructions written in the DNA dialect to the same instructions written in the RNA dialect. The conversion of DNA-encoded information to its RNA-encoded equivalent is known as **transcription.** The product of transcription is a **transcript:** a molecule of

messenger RNA (mRNA)
in prokaryotes, a molecule
of RNA that undergoes processing to become an mRNA
in eukaryotes.

In the second stage of
gene expression, the cellular
machinery translates mRNA
into its polypeptide equivalent in the language of
amino acids. This decoding
of nucleotide information to
a sequence of amino acids is
known as **translation.** It
takes place on molecular
workbenches called **ribo-**
somes, which are composed of proteins and **ribosomal RNAs (rRNAs),** and it
depends on the "dictionary" known as the **genetic code,** which defines each amino
acid in terms of specific sequences of three nucleotides. Translation also depends
on **transfer RNAs (tRNAs),** small RNA adaptor molecules that place specific
amino acids at the correct position in a growing polypeptide chain.

The Central Dogma does not explain the behavior of all genes. As Crick himself realized, a large subset of genes is transcribed into RNAs that are never translated into proteins. The genes encoding rRNAs and tRNAs belong to this group.
In addition, scientists later found that certain viruses contain an enzyme that can
reverse the DNA-to-RNA flow of information by copying RNA to DNA in a process
called **reverse transcription.**

Four general themes emerge from our discussion of gene expression. First,
the pairing of complementary bases is key to the transfer of information
from DNA to RNA, and from RNA to protein. Second, the polarities (directionality) of DNA, RNA, and polypeptides help guide the mechanisms of gene
expression. Third, like DNA replication and recombination, gene expression
requires an input of energy and the participation of specific proteins and macromolecular assemblies, such as ribosomes. Finally, mutations that change genetic
information or obstruct the flow of its expression can have dramatic effects on
phenotype.

Figure 8.1 *C. elegans:* **An ideal subject for genetic analysis.** Micrograph of several adult worms.

Figure 8.2 Gene expression: The flow of genetic information from DNA via RNA to protein. In transcription, the enzyme RNA polymerase copies DNA to produce an RNA tran-
script. In translation, the cellular machinery uses instructions in mRNA to synthesize a
polypeptide, following the rules of the genetic code.

DNA

Transcription

RNA transcript: serves directly as mRNA in prokaryotes; processed to become mRNA in eukaryotes

Translation

Polypeptide

8.1 The Genetic Code

A code is a system of symbols that equates information
in one language with information in another. A useful
analogy for the genetic code is the Morse code, which
uses dots and dashes to transmit messages over radio or
telegraph wires. Various groupings of the dot-dash symbols represent the 26 letters of the English alphabet.
Because there are many more letters than the two symbols
(dot or dash), groups of one, two, three, or four dots or
dashes in various combinations represent individual letters. For example, the symbol for C is dash dot dash dot
(– · – ·), the symbol for O is dash dash dash (– – –), D
is dash dot dot (– · ·), and E is a single dot (·). Because

anywhere from one to four symbols specify each letter,
the Morse code requires a symbol for "pause" (in practice,
a short interval of time) to signify where one letter ends
and the next begins.

Triplet codons of nucleotides represent individual amino acids

The language of nucleic acids is written in four nucleotides—A, G, C, and T in the DNA dialect; A, G, C,
and U in the RNA dialect—while the language of proteins is written in amino acids. The first hurdle to be
overcome in deciphering how sequences of nucleotides

can determine the order of amino acids in a polypeptide is to determine how many amino acid "letters" exist. Over lunch one day at a local pub, Watson and Crick produced the now accepted list of the 20 amino acids that are genetically encoded by DNA or RNA. They created the list by analyzing the known amino acid sequences of a variety of naturally occurring polypeptides. Amino acids that are present in only a small number of proteins or in only certain tissues or organisms did not qualify as standard building blocks; Crick and Watson correctly assumed that such amino acids arise when proteins undergo modification after their synthesis. By contrast, amino acids that are present in most, though not necessarily all, proteins made the list. The question then became, How can four nucleotides encode 20 amino acids?

Like the Morse code, the four nucleotides encode 20 amino acids through specific groupings of A, G, C, and T or A, G, C, and U. Researchers initially arrived at the number of letters per grouping by deductive reasoning and later confirmed their guess by experiment. They reasoned that if only one nucleotide represented an amino acid, there would be information for only four amino acids: A would encode one amino acid; G, a second amino acid; and so on. If two nucleotides represented each amino acid, there would be $4^2 = 16$ possible combinations of couplets.

Of course, if the code consisted of groups containing one *or* two nucleotides, it would have $4 + 16 = 20$ groups and could account for all the amino acids, but there would be nothing left over to signify the pause required to denote where one group ends and the next begins. Groups of three nucleotides in a row would provide $4^3 = 64$ different triplet combinations, more than enough to code for all the amino acids. If the code consisted of doublets and triplets, a signal denoting a pause would once again be necessary. But a triplets-only code would require no symbol for "pause" if the mechanism for counting to three and distinguishing among successive triplets was very reliable.

Although this kind of reasoning generates a hypothesis, it does not prove it. As it turned out, however, the experiments described later in this chapter did indeed demonstrate that groups of three nucleotides represent all 20 amino acids. Each nucleotide triplet is called a **codon.** Each codon, designated by the bases defining its three nucleotides, specifies one amino acid. For example, GAA is a codon for glutamic acid (Glu), and GUU is a codon for valine (Val). Because the code comes into play only during the translation part of gene expression, that is, during the decoding of messenger RNA to polypeptide, geneticists usually present the code in the RNA dialect of A, G, C, and U, as depicted in **Fig. 8.3.** When speaking of genes, they can substitute T for U to show the same code in the DNA dialect.

Figure 8.3 The genetic code: 61 codons represent th 20 amino acids, while 3 codons signify stop. To read th code, find the first letter in the *left column*, the second letter along the *top*, and the third letter in the *right column;* this reading corresponds to the 5′-to-3′ direction along the mRNA.

If you knew the sequence of nucleotides in a ge or its transcript as well as the sequence of amino aci in the corresponding polypeptide, you could then dedu the genetic code without understanding how the und lying cellular machinery actually works. Although tec niques for determining both nucleotide and amino ac sequence are available today, this was not true wh researchers were trying to crack the genetic code in t 1950s and 1960s. At that time, they could establish polypeptide's amino acid sequence, but not the nucleoti sequence of DNA or RNA. Because of their inability read nucleotide sequence, they used an assortment genetic and biochemical techniques to fathom the coc They began by examining how different mutations ir single gene affected the amino acid sequence of t gene's polypeptide product. In this way, they were ak to use the abnormal (specific mutations) to understa the normal (the general relationship between genes a polypeptides).

Geneticists reasoned on theoretical grounds that codon composed of three nucleotides would provide the simples mechanism by which genes could encode the 20 amin acids commonly found in proteins.

A gene's nucleotide sequence is colinear with the amino acid sequence of the encoded polypeptide

As you know, DNA is a linear molecule with base pairs following one another down the intertwined chains. Proteins, by contrast, have complicated three-dimensional structures. Even so, if unfolded and stretched out from N terminus to C terminus, proteins have a one-dimensional, linear structure—a specific sequence of amino acids. If the information in a gene and its corresponding protein are colinear, the consecutive order of bases in the DNA from the beginning to the end of the gene would stipulate the consecutive order of amino acids from one end to the other of the outstretched protein.

In the 1960s, Charles Yanofsky was the first to compare maps of mutations within a gene to the particular amino acid substitutions that resulted. He began by generating a large number of *trp*⁻ auxotrophic mutants in *E. coli* that carried mutations in the *trpA* gene for a subunit of the enzyme tryptophan synthetase. He next made a fine structure recombinational map of these mutations (analogous to Benzer's fine structure map for the *rII* region of bacteriophage T4, discussed in Chapter 7). Yanofsky then purified and determined the amino acid sequence of the mutant tryptophan synthetase subunits. As **Fig. 8.4a** illustrates, his data showed that the order of mutations mapped within the DNA of the gene by recombination was indeed colinear with the positions of the amino acid substitutions occurring in the resulting mutant proteins. In spite of this colinearity in order, distances on the genetic map (measured in map units) do not exactly reflect the number of amino acids between the amino acid substitutions. The reason is that recombination as seen on this very high resolution map does not occur with an equal probability at every base pair within the gene.

By carefully examining the results of his analysis, Yanofsky deduced key features of the relationship between nucleotides and amino acids, in addition to his confirmation of the existence of colinearity.

Evidence that a codon is composed of more than one nucleotide

Yanofsky observed that different **point mutations** (changes in only one nucleotide pair) may affect the same amino acid. In one example shown in Fig. 8.4a, mutation #23 changed the glycine (Gly) at position 211 of the wild-type polypeptide chain to arginine (Arg), while mutation #46 yielded glutamic acid (Glu) at the same position. In another

Figure 8.4 Mutations in a gene are colinear with the sequence of amino acids in the encoded polypeptide. **(a)** The relationship between the genetic map of *E. coli's trpA* gene and the positions of amino acid substitutions in mutant tryptophan synthetase proteins. **(b)** Codons must include two or more base pairs. When two mutant strains with different amino acids at the same position were crossed, recombination could produce a wild-type allele.

(a) Colinearity of genes and proteins

(b) Recombination within a codon

example, mutation #78 changed the glycine at position 234 to cysteine (Cys), while mutation #58 produced aspartic acid (Asp) at the same position. In both cases, Yanofsky also found that recombination could occur between the two mutations that changed the identity of the same amino acid; such recombination would produce a wild-type tryptophan synthetase gene (**Fig. 8.4b**). Because the smallest unit of recombination is the base pair, two mutations capable of recombination—in this case, in the same codon because they affect the same amino acid—must be in different (although nearby) nucleotides. Thus, a codon must contain more than one nucleotide.

Evidence that each nucleotide is part of only one codon

As Fig. 8.4a illustrates, each of the point mutations in the tryptophan synthetase gene characterized by Yanofsky alters the identity of only a single amino acid. This is also true of the point mutations examined in many other genes, such as the human genes for rhodopsin and hemoglobin (see Chapter 7). Because point mutations change only a single nucleotide pair, and most point mutations affect only a single amino acid in a polypeptide, each nucleotide

in a gene must influence the identity of only a single amino acid. In contrast, if a nucleotide were part of more than one codon, a mutation in that nucleotide would affect more than one amino acid.

> Comparison of recombination maps of mutations with the amino acid sequences of mutant polypeptides established colinearity: The order of nucleotides in the gene corresponds to the order of amino acids in the polypeptide. Further analysis demonstrated that a single codon must contain more than one nucleotide, and that each nucleotide in the gene helps encode only a single amino acid.

Nonoverlapping triplet codons are set in a reading frame

Although the most efficient code to specify 20 amino acids requires three nucleotides per codon, more complicated scenarios are possible. But in 1955, Francis Crick and Sydney Brenner obtained convincing evidence for the triplet nature of the genetic code in studies of mutations in the bacteriophage T4 *rIIB* gene (**Fig. 8.5**). They induced the

Figure 8.5 Studies of frameshift mutations in the bacteriophage T4 *rIIB* gene showed that codons consist of three nucleotides. (a) The mutagen proflavin slips between adjacent base pairs, eventually causing a deletion or insertion. **(b)** Treatment with proflavin produces a mutation at one site (FC0). A second proflavin exposure results in a second mutation (FC7) within the same gene, which suppresses FC0. **(c)** When the revertant is crossed with a wild-type strain, crossing-over separates the two *rIIB⁻* mutations FC0 and FC7. The reversion to an *rIIB⁺* phenotype was thus the result of intragenic suppression. **(d)** Evidence for a triplet code.

(a) The mutagen proflavin can insert between two base pairs.

(b) Consequences of exposure to proflavin

(c) *rIIB⁺* revertant X wild type yields *rIIB⁻* recombinants.

(d) Different sets of mutations generate either a mutant or a normal phenotype.

Proflavin-induced mutations (+) insertion (−) deletion	Phenotype
− or +	Mutant
− − or + +	Mutant
− − − − or − − − − − or + + + + or + + + + +	Mutant
− +	Wild type
− − − or − − − − − or + + + or + + + + +	Wild type

mutations with proflavin, an intercalating mutagen that can insert itself between the paired bases stacked in the center of the DNA molecule (Fig. 8.5a). Their assumption was that proflavin would act like other mutagens, causing single-base substitutions. If this were true, it would be possible to generate revertants through treatment with other mutagens that might restore the wild-type DNA sequence.

Surprisingly, genes with proflavin-induced mutations did not revert to wild type upon treatment with other mutagens known to cause nucleotide substitutions. Only further exposure to proflavin caused proflavin-induced mutations to revert to wild type (Fig. 8.5b). Crick and Brenner had to explain this observation before they could proceed with their phage experiments. With keen insight, they correctly guessed that proflavin does not cause base substitutions; instead, it causes insertions or deletions. This hypothesis explained why base-substituting mutagens could not cause reversion of proflavin-induced mutations; it was also consistent with the structure of proflavin. By intercalating between base pairs, proflavin would distort the double helix and thus interfere with the action of enzymes that function in the repair, replication, or recombination of DNA. The result would be the deletion or addition of one or more nucleotide pairs to the DNA molecule (review Figure 7.10 on pp. 210–211).

Evidence for a triplet code

Crick and Brenner began their experiments with a particular proflavin-induced *rIIB⁻* mutation they called FC0. They next treated this mutant strain with more proflavin to isolate an *rIIB⁺* revertant (Fig. 8.5b). By recombining this revertant with wild-type bacteriophage T4, Crick and Brenner were able to show that the revertant's chromosome actually contained two different *rIIB⁻* mutations (Fig. 8.5c). One was the original FC0 mutation; the other was the newly induced FC7. Either mutation by itself yields a mutant phenotype, but their simultaneous occurrence in the same gene yielded an *rIIB⁺* phenotype. Crick and Brenner reasoned that if the first mutation was the deletion of a single base pair, represented by the symbol (−), then the counteracting mutation must be the insertion of a base pair, represented as (+). The restoration of gene function by one mutation canceling another in the same gene is known as **intragenic suppression**. On the basis of this reasoning, they went on to establish T4 strains with different numbers of (+) and (−) mutations in the same chromosome. Figure 8.5d tabulates the phenotypes associated with each combination of proflavin-induced mutations.

In analyzing the data, Crick and Brenner assumed that each codon is a trio of nucleotides and that for each gene there is a single starting point. This starting point establishes a **reading frame**: the partitioning of groups of three nucleotides such that the sequential interpretation of each triplet generates the correct order of amino acids in the resulting polypeptide chain. If codons are read in order

from a fixed starting point, one mutation will counteract another if the two are equivalent mutations of opposite signs—that is, (−) and (+). In such a case, each insertion compensates for each deletion, and this counterbalancing restores the reading frame (**Fig. 8.6a**). The gene would only regain its wild-type activity, however, if the portion of the polypeptide encoded between the two mutations of opposite sign is not required for protein function, because in the double mutant, this region would have an improper amino acid sequence.

Similarly, if a gene sustains three or multiples of three changes of the same sign, the encoded polypeptide

Figure 8.6 Codons consist of three nucleotides read in a defined reading frame. The phenotypic effects of proflavin-induced frameshift mutations depend on whether the reading frame is restored and whether the part of the gene with an altered reading frame specifies an essential or nonessential region of the polypeptide.

correct triplet
incorrect triplet

(a) Intragenic suppression: 2 mutations of opposite sign.
Single base insertion (+) and single base deletion (−)

ATG AAC AAT GCG CCG GAG GAA GCG GAC
↓
ATG AAC AAT CGC GCCG GAG GA GCG GAC

(b) Intragenic suppression: 3 mutations of the same sign.
Three single base deletions (− − −)

ATG AAC AAT GCG CCG GAG GAA GCG GAC
↓
ATG AAC AA GCG C G G G GAA GCG GAC

Three single base insertions (+ + +)

ATG AAC AAT GCG CCG GAG GAA GCG GAC
↓
ATG AAC AAT GGCGCTCGGCAG GAA GCG GAC

(c) Some frameshift mutations.
Single base deletion (−)

ATG AAC AAT GCG CCG GAG GAA GCG GAC
↓
ATG AAC AA GCG CCG GAG GAA GCG GAC

Single base insertion (+)

ATG AAC AAT GCG CCG GAG GAA GCG GAC
↓
ATG AAC AAT GGCGCCG GAG GAA GCG GAC

can still function, because the mutations do not alter the reading frame for the majority of amino acids (**Fig. 8.6b**). The resulting polypeptide will, however, have one extra or one fewer amino acid than normal (designated by three plus signs (+) or three minus signs (−), respectively), and the region encoded by the part of the gene between the first and the last mutations will not contain the correct amino acids.

By contrast, a single nucleotide inserted into or deleted from a gene alters the reading frame and thereby affects the identity of not only one amino acid but of all other amino acids beyond the point of alteration (**Fig. 8.6c**). Changes that alter the grouping of nucleotides into codons are called **frameshift mutations:** They shift the reading frame for all codons beyond the point of insertion or deletion, almost always abolishing the function of the polypeptide product.

A review of the evidence tabulated in Fig. 8.5d supports all these points. A single (−) or a single (+) mutation destroyed the function of the *rIIB* gene and produced an *rIIB*⁻ phage. Similarly, any gene with two base changes of the same sign (− − or + +) or with four or five insertions or deletions of the same sign (for example, + + + +) also generated a mutant phenotype. However, genes containing three or multiples of three mutations of the same sign (for example, + + + or − − − − − −), as well as genes containing a (+ −) pair of mutations, generated *rIIB*⁺ wild-type individuals. In these last examples, intragenic suppression allowed restitution of the reading frame and thereby restored the lost or aberrant genetic function produced by other frameshift mutations in the gene.

Evidence that most amino acids are specified by more than one codon

As Fig. 8.6a illustrates, intragenic suppression occurs only if, in the region between two frameshift mutations of opposite sign, a gene still dictates the appearance of amino acids—even if these amino acids are not the same as those appearing in the normal protein. If the frameshifted part of the gene encodes instructions to stop protein synthesis by introducing, for example, a triplet that does not correspond to any amino acid, then wild-type polypeptide production will not continue. The reason is that polypeptide synthesis would stop before the compensating mutation could reestablish the correct reading frame.

The fact that intragenic suppression occurs as often as it does suggests that the code includes more than one codon for some amino acids. Recall that there are 20 common amino acids but $4^3 = 64$ different combinations of three nucleotides. If each amino acid corresponded to only a single codon, there would be $64 - 20 = 44$ possible triplets not encoding an amino acid. These noncoding triplets would act as "stop" signals and prevent further polypeptide synthesis. If this happened, more than half of all frameshift mutations (44/64) would cause protein synthesis to stop at the first codon after the mutation, and the chances of extending the protein each amino acid farther down the chain would diminish exponentially. As a result, intragenic suppression would rarely occur. However, we have seen that many frameshift mutations of one sign can be offset by mutations of the other sign. The distances between these mutations, estimated by recombination frequencies, are in some cases large enough to code for more than 50 amino acids, which would be possible only if most of the 64 possible triplet codons specified amino acids. Thus, the data of Crick and Brenner provide strong support for the idea that the genetic code is **degenerate:** Two or more nucleotide triplets specify most of the 20 amino acids (see the genetic code in Fig. 8.3 on p. 248).

> Work with frameshift mutations in the bacteriophage T4 *rIIB* gene established that (1) codons consist of three adjacent nucleotides; (2) each gene has a specific starting point to set a reading frame for triplets; and (3) the genetic code is degenerate, with some amino acids specified by more than one codon.

Cracking the code: Which codons represent which amino acids?

Although the genetic experiments just described allowed remarkably prescient insights about the nature of the genetic code, they did not establish a correspondence between specific codons and specific amino acids. The discovery of messenger RNA and the development of techniques for synthesizing simple messenger RNA molecules had to occur first, so that researchers could manufacture simple proteins in the test tube.

The discovery of messenger RNAs

In the 1950s, researchers exposed eukaryotic cells to amino acids tagged with radioactivity and observed that protein synthesis incorporating the radioactive amino acids into polypeptides takes place in the cytoplasm, even though the genes for those polypeptides are sequestered in the cell nucleus. From this discovery, they deduced the existence of an intermediate molecule, made in the nucleus and capable of transporting DNA sequence information to the cytoplasm, where it can direct protein synthesis. RNA was a prime candidate for this intermediary information-carrying molecule.

Because of RNA's potential for base pairing with a strand of DNA, one could imagine the cellular machinery copying a strand of DNA into a complementary strand of RNA in a manner analogous to the DNA-to-DNA copying of DNA replication. Subsequent studies in eukaryotes using radioactive uracil, a base found only in RNA, showed that although the molecules are synthesized in the nucleus, at least some of them migrate to the cytoplasm. Among those RNA molecules that migrate to the cytoplasm are the messenger RNAs, or mRNAs, depicted in Fig. 8.2 on p. 247. They arise in the nucleus from the transcription of DNA sequence information and then move (after processing) to the cytoplasm, where they determine the proper order of amino acids during protein synthesis.

Using synthetic mRNAs and *in vitro* translation

Knowledge of mRNA served as the framework for two experimental breakthroughs that led to the deciphering of the genetic code. In the first, biochemists obtained cellular extracts that, with the addition of mRNA, synthesized polypeptides in a test tube. They called these extracts "*in vitro* translational systems." The second breakthrough was the development of techniques enabling the synthesis of artificial mRNAs containing only a few codons of known composition. When added to *in vitro* translational systems, these simple, synthetic mRNAs directed the formation of very simple polypeptides.

In 1961, Marshall Nirenberg and Heinrich Matthaei added a synthetic poly-U (5′. . . UUUUUUUUUUU . . . 3′) mRNA to a cell-free translational system derived from *E. coli*. With the poly-U mRNA, phenylalanine (Phe) was the only amino acid incorporated into the resulting polypeptide (**Fig. 8.7a**). Because UUU is the only possible triplet in poly-U, UUU must be a codon for phenylalanine. In a similar fashion, Nirenberg and Matthaei showed that CCC encodes proline (Pro), AAA is a codon for lysine (Lys), and GGG encodes glycine (Gly) (**Fig. 8.7b**).

The chemist Har Gobind Khorana later made mRNAs with repeating dinucleotides, such as poly-UC (5′. . . UCUCUCUC . . . 3′), repeating trinucleotides, such as poly-UUC, and repeating tetranucleotides, such as poly-UAUC, and used them to direct the synthesis of slightly more complex polypeptides. As Fig. 8.7b shows, his results limited the coding possibilities, but some ambiguities remained. For example, poly-UC encodes the polypeptide N . . . Ser-Leu-Ser-Leu-Ser-Leu . . . C in which serine and leucine alternate with each other. Although the mRNA contains only two different codons (5′ UCU 3′ and 5′ CUC 3′), it is not obvious which corresponds to serine and which to leucine.

Nirenberg and Philip Leder resolved these ambiguities in 1965 with experiments in which they added short, synthetic mRNAs only three nucleotides in length to an *in vitro* translational system containing 1 radioactive amino acid and 19 unlabeled amino acids, all attached to tRNA molecules. They then poured through a filter the mixture of synthetic mRNAs and translational systems containing a tRNA-attached, radioactively labeled amino acid (**Fig. 8.8**). tRNAs carrying an amino acid normally go right through a filter. If, however, a tRNA carrying an amino acid binds to a ribosome, it will stick in the filter,

Figure 8.7 How geneticists used synthetic mRNAs to limit the coding possibilities. (a) Poly-U mRNA generates a poly-phenylalanine polypeptide. **(b)** Polydi-, polytri-, and polytetra-nucleotides encode simple polypeptides. Some synthetic mRNAs, such as poly-GUAA, contain stop codons in all three reading frames and thus specify the construction only of short peptides.

(a) Poly-U mRNA encodes polyphenylalanine.

Synthetic mRNA

In vitro translational system plus radioactive amino acids

Analyze radioactive polypeptides synthesized

(b) Analyzing the coding possibilities.

Synthetic mRNA		Polypeptides synthesized
		Polypeptides with one amino acid
poly-U	UUUU ...	Phe-Phe-Phe ...
poly-C	CCCC ...	Pro-Pro-Pro ...
poly-A	AAAA ...	Lys-Lys-Lys ...
poly-G	GGGG ...	Gly-Gly-Gly ...
Repeating dinucleotides		Polypeptides with alternating amino acids
poly-UC	UCUC ...	Ser-Leu-Ser-Leu ...
poly-AG	AGAG ...	Arg-Glu-Arg-Glu ...
poly-UG	UGUG ...	Cys-Val-Cys-Val ...
poly-AC	ACAC ...	Thr-His-Thr-His ...
Repeating trinucleotides		Three polypeptides each with one amino acid
poly-UUC	UUCUUCUUC ...	Phe-Phe.... and Ser-Ser.... and Leu-Leu....
poly-AAG	AAGAAGAAG ...	Lys-Lys.... and Arg-Arg.... and Glu-Glu....
poly-UUG	UUGUUGUUG ...	Leu-Leu.... and Cys-Cys.... and Val-Val....
poly-UAC	UACUACUAC ...	Tyr-Tyr.... and Thr-Thr.... and Leu-Leu....
Repeating tetranucleotides		Polypeptides with repeating units of four amino acids
poly-UAUC	UAUCUAUC ...	Tyr-Leu-Ser-Ile-Tyr-Leu-Ser-Ile...
poly-UUAC	UUACUUAC ...	Leu-Leu-Thr-Tyr-Leu-Leu-Thr-Tyr...
poly-GUAA	GUAAGUAA ...	none
poly-GAUA	GAUAGAUA ...	none

because this larger complex of ribosome, amino-acid-carrying tRNA, and small mRNA cannot pass through the filter. Nirenberg and Leder could thus use this approach to see which small mRNA caused the entrapment of which radioactively labeled amino acid. For example, they knew from Khorana's earlier work that CUC encoded either serine or leucine. When they added the synthetic triplet CUC to an *in vitro* system where the radioactive amino acid was serine, this tRNA-attached amino acid passed through the filter, and the filter thus emitted no radiation. But when they added the same triplet to a system where the radioactive amino acid was leucine, the filter lit up with radioactivity, indicating that the radioactively tagged leucine attached to a tRNA had bound to the

Figure 8.8 Cracking the genetic code with mini-mRNAs.

Nirenberg and Leder added trinucleotides of known sequence, in combination with tRNAs charged with a radioactive amino acid, to an *in vitro* extract containing ribosomes. If the trinucleotide specified the radioactive amino acid, the amino acid-bearing tRNA formed a complex with the ribosomes that could be trapped on a filter. The experiments shown here indicate that the codon CUC specifies leucine, not serine.

Figure 8.9 Correlation of polarities in DNA, mRNA, and polypeptide.

The template strand of DNA is complementary to both the RNA-like DNA strand and the mRNA. The 5′-to-3′ direction in an mRNA corresponds to the N-terminus-to-C-terminus direction in the polypeptide.

ribosome-mRNA complex and gotten stuck in the filter. CUC thus encodes leucine, not serine. Nirenberg and Leder used this technique to determine all the codon–amino acid correspondences shown in the genetic code table (see Fig. 8.3 on p. 248).

Polarities: 5′-to-3′ in mRNA corresponds to N-to-C in the polypeptide

In studies using synthetic mRNAs, when investigators added the six-nucleotide-long 5′ AAAUUU 3′ to an *in vitro* translational system, the product N-Lys-Phe-C emerged, but no N-Phe-Lys-C appeared. Because AAA is the codon for lysine and UUU is the codon for phenylalanine, this means that the codon closest to the 5′ end of the mRNA encoded the amino acid closest to the N terminus of the corresponding polypeptide. Similarly, the codon nearest the 3′ end of the mRNA encoded the amino acid nearest the C terminus of the resulting polypeptide.

To understand how the polarities of the macromolecules participating in gene expression relate to each other, remember that although the gene is a segment of a DNA double helix, only one of the two strands serves as a template for the mRNA. This strand is known as the **template strand.** The other strand is the **RNA-like strand,** because it has the same polarity and sequence (written in the DNA

dialect) as the RNA. Note that some scientists use the terms *sense strand* or *coding strand* as synonyms for the RNA-like strand; in these alternative nomenclatures, the template strand would be the *antisense strand* or the *noncoding strand.* **Figure 8.9** diagrams the respective polarities of a gene's DNA, the mRNA transcript of that DNA, and the resulting polypeptide.

Nonsense codons and polypeptide chain termination

Although most of the simple, repetitive RNAs synthesized by Khorana were very long and thus generated very long polypeptides, a few did not. These RNAs had signals that stopped construction of a polypeptide chain. As it turned out, three different triplets—UAA, UAG, and UGA—do not correspond to any of the amino acids. When these codons appear in frame, translation stops. As an example of how investigators established this fact, consider the case of poly-GUAA (review Fig. 8.7b). This mRNA will not generate a long polypeptide because in all possible reading frames, it contains the **stop codon** UAA.

The three stop codons that terminate translation are also known as **nonsense codons.** For historical reasons, researchers often refer to UAA as the *ocher* codon, UAG as the *amber* codon, and UGA as the *opal* codon. The historical basis of this nomenclature is the last name of one of the early investigators—Bernstein—which means "amber" in German; ocher and opal derive from their similarity with amber as semiprecious materials.

The addition of synthetic mRNAs to *in vitro* translation systems allowed biochemists to determine which codons specify which amino acids.

The genetic code: A summary

The genetic code is a complete, unabridged dictionary equating the 4-letter language of the nucleic acids w the 20-letter language of the proteins. The following list summarizes the code's main features:

1. *Triplet codons:* As written in Fig. 8.3 on p. 248, the code shows the 5'-to-3' sequence of the three nucleotides in each mRNA codon; that is, the first nucleotide depicted is at the 5' end of the codon.
2. The codons are *nonoverlapping.* In the mRNA sequence 5' GAAGUUGAA 3', for example, the first three nucleotides (GAA) form one codon; nucleotides 4 through 6 (GUU) form the second; and so on. Each nucleotide is part of only one codon.
3. The code includes three *stop,* or *nonsense, codons:* UAA, UAG, and UGA. These codons do not encode an amino acid and thus terminate translation.
4. The code is *degenerate,* meaning that more than one codon may specify the same amino acid. The code is nevertheless unambiguous, because each codon specifies only one amino acid.
5. The cellular machinery scans mRNA from a fixed starting point that establishes a *reading frame.* As we see later, the nucleotide triplet AUG, which specifies the amino acid methionine, serves in certain contexts as the **initiation codon,** marking where in an mRNA the code for a particular polypeptide begins.
6. *Corresponding polarities:* Moving from the 5' to the 3' end of an mRNA, each successive codon is sequentially interpreted into an amino acid, starting at the N terminus and moving toward the C terminus of the resulting polypeptide.
7. Mutations may modify the message encoded in a sequence of nucleotides in three ways. *Frameshift mutations* are nucleotide insertions or deletions that alter the genetic instructions for polypeptide construction by changing the reading frame. *Missense mutations* change a codon for one amino acid to a codon for a different amino acid. *Nonsense mutations* change a codon for an amino acid to a stop codon.

The effects of mutations on polypeptides helped verify the code

The experiments that cracked the genetic code by assigning codons to amino acids were all *in vitro* studies using cell-free extracts and synthetic mRNAs. A logical question thus arose: Do living cells construct polypeptides according to the same rules? Early evidence that they do came from studies analyzing how mutations actually affect the amino acid composition of the polypeptides encoded by a gene. Most mutagens change a single nucleotide in a codon. As a result, most missense mutations that change the identity of a single amino acid should be single-nucleotide substitutions, and analyses of these substitutions should conform to the code. Yanofsky, for example, found two *trp*⁻ auxotrophic mutations in the *E. coli*

tryptophan synthetase gene that produced two different amino acids (arginine, or Arg, and glutamic acid, or Glu) at the same position—amino acid 211—in the polypeptide chain (**Fig. 8.10a**). According to the code, both of these mutations could have resulted from single-base changes in the GGA codon that normally inserts glycine (Gly) at position 211.

Even more telling were the *trp*⁺ revertants of these mutations subsequently isolated by Yanofsky. As Fig. 8.10a illustrates, single-base substitutions could also explain the amino acid changes in these revertants. Note that some of these substitutions restore Gly to position 211 of the polypeptide, while others place amino acids such as Ile, Thr, Ser, Ala, or Val at this site in the tryptophan synthetase molecule. The substitution of these other amino acids for Gly at position 211 in the polypeptide chain is compatible with (that is, largely conserves) the enzyme's function.

Figure 8.10 Experimental verification of the genetic code. (a) Single-base substitutions can explain the amino acid substitutions of *trp*⁻ mutations and *trp*⁺ revertants. **(b)** The genetic code predicts the amino acid alterations (*yellow*) that would arise from single-base-pair deletions and suppressing insertions.

(a) Altered amino acids in *trp*⁻ mutations and *trp*⁺ revertants

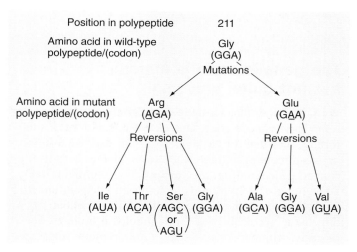

(b) Amino acid alterations that accompany intragenic suppression

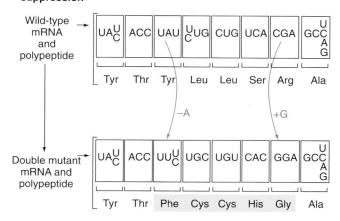

Yanofsky obtained better evidence yet that cells use the genetic code *in vivo* by analyzing proflavin-induced frame-shift mutations of the tryptophan synthetase gene (**Fig. 8.10b**). He first treated populations of *E. coli* with proflavin to produce *trp*⁻ mutants. Subsequent treatment of these mutants with more proflavin generated some *trp*⁺ revertants among the progeny. The most likely explanation for the revertants was that their tryptophan synthetase gene carried both a single-base-pair deletion and a single-base-pair insertion (− +). Upon determining the amino acid sequences of the tryptophan synthetase enzymes made by the revertant strains, Yanofsky found that he could use the genetic code to predict the precise amino acid alterations that had occurred by assuming the revertants had a specific single-base-pair insertion and a specific single-base-pair deletion.

Yanofsky's results helped confirm not only amino acid codon assignments but other parameters of the code as well. His interpretations make sense only if codons do not overlap and are read from a fixed starting point with no pauses or commas separating the adjacent triplets.

> The effects of specific mutations on the amino acid sequence of the encoded polypeptide are consistent with the genetic code table shown in Fig. 8.3.

The genetic code is almost, but not quite, universal

We now know that virtually all cells alive today use the same basic genetic code. One early indication of this uniformity was that a translational system derived from one organism could use the mRNA from another organism to convert genetic information to the encoded protein. Rabbit hemoglobin mRNA, for example, when injected into frog eggs or added to cell-free extracts from wheat germ, directs the synthesis of rabbit hemoglobin proteins. More recently, comparisons of DNA and protein sequences have revealed a perfect correspondence according to the genetic code between codons and amino acids in almost all organisms examined.

Conservation of the genetic code

The universality of the code is an indication that it evolved very early in the history of life. Once it emerged, it remained constant over billions of years, in part because evolving organisms would have little tolerance for change. A single change in the genetic code could disrupt the production of hundreds or thousands of proteins in a cell—from the DNA polymerase that is essential for replication to the RNA polymerase that is required for gene expression to the tubulin proteins that compose the mitotic spindle—and such a change would therefore be lethal.

Exceptional genetic codes

Researchers were thus quite amazed to observe a few exceptions to the universality of the code. In some species of the single-celled eukaryotic protozoans known as ciliates, the codons UAA and UAG, which are nonsense codons in most organisms, specify the amino acid glutamine; in other ciliates, UGA, the third stop codon in most organisms, specifies cysteine. These ciliates use the remaining nonsense codons as stop codons.

Other systematic changes in the genetic code exist in mitochondria, the semiautonomous, self-reproducing organelles within eukaryotic cells that are the sites of ATP formation. Each mitochondrion has its own chromosomes and its own apparatus for gene expression (which we describe in detail in Chapter 14). In the mitochondria of yeast, CUA specifies threonine instead of leucine.

It may be that ciliates and mitochondria tolerated these changes in the genetic code because the alterations affected very few proteins. For instance, the nonsense codon UGA might have found only infrequent use in one kind of primitive ciliate, so its switch to a "sense" codon would not have made a tremendous difference in protein production. Similarly, mitochondria might have survived a few changes in the code because they synthesize only a handful of proteins.

The experimental evidence presented so far helped define a nearly universal genetic code. But although cracking the code made it possible to understand the broad outlines of information flow between gene and protein, it did not explain exactly how the cellular machinery accomplishes gene expression. This is our focus as we present the details of transcription and translation.

8.2 Transcription: From DNA to RNA

Transcription is the process by which the polymerization of ribonucleotides guided by complementary base pairing produces an RNA transcript of a gene. The template for the RNA transcript is one strand of that portion of the DNA double helix that composes the gene.

RNA polymerase synthesizes a single-stranded RNA copy of a gene

Figure 8.11 depicts the basic components of transcription and illustrates key events in the process as it occurs in the bacterium *E. coli*. This figure divides transcription into successive phases of *initiation, elongation,* and *termination.* The following four points are of particular importance:

1. The enzyme **RNA polymerase** catalyzes transcription.
2. DNA sequences near the beginning of genes, called **promoters,** signal RNA polymerase where to begin

Transcription in Bacterial Cells

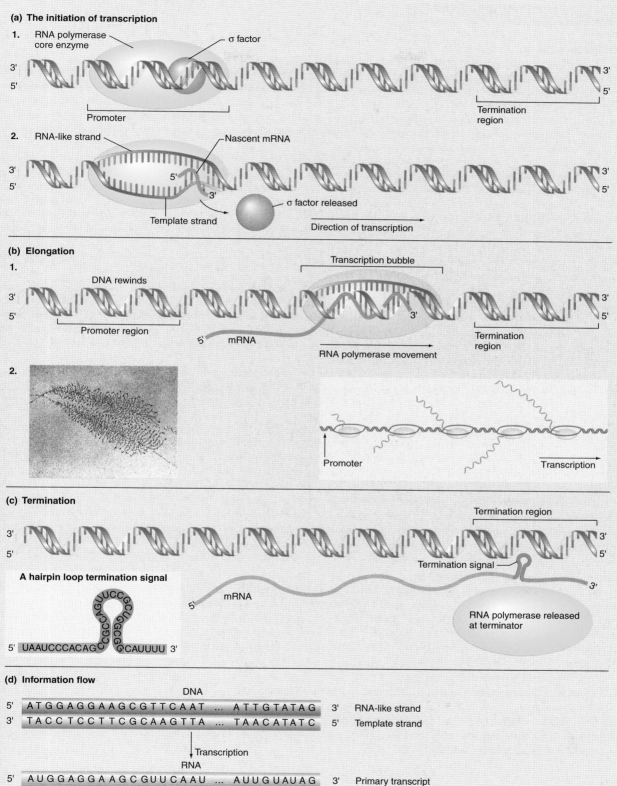

(a) The initiation of transcription

1.

RNA polymerase core enzyme

σ factor

3'
5'

Promoter

Termination region

2.

RNA-like strand

Nascent mRNA

3'
5'

5'

3'

σ factor released

Template strand

Direction of transcription

(b) Elongation

1.

DNA rewinds

Transcription bubble

3'
5'

Promoter region

3'

5' mRNA

Termination region

RNA polymerase movement

2.

Promoter

Transcription

(c) Termination

Termination region

3'
5'

Termination signal

A hairpin loop termination signal

mRNA
5'

3'

RNA polymerase released at terminator

5' UAAUCCCACAG GUUCCG...CCGCCG...GGCGG CAUUUU 3'

(d) Information flow

DNA

5' ATGGAGGAAGCGTTCAAT ... ATTGTATAG 3' RNA-like strand
3' TACCTCCTTCGCAAGTTA ... TAACATATC 5' Template strand

↓ Transcription

RNA

5' AUGGAGGAAGCGUUCAAU ... AUUGUAUAG 3' Primary transcript

(Continued)

FEATURE FIGURE 8.11 (Continued)

(a) The Initiation of Transcription

1. *RNA polymerase binds to double-stranded DNA at the beginning of the gene to be copied.* RNA polymerase recognizes and binds to **promoters,** specialized DNA sequences near the beginning of a gene where transcription will start. Although specific promoters vary substantially, all promoters in *E. coli* contain two characteristic short sequences of 6–10 nucleotide pairs that help bind RNA polymerase (Fig. 8.12). In bacteria, the complete RNA polymerase (the *holoenzyme*) consists of a core enzyme, plus a σ (sigma) subunit involved only in initiation. The σ subunit reduces RNA polymerase's general affinity for DNA but simultaneously increases RNA polymerase's affinity for the promoter. As a result, the RNA polymerase holoenzyme can hone in on a promoter and bind tightly to it, forming a so-called *closed promoter complex.*

2. *After binding to the promoter, RNA polymerase unwinds part of the double helix, exposing unpaired bases on the template strand.* The complex formed between the RNA polymerase holoenzyme and an unwound promoter is called an *open promoter complex.* The enzyme identifies the template strand and chooses the two nucleotides with which to initiate copying. Guided by base pairing with these two nucleotides, RNA polymerase aligns the first two ribonucleotides of the new RNA, which will be at the 5′ end of the final RNA product. The DNA transcribed into the 5′ end of the mRNA is often called the *5′ end of the gene.* RNA polymerase then catalyzes the formation of a phosphodiester bond between the first two ribonucleotides. Soon thereafter, the RNA polymerase releases the σ subunit. This release marks the end of initiation.

(b) Elongation: Constructing an RNA Copy of the Gene

1. *When the σ subunit separates from the RNA polymerase, the enzyme loses its enhanced affinity for the promoter sequence and regains its strong generalized affinity for any DNA.* These changes enable the core enzyme to leave the promoter yet remain bound to the gene. The core enzyme now moves along the chromosome, unwinding the double helix to expose the next single-stranded region of the template. The enzyme extends the RNA by linking a ribonucleotide positioned by complementarity with the template strand to the 3′ end of the growing chain. As the enzyme extends the mRNA in the 5′-to-3′ direction, it moves in the antiparallel 3′-to-5′ direction along the DNA template strand.

The region of DNA unwound by RNA polymerase is called the **transcription bubble.** Within the bubble, the nascent RNA chain remains base paired with the DNA template, forming a DNA-RNA hybrid. However, in those parts of the gene behind the bubble that have already been transcribed, the DNA double helix re-forms, displacing the RNA, which hangs out of the transcription complex as a single strand with a free 5′ end.

2. *Once an RNA polymerase has moved off the promoter, other RNA polymerase molecules can move in to initiate transcription.* If the promoter is very strong, that is, if it can rapidly attract RNA polymerase, the gene can undergo transcription by many RNA polymerases simultaneously. Here we show an electron micrograph and an artist's interpretation of simultaneous transcription by several RNA polymerases. As you can see, the promoter for this gene lies very close to where the shortest RNA is emerging from the DNA.

Geneticists often use the direction traveled by RNA polymerase as a reference when discussing various features within a gene. If for example, you started at the 5′ end of a gene at point A and moved along the gene in the same direction as RNA polymerase to point B, you would be traveling in the **downstream** direction. If by contrast, you started at point B and moved in the opposite direction to point A, you would be traveling in the **upstream** direction.

(c) Termination: The End of Transcription

RNA sequences that signal the end of transcription are known as **terminators.** There are two types of terminators: *intrinsic terminators,* which cause the RNA polymerase core enzyme to terminate transcription on its own, and *extrinsic terminators,* which require proteins other than RNA polymerase—particularly a polypeptide known as *rho*—to bring about termination. All terminators, whether intrinsic or extrinsic, are specific sequences in the mRNA that are transcribed from specific DNA regions. Terminators often form **hairpin loops** in which nucleotides within the mRNA pair with nearby complementary nucleotides. Upon termination, RNA polymerase and a completed RNA chain are both released from the DNA.

(d) The Product of Transcription Is a Single-Stranded Primary Transcript

The RNA produced by the action of RNA polymerase on a gene is a single strand of nucleotides known as a *primary transcript.* The bases in the primary transcript are complementary to the bases between the initiation and termination sites in the template strand of the gene. The ribonucleotides in the primary transcript include a start codon, the codons that specify the remaining amino acids of the polypeptide, and a stop codon.

transcription. As seen in **Fig. 8.12,** most bacterial gene promotors share two short regions that have almost identical nucleotide sequences. These are the sites at which RNA polymerase makes particularly strong contact with the promoters.

3. RNA polymerase adds nucleotides to the growing RN polymer in the 5′-to-3′ direction. The chemical mech nism of this nucleotide-adding reaction is similar to th formation of phosphodiester bonds between nucleotid during DNA replication (review Fig. 6.19 on p. 182)

Figure 8.12 The promoters of 10 different bacterial genes. Only the sequence of the RNA-like strand is shown; numbering starts at the first transcribed nucleotide (+1). **(a)** Most promoters are upstream of the start point of transcription. **(b)** All promoters in *E. coli* share two different short stretches of nucleotides (*yellow*) that are essential for recognition of the promoter by RNA polymerase. The most common nucleotides at each position in each stretch constitute a *consensus sequence;* invariant nucleotides within the consensus are in **bold**.

(a) Transcription initiation signals in bacteria

(b) Strong *E. coli* promoters

X1	ATGCATTTTTCCGCTTGTCTTCCTGA • • GCCGACTCCCTATAATGCGCCTCCATCGACACGGCGGAT
(DXE)₂	CCTGAAATTCAGGGTTGACTCTGAAA • • GAGGAAAGCGTAATATAC • GCCACCTCGCGACAGTGAGC
A1	TTTTAAATTTCCTCTTGTCAGGCCGG • • AATAACTCCCTATAATGCGCCACCACTGACACGGAACAA
A2	GCAAAAATAAATGCTTGACTCTGTAG • CGGGAAGGCGTATTATGC • ACACCCCGCGCCGCTGAGAA
PR	TAACACCGTGCGTGTTGACTATTTTA • CCTCTGGCGGTGATAATGG • • TTGCATGTACTAAGGAGGT
PL	TATCTCTGGCGGTGTTGACATAAATA • CCACTGGCGGTGATACTGA • • GCACATCAGCAGGACGCAC
A3	GTGAAACAAACGGTTGACAACATGA • AGTAAACACGGTACGATGT • ACCACATGAAACGACAGTGA
A1	TATCAAAAAGAGTATTGACTTAAAGT • CTAACCTATAGGATACTT A • CAGCCATCGAGAGGGACACG
A2	ACGAAAAACAGGTATTGACAACATGAAGTAACATGCAGTAAGATAC • AAATCGCTAGGTAACACTAG
VIII	GATACAAATCTCCGTTGTACTTTGTT • • TCGCGCTTGGTATAATCG • CTGGGCGTCAAAGATGAGTG

–35 region		–10 region	+1
Consensus	**TTG**ACAT ———— 15 – 17 bp ————	**TATAAT**	5′ ———————→ 3′ Primary transcript

with one exception: Transcription uses ribonucleotide triphosphates (ATP, CTP, GTP, and UTP) instead of deoxyribonucleotide triphosphates. Hydrolysis of the high-energy bonds in each ribonucleotide triphosphate provides the energy needed for elongation.

Sequences in the RNA products, known as **terminators,** tell RNA polymerase where to stop transcription.

As you examine Fig. 8.11, bear in mind that a gene consists of two antiparallel strands of DNA, as mentioned earlier. One—the *RNA-like strand*—has the same polarity and sequence (except for T instead of U) as the emerging RNA transcript. The second—the *template strand*—has the opposite polarity and a complementary sequence that enables it to serve as the template for making the RNA transcript. When geneticists refer to the sequence of a gene, they usually mean the sequence of the RNA-like strand.

Although the transcription of all genes in all organisms roughly follows the general scheme shown in Fig. 8.11, important variations can be found in the details. For example, transcription of different genes in bacteria can be initiated by alternative sigma (σ) factors. In eukaryotes, promoters are more complicated than those in bacteria, and there are three different kinds of RNA polymerase that can transcribe different classes of genes. Chapters 15 and 16 describe how prokaryotic and eukaryotic cells can exploit these and other variations to control when, where, and at what level a given gene is expressed. Finally, the Genetics and Society box "HIV and Reverse Transcription" starting on the following page describes how the AIDS virus uses an exceptional form

of transcription, known as **reverse transcription,** to construct a double strand of DNA from an RNA template.

The result of transcription is a single strand of RNA known as a **primary transcript** (see Fig. 8.11d). In prokaryotic organisms, the RNA produced by transcription is the actual messenger RNA that guides protein synthesis. In eukaryotic organisms, by contrast, most primary transcripts undergo *processing* in the nucleus before they migrate to the cytoplasm to direct protein synthesis. This processing has played a fundamental role in the evolution of complex organisms.

> RNA polymerase, the key enzyme of transcription, recognizes the promoter at the beginning of a gene and then uses complementary base pairing with the DNA template strand to add RNA nucleotides to the 3′ end of the growing transcript. When RNA polymerase detects a terminator, it dissociates from both the DNA and the transcript.

In eukaryotes, RNA processing after transcription produces a mature mRNA

Some RNA processing in eukaryotes modifies only the 5′ or 3′ ends of the primary transcript, leaving the information content of the rest of the mRNA untouched. Other processing deletes blocks of information from the middle of the primary transcript, so the content of the mature mRNA is related, but not identical, to the complete set of DNA nucleotide pairs in the original gene.

G E N E T I C S   A N D   S O C I E T Y

HIV and Reverse Transcription

The AIDS-causing human immunodeficiency virus (HIV) is the most intensively analyzed virus in history. From laboratory and clinical studies spanning more than a decade, researchers have learned that each viral particle is a rough-edged sphere consisting of an outer envelope enclosing a protein matrix, which, in turn, surrounds a cut-off cone-shaped core (**Fig. A**). Within the core lies an enzyme-studded genome: two identical single strands of RNA associated with many molecules of an unusual DNA polymerase known as **reverse transcriptase.**

During infection, the AIDS virus binds to and injects its cone-shaped core into cells of the human immune system (**Fig. B**). It next uses reverse transcriptase to copy its RNA genome into double-stranded DNA molecules in the cytoplasm of the host cell. The double helixes then travel to the nucleus where another enzyme inserts them into a host chromosome. Once integrated into a host-cell chromosome, the viral genome can do one of two things. It can commandeer the host cell's protein synthesis machinery to make hundreds of new viral particles that bud off from the parent cell, taking with them part of the cell membrane and sometimes resulting in the host cell's death. Alternatively, it can lie latent inside the host chromosome, which then copies and transmits the viral genome to two new cells with each cell division.

The events of this life cycle make HIV a **retrovirus:** an RNA virus that after infecting a host cell copies its own single strands of RNA into double helixes of DNA, which a viral enzyme then integrates into a host chromosome. RNA viruses that are not retroviruses simply infect a host cell and then use the cellular machinery to make more of themselves, often killing the host cell in the process. The viruses that cause hepatitis A, many types of the common cold, and rabies are this latter type of RNA virus. Unlike retroviruses, they are not transmitted by cell division to a geometrically growing number of new cells.

Reverse transcription, the foundation of the retroviral life cycle, is inconsistent with the one-way, DNA-to-RNA-to-protein flow of genetic information. Because it was so unexpected, the phenomenon of reverse transcription encountered great resistance in the scientific community when first reported by Howard Temin of the University of Wisconsin and David Baltimore, then of MIT. Now, however, it is an established fact. Reverse transcriptase is a remarkable DNA polymerase that can construct a DNA polymer from either an RNA or a DNA template.

Figure A   Structure of the AIDS virus

HIV viral particle

Core
Protein matrix
RNA
Reverse transcriptase
Bilipid outer layer

Figure B   Life cycle of the AIDS virus

3. DNA copy of virus genome enters nucleus.
4. DNA copy of virus genome integrates into host chromosome.
Host DNA
2. Core disintegrates, releasing RNA. Reverse transcriptase produces DNA from viral RNA genome.
5. Transcription of integrated virus makes viral RNA genome.
1. Virus particles attach to host cell membrane.
Host cell
6. Core forms; new virus particles bud from host cell.

Adding a 5′ methylated cap and a 3′ poly-A tail

The nucleotide at the 5′ end of a eukaryotic mRNA is a G in reverse orientation from the rest of the molecule; it is connected through a triphosphate linkage to the first nucleotide in the primary transcript. This "backward G" is not transcribed from the DNA. Instead, a special *capping enzyme* adds it to the primary transcript after polymerization of the transcript's first few nucleotides. Enzymes known as *methyl transferases* then add methyl (–CH$_3$) groups to the backward G and to one or more of the succeeding nucleotides in the RNA, forming a so-called **methylated cap** (**Fig. 8.13**).

Like the 5′ methylated cap, the 3′ end of most eukaryotic mRNAs is not encoded directly by the gene. In a large majority of eukaryotic mRNAs, the 3′ end consists of 100–200 A's, referred to as a **poly-A tail** (**Fig. 8.1**). Addition of the tail is a two-step process. First, a ribonuclease cleaves the primary transcript to form a new end; cleavage depends on the sequence AAUAAA, which is found in poly-A-containing mRNAs 11–30 nucleotides upstream of the position where the tail is added. Next the enzyme *poly-A polymerase* adds A's onto the 3′ end exposed by cleavage.

Unexpectedly, both the methylated cap and the poly-A tail are critical for the efficient translation of the mRNA into protein, even though neither helps specify an amino acid. Recent data indicate that particular *eukaryotic translation initiation factors* bind to the 5′ cap, while *poly-A binding protein* associates with the tail at the 3′ end of the mRNA. The interaction of these proteins shapes the mRNA molecule into

In addition to its comprehensive copying abilities, reverse transcriptase has another feature not seen in most DNA polymerases: inaccuracy. As we saw in Chapter 7, normal DNA polymerases replicate DNA with an error rate of one mistake in every million nucleotides copied. Reverse transcriptase, however, introduces one mutation in every 5000 incorporated nucleotides.

HIV uses this capacity for mutation, in combination with its ability to integrate its genome into the chromosomes of immune-system cells, to gain a tactical advantage over the immune response of its host organism. Cells of the immune system seek to overcome an HIV invasion by multiplying in response to the proliferating viral particles. The numbers are staggering. Each day of infection in every patient, from 100 million to a billion HIV particles are released from infected immune-system cells. As long as the immune system is strong enough to withstand the assault, it may respond by producing as many as 2 billion new cells daily. Many of these new cells produce antibodies targeted against proteins on the surface of the virus.

But just when an immune response wipes out those viral particles carrying the targeted protein, virions incorporating new forms of the protein resistant to the current immune response make their appearance. After many years of this complex chase, capture, and destruction by the immune system, the changeable virus outruns the host's immune response and gains the upper hand. Thus, the intrinsic infidelity of HIV's reverse transcriptase, by enhancing the virus's ability to compete in the evolutionary marketplace, increases its threat to human life and health.

This inherent mutability has undermined two potential therapeutic approaches toward the control of AIDS: drugs and vaccines. Some of the antiviral drugs approved in the United States for treatment of HIV infection—AZT (zidovudine), ddC (dideoxycytidine), and ddI (dideoxyinosine)—block viral replication by interfering with the action of reverse transcriptase. Each drug is similar to one of the four nucleotides, and when reverse transcriptase incorporates one of the drug molecules rather than a genuine nucleotide into a growing DNA polymer, the enzyme cannot extend the chain any further. However, the drugs are toxic at high doses and thus can be administered only at low doses that do not destroy all viral particles. Because of this limitation and the virus's high rate of mutation, mutant reverse transcriptases soon appear that work even in the presence of the drugs.

Similarly, researchers are having trouble developing safe, effective vaccines. Because HIV infects cells of the immune system and a vaccine works by stimulating immune-system cells to multiply, some of the vaccines tested so far actually increase the activity of the virus; others have only a weak effect on viral replication. Moreover, if it were possible to produce a vaccine that could generate a massive immune response against one, two, or even several HIV proteins at a time, such a vaccine might be effective for only a short while—until enough mutations built up to make the virus resistant.

For these reasons, the AIDS virus will most likely not succumb entirely to drugs or vaccines that target proteins active at various stages of its life cycle. Combinations of these therapeutic tools will nonetheless remain an important part of the medical arsenal for prolonging an AIDS patient's life. In 1996, for example, medical researchers found that a therapeutic "cocktail" including at least one anti-reverse-transcriptase drug and a relatively new kind of drug known as a protease inhibitor (which blocks the enzymes that cleave a long, inactive polyprotein into shorter, functional viral proteins) could reduce the viral load of some very sick AIDS patients to undetectable levels, thereby relieving their disease symptoms. One year later, however, a clinical study revealed that for slightly more than 50% of patients receiving the drug cocktail in a San Francisco hospital, the treatment lost its effectiveness after six months.

A self-preserving capacity for mutation, perpetuated by reverse transcriptase, is surely one of the main reasons for HIV's success. Ironically, it may also provide a basis for its subjugation. Researchers are studying what happens when the virus increases its mutational load. If reverse transcriptase's error rate determines the size and integrity of the viral population in a host organism, greatly accelerated mutagenesis might push the virus beyond the error threshold that allows it to function. In other words, too much mutation might destroy the virus's infectivity, virulence, or capacity to reproduce. If geneticists could figure out how to make this happen, they might be able to give the human immune system the advantage it needs to overrun the virus.

circle. This circularization both enhances the initial steps translation and stabilizes the mRNA in the cytoplasm by creasing the length of time it can serve as a messenger.

emoving introns from the primary anscript by RNA splicing

nother kind of RNA processing became apparent in the e 1970s, after researchers had developed techniques that abled them to analyze nucleotide sequences in both DNA d RNA. Using these techniques, which we describe in apter 9, they began to compare eukaryotic genes with e mRNAs derived from them. Their expectation was that st as in prokaryotes, the DNA nucleotide sequence of a ne's RNA-like strand would be identical to the RNA nucleotide sequence of the messenger RNA (with the exception of U replacing T in the RNA). Surprisingly, they found that the DNA nucleotide sequences of many eukaryotic genes are much longer than their corresponding mRNAs, suggesting that RNA transcripts, in addition to receiving a methylated cap and a poly-A tail, undergo extensive internal processing.

An extreme example of the length difference between primary transcript and mRNA is seen in the human gene for dystrophin (**Fig. 8.15**). Abnormalities in the dystrophin gene underlie the genetic disorder of Duchenne muscular dystrophy (DMD). The dystrophin gene is 2.5 million nucleotides—or 2500 kilobases (kb)—long, whereas the corresponding mRNA is roughly 14,000 nucleotides, or 14 kb, in length. Obviously the gene contains DNA sequences that are not present in the mature mRNA. Those regions

Figure 8.13 Structure of the methylated cap at the 5′ end of eukaryotic mRNAs. Capping enzyme connects a backward G to the first nucleotide of the primary transcript through a triphosphate linkage. Methyl transferase enzymes then add methyl groups to this G and to one or two of the nucleotides first transcribed from the DNA template.

of the gene that do end up in the mature mRNA are scattered throughout the 2500 kb of DNA.

Exons and Introns Sequences found in both a gene's DNA and the mature messenger RNA are called **exons** (for "expressed regions"). The sequences found in the DNA of the gene but not in the mature mRNA are known as **introns**

Figure 8.14 How RNA processing adds a tail to the 3′ end of eukaryotic mRNAs. A ribonuclease recognizes AAUAAA in a particular context of the primary transcript and cleaves the transcript 11–30 nucleotides downstream to create a new 3′ end. The enzyme poly-A polymerase then adds 100–200 A's onto this new 3′ end.

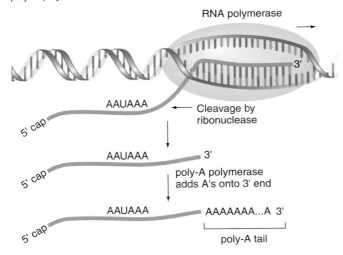

(for "intervening regions"). Introns interrupt, or separate, the exon sequences that actually end up in the mature mRNA.

The *DMD* gene has more than 80 introns; the mean intron length is 35 kb, but one intron is an amazing 400 k long. Other genes in humans generally have many fewe introns, while a few have none—and the introns range from 50 bp to over 100 kb. Exons, in contrast, vary in size from 50 bp to a few kilobases; in the *DMD* gene, the mean exon length is 200 bp. The greater size variation seen in intron compared to exons reflects the fact that introns do no encode polypeptides and do not appear in mature mRNA As a result, fewer restrictions exist on the sizes and bas sequences of introns.

Mature mRNAs must contain all of the codons that a translated into amino acids, including the initiation and term nation codons. In addition, mature mRNAs have sequence at their 5′ and 3′ ends that are not translated, but that nevert less play important roles in regulating the efficiency of trans lation. These sequences, called the **5′- and 3′-untranslate regions** (5′ and 3′ UTRs), are located just after the met ylated cap and just before the poly-A tail, respectively. Excep ing the cap and tail themselves, all of the sequences in mature mRNA, including all of the codons and both UTR must be transcribed from the gene's exons. Introns can interru a gene at any location, even between the nucleotides makin up a single codon. In such a case, the three nucleotides of t codon are present in two different (but successive) exons.

How do cells make a mature mRNA from a gene who coding sequences are interrupted by introns? The answer

Figure 8.15 The human dystrophin gene: An extreme example of RNA splicing. Though the dystrophin gene is 2500 kb (or 2.5 Mb) long, the dystrophin mRNA is only 14 kb long. More than 80 introns are removed from the 2500 kb primary transcript to produce the mature mRNA (which is not drawn to scale).

Splicing removes introns from a primary transcript.

at cells first make a primary transcript containing all of gene's introns and exons, and then they remove the trons from the primary transcript by **RNA splicing,** the ocess that deletes introns and joins together successive ons to form a mature mRNA consisting only of exons ig. 8.15). Because the first and last exons of the primary nscript become the 5′ and 3′ ends of the mRNA, while intervening introns are spliced out, a gene must have

one more exon than it does introns. To construct the mature mRNA, splicing must be remarkably precise. For example, if an intron lies within a codon, splicing must remove the intron and reconstitute the codon without disrupting the reading frame of the mRNA.

The Mechanism of RNA Splicing Figure 8.16 illustrates how RNA splicing works. Three types of short sequences

Figure 8.16 How RNA processing splices out introns and joins adjacent exons. (a) Three short sequences within the primary nscript determine the specificity of splicing. (1) The splice-donor site occurs where the 3′ end of an exon abuts the 5′ end of an intron. In st splice-donor sites, a GU dinucleotide (*arrows*) that begins the intron is flanked on either side by a few purines (Pu; that is, A or G). (2) The ice-acceptor site is at the 3′ end of the intron where it joins with the next exon. The final nucleotides of the intron are always AG (*arrows*) preded by 12–14 pyrimidines (Py; that is, C or U). (3) The branch site, which is located within the intron about 30 nucleotides upstream of the ce acceptor, must include an A (*arrow*) and is usually rich in pyrimidines. **(b)** Two sequential cuts, the first at the splice-donor site and the secd at the splice-acceptor site, remove the intron, allowing precise splicing of adjacent exons.

(a) Short sequences dictate where splicing occurs.

(b) Two sequential cuts remove the intron.

within the primary transcript—**splice donors, splice acceptors,** and **branch sites**—help ensure the specificity of splicing. These sites make it possible to sever the connections between an intron and the exons that precede and follow it, and then to join the formerly separated exons.

The mechanism of splicing involves two sequential cuts in the primary transcript. The first cut is at the splice-donor site, at the 5′ end of the intron. After this first cut, the new 5′ end of the intron attaches, via a novel 2′–5′ phosphodiester bond, to an A at the branch site located within the intron, forming a so-called *lariat structure*. The second cut is at the splice-acceptor site, at the 3′ end of the intron; this cut removes the intron. The discarded intron is degraded, and the precise splicing of adjacent exons completes the process of intron removal.

SnRNPs and the Spliceosome Splicing normally requires a complicated intranuclear machine called the **spliceosome,** which ensures that all of the splicing reactions take place in concert (**Fig. 8.17**). The spliceosome consists of four subunits known as small nuclear ribonucleoproteins, or snRNPs (pronounced "snurps"). Each snRNP contains one or two small nuclear RNAs (snRNAs) 100–300 nucleotides long, associated with proteins in a discrete particle. Certain snRNAs can base pair with the splice donor and splice acceptor sequences in the primary transcript, so these snRNAs are particularly important in bringing together the two exons that flank an intron. Given the complexities of spliceosome structure, it is remarkable that a few primary transcripts can splice themselves without the aid of a spliceosome or any additional factor. These rare primary transcripts function as **ribozymes:** RNA molecules that can act as enzymes and catalyze a specific biochemical reaction.

It might seem strange that eukaryotic genes incorporate DNA sequences that are spliced out of the mRNA before translation and thus do not encode amino acids. No one knows exactly why introns exist. One hypothesis proposes that they make it possible to assemble genes from various exon building blocks, which encode modules of protein function. This type of assembly would allow the shuffling of exons to make new genes, a process that appears to have played a key role in the evolution of complex organisms. The exon-as-module proposal is attractive because it is easy to understand the selective advantage of the potential for exon shuffling. Nevertheless, it remains a hypothesis without proof. There is no hard evidence for or against the hypothesis, and introns may have become established through means that scientists have yet to imagine.

Alternative splicing: Different mRNAs from the same primary transcript

Normally, RNA splicing joins together the splice donor and splice acceptor at the opposite ends of an intron, resulting in

Figure 8.17 Splicing is catalyzed by the spliceosome. (*Top*) The spliceosome is assembled from four snRNP subunits, each of which contains one or two snRNAs and several proteins. (*Bottom*) A view of three spliceosomes in the electron microscope.

Spliceosome components

Five snRNAs (small nuclear RNAs)   +   ~50 proteins

Four snRNPs (small nuclear ribonucleic particles), which assemble into a spliceosome

Proteins

snRNA

removal of the intron and fusion of two successive—a now adjacent—exons. For some genes, however, RN splicing during development is regulated so that at cert times or in certain tissues, some splicing signals may ignored. As an example, splicing may occur between splice donor site of one intron and the splice acceptor site a different intron downstream. Such **alternative splici** produces different mRNA molecules that may encode rela proteins with different—though partially overlapping amino acid sequences and functions. In effect then, alt native splicing can tailor the nucleotide sequence o primary transcript to produce more than one kind of po peptide. Alternative splicing largely explains how 20,000–30,000 genes in the human genome can enc he hundreds of thousands of different proteins estimated ɔ exist in human cells.

In mammals, alternative splicing of the gene encod-ng the antibody heavy chain determines whether the anti-ody proteins become embedded in the membrane of the ᵬ lymphocyte that makes them or are instead secreted into ᴧe blood. The antibody heavy-chain gene has eight exons nd seven introns; exon number 6 has a splice-donor site ⱱithin it. To make the membrane-bound antibody, all xons except for the right-hand part of number 6 are ᴊined to create an mRNA encoding a hydrophobic (water-ᴧating, lipid-loving) C terminus (**Fig. 8.18a**). For the ᴈcreted antibody, only the first six exons (including the ᴇght part of 6) are spliced together to make an mRNA

igure 8.18 Different mRNAs can be produced from ᴧe same primary transcript. (a) Alternative splicing of the imary transcript for the antibody heavy chain produces mRNAs that code different kinds of antibody proteins. **(b)** Rare trans-splicing ents combine exons from different genes into one mature mRNA.

) **Alternative splicing produces two different mRNAs from the same gene.**

Trans-splicing combines exons from different genes.

encoding a heavy chain with a hydrophilic (water-loving) C terminus. These two kinds of mRNAs formed by alter-native splicing thus encode slightly different proteins that are directed to different parts of the body. We provide more details about the function of these antibody proteins in Chapter 20.

A rare and unusual strategy of alternative splicing, seen in *C. elegans* and a few other eukaryotes, is **trans-splicing,** in which the spliceosome joins an exon of one gene with an exon of another gene (**Fig. 8.18b**). Special nucleotide sequences in the RNAs make trans-splicing possible.

> In eukaryotic cells, RNA processing follows transcription to generate an mRNA. Processing steps include additions of a methylated cap to the RNA's 5'-end and a poly-A tail to the 3' end, as well as the removal of introns from the primary transcript by splicing. Alternative splicing of exons can yield different mRNAs from the same primary transcript.

8.3 Translation: From mRNA to Protein

Translation is the process by which the sequence of nucleo-tides in a messenger RNA directs the assembly of the correct sequence of amino acids in the corresponding polypeptide. Translation takes place on ribosomes that coordinate the movements of transfer RNAs carrying spe-cific amino acids with the genetic instructions of an mRNA. As we examine the cell's translation machinery, we first describe the structure and function of tRNAs and ribosomes; and we then explain how these components interact during translation.

Transfer RNAs mediate the translation of mRNA codons to amino acids

No obvious chemical similarity or affinity exists between the nucleotide triplets of mRNA codons and the amino acids they specify. Rather, *transfer RNAs (tRNAs)* serve as adaptor molecules that mediate the transfer of informa-tion from nucleic acid to protein.

The structure of tRNA

Transfer RNAs are short, single-stranded RNA molecules 74–95 nucleotides in length. Several of the nucleotides in tRNAs contain modified bases produced by chemical alterations of the principal A, G, C, and U nucleotides (**Fig. 8.19a**). Each tRNA carries one particular amino acid, and cells must have at least one tRNA for each of the 20 amino acids specified by the genetic code. The

Figure 8.19 tRNAs mediate the transfer of information from nucleic acid to protein.

(a) Many tRNAs contain modified bases produced by chemical alterations of A, G, C, and U. **(b)** The primary structures of tRNA molecules fold to form characteristic secondary and tertiary structures. The anticodon and the amino acid attachment site are at opposite ends of the L-shaped structure.

(a) Some tRNAs contain modified bases.

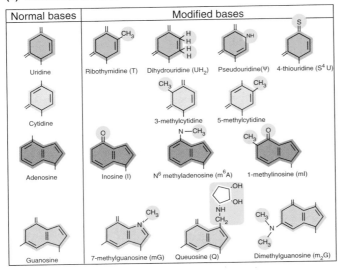

(b) Each tRNA has a primary, secondary, and tertiary structure.

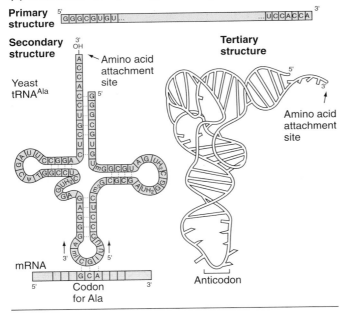

Figure 8.20 Aminoacyl-tRNA synthetases catalyze the attachment of tRNAs to their corresponding amino acids.

The aminoacyl-tRNA synthetase first activates the amino acid, forming an AMP-amino acid. The enzyme then transfers the amino acid's carboxyl group from AMP to the hydroxyl (−OH) group of the ribose at the 3′ end of the tRNA, producing a charged tRNA.

create a characteristic cloverleaf shape; this is the tRNA's secondary structure.

3. Folding in three-dimensional space creates a tertiary structure that looks like a compact letter L.

At one end of the L, the tRNA carries an **anticodon**, three nucleotides complementary to an mRNA codon specifying the amino acid carried by the tRNA (Fig. 8.19b). The anticodon never forms base pairs with other regions of the tRNA; it is always available for base pairing with its complementary mRNA codon. As with other complementary base sequences, during pairing at the ribosome, the strands of anticodon and codon run antiparallel to each other. If, for example, the anticodon is 3′ CCU 5′, the complementary mRNA codon is 5′ GGA 3′, specifying the amino acid glycine.

At the other end of the L, where the 5′ and 3′ ends of the tRNA strand are found, enzymes known as **aminoacyl-tRNA synthetases** connect the tRNA to the amino acid that corresponds to the anticodon (**Fig. 8.20**). These enzymes are extraordinarily specific, recognizing unique features of a particular tRNA—despite its general structural similarities with all other tRNAs—while also recognizing the corresponding amino acid (see the opening figure of the chapter on p. 246).

Aminoacyl-tRNA synthetases are, in fact, the only molecules that read the languages of both nucleic acid and protein. They are thus the actual molecular translators. At least one aminoacyl-tRNA synthetase exists for each of the 20 amino acids, and like tRNA, each synthetase functions with only one amino acid. Figure 8.20 shows the two-step process that establishes the covalent bond

name of a tRNA reflects the amino acid it carries. For example, tRNA^{Gly} carries the amino acid glycine.

As **Fig. 8.19b** shows, it is possible to consider the structure of a tRNA molecule on three levels.

1. The nucleotide sequence of a tRNA constitutes the primary structure.
2. Short complementary regions within a tRNA's single strand can form base pairs with each other to

Figure 8.21 Base pairing between an mRNA codon and a tRNA anticodon determines which amino acid is added to a growing polypeptide. A tRNA with an anticodon for cysteine, but carrying the amino acid alanine, adds alanine whenever the mRNA codon for cysteine appears.

between an amino acid and the 3′ end of its corresponding tRNA. A tRNA covalently coupled to its amino acid is called a **charged tRNA.** The bond between the amino acid and tRNA contains substantial energy that is later used to drive peptide bond formation.

The critical role of base pairing between codon and anticodon

While attachment of the appropriate amino acid charges a tRNA, the amino acid itself does not play a significant role in determining where it becomes incorporated in a growing polypeptide chain. Instead, the specific interaction between a tRNA's anticodon and an mRNA's codon makes that decision. A simple experiment illustrates this point (Fig. 8.21). Researchers can subject a charged tRNA to chemical treatments that, without altering the structure of the tRNA, change the amino acid it carries. One treatment replaces the cysteine carried by tRNA^{Cys} with alanine. When investigators then add the tRNA^{Cys} charged with alanine to a cell-free translational system, the system incorporates *alanine* into the growing polypeptide wherever the mRNA contains a cysteine codon complementary to the anticodon of the tRNA^{Cys}.

Transfer RNAs mediate the relationship between codons in the mRNA and the amino acids in the polypeptide product. At one end of the "L" formed by a tRNA molecule are the three nucleotides of the anticodon that can base pair with complementary codons. At the other end of the L, the proper amino acid is covalently coupled to the tRNA by a specific aminoacyl-tRNA synthetase enzyme.

Wobble: One tRNA, more than one codon

Although at least one kind of tRNA exists for each of the 20 amino acids, cells do not necessarily carry tRNAs with

anticodons complementary to all of the 61 possible codon triplets in the genetic code. *E. coli,* for example, makes 79 different tRNAs containing 42 different anticodons. Although several of the 79 tRNAs in this collection obviously have the same anticodon, $61 - 42 = 19$ of 61 potential anticodons are not represented. Thus 19 mRNA codons will not find a complementary anticodon in the *E. coli* collection of tRNAs. How can an organism construct proper polypeptides if some of the codons in its mRNAs cannot locate tRNAs with complementary anticodons?

The answer is that some tRNAs can recognize more than one codon for the amino acid with which they are charged. That is, the anticodons of these tRNAs can interact with more than one codon for the same amino acid, in keeping with the degenerate nature of the genetic code. Although researchers do not fully understand this "promiscuous" base pairing between codons and anticodons, Francis Crick spelled out a few of the rules that govern it.

Crick reasoned first that the 3′ nucleotide in many codons adds nothing to the specificity of the codon. For example, 5′ GGU 3′, 5′ GGC 3′, 5′ GGA 3′, and 5′ GGG 3′ all encode glycine (review Fig. 8.3 on p. 248). It does not matter whether the 3′ nucleotide is U, C, A, or G as long as the first two letters are GG. The same is true for other amino acids encoded by four different codons, such as valine, where the first two bases must be GU, but the third base can be U, C, A, or G.

For amino acids specified by two different codons, the first two bases of the codon are, once again, always the same, while the third base must be either one of the two purines (A or G) or one of the two pyrimidines (U or C). Thus, 5′ CAA 3′ and 5′ CAG 3′ are both codons for glutamine; 5′ CAU 3′ and 5′ CAC 3′ are both codons for histidine. If Pu stands for either purine and Py stands for either pyrimidine, then CAPu represents the codons for glutamine, while CAPy represents the codons for histidine.

In fact, the 5′ nucleotide of a tRNA's anticodon can often pair with more than one kind of nucleotide in the 3′ position of an mRNA's codon. (Recall that after base pairing, the bases in the anticodon run antiparallel to the bases in the codon.) A single tRNA charged with a particular amino acid can thus recognize several or even all of the codons for that amino acid. This flexibility in base pairing between the 3′ nucleotide in the codon and the 5′ nucleotide in the anticodon is known as **wobble (Fig. 8.22a).** The combination of normal base pairing at the first two positions of a codon with wobble at the third position clarifies why multiple codons for a single amino acid usually start with the same two letters.

Crick's "wobble rules," shown in **Fig. 8.22b,** delimit what kind of flexibility in base pairing is consistent with the genetic code. For example, methionine (Met) is specified by a single codon (5′ AUG 3′). As a result, Met-specific tRNAs must have a C at the 5′ end of their anticodons (5′ CAU 3′), because this is the only nucleotide at that position that can

Figure 8.22 Wobble: Some tRNAs recognize more than one codon for the amino acid they carry. (a) The G at the 5′ end of the anticodon shown here can pair with either U or C at the 3′ end of the codon. **(b)** The chart shows the pairing possibilities for other nucleotides at the 5′ end of an anticodon; I = inosine.

(a)

(b)

Wobble Rules		
5′ end of anticodon	→ can pair with →	3′ end of codon
G		U or C
C		G
A		U
U		A or G
I		U, C, or A

base pair only with the G at the 3′ end of the Met codon. By contrast, a single isoleucine-specific tRNA with the modified nucleotide inosine (I) at the 5′ position of the anticodon can recognize all three codons (5′ AUU 3′, 5′ AUC 3′, and 5′ AUA 3′) for isoleucine.

"Wobble" refers to the observation that the nucleotide at the 5′ position of a tRNA's anticodon can often pair with different nucleotides at the 3′ position of an mRNA codon. Wobble explains why alternative codons for a single amino acid usually start with the same two nucleotides.

Ribosomes are the sites of polypeptide synthesis

Ribosomes facilitate polypeptide synthesis in various ways. First, they recognize mRNA features that signal the start of translation. Second, they help ensure accurate interpretation of the genetic code by stabilizing the interactions between tRNAs and mRNAs; without a ribosome, codon-anticodon recognition, mediated by only three base pairs, would be extremely weak. Third, they supply the enzymatic activity that links the amino acids in a growing polypeptide chain. Fourth, by moving 5′ to 3′ along an mRNA molecule, they expose the mRNA codons in sequence, ensuring the linear addition of amino acids. Finally, ribosomes help end polypeptide synthesis by dissociating both from the mRNA directing polypeptide construction and from the polypeptide product itself.

Figure 8.23 The ribosome: Site of polypeptide synthesis (a) A ribosome has two subunits, each composed of rRNA and various proteins. **(b)** The small subunit initially binds to mRNA. The large subunit contributes the enzyme peptidyl transferase, which catalyzes the formation of peptide bonds. The two subunits together form the A, P, and E tRNA binding sites.

(a) A ribosome has two subunits composed of RNA and protein

(b) Different parts of a ribosome have different functions.

The structure of ribosomes

In *E. coli*, ribosomes consist of 3 different **ribosomal RNA (rRNAs)** and 52 different ribosomal proteins **(Fig. 8.23a)**. These components associate to form two different ribosomal subunits called the 30S subunit and the 50S subunit (with S designating a coefficient of sedimentation related to the size and shape of the subunit; the 30S subunit is smaller than the 50S subunit). Before translation begins, the two subunits exist as separate entities in the cytoplasm. Soon after the start of translation, they come together to reconstitute a complete ribosome. Eukaryotic ribosomes have more components than their prokaryotic counterparts, but they still consist of two dissociable subunits.

Functional domains of ribosomes

The small 30S subunit is the part of the ribosome that initially binds to mRNA. The larger 50S subunit contributes an enzyme known as **peptidyl transferase,** which catalyzes formation of the peptide bonds joining adjacent amino acids **(Fig. 8.23b)**. Both the small and the large subunits contribute to three distinct tRNA binding areas known as the **aminoacyl** (or **A**) **site,** the **peptidyl** (or **P**) **site,** and the e (or **E**) **site.** Finally, other regions of the ribosome distributed over the two subunits serve as points of contact for some of the additional proteins that play a role in translation.

Figure 8.24 The large subunit of a bacterial ribosome. Various ribosomal proteins are *lavender*, 23S rRNA is in *gold* and *white*, and 5S rRNA is *maroon* and *white*. The tRNA in the A site is *green*; the tRNA in the P site is *red*; no tRNA is shown in the E site. The superimposed box shows the location where new peptide bonds are formed.

Using X-ray crystallography and elegant techniques of electron microscopy, researchers have recently gained a remarkably detailed view of the complicated structure of the ribosome. **Figure 8.24** shows the large subunit of a bacterial ribosome; the small subunit was computationally removed for better visualization of the charged tRNAs occupying the A and P sites. With this illustration, you can see that the rRNAs occupy most of the space in the central part of the ribosome, while the various ribososomal proteins are studded around the exterior. Surprisingly, no proteins are found close to the region between the two tRNAs where peptide bonds are formed. This finding supports the conclusions of biochemical experiments that peptidyl transferase is actually a function of the 50S subunit's rRNA rather than any protein component of the ribosome; in other words, the rRNA acts as a *ribozyme* that joins amino acids together.

The ribosome is a complex made of various proteins and rRNAs at which polypeptide synthesis takes place. The large and small subunits of the ribosome together form three binding sites (A, P, and E) for tRNA molecules.

Ribosomes and charged tRNAs collaborate to translate mRNAs into polypeptides

As was the case for transcription, translation consists of three phases: an **initiation** phase that sets the stage for polypeptide synthesis; **elongation,** during which amino acids are added to a growing polypeptide; and a **termination** phase that brings polypeptide synthesis to a halt and enables the ribosome to release a completed chain of amino acids. **Figure 8.25** illustrates the details of the process, focusing on translation as it occurs in bacterial cells. As you examine the figure, note the following points about the flow of information during translation.

- The first codon to be translated—the initiation codon—is an AUG set in a special context at the 5' end of the gene's reading frame (*not* precisely at the 5' end of the mRNA).
- Special initiating tRNAs carrying a modified form of methionine called formylmethionine (fMet) recognize the initiation codon.
- The ribosome moves along the mRNA in the 5'-to-3' direction, revealing successive codons in a stepwise fashion.
- At each step of translation, the polypeptide grows by the addition of the next amino acid in the chain to its C terminus.
- Translation terminates when the ribosome reaches a UAA, UAG, or UGA nonsense codon at the 3' end of the gene's reading frame.

These points explain the biochemical basis of colinearity, that is, the correspondence between the 5'-to-3' direction in the mRNA and the N-terminus-to-C-terminus direction in the resulting polypeptide.

During elongation, the translation machinery adds about 2–15 amino acids per second to the growing chain. The speed is higher in prokaryotes and lower in eukaryotes. At these rates, construction of an average size 300-amino-acid polypeptide (from an average-length mRNA that is somewhat longer than 1000 nucleotides) could take as little as 20 seconds or as long as 2.5 minutes.

Several details have been left out of Fig. 8.25 so that you can concentrate on the flow of information during translation. In particular, this figure does not depict the important roles played by protein translation factors, which help shepherd mRNAs and tRNAs to their proper locations on the ribosome. Some translation factors also carry GTP to the ribosome, where hydrolysis of the high-energy bonds in the GTP helps power certain molecular movements (such as translocation of the ribosome along the mRNA). The book's website (www.mhhe.com/hartwell4) provides a wealth of information on the details of translation, including links to remarkable animations illustrating each step of the process.

Ribosomes initiate mRNA translation at AUG initiation codons. During elongation, the ribosome moves along the mRNA in the 5'-to-3' direction, while tRNAs base paired with mRNA codons move through the ribosome's A, P, and E sites. The ribosome's peptidyl transferase forms peptide bonds between successive amino acids. Translation terminates at stop codons in the mRNA.

Translation of mRNAs on Ribosomes

Initiation phase

(a) Initiation: Setting the stage for polypeptide synthesis The first three nucleotides of an mRNA do not serve as the first codon to be translated into an amino acid. Instead, a special signal indicates where along the mRNA translation should begin. In prokaryotes, this signal is called the **ribosome binding site,** and it has two important elements. The first is a short sequence of six nucleotides—usually 5′ . . . AGGAGG . . . 3′—named the **Shine-Dalgarno box** after its discoverers. The second element in an mRNA's ribosome binding site is the triplet 5′ AUG 3′, which serves as the initiation codon.

A special initiator tRNA, whose 5′ CAU 3′ anticodon is complementary to AUG, recognizes an AUG preceded by the Shine-Dalgarno box of a ribosome binding site. The initiator tRNA carries **N-formylmethionine (fMet),** a modified methionine whose amino end is blocked by a formyl group. The specialized fMet tRNA functions only at an initiation site. An AUG codon located within an mRNA's reading frame is recognized by a different tRNA that is charged with an unmodified methionine. This tRNA cannot start translation.

During initiation, the 3′ end of the 16S rRNA in the 30S ribosomal subunit binds to the mRNA's Shine-Dalgarno box (*not shown*), the fMet tRNA binds to the mRNA's initiation codon, and a large 50S ribosomal subunit associates with the small subunit to round out the ribosome. At the end of initiation, the fMet tRNA sits in the P site of the completed ribosome. Proteins known as **initiation factors** (*not shown*) play a transient role in the initiation process.

In eukaryotes, the small ribosomal subunit binds first to the methylated cap at the 5′ end of the mature mRNA. It then migrates to the initiation site—usually the first AUG it encounters as it scans the mRNA in the 5′-to-3′ direction. The initiator tRNA in eukaryotes carries unmodified methionine (Met) instead of fMet.

(b) Elongation: The addition of amino acids to a growing polypeptide Proteins known as **elongation factors** (*not shown*) usher the appropriate tRNA into the A site of the ribosome. The anticodon of this charged tRNA must recognize the next codon in the mRNA. The ribosome simultaneously holds the initiating tRNA at its P site and the second tRNA at its A site so that peptidyl transferase can catalyze formation of a peptide bond between the amino acids carried by the two tRNAs. As a result, the tRNA at the A site now carries two amino acids. The N terminus of this dipeptide is fMet; the C terminus is the second amino acid, whose carboxyl group remains covalently linked to its tRNA.

Following formation of the first peptide bond, the ribosome moves, exposing the next mRNA codon. The ribosome's movement requires the help of elongation factors and an input of energy. As the ribosome moves, the initiating tRNA, which no longer carries an amino acid, is transferred to the E site, and the other tRNA carrying the dipeptide shifts from the A site to the P site.

The empty A site now receives another tRNA, whose identity is determined by the next codon in the mRNA. The uncharged initiating tRNA is bumped off the E site and leaves the ribosome. Peptidyl transferase then catalyzes formation of a second peptide bond, generating a chain of three amino acids connected at its C terminus to the tRNA currently in the A site. With each subsequent round of ribosome movement and peptide bond formation, the peptide chain grows one amino acid longer. Note that each tRNA moves from the A site to the P site to the E site (excepting the initiating tRNA, which first enters the P site).

Because the elongation machinery adds amino acids to the C terminus of the lengthening polypeptide, polypeptide synthesis proceeds from the N terminus to the C terminus. As a result, fMet in prokaryotes (Met in eukaryotes), the first amino acid in the

Elongation phase

Ribosome moves toward 3' end of mRNA at this step

Direction of ribosome movement

growing chain, will be the N-terminal amino acid of all finished polypeptides prior to protein processing. Moreover, the ribosome must move along the mRNA in the 5′-to-3′ direction so that the polypeptide can grow in the N-to-C direction.

Once a ribosome has moved far enough away from the mRNA's ribosome binding site, that site becomes accessible to other ribosomes. In fact, several ribosomes can work on the same mRNA at one time. A complex of several ribosomes translating from the same mRNA is called a **polyribosome.** This complex allows the simultaneous synthesis of many copies of a polypeptide from a single mRNA.

Polyribosome

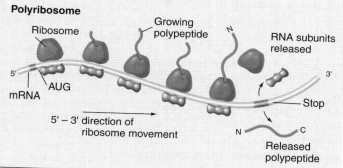

(c) **Termination: The ribosome releases the completed polypeptide** No normal tRNAs carry anticodons complementary to the three nonsense (stop) codons UAG, UAA, and UGA. Thus, when movement of the ribosome brings a nonsense codon into the ribosome's A site, no tRNAs can bind to that codon. Instead, proteins called **release factors** recognize the termination codons and bring polypeptide synthesis to a halt. The tRNA specifying the C-terminal amino acid releases the completed polypeptide, the same tRNA as well as the mRNA separate from the ribosome, and the ribosome dissociates into its large and small subunits.

Termination phase

Processing after translation can change a polypeptide's structure

Protein structure is not irrevocably fixed at the completion of translation. Several different processes may subsequently modify a polypeptide's structure. Cleavage may remove amino acids, such as the N-terminal fMet, from a polypeptide (**Fig. 8.26a**), or it may generate several smaller polypeptides from one larger product of translation (**Fig. 8.26b**). In the latter case, the larger polypeptide made before it is cleaved into smaller polypeptides is often called a **polyprotein.** The addition of chemical constituents, such as phosphate groups, methyl groups, or even carbohydrates, to specific amino acids may also modify a polypeptide after translation (**Fig. 8.26c**). Such cleavages and additions are known as **posttranslational modifications.** Posttranslational changes to a protein can be very important: For example, the biochemical function of many enzymes directly depends on the addition (or sometimes removal) of phosphate groups.

Figure 8.26 Posttranslational processing can modify polypeptide structure. Cleavage may remove an amino acid from the N terminus of a polypeptide **(a)** or split a larger *polyprotein* into two or more smaller functional proteins **(b)**. **(c)** Chemical reactions may add a phosphate or other functional group to an amino acid in the polypeptide.

(a) Cleavage may remove an amino acid.

(b) Cleavage may split a polyprotein.

(c) Addition of chemical constituents may modify a protein.

8.4 Differences in Gene Expression Between Prokaryotes and Eukaryotes

The processes of transcription and translation in eukaryotes and prokaryotes are similar in many ways but also are affected by certain differences, including (1) the presence of a nuclear membrane in eukaryotes, (2) variations in the way in which translation is initiated, and (3) the need for additional transcript processing in eukaryotes.

In eukaryotes, the nuclear membrane prevents the coupling of transcription and translation

In *E. coli* and other prokaryotes, transcription takes place in an open intracellular space undivided by a nuclear membrane; translation occurs in the same open space and is sometimes coupled directly with transcription (**Table 8.1**). This coupling is possible because transcription extends mRNAs in the same 5′-to-3′ direction as the ribosome moves along the mRNA. As a result, ribosomes can begin to translate a partial mRNA that the RNA polymerase is still in the process of transcribing from the DNA.

The coupling of transcription and translation has significant consequences for the regulation of gene expression in prokaryotes. For example, in an important regulatory mechanism called *attenuation,* which we describe in Chapter 15, the rate of translation of some mRNAs directly determines the rate at which the corresponding genes are transcribed into these mRNAs.

Such coupling cannot occur in eukaryotes because the nuclear envelope physically separates the sites of transcription and RNA processing in the nucleus from the sites of translation in the cytoplasm. As a result, translation in eukaryotes can affect the rate at which genes are transcribed only in more indirect ways.

Prokaryotes and eukaryotes initiate translation differently

In prokaryotes, translation begins at a ribosome binding site on the mRNA, which is defined by a short, characteristic sequence of nucleotides called a *Shine-Dalgarno box* adjacent to an initiating AUG codon (review Fig. 8.25a). There is nothing to prevent an mRNA from having more than one ribosome binding site, and, in fact, many prokaryotic messages are **polycistronic:** They contain the information of several genes (sometimes referred to as *cistrons;* see Chapter 7), each of which can be translated independently starting at its own ribosome binding site (Table 8.1).

In eukaryotes, by contrast, the small ribosomal subunit first binds to the methylated cap at the 5′ end of the mature mRNA and then migrates to the initiation site.

TABLE 8.1	Differences Between Prokaryotes and Eukaryotes in the Details of Gene Expression	
	Prokaryotes	**Eukaryotes**
Overview	1. No nucleus. Transcription and translation take place in the same cellular compartments, and translation is often coupled to transcription.	1. Nucleus separated from the cytoplasm by a nuclear membrane. Transcription takes place in the nucleus, while translation occurs in the cytoplasm. Direct coupling of transcription and translation is not possible.
	2. Genes are not divided into exons and introns.	2. The DNA of a gene consists of exons separated by introns; the exons are defined by posttranscriptional splicing, which deletes the introns.
Transcription	1. One RNA polymerase consisting of five subunits.	1. Several kinds of RNA polymerase, each containing 10 or more subunits; different polymerases transcribe different genes.
	2. Primary transcripts are the actual mRNAs; they have a triphosphate start at the 5′ end and no tail at the 3′ end.	2. Primary transcripts undergo processing to produce mature mRNAs that have a methylated cap at the 5′ end and a poly-A tail at the 3′ end.
Translation	1. Unique initiator tRNA carries formylmethionine.	1. Initiator tRNA carries methionine.
	2. mRNAs have multiple ribosome binding sites and can thus direct the synthesis of several different polypeptides.	2. mRNAs have only one start site and can thus direct the synthesis of only one kind of polypeptide.
	3. Small ribosomal subunit immediately binds to the mRNA's ribosome binding site.	3. Small ribosomal subunit binds first to the methylated cap at the 5′ end of the mature mRNA and then scans the mRNA to find the ribosome binding site.

this site is almost always the first AUG codon encountered by the ribosomal subunit as it moves along, or scans, the mRNA in the 5′-to-3′ direction (see Fig. 8.25a and Table 8.1). The mRNA region between the 5′ cap and the initiation codon is sometimes referred to as either the *5′-untranslated region (5′ UTR)* or the *5′-untranslated leader*. Because of this scanning mechanism, initiation in eukaryotes takes place at only a single site on the mRNA, and each mRNA contains the information for translating only a single kind of polypeptide.

Another translational difference between prokaryotes and eukaryotes is in the composition of the initiating tRNA. In prokaryotes, as already mentioned, this tRNA carries a modified form of methionine known as *N*-formylmethionine, while in eukaryotes, it carries an unmodified methionine (see Table 8.1). Thus, immediately after translation, eukaryotic polypeptides all have Met (instead of fMet) at their N termini. Posttranslational cleavage events in both prokaryotes and eukaryotes often create mature proteins that no longer have N-terminal fMet or Met (see Fig. 8.26a).

Eukaryotic mRNAs require more processing than prokaryotic mRNAs

Table 8.1 reviews other important differences in gene structure and expression between prokaryotes and eukaryotes.

In particular, introns interrupt eukaryotic, but not prokaryotic, genes such that the splicing of a primary transcript is necessary for eukaryotic gene expression. Other types of RNA processing that occur in eukaryotes but not prokaryotes add a methylated cap and a poly-A tail, respectively, to the 5′ and 3′ ends of the mRNAs.

> Because mRNA in eukaryotes must leave the nucleus for translation, transcription and translation cannot be coupled, as in prokaryotes. Eukaryotic mRNAs also initiate translation at a single site, rather than at multiple ribosome binding sites. Finally, in eukaryotes additional processing steps including splicing are required to form mature mRNAs.

8.5 A Comprehensive Example: Computerized Analysis of Gene Expression in *C. elegans*

Caenorhabditis elegans is a soil-living roundworm about 1 mm in length. Feeding on bacteria, it grows from fertilized egg to adult—either hermaphrodite or male—in just three days. Each hermaphrodite produces between 250 and 1000 progeny. Because of its small size, short life cycle, and capacity for prolific reproduction, *C. elegans* is an ideal subject for genetic analysis.

As you read at the beginning of this chapter, geneticists have determined the precise sequence of nearly all of the 100 million base pairs in the haploid genome of the tiny nematode *C. elegans*. Using their knowledge of gene structure and gene expression, they have also programmed computers to locate the sequences within the genome likely to be genes. Their programs include instructions to search for possible exons by looking for **open reading frames (ORFs)**: strings of amino acid–encoding nucleotide triplets uninterrupted by in-frame nonsense (stop) codons. Other algorithms ignore potential introns, identified as sequences lying between likely splice-donor and splice-acceptor sites.

Once the computer has retrieved regions likely to be genes, the researchers ask it to use the genetic code to project the amino acid sequences of the polypeptides encoded by these genes. Finally, they scan computerized databases for similar amino acid sequences in the polypeptides of other organisms. If they find a similar sequence in a polypeptide of known function in another organism, they can conclude that the *C. elegans* version of the polypeptide probably has a parallel function.

Geneticists now know many characteristics of the *C. elegans* genome

Investigators have discovered that the *C. elegans* genome contains roughly 20,000 genes, of which approximately 15% encode components of the worm's gene-expression machinery. Many of these gene-expression components are proteins. For example, more than 60 genes encode proteins that function as parts of the ribosome workbench, while more than 300 genes encode **transcription factors**: DNA-binding proteins that regulate transcription.

By contrast, a large contingent of expression-related genes produce RNAs that are not translated into protein. There are 659 tRNA genes in the *C. elegans* genome, about 100 rRNA genes, and 72 genes for spliceosomal RNAs. The relatively high numbers of RNA-encoding genes reflect the fact that the genome contains several identical or near-identical copies of these untranslated genes. For example, even though there are 72 spliceosomal RNA genes, there are only 5 different kinds of spliceosomal RNAs.

Computerized predictions based on genomic DNA sequences alone are valuable but not infallible tools. Computer programs are currently very good at predicting the introns and exons and the primary amino acid sequence of genes encoding proteins that are well conserved in evolution. But certain details of the transcription and translation of these genes cannot be established without isolating and characterizing their corresponding mRNAs. For example, although the computer can accurately locate the protein-coding exons of a gene, the gene may contain additional exons and introns at its 5′ or 3′ ends that are more difficult for the computer to find. Similarly, without biochemical analysis of the gene's RNA products, it is not possible to know whether alternative splicing of the gene's primary transcript produces different mRNAs.

A *C. elegans* collagen gene illustrates principles of gene structure

Using techniques described in Chapters 9 and 10, researchers have obtained both the genomic DNA and the mRNA sequences for many *C. elegans* genes. These data allow an examination of the structure of these genes in nucleotide-by-nucleotide detail. One of these genes encodes a particular type of collagen protein. This single-polypeptide protein is a component of the hard cuticle that surrounds and protects the worm. Related forms of collagen occur in all multicellular animals. In vertebrates, collagen is the most abundant protein, found in bones, teeth, cartilage, tendons, and other tissues.

Figure 8.27 shows a diagram of the collagen gene as well as the complete sequence of the gene, its primary RNA transcript, the mature mRNA, and the polypeptide product. As you can see, the gene's structural features include three exons and two introns, as well as the signals that allow transcription, RNA processing, and translation into collagen. Note that the ATG-initiated reading frame for the protein begins only in the second exon. The reason is that the entire first exon and the first four nucleotides of the second exon correspond to the 5′-untranslated region (5′-UTR). Similarly

Figure 8.27 Expression of a *C. elegans* gene for collagen. (a) Landmarks in the collagen gene. **(b)** Comparison of the sequence of the collagen gene's DNA with the sequence of nucleotides in the mature mRNA (*purple*) pinpoints the start of transcription, the location of exons (*red*) and introns (*green*), and the position of the AAUAAA poly-A addition signal (*underlined in purple*). Translation of the mRNA according to the genetic code determines the amino acids of the protein product.

(a) A collagen gene of *C. elegans*

(b) Sequence of a *C. elegans* collagen gene, mRNA, and polypeptide

RNA-like strand 5'... ACAACACTAGGTATAAAGCGGAAGTGGTGGCTTTAAAAT CACTTGGCTTCTAAAGTCCAGTGACAG GTAAG

Template strand 3'...TGTTGTGATC CATATTTCGCC TTCACCACCGAAATTT AGTGAACCGAAGATTTCAGGTCACTGTC CATTC

mRNA   5' cap– CACUUGGCUUCUAAAGUCCAGUGACAG

GTTCTCGTTACTTCCGTCTCGATTACTAAGATTTGATTACTTTTAG AAAAATGACCGAAGATCCAAAGCAGATTGCCCAGGAGACTGAG...
CAAGAGCAATGAAGGCAGAG CTAATGATTCTAAAC TAATGAAAAT CTTTTTACTGGCTTCTAGGTTTCGTC TAACGGGTCCTCTGACTC...
                                AAAAAUGACCGAAGAUCCAAAGCAGAUUGCCCAGG AGACUGAG...
Polypeptide   Met Thr Glu Asp Pro Lys Gln Ile Ala Gln Glu Thr Glu...

GTTGAATTC TGCCAACACAGA TCAAATGGACTTTGGGATGAGTAT AAGAGAGTATGTTTTTTTTGTTGAATAATTTTAATTTTAGTTAAATGTTT
CAACTTAAG ACGGTTGTGTCTAGTTTACCTGAAACCCTACTCATATTCTCTCATACAAAAAAAACAACTTATTAAAATTAAAATCAATTTACAAA
GUUGAAUUCUGCCAACACAGAUCAAAUGGACUUUGGGAU GUGUAUAAG AGA
Val Glu Phe Cys Gln His Arg Ser Asn Gly Leu Trp Asp Glu Tyr Lys Arg

GATTTCAGTTCCAAGGAGTTTCTGGAGTTGAAGGACGTATCAAGAGAGACGCATATCACCGTAGCCTCGGAGTTTCTGGTGCTTCCCGC
CTAAAGTC AAGGTTCCTCAAAGACCTCAACTTCCTGCATAGTTCTCTCTGCGTATAGTGGCATCGGAGCCTCAAAGACCACGAAGGGCG
        UUCCAAGG AGUUUCUGGAGUUGAAGGACGUAUCAAGAGAG ACGCAUAUCACCGUAGCCUCGGAGUUUCUGGUGCUUCCCGC
        Phe Gln Gly Val Ser Gly Val Glu Gly Arg Ile Lys Arg Asp Ala Tyr His Arg Ser Leu Gly Val Ser Gly Ala Ser Arg

AAGGCTCGTCGTCAATCTTATGGAAATGACGCTGCTGTCGGAGGATTCGGTGGATCATCTGGAGGATCATGCTGCTCATGCGGATCT...
TTCCGAGCAGCAGTTAGAATACCTTTACTGCGACGACAGCCTCCTAAGCCACCTAGTAGACCTCCTAGTACGACGAGTACGCCTAGA...
AAGGCUCGUCGUCAAUCUUAUGGAAAUGACGCUGCUGUCGGAGGAUUCGGUGGAUCAUCUGGAGGAUCAUGCUGCUCAUGCGGAUCU...
Lys Ala Arg Arg Gln Ser Tyr Gly Asn Asp Ala Ala Val Gly Gly Phe Gly Gly Ser Ser Gly Gly Ser Cys Cys Ser Cys Gly Ser...

CCAGGACAAGCTGGAGCACCAGGACAAGATGGAGAGAGTGGATCCGAGGGAGCTTGCGATCACTGCCCACCACCACGTACCGCTCCA
GGTCCTGTTCGACCTCGTGGTCCTGTTCTACCTCTCTCACCTAGGCTCCCTCGAACGCTAGTGACGGGTGGTGGTGCATGGCGAGGT
CCAGGACAAGCUGGAGCACCAGGACAAGAUGGAGAGAGUGGAUCCGAGGGAGCUUGCGAUCACUGCCCACCACCACGUACCGCUCCA
Pro Gly Gln Ala Gly Ala Pro Gly Gln Asp Gly Glu Ser Gly Ser Glu Gly Ala Cys Asp His Cys Pro Pro Pro Arg Thr Ala Pro

GGATATTAAGCGCTTCAATGACATCTCATTTGATTATCTCTGCTTTATCTCATTTGTATGTTTTGTGTATGAAAAACGAACACACTTAGAATAG
CCTATAATTCGCGAAGTTACTGTAGAGTAAACTAATAGAGACGAAATAGAGTAAACATACAAAACACATACTTTTTGCTTGTGTGAATCTTATC
GGAUAUUAAGCGCUUCAAUGACAUCUCAUUUGAUUAUCUCUGCUUUAUCUCAUUUGUAUGUUUUGUGUAUGAAAAACGAACACACUUAGA AUAG
Gly Tyr Stop

TGGAATAAATGATTTCATTACAAATTTGAAAT TGAATAAGACAAATGTGAAATGAAAGTATAAAAGAAAATGAGAGAC...3'
ACCTTATTTACTAAAGTAATGTTTAAACTTTAACTTATTCTGTTTACACTTTACTTTCATATTTTCTTTTACTCTCTG...5'
UGG AAUAAAUGAUUUCAUUACAAAUUUGAAAUUGAAAAAAAAAA...
(poly (A))

---

he third exon contains both amino acid-specifying codons, as well as sequences transcribed into an untranslated region near the 3' end of the mature mRNA (the 3'-UTR) just upstream of the poly-A tail.

The general structure of the collagen gene is similar to the structure of most eukaryotic genes. This is because the basic pattern of gene expression has remained substantially the same throughout evolution, even though details, such as gene length, exon number, and the spacing or size of the untranslated 5' and 3' ends, vary from gene to gene and from organism to organism.

Gene expression in *C. elegans* involves trans-splicing and polycistronic transcripts

he sequencing of the 100 million nucleotides in the *C. elegans* genome not only led to the identification of 20,000 genes but also helped reveal some uncommon features in the way the worm expresses its genes. In rare instances, worms use trans-splicing to create an mRNA from the primary transcripts of two different genes (review Fig. 8.18b on p. 265); before observing trans-splicing in the nematode, researchers had seen it mainly in trypanosomes, the single-celled protozoans that cause sleeping sickness.

Like bacteria, *C. elegans* transcribes some groups of adjacent genes as one long polycistronic primary transcript; it is one of the very few eukaryotic organisms in which researchers have observed this predominantly prokaryotic phenomenon. Polycistronic transcripts are permissible in *C. elegans* because they are processed by trans-splicing into mature mRNAs for individual genes. Researchers will be able to apply these insights clarifying *C. elegans'* mechanisms of gene expression to studies of the worm's growth and development (see the genetic portrait of *C. elegans* on our website: www.mhhe.com/hartwell4).

8.6 The Effect of Mutations on Gene Expression and Gene Function

We have seen that the information in DNA is the starting point of gene expression. The cell transcribes that information into mRNA and then translates the mRNA information into protein. Mutations that alter the nucleotide pairs of DNA may modify any of the steps or products of gene expression.

Mutations in a gene's coding sequence may alter the gene product

Because of the nature of the genetic code, mutations in a gene's amino acid-encoding exons generate a range of repercussions (**Fig. 8.28a**).

Silent mutations

One consequence of the code's degeneracy is that some mutations, known as **silent mutations,** can change a codon into a mutant codon that specifies exactly the same amino acid. The majority of silent mutations change the third nucleotide of a codon, the position at which most codons for the

same amino acid differ. For example, a change from GCA to GCC in a codon would still yield alanine in the protein product. Because silent mutations do not alter the amino acid composition of the encoded polypeptide, such mutations have no effect on any of the phenotypes influenced by the gene.

Missense mutations

Mutations that change a codon into a mutant codon that specifies a different amino acid are called **missense mutations.** If the substituted amino acid has chemical properties similar to the one it replaces, then it may have little or no effect on protein function. Such substitutions are *conservative.* For example, a mutation that alters a GAC codon for aspartic acid to a GAG codon for glutamic acid is a conservative substitution because both amino acids have acidic R groups.

By contrast, *nonconservative* missense mutations that cause substitution of an amino acid with very different properties are likely to have more noticeable consequences. A change of the same GAC codon for aspartic acid to GCC, a codon for alanine (an amino acid with an uncharged, nonpolar R group), is an example of a nonconservative substitution.

The effect on phenotype of any missense mutation is difficult to predict because it depends on how a particular amino acid substitution changes a protein's structure and function.

Nonsense mutations

Mutations known as **nonsense mutations** change an amino acid–specifying codon to a premature stop codon. Nonsense mutations therefore result in the production of proteins smaller than those encoded by wild-type alleles of the same gene. The shorter, *truncated proteins* lack all amino acids between the amino acid encoded by the mutant codon and the C terminus of the normal polypeptide. The mutant polypeptide will be unable to function if it requires the missing amino acids for its activity.

Frameshift mutations

Frameshift mutations result from the insertion or deletion of nucleotides within the coding sequence (the series of codons specifying the amino acids of the gene product). As discussed earlier, if the number of extra or missing nucleotides is not divisible by 3, the insertion or deletion will skew the reading frame downstream of the mutation. As a result, frameshift mutations cause unrelated amino acids to appear in place of amino acids critical to protein function, destroying or diminishing polypeptide function.

Figure 8.28 How mutations in a gene can affect its expression. (a) Mutations in a gene's coding sequences. *Silent mutations* do not alter the protein's primary structure. *Missense mutations* replace one amino acid with another. *Nonsense mutations* shorten a polypeptide by replacing a codon with a stop signal. *Frameshift mutations* result in a change in reading frame downstream of the addition or deletion. **(b)** Mutations outside the coding region can also disrupt gene expression.

(a) Types of mutation in a gene's coding sequence

Wild-type mRNA	5' GCU GGA GCA CCA GGA CAA GAU GGA 3'	
Wild-type polypeptide	N Ala Gly Ala Pro Gly Gln Asp Gly C	
Silent mutation	GCU GGA GCC CCA GGA CAA GAU GGA Ala Gly Ala Pro Gly Gln Asp Gly	
Missense mutation	GCU GGA GCA CCA AGA CAA GAU GGA Ala Gly Ala Pro Arg Gln Asp Gly	
Nonsense mutation	GCU GGA GCA CCA GGA UAA GAU GGA Ala Gly Ala Pro Gly Stop	
Frameshift mutation	GCU GGA GCC ACC AGG ACA AGA UGG A Ala Gly Ala Thr Arg Thr Arg Trp	

(b) Mutations outside the coding sequence

Promoter | Ribosome binding site or 5'-untranslated leader | Sites needed for splicing | In-frame stop codon (TAG) | Transcription termination

Exon   Intron   Exon

> Silent mutations have no effect on the encoded polypeptide or on phenotype. The phenotypic consequences of missense, nonsense, and frameshift mutations depend upon how the specific changes in amino acid sequence influence the function of the gene product.

Mutations outside the coding sequence can also alter gene expression

Mutations that produce a variant phenotype are not restricted to alterations in codons. Because gene expression depends on several signals other than the actual coding sequence, changes in any of these critical signals can disrupt the process (see **Fig. 8.28b**).

We have seen that promoters and termination signals in the DNA of a gene instruct RNA polymerase where to start and stop transcription. Changes in the sequence of a promoter that make it hard or impossible for RNA polymerase to recognize the site diminish or prevent transcription. Mutations in a termination signal can diminish the amount of mRNA produced and thus the amount of gene product.

In eukaryotes, most primary transcripts have splice-acceptor sites, splice-donor sites, and branch sites that allow splicing to join exons together with precision in the mature mRNA. Changes in a splice-acceptor or donor site can obstruct splicing. In some cases, the result will be the absence of mature mRNA and thus no polypeptide. In other cases, the splicing errors can yield aberrantly spliced mRNAs that encode altered forms of the protein.

Mature mRNAs have ribosome binding sites and in-frame stop codons indicating where translation should start and stop. Mutations affecting a ribosome binding site would lower the affinity of the mRNA for the small ribosomal subunit; such mutations are likely to diminish the efficiency of translation and thus the amount of polypeptide product. Mutations in a stop codon would produce longer than normal proteins that might be unstable or nonfunctional.

Most mutations outside the coding sequence, such as in promoters and transcription termination signals, affect the amount but not the nature of the protein product. Rare exceptions include mutations that lead to incorrectly spliced mRNAs, or that convert a stop codon into a codon for an amino acid.

Most mutations that affect gene expression reduce gene function

Mutations affect phenotype by changing either the amino acid sequence of a protein or the amount of the protein produced. Any mutation inside or outside a coding region that reduces or abolishes protein activity in one of the many ways previously described is a **loss-of-function mutation.**

Recessive loss-of-function alleles

Loss-of-function alleles that completely block the function of a protein are called **null,** or **amorphic, mutations**

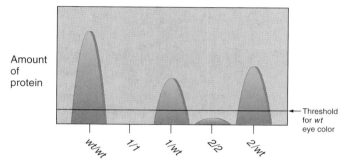

Figure 8.29 Why some mutant alleles are recessive. Researchers subjected fly extracts to "rocket" immunoelectrophoresis to quantify the amount of an enzyme called xanthine dehydrogenase. Flies need only 10% of the enzyme produced in wild-type strains (*wt/wt*) to have normal eye color. Null allele 1 and hypomorphic allele 2 are recessive to wild type because 1/*wt* or 2/*wt* heterozygotes have enough enzyme for normal eye color.

(**Fig. 8.29**). Such mutations either prevent synthesis of the protein or promote synthesis of a protein incapable of carrying out any function. For example, a deletion of an entire gene would by definition be a null allele. In an A^+/a heterozygote, in which allele a is recessive to wild-type allele A^+, the A^+ allele would generate functional protein, while the null a allele would not. If the amount of protein produced by the single A^+ allele (usually, though not always, half the amount produced in an A^+/A^+ cell) is above the threshold amount sufficient to fulfill the normal biochemical requirements of the cell, the phenotype of the A^+/a heterozygote will be wild type. For the large number of genes that function in this way, A^+/A^+ cells actually make more than twice as much of the protein needed for the normal phenotype.

A **hypomorphic mutation** is a loss-of-function mutation that produces either much less of a protein or a protein with very weak but detectable function (Fig. 8.29). In a B^+/b heterozygote, where b is a hypomorphic allele recessive to wild-type allele B^+, the amount of protein activity will be somewhat greater than half the amount in a B^+/B^+ cell. Usually, this is enough activity to fulfill the normal biochemical requirements of the cell. Most hypomorphic mutations are detectable only in homozygotes, and only if the reduction in protein amount or function is sufficient to cause an abnormal phenotype.

Incomplete dominance

Some combinations of alleles generate phenotypes that vary continuously with the amount of functional gene product, giving rise to incomplete dominance. For example, loss-of-function mutations in a single pigment-producing gene can generate a red-to-white spectrum of flower colors, with the white resulting from the absence of an enzyme in a biochemical pathway (**Fig. 8.30**). Consider three alleles of the gene encoding this enzyme: R^+ specifies a

Figure 8.30 When a phenotype varies continuously with levels of protein function, incomplete dominance results.

high, wild-type amount of the enzyme; r^{50} generates half the normal amount of the same enzyme (or the full amount of an altered form that has half the normal level of activity); and r^0 is a null allele. R^+/r^0 heterozygotes produce pink flowers whose color is halfway between red and white because one-half the R^+/R^+ level of enzyme activity is not enough to generate a full red. Combining R^+ or r^0 with the r^{50} allele produces pigmentation intermediate between red and pink or between pink and white.

Rare dominant loss-of-function alleles

With phenotypes that are exquisitely sensitive to the amount of functional protein produced, even a relatively small change of twofold or less can cause a switch between distinct phenotypes. For example, a heterozygote for a null loss-of-function mutation that generates only half the normal amount of functional gene product may look completely different from the wild type.

The T locus in mice has just such a mutation, with an easy-to-visualize dominant phenotype (**Fig. 8.31a**). Mice require the wild-type protein product of the T-locus gene during embryogenesis for the normal development of the posterior portion of the spinal cord and tail. Embryos heterozygous for a null mutation at the T locus produce only half the normal amount of the T-determined protein, and they mature into viable offspring that are normal in all respects except for the absence of the distal two-thirds of their tail. The severely shortened tail reflects the embryo's sensitivity to the level of T-gene product available during morphogenesis; half the normal amount of T protein is below the threshold needed for normal development.

Geneticists sometimes use the term **haploinsufficiency** to describe situations in which one wild-type allele does not provide enough of a gene product. Only a minority of phenotypes are so sensitive to the amount of a particular protein. Thus, as described earlier, null and hypomorphic alleles usually produce phenotypes that are recessive to wild type.

In another mechanism leading to dominance, some alleles of genes encode subunits of multimers that block the activity of the subunits produced by normal alleles.

Such blocking alleles cause a loss of function of the gene product in the organism, and are called **dominant negative,** or **antimorphic, alleles.** Consider, for example, a gene encoding a polypeptide that associates with three other identical polypeptides in a four-subunit enzyme. All four subunits are products of the same gene. If a dominant mutant allele D directs the synthesis of a polypeptide that can still assemble into aggregates but whose presence in the multimer—even as one subunit out of four—abolishes enzyme function, the chance of a heterozygote producing a multimer composed solely of functional wild-type d^+ subunits is 1 in 16: $(1/2)^4 = 1/16 = 6.25\%$ (**Fig. 8.31b**). As a result, total enzyme activity in D/d^+ heterozygotes is far less than that seen in wild-type d^+/d^+ homozygotes. Dominant negative mutations can also affect subunits in multimers composed of more than one type of polypeptide. The *Kinky* allele at the *fused* locus in mice is an example of such a dominant negative mutation (**Fig. 8.31c**).

> Most loss-of-function (null or hypomorphic) mutations are recessive because half the normal amount of gene product is usually sufficient for a wild-type phenotype. Exceptions occur when intermediate levels of gene products cause intermediate phenotypes (incomplete dominance), when half the amount of gene product yields an abnormal phenotype (haploinsufficiency), or when a mutant polypeptide blocks the action of the wild-type polypeptide (dominant negative alleles).

Unusual gain-of-function alleles are almost always dominant

Because there are many ways to interfere with a gene's ability to make sufficient amounts of active protein, the large majority of mutations in most genes are loss-of-function alleles. However, rare mutations that enhance a protein's function or even confer a new activity on a protein produce **gain-of-function alleles.** Because a single such allele by itself can produce sufficient excess protein to alter phenotype, these unusual gain-of-function mutations are almost always dominant to wild-type alleles.

A **hypermorphic mutation** is a gain-of-function mutation that generates either more protein than the wild-type allele or the same amount of a more efficient protein. A hypermorphic mutation in the rhodopsin gene produces a rhodopsin protein that is activated whether or not light is present, resulting in constant, low-level stimulation of rhodopsin in the photoreceptor cells that detect black and white. These cells, known as rod cells, function primarily at night. People with the mutation can still see in bright daylight, but they have congenital night blindness. The blindness probably arises because the constant rhodopsin stimulation prevents adaptation of the rod cells to the very low light intensities present at night.

Figure 8.31 Why some mutant alleles are dominant. (a) Mice heterozygous for a null mutation of the *T* locus (*T/+*) have tails shorter than wild type (*+/+*). **(b)** With proteins composed of four subunits encoded by a single gene, a dominant negative mutant may inactivate 15 out of every 16 multimers. **(c)** The *Kinky* allele in mice is a dominant negative mutation that causes a kink in the tail. **(d)** A neomorphic dominant mutation in the fly *Antennapedia* gene causes ectopic expression of a leg-determining gene in structures that normally produce antennae. The photo at *left* shows two legs growing out of the head; a normal fly head is shown at *right*.

(a) Haploinsufficiency

(b) Dominant negative mutations

Functional Enzyme	Nonfunctional Enzyme			
$d^+d^+d^+d^+$	$d^+d^+d^+D$	$d^+d^+D\,d^+$	$d^+\,D\,d^+d^+$	$D\,d^+d^+d^+$
	$d^+d^+D\,D$	$d^+D\,D\,d^+$	$d^+\,D\,d^+D$	$D\,d^+D\,d^+$
	$D\,d^+d^+D$	$D\,D\,d^+d^+$	$d^+\,D\,D\,D$	$D\,d^+D\,D$
	$D\,D\,d^+D$	$D\,D\,D\,d^+$	$D\,D\,D\,D$	

D = dominant mutant subunit
d^+ = wild-type subunit

(c) *Kinky*: A dominant negative mutation

(d) A result of ectopic expression

A very rare class of dominant gain-of-function alleles arises from **neomorphic mutations** that generate a novel phenotype. Some neomorphic mutations produce proteins with a new function, while others cause genes to produce the normal protein but at an inappropriate time or place. A striking example of inappropriate protein production is the *Drosophila* gene *Antennapedia,* active during embryonic and larval stages. Normally, the gene makes its protein product in tissues destined to become legs; the protein ensures that these tissues develop into legs and not, for example, head structures such as antennae. Dominant mutations of the gene cause production of the protein in the head region of the animal, where the

Antennapedia gene is not normally active. Here, the misplaced protein causes tissues that would normally develop into antennae to develop into legs (**Fig. 8.31d**). Production of a protein outside of its normal place or time is called **ectopic expression.**

Rare gain-of-function mutations, which are typically dominant, include hypermorphic mutations that generate greater protein function than normal, and neomorphic mutations that either produce proteins with new functions or express normal proteins inappropriately (ectopic expression).

TABLE 8.2   Mutations Classified by Their Effects on Protein Function

	Loss-of-Function			Gain-of-Function	
Mutation Type	Hypomorphic (leaky)	Amorphic (null)	Antimorphic (dominant negative)*	Hypermorphic	Neomorphic (ectopic expression)
Occurrence	Common	Common	Rare	Rare	Rare
Possible Dominance Relations	Usually recessive to wild type Can be incompletely dominant if phenotype varies continuously with gene product Can be dominant in cases of haploinsufficiency		Usually dominant or incompletely dominant	Usually dominant or incompletely dominant	Usually dominant or incompletely dominant

*Some scientists, focusing on the protein encoded by the mutant allele rather than on the total level of active protein in the cell, classify antimorphic alleles as gain-of-function mutations.

The effects of a mutation can be difficult to predict

As previously noted, most mutations constitute loss-of-function alleles. This is because many changes in amino acid sequence are likely to disrupt a protein's function, and because most alterations in gene regulatory sites, such as promoters, will make those sites less efficient. Nonetheless, rare mutations at almost any location in a gene can result in a gain of function.

Consider, for example, a protein with a region of amino acids near its C terminus that prevents the protein from functioning except under particular conditions. A nonsense mutation that removes the amino acids needed for this negative regulation might be a hypermorphic allele: The protein would work all the time, not just under the proper conditions. In another example, the *Antennapedia* mutation shown in Fig. 8.31d results from an unusual alteration in the gene's promoter that causes *Antennapedia* to be transcribed in the wrong tissues of the animal.

Even when you know how a mutation affects gene function, you cannot always predict whether the mutation will be dominant or recessive to wild type (**Table 8.2**). Although most loss-of-function mutations are recessive and almost all gain-of-function mutations are dominant, exceptions to these generalizations exist. The reason is that dominance relations between the wild-type and mutant alleles of genes in diploid organisms depend on how drastically a mutation influences protein production or activity, and how thoroughly phenotype depends on the normal wild-type level of the protein.

Mutations in genes encoding the molecules that implement expression may have global effects

Gene expression depends on an astonishing number and variety of macromolecules (**Table 8.3**). A separate gene

TABLE 8.3   The Cellular Components of Gene Expression

Function	Cellular Components
Transcription*	Core RNA polymerase Sigma subunit Rho factor
Splicing and RNA Processing	snRNAs Protein components of spliceosomes Additional splicing factors Capping enzyme Methyl transferases Poly-A polymerase
Translation	mRNAs tRNAs Aminoacyl-tRNA synthetases rRNAs Protein components of ribosomes Translation factors
Protein Processing	Deformylases Amino peptidases Proteases Methylases Hydroxylases Glycosylases Kinases Phosphatases

*For simplicity, we list here only proteins from prokaryotic organisms involved in transcription. The cellular components needed for transcription in eukaryotic organisms are more complex; for example, eukaryotes have three different kinds of RNA polymerase, each made of numerous subunits.

encodes the subunits of each macromolecule. The gene for all the proteins are transcribed and translated the same as any other gene. The genes for all the rRNAs, tRNAs, and snRNAs are transcribed but *not* translated. Many mutations in these genes have a dramatic effect on phenotype.

Lethal mutations affecting the machinery of gene expression

Mutations in the genes encoding molecules that implement gene expression, such as ribosomal proteins or rRNAs, are often lethal because such mutations adversely affect the synthesis of all proteins in a cell. Even a 50% reduction in the amount of some of the proteins enumerated in Table 8.3 can have severe repercussions. In *Drosophila,* for example, null mutations in many of the genes encoding the various ribosomal proteins are lethal when homozygous. This same mutation in a heterozygote causes a dominant *Minute* phenotype in which the slow growth of cells delays the fly's development.

Mutations in tRNA genes that can suppress mutations in protein-coding genes

If more than one gene encoded the same molecule with a role in gene expression, a mutation in one of these genes would not necessarily be lethal and might even be useful. Bacterial geneticists have found, for example, that mutations in certain tRNA genes can suppress the effect of a nonsense mutation in other genes. The tRNA-gene mutations that have this effect give rise to **nonsense suppressor tRNAs.** Consider, for instance, an otherwise wild-type *E. coli* population with an in-frame UAG nonsense mutation in the tryptophan synthetase gene. All cells in this population make a truncated, nonfunctional form of the tryptophan synthetase enzyme and are thus tryptophan auxotrophs (trp^-) unable to synthesize tryptophan (**Fig. 8.32a**). Subsequent exposure of these auxotrophs to mutagens, however, generates some trp^+ cells that carry two mutations: one is the original tryptophan synthetase nonsense mutation, the second is a mutation in the gene that encodes a tRNA for the amino acid tyrosine. Evidently, the mutation in the tRNA gene suppresses the effect of the nonsense mutation, restoring the function of the tryptophan synthetase gene.

As **Fig. 8.32b** illustrates, the basis of this nonsense suppression is that the tRNA^{Tyr} mutation changes an anticodon that recognizes the codon for tyrosine to an anticodon complementary to the UAG stop codon. The mutant tRNA can therefore insert tyrosine into the polypeptide at the position of the in-frame UAG nonsense mutation, allowing the cell to make at least some full-length enzyme. Similarly, mutations in the anticodons of other tRNA genes can suppress UGA or UAA nonsense mutations.

Cells with a nonsense-suppressing mutation in a tRNA gene can survive only if two conditions coexist with the mutation. First, the cell must have other tRNAs that recognize the same codon as the suppressing tRNA recognized before mutation altered its anticodon. Without

such tRNAs, the cell has no way to insert the proper amino acid in response to that codon (in our example, the codon for tyrosine). Second, the suppressing tRNA must have only a weak affinity for the stop codons normally found at the ends of mRNA coding regions. If this were not the case, the suppressing tRNA would wreak havoc in the cell, producing a whole array of aberrant polypeptides that are longer than normal. One way cells guard against this possibility is that for many genes, termination depends on two stop codons in a row. Because a suppressing tRNA's chance of inserting an amino acid at both of these codons is very low, only a small number of extended proteins arise.

Figure 8.32 Nonsense suppression. (a) A nonsense mutation that generates a stop codon causes production of a truncated, nonfunctional polypeptide. **(b)** A second, nonsense-suppressing mutation in a tRNA gene causes addition of an amino acid in response to the stop codon, allowing production of a full-length polypeptide.

(a) A nonsense mutation

(b) A nonsense-suppressor tRNA

Mutations altering the genes involved in gene expression are often lethal. Important exceptions include mutations in tRNA genes that can suppress nonsense mutations in protein-coding genes. The suppressing tRNAs insert amino acids into the growing polypeptide chains in response to premature stop codons in the mRNAs.

Connections

Our knowledge of gene expression enables us to redefine the concept of a gene. A gene is not simply the DNA that is transcribed into the mRNA codons specifying the amino acids of a particular polypeptide. Rather, *a gene is all the DNA sequences needed for expression of the gene into a polypeptide product.* A gene therefore includes the promoter sequences that govern where transcription begins and, at the opposite end, signals for the termination of transcription. A gene also must include sequences dictating where translation of the mRNA starts and stops. In addition to all of these features, eukaryotic genes contain introns that are spliced out of the primary transcript to make the mature mRNA. Because of introns, most eukaryotic genes are much larger than prokaryotic genes.

Even with introns, a single gene carries only a very small percentage of the nucleotide pairs in the chromosomes that make up a genome. The average gene in *C. elegans* is about 4000 nucleotide pairs in length, and there are roughly 20,000 genes. The worm's haploid genome, however, contains approximately 100 million nucleotide pairs distributed among six chromosomes containing an average of 16–17 million nucleotide pair apiece. In humans, where genes tend to have more introns, the average gene is 16,000 nucleotide pairs in length and there are 20,000–30,000 of them. But the haploid human genome has roughly 3 billion (3,000,000,000) nucleotide pairs distributed among 23 chromosomes containing an average of 130 million nucleotide pair apiece.

In Chapters 9 and 10, we describe how researchers analyze the mass of genetic information in the chromosomes of a genome as they try to discover what parts of the DNA are genes and how those genes influence phenotype. They begin their analysis by breaking the DNA into pieces of manageable size, making many copies of those pieces to obtain enough material for study, and characterizing the pieces down to the level of nucleotide sequence. They then try to reconstruct the DNA sequence of an entire genome by determining the spatial relationship between the many pieces. Finally, they use the knowledge they have obtained to examine the genomic variation that make individuals unique.

ESSENTIAL CONCEPTS

1. Gene expression is the process by which cells convert the DNA sequence of a gene to the RNA sequence of a transcript, and then decode the RNA sequence as the amino acid sequence of a polypeptide.

2. The nearly universal genetic code consists of 64 codons, each one composed of three nucleotides. Sixty-one codons specify amino acids, while three—UAA, UAG, and UGA—are nonsense or stop codons. The code is degenerate because more than one codon can specify each amino acid except methionine and tryptophan. The codon AUG in the context of a ribosome binding site is the initiation codon; it establishes the reading frame that groups nucleotides into non-overlapping codon triplets.

3. Transcription is the first stage of gene expression. During transcription, RNA polymerase synthesizes a single-stranded primary transcript from a DNA template. In initiation, RNA polymerase binds to the promoter sequence of the DNA and unwinds the double helix to expose bases for pairing. During elongation, the enzyme extends the RNA in the 5'-to-3' direction by catalyzing bond formation between successively aligned nucleotides.

Termination occurs when terminator sequences in the RNA cause RNA polymerase to dissociate from the DNA.

4. In prokaryotes, the primary transcript is the messenger RNA (mRNA). In eukaryotes, RNA processing after transcription produces a mature mRNA. RNA processing adds a methylated cap to the 5' end and a poly-A tail to the 3' end of eukaryotic mRNA. An important aspect of processing is RNA splicing, during which the spliceosome removes introns from the primary transcript and joins together the remaining exons. Alternative splicing allows production of different mRNAs from the same primary transcript.

5. Translation occurs when the cell synthesizes protein according to instructions in the mRNA. This process takes place on ribosomes, which are composed of protein and ribosomal RNA (rRNA). Ribosomes have three binding sites for transfer RNA (tRNAs)—A, P, and E sites—and they also supply the ribozyme known as peptidyl transferase, which catalyzes formation of peptide bonds between amino acids.

6. Individual aminoacyl-tRNA synthetases connect the correct amino acids to their corresponding tRNAs; a tRNA carrying an amino acid is said to be charged. Each charged tRNA has an anticodon complementary to the mRNA codon specifying the amino acid the tRNA carries. Because of wobble, some tRNA anticodons recognize more than one mRNA codon.

7. To initiate translation, the small subunit of the ribosome binds to a ribosome-binding site on the mRNA that includes the AUG initiation codon. Special tRNAs carry the amino acid fMet in prokaryotes or Met in eukaryotes to the ribosomal P site. This amino acid becomes the N terminus of the growing polypeptide. After initiation has begun, a charged tRNA complementary to the next codon of the mRNA enters the A site of the ribosome.

8. During elongation, the carboxyl group of the amino acid connected to a tRNA at the ribosome's P site becomes bonded to the amino acid carried by the tRNA at the A site. The ribosome then travels three nucleotides toward the 3' end of the mRNA. The 5'-to-3' direction in the mRNA thus corresponds to the N-terminus-to-C-terminus direction in the polypeptide under construction.

9. Termination occurs when the ribosome encounters a nonsense (stop) codon. The ribosome then releases the mRNA and disconnects the completed polypeptide from the tRNA to which it was attached.

10. Posttranslational processing may alter a polypeptide by adding or removing chemical constituents or by cleaving the polypeptide into smaller molecules.

11. Mutations in a gene may modify the message encoded in a sequence of nucleotides. Silent mutations usually change the third letter of a codon and have no effect on polypeptide production. Missense mutations change the codon for one amino acid to the codon for another amino acid. Nonsense mutations change a codon for an amino acid to a stop codon. Frameshift mutations change the reading frame of a gene, altering the identity of all subsequent amino acids.

12. Mutations outside coding sequences that alter signals required for transcription, mRNA splicing, or translation can modify gene expression by altering the amount, time, or place of protein production.

13. Loss-of-function mutations reduce or completely block gene expression. Most loss-of-function alleles are recessive to wild-type alleles, but in haploinsufficiency, half the normal gene product is not enough for a normal phenotype, so the mutant allele is dominant to wild type. Certain loss-of-function alleles can have dominant effects by disrupting function of wild-type protein subunits in a complex.

14. Rare gain-of-function mutations cause either increased protein production or synthesis of a protein with enhanced activity. Some gain-of-function alleles confer a novel function on a gene; one example is ectopic expression, in which the gene product is made in the wrong tissue or at the wrong time in development. Most gain-of-function mutations are dominant.

15. Mutations in genes that encode molecules of the gene-expression machinery are often lethal. Exceptions include mutations in tRNA genes that suppress nonsense mutations in polypeptide-encoding genes.

On Our Website   www.mhhe.com/hartwell4

Annotated Suggested Readings and Links to Other Websites

- Research articles, both historical and recent, describing experiments leading to the elucidation of the genetic code and to our current understanding of the mechanisms responsible for gene expression.

- Animations and high-resolution molecular models illustrating the events occuring during transcription, RNA processing, and translation.

- A database of the *Caenorhabditis elegans* genome.

Specialized Topics

- A comprehensive view of the molecular details of translation, focusing on the roles played by various translation factors in initiation, elongation, and termination.

Solved Problems

I. A geneticist examined the amino acid sequence of a particular protein in a variety of *E. coli* mutants. The amino acid in position 40 in the normal enzyme is glycine. The following table shows the substitutions the geneticist found at amino acid position 40 in six mutant forms of the enzyme.

mutant 1	cysteine
mutant 2	valine
mutant 3	serine
mutant 4	aspartic acid
mutant 5	arginine
mutant 6	alanine

Determine the nature of the base substitution that must have occurred in the DNA in each case. Which of these mutants would be capable of recombination with mutant 1 to form a wild-type gene?

Answer

To determine the base substitutions, use the genetic code table (see Fig. 8.3 on p. 248). The original amino acid was glycine, which can be encoded by GGU, GGC, GGA, or GGC. Mutant 1 results in a cysteine at position 40; Cys codons are either UGU or UGC. A change in the base pair in the DNA encoding the first position in the codon (a G–C to T–A transversion) must have occurred, and the original glycine codon must therefore have been either GGU or GGC. Valine (in mutant 2) is encoded by GUN (with N representing any one of the four bases), but assuming that the mutation is a single base change, the Val codon must be either GUU or GUC. The change must have been a G–C to T–A transversion in the DNA for the second position of the codon. To get from glycine to serine (mutant 3) with only one base change, the GGU or GGC would be changed to AGU or AGC, respectively. There was a transition (G–C to A–T) at the first position. Aspartic acid (mutant 4) is encoded by GAU or GAC, so the DNA of mutant 4 is the result of a G–C to A–T transition at position 2. Arginine (mutant 5) is encoded by CGN, so the DNA of mutant 5 must have undergone a G–C to C–G transversion at position 1. Finally, alanine (mutant 6) is encoded by GCN, so the DNA of mutant 6 must have undergone a G–C to C–G transversion at position 2. Mutants 2, 4, and 6 affect a base pair different from that affected by mutant 1, so they could recombine with mutant 1.

In summary, the sequence of nucleotides on the RNA-like strand of the wild-type and mutant genes at this position must be

wild type	5′ G G T/C 3′
mutant 1	5′ <u>T</u> G T/C 3′
mutant 2	5′ G <u>T</u> T/C 3′
mutant 3	5′ <u>A</u> G T/C 3′
mutant 4	5′ G <u>A</u> T/C 3′
mutant 5	5′ <u>C</u> G T/C 3′
mutant 6	5′ G <u>C</u> T/C 3′

II. The double-stranded circular DNA molecule that forms the genome of the SV40 virus can be denatured into single-stranded DNA molecules. Because the base composition of the two strands differs, the strands can be separated on the basis of their density into two strands designated W(atson) and C(rick). When each of the purified preparations of the single strands was mixed with mRNA from cells infected with the virus, hybrids were formed between the RNA and DNA. Closer analysis of these hybridizations showed that RNAs that hybridized with the W preparation were different from RNAs that hybridized with the C preparation. What does this tell you about the transcription templates for the different classes of RNAs?

Answer

An understanding of transcription and the polarity of DNA strands in the double helix are needed to answer this question. *Some genes use one strand of the DNA as a template; others use the opposite strand as a template.* Because of the different polarities of the DNA strands, one set of genes would be transcribed in a clockwise direction on the circular DNA (using say the W strand as the template), and the other set would be transcribed in a counterclockwise direction (with the C strand as template).

III. Geneticists interested in human hemoglobins have found a very large number of mutant forms. Some of these mutant proteins are of normal size, with amino acid substitutions, while others are short, due to deletions or nonsense mutations. The first extra-long example was named Hb Constant Spring, in which the β globin has several extra amino acids attached at the C-terminal end. What is a plausible explanation for its origin? Is it likely that Hb Constant Spring arose from failure to splice out an intron?

Answer

An understanding of the principles of translation and RNA splicing are needed to answer this question. Because there is an extension on the C-terminal end of the protein, *the mutation probably affected the termination (nonsense) codon rather than affecting splicing of the RNA.* This could have been a base change or a frameshift or a deletion that altered or removed the termination codon. The information in the mRNA beyond the normal stop codon would be translated until another stop codon in the mRNA was reached. A splicing defect could explain Hb Constant Spring only in the more unlikely case that an incorrectly spliced mRNA would encode a protein much longer than normal.

Problems

Interactive Web Exercise

As part of its effort to annotate the human genome, the National Center for Biotechnology Information (NCBI) maintains a database called Sequence View. The files in this database show the structure of genes at the level of base pairs. The Interactive Web Exercise for this chapter at www. mhhe.com/hartwell4 (Chapter 8) provides you with an opportunity to enhance your understanding of gene organization and function by exploring one such file in detail.

Vocabulary

1. For each of the terms in the left column, choose the best matching phrase in the right column.

a. codon	1. removing base sequences corresponding to introns from the primary transcript
b. colinearity	2. UAA, UGA, or UAG
c. reading frame	3. the strand of DNA that has the same base sequence as the primary transcript
d. frameshift mutation	4. a transfer RNA molecule to which the appropriate amino acid has been attached
e. degeneracy of the genetic code	5. a group of three mRNA bases signifying one amino acid
f. nonsense codon	6. most amino acids are not specified by a single codon
g. initiation codon	7. using the information in the nucleotide sequence of a strand of DNA to specify the nucleotide sequence of a strand of RNA
h. template strand	8. the grouping of mRNA bases in threes to be read as codons
i. RNA-like strand	9. AUG in a particular context
j. intron	10. the linear sequence of amino acids in the poly peptide corresponds to the linear sequence of nucleotide pairs in the gene
k. RNA splicing	11. produces different mature mRNAs from the same primary transcript
l. transcription	12. addition or deletion of a number of base pairs other than three into the coding sequence
m. translation	13. a sequence of base pairs within a gene that is not represented by any bases in the mature mRNA
n. alternative splicing	14. the strand of DNA having the base sequence complementary to that of the primary transcript
o. charged tRNA	15. using the information encoded in the nucleotide sequence of an mRNA molecule to specify the amino acid sequence of a polypeptide molecule
p. reverse transcription	16. copying RNA into DNA

Section 8.1

2. Match the hypothesis from the left column to the observation from the right column that gave rise to it.

a. existence of an intermediate messenger between DNA and protein	1. two mutations affecting the same amino acid can recombine to give wild type
b. the genetic code is nonoverlapping	2. one or two base deletions (or insertions) in a gene disrupt its function; three base deletions (or insertions) are often compatible with function
c. the codon is more than one nucleotide	3. artificial messages containing certain codons produced shorter proteins than messages not containing those codons
d. the genetic code is based on triplets of bases	4. protein synthesis occurs in the cytoplasm, while DNA resides in the nucleus
e. stop codons exist and terminate translation	5. artificial messages with different base sequences gave rise to different proteins in an *in vitro* translation system
f. the amino acid sequence of a protein depends on the base sequence of an mRNA	6. single base substitutions affect only one amino acid in the protein chain

3. How would the artificial mRNA 5′. . GUGUGUGU . . 3′ be read according to each of the following models for the genetic code?
   a. two-base, not overlapping
   b. two-base, overlapping
   c. three-base, not overlapping
   d. three-base, overlapping
   e. four-base, not overlapping

4. An example of a portion of the T4 *rIIB* gene in which Crick and Brenner had recombined one + and one − mutation is shown here. (The RNA-like strand of the DNA is shown.)

   ```
   wild type   5′ AAA AGT CCA TCA CTT AAT GCC 3′
   mutant      5′ AAA GTC CAT CAC TTA ATG GCC 3′
   ```

   a. Where are the + and − mutations in the mutant DNA?
   b. What alterations in amino acids occurred in this double mutant, which produces wild-type plaques?
   c. How can you explain the fact that amino acids are different in the double mutant compared to the wild-type sequence, yet the phage is wild type?

5. In the *HbS* allele (sickle-cell allele) of the human β-globin gene, the sixth amino acid in the β-globin chain is changed from glutamic acid to valine. In *HbC*, the sixth amino acid in β globin is changed from glutamic acid to lysine. What would be the order of these two mutations within the map of the β-globin gene?

6. The following diagram describes the mRNA sequence of part of the *A* gene and the beginning of the *B* gene of phage φX174. In this phage, there are some genes that are read in overlapping reading frames. For example, the code for the *A* gene is used for part of the *B* gene, but the reading frame is displaced by one base. Shown here is the single mRNA with the codons for proteins A and B indicated.

```
aa    5   6   7   8   9   10  11  12  13  14  15  16
A     AlaLysGluTrpAsnAsnSerLeuLysThrLysLeu

mRNA  GCUAAAGAAUGGAACAACUCACUAAAAACCAAGCUG

B              MetGluGlnLeuThrLysAsnGlnAla
Aa             1   2   3   4   5   6   7   8   9
```

Given the following amino acid (aa) changes, indicate the base change that occurred in the mRNA and the consequences for the other protein sequence.

a. Asn at position 10 in protein A is changed to Tyr.

b. Leu at position 12 in protein A is changed to Pro.

c. Gln at position 8 in protein B is changed to Leu.

d. The occurrence of overlapping reading frames is very rare in nature. When it does occur, the extent of the overlap is not very long. Why do you think this is the case?

7. The amino acid sequence of part of a protein has been determined:

N . . . Gly Ala Pro Arg Lys . . . C

A mutation has been induced in the gene encoding this protein using the mutagen proflavin. The resulting mutant protein can be purified and its amino acid sequence determined. The amino acid sequence of the mutant protein is exactly the same as the amino acid sequence of the wild-type protein from the N terminus of the protein to the glycine in the preceding sequence. Starting with this glycine, the sequence of amino acids is changed to the following:

N . . . Gly His Gln Gly Lys . . . C

Using the amino acid sequences, one can determine the sequence of 14 nucleotides from the wild-type gene encoding this protein. What is this sequence?

8. When the artificial mRNA 5′ . . . UCUCUCUC . . . 3′ was added to an *in vitro* protein synthesis system, investigators found that proteins composed of alternating leucine and serine were made. What experiments were done to determine whether leucine was specified by CUC and serine by UCU, or vice versa?

9. Identify all the amino acid–specifying codons where a point mutation (a single base change) could generate a nonsense codon.

10. Translate all the sequences shown in Fig. 8.6 on p. 251, assuming that in each case the RNA-like strand of the gene is depicted.

11. A particular protein has the amino acid sequence

N . . . Ala-Pro-His-Trp-Arg-Lys-Gly-Val-Thr . . . C

within its primary structure. A geneticist studying mutations affecting this protein discovered that several of the mutants produced shortened protein molecules that terminated within this region. In one of them, the His became the terminal amino acid.

a. What DNA single-base change(s) would cause the protein to terminate at the His residue?

b. What other potential sites do you see in the DNA sequence encoding this protein where mutation of a single base pair would cause premature termination of translation?

12. In studying normal and mutant forms of a particular human enzyme, a geneticist came across a particularly interesting mutant form of the enzyme. The normal enzyme is 227 amino acids long, but the mutant form was 312 amino acids long, having that extra 85 amino acids as a block in the middle of the normal sequence. The inserted amino acids do not correspond in any way to the normal protein sequence. What are possible explanations for this phenomenon? How would you distinguish among them?

13. How many possible open reading frames (frames without stop codons) are there that extend through the following sequence?

```
5′... CTTACAGTTTATTGATACGGAGAAGG...3′
3′... GAATGTCAAATAACTATGCCTCTTCC...5′
```

14. a. In Fig. 8.4 on p. 249, the physical map (the number of base pairs) is not exactly equivalent to the genetic map (in map units). Explain this apparent discrepancy.

b. In Fig. 8.4, which region shows the highest rate of recombination, and which the lowest?

15. The sequence of a segment of mRNA, beginning with the initiation codon, is given here, along with the corresponding sequences from several mutant strains.

```
Normal     AUGACACAUCGAGGGGUGGUAAACCCUAAG...
Mutant 1   AUGACACAUCCAGGGGUGGUAAACCCUAAG...
Mutant 2   AUGACACAUCGAGGGUGGUAAACCCUAAG...
Mutant 3   AUGACGCAUCGAGGGGUGGUAAACCCUAAG...
Mutant 4   AUGACACAUCGAGGGGUUGGUAAACCCUAAG...
Mutant 5   AUGACACAUUGAGGGGUGGUAAACCCUAAG...
Mutant 6   AUGACAUUUACCACCCCUCGAUGCCCUAAG...
```

a. Indicate the type of mutation present in each and translate the mutated portion of the sequence into an amino acid sequence in each case.

b. Which of the mutations could be reverted by treatment with EMS (ethylmethane sulfonate; see Fig. 7.10 on pp. 210–211)? With proflavin?

6. You identify a proflavin-generated allele of a gene that produces a 110-amino acid polypeptide rather than the usual 157-amino acid protein. After subjecting this mutant allele to extensive proflavin mutagenesis, you are able to find a number of intragenic suppressors located in the part of the gene between the sequences encoding the N terminus of the protein and the original mutation but no suppressors located in the region between the original mutation and the sequences encoding the usual C terminus of the protein. Why do you think this is the case?

Section 8.2

7. Describe the steps in transcription that require complementary base pairing.

8. Chapters 6 and 7 explained that mistakes made by DNA polymerase are corrected either by proofreading mechanisms during DNA replication or by DNA repair systems that operate after replication is complete. The overall rate of errors in DNA replication is about 1×10^{-10}, that is, one error in 10 million base pairs. RNA polymerase also has some proofreading capability, but the overall error rate for transcription is significantly higher (1×10^{-4}, or one error in each 10,000 nucleotides). Why can organisms tolerate higher error rates for transcription than for DNA replication?

9. The coding sequence for gene F is read from left to right on the following figure. The coding sequence for gene G is read from right to left. Which strand of DNA (top or bottom) serves as the template for transcription of each gene?

10. If you mixed the mRNA of a human gene with the genomic DNA for the same gene and allowed the RNA and DNA to form a hybrid, what would you be likely to see in the electron microscope? Your figure should include hybridization involving both DNA strands (template and RNA-like) as well as the mRNA.

Section 8.3

11. Describe the steps in translation that require complementary base pairing.

12. Locate as accurately as possible the listed items that are shown on the following figure. Some items are not shown. (a) 5′ end of DNA template strand; (b) 3′ end of mRNA; (c) ribosome; (d) promoter; (e) codon; (f) an amino acid; (g) DNA polymerase; (h) 5′ UTR; (i) centromere; (j) intron; (k) anticodon; (l) N terminus; (m) 5′ end of charged tRNA; (n) RNA polymerase; (o) 3′ end of uncharged tRNA; (p) a nucleotide; (q) mRNA cap; (r) peptide bond; (s) P site; (t) aminoacyl-tRNA synthetase; (u) hydrogen bond; (v) exon; (w) 5′ AUG 3′; (x) potential "wobble" interaction.

23. Concerning the figure for the previous problem (#22):
  a. Which process is being represented?
  b. What is the next building block to be added to the growing chain in the figure? To what end of the growing chain will this building block be added? How many building blocks will there be in the chain when it is completed?
  c. What other building blocks have a known identity?
  d. What details could you add to this figure that would be different in a eukaryotic cell versus a prokaryotic cell?

Section 8.4

24. In prokaryotes, a search for genes in a DNA sequence involves scanning the DNA sequence for long open reading frames (that is, reading frames uninterrupted by stop codons). What problem can you see with this approach in eukaryotes?

25. The yeast gene encoding a protein found in the mitotic spindle was cloned by a laboratory studying mitosis. The gene encodes a protein of 477 amino acids.
  a. What is the minimum length in nucleotides of the protein-coding part of this yeast gene?
  b. A partial sequence of one DNA strand in an exon containing the middle of the coding region of the yeast gene is given here. What is the sequence of nucleotides of the mRNA in this region of the gene? Show the 5′ and 3′ directionality of your strand.

    5′ GTAAGTTAACTTTCGACTAGTCCAGGGT 3′

  c. What is the sequence of amino acids in this part of the yeast mitotic spindle protein?

26. The sequence of a complete eukaryotic gene encoding the small protein Met Tyr Arg Gly Ala is shown here. All of the written sequences on the template strand are transcribed into RNA.

5′ CCCCTATGCCCCCCTGGGGGAGGATCAAAACACTTACCTGTACATGGC 3′
3′ GGGGATACGGGGGGGACCCCCTCCTAGTTTTGTGAATGGACATGTACCG 5′

  a. Which strand is the template strand? Which direction (right to left or left to right) does RNA polymerase move along the template as it transcribes this gene?
  b. What is the sequence of the nucleotides in the processed mRNA molecule for this gene? Indicate the 5′ and 3′ polarity of this mRNA.
  c. A single base mutation in the gene results in synthesis of the peptide Met Tyr Thr. What is the sequence of nucleotides making up the mRNA produced by this mutant gene?

27. Using recombinant DNA techniques (which will be described in Chapter 9), it is possible to take the DNA of a gene from any source and place it on a chromosome in the nucleus of a yeast cell. When you take the DNA for a human gene and put it into a yeast cell chromosome, the altered yeast cell can make the human protein. But when you remove the DNA for a gene normally present on yeast mitochondrial chromosomes and put it on a yeast chromosome in the nucleus, the yeast cell cannot synthesize the correct protein, even though the gene comes from the same organism. Explain. What would you need to do to ensure that such a yeast cell could make the correct protein?

28. a. The genetic code table shown in Fig. 8.3 on p. 248 applies both to humans and to *E. coli*. Suppose that you have purified a piece of DNA from the human genome containing the entire gene encoding the hormone insulin. You now transform this piece of DNA into *E. coli*. Why can't *E. coli* cells containing the human insulin gene actually make insulin?

   b. Pharmaceutical companies have actually been able to obtain *E. coli* cells that make human insulin; such insulin can be purified from the bacterial cells and used to treat diabetic patients. How were the pharmaceutical companies able to create such "bacterial factories" for making insulin?

Section 8.5

29. Arrange the following list of eukaryotic gene elements in the order they would appear in the genome and in the direction traveled by RNA polymerase along the gene. Assume the gene's single intron interrupts the open reading frame. Note that some of these names are abbreviated and thus do not distinguish between elements in DNA versus RNA. For example, "splice-donor site" is an abbreviation for "DNA sequences transcribed into the splice-donor site" because splicing takes place on the gene's RNA transcript, not on the gene itself. Geneticists often use this kind of shorthand for simplicity, even though it is imprecise. (a) splice-donor site; (b) 3′ UTR; (c) promoter; (d) stop codon; (e) nucleotide to which methylated cap is added; (f) initiation codon; (g) transcription terminator; (h) splice-acceptor site; (i) 5′ UTR; (j) poly-A addition site; (k) splice branch site.

30. Concerning the list of eukaryotic gene elements in the previous problem (#29):

   a. Which of the element names in the list are abbreviated? (That is, which of these elements actually occur in the gene's primary transcript or mRNA rather than in the gene itself?)

   b. Which of the elements in the list are found partly or completely in the first exon of this gene (or the RNA transcribed from this exon)? In the intron? In the second exon?

Section 8.6

31. Do you think each of the following types of mutation would have very severe effects, mild effects, or no effect at all?

   a. Nonsense mutations occurring in the sequences encoding amino acids near the N terminus of the protein

   b. Nonsense mutations occurring in the sequences encoding amino acids near the C terminus of the protein

   c. Frameshift mutations occurring in the sequences encoding amino acids near the N terminus of the protein

   d. Frameshift mutations occurring in the sequences encoding amino acids near the C terminus of the protein

   e. Silent mutations

   f. Conservative missense mutations

   g. Nonconservative missense mutations affecting the active site of the protein

   h. Nonconservative missense mutations not in the active site of the protein

32. Null mutations are valuable genetic resources because they allow a researcher to determine what happens to an organism in the complete absence of a particular protein. However, it is often not a trivial matter to determine whether a mutation represents the null state of the gene.

   a. Geneticists sometimes use the following test for the "nullness" of an allele in a diploid organism. If the abnormal phenotype seen in a homozygote for the allele is identical to that seen in a heterozygote where one chromosome carries the allele in question and the homologous chromosome is known to be completely deleted for the gene, then the allele is null. What is the underlying rationale for this test? What limitations might there be in interpreting such a result?

   b. Can you think of other methods to determine whether an allele represents the null state of a particular gene?

33. The following is a list of mutations that have been discovered in a gene that has more than 60 exons and encodes a very large protein of 2532 amino acids. Indicate whether or not each mutation could cause a detectable change in the size or the amount of mRNA and/or a detectable change in the size or the amount of the protein product. (Detectable changes in size or amount must be greater than 1% of normal values.) What kind of change would you predict?

   a. Lys576Val (changes amino acid 576 from lysine into valine)

   b. Lys576Arg

   c. AAG576AAA (changes codon 576 from AAG to AAA)

   d. AAG576UAG

e. Met1Arg (there are at least two possible scenarios for this mutation)
f. promoter mutation
g. one base-pair insertion into codon 1841
h. deletion of codon 779
i. IVS18DS, G–A, + 1 (this mutation changes the first nucleotide in the eighteenth intron of the gene, causing exon 18 to be spliced to exon 20, thus skipping exon 19)
j. deletion of the poly-A addition site
k. G-to-A substitution in the 5′ UTR
l. insertion of 1000 base pairs into the sixth intron (this particular insertion does not alter splicing)

4. Considering further the mutations described in the previous problem (#33):
a. Which of the mutations could be null mutations?
b. Which of the mutations would be most likely to result in an allele that is recessive to wild type?
c. Which of the mutations could result in an allele dominant to wild type? What mechanism(s) could explain this dominance?

5. When 1 million cells of a culture of haploid yeast carrying a *met*⁻ auxotrophic mutation were plated on petri plates lacking methionine (met), five colonies grew. You would expect cells in which the original *met*⁻ mutation was reversed (by a base change back to the original sequence) would grow on the media lacking methionine, but some of these apparent reversions could be due to a mutation in a different gene that somehow suppresses the original *met*⁻ mutations. How would you be able to determine if the mutations in your five colonies were due either to a precise reversion of the original *met*⁻ mutation or to the generation of a suppressor mutation in a gene on another chromosome?

6. a. What are the differences between null, hypomorphic, hypermorphic, dominant negative, and neomorphic mutations?
b. For each of these kinds of mutations, would you predict they would be dominant or recessive to a wild-type allele in producing a mutant phenotype?

7. A mutant *B. adonis* bacterium has a nonsense suppressor tRNA that inserts glutamine (Gln) to match a UAG (but not other nonsense) codons.
a. What is the anticodon of the suppressing tRNA? Indicate the 5′ and 3′ ends.
b. What is the sequence of the template strand of the wild-type tRNA^Gln-encoding gene that was altered to produce the suppressor, assuming that only a single-base-pair alteration was involved?
c. What is the *minimum* number of tRNA^Gln genes that could be present in a wild-type *B. adonis* cell? Describe the corresponding anticodons.

38. You are studying mutations in a bacterial gene that codes for an enzyme whose amino acid sequence is known. In the wild-type protein, proline is the fifth amino acid from the amino terminal end. In one of your mutants with nonfunctional enzyme, you find a serine at position number 5. You subject this mutant to further mutagenesis and recover three different strains. Strain A has a proline at position number 5 and acts just like wild type. Strain B has tryptophan at position number 5 and also acts like wild type. Strain C has no detectable enzyme function at any temperature, and you can't recover any protein that resembles the enzyme. You mutagenize strain C and recover a strain (C-1) that has enzyme function. The second mutation in C-1 responsible for the recovery of enzyme function does not map at the enzyme locus.
a. What is the nucleotide sequence in both strands of the wild-type gene at this location?
b. Why does strain B have a wild-type phenotype? Why does the original mutant with serine at position 5 lack function?
c. What is the nature of the mutation in strain C?
d. What is the second mutation that arose in C-1?

39. Another class of suppressor mutations, not described in the chapter, are mutations that suppress missense mutations.
a. Why would bacterial strains carrying such missense suppressor mutations generally grow more slowly than strains carrying nonsense suppressor mutations?
b. What other kinds of mutations can you imagine in genes encoding components needed for gene expression that would suppress a missense mutation in a protein-coding gene?

40. Yet another class of suppressor mutations not described in the chapter are mutations in tRNA genes that can suppress frameshift mutations. What would have to be true about a tRNA that could suppress a frameshift mutation involving the insertion of a single base pair?

41. There is at least one nonsense suppressing tRNA known that can suppress more than one type of nonsense codon.
a. What is the anticodon of such a suppressing tRNA?
b. What stop codons would it suppress?
c. What are the amino acids most likely to be carried by this nonsense suppressing tRNA?

42. An investigator was interested in studying UAG nonsense suppressor mutations in bacteria. In one species of bacteria, she was able to select two different mutants of this type, one in a *tRNA^Tyr* gene and the other in a *tRNA^Gln* gene, but in a second species, she was not able to obtain any such nonsense suppressor mutations, even after very extensive effort. What could explain the difference between the two species?

Digital Analysis of DNA

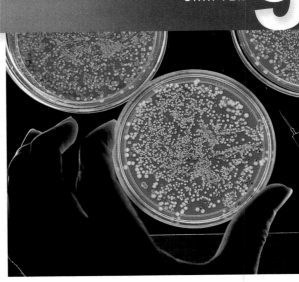

Colonies of bacterial cell clones containing recombinant DNA molecules.

The vivid red color of our blood arises from its life-sustaining ability to carry oxygen. This ability, in turn, derives from billions of red blood cells suspended in proteinaceous solution, each one packed with close to 280 million molecules of the protein pigment known as hemoglobin (**Fig. 9.1a**). A normal adult hemoglobin molecule consists of four polypeptide chains, two alpha (α) and two beta (β) globins, each surrounding an iron-containing small molecular structure known as a heme group (**Fig. 9.1b**). The iron atom within the heme sustains a reversible interaction with oxygen, binding it firmly enough to hold it on the trip from lungs to body tissue but loosely enough to release it where needed. The intricately folded α and β chains protect the iron-containing hemes from substances in the cell's interior. Each hemoglobin molecule can carry up to four oxygen atoms, one per heme, and these oxygenated hemes impart a scarlet hue to the pigment molecules and thus to the blood cells that carry them.

CHAPTER OUTLINE

- 9.1 Sequence-Specific DNA Fragmentation
- 9.2 Cloning Fragments of DNA
- 9.3 Hybridization
- 9.4 The Polymerase Chain Reaction
- 9.5 DNA Sequence Analysis
- 9.6 Bioinformatics: Information Technology and Genomes
- 9.7 The Hemoglobin Genes: A Comprehensive Example

The genetically determined molecular composition of hemoglobin changes several times during human development, enabling the molecule to adapt its oxygen-transport function to the varying environments of the embryo, fetus, newborn, and adult (**Fig. 9.1c**). In the first five weeks after conception, the red blood cells carry *embryonic hemoglobin,* which consists of two α-like zeta (ζ) chains and two β-like epsilon (ϵ) chains. Thereafter, throughout the rest of gestation, the cells contain *fetal hemoglobin,* composed of two bona fide α chains and two β-like gamma (γ) chains. Then, shortly before birth, production of *adult hemoglobin,* composed of two α and two β chains, begins to climb. By the time an infant reaches three months of age, almost all of his or her hemoglobin is of the adult type.

Evolution of the various forms of hemoglobin maximized the delivery of oxygen to an individual's cells at different stages of development. The early embryo, which is not yet associated with a fully functional placenta, has the least access to oxygen in the maternal circulation. Both embryonic and fetal hemoglobin evolved to bind oxygen more tightly than adult hemoglobin does; they thus facilitate the transfer of maternal oxygen to the embryo or fetus. All the hemoglobins readily release their oxygen to cells, which have an even lower level of oxygen than any source of the gas. After birth, when oxygen is abundantly available in the lungs, adult hemoglobin, with its more relaxed kinetics of oxygen binding, allows for the most efficient pickup and delivery of the vital gas.

Hemoglobin disorders are the most common genetic diseases in the world and include sickle-cell anemia, which arises from an altered β chain, and thalassemia, which results from decreases in the amount of either α- or β-chain production.

Figure 9.1 Hemoglobin is composed of four polypeptide chains that change during development. (a) Scanning electron micrograph of adult human red blood cells loaded with hemoglobin. **(b)** Adult hemoglobin consists of two α and two β polypeptide chains, each associated with an oxygen-carrying heme group. **(c)** The hemoglobin carried by red blood cells switches during human development from an embryonic form containing two α-like ξ chains and two β-like ε chains, to a fetal form containing two α chains and two β-like γ chains, and finally to the adult form containing two α and two β chains. In a small percentage of adult hemoglobin molecules, a β-like δ chain replaces the actual β chain. The α-like chains are represented in *magenta,* and β-like chains are represented in *green.*

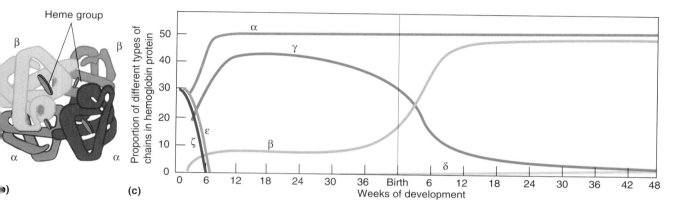

The hemoglobin genes lie buried in a diploid human genome containing 6 billion base pairs distributed among 46 different strings of DNA (the chromosomes) that range in size from 60 million to 360 million base pairs each. In this chapter, we describe the powerful tools of modern molecular analysis that medical researchers now use to search through these enormously long strings of information for genes such as the hemoglobin genes, which may be only several thousand base pairs in length. Initially, these tools took advantage of isolated enzymes and biochemical reactions that occur naturally within the simplest life-forms, bacterial cells. But over the last two decades, biologists have collaborated with chemists, engineers, and computer scientists to expand the toolkit to include automated chemical procedures not found in nature. Researchers now refer to the whole kit of modern tools and reactions as **biotechnology.**

Biotechnology emerged from a technological revolution that began in the mid-1970s, when researchers gained the ability to read the digital information contained within any isolated sequence of DNA base pairs. For the first time, the genotypes of organisms could be determined even when they did not express a distinguishable phenotype. Geneticists can use the tools of biotechnology to gather information unobtainable in any other way or to analyze the results of breeding and cytological studies with greater speed and accuracy than ever before.

9.1 Sequence-specific DNA Fragmentation

Every intact diploid human body cell, including the precursors of red blood cells, carries two nearly identical sets of 3 billion base pairs of information that, when unwound, extend 2 meters in length. If you could enlarge the cell nucleus to the size of a basketball, the unwound DNA would have the diameter of a fishing line and a length of 200 kilometers. This is much too much material and information to study as a whole. To reduce its complexity, researchers first cut the genome into "bite-size" pieces.

Restriction enzymes fragment the genome at specific sites

Researchers use restriction enzymes to cut the DNA released from the nuclei of cells at specific sites. These well-defined cuts generate fragments suitable for manipulation and characterization. A **restriction enzyme** recognizes a specific sequence of bases anywhere within the genome and then severs two covalent bonds (one in each strand) in the sugar-phosphate backbone at particular positions within or near that sequence. The fragments generated by restriction enzymes are referred to as **restriction fragments,** and the act of cutting is often called **digestion.**

Restriction enzymes originate in and can be purified from bacterial cells. The enzymes protect these prokaryotic cells from viral infection by digesting viral DNA. Bacteria shield their DNA from digestion by their own restriction enzymes through the selective addition of methyl groups (—CH₃) to the restriction recognition sites in their DNA. In the test tube, restriction enzymes from bacteria recognize target sequences of 4–8 bp in DNA isolated from any other organism and cut the DNA at or near these sites. **Table 9.1** lists the names, recognition

sequences, and microbial origins of just 10 of the more than 100 commonly used restriction enzymes.

For the majority of these enzymes, the recognition site contains 4–6 base pairs and exhibits a kind of palindromic symmetry in which the base sequences of each of the two DNA strands are identical when read in the 5′-to 3′ direction. Because of this, base pairs on either side of a central line of symmetry are mirror images of each other. Each enzyme always cuts at the same place relative to its specific recognition sequence, and most enzymes make their cuts in one of two ways: either straight through both DNA strands right at the line of symmetry to produce fragments with **blunt ends,** or displaced equally in opposite directions from the line of symmetry by one or more bases to generate fragments with single-stranded ends (**Fig. 9.2**). Geneticists often refer to these protruding single strands as **sticky ends.** They are considered "sticky" because they are free to base pair with a complementary sequence from the DNA of *any* organism cut by the same restriction enzyme. (The Tools of Genetics box on p. 29 of this chapter and the Tools of Genetics box on pp. 177–17 of Chapter 6 contain more information on restriction enzymes.)

> Restriction enzymes recognize specific short sequences of bases and cut each strand of DNA at specific locations in or near the target sequence. The result of digesting a particular genome with a particular restriction enzyme is a collection of restriction fragments of defined length and composition.

Enzyme	Sequence of Recognition Site	Microbial Origin
TABLE 9.1	**Ten Commonly Used Restriction Enzymes**	
TaqI	5′ T C G A 3′ / 3′ A G C T 5′	*Thermus aquaticus* YTI
RsaI	5′ G T A C 3′ / 3′ C A T G 5′	*Rhodopseudomonas sphaeroides*
Sau3AI	5′ G A T C 3′ / 3′ C T A G 5′	*Staphylococcus aureus* 3A
EcoRI	5′ G A A T T C 3′ / 3′ C T T A A G 5′	*Escherichia coli*
BamHI	5′ G G A T C C 3′ / 3′ C C T A G G 5′	*Bacillus amyloliquefaciens* H.
HindIII	5′ A A G C T T 3′ / 3′ T T C G A A 5′	*Haemophilus influenzae*
KpnI	5′ G G T A C C 3′ / 3′ C C A T G G 5′	*Klebsiella pneumoniae* OK8
ClaI	5′ A T C G A T 3′ / 3′ T A G C T A 5′	*Caryophanon latum*
BssHII	5′ G C G C G C 3′ / 3′ C G C G C G 5′	*Bacillus stearothermophilus*
NotI	5′ G C G G C C G C 3′ / 3′ C G C C G G C G 5′	*Nocardia otitidiscaviarum*

Figure 9.2 Restriction enzymes cut DNA molecules at specific locations to produce restriction fragments with either blunt or sticky ends. (a) The restriction enzyme *Rsa*I produces blunt-ended restriction fragments. **(b)** *Eco*RI produces sticky ends with a 5′ overhang. **(c)** *Kpn*I produces sticky ends with a 3′ overhang.

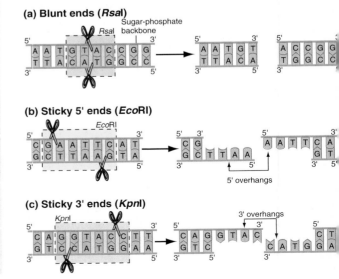

(a) Blunt ends (*Rsa*I)

(b) Sticky 5′ ends (*Eco*RI)

5′ overhangs

(c) Sticky 3′ ends (*Kpn*I)

3′ overhangs

TOOLS OF GENETICS

Serendipity in Science: The Discovery of Restriction Enzymes

Most of the tools and techniques for cloning and analyzing DNA fragments emerged from studies of bacteria and the viruses that infect them. Molecular biologists had observed, for example, that viruses able to grow abundantly on one strain of bacteria grew poorly on a closely related strain of the same bacteria. While examining the mechanisms of this discrepancy, they discovered restriction enzymes.

To follow the story, one must know that researchers compare rates of viral proliferation in terms of *plating efficiency:* the fraction of viral particles that enter and replicate inside host bacterial cells, causing the cells to lyse and release viral progeny. These progeny go on to infect and replicate inside neighboring cells, which in turn lyse and release further virus particles. When a petri dish is coated with a continuous "lawn" of bacterial cells, an active viral infection can be observed as a visibly cleared spot, or plaque, where bacteria have been eliminated (see Fig. 7.20 on pp. 220–221). The plating efficiency of lambda virus grown on *E. coli* C is nearly 1.0. This means that 100 original virus particles will cause close to 100 plaques on a lawn of *E. coli* C bacteria.

The plating efficiency of the same virus grown on *E. coli* K12 is only 1 in 10^4, or 0.0001. The ability of a bacterial strain to prevent the replication of an infecting virus, in this case the growth of lambda on *E. coli* K12, is called **restriction.**

Restriction is rarely absolute. Although lambda virus grown on *E. coli* K12 produces almost no progeny (the viruses infect cells but can't replicate inside them), a few viral particles inside a few cells do manage to proliferate. If their progeny are then tested on *E. coli* K12, the plating efficiency is nearly 1.0. The phenomenon in which growth on a restricting host modifies a virus so that succeeding generations grow more efficiently on that same host is known as **modification.**

What mechanisms account for restriction and modification? Studies following viral DNA after bacterial infection found that during restriction, the viral DNA is broken into pieces and degraded (**Fig. A**). When the enzyme responsible for the initial breakage was isolated, it was found to be an endonuclease, an enzyme that breaks the phosphodiester bonds in the viral DNA molecule, usually making double-strand cuts at a specific sequence in the viral chromosome. Because this breakage restricts the biological activity of the viral DNA, researchers called the enzymes that accomplish it *restriction enzymes.* Subsequent studies showed that the small percentage of viral DNA that escapes digestion and goes on to generate new viral particles has been modified by the addition of methyl groups during its replication in the host cell. Researchers named the enzymes that add methyl groups to specific DNA sequences **modification enzymes.**

Biologists have identified a large number of complementary restriction-modification systems in a variety of bacterial strains. Purification of the systems has yielded a mainstay of recombinant DNA technology: the battery of restriction enzymes used to cut DNA *in vitro* for cloning, mapping, and ligation (see Table 9.1 on p. 292).

This example of serendipity in science sheds some light on the debate between administrators who distribute and oversee

Figure A Operation of the restriction enzyme/modification system in nature. (1) *E. coli* strain C does not have a functional restriction enzyme/modification system and is susceptible to infection by the lambda phage. (2) In contrast, *E. coli* strain K12 generally resists infection by the viral particles produced from a phage infection of *E. coli* C. This is because *E. coli* K12 makes several restriction enzymes, including *Eco*RI, which cut the lambda DNA molecule before its genes can be expressed. (3) However, in rare K12 cells, the lambda DNA is modified by an enzyme that protects its recognition sites from the host cell's restriction enzymes. This modified lambda DNA can now replicate and generate phage particles, which eventually destroy the bacterial cell.

research funding and scientists who carry out the research. Microbial investigators did not set out to find restriction enzymes; they could not have known these enzymes would be one of their finds. Rather, they sought to understand the mechanisms by which viruses infect and proliferate in bacteria. Along the way, they discovered restriction enzymes and how they work. The politicians and administrators in charge of allocating funds often want to direct research spending to urgent health or agricultural problems while the scientists in charge of laboratory research call for a broad distribution of funds to all projects investigating interesting biological phenomena. The validity of both views suggests the need for a balanced approach to the funding of research activities.

Different restriction enzymes produce fragments of different length

The average length of the fragments that a particular restriction enzyme generates can be calculated and the information used to estimate the approximate number and distribution of recognition sites in a genome. The estimate depends on two simplifying assumptions: first, that each of the four bases occurs in equal proportions such that a genome is composed of 25% A, 25% T, 25% G, and 25% C; second, that the bases are randomly distributed in the DNA sequence. Although these assumptions are never precisely valid, they enable us to determine the average distance between recognition sites of any length by the general formula 4^n, where n is the number of bases in the site (**Fig. 9.3**).

Size of restriction enzyme recognition site and fragment length

According to the 4^n formula, *Rsa*I, which recognizes the four-base-sequence GTAC, will cut on average once every 4^4, or every 256 base pairs (bp), creating fragments averaging 256 bp in length. By comparison, the enzyme *Eco*RI, which recognizes the six-base-sequence GAATTC, will cut on average once every 4^6, or 4096 bp; because 1000 base pairs = 1 kilobase pair, researchers often round off this large number to roughly 4.1 kilobase pairs, abbreviated 4.1 kb. Similarly, an enzyme such as *Not*I, which recognizes the eight bases GCGGCCGC,

Figure 9.3 The number of base pairs in a recognition site determines the average distance between sites in a genome and thus the size of fragments produced. *Rsa*I recognizes and cuts at a 4 bp site, *Eco*RI cuts at a 6 bp site, and *Not*I cuts at an 8 bp site. **(b)** *Rsa*I, *Eco*RI, and *Not*I restriction sites in a 200 kb region of human chromosome 11, followed by the names and locations of genes in this region.

will cut on average every 4^8 bp, or every 65.5 kb. Note however, that because the actual distances between re striction sites for any enzyme vary considerably, very few of the fragments produced by the three enzymes men tioned here will be precisely 65.5 kb, 4.1 kb, or 256 bp in length.

Geneticists often need to produce DNA fragments o a particular length—larger ones to study the organizatio of a chromosomal region, smaller ones to examine a whol gene, and ones that are smaller still for DNA sequenc analysis (that is, for the determination of the precise orde of bases in a DNA fragment). If their goal is 4 kb frag ments, they have a range of six-base-cutter enzymes t choose from. Exposing the DNA to a six-base cutter fo a long enough time gives the restriction enzyme ampl opportunity for digestion. The result is a **complete diges** in which the DNA has been cut at every one of the rec ognition sites it contains.

Geneticists use enzyme-specific recognition-site size and time of exposure to the enzyme to create complete or partial digests of DNA genomes, depending on what is needed fo a particular experiment.

Different restriction enzymes produce different numbers of fragments

We have seen that the four-base cutter *Rsa*I cuts th genome on average every 4^4 (256) bp. If you expose the haploid human genome with its 3 billion bp to *Rsa* for a sufficient time under appropriate conditions, yo would ensure that all of the recognition sites in th genome that can be cleaved will be cleaved, and yo would get

$$\frac{3,000,000,000\,bp}{\sim 256\,bp} = \begin{array}{l}\sim 12,000,000 \text{ fragments that are}\\ \sim 256 \text{ bp in average length}\end{array}$$

By comparison, the six-base cutter *Eco*RI cuts th DNA on average every 4^6 (4096) bp, or every 4.1 kb. you exposed the haploid human genome with its 3 billi bp, or 3 million kb, to *Eco*RI in the proper way, y would get

$$\frac{3,000,000,000\,bp}{\sim 4100\,bp} = \begin{array}{l}\sim 700,000 \text{ fragments that are}\\ \sim 4.1 \text{ kb in average length}\end{array}$$

And if you exposed the same haploid human genor to the eight-base cutter *Not*I, which cuts on average eve 4^8 (65,536) bp, or 65.5 kb, you would obtain

$$\frac{3,000,000,000\,bp}{\sim 65,500\,bp} = \begin{array}{l}\sim 46,000 \text{ fragments that are}\\ \sim 65.5 \text{ kb in average length}\end{array}$$

(a) Calculating Average Restriction Fragment Size

1. Probability that a four-base recognition site will be found in a genome =

    1/4 × 1/4 × 1/4 × 1/4 = 1/256

2. Probability that a six-base recognition site will be found =

    1/4 × 1/4 × 1/4 × 1/4 × 1/4 × 1/4 = 1/4096

(b)

Clearly, the larger the recognition site, the smaller the number of fragments generated by enzymatic digestion.

Restriction enzymes were first used to study the very small genomes of viruses such as bacteriophage lambda (λ), whose genome has a length of approximately 48.5 kb, and the animal tumor virus SV40, whose genome has a length of 5.2 kb. We now know that the six-base cutter *Eco*RI digests lambda DNA into 5 fragments, and the four-base cutter *Rsa*I digests SV40 into 12 fragments. But when molecular biologists first used restriction enzymes to digest these viral genomes, they also needed a tool that could distinguish the different fragments in a genome from each other and determine their sizes. That tool is gel electrophoresis.

> By using different restriction enzymes, scientists can generate different numbers of unique fragments from a single genome. The larger the recognition site, the smaller the number of fragments.

Gel electrophoresis distinguishes DNA fragments according to size

Electrophoresis is the movement of charged molecules in an electric field. Biologists use it to separate many different types of molecules, for example, DNA of one length from DNA of other lengths, DNA from protein, or one kind of protein from another. In this discussion, we focus on its application to the separation of DNA fragments of varying length in a gel (**Fig. 9.4**). To carry out such a separation, you place a solution of DNA molecules into indentations called wells at one end of a porous gel-like matrix. When you then place the gel in a buffered aqueous solution and set up an electric field between bare wires at either end connected to a power supply, the electric field causes all charged molecules in the wells to migrate in the direction of the electrode having an opposite charge. Because all of the phosphate groups in the backbone of DNA carry a net negative charge in a solution near neutral pH, DNA molecules are pulled through a gel toward the wire with a positive charge.

Several variables determine the rate at which DNA molecules (or any other molecules) move during electrophoresis. These variables are the strength of the electric field applied across the gel, the composition of the gel, the charge per unit volume of molecule (known as *charge density*), and the physical size of the molecule. The only one of these variables that actually differs among any set of linear DNA fragments migrating in a particular gel is size. The reason is that all molecules placed in a well are subjected to the same electric field and the same gel matrix, and all DNA molecules have the same charge density (because the charge of all nucleotide pairs is nearly

identical). As a result, only differences in size cause different linear DNA molecules to migrate at different speeds during electrophoresis.

With linear DNA molecules, differences in size are proportional to differences in length: the longer the molecule, the larger the volume it occupies as a random coil. The larger the volume a molecule occupies, the less likely it is to find a pore in the gel matrix big enough to squeeze through and the more often it will bump into the matrix. And the more often the molecule bumps into the matrix, the lower its rate of migration (also referred to as its mobility). With this background, you can follow the steps of **Fig. 9.4a** to determine the length of the restriction fragments in the DNA under analysis.

When electrophoresis is completed, the gel is incubated with a fluorescent DNA-binding dye called ethidium bromide. After the unbound dye has been washed away, it is easy to visualize the DNA by placing the gel under an ultraviolet light. The actual size of restriction fragments observed on gels is determined by comparison to migration distances of known *marker fragments* that are subjected to electrophoresis in an adjacent lane of the gel.

DNA molecules range in size from small fragments of less than 10 bp to whole human chromosomes that have an average length of 130,000,000 bp. No one sizing procedure has the capacity to separate molecules throughout this enormous range. To detect DNA molecules in different size ranges, researchers use a variety of protocols based mainly on two kinds of gels: polyacrylamide (formed by covalent bonding between acrylamide monomers), which is good for distinguishing smaller DNA fragments, and agarose (formed by the noncovalent association of agarose polymers), which is suitable for looking at larger fragments. **Figure 9.4b** illustrates these differences.

> Gel electrophoresis is used to separate and measure the different lengths of DNA molecules present in a complex solution.

Restriction maps provide sequence-specific landmarks in the DNA terrain

Researchers can use restriction enzymes not only as molecular scissors to create unique DNA fragments but also as an analytic tool to create maps of viral genomes and other purified DNA fragments. These maps, called *restriction maps,* show the relative order and distances between multiple restriction sites, which thus act as landmarks along a DNA molecule.

The derivation of a restriction map can be approached in several ways. One of the most commonly used methods

FEATURE FIGURE 9.4

Gel Electrophoresis

(a)

1. Attach a comb to a clear acrylic plate with clamps.

2. Pour heated molten agarose into plate. Allow to cool and harden.

3. Remove comb from gel; shallow wells are left in gel. Remove gel from plate.

4. A micropipette is used to load DNA samples into each well. Each sample contains a blue dye to make it easier to see.

5. Electrode wires are placed along each end of the gel and are attached to a power supply. The current is switched on, and DNA molecules in each sample migrate toward the "+" end of the box (along the paths depicted with orange arrows). Electrophoresis continues for 1–20 hours.

6. Remove gel from gel box. Incubate with ethidium bromide, then wash to remove excess dye.

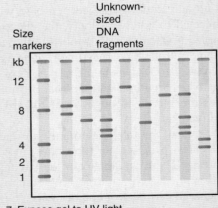

7. Expose gel to UV light.
DNA molecules will appear as red bands. A photo of the bands will provide a black-and-white image. The sizes of the bands in the unknown samples can be calibrated by comparison to size markers that have been run in the leftmost lane of the gel.

(a) **Preparing the gel.** To prepare an agarose gel containing wells for samples, you follow the steps illustrated in (a)1.–3. You then place the prepared gel on a base inside a gel tank that contains a buffered solution. With a micropipette, you load a different DNA sample into each well (step 4). A special "size marker" sample containing DNA fragments of known size is loaded into the first well. You now connect wires at either end of the box to a power supply, turn on the electric current, and allow the fragments to migrate for 1–20 hours. You then remove the gel from the electrophoresis chamber and place it into a box containing a solution of ethidium bromide, a fluorescent dye that will bind tightly to any DNA fragments in the gel. After incubating the gel for several hours, you immerse the gel in water to wash away any unbound dye molecules. Then, with exposure to ultraviolet light, the bound dye absorbs photons in the UV range and gives off photons in the visible red range. The DNA molecules appear as red bands, and a digital image shows the relative positions to which they have migrated in the gel.

To determine the length of a DNA fragment, you chart the mobility of the band composed of that fragment relative to the migration of the size marker bands in the first gel lane.

(b) Different types of gels separate different-sized DNA molecules. Gels can be composed of two different types of chemical matrices: polyacrylamide and agarose. Polyacrylamide, which has smaller pores, can separate DNA molecules in the range of 10–500 nucleotides in length; agarose separates only larger molecules. The polyacrylamide gel on the *left* was used to separate restriction fragments formed by the digestion of eight different DNA samples with an enzyme that recognizes a four-base sequence. The fragments *a–n* range in size from 90–340 bases in length. The agarose gel on the *right* was used to separate restriction fragments in a series of complex samples digested with *Eco*RI. The first lane contains size markers ranging in size from 2.2 kb to 8.3 kb. The other lanes contain digested whole genomic DNA from different mice. The mouse genome contains approximately 700,000 unique *Eco*RI restriction fragments, which appear as a smear when stained with ethidium bromide.

volves digestion with multiple restriction enzymes—alone
mixed together—followed by gel electrophoresis to
sualize the fragments produced. If the relative arrangement
sites for the various restriction enzymes employed does
t create too many fragments, the data obtained can pro-
le enough information to piece together a map showing
e position of each restriction site. **Figure 9.5** shows how
rocess of elimination allows you to infer the arrange-
nt of restriction sites consistent with the results of three
s of digestions using either of two enzymes alone or
th enzymes simultaneously.

Today, molecular biologists can use automated DNA
juencing and bioinformatics to rapidly obtain detailed
ormation on the size and sequence of any DNA mole-
le in the size range of SV40 or bacteriophage λ. We

describe sequencing and bioinformatics techniques later
in this chapter.

> Restriction maps are constructed through a process of logical
> deduction based on the sizes of restriction fragments obtained
> after digestion with two or more restriction enzymes both
> separately and together. Restriction fragment sizes are deter-
> mined by gel electrophoresis.

9.2 Cloning Fragments of DNA

While restriction enzyme digestion and gel electrophoresis
provide a means for analyzing simple DNA molecules, the
genomes of animals, plants, and even microorganisms are

Figure 9.5 How to infer a restriction map from the sizes of restriction fragments produced by two restriction enzymes. (a) Divide a purified preparation of cloned DNA into three aliquots; expose the first aliquot to *Eco*RI, the second to *Bam*HI, and the third to both enzymes. **(b)** Now separate by gel electrophoresis the restriction fragments that result from each digestion and determine their sizes in relation to defined markers. **(c)** Finally, use a process of elimination to derive the only arrangement that can account for the results obtained with all three samples.

far too large to be analyzed in this way. For example, the *E. coli* genome is approximately 4200 kb or 4.2 megabases (Mb) in length. An *Eco*RI digestion of this genome would produce approximately 1000 fragments. If you subjected these complex mixtures of DNA fragments to gel electrophoresis, all you would see at the end is a smear rather than discrete bands (review Fig. 9.4b). To study any one fragment within this complex mixture, it first must be purified away from all the other fragments and then amplified, that is, used to make many identical copies of the

originally purified molecule. Researchers can then apply chemical and physical techniques—including restriction mapping and DNA sequencing—to analyze the isolated DNA fragment.

Scientists now use two strategies to accomplish the purification and amplification of individual fragments: *molecular cloning,* which replicates individual fragments of previously uncharacterized DNA, and the *polymerase chain reaction* (or *PCR*), which can purify and amplify a previously sequenced genomic region (or a transcribed version of it) from any source much more rapidly than cloning. Here we present the protocol for the molecular cloning of DNA. Later in the chapter, we describe PCR.

Molecular cloning is the process that takes a complex mixture of restriction fragments and uses living cells to purify and make many exact replicas of just one fragment at a time. It consists of two basic steps. In the first, DNA fragments that fall within a specified range of size are inserted into specialized chromosome-like carriers called *vectors,* which ensure the transport, replication, and purification of individual inserts. In the second step, the combined vector-insert molecules are transported into living cells, and the cells make many copies of these molecules. Because all the copies are identical, the group of replicated DNA molecules is known as a **DNA clone.** DNA clones may be purified for immediate study or stored within cells or viruses as collections of clones known as *libraries* for future analysis. We now describe each step of molecular cloning.

Cloning step 1: Splicing inserts to vectors produces recombinant DNA

On their own, restriction fragments cannot reproduce themselves in a cell. To make replication possible, it is necessary to splice each fragment to a **vector:** A specialized DNA sequence that can enter a living cell, signal its presence to an investigator by conferring a detectable property on the host cell, and provide a means of replication for itself and the foreign DNA inserted into it. A vector must also possess distinguishing physical traits, such as size or shape, by which it can be purified away from the host cell's genome. Several types of vectors are in use and each one behaves as a chromosome capable of accepting foreign DNA inserts and replicating independently of the host cell's genome. The cutting and splicing together of vector and inserted fragment—DNA from two different origins—creates a **recombinant DNA molecule.**

Sticky ends and base pairing

Two characteristics of single-stranded, or "sticky," ends provide a basis for the efficient production of a vector-insert recombinant: The ends are available for base pairing, and no matter what the origin of the DNA (bacterial or human, for example), two sticky ends produced with the same enzyme are complementary in sequence. You simply cut the vector with the same restriction enzyme used to generate the fragment of genomic DNA and mix the digested vector and genomic DNAs together in the presence of DNA ligase. You then allow time for the base pairing of complementary sticky ends and for the ligase to stabilize the molecule. Certain laboratory "tricks" (discussed later) help prevent two or more genomic fragments from joining with each other rather than with vectors.

Choice of vectors

Available vectors differ from one another in biological properties, carrying capacity, and the type of host they can infect. The simplest vectors are minute circles of double-stranded DNA known as **plasmids** that can gain admission to and replicate in the cytoplasm of many kinds of bacterial cells, independently of the bacterial chromosomes (**Fig. 9.6**). The most useful plasmids contain several recognition sites, one for each of several different restriction enzymes, for example, one *Eco*RI site, one *Hpa*I site, and so forth. This provides flexibility in the choice of enzymes that can be used to digest the DNA containing the fragment, or fragments, of interest. Exposure to any one of these restriction enzymes opens up the vector at the corresponding recognition site, allowing the insertion of a foreign DNA fragment, without at the same time splitting the plasmid into many pieces (Fig. 9.6).

Each plasmid vector carries an origin of replication and a gene for resistance to a specific antibiotic. The origin of replication enables it to replicate independently inside a bacterium. The gene for antibiotic resistance confers on the host cell the ability to survive in a medium containing a specific antibiotic; the resistance gene thereby enables experimenters to select for propagation only those bacterial cells that contain a plasmid (Fig. 9.7). Antibiotic resistance genes and other vector genes that make it possible to pick out cells harboring a particular DNA molecule are called **selectable markers.** Plasmids fulfill the final requirement for vectors—ease of purification—because they can be purified away from the genomic DNA of the bacterial host by several techniques that take advantage of size and other differences, described later. Plasmid vector restriction sites useful for cloning are ones that do not interrupt either the vector origin of replication or the coding region of the selectable marker.

The largest-capacity vectors are *artificial chromosomes:* recombinant DNA molecules formed by combining multiple chromosomal replication and segregation elements of a specific host with a DNA insert. A bacterial

artificial chromosome (BAC) can accommodate a DNA insert of 300 kb.

Figure 9.6 Creating recombinant DNA molecules with plasmid vectors. (a) Human genomic DNA is cut with *Eco*RI to produce a mixture of fragments. A plasmid vector is also cut with *Eco*RI at its single *Eco*RI recognition site. The two are mixed together in the presence of the enzyme ligase, which sutures them to each other to form circular recombinant DNA molecules. **(b)** *E. coli* cells transformed with recombinant plasmids are recognized by their growth in the presence of ampicillin.

(a) Human DNA

*Eco*RI site

Plasmid vectors

*Eco*RI site

Origin of replication

Gene for ampicillin resistance

Human DNA and plasmid vectors are cut with *Eco*RI.

Cleaved fragments and vectors are combined in the presence of ligase.

Ligase

(b) Recombinant plasmids are added to a population of *E. coli* cells.

Host chromosome

Plasmid

E. coli plated onto medium containing ampicillin. Only cells containing recombinant plasmids are able to grow.

The first step in the creation of recombinant DNA clones is the ligation of the DNA of interest to a vector, such as a plasmid or an artificial chromosome. Vectors contain one or more origins of replication and a selectable marker, such as an antibiotic resistance gene, so that the recombinant molecule can be replicated and identified.

Figure 9.7 How to identify transformed bacterial cells containing plasmids with DNA inserts. (a) Plasmid vectors are often constructed so that they contain the *E. coli lacZ* gene with a restriction site right in the middle of the gene. If the vector reanneals to itself without inclusion of an insert, the *lacZ* gene will remain uninterrupted; if it accepts an insert, the gene will be interrupted. **(b)** Transformation: When added to a culture of bacteria, plasmids enter about 1 in 1000 cells. **(c)** Only cells transformed by a plasmid carrying a gene for ampicillin resistance will form colonies on petri plates. **(d)** Cells containing vectors that have reannealed to themselves without the inclusion of an insert will express the uninterrupted *lacZ* gene. The polypeptide product of the gene is β-galactosidase. Reaction of this enzyme with a substrate known as X-Gal produces a molecule that turns the cell blue. Any cells containing recombinant plasmids will not generate active β-galactosidase and will therefore not turn blue.

(a) A recombinant plasmid

(b) Transformation: foreign DNA enters the host cell

(c) Selecting cells that have received a plasmid

(d) Distinguishing cells carrying recombinant molecules from cells carrying just non-recombinant vector DNA

then use the disruption of *lacZ* gene function to distin guish insert-containing recombinant molecules from vec tors without inserts. Many of the plasmid vectors use today incorporate most if not all of the features depicte in Fig. 9.7.

Cloning step 2: Host cells take up and amplify recombinant DNA

Although each type of vector functions in a slightly different way and enters a specific kind of host, the general scheme of entering a host cell and taking advantage of the cellular environment to replicate itself is the same for all. We divide our discussion of this step of cloning into three parts: getting foreign DNA into the host cell; selecting cells that have received a DNA molecule; and distinguishing insert-containing recombinant molecules from vectors without inserts. Figure 9.7 illustrates the three-part process with a plasmid vector containing an origin of replication, the gene for resistance to ampicillin (amp^R), and the *E. coli lacZ* gene, which encodes the enzyme β-galactosidase. By constructing the vector with a common restriction site like *Eco*RI right in the middle of the *lacZ* gene, researchers can insert foreign DNA into the gene at that location and

Transformation of host cells

Transformation, as you saw in Chapter 6, is the proces by which a cell or organism takes up a foreign DN molecule, changing the genetic characteristics of that ce or organism. What we now describe is similar to wh Avery and his colleagues did in the transformation exper ments that determined DNA was the molecule of heredi (see p. 166 of Chapter 6), but the method outlined here more efficient.

First, recombinant DNA molecules are added to a su pension of specially prepared *E. coli*. Under condition favoring entry, such as suspension of the bacterial cel in a cold $CaCl_2$ solution or treatment of the solution wi high-voltage electric shock (a technique known as *ele troporation*), the plasmids will enter about 1 in 1000 ce

Fig. 9.7b). These protocols increase the permeability of the bacterial cell membrane, in essence punching temporary holes through which the DNA gains entry. The probability that any one plasmid will enter any one cell is so low (0.001) that the probability of simultaneous entry of two plasmids into a single cell is insignificant (0.001 × 0.001 = 0.000001).

Identification and isolation of transformed cells

To identify the 0.1% of cells housing a plasmid, the bacteria-plasmid mixture is decanted onto a plate containing agar, nutrients, and ampicillin. Only cells transformed by a plasmid providing resistance to ampicillin will be able to grow and multiply in the presence of the antibiotic. The plasmid's origin of replication enables it to replicate in the bacterial cell independently of the bacterial chromosome; in fact, most plasmids replicate so well that a single bacterial cell may end up with hundreds of identical copies of the same plasmid molecule.

Each viable plasmid-containing bacterial cell will multiply to produce a distinct spot on an agar plate, consisting of a colony of tens of millions of genetically identical cells. The colony as a whole is considered a **cellular clone.** Such clones can be identified when they have grown to about 1 mm in diameter. (**Fig. 9.7c,** see also the chapter opening photo on p. 290). The millions of identical plasmid molecules contained within a colony together make up a **DNA clone.** They can be purified away from other cellular material as described in a following section.

Screening for insert-containing DNA molecules

If prepared under proper conditions, most treated plasmids contain an insert. Some plasmids, however, slip through without one. **Figure 9.7d** shows how the system we are discussing distinguishes cells with only vectors from cells with vectors containing inserts.

The medium on which the transformed, ampicillin-resistant bacteria grow contains, in addition to nutrients and ampicillin, a chemical compound known as X-Gal. This compound serves as a substrate for the reaction catalyzed by the intact β-galactosidase enzyme (the protein encoded by the *lacZ* gene); one product of the reaction is a new, blue-colored chemical. Cells containing vectors without inserts turn blue because they carry the original intact β-galactosidase gene. Cells containing plasmids with inserts remain colorless, because the interrupted *lacZ* gene does not allow production of functional β-galactosidase enzyme. This process of engineering an insert to interrupt a host gene is termed *insertional inactivation.*

> The vector component of the recombinant DNA molecule (1) provides a receptacle for the DNA fragment of interest, (2) carries a selectable marker, (3) hijacks the cell's biochemical machinery to amplify the recombinant molecule, (4) provides a means for distinguishing recombinant molecules from vector-only molecules, and (5) can be trimmed away to allow purification of the amplified insert DNA.

Libraries are collections of cloned fragments

Moving step by step from the DNA of any organism to a single purified DNA fragment is a long and tedious process. Fortunately, scientists do not have to return to step 1 every time they need to purify a new genomic fragment from the same organism. Instead, they can build a **genomic library:** A long-lived collection of cellular clones that contains copies of every sequence in the whole genome inserted into a suitable vector. Like traditional book libraries, genomic libraries store large amounts of information for retrieval upon request. They make it possible to start a new cloning project at an advanced stage, when the initial cloning step has already been completed and the only difficult task left is to determine which of the many clones in a library contains the DNA sequence of interest. Once the correct cellular or viral clone is identified, it can be amplified to yield a large amount of the desired genomic fragment.

Genomic libraries

If you digested the genome of a single cell with a restriction enzyme and ligated every fragment to a vector with 100% efficiency, and you then transformed all of these recombinant DNA molecules into host cells with 100% efficiency, the resulting set of clones would represent the entire genome in a fragmented form. A hypothetical collection of cellular clones that includes one copy—and one copy only—of every sequence in the entire genome would be a *complete genomic library.*

How many clones are present in this hypothetical library? If you started with the 3,000,000 kb of DNA from a haploid human sperm and reliably cut it into a series of 150 kb restriction fragments, you would generate 3,000,000/150 = 20,000 genomic fragments. If you placed each and every one of these fragments into BAC cloning vectors that were then transformed into *E. coli* host cells, you would create a perfect library of 20,000 clones that collectively carry every locus in the genome. The number of clones in this perfect library defines a **genomic equivalent.** To find the number of clones that constitute one genomic equivalent for any library, you simply divide the length of the genome (here, 3,000,000 kb) by the average size of the inserts carried by the library's vector (in this case, 150 kb).

In real life, it is impossible to obtain a perfect library. Each step of cloning is far from 100% efficient, and the DNA of a single cell does not supply sufficient raw material for the process. Researchers must thus harvest DNA from the millions of cells in a particular tissue or organism. If you make a genomic library with this DNA by collecting only one genomic equivalent (20,000 clones for a human library in BAC vectors), then by chance some human DNA fragments will appear more than once, while others will not be present at all. Including four to five genomic equivalents produces an average of four to five clones for each locus, and a 95% probability that any individual locus is present at least once.

cDNA libraries

Often, only the information in a gene's coding sequence is of experimental interest, and it would be advantageous to limit analysis to the gene's exons without having to determine the structure of the introns as well. Because coding sequences account for a very small percentage of genomic DNA in higher eukaryotes, however, it is inefficient to look for them in genomic libraries. The solution is to generate **cDNA libraries,** which store sequences copied into DNA from all the RNA transcripts present in a particular cell type, tissue, or organ. Because they are obtained from RNA transcripts, these sequences carry only exon information.

To produce DNA clones from mRNA sequences, researchers rely on a series of *in vitro* reactions that mimic several stages in the life cycle of viruses known as **retroviruses.** Retroviruses, which include among their ranks the HIV virus that causes AIDS, carry their genetic information in molecules of RNA. As part of their gene-transmission kit, retroviruses also contain the unusual enzyme known as **RNA-dependent DNA polymerase,** or simply **reverse transcriptase** (review the Genetics and Society box in Chapter 8, pp. 260–261). After infecting a cell, a retrovirus uses reverse transcriptase to copy its single strand of RNA into a mirror-image-like strand of complementary DNA, often abbreviated as **cDNA.** The reverse transcriptase, which can also function as a DNA-dependent DNA polymerase, then makes a second strand of DNA complementary to this first cDNA strand (and equivalent in sequence to the original RNA template). Finally, this double-stranded DNA copy of the retroviral RNA chromosome integrates into the host cell's genome. Although the designation cDNA originally meant a single strand of DNA complementary to an RNA molecule, it now refers to any DNA—single- or double-stranded—derived from an RNA template.

Suppose you were interested in studying the structure of a mutant β-globin protein. You have already analyzed hemoglobin obtained from a patient carrying this mutation and found that the alteration affects the amino acid structure of the protein itself and not its regulation, so you now need only look at the sequence of the mutant gene's coding region to understand the primary genetic defect. To establish a library enriched for the mutant gene sequence and lacking all the extraneous information, you would first obtain mRNA from the cytoplasm of the patient's red blood cell precursors (**Fig. 9.8a**). About 80% of the total mRNA in these red blood cells is from the α- and β-hemoglobin genes, so the mRNA preparation contains a much higher proportion of the sequence corresponding to the β-globin (*HBB*) gene than do the genomic sequences found in a cell's nuclear DNA.

The addition of reverse transcriptase to the total mRNA preparation—as well as ample amounts of the four deoxyribonucleotide triphosphates and primers to initiate synthesis—generates single-stranded cDNA bound to the mRNA template (**Fig. 9.8b**). The primers used in this reaction would be oligo(dT)—single-stranded fragments of DNA containing about 20 T's in a row—that can bind through hybridization to the poly-A tail at the 3′ end of eukaryotic mRNAs and initiate polymerization of the first cDNA strand. Upon exposure to high temperature, the mRNA-cDNA hybrids separate, or denature, into single strands. The addition of an RNase enzyme that digests the original RNA strands leaves intact single strands of cDNA (**Fig. 9.8c**). Most of these fold back on themselves at their 3′ end to form transient hairpin loops via base pairing with random complementary nucleotides in nearby sequences in the same strand. These hairpin loops serve as primers for synthesis of the second DNA strand. Now the addition of DNA polymerase, in the presence of the requisite deoxyribonucleotide triphosphates, initiates the production of a second cDNA strand from the just synthesized single-stranded cDNA template (**Fig. 9.8d**).

After using restriction enzymes and ligase to insert the double-stranded cDNA into a suitable vector (**Fig. 9.8e**) and then transforming the vector-insert recombinants into appropriate host cells, you would have a library of double-stranded cDNA fragments, with the cDNA fragment in each individual clone corresponding to an mRNA molecule in the red blood cells that served as your sample. This library includes only the exons from that part of the genome that the red blood precursors were actively transcribing for translation into protein. For genes expressed infrequently or in very few tissues, you would have to screen many clones of a cDNA library to find the gene of interest. For highly expressed genes, such as the *HBB* gene, you would have to screen only a few clones in a red blood cell precursor library.

Genomic versus cDNA libraries

Figure 9.9 compares genomic and cDNA libraries. The main advantage of genomic libraries is that the genomic clones within them represent all regions of DNA equally

(a) Red blood cell precursors

Release mRNA from cytoplasm and purify.

Figure 9.8 Converting RNA transcripts to cDNA. **(a)** Obtain mRNA from red blood cell precursors. **(b)** Create a hybrid cDNA-mRNA molecule using reverse transcriptase. **(c)** Heat the mixture to separate mRNA and cDNA strands, and then eliminate the mRNA transcript. The 3′ end of the cDNA strands loops around and binds by chance to complementary nucleotides within the same strand, forming the primer for DNA polymerization. **(d)** Create a second cDNA strand complementary to the first. After the reaction is completed, the enzyme S1 nuclease is used to cleave the "hairpin loop" at one end. **(e)** Insert the newly created double-stranded DNA molecule into a vector for cloning.

(b) Add oligo(dT) primer. Treat with reverse transcriptase in presence of dATP, dCTP, dGTP, and dTTP.

(c) Denature cDNA-mRNA hybrids and digest mRNA with RNase. 3′ end of cDNA folds back on itself and acts as primer.

Figure 9.9 A comparison of genomic and cDNA libraries. Every tissue in a multicellular organism can generate the same genomic library, and the DNA fragments in that library collectively carry all the DNA of the genome. On average, the clones of a genomic library represent every locus an equal number of times. By contrast, every tissue in a multicellular organism generates a different cDNA library. Clones of a cDNA library represent only the fraction of the genome that is being actively transcribed in that tissue. The frequency with which particular fragments appear in a cDNA library is proportional to the level of the corresponding mRNA in that tissue.

(d) The first cDNA strand acts as a template for synthesis of the second cDNA strand in the presence of the four deoxynucleotides and DNA polymerase

(e) Insert cDNA into vector.

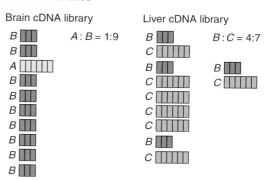

Recombinant DNA Technology and Pest-resistant Crops

The U.S. Department of Agriculture estimates that caterpillar pests such as the European corn borer, corn rootworm, and cotton bollworm are responsible for $1 billion in lost revenue each year in the United States alone. Farmers can spray their crops with pesticides, but the process is costly, labor intensive, not completely effective, and in some cases, harmful to workers in the field and to beneficial insects.

Organic farmers choose to use pesticides that only exist, or are produced, naturally. For the last 30 years, they have taken advantage of the protein-based mechanism evolved by the common soil bacterium *Bacillus thuringiensis kurstaki* (abbreviated *Bt*) to protect itself from being eaten by the same caterpillars that cause so many problems for farmers. About a dozen genes in the microbe code for crystalline (CRY) polypeptides that function as specialized endotoxins. When a caterpillar ingests the bacteria, the CRY proteins bind to specific intestinal membrane sites and disrupt digestion, leading to the insect's rapid death. CRY binding is highly specific for proteins found only in the larvae of moths and butterflies and not in any vertebrate species. Even high dosages of CRY proteins have no toxic or allergenic effects on birds, mammals, reptiles, or amphibians.

In the mid-1980s, agricultural molecular biologists realized they could use the newly developed tools of recombinant DNA technology to create genetically modified (GM) crops that would be resistant to insect infestation, without the need for pesticide applications. Based on the extensive safety record associated with whole-organism *Bt* use and a detailed understanding of the biochemical mechanism of CRY pesticidal action, researchers developed a strategy for creating plants that expressed a *cry* gene within their own cells as follows. They cloned a *cry* family gene named *cry1Ab* into a plasmid vector, cut out the insert with a restriction enzyme, and purified the insert. Next, they ligated a restriction fragment containing a plant gene intron (required to stabilize RNA transcripts) to the 5′ end of the coding region. At the 5′ end of this joined molecule, they added another restriction fragment containing a promoter from a plant virus; at the 3′ end of the construct, they attached a special plant transcription termination signal sequence. They then inserted this four-part *cry*-gene construct into a bacterial plasmid vector resembling the one shown in Fig. 9.7, which was used to transform a bacterial culture. Finally, they identified bacterial clones containing the construct based on antibiotic resistance and the absence of *lacZ* production and used these clones to produce a purified DNA insert containing the *cry* gene and associated genetic elements (**Fig. A**).

Cells from many different plant species can be grown in petri dishes where DNA transformation with the recombinant *cry*

Figure A DNA construct with recombinant gene that can express CRY protein in plants

Figure B Global area of biotech crops (million hectares; 1996–2004). Increase of 20% 13.3 million hectares, or 32.9 million acres, between 2003 and 2004.

insert can easily occur. Transformed cells are identified, isolated, and then grown under conditions that allow them to regenerate whole plants. Genetically modified plants containing the *cry* gene were grown commercially for the first time in 1996 (**Fig. B**). By 2004, *cry* genes had been used to create insect-resistant canola, cotton, corn, papaya, potato, rice, soybean, squash, sugar beet, tomato, and wheat. These and other genetically modified crops were being grown on over 80 million hectares (8 billion acres) of land around the world, in both industrialized and developing countries.

Before genetically modified plants can be grown commercially, they must pass stringent tests for efficacy and safety on a case-by-case basis. In the case of corn engineered to express the *cry1Ab* gene, the CRY protein product was detected at a level of three parts per 10 million (0.0000003) in corn and is nonexistent in extracted corn syrup used for soft-drink production. As expected, no difference could be detected between the GM and non-GM variety in amino acids, vitamins, carbohydrates or any other nutritional characteristic. (In contrast, large differences *do* exist between traditional corn varieties bred for

different purposes, such as pig feed, corn syrup, or direct human consumption.)

GM foods currently on the American market have not been associated with any kind of negative health effect in any person. This doesn't mean that all future GM plants will be without ill effect and risk free, but risk assessment only makes sense in comparison to the substitute foods that people would eat in the absence of a particular GM product. In some situations, the risk exists for genetically engineered traits to migrate unintentionally into wild plants. Indeed, most scientists take this risk more seriously than alleged health risks. With a scientifically informed regulatory process, the risk of significant eco-harm can be assessed up front and included in the decision to implement, redesign, or reject a particular GM technology on a case-by-case basis.

As shown in Fig. B, the global area devoted to planting GM crops continues to increase at a rapid pace in both industrialized and developing countries. As the world's human population increases, the use of GM crops may help solve the problems of mass starvation, especially in less developed countries.

and show what the intact genome looks like in the region of each clone. The chief advantage of cDNA libraries is that the cDNA clones reveal which parts of the genome contain the information used in making proteins in specific tissues, as determined from the prevalence of the mRNAs for the genes involved. To gain as much information as possible about a gene's structure and function, researchers rely on both types of libraries.

> A genomic library is a collection of cloned DNA fragments, each of which is equivalent to a portion of an organism's genome. In an ideal library, every region of the genome is represented in a equal number of clones. By contrast, a cDNA library contains only sequences present in the mRNA transcripts of the particular source tissue.

9.3 Hybridization

Once you have collected the hundreds of thousands of human DNA fragments in a genomic or cDNA library, how do you find the gene you wish to study, the proverbial "needle in the haystack"? For example, how would you go about finding a genomic clone containing the *HBB* gene and its surrounding non-transcribed region? One way is to take advantage of hybridization—the natural propensity of complementary single-stranded molecules of DNA or RNA to base pair and form stable double helixes. Once a β-globin cDNA clone is available, it can be denatured (separated into single strands), linked with a radioactive or fluorescent tag, and then used to probe a whole genome library that is spread out as a series of colonies on one or more petri plates. The tagged DNA probe will hybridize with denatured DNA from the genomic clones that contain a complementary sequence. After nonhybridizing probe is washed away, only the tiny number of β-globin-containing clones (among the hundreds of thousands in the library) are tagged by virtue of their hybridization to the probe. Individual cellular clones can then be retrieved from the library and put into culture to produce larger amounts of material in preparation for recovery of the purified DNA insert.

Hybridization has a single critical requirement: The region of complementarity between two single strands must be sufficiently long and accurate to produce a large enough number of hydrogen bonds to generate a cohesive force. Accuracy refers to the percentage of bases within the complementary regions that are actual complements of each other (C–G or A–T). The cohesive force formed by adding together large numbers of hydrogen bonds counteracts the thermal forces that tend to disrupt the double helix. If two single strands form hydrogen bonds between 15 or more contiguous base pairs, the combined force is sufficient. Hybridization can occur between any two

single strands of nucleic acid: DNA/DNA, DNA/RNA, or RNA/RNA.

DNA probes are used to screen libraries

DNA probes are purified fragments of single-stranded DNA 25 to several thousand nucleotides in length that are subsequently labeled with a radioactive isotope (typically ^{32}P) or a fluorescent dye. DNA probes can be produced from previously cloned fragments of DNA, from purified fragments of DNA amplified by PCR (described in the next section), or from short single strands of chemically synthesized DNA.

In chemical synthesis, an automated DNA synthesizer adds specified nucleotides, one at a time, through chemical reactions, to a growing DNA strand (**Fig. 9.10a**). Modern synthesizers can produce specific sequences up to 100 nucleotides in length. An investigator can instruct the DNA synthesizer to construct a particular sequence of A's, T's, C's, and G's. Within a few hours, the machine produces the desired short DNA chains, which are known as **oligonucleotides.**

With the availability of oligonucleotide synthesis, it is possible to generate probes indirectly from a polypeptide sequence whose corresponding gene coding sequence is unknown, rather than directly from a known DNA sequence. This process is known as *reverse translation* (**Fig. 9.10b**). To perform a reverse translation, an investigator first translates the amino acid sequence of a protein into a DNA sequence via the genetic code dictionary. Recall, however, that the genetic code is "degenerate," i.e., most individual amino acids are represented by more than one codon. Without knowing the coding DNA sequence, it is impossible to predict which of several codons is actually used in the genome. To simplify the task, investigators choose peptide sequences containing amino acids encoded by as few potential codons as possible. They must then synthesize a mixture of oligonucleotides containing all possible combinations of codons for each amino acid. This is no problem for an automated DNA synthesizer: An investigator can direct the machine to add in a defined mixture of nucleotides (A and G, for example) at each ambiguous position in the oligonucleotide. With this indirect method of obtaining a DNA probe, researchers can locate and clone genes even if they have only partial coding information based on the proteins the genes encode.

Hybridization can occur between single strands that are not completely complementary, including related sequence from different species. In general, two single DNA strands that are longer than 50–100 bp will hybridize so long as the extent of their complementarity is more than 80% even though mismatches may appear throughout the resulting hybrid molecule. Imperfect hybrids are less

Figure 9.10 How to make oligonucleotide probes for screening a library. (a) A DNA synthesizer is a machine that automates the addition through chemical reactions of specified nucleotides to the growing DNA chains, known as oligonucleotides. The bottles contain solutions of A, T, C, and G, along with reagents used in the reactions. **(b)** Reverse translation. An amino acid sequence can be "reverse translated" into a degenerate DNA sequence, which can be programmed into a DNA synthesizer to create a set of oligonucleotides that must include the one present in the actual genomic DNA.

(a) A DNA synthesizer

(b) Synthesizing DNA probes based on reverse translation

Protein sequence	Glu	Asp	Met	Trp	Tyr
↓					
Degenerate coding sequences	GAA	GAT	ATG	TGG	TAT
	GAG	GAC			TAC
↓					
Sequences that must be present in the probe					

GAAGATATGTGGTAT
GAGGATATGTGGTAT
GAAGACATGTGGTAT
GAGGACATGTGGTAT
GAAGATATGTGGTAC
GAGGATATGTGGTAC
GAAGACATGTGGTAC
GAGGACATGTGGTAC

Hybridization is the process through which complementary DNA strands base pair to form stable double-helical structures. Hybridization occurs even between strands that have small numbers of mismatches. A purified DNA fragment can be tagged and used as a probe to screen genomic or cDNA libraries of any species for clones containing related DNA sequences. DNA probes can be produced from previously cloned fragments or from synthesized oligonucleotides.

Southern blots allow visualization of rare DNA fragments in complex samples

Researchers use hybridization to screen a library of thousands of clones for particular ones complementary to specific probes. Hybridization with a cloned probe can also provide information about similar DNA regions in a whole-genome sample. The protocol for accomplishing this task combines gel electrophoresis (review discussion on pp. 295–297) with the hybridization of DNA probes to DNA targets immobilized on nitrocellulose paper.

Suppose you had a clone of a gene called *H2K* from the mouse major histocompatibility complex (MHC). The *H2K* gene plays a critical role in the body's ability to mount an immune response to foreign cells. You want to know whether other genes in the mouse genome are similar to *H2K* and, by extrapolation, also play a role in the immune response. To get an estimate of the number of *H2K*-like genes that exist in the genome, you could turn to a hybridization technique called the **Southern blot,** named for Edward Southern, the British scientist who developed it. **Figure 9.11** illustrates the details of the technique.

Southern blotting can identify individual *H2K*-like DNA sequences within the uncloned expanse of DNA present in a mammalian genome. Cutting the total genomic DNA with *Eco*RI produces about 700,000 different fragments. When you separate these fragments by gel electrophoresis and stain them with ethidium bromide, all you see is a smear, because it is impossible to distinguish 700,000 fragments spread over a distance of some 10 cm (Fig. 9.11). But you can blot the smear of fragments to a nitrocellulose filter paper and probe the resulting blot with a labeled *H2K* clone, which picks out the bands containing the *H2K*-like gene sequences. The result shown in Fig. 9.11 is a pattern of approximately two dozen fragments that constitute a series of related MHC genes within the mouse genome. The Southern blot thus makes it possible to start with a very complex mixture and identify the small number of fragments among hundreds of thousands within a whole genome that are related to your original clone.

Southern blotting can also determine the location of one cloned sequence (such as a 1.4 kb human β-globin cDNA sequence from a plasmid vector) within a larger

stable than perfect ones, but geneticists can exploit this difference in stability to evaluate the similarity between molecules from two different sources. Hybridization, for example, occurs between the mouse and human genes for the cystic fibrosis protein. Researchers can thus use the human genes to identify and isolate the corresponding mouse sequences and then use these sequences to develop a mouse carrying a defective cystic fibrosis gene. Such a mouse provides a model for cystic fibrosis in a species that, unlike humans, can be used in experimental analysis.

Southern Blot Analysis

Genomic DNA was purified from the tissues of seven mice, and each sample was subjected to digestion with the restriction enzymes *Eco*RI. Digested samples were separated by electrophoresis in an agarose gel, as illustrated in Fig. 9.4.

Stain with
ethidium bromide
to visualize total
genomic DNA under
UV illumination.

Next you place the gel in a strongly alkaline solution to denature the DNA, and then in a neutralizing solution. You now cover the gel containing the separated DNA restriction fragments with a piece of nitrocellulose filter paper. On top of the filter paper, you place a stack of paper towels, and beneath the gel, a sponge saturated with buffer. Within this setup, the dry paper towels act as a blotter, pulling liquid from the buffer-saturated sponge, through the gel, the nitrocellulose filter, and into the towels themselves. The large DNA molecules do not pass through the filter into the paper towels. Instead, they become trapped at points directly above their locations in the gel, forming a Southern blot: the nitrocellulose filter containing DNA fragments in a pattern that is a replica of their migration pattern in the gel.

Buffer solution

Sponge
Gel
Nitrocellulose paper
Stacked paper towels

↑ shows direction of DNA movement
from gel into filter

The Southern blot is removed from the blotting apparatus, incubated with NaOH to denature the transferred DNA, and then baked and exposed to UV radiation to attach the single-stranded DNA to the blot.

The blot is incubated with radioactive probe for a mouse major histocompatibility gene *H2K*.

The distribution of unlabeled mouse genomic restriction fragments transferred from the gel to the blot is shown in *black*; *red bands* indicate locations on the blot where the *H2K* probe has hybridized to homologous mouse genomic DNA fragments.

High temperature

UV exposure

Blot is removed,

washed, and exposed to X-ray film.

Detection of radioactive label

A B C D E F G

15.0 —

9.1 —

5.3 —

3.3 —

2.0 —

1
2a
2b
3
5
7
8
9
10
11
12
13
14
15
16

In each genomic DNA sample, the *H2K* probe hybridizes to all 20–30 major histocompatability-related genes present within the mouse genome.

cloned sequence (such as 30 kb genomic clone containing the β-globin locus and surrounding genome). Suppose you want to use these two clones to discover the location of the gene within the genomic clone as well as to learn which parts of the full gene are exons and which parts are introns. To answer both of these questions in a very straightforward fashion you would turn to Southern blotting.

First you would use gel electrophoresis of restriction-enzyme digested DNA from the 30 kb, to construct a restriction map. Next, you would transfer the restriction fragments from the gel onto a filter paper and probe the filter by hybridization to the labeled β-globin cDNA clone. A system for detecting location and intensity of the label, which can be either radioactive or fluorescent, then shows the precise restriction fragments that carry coding regions of the *HBB* gene. With very high resolution restriction maps of genomic subclones and high-resolution gel electrophoresis of small restriction fragments, you could distinguish restriction fragments containing exons from the other fragments that contain the introns of the *HBB* gene or a flanking sequence.

> In the Southern blot technique, restriction fragments from a complex genome are separated by gel electrophoresis and transferred by blotting to a nitrocellulose filter. DNA sequences of interest in the complex genome are identified by hybridization to a tagged DNA probe.

9.4 The Polymerase Chain Reaction

Genes are rare targets in a complex genome: The *HBB* gene, for example, spans only about 1400 of the 3,000,000,000 nucleotide pairs in the haploid human genome. Cloning overcomes the problem of studying such rarities by amplifying large amounts of a specific DNA fragment in isolation. But cloning is a tedious, labor-intensive process. Once a sequence is known, or even partially known, molecular biologists now use an alternative method to recover versions of the same sequence from any source material: the **polymerase chain reaction,** or **PCR.** First developed in 1985, PCR is faster, less expensive, and more flexible in application than cloning. From a complex mixture of DNA—like that present in a person's blood sample—PCR can isolate a purified DNA fragment in just a few hours.

PCR is also extremely efficient. In creating a genomic or cDNA library, a large number of cells from one or more tissues are necessary as the source of DNA or mRNA. By contrast, the single copy of a genome present in one sperm cell or the minute amount of severely degraded DNA recovered from the bone marrow of a 30,000-year-old Neanderthal skeleton provides enough material for PCR to make a billion or more copies of a target DNA sequence in an afternoon.

PCR generates copies of target DNA exponentially

The polymerase chain reaction is a kind of reiterative loop in which an operation is repeatedly applied to the product of earlier rounds of the same operation. You can liken it to the operation of an imaginary generously paying automatic slot machine. You start the machine by inserting a quarter, at which point the handle cranks, and the machine pays out two quarters; it then reinserts those two coins, cranks, and produces four quarters; reinserts the four, cranks, and spits out eight coins, and so on. By the twenty-second round, this fantasy machine delivers more than 4 million quarters.

The PCR operation brings together and exploits the method of DNA hybridization described earlier in this chapter and the essential features of DNA replication described in Chapter 6. Once a specific genomic region (which may range in size from a few dozen base pairs to 25 kb in length) has been chosen for amplification, an investigator uses prior knowledge of the sequence to synthesize two oligonucleotides that correspond to the two ends of the target region. One oligonucleotide is complementary to one strand of DNA at one end of the region; the other oligonucleotide is complementary to the other strand at the other end of the region. The process of amplification is initiated by the hybridization of these oligonucleotides to denatured DNA molecules within the sample. The oligonucleotides act as primers directing DNA polymerase to create new strands of DNA complementary to both strands between the two primed sections (**Fig. 9.12**).

This initial replication is followed by subsequent rounds in which both the starting DNA and the copies synthesized in previous steps become templates for further replication, resulting in an exponential increase by doubling the number of copies of the replicated region with each step. Figure 9.12 diagrams the steps of the PCR operation, showing how you could use it to obtain many copies of a small portion of the *HBB* gene for further study.

> PCR is a powerful tool used to isolate and make large quantities of a defined DNA fragment from a complex genome. PCR takes advantage of hybridization and synthetic oligonucleotides. Its starting material can be as small as a single cell. Because amplification is exponential, a single DNA molecule can be copied into trillions of copies in a single day.

PCR products can be used just like cloned restriction fragments

When properly executed, PCR provides all the highly enriched DNA you could want for unambiguous analysis of many types. PCR products can be labeled to produce hybridization probes or can be sequenced (as described in the next section) to determine the exact genetic information

FEATURE FIGURE 9.12

Polymerase Chain Reaction

Suppose you are a physician and wish to understand the molecular details of the *HBB* gene mutation that causes the expression of a novel form of anemia in one of your patients. To characterize the potentially novel allele, you would turn to PCR. You begin by preparing a small amount of genomic DNA from skin, blood, or other tissue that is easy to obtain from your patient suffering from the novel anemia. You then synthesize two specific oligonucleotide primers, each a short single-stranded chain of 16–26 nucleotides,

whose sequence is chosen from the already known sequence of the wild-type β-globin allele. One of these oligonucleotides (arbitrarily called the "left primer" in the diagram) is equivalent in sequence to a section of DNA along a 5′ strand adjacent to the target region (colored *blue* in the diagram). The second oligonucleotide, the "right primer," is equivalent to a sequence on the opposite adjacent 5′ strand. As you can see, the target DNA amplified by PCR is that stretch of the genome lying between the two primers.

Next you put the patient's genomic DNA in a test tube along with the specially prepared primers, a solution of the four deoxynucleotides, and *Taq* DNA polymerase, a specialized polymerase obtained from *Thermus aquaticus* bacteria living in hot springs. This specialized DNA polymerase remains active at the high

temperatures employed during the PCR protocol. Now place the test tube with these components in a machine called a thermal cycler, which repeatedly changes the temperature of incubation according to a preset program with three phases.

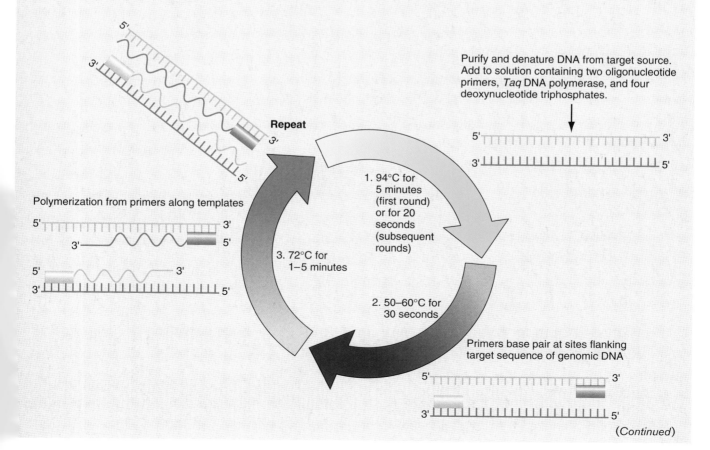

(*Continued*)

In a typical program, the cycler (1) heats the solution to 94°C for 5 minutes. At this temperature, the target DNA separates into single strands. (2) The temperature is next lowered to 50–60°C for 30 seconds to allow the primers to base pair with complementary sequences in the single-stranded genomic DNA. Specifics of both temperature and timing within these ranges depend on the length and GC:AT ratio of the primer sequences. (3) The thermal cycler then raises the temperature to 72°C, the temperature at which the *Taq* polymerase functions best. Holding the temperature at 72°C for 1–5 minutes (depending on the length of the target

sequence) allows DNA polymerization to proceed. At the end of this period, with the completion of DNA synthesis, the first round of PCR is over, and the amount of target DNA has doubled.

To start the next round, the cycler again raises the temperature to 94°C, but this time for only about 20 seconds, to denature the short stretches of DNA consisting of one of the original strands of genomic DNA and a newly synthesized complementary strand initiated by a primer. These short single strands become the templates for the second round of replication because the synthesized primers are able to base pair to them.

(1) Denature strands   (2) Base pairing of primers   (3) Polymerization from primers along templates

The machine repeats the cycle again and again, generating an exponential increase in the amount of target sequence: 22 repetitions produce over a million copies of the target sequence; 32 repetitions over a billion. The length of the accumulating DNA

strands becomes fixed at the length of the DNA between the 5′ ends of the two primers, as shown. This is because, beginning with round 3, the 5′ end of a majority of templates is defined by a primer that has been incorporated in one strand of a PCR product.

hey contain. Because the products are obtained without loning, it is possible to amplify and learn the sequence of a specific DNA segment in a very short time. In fact, in hecking for a particular hemoglobin mutation, one could tart with a blood sample and determine a DNA sequence within two days.

As an analytic tool, PCR has several advantages over loning. First, it provides the ultimate in sensitivity: The minimum input is a single DNA molecule. Second, as we ave seen, it is very fast, requiring no more than a few hours o generate enough amplified DNA for analysis. Third, in he sometimes highly competitive research world, it is an gent of democracy: Once the base sequence of the oli onucleotide primers that allow the amplification of a articular target region appears in print, anyone with the elatively small amount of funds needed to synthesize or uy these primers can reproduce the reaction.

PCR is nevertheless unsuitable in certain situations. Because the protocol only copies DNA fragments up to 5 kb in length, it cannot amplify larger regions of inter st. And because the synthesis of PCR primers depends n sequence information from the vicinity of the target egion, the protocol cannot serve as the starting point for ne analysis of genes or genomic regions that have not yet een cloned and sequenced.

PCR has many uses

CR is one of the most powerful techniques in molecular iology. Its originator, Kary Mullis, received the 1993 obel Prize in chemistry for his 1985 invention of this ol for genetic analysis. PCR has made molecular analy s an essential component of genotype detection and gene apping; we describe its applications in these areas in hapters 10 and 11. In addition, PCR has revolutionized volutionary studies, enabling researchers to analyze equences from both living and extinct organisms and to etermine the relatedness between these organisms with reater accuracy than ever before (Chapter 22 discusses volution at the molecular level). The study of gene diver ty at the nucleotide level in populations has been facili ted tremendously by PCR, and it has greatly simplified ie process of monitoring genetic changes in a group over me (see Chapter 19 for the details of population genetics). inally, PCR has helped bring molecular genetics to many elds outside of traditional genetics. The following exam le of its use in diagnosing infectious disease provides an kling of its potential impact on medicine.

AIDS, like other viral diseases, though not inherited, is one sense a genetic disease, because it is caused by the ctivity of foreign DNA inside a subgroup of somatic cells. IV, the virus associated with AIDS, gains entry to a per n's body through the bloodstream or lymphatic system, en docks at specific membrane receptors on a few types of hite blood cells, fuses with the cell membrane, and releases RNA chromosome, along with several copies of reverse

transcriptase, into the cell (see the Genetics and Society box on pp. 260–261 in Chapter 8). Once inside the cell, the reverse transcriptase copies the RNA to cDNA. The double-stranded DNA copy of the viral genome then integrates itself into the host genome where, known as a *provirus* or *endogenous retrovirus,* it can lie latent for up to 10 years or become active at any time. When activated, it directs the cellular machinery to make more viral particles.

Standard tests for HIV detect antibodies to the virus, but it may take several months for the antibodies produced by an infected person's immune system to reach levels that are measurable in the blood. Then, in another few months, when ongoing viral activity inside many types of circulating white blood cells subsides, most of the antibodies may disappear from the circulation. The reason is that once the viral particles have entered the latent state, they are literally in hiding (inside chromosomal DNA) and able to avoid detection by the immune system.

With PCR, it is possible to detect small amounts of virus circulating in the blood or lymph very soon after infection, before antibody production is in full swing. PCR can also detect viral DNA incorporated in the genome of any cell, picking up as few as 1–10 copies of viral DNA per million cells. Thus, with PCR, it becomes possible to confirm and begin treating HIV infection during the critical period before antibodies reach measurable levels. It also becomes possible to follow the progress of each person's HIV infection and tailor therapies accordingly, using a large dose of certain drugs to combat a large amount of viral activity but small doses of perhaps other drugs to prevent a small number of cells from emerging from latency.

> Once a reference DNA sequence has been established, PCR can be used to pick out variant forms of that sequence in any DNA sample. PCR amplifies any sequence between the primers used, even if the order of bases is slightly different, and it allows screening of thousands of samples very quickly.

9.5 DNA Sequence Analysis

The DNA sequence of a genome provides a staggering amount of practical information. Restriction enzyme recognition sites are immediately visible. Open reading frames of genes are recognized and translated amino acids sequences are inferred. These primary polypeptide structures provide information about possible protein structure and function. Comparison of genomic and cDNA sequences immediately shows how a gene is divided into exons and introns and may suggest whether alternative splicing of the gene's primary transcript occurs. Even an exploration of the DNA sequences between genes can provide important information about the evolution of genomes as explained later in Section 9.6.

Although scientists have known since the 1953 discovery of the double helix that genes and genomes are defined by sequences of base pairs, it wasn't until the early 1970s that the first specific sequences of genomic DNA were determined directly by chemical methods. The first DNA sequence to be determined was a 24 base-pair region of the *E. coli* genome that binds to the *lac* repressor:

TGGAATTGTGAGCGGATAACAATT

ACCTTAACACTCGCCTATTGTTAA

It was "a laborious process that took several years," according to Walter Gilbert. The frustration of that experience galvanized Gilbert and his colleague Alan Maxam to invent a general-purpose sequencing method based on the chemical cleavage of DNA molecules at specific nucleotide types. A second technology, developed by Fred Sanger, during the same mid-1970s time frame, was based on the enzymatic extension of DNA strands to a defined terminating base. Gilbert and Sanger both won the Nobel Prize for their contribution to DNA sequencing technology. Their techniques have a similar throughput of 500–700 bases obtained in each several-day-long experiment, and a similar accuracy, which approaches 99.9%. But only the Sanger technique was readily amenable to automation, and DNA sequencing reaches its full potential only with automation.

Sanger sequencing generates sets o nested fragments separated by size

There are two steps to the Sanger method of sequenc whose object is to reveal the order of base pairs in an lated DNA molecule. The first step is the generation complete series of single-stranded subfragments con mentary to a portion of the DNA template under anal (Although both strands of a DNA fragment are presen a typical DNA sample, only one is used as a template sequencing.) Each subfragment differs in length by a si nucleotide from the preceding and succeeding fragme the graduated set of fragments is known as a *nested a* A critical feature of the subfragments is that each on distinguishable according to its terminal 3′ base. Thus, subfragment has two defining attributes—relative le and one of four possible terminating nucleotides.

In the second step of the sequencing process, bi gists analyze the mixture of DNA subfragments thr polyacrylamide gel electrophoresis, under conditions allow the separation of DNA molecules differing in le by just a single nucleotide.

The original Sanger sequencing procedure (illustr in **Fig. 9.13**) begins with the denaturing into single str

---

FEATURE FIGURE 9.13

Sanger Sequencing

Begin by mixing the purified, denatured DNA with a labeled oligonucleotide primer that is complementary to a particular site on one strand of the cloned insert. Add DNA polymerase and the four deoxynucleotide triphosphates.

Next divide the mixture into four aliquots and, into each one, add a small amount of a single chain-terminating dideoxyribo-

nucleotide triphosphate abbreviated as "dideoxynucleotid triphosphate" or simply "ddNTP". One aliquot, for examp contains the deoxynucleotides A, T, C, and G spiked wi the dideoxynucleotide analog of T. Polymerization from th primer strand continues until, by chance, the dideoxynucleoti is incorporated.

Because a dideoxynucleotide analog has no oxygen at the 3′ position in the sugar, its incorporation prevents the further addition of nucleotides to the strand and thus terminates a growing chain wherever it becomes incorporated in place of an actual deoxynucleotide. The aliquot that has the dideoxy form of thymidine, for example, will generate a population of DNA molecules that terminate at each of the thymidines in the original template strand under analysis.

Incorporation of normal deoxy-T allows further chain elongation.

Incorporation of dideoxy-T causes chain termination.

FEATURE FIGURE 9.13 (Continued)

Gel analysis of fragments

| ddA | ddG | ddC | ddT |

Sequence of synthesized DNA
3'
T
G
T
A
T
G
C
C
T
A
A
G
5'

Sequence of template DNA
5'
A
C
A
T
A
C
G
G
A
T
T
C
3'

Then use electrophoresis on a polyacrylamide gel to separate the fragments in each of the four aliquots according to size. The resolution of the gel is such that you can distinguish DNA molecules that differ in length by only a single base. The appearance of a DNA fragment of a particular length demonstrates the presence of a particular nucleotide at that position in the strand.

Suppose, for example, that the aliquot polymerized in the presence of dideoxythymidine shows fragments 32, 35, and 39 bases in length. These fragments indicate that thymidine is present at those positions in the strand of nucleotides. In practice, one does not independently determine the exact lengths of each fragment. Instead, one starts at the bottom of the gel, looks at which of the four lanes has a band in it, records that base, then moves up one position and determines which lane has the next band, and so on. In this way, it is possible to read several hundred bases from a single set of reactions.

of the DNA to be sequenced. The single strands are then mixed in solution with DNA polymerase, the four deoxynucleotide triphosphates, and a radioactively labeled oligonucleotide primer complementary to DNA adjacent to the 3' end of the template strand under analysis. The solution is next divided into four aliquots. To each one, an investigator adds a small amount of a single type of a nucleotide triphosphate lacking the 3'-hydroxyl group that is critical for the formation of the phosophodiester bonds that lead to chain extension (review Fig. 6.7); this nucleotide analogue is called a **dideoxyribonucleotide** (or **dideoxynucleotide**), and it comes in four forms: **ddTTP, ddATP, ddGTP,** or **ddCTP** (abbreviated even further as ddT, ddA, ddG, and ddC).

In each sample reaction tube, the oligonucleotide primer hybridizes at the same location on the template DNA strand. As a primer, it will supply a free 3' end for DNA chain extension by DNA polymerase. The polymerase adds nucleotides to the growing strand that are complementary to those of the sample's template strand (that is, the actual DNA strand under analysis). The addition of nucleotides continues until, by chance, a dideoxynucleotide is incorporated instead of a normal nucleotide. The absence of a 3'-hydroxyl group in the dideoxynucleotide prevents the DNA polymerase from forming a phosphodiester bond with any other nucleotide, ending the polymerization for that new strand of DNA. Next, after allowing enough time for the polymerization of all molecules to reach completion, an investigator releases the templates from the newly synthesized strands by denaturing the DNA at high temperature. Each sample tube now holds a whole collection of

single-stranded radioactive DNA chains as well as the nonradioactive single strands of the template DNA. The lengths of the radioactive chains reflect the distance from the 5' end of the oligonucleotide primer to the position in the sequence at which the specific dideoxynucleotide present in that particular tube was incorporated into the growing chain.

The samples in the four tubes are now electrophoresed in adjacent lanes on a polyacrylamide gel, and the gel is subjected to a system that detects the presence of the radioactive label. Because the template strands are not labeled, they do not show up. The investigator reads out the sequence of the radioactive strand by starting at the bottom and moving up, determining which lane carries each subsequent band in the ascending series, as shown in Fig. 9.13. As you ascend, each band represents a chain that is one nucleotide longer than the chain of the band below. Once the sequence of the newly synthesized DNA is known, it is a simple matter to convert this sequence into the complementary sequence of the template strand under analysis.

To automate the DNA sequencing process, molecular geneticists changed the method of labeling the newly formed complementary DNA strands. Instead of placing a single radioactive label on the primer oligonucleotide, they labeled each of the four chain-terminating dideoxynucleotides with a different color fluorescent dye. As a result, instead of four separate reactions, all four dideoxynucleotides could be combined in a single reaction mixture that could be analyzed in a single lane on a gel (**Fig. 9.14**). A DNA sequencing machine follows the DNA chains of each length in the ascending

Figure 9.14 Automated sequencing. (a) For automated sequencing, the Sanger protocol is performed with all four fluorescently labeled terminating nucleotides present in a single reaction. At completion of the reaction, DNA fragments terminating at every base in the sequence are present and color coded by the identity of the terminating base. Separation by gel electrophoresis is next. As each fragment moves past a laser beam, the color of the terminal base is detected and recorded. **(b)** Image of a sequencing gel. Each lane displays the sequence obtained with a separate DNA sample and primer. **(c)** The raw data are displayed as peaks of four different colors, called a chromatogram. The base-calling software produces a text sequence of the newly synthesized, complementary DNA strand from left to right, which corresponds to the 5′-to-3′ direction. The machine records any ambiguity in the base call as an "N"; Ambiguity may be due to a mixture of alleles in the starting sample or technical failure. In large-scale sequencing projects, each genomic region is sequenced multiple times on both strands, which allows resolution of most ambiguities.

(a) Automated sequencing

1. Generate nested array of fragments; each with a fluorescent label corresponding to the terminating 3′ base.

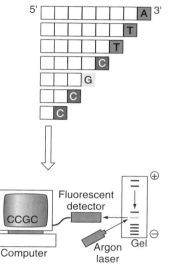

2. Fragments separated by electrophoresis in a single vertical gel lane.

3. As migrating fragments pass through the scanning laser, they fluoresce. A fluorescent detector records the color order of the passing bands. That order is translated into sequence data by base-calling software.

(b) Fluorescent bands in a sequencing gel

(c) Chromatogram and inferred sequence

NGCTTTGGAGAAAGGCTCCATTGNCAATCAAGACACACAGAGGTGTCCTCTTTTTCCCCTGGTCAGCGNCCAGGTACATNGCACCAAGGCTGCGTAGTGAACTTGNCACCAGNCCATGGAC
(For ease of readability, the yellow color of G nucleotides has been replaced by black.)

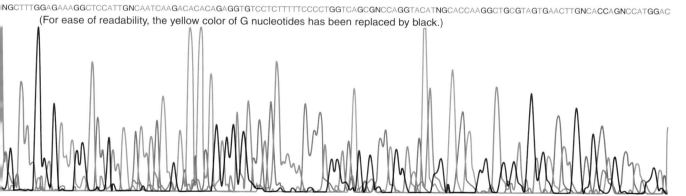

ries through a special detector that can distinguish the different colors associated with each terminating dideoxynucleotide. Thus, in each lane of a gel, it is possible to run a different DNA fragment for complete sequence analysis.

Sanger sequencing begins with hybridization of a DNA primer to the template DNA under analysis. DNA polymerase extends the primer until, by chance, a particular dideoxynucleotide is incorporated, stopping the polymerization. The result is a nested set of DNA fragments tagged according to their terminating base.

9.6 Bioinformatics: Information Technology and Genomes

By 1979, before the Sanger technique became automated, the molecular biology community had collectively determined close to 100,000 base pairs of sequence. With the introduction of commercial DNA sequencer machines in 1986, the rate at which sequence data were generated continued to climb exponentially. The informal labor-intensive systems biologists used to interpret and share experimental results were simply not up to the task of dealing with so much data.

Digital computers are a perfect match for digital genomes

The digital language used by computers for information storage and processing is ideally suited to handle the digital code that exists naturally in genomes as each base-pair unit of DNA sequence has only four possible values on one strand—namely, adenine, cytosine, guanine, or thymine—paired to a complementary base on the second strand. These four values can be represented in two digits of binary code (00, 01, 10, and 11).

Keeping pace with the 1970's and 1980's revolution in biological data generation, a parallel revolution was occurring in information technology. The Internet came into existence along with personal computers that were linked together to establish rapid transmission of electronic data from one lab to another. It was a straightforward task to channel the output of DNA sequencer machines directly into electronic storage media, from which sequences were available for analysis and transmission to other scientists.

DNA sequences online

The first official repository for DNA sequences was the GenBank database, established by the National Institutes of Health in 1982. GenBank served as an open-access, permanent online repository of sequence data generated in all molecular biology laboratories around the world prior to 2007. Individual scientists deposited their sequences electronically, and anyone in the world with an Internet connection can download and analyze them. From its establishment, the GenBank database doubled in size every 18 months, from less than 1 million base pairs initially to a total of nearly 100 billion base pairs by the beginning of 2008 (**Fig. 9.15a**).

In 2008, however, a new generation of nanotechnology-based DNA sequencers provided scientists with the ability to obtain over 100 billion base pairs of sequence data—more than the combined total of global scientific output from 197 until 2007—in a single experiment (**Fig. 9.15b**). As the cos of sequencing continues to drop, and billion-base-pa sequencing experiments become routine, it is no longer fea sible for GenBank to act as an all-inclusive repository fc the primary sequences generated by the world's scientists.

Hacking the genome

The meaning of DNA sequences in terms of organism func tion must be interpreted through software programs. Th initial programs analyzed sequences for previously define biological landmarks, including restriction-enzyme recogn tion sites and amino acid sequences encoded in open readin frames. Software was also developed to search for hidde sequence patterns, and to identify statistically significai similarities among different sequences. Results obtaine from software-driven studies led to new biological unde standing, which was incorporated into more sophisticate computer programs, which led to further understanding, ai so on. The integration of biological data and computer anal sis gave rise to the new field of bioinformatics.

Bioinformatics provides tools for visualizing functional features of genomes

Bioinformatics is the science of using computation methods—specialized software—to decipher the biologic

Figure 9.15 Accumulation of genome sequence data. (a) Growth of total sequence data deposited in GenBank. In the 25-year period from 1983 to 2008, GenBank's accumulated data repository grew 10,000-fold to nearly 100 billion base pairs. **(b)** Ultrahigh-throughput DNA sequencing. Millions of DNA clones are sequenced simultaneously as individual glowing dots on a microscope slide. At each step of the sequencing process, each dot fluoresces one of four colors corresponding to each of the four bases.

(a)

Growth of GenBank

Base pairs (y-axis): 1e + 11, 1e + 10, 1e + 09, 1e + 08, 1e + 07, 1e + 06, 100,000

Date (mm/yy) (x-axis): 1/82 1/85 1/88 1/91 1/94 1/97 1/00 1/03 1/06 1/09

(b)   Images   Image Analysis   Base Calling   Aligned Reads meaning of information contained within organismal systems. Among the most important bioinformatics tools are those that allow researchers to visualize genomic data through graphic presentations constructed on-the-fly for online viewing through a web browser. The National Center for Biotechnology Information (NCBI: http://www.ncbi.nlm.nih.gov/) was established in 1988 to oversee GenBank, create additional public databases of biological information, and develop bioinformatic applications for analyzing, systemizing, and disseminating the data. This section provides some examples of bioinformatics tools, developed by scientists at NCBI and elsewhere, that can be accessed through any web browser to visualize publicly available genome data.

The species RefSeq

Comparisons of experimental data involving DNA sequences generated by different laboratories are critically dependent on the use of a universally agreed-upon standard for analysis. This role is played by a species reference sequence, abbreviated as RefSeq. A RefSeq is a single, complete, annotated version of the species genome that is freely available online. A RefSeq need not be derived from a single individual, and it need not contain the most common genetic variants found in species members. Rather, it is simply an arbitrary, but well-characterized, example against which all newly obtained sequences from that species can be compared. By March 2009, whole-genome RefSeqs had been established for each of 8054 species, including our own (http://www.ncbi.nlm.nih.gov/RefSeq/).

Visualizing genes

A number of web-based programs have been developed that allow a user to visualize public and private genome data. Among the most popular is the UCSC Genome Browser developed at the University of California, Santa Cruz (http://genome.ucsc.edu/). The UCSC Genome Browser was used to visualize the genes identified in the human RefSeq (**Fig. 9.16**). At different levels of resolution, it becomes possible for a viewer to gain insight into different aspects of human genome organization.

Figure 9.16a depicts the locations of all identified genes along the 158,821,424 bp length of human RefSeq chromosome 7 lined up beneath the chromosomal ideogram. The 1503 genes are each represented by a separate blue box indicating location and length. Although very little molecular detail is visible at this resolution, you can see immediately that the density of genes varies enormously along the chromosome. Some regions—for example, around the 100 Mb mark—are particularly rich in genes, whereas other regions are "gene deserts." Furthermore, long-range repeating patterns of either gene density or gene sizes are absent.

Variation in gene density is even more apparent when you zoom into a 3 Mb region around the *CFTR* gene at position 117 Mb on the long arm of the chromosome (**Fig. 9.16b**). Each gene in the region is now clearly visible

as a separate group of vertically extended lines or boxes linked together by a horizontal line; vertical extensions represent exons, and lines represent spliced-out introns. When visible, arrows along an intron indicate the direction of transcription. You can see that nine nonoverlapping genes are located in the leftmost 1.7 Mb of the region, whereas none are in the remaining 1.3 Mb. The variation in the lengths of genes is also apparent in this view.

Visualizing gene structure and functional capacity

Transcribed genomic regions, exon-intron structures, and locations of protein-coding regions are best visualized by switching to the NCBI Sequence Viewer (http://www.ncbi.nlm.nih.gov/nuccore/89161213?content=5&v=116750000:117350000&report=graph). A 540 kb region around *CFTR* is shown in **Fig. 9.16c,** where transcription units are indicated with green bars (containing arrows that indicate the direction of transcription), the exon/intron structure of each gene is shown beneath with blue boxes and connecting lines, the spliced RNA product is indicated with red boxes, and genomic regions corresponding to polypeptide products are in black. Each of the three well-defined genes in this region encodes multiple polypeptides extending across different portions of mature transcripts.

Whole-genome comparisons distinguish genomic elements conserved by natural selection

Nearly a century before the DNA double helix was discovered, Charles Darwin proposed the evolution of species from now-extinct ancestors by a process of "descent with modification." We now know that the actual entity undergoing descent with modification is the DNA sequence that defines an organism's genome. Based on Darwin's model of evolution, molecular biologists anticipated that related species would have related genomes. But they did not know how closely related two species would have to be for DNA sequence homology to be recognized.

How can you tell whether DNA sequences from two sources are similar by chance or by common origin? As an example of a null hypothesis, consider a specific, but random, 50 bp sequence and calculate the probability that an independently derived DNA segment could be 100% identical, just by chance. The probability of occurrence of any DNA sequence of length n is obtained simply by raising 0.25 (the chance occurrence of the same base at a particular position) to the 50th power (the number of independent chance events required): $(0.25)^{50} = 8 \times 10^{-31}$. For all intents and purposes, this probability is essentially zero, which negates the null hypothesis and tells us that two perfectly matched 50 bp DNA sequences found in nature are almost certainly derived from the same ancestral sequence, rather than by chance.

Figure 9.16 Visualizing genes of the human RefSeq genome with the UCSC Genome Browser. (a) Locations of the 1503 genes identified along the 158,821,424 bp length of human chromosome 7. **(b)** A 3 Mb pair region of chromosome 7 between sequence positions 116,000,001 and 119,000,000, showing the locations and lengths of nine genes labeled on the left with their official names. The genomic region from 117,700,000 to 119,000,000 is a "gene desert." **(c)** Visualization of a 540 kb region of chromosome 7 containing the *CFTR* gene with the NCBI Sequence Viewer.

DNA sequence conservation

A segment of DNA is said to be a *homolog* of a sequence in another species when the two show evidence of derivation from the same DNA sequence in a common ancestor. For perfectly matched sequences that are 50 bp in length or longer, the evidence is clear. But evidence for homology of imperfectly matched DNA regions requires a more sophisticated statistical analysis, a task that is readily performed by specialized bioinformatics programs. When homologs of a DNA sequence are found in many differe species, the sequence is said to be *conserved*.

A traditional phylogenetic tree, like the one shown i **Fig. 9.17a,** depicts the relatedness of multiple species each other, with branch points that represent a series of nested common ancestors. When the human genome compared as a whole with other representative vertebra species, the percentage of sequence conservation is rel tively high for chimps and monkeys, but general

(a)

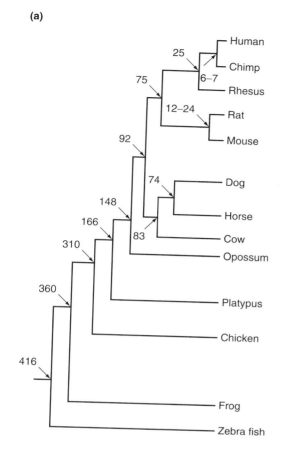

Figure 9.17 Species relatedness and genome conservation between *H. sapiens* and other vertebrates. (a) A phylogenetic tree showing branch points at which organisms diverged; the number at each branch point represents millions of years before the present. **(b)** Relatedness of the *H. sapiens* genome to that of other vertebrates is evaluated according to two bioinformatic measures: In **column 1,** the proportion of the complete human genome sequence that is found in the species being compared; and in **column 2,** the proportions of human protein-coding sequences that are found in each vertebrate genome.

(b)

Scientific name	Common name	1	2
Homo sapiens	Human	100%	100%
Pan troglodytes	Chimp	93.9%	96.58%
Macaca mulatta	Rhesus	85.1%	96.31%
Rattus norvegicus	Rat	35.7%	94.47%
Mus musculus	Mouse	37.6%	95.36%
Canis familiaris	Dog	55.4%	95.18%
Equus caballus	Horse	58.8%	92.70%
Bos taurus	Cow	48.2%	94.78%
Monodelphis domestica	Opossum	11.1%	91.43%
Ornithorhynchus anatinus	Platypus	8.2%	86.43%
Gallus gallus	Chicken	3.8%	88.61%
Xenopus tropicalls	Frog	2.6%	87.44%
Danio rerio	Zebra fish	2.0%	82.38%

decreases as the elapsed time to a common ancestor increases (**Fig. 9.17b**). At a distance of over 400 million years, the fish genome contains only 2% of the DNA sequences present in the human genome. In contrast, when comparisons are restricted to human protein-coding sequences, conservation levels remain high—at more than 82%—throughout vertebrate evolution.

Functional DNA sequences such as protein-coding regions are subject to loss or lessening of function by at least some mutations. As a result, they evolve more slowly than nonfunctional sequences, which are not similarly constrained by functional requirements. Unconstrained sequence divergence would eventually eliminate all evidence of common ancestry. Thus, whole-genome comparison results have biological function.

Homology mapping of genomes

With a genome visualization tool, it becomes possible to explore DNA sequence conservation directly along the genome, as well as across evolutionary time. An example of cross-species homology analysis is shown in **Fig. 9.18** for a 100 kb region containing the *HOXA* family of genes. The locations and exon/intron structures of the 10 human RefSeq genes are displayed in the bottom row. Above this row are homology maps for five representative vertebrate species; conservation of sequence homology is indicated with dark lines or blocks.

As anticipated from whole-genome data, nearly complete conservation of human sequences exists across the entire region in a chimp genome. In other mammals, represented here by the mouse, conservation is also apparent

Figure 9.18 Homology map for a 100 kb region of the human genome. Conservation of DNA sequences across a region of chromosome 7 from sequence position 27,092,501 to 27,192,500 containing the *HOXA* gene family.

across the entire region, but the pattern is choppy, indicating small regions of conservation interspersed with small regions that are not conserved.

As we move farther across the phylogenetic landscape to frogs and fish, we can more clearly distinguish sequences subject to evolutionary constraints from those that are not. The coding regions of the *HOXA* genes are all conserved; these genes are critical to proper development of all vertebrates. But in addition, other conserved DNA sequences can be observed at locations between coding regions. Although these sequences do not have coding potential, they may be sites of sequence-specific binding to proteins required for gene regulation or local chromatin structure.

Digital computer technology has proved to be an ideal tool for use with the four-value DNA code. Bioinformatics allows visualization of the functional features of genomes at almost any scale, as well as comparison of genome features. These whole-genome comparisons enable identification of genomic elements conserved by natural selection.

9.7 The Hemoglobin Genes: A Comprehensive Example

Geneticists have used the tools of biotechnology and bioinformatics to analyze the clusters of related genes that make up the α- and β-globin loci. Fundamental insights from these studies have helped explain how the linear information of DNA encompasses all the instructions for development of the hemoglobin system, including the changes in globin expression during normal development. The studies have also clarified how the globin genes evolved and how a large number of different mutations produce the phenotypic permutations that give rise to a range of globin-related disorders. In this section, we'll see the details of the hemoglobin system as revealed by DNA technology.

Hemoglobin genes occur in two clusters on two chromosomes

The α-globin (*HBA*) gene cluster contains five functional genes and spans about 28 kb on chromosome 16 (**Fig. 9.19a**). All the genes in the α-gene cluster are oriented in the same direction; that is, they all use the same strand of DNA as the template for transcription. Moving in the 5′-to-3′ direction along the RNA-like strand, the α or α-like genes appear in the order *HBZ*, *HBM*, *HBA2*, *HBA1*, and *HBQ1*. The genes in the β-gene cluster, like those in the α-gene cluster, all have the same orientation. The β-globin (*HBB*) cluster covers 45 kb on chromosome 11 and also contains five functional genes in the order *HBE*, *HBG2*, *HBG1*, *HBD,* and *HBB* (**Fig. 9.19b**). Geneticists refer to the chromosomal region carrying all of the *HBA*-like genes as the **α-globin locus** and the region containing the *HBB*-like genes as the **β-globin locus.** Note that the term **locus** signifies a location

on a chromosome; that location may be as small as a single nucleotide or as large as a cluster of related genes.

Correlation of globin gene order with timing of expression

The linear organization of the genes in the α- and β-gene clusters reflects the order in which they are expressed during development. For the α-like chains, that temporal order is *HBZ* during the first five weeks of embryonic life, followed by *HBA2* and *HBA1* during fetal and adult life. For the β-like chains, the order is *HBE* during the first five weeks of embryonic life; then *HBG2* and *HBG1* during fetal life and finally, within a few months of birth, mostly *HBB* but also some δ chains (see Fig. 9.1 on p. 291 and Fig. 9.19).

The fact that the order of genes on the chromosome parallels the order of their expression during development suggests that whatever mechanism turns these genes on and off takes advantage of their relative positions. We now understand what that mechanism is: A *locus control region* (or *LCR*) associated with specialized DNA binding proteins at the 5′ end of each locus works its way down the locus, bending the chromatin back on itself to turn genes on and off in order. We describe this regulatory mechanism in more detail in Chapter 18.

Fetal globin expression in adults caused by a deletion

One consequence of a master regulatory element that controls an entire gene complex is seen in a rare medical condition with a surprising prognosis. In some adults, the red blood cell precursors express neither the *HBB* nor the *HBD* genes. Although this should be a lethal situation, these adults remain healthy. Cloning and sequence analysis of the β-globin locus from affected adults show that they have a deletion extending across the *HBB* and *HBD* genes. Because of this deletion, the master regulatory control can't switch around birth, as it normally would, from γ-globin production to β- and δ-globin production (**Fig. 9.19c**). People with this rare condition continue to produce large amounts of fetal γ globin throughout adulthood, and that γ globin is sufficient to maintain a near-normal level of health.

Geneticists have found that the hemoglobin genes occur in two clusters in two separate chromosomes. The genes in the two clusters are transcribed in order at different stages of development, explaining how the structure of hemoglobin changes from embyro to adult.

Globin-related diseases result from a variety of mutations

By comparing DNA sequences from affected individuals with those from healthy individuals, researchers have learned that there are two general classes of disorders arising from alterations in the hemoglobin genes. In one

Figure 9.19 The genes for the polypeptide components of human hemoglobin are located in two genomic clusters on two different chromosomes. **(a)** Schematic representation of the *HBA* gene cluster on chromosome 16. The *HBA* gene homologs are indicated with *green* boxes. Transcripts are shown below active genes by a series of boxes, representing exons, connected with lines representing introns. The translated portions of each transcript are indicated in *red,* and the translation products are represented below transcripts in *black.* Sites of posttranslation modification, including heme-binding, acetylation, and glycosylation are also shown. The cluster contains five functional genes and two pseudogenes (designated with the appended letter P). **(b)** Schematic representation of the *HBB* gene cluster on chromosome 11; this cluster has five functional genes and one pseudogene. (The pseudogene HBBP is actually transcribed, but the transcript is not translated.) Upstream from both the *HBA* an *HBB* gene clusters lie the locus control regions (LCR) (which is only shown for the β-globin locus here). **(c)** In this example of a mutant chromosome, the adult *HBB* genes β and δ have been deleted; as a result, the LCR cannot switch from activating the fetal genes to activating the adult genes, and the fetal genes remain active in the adult.

lass, mutations change the amino acid sequence and thus the three-dimensional structure of the α- or β-globin chain, nd these structural changes result in an altered protein vhose malfunction causes the destruction of red blood ells. Diseases of this type are known as hemolytic ane-nias (**Fig. 9.20a**). An example is sickle-cell anemia, aused by an A-to-T substitution in the sixth codon of the -globin chain. This simple change in DNA sequence ters the sixth amino acid in the chain from glutamic acid valine, which, in turn, modifies the form and function ' the affected hemoglobin molecules. Red blood cells car-ing these altered molecules often have abnormal shapes at cause them to block blood vessels or be degraded.

The second major class of hemoglobin-related genetic seases arises from DNA mutations that reduce or minate the production of one of the two globin poly-ptides. The disease state resulting from such mutations known as thalassemia, from the Greek words *thalassa* caning "sea" and *emia* meaning "blood"; the name arose m the observation that a relatively high rate of this ood disease occurs among people who live near the diterranean Sea. Several different types of mutation cause thalassemia, including those that delete an entire A or *HBB* gene, those that alter the sequence in regions are outside the gene but necessary for its regulation,

or those that alter the sequence within the gene such that no protein can be produced. The consequence of these changes in DNA sequence is the total absence or a defi-cient amount of one or the other of the normal hemo-globin chains. Because there are two *HBA* genes (*HBA1* and *HBA2*) that see roughly equal expression beginning a few weeks after conception, individuals carrying dele-tions within the α-globin locus may be missing anywhere from one to four copies in total (**Fig. 9.20b**). A person lacking only one would be a heterozygote for the dele-tion of one of two *HBA* genes; a person missing all four would be a homozygote for deletions of both *HBA* genes. The range of mutational possibilities explains the range of phenotypes seen in α-thalassemia. Individuals miss-ing only one of four possible copies of the α genes are normal; those lacking two of the four have a mild ane-mia, and those without all four die before birth.

The fact that the *HBA* genes are expressed early in fetal life explains why the α-thalassemias are detrimental *in utero.* By contrast, β-thalassemia major, the disease occurring in people who are homozygotes for most dele-tions of the single *HBB* gene, also usually results in death, but not until soon after birth. These individuals survive that long because the *HBB* homolog *HBD* is expressed in the fetus (review Fig. 9.1 on p. 291).

Figure 9.20 Mutations in the DNA for hemoglobin produce two classes of disease. (a.1) The major types of hemoglobin variants causing hemolytic anemias. (a.2) The basis of sickle-cell anemia. (a.3) Sickling red blood cells appear as crescents among more rounded nonsickling cells. (b.1) Thalassemias associated with deletions in the α-globin polypeptide. (b.2) The physiological basis of β-thalassemia major. (b.3) Child suffering from β-thalassemia major.

(a.1) Major types of structural variants causing hemolytic anemias

Name	Molecular basis of mutation	Change in polypeptide	Pathophysiological effect of mutation	Inheritance
HbS	Single nucleotide substitution	β 6 Glu ↓ Val	Deoxygenated HbS polymerizes → sickle cells → vascular occlusion and hemolysis	Autosomal Recessive
HbC	Single nucleotide substitution	β 6 Glu ↓ Lys	Oxygenated HbC tends to crystallize → less deformable cells → mild hemolysis; the disease in HbS:HbC compounds is like mild sickle-cell anemia	Autosomal Recessive
Hb Hammer-smith	Single nucleotide substitution	β 42 Phe ↓ Ser	An unstable Hb → Hb precipitation → hemolysis; also low O_2 affinity	Autosomal Dominant

(b.1) Clinical results of various α-thalassemia genotypes

Clinical condition	Genotype	Number of functional α genes	α-chain production
Normal	*HBZ* *HBA2* *HBA1* HBAHBA/HBAHBA	4	100%
Silent carrier	HBAHBA/HBA—	3	75%
Heterozygous α-thalassemia— mild anemia	HBA—/HBA— or HBAHBA/— —	2	50%
HbH ($β_4$) disease— moderately severe anemia	HBA—/— —	1	25%
Homozygous α-thalassemia— lethal	— —/— —	0	0%

(a.2) Basis of sickle-cell anemia

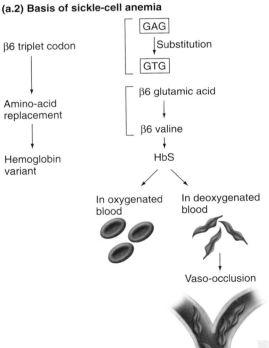

β6 triplet codon → Amino-acid replacement → Hemoglobin variant

GAG → │Substitution → GTG

β6 glutamic acid → β6 valine → HbS

In oxygenated blood

In deoxygenated blood → Vaso-occlusion

(a.3)

(b.3)

(b.2) A β-thalassemia patient makes only α globin, not β globin.

α β

Four α subunits combine to make abnormal hemoglobin.

Abnormal hemoglobin molecules clump together, altering shape of red blood cells. Abnormal cells carry reduced amounts of oxygen.

To compensate for reduced oxygen level, medullary cavities of bones enlarge to produce more red blood cells.

The spleen enlarges to remove excessive number of abnormal red blood cells.

— spleen

Too few red blood cells in circulation result in anemia.

Figure 9.21 Regulatory regions affecting globin gene expression. (a) Mutations in the TATA box associated with the *HBB* gene can eliminate transcription and cause β-thalassemia. **(b)** A locus control region is present 25–50 kb upstream of the *HBA* gene cluster. The function of the LCR is to open up the chromatin domain associated with the complete cluster of *HBA* genes. Mutations in the LCR can prevent expression of all the *HBA* genes, resulting in severe α-thalassemia.

(a) Promoter region of the *HBB* gene

(b) Locus control region of the *HBA* locus

Figure 9.22 Evolution of the globin gene family. Duplication of an ancestral gene followed by divergence of the separate duplication products established the α- and β-globin lineages. Further rounds of duplication and divergence within the separate lineages generated the two sets of genes and pseudogenes of the globin gene family.

Comparisons of the altered DNA sequences from affected individuals with wild-type sequences from healthy individuals have helped illuminate the sequences necessary for normal hemoglobin expression. In some β-thalassemia patients, for example, disease symptoms arise from the alteration of a few nucleotides adjacent to the 5′ end of the coding region for the β chain. Data of this type have defined sequences that are important for expression of the β-globin locus. One such segment is the TATA box, a sequence found in many eukaryotic promoters (**Fig. 9.21a;** see Chapter 18 for a more detailed discussion). In other thalassemia patients, the entire α-globin locus and adjacent regulatory segments, including the TATA box, are intact, but a mutation has altered the LCR found far to the 5′ side of all the α-like genes. This LCR is necessary for a high level of tissue-specific expression of all α-like genes in red blood cell progenitors (**Fig. 9.21b**). Mutations in the TATA box or the locus control region, depending on how disruptive they are, produce α- or β-thalassemias of varying severity.

Disease-causing mutations in the globin genes range from the point mutation that causes sickle-cell anemia to the variety of mutations that cause thalassemia, including deletions, frameshifts, and changes to regulatory genes.

ll of the globin genes can be aced back to a single ancestral NA sequence

ith the use of bioinformatics, researchers can see that the human globin genes form a closely related group, gene family, that evolved by duplication and diver-

gence from one ancestral gene (**Fig. 9.22**). The two DNA sequence products of a duplication event, which start out identical, eventually diverge as they accumulate different mutations. The members of a gene family may be grouped together on one chromosome (like the very closely related *HBB* genes) or dispersed on different chromosomes (like the less closely related *HBA* and *HBB* clusters). All the β-like genes are exactly the same length and have two introns at exactly the same positions (Fig. 9.20b). Four of the five α-like genes also have two introns at exactly the same positions, but these positions are different from those of the β genes. (The first intron of the *HBZ* gene has been lengthened by subsequent insertion of DNA.) The sequences of all the β-like genes are more similar to each other than they are to the α-like sequences, and vice versa. These comparisons suggest that a single ancestral globin gene duplicated, and one copy moved to another chromosome. With time, one of the two gene copies gave rise to the α lineage, the other to the β lineage. Each lineage then underwent further duplications to generate the present array of three α-like and five β-like genes in humans.

Interestingly, the duplications also produced genes that eventually lost the ability to function. Molecular geneticists made this last deduction from data showing two additional α-like sequences within the α locus and one β-like sequence within the β locus that no longer have the capacity for proper expression. The reading frames are interrupted by frameshifts, missense mutations, and nonsense codons, while regions needed to control the expression of the genes have lost key DNA signals. Sequences that look like, but do not function as, a gene are known as **pseudogenes;** they occur throughout all higher eukaryotic genomes.

Connections

The tools of recombinant DNA technology grew out of an understanding of the DNA molecule and its interaction with the enzymes that operate on DNA in normal cells. Geneticists use the tools singly or in combination to look at DNA directly. Through cloning, hybridization, PCR, and sequencing, they have been able to isolate the genes that encode, for example, the hemoglobin proteins; identify sequences near the genes that regulate their expression; determine the complete nucleotide sequence of each gene; and discover the changes in sequence produced by the hundreds of mutations that affect hemoglobin production. The results give a fascinating and detailed picture of how the nucleotides along a DNA molecule determine protein structure and function and how mutations in sequence produce far-ranging and varied effects on human health. The methods of classical genetics that we examined in Chapters 2–5 complement those of recombinant DNA technology to produce an integrated picture of genes and genomes at many levels.

In Chapter 10, we describe how the use of recombinant DNA technology has expanded from the analysis of single genes and gene complexes to the sequencing and examination of whole genomes. Through the automation of sequencing and high-powered computer analysis of the data, scientific teams have determined the DNA sequence of the entire human genome and the genomes of many other organisms as well.

ESSENTIAL CONCEPTS

1. An intact eukaryotic genome is too complex for most types of analysis. Geneticists have appropriated the enzymes that normally operate on foreign DNA molecules inside a bacterial cell and used them in the test tube to create the tools of recombinant DNA technology. Restriction enzymes cut DNA at defined sites, ligase splices the pieces together, DNA polymerase makes DNA copies, and reverse transcriptase copies RNA into DNA.

2. Gel electrophoresis provides a method for separating DNA fragments according to their size. When biologists subject a viral genome, plasmid, or small chromosome to restriction digestion and gel electrophoresis, they can observe the resulting DNA fragments by ethidium bromide staining. They then determine the size of the fragments by comparing their migration within the gel with the migration of known marker fragments.

3. New technologies have allowed cloning of DNA fragments. Restriction fragments and cloning vectors with matching sticky ends can be spliced together to produce recombinant DNA molecules. A cloning vector is a DNA sequence that can enter a host cell, produce a selectable phenotype, and provide a means of replicating and purifying both itself and any DNA to which it is spliced.

4. Once inside a living cell, vector-insert recombinants are replicated during each cell cycle, just as the cell's own chromosomes are. A cellular clone consists of the millions of cells arising from consecutive divisions of a single cell. The vector-insert recombinant molecules inside the cells of a clone, often referred to as DNA clones, can be purified by procedures that separate recombinant molecules from host DNA. Restriction enzymes can cut away the insert, which can then undergo purification processing.

5. Genomic libraries are random collections of vector-insert recombinants containing DNA fragments of a given species. The most useful libraries carry at least four to five genomic equivalents. cDNA libraries carry DNA copies of the RNA transcripts produced in a particular tissue at a particular time. The clones in a cDNA library represent only that part of the genome transcribed and spliced into mRNA in the cells of a specific tissue, organ, or organism.

6. Hybridization is the process whereby complementary DNA strands form stable double helixes. Hybridization makes it possible to use previously purified DNA fragments as labeled probes. Biologists use such probes to identify clones containing identical or similar sequences within genomic or cDNA libraries. Hybridization can also be used with gel electrophoresis as part of the technique called Southern blotting. Southern blot hybridization allows an investigator to determine the numbers and positions of complementary sequences within isolated DNA fragments or whole genomes of any complexity.

7. The polymerase chain reaction (PCR) is a method for the rapid purification and amplification of a single DNA fragment from a complex mixture such as the whole human genome. The DNA fragment to be amplified is defined by a pair of oligonucleotide primers complementary to either end on opposite strands. The PCR procedure operates through a reiterative loop that amplifies the sequence between the primers in an exponential manner. PCR is used in place of cloning to purify DNA fragments whenever sequence information for primers is already available.

8. Sequencing provides the ultimate description of a cloned fragment. Automation has increased the speed and scope of sequencing.

9. Bioinformatics uses specialized software to analyze and interpret DNA sequence data. Many bioinformatics applications provide a web-based visual gateway into genome data that is freely accessible online. Bioinformatic comparisons of genomes from different species reveal conserved DNA sequences that must have essential functions since they have been conserved over evolutionary time.

On Our Website   www.mhhe.com/hartwell4

Annotated Suggested Readings and Links to Other Websites

- Foundational articles describing recombinant DNA technology
- Original DNA sequencing articles
- More on the human α- and β-globin loci and their associated diseases

- More on the use of restriction site analysis in the diagnosis of sickle-cell syndrome
- History of the biotechnology industry

Specialized Topics

- Agricultural biotechnology

Solved Problems

I. The following map of the plasmid cloning vector pBR322 shows the locations of the ampicillin (amp) and tetracycline (tet) resistance genes as well as two unique restriction enzyme recognition sites, one for *Eco*RI and one for *Bam*HI. You digested this plasmid vector with both *Eco*RI and *Bam*HI enzymes and purified the large *Eco*RI-*Bam*HI vector fragment. You also digested the cellular DNA that you want to insert into the vector with both *Eco*RI and *Bam*HI. After mixing the plasmid vector and the fragments together and ligating, you transformed an ampicillin-sensitive strain of *E. coli* and selected for ampicillin-resistant colonies. If you test all of your selected ampicillin-resistant transformants for tetracycline resistance, what result do you expect, and why?

Answer

This problem requires an understanding of vectors and the process of combining DNAs using sticky ends generated by restriction enzymes.

The plasmid must be circular to replicate in *E. coli*, and, in this case, a circular molecule will be formed only if the insert fragment joins with the cut vector DNA. The cut vector will not be able to religate without an inserted fragment because the *Bam*HI and *Eco*RI sticky ends are not complementary and cannot base pair. All ampicillin-resistant colonies therefore contain a *Bam*HI-*Eco*RI fragment ligated to the *Bam*HI-*Eco*RI sites of the vector. Fragments cloned at the *Bam*HI-*Eco*RI site interrupt and therefore inactivate the tetracycline resistance gene. *All ampicillin-resistant clones will be tetracycline sensitive.*

II. The gene for the human peptide hormone somatostatin (encoding nine amino acids) is completely contained on an *Eco*RI (5′ G∧AATTC 3′) fragment, which can be cut out of the larger fragment shown below. (The ∧ symbol indicates the site where the sugar-phosphate backbone is cut by the restriction enzyme.)

a. What is the amino acid sequence of human somatostatin?

b. Indicate the direction of transcription of this gene.

c. The first step in synthesizing large amounts of human somatostatin for pharmacological treatments involves constructing a so-called fusion gene. In this fusion construct, the N terminus of the protein encoded by the fusion gene consists of the N-terminal half of the *lacZ* gene (encoding β-galactosidase), while the remainder of the product of the fusion gene is human somatostatin. A family of three plasmid vectors for the construction of such a fusion gene has been created. All of these vectors have an ampicillin resistance gene and part of the *lacZ* gene encoding the first 583 amino acids of the β-galactosidase protein. The *Eco*RI fragment (that is, the fragment produced by cutting with *Eco*RI) containing human somatostatin

```
5′  GCCG^AATT CGATCCTATCAACACGAAGTGAAAGTCTTACAACCCATG^AATT CGATTCG  3′
3′  CGGC TTAA^GCTAGGATAGTTGTGCTTCACTTTCAGAATGTTGGGTAC TTAA^GCTAAGC  5′
```

can be inserted into the single *Eco*RI restriction site on the vectors. The sequence of three vectors in the vicinity of the *Eco*RI site is shown here. The numbers refer to amino acids in the β-galactosidase protein with the N-terminal amino acid being number 1. The DNA sequence presented is the same as that of the *lacZ* mRNA (with T's replacing the U's found in RNA). In which of these three vectors must the *Eco*RI fragment containing human somatostatin be inserted to generate a fusion protein with an N-terminal region from β-galactosidase and a C-terminal region from human somatostatin?

```
              582 583                          EcoRI
              Gly Asn                         ┌─────┐
pWR590-1   5′ GGCAACCGGGCGAGCTCGAATTCG
```

```
              582 583                      EcoRI
              Gly Asn                     ┌─────┐
pWR590-2   5′ GGCAACCCGGGCGAGCTCGAATTC
```

```
              582 583                       EcoRI
              Gly Asn                      ┌─────┐
pWR590-3   5′ GGCAACGGGGCAGCTCGAATTCGA
```

Answer

This problem requires an understanding of the sticky ends formed by restriction enzyme digestion and the requirement of appropriate reading frames for the production of proteins.

a. The only complete open reading frame (ATG start codon to a stop codon) is found on the bottom strand (underlined on the following figure). *The amino acid sequence is Met-Gly-Cys-Lys-Thr-Phe-The-Ser-Cys.*

b. Based on the amino acid sequence determined for part *a, the gene must be transcribed from right to left.*

c. The cut site for *Eco*RI is after the G at the 5′ end of the *Eco*RI recognition sequence on each strand. For each of the three vectors, the cut will be shifted relative to the reading frame of the *lacZ* gene by one base. The *Eco*RI fragment containing somatostatin

can ligate to the vector in two possible orientations but because we know the sequence on the bottom strand codes for the protein, a fusion protein will be produced only if the fragment is inserted with the coding sequence on the same strand as the vector coding sequences. Consider only this orientation to determine which vector will produce the fusion protein. The *Eco*RI fragment to be inserted into the vector next to the *lacZ* gene has five nucleotides that precede the first codon of the somatostatin gene (see following figure) and therefore requires one more nucleotide to match the reading frame of the vector. For pWR590-1, the cut results in an in-frame end; pWR590-2 has one base extra beyond the reading frame; pWR590-3 has a two-base extension past the reading frame. *The EcoRI fragment must be inserted in the vector pWR590-2 to get somatostatin protein produced.*

III. Imagine you have cloned a 14.7 kb piece of DNA which contains restriction sites as shown here.

```
        B  E        H    B  E
        |  |        |    |  |
     ───┴──┴────────┴────┴──┴─────────
      2   1.4   3.5    3   0.8    4    kb
```

B = *Bam*HI site, E = *Eco*RI site,
H = *Hind*III site

Numbers under the segments represent the sizes of the regions in kilobases (kb). You have labeled the left end of the molecule with ^{32}P. What radioactive bands would you expect to see following electrophoresis if you did a complete digestion with *Bam*HI? *Eco*RI? *Hind*III?

Answer

This problem deals with partial and complete digests and radioactive labeling of fragments. Only the left-most fragment would be seen after complete digestion with any of the three enzymes because only the left end contains radioactivity. *Radioactive bands seen after digestion with BamHI: 2 kb; EcoRI: 3.4 kb; and HindIII: 6.9 kb.*

```
5′ GCCG^AATT CGATCCTATCAACACGAAGTGAAAGTCTTACAACCCATG^AATT CGATTCG
3′ CGGCTTAA^GCTAGGATAGTTGTGCTTCACTTTCAGAATGTTGGGTACTTAA^GCTAAGC
```

![Problems banner]

Problems

Vocabulary

1. Match each of the terms in the left column to the best-fitting phrase from the right column.

a. oligonucleotide

    1. a DNA molecule used for transporting, replicating, and purifying a DNA fragment

b. vector

    2. a collection of the DNA fragments of a given species, inserted into a vector

c. sticky ends

    3. DNA copied from RNA by reverse transcriptase

d. recombinant DNA

    4. stable binding of single-stranded DNA molecules to each other

e. reverse translation

    5. efficient and rapid technique for amplifying the number of copies of DNA fragment

f. genomic library

    6. computational method for determining the possible sequence of base pairs associated with a particular region a polypeptide

g. genomic equivalent

    7. contains genetic material from two different organisms

h. cDNA

    8. the number of DNA fragments that are sufficient in aggregate length to contain the entire genome of a specified organism

i. PCR

9. short single-stranded sequences found at the ends of many restriction fragments

j. hybridization

10. a short DNA fragment that can be synthesized by a machine

Section 9.1

2. Approximately how many restriction fragments would result from the complete digestion of the human genome (3×10^9 bases) with the following restriction enzymes? (The recognition sequence for each enzyme is given in parentheses, where N means any of the four nucleotides.)
   a. *Sau*3A (ᴧGATC)
   b. *Bam*HI (GᴧGATCC)
   c. *Sfi*I (GGCCNNNNᴧNGGCC)

3. Why do longer DNA molecules move more slowly than shorter ones during electrophoresis?

4. You have a circular plasmid containing 9 kb of DNA, and you wish to map its *Eco*RI and *Bam*HI sites. When you digest the plasmid with *Eco*RI and run the resulting DNA on a gel, you observe a single band at 9 kb. You get the same result when you digest the DNA with *Bam*HI. When you digest with a mixture of both enzymes, you observe two bands, one 6 kb and the other 3 kb in size. Explain these results. Draw a map of the restriction sites.

5. The linear bacteriophage λ genomic DNA has at each end a single-strand extension of 20 bases. (These are "sticky ends" but are not, in this case, produced by restriction enzyme digestion.) These sticky ends can be ligated to form a circular piece of DNA. In a series of separate tubes, either the linear or circular forms of the DNA are digested to completion with *Eco*RI, *Bam*HI, or a mixture of the two enzymes. The results are shown here.

a. Which of the samples (A or B) represents the circular form of the DNA molecule?
b. What is the total length of the linear form of the DNA molecule?
c. What is the total length of the circular form of the DNA molecule?

d. Draw a restriction map of the linear form of the DNA molecule. Label all restriction enzyme sites as *Eco*RI or *Bam*HI.

6. The following fragments were found after digestion of a circular plasmid with restriction enzymes as noted. Draw a restriction map of the plasmid.

   *Eco*RI: 7.0 kb
   *Sal*I: 7.0 kb
   *Hin*dIII: 4.0, 2.0, 1.0 kb
   *Sal*I + *Hin*dIII: 2.5, 2.0, 1.5, 1.0 kb
   *Eco*RI + *Hin*dIII: 4.0, 2.0, 0.6, 0.4 kb
   *Eco*RI + *Sal*I: 2.9, 4.1 kb

Section 9.2

7. What purpose do selectable markers serve in vectors?

8. Why do geneticists studying eukaryotic organisms often construct cDNA libraries, whereas geneticists studying bacteria almost never do? Why would bacterial geneticists have difficulties constructing cDNA libraries even if they wanted to?

9. A plasmid vector pBS281 is cleaved by the enzyme *Bam*HI (GᴧGATCC), which recognizes only one site in the DNA molecule. Human DNA is digested with the enzyme *Mbo*I (ᴧGATC), which recognizes many sites in human DNA. These two digested DNAs are now ligated together. Consider only those molecules in which the pBS281 DNA has been joined with a fragment of human DNA. Answer the following questions concerning the junction between the two different kinds of DNA.
   a. What proportion of the junctions between pBS281 and all possible human DNA fragments can be cleaved with *Mbo*I?
   b. What proportion of the junctions between pBS281 and all possible human DNA fragments can be cleaved with *Bam*HI?
   c. What proportion of the junctions between pBS281 and all possible human DNA fragments can be cleaved with *Xor*II (CᴧGATCG)?
   d. What proportion of the junctions between pBS281 and all possible human DNA fragments can be cleaved with *Eco*RII (Pu Pu A ^ T Py Py)? (Pu and Py stand for purine and pyrimidine, respectively.)
   e. What proportion of all possible junctions that can be cleaved with *Bam*HI will result from cases in which the cleavage site in human DNA was not a *Bam*HI site in the human chromosome?

10. Consider three different kinds of human libraries: a genomic library, a brain cDNA library, and a liver cDNA library.
    a. Assuming inserts of approximately equal size, which would contain the greatest number of different clones?

b. Would you expect any of these not to overlap the others at all in terms of the sequences it contains? Explain.

c. How do these three libraries differ in terms of the starting material for constructing the clones in the library?

11. As a molecular biologist and horticulturist specializing in snapdragons, you have decided that you need to make a genomic library to characterize the flower color genes of snapdragons.

a. How many genomic equivalents would you like to have represented in your library to be 95% confident of having a clone containing each gene in your library?

b. How do you determine the number of clones that should be isolated and screened to guarantee this number of genomic equivalents?

12. Imagine that you are a molecular geneticist studying a particular gene in which mutations cause a serious human disease. The gene, including its flanking regulatory sequences, spans 200 kb of DNA. The distance from the first to the last coding base is 140 kb, which is divided among 10 exons and 9 introns. The exons contain a total of 9.7 kb, and the introns contain 130.3 kb of DNA. You would like to obtain the following for your work: (a) an intact clone of the whole gene, including flanking sequences; (b) a clone containing the entire coding sequences but no noncoding sequences; and (c) a clone of exon 3, which is the site of the most common disease-causing mutation in this gene. For each of these clones, describe the source of the human DNA to be inserted into the vector, and decide whether you would use a plasmid vector or a BAC vector. (Note: where possible, it is technically easier to use plasmids than BACs as vectors.) Explain your answers.

13. A 49 bp *Eco*RI fragment containing the somatostatin gene was inserted into the vector pWR590 shown below. The sequence of the inserted fragment is

```
5' AATTCGATCCTATCAACACGAAGTGAAAGTCTTACAACCCATGAATTCG 3'
3'    GCTAGGATAGTTGTGCTTCACTTTCAGAATGTTGGGTACTTAAGCTTAA 5'
```

Distances between adjacent restriction sites in the pWR590 vector are indicated in the diagram. What are the patterns of restriction digests with *Eco*RI (G⌃AATTC) or with *Mbo*I (⌃GATC) before and after cloning the somatostatin gene into the vector? E = *Eco*RI, M = *Mbo*I)

pWR590

14. The *Notch* gene involved in *Drosophila* development is contained within a restriction fragment of *Drosophila* genomic DNA produced by cleavage with the enzyme *Sal*I. The restriction map of this *Drosophila* fragment for several enzymes (*Sal*I, *Pst*I, and *Xho*I) is shown here; numbers indicate the distances between adjacent restriction sites. This fragment is cloned by sticky end ligation into the single *Sal*I site of a bacterial plasmid vector that is 5.2 kb long. The plasmid vector has no restriction sites for *Pst*I or *Xho*I enzymes.

Make a sketch of the expected patterns seen after agarose gel electrophoresis and staining of a *Sal*I digest (alone), of a *Pst*I digest (alone), of a *Xho*I digest (alone), of the plasmid containing vector and *Drosophila* fragment. Indicate the fragment sizes in kilobases.

15. Your undergraduate research advisor has assigned you a task: Insert an *Eco*RI-digested fragment of frog DNA into an *E. coli* plasmid that carries a *lacZ* gene with an *Eco*RI site in the middle (see Fig. 9.7 on p. 300). Your advisor suggests that after you digest your plasmid with *Eco*RI, you should treat the plasmid with the enzyme alkaline phosphatase. This enzyme removes phosphate groups that may be located at the 5′ ends of DNA strands. You will then add the fragment of frog DNA to the vector and join the two together with the enzyme DNA ligase.

You don't quite follow your advisor's reasoning, so you set up two ligations, one with plasmid that was treated with alkaline phosphatase and the other without such treatment. Otherwise, the ligation mixtures are identical. After the ligation reactions are completed, you transform a small aliquot (portion) of each ligation into *E. coli* and spread the cells on petri plates containing both ampicillin and Xgal. The next day you observe 100 white colonies and one blue colony on the plate transformed with alkaline-phosphatase-treated plasmids and 100 blue colonies and one white colony on the plate transformed with plasmids that had not been treated with alkaline phosphatase.

a. Explain the results seen on the two plates.

b. Why was your research advisor's suggestion a good one?

c. Why would you normally treat plasmid vectors with alkaline phosphatase but not the DNA fragments you want to add to the vector?

Section 9.3

16. a. Given the following restriction map of a cloned 10 kb piece of DNA, what size fragments would you see after digesting this linear DNA fragment with each of the enzymes or combinations of enzymes

listed? (1) *Eco*RI, (2) *Bam*HI, (3) *Eco*RI + *Hind*III, (4) *Bam*HI + *Pst*I, and (5) *Eco*RI + *Bam*HI.

b. What fragments in the last three double digests would hybridize on a Southern blot with a probe made from the 4 kb *Bam*HI fragment?

```
E    H H    E    B          P          B      E
+----+-+----+----+----------+----------+------+
 1.5  0.6 1.0  1.2    2.1        1.9       1.7  kb
```

17. Human genomic DNA was digested with the various restriction enzymes noted in the list below. These digests were subjected to electrophoresis on an agarose gel; the DNA separated in the gel was then stained with ethidium bromide, and a photograph of the fluorescence was taken. The DNA in the gel was transferred to a nitrocellulose filter to make a Southern blot, and this blot was then probed with a radioactive 5 kb-long fragment of cloned human DNA with *Eco*RI sites at both ends. The sizes of the dark bands seen on an X-ray film exposed to the Southern blot for each digest were

*Eco*RI: 5 kb
*Kpn*I: 2.5 kb, 6 kb
*Hind*III: 8 kb
*Eco*RI + *Kpn*I: 4 kb, 1 kb
*Eco*RI + *Hind*III: 5 kb
*Kpn*I: + *Hind*III: 2.5 kb, 4.5 kb

a. Why were these digests separated by electrophoresis on agarose gels rather than polyacrylamide gels?

b. Describe what you would see on the photograph of the ethidium bromide–stained gel.

c. In this problem, the sums of the sizes of all the dark bands seen on the X-ray film of the Southern blot are not the same for all the digests reported. However, in previous problems involving restriction mapping (such as Problems 5, 6, 14 and 16), all the digests of a particular DNA sample produce fragments the sum of whose sizes are the same. Explain this difference.

d. Draw a restriction map that accounts for the results of this Southern blot.

e. Can you orient the restriction map you drew in part *d* to the centromere-to-telomere direction along the human chromosome on which these DNA sequences are located?

8. You have cloned and characterized a particularly interesting protein-coding gene from the bacterium *Bacillus subtilis,* and you would like to isolate the corresponding, homologous gene from the rare, poorly characterized bacterial species *Beneckea nigripulchritudo* that infects certain shrimp. You decide to make degenerate probes to identify, by hybridization, clones containing this homologous gene. The amount of degeneracy is a

potential problem because the more types of different DNA molecules contained in the probe, the worse the signal-to-noise ratio in the hybridization experiment. How can you minimize the degeneracy? Be as specific as possible, mentioning such factors as the length of the probe and the region of DNA you will choose to synthesize by reverse translation.

19. It is possible to use hybridization techniques similar to those described for the Southern blot procedure (Fig. 9.11 on pp. 308–309) to identify within a library particular clones homologous to a nucleic acid probe. The idea is to transfer some DNA from the colonies growing on a plate to a nitrocellulose filter, hybridize the filter with the radioactive probe, and then pick cells from the original plate that correspond to the positions of probe hybridization. With this idea in mind, place in an appropriate order the following steps that could be used.

a. Mix together BAC vector DNA and hoot owl DNA with ligase.

b. Expose nitrocellulose paper disks to UV radiation and baking.

c. Extract genomic DNA from hoot owl cells.

d. Visualize labeled DNA fragments.

e. Produce a labeled DNA probe to the *idiosynchratase* gene.

f. Completely digest BAC vector DNA with the restriction enzyme *Hind*III.

g. Place nitrocellulose paper disks onto the agar surface to transfer colonies.

h. Incubate DNA probe with nitrocellulose paper disks.

i. Distribute bacteria onto a petri plate containing agar and nutrients and allow growth into colonies.

j. Partially digest hoot owl genomic DNA with the restriction enzyme *Hind*III.

k. Transform bacteria.

Section 9.4

20. Using PCR, you want to amplify a ~1 kb exon of the human autosomal gene encoding the enzyme phenylalanine hydroxylase from the genomic DNA of a patient suffering from the autosomal recessive condition phenylketonuria (PKU).

a. Why might you wish to perform this PCR amplification in the first place, given that the sequence of the human genome has already been determined?

b. Calculate the number of template molecules that are present if you set up a PCR reaction using 1 nanogram (1×10^{-9} grams) of chromosomal DNA as the template. Assume that each haploid genome contains only a single gene for phenylalanine hydroxylase and that the molecular weight of a base pair is 660 grams per mole. The human genome contains 3×10^9 base pairs.

c. Calculate the number of PCR product molecules you would obtain if you perform 25 PCR cycles and the yield from each cycle is exactly twice that of the previous cycle. What would be the mass of these PCR products taken together?

21. Which of the following set(s) of primers could you use to amplify the target DNA sequence below, which is part of the last protein-coding exon of the *CFTR* gene?

```
5' GGCTAAGATCTGAATTTTCCGAG ... TTGGGCAATAATGTAGCGCCTT 3'
3' CCGATTCTAGACTTAAAAGGCTC ... AACCCGTTATTACATCGCGGAA 5'
```

a. 5' GGAAAATTCAGATCTTAG 3';
   5' TGGGCAATAATGTAGCGC 3'
b. 5' GCTAAGATCTGAATTTTC 3';
   3' ACCCGTTATTACATCGCG 5'
c. 3' GATTCTAGACTTAAAGGC 5';
   3' ACCCGTTATTACATCGCG 5'
d. 5' GCTAAGATCTGAATTTTC 3';
   5' TGGGCAATAATGTAGCGC 3'

22. Problem 21 raises several interesting questions about the design of PCR primers.
   a. PCR is important because it can amplify a single region of DNA from a complex genome. How can you be sure that the two primers you chose as your answer to Problem 21 will amplify only an exon of the *CFTR* gene from a sample of human genomic DNA?
   b. The protocol for PCR shown in Fig. 9.12 on pp. 311–312 states that each of the primers used should be 16–26 nucleotides long. (i) Why do you think the lower limit would be approximately 16? (ii) The upper limit of 26 nucleotides is not absolute. For some applications of PCR, it is possible to use longer primers, but at the risk of introducing potential difficulties. What complications or disadvantages might be associated with longer primers?
   c. Suppose that one of the primers you designed in your answer to Problem 21 had a mismatch with a single base in the genomic DNA of a particular individual. Would you be more likely to obtain a PCR product from this genomic DNA if the mismatch were at the 5' end or at the 3' end of the primer? Why?
   d. Suppose you wanted to clone the region you amplified in Problem 21 into a plasmid vector with a single site for the restriction enzyme *EcoRI*? How could you modify the PCR primers to produce a PCR product with *EcoRI* sites at both ends?

23. You wish to purify large amounts of the part of the CFTR protein that is encoded by the last protein coding exon shown in Problem 21 and that begins with the amino acid sequence

N...Leu Arg Ser Glu Phe Ser Glu...C

and ends with the sequence

N...Trp Ala Ile Met (C terminus)

You will start this process by cloning an appropriate PCR product into the pMore vector, part of whose sequence is shown in the following. The pMore vector makes large amounts of maltose binding protein (MBP) when transformed into *E. coli*. The amino acids shown with the vector sequence correspond to the C-terminal end of MBP. To do the cloning, you will digest both the pMore vector and your PCR product with both the *EcoRI* (G^AATTC) and *SalI* (G^TCGAC) restriction enzymes and then ligate the pieces together. The vector has only a single site for each of these enzymes.

```
5'...AGGATTTCAGAATTCGGATCCTCTAGAGTCGACCTGTAGGGCAA...3'
     ArgIleSerGluPheGlySerSerArgValAspLeup
```

a. As discussed in Solved Problem II on pp. 327–328, a fusion protein contains amino acid sequences derived from two or more naturally occurring polypeptides. Describe the fusion protein that will be made when the PCR product is ligated into the vector. What are the orientations of the parts of MBP and CFTR relative to that of the fusion protein?
b. What advantages might there be for cutting the vector and PCR product with two restriction enzymes instead of one?
c. Design PCR primers that will allow you to construct the desired recombinant DNA molecule. Note (i) that the sequence shown in Problem 23 has neither *EcoRI* nor *SalI* sites, (ii) that additional nucleotides can be added to appropriate locations in the PCR primers, and (iii) that restriction enzymes require about 5 nucleotides on either side of the restriction site for the enzymes to work. This problem is extremely difficult, but will help you integrate a great deal of information about gene structure and recombinant DNA technology.
d. MBP can bind to the sugars amylose and maltose. The last 20 amino acids at the C terminus of MBP are not required for this property. It is also possible to synthesize chemically an amylose resin (beads with covalently bound amylose). How would these facts be helpful in allowing you to purify a large amount of a region of the CFTR protein?

Section 9.5

24. Several of the techniques discussed in this chapter, particularly restriction mapping and methods based on DNA hybridization such as Southern blots, are still often used for studying genes in unusual organisms. However, in the twenty-first century, these techniques are used much more rarely than in the late twentieth century for studying genes in humans or in model organisms such as yeast, *C. elegans*, *Drosophila*, or mice. What has changed with the millenium, and what new techniques have arisen as replacements?

25. Which of the following processes used in biotechnology relies on specific enzymes? What are those enzymes? What is the basis for any of these processes that are not enzyme based?
  a. DNA ligation
  b. cleavage of DNA at specific sites
  c. DNA hybridization
  d. DNA sequencing
  e. cDNA synthesis
  f. PCR

26. a. If you are presented with the following sequencing autoradiogram, what can you say about the sequence of the template strand used in these sequencing reactions?
  b. If the template for sequencing is the strand that resembles the mRNA, write out the sequence of the mRNA insofar as it can be determined.
  c. Is this portion of the genome likely to be within a coding region? Explain your answer.

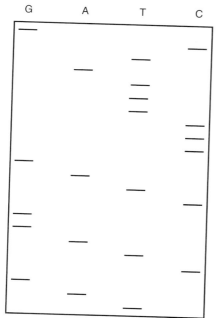

27. You read the following sequence directly from a gel.

5′ TCTAGCCTGAACTAATGC 3′

  a. Make a drawing that reproduces the autoradiogram from which this sequence was read. How would you know the reading frame if you are reading this short sequence off a gel?
  b. Assuming this sequence is from an exon in the middle of a gene, does this newly synthesized strand or the template strand have the same sequence as the mRNA for the gene (except that T's are present instead of U's)? Justify your answer.
  c. Using the genetic code table, give the amino acid sequence of the hexapeptide (six amino acids) translated from the 18-base message. Indicate which is the amino terminal end of the peptide.

28. The following figure portrays a trace derived from the automated sequencing of a certain PCR product produced by the amplification of the genomic DNA from a particular person's cells. The left-to-right orientation of the peaks on the trace corresponds to smaller-to-larger fragments of DNA. The height of the peaks is unimportant. (red = T; green = A; black = G; purple = C)
  a. What does the green peak at the left end of the trace signify? Be as precise as possible.
  b. Write the sequence of DNA revealed by this trace, indicating the 5′-to-3′ orientation.
  c. What do you think is meant by "residue position"? That is, what is located at residue position 1?
  d. Explain the apparent anomaly at residue position 370.

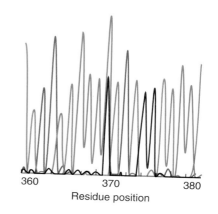

Section 9.6

29. Referring to Fig. 9.16 on p. 320:
  a. What is the significance of the RefSeq genes' appearing to pile up in the vertical direction on part *a* of the figure?
  b. What is the approximate location of the longest "gene desert" on human chromosome 7 (that is, the longest region devoid of genes)?
  c. What is the approximate location of the centromere on human chromosome 7?
  d. Is the *CFTR* gene located on the short arm or the long arm of human chromosome 7?
  e. In which direction is the *CFTR* gene transcribed: toward the centromere, or away from the centromere?
  f. What is the approximate number of exons in the *CFTR* gene? Why is this number only an approximation?

30. You have just determined the DNA sequence of part of a chromosome in a rare, newly discovered vertebrate species. How would you try to annotate this sequence; that is, how could you find any genes or other functionally important DNA regions contained in this part of the genome? How would you determine whether any of the genes you found undergo alternative splicing in different tissues?

CHAPTER 10

Genomes and Proteomes

Chromosome

Nucleus

DNA

Cell

Since the mid-nineteenth century, three advances have radically transformed the field of genetics: Mendel's discovery of fundamental principles in the 1860s, Watson and Crick's elucidation of DNA structure in 1953, and the Human Genome Project from 1990 to the present. In this chapter, we discuss the Human Genome Project and the field of genomics that it spawned.

The **Human Genome Project** was initiated to sequence and analyze the human genome in conjunction with the genomes of several model organisms. A "genome" is the total digital information contained within the DNA sequences of an organism's chromosomes. Although the human genome is contained within 46 chromosomes, 99.9% of the information in each autosome is the same as in its partner homolog. Thus, each pair of autosomes (22 pairs) is counted only once, together with the X and Y chromosomes, for a total of 24 chromosomes that roughly describe the information content of the human genome. These 24 strings of G's, C's, T's, and A's contain a total of approximately 3 billion nucleotides and range in size from 45 million to 250 million bp.

Genomics, the study of whole genomes, is a branch of biology dedicated to the development and application of more effective mapping, sequencing, and computational tools. Genomicists use large-scale, or global, molecular techniques for linkage analysis, physical mapping, and the sequencing of genomes to generate vast amounts of data, which they then analyze by computer. Sophisticated programs enable genomicists to predict the existence and, in some cases, the general functions of previously undefined genes. These predictions can then be verified by molecular biology techniques.

The first meeting on the Human Genome Project took place in Santa Cruz, California, in the spring of 1985. The chancellor of the University of California at Santa Cruz had assembled 12 biologists of diverse backgrounds to explore the idea of starting an institute to sequence the human genome. After two days of heated discussion, the 12 biologists concluded that it would, indeed, be possible to develop the technology required to accomplish this then seemingly impossible objective. However, the group was split on whether it would be a good idea for the scientific community.

Two aspects of their discussion were striking. First, the concept of the Human Genome Project introduced the idea of *discovery science*—a new scientific approach to biology. In **discovery science,** one seeks to identify all the elements of a biological system—for instance, the complete sequences of the 24 chromosomes that contain

The human genome, present in the nucleus of each cell, contains the instructions for transforming a single fertilized egg cell into an adult with 10^{14} cells. Each genome has ≈ 3 billion letters of the DNA language divided among 24 distinct chromosomes ranging in size from 45 million to 280 million letters. The Human Genome Project undertook the challenging task of deciphering this book of life.

CHAPTER OUTLINE

- 10.1 Large-Scale Genome Mapping and Analysis
- 10.2 Major Insights from the Human and Model Organism Genome Sequences
- 10.3 Global Analysis of Genes and Their mRNAs
- 10.4 Global Analysis of Proteomes
- 10.5 Repercussions of the Human Genome Project and High-Throughput Technology

the 3 billion nucleotides of the human genome—and place them in a database to enrich the infrastructure of biology. Discovery science stands in contrast to hypothesis-driven approaches to biology, in which one asks questions and seeks experimental verification of possible answers. Second, the Human Genome Project required the development of very fast and reliable ("high-throughput") automated DNA sequencing technology as well as the computational tools necessary for capturing, storing, and analyzing the vast amounts of cloning, mapping, and sequence data associated with obtaining genome sequences.

Not surprisingly, most biologists initially viewed the Human Genome Project with skepticism. They thought the project would not be particularly worthwhile because about only 2% of the genome codes for proteins; the remaining 98%, they argued, must be just "junk." In the mid-1980s, most biologists also believed that the Human Genome Project was not really a scientific endeavor because it was not hypothesis-driven. Many did not understand how the discovery approach to determining the sequence of the human genome would revolutionize the power and potential of genetic and other biological studies. Finally, some viewed the Human Genome Project as "big science" that would inappropriately compete for funds with more fruitful and productive, small-scale hypothesis-driven science.

In 1988, the National Academy of Sciences appointed a committee (half proponents and half opponents) to consider the scientific merits of the Human Genome Project. After a year of vigorous debate and analysis, the committee unanimously endorsed the project, marking a major turning point in its acceptance. The government-funded Human Genome Project began in 1990 with a projected 15-year time scale and a $3 billion budget for completing the human genome sequence.

A rough sequence draft of the human genome was completed in February 2001 (**Fig. 10.1**); in this "draft" the sequence did not yet have an appropriate level of accuracy (an error rate of 1/10,000), and it had some gaps. An accurate sequence covering 97% of the genome was completed in 2003, two years ahead of the originally proposed 2005 finish date. The early finish was in part catalyzed by the 1998 promise of Celera, a private company, to complete a draft of the genome in just three years, employing a novel sequencing strategy. The federally supported genome effort reacted by moving its timetable ahead by several years. By July 2009, whole-genome sequences had been completed for 2133 distinct species, including 30 different mammals that all have genomes of approximately the same size as humans (**Table 10.1**).

By comparing the DNA of other organisms to that of humans, researchers seek to uncover genes and other critical DNA elements that are conserved across evolutionary lines. The Human Genome Project catalyzed efforts to sequence these myriad species. Such sequencing projects have revolutionized the study of microbiology as well as that of genetics, molecular biology, and plant development.

In other accomplishments, production of a human genome–wide genetic map has made it possible to identify 2359 genes causing different human diseases (as of July 2009). The identification of genes predisposing individuals to specific diseases creates new opportunities for diagnosis and therapy as well as for understanding the biology of the disease.

Figure 10.1 DNA sequence coverage of the first rough draft of the human genome. For each chromosome, the first draft coverage—the proportion of the chromosome sequenced—is shown along with the summed length of sequence gaps. This first draft included 93% of the total human genome. Targeted sequencing of gaps was performed over the five years following the draft release, and in March 2006, a finished human genome sequence with greater than 99% coverage and 99.99% accuracy was published.

Chromosome	Including gaps	Sequenced	Gaps
1	247,249,719	224,999,719	22,250,000
2	242,951,149	237,712,649	5,238,500
3	199,501,827	194,704,827	4,797,000
4	191,273,063	187,297,063	3,976,000
5	180,857,866	177,702,766	3,155,100
6	170,899,992	167,273,992	3,626,000
7	158,821,424	154,952,424	3,869,000
8	146,274,826	142,612,826	3,662,000
9	140,273,252	120,143,252	20,130,000
10	135,374,737	131,624,737	3,750,000
11	134,452,384	131,130,853	3,321,531
12	132,349,534	130,303,534	2,046,000
13	114,142,980	95,559,980	18,583,000
14	106,368,585	88,290,585	18,078,000
15	100,338,915	81,341,915	18,997,000
16	88,827,254	78,884,754	9,942,500
17	78,774,742	77,800,220	974,522
18	76,117,153	74,656,155	1,460,998
19	63,811,651	55,785,651	8,026,000
20	62,435,964	59,505,253	2,930,711
21	46,944,323	34,171,998	12,772,325
22	49,691,432	34,851,332	14,840,100
X	154,913,754	151,058,754	3,855,000
Y	57,772,954	25,652,954	32,120,000
M	16,571	16,571	0
Total genome	**3,080,436,051**	**2,858,034,764**	**222,401,287**

TABLE 10.1	Number of Species with Finished Whole-Genome Sequences Deposited at the National Center for Biotechnology Information as of February 1, 2010		
Organism	Whole Genome	In Progress	Total
Prokaryotes	1058	2354	3412
Mammals	56	69	125
Birds	2	12	14
Fishes	15	17	32
Insects	36	7	43
Flatworms	3	2	5
Roundworms	12	14	26
Amphibians	1	0	1
Reptiles	1	0	1
Other animals	11	18	29
Plants	25	88	113
Fungi	129	91	220
Protists	54	58	112
Total	1403	2730	4133

Another significant aspect of the Human Genome Project is that it includes in its statement of purpose the consideration of the social, ethical, and legal challenges emerging from its projected results; for example, the issue of genetic privacy. It was the first scientific project to do so. At the suggestion of James Watson, the first director, 3% to 5% of the project's research funds were dedicated to the study of ethical, legal, and social implications (ELSI) of mapping the genome. A critical concept is the education of society about the new genetics so that public and private figures alike can make informed decisions about resource allocations and the rules and regulations governing applications of the new technologies.

As we describe the tools and potential applications of genomics, we encounter a compelling general theme: The social and personal repercussions of the information gained from genomic analysis are generating new areas of biological concern that require close attention as the new knowledge unfolds.

10.1 Large-Scale Genome Mapping and Analysis

The genomes of microbes and eukaryotes range from the 700,000 base pairs (700 kb) in a single microbial chromosome to more than 3 billion base pairs (3 gigabase pairs, or 3 Gb) distributed among the 5–96 chromosomes of various mammals to even larger genomes. **Table 10.2** gives the genome sizes of representative microbes, plants, and animals. One amoeba, *Amoeba dubia,* has a genome of more than 600 billion base pairs, and wheat has a

genome of 15 billion base pairs. To put these numbers in perspective, the human genome is 200 times larger than the yeast genome and 200 times smaller than the genome of *Amoeba dubia.* Thus, the information content of a genome is not necessarily proportional to the complexity of the organism it defines. The large size of some genomes presents fascinating challenges for their ultimate characterization and analysis.

Genomicists face major challenges in dealing with this immense body of data. One of these is how to make sequences accurately. In this section, we consider both

TABLE 10.2	A Comparison of the Developmental Complexity and Genome Features* of Model Organisms					
Organism		**Developmental Complexity**	**Genome Size* (Megabases)**	**Number of Genes**	**# of Genes per Million bp Sequenced**	**Date Genome Finished**
Type	**Species**					
Bacterium	*Escherichia coli*	1-cell prokaryote	4.64	3244	905	1997
Yeast	*Saccharomyces cerevisiae*	1-cell eukaryote	12.07	6201	483	1996
Worm	*Caenorhabditis elegans*	≈ 1000 cells	100	21,188	197	1998
Fly	*Drosophila melanogaster*	$\approx 50,000$ cells	180	22,606	117	2000
Mustard weed	*Arabidopsis thaliana*	10^{10} cells	125	33,500	221	2000
Rice (draft)	*Oryza sativa*	5×10^{10} cells	466/420	29,437	127–155/82–128	2002
Mouse	*Mus musculus*	10^{11} cells	3200	61,818	10–13	2005
Human	*Homo sapiens*	10^{14} cells	3200	45,416	18	2003

Haploid genome size, including heterochromatic DNA.

Note: For the sequenced genomes of model organisms, gene numbers are taken from the original sequence publications; most numbers have since changed slightly. For rice, two different strains have been sequenced: *Oryza sativa* L. ssp. *Japonica* and *Oryza sativa* L. ssp. *Indica*.

physical maps of markers on chromosomes and sequence maps that provide high resolution.

Long-range physical maps are produced using the FISH protocol

Chromosomal maps show the location of genes, genetic markers, centromeres, telomeres, and other points of interest along the chromosome of an organism. In Chapter 5, we described techniques for mapping a small number of loci in a relatively small region of a genome. Geneticists use the terms "linkage" and "genetic" interchangeably when talking about maps made through analyses of recombination frequencies. Here we examine how genomicists expand on these techniques to produce physical and sequence maps for a whole genome.

The analysis of the human genome focused initially on a genomewide linkage map, then a physical map, and finally a sequence map. These maps were successively integrated into each other. The linkage map was produced by a global genomewide approach; the physical map by a hierarchical divide and conquer approach; and the sequence map by both strategies.

A *physical map* is a constellation of overlapping DNA fragments that are ordered and oriented and span each of the chromosomes in a genome. Physical maps, the molecular counterparts of linkage maps, are based on the direct analysis of genomic DNA. Such maps chart the actual number of base pairs (bp), kilobases (kb), or megabases (Mb) that define and separate a locus, or site, from its neighbors in a particular region of a particular chromosome. Linkage and physical maps can be roughly calibrated against one another. For example, in humans, 1 cM $\approx$ 1 Mb, whereas in mice, 1 cM $\approx$ 2 Mb.

As we saw in Fig. 9.6 on p. 299, geneticists build relatively short-range physical maps by exposing DNA clones to two or more restriction enzymes and comparing the fragments produced in this way; they then use hybridization probes to ascribe a precise position to the genes and markers included in the mapped clone. The major difference between the physical maps discussed earlier and those developed by genomicists is one of scale. A map of a plasmid clone, for example, might span 10,000 bp of genomic DNA. Here we learn how molecular geneticists map a human chromosome averaging 130,000,000 bp in length (approximately 13,000 times longer than a single plasmid). Figure 10.1 shows the length of each human chromosome, the portion that was originally sequenced, and the total length of unsequenced gaps.

A summary of karyotyping

You learned in Chapter 4 that the chromosomes of actively dividing cells in metaphase of mitosis, when stained with a Giemsa dye and viewed in the light microscope, show an identifiable series of dark and light regions termed bands and interbands (Fig. 4.4 on p. 82 and **Fig. 10.2a**). The number, intensity, and width of each band and interband are highly reproducible characteristics that a skilled cytogeneticist can use to distinguish each pair of homologs from all other chromosomes in a cell (see Chapter 12 for details). The visual description of a complete set of chromosomes in one cell of an organism is a *karyotype*.

For convenience, investigators convert the light and dark bands actually observed under the microscope into black-and-white diagrams of the chromosomes called **idiograms** (Fig. 10.2a and b). In these diagrams, the autosomes are numbered in order of descending length. The

Figure 10.2 The human karyotype: Banding distinguishes the chromosomes. (a) Photograph of a complete set of human chromosomes stained at metaphase. **(b)** Idiograms for the complete set of human chromosomes. **(c)** Chromosome 7 at three different levels of banding resolution. As staining techniques improve, what previously appeared as a single band resolves into a series of bands and interbands, producing more and more bands along each chromosome. Thus, at the resolution on the left 7q31 appears as one band. At a slightly higher resolution (middle), 7q31 becomes two bands (7q31.1 and 7q31.3) flanking an interband (7q31.2); and at an even higher resolution (right), 7q31.3 itself appears as two bands (7q31.31 and 7q31.33) and an interband (7q31.32).

shorter arm of each chromosome is designated "p" (for *petit*) and the longer arm is "q" (for queue, the French word for "tail"). Karyotypers number each band and interband, starting at the centromere and moving out along each arm toward the telomere.

Spectral karyotyping (SKY): A FISH application

Figure 10.3 shows the elegant SKY (spectral karyotyping) method for constructing karyotypes which makes it easy to identify individual chromosomes. The SKY technique is a specialized application of a more general protocol known as **fluorescent *in situ* hybridization,** or **FISH,** which is used to locate regions in the genome that are homologous to a nucleic acid probe. **Figure 10.4** illustrates the steps of the FISH protocol. In spectral karyotyping, each probe for *in situ* hybridization is made from multiple DNAs that originated from positions scattered along the length of individual chromosomes. The probe

for chromosome 1 is labeled with a group that fluoresce in one color; the probe for chromosome 2 is tagged with fluorescence of a different color, and so forth, so that each of the 24 human chromosomes in a SKY karyotype can be recognized by its color (Fig. 10.3).

For the purposes of map making, FISH is more commonly used to show the location of a particular DNA sequence within the genome. In a mapping experiment, a single DNA probe is labeled with a fluorescent tag and hybridized with the chromosomes. The site(s) of hybridization appear under the microscope as discrete spots of illumination that indicate the chromosomal location of the DNA in the probe (Fig. 10.4b).

Karyotypic analysis thus enables the generation of low-resolution physical maps that locate cloned genes and markers on particular parts of chromosomes. Geneticists use the cloning techniques described in Chapter 9 to expand these maps with a much finer resolution of loci. The ultimate goal of high-resolution physical mapping

Figure 10.3 A SKY chromosomal *in situ* hybridization. Each chromosome has a distinctive color, and homologs match each other. X and Y are shown at the bottom right.

Figure 10.4 The FISH protocol. (a) The technique. (1) First, drop cells arrested in the metaphase stage of the cell cycle onto a microscope slide. The cells burst open with the chromosomes spread apart. (2) Next, fix the chromosomes and gently denature the DNA within them such that the overall chromosomal structure is maintained even though each DNA double helix opens up at numerous points. (3) Label a DNA probe with a fluorescent dye, add it to the slide, incubate long enough for hybridization to occur, and wash away unhybridized probe. (4) View the slide under a specialized fluorescence microscope that utilizes UV. The UV light causes the bound probe to fluoresce in the visible range of the spectrum. **(b)** A fluorescence micrograph of a baby hamster kidney cell subjected to FISH analysis. The four yellow spots show the locations at which a particular probe hybridizes to the two sister chromatids of two homologous chromosomes.

(a)

1. Drop cells onto a glass slide.

2. Gently denature DNA by treating briefly with DNase.

3. Add hybridization probes labeled with fluorescent dye and wash away unhybridized probe.

Fluorescent probes

Fluorescent dye

Fluorescence microscope

Eyepiece

Barrier filter 2 (further blockage of stray UV rays)

UV source

Mirror to UV light; transparent to visible light

Barrier filter 1 (blocks dangerous short UV rays, allows needed long UV rays to pass through)

Objective lens

Object

4. Expose to ultraviolet (UV) light. Take picture of fluorescent chromosomes.

(b)

the generation of one large contig for each chromosome in a genome. A **contig** (from the word *contiguous*) is a set of two or more overlapping cloned DNA fragments that together cover an uninterrupted stretch of the genome.

Once a combination of approaches to generating whole chromosome contigs has produced an ordered array of overlapping clones for all the chromosomes in the genome, researchers can study the clones of each contig in greater detail. In this way, they can locate and analyze genes and markers of interest. A computer can then combine all the information for all the clones into a detailed physical map showing a variety of landmarks across the contigs of all the chromosomes in the genome.

Fluorescent in situ hybridization (FISH) allows long-range physical mapping of chromosomes using fluorescent probes to locate homologous regions. Spectral karyotyping (SKY) employs probes of different colors to tag regions of different chromosomes, so that each chromosome pair can be readily identified. The goal of physical mapping is to produce a contig, or contiguous map, of a chromosome.

Sequence maps have the highest resolution

Sequence maps show the order of nucleotides in a cloned piece of DNA. The goal of the Human Genome Project was the determination of the complete nucleotide sequence for every chromosome in the genome (of humans and model organisms). Two basic strategies have been employed for sequencing genomes: the *hierarchical shotgun approach* and the *whole-genome shotgun approach*. The term **shotgun** means that the overlapping insert fragments to be sequenced have been randomly generated either from large insert clones (BACs) or from the whole genome by shearing with sound (sonication) or by partial digestion with restriction enzymes.

The hierarchical shotgun sequencing strategy

The publicly funded effort to obtain a draft sequence of the human genome employed the hierarchical shotgun strategy (**Fig. 10.5**). In this multistep approach, researchers first generate a genomic BAC library, develop

Figure 10.5 Idealized representation of the hierarchical shotgun sequencing strategy. (a) Construct a library by fragmenting the target genome and cloning it into a large fragment cloning vector, in this case, BAC vectors. **(b)** Organize the genomic DNA fragments represented in the library into a physical map, and select and sequence the BAC clones on a minimum tiling path by the random shotgun strategy. The minimum tiling path is indicated by the darker clones. **(c)** Assemble the cloned shotgun sequences to reconstruct the sequence of the genome.

Hierarchical shotgun sequencing

(a) Genomic DNA

(b) BAC library

Organized mapped large clone contigs

BAC to be sequenced from minimum tiling path

(c) Shotgun clones

Shotgun sequence   ...ACCGTAAATGGGCTGATCATGCTTAAA
            TGATCATGCTTAAACCCTGTGCATCCTACTG...

Assembly ...ACCGTAAATGGGCTGATCATGCTTAAACCCTGTGCATCCTACTG...

map of overlapping BAC clones across the genome, and then select a set of minimally overlapping BACs across the genome. The final, minimally overlapping set of BACs is called a **minimal tiling path** of BAC clones.

To sequence each BAC clone on the minimal tiling path, a researcher randomly shears it into ≈2 kb fragments, clones these fragments in plasmids, and then sequences both ends of a sufficient number of plasmid inserts to generate 10-fold coverage across the BAC insert. If the BAC insert is 200 kb and 2000 bp (or 2 kb) are sequenced for each plasmid insert (1000 bp from each end), the sequencing of each BAC would require the sequencing of 200 kb/BAC × 10/2 kb/plasmid = 1000 plasmids/BAC.

One advantage of this divide and conquer strategy is that you need to assemble only about 1000 plasmid insert sequences for each BAC. The data from the linkage maps (showing SSRs or SNPs) and the physical maps (showing gene locations and STS maps) are also used to help assemble the sequence maps of the individual chromosomes. The hierarchical shotgun strategy requires a fair amount of front-end work to create the physical map of BAC clones and to generate a plasmid library for each of the 20,000 or so BAC clones to be sequenced.

The whole-genome shotgun sequencing strategy

The private company Celera employed the whole-genome shotgun strategy to obtain its draft sequence of the human genome. In this approach, the whole-genome DNA is randomly sheared three times, first to construct a plasmid library with ≈2 kb inserts, second to generate a plasmid library with ≈10 kb inserts, and third to produce a BAC library of ≈200 kb inserts (**Fig. 10.6**). In theory, it should be possible to sequence the 2 kb and 10 kb inserts to attain approximately 6-fold and 3-fold coverage, respectively (3×10^9 [the genome] × 6/2000 [bp sequenced per insert, assuming each sequencing reaction—can sequence 1000 bp, times two ends per insert.] = 9×10^6 plasmid clones; and $3 \times 10^9 \times 3/2000 = 4.5 \times 10^6$ plasmid clones). One could then sequence the insert ends from the 200 kb BAC library to a 1-fold coverage ($3 \times 10^9 \times 1/2000 = 1.5 \times 10^6$ BACs). The 6-fold plus 3-fold plus 1-fold coverages would amount to a 10-fold coverage. (In the Celera draft, the total coverage was about 6-fold.) A genomewide shotgun computer program would then assemble all these sequences into the chromosomal strings.

The whole-genome shotgun strategy has several advantages: First, it does not require the construction of a physical map, and it depends on the construction of only one BAC and two plasmid libraries. Second, it overcomes the problem posed by repeat sequences scattered throughout the genome because paired end sequences from clones of three insert sizes, 2 kb, 10 kb, and 200 kb, make it possible to bridge most lengths of repetitive sequences. Third, it relies on only a single highly automated and very mature technology—DNA sequencing. In the end, the Celera effort did incorporate data from the public effort

Figure 10.6 Hypothetical whole-genome shotgun sequencing strategy. Only three libraries of differing-sized fragments, here 2 kb, 10 kb, and 200 kb, need to be constructed. The big challenge is to assemble these sequences when they include large numbers of repeats.

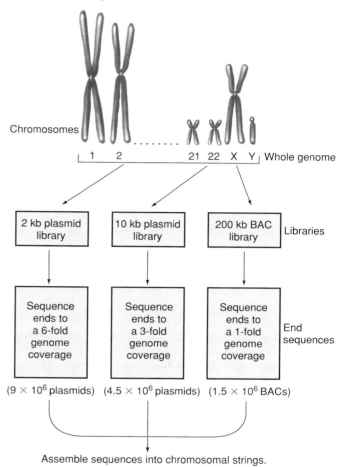

Assemble sequences into chromosomal strings.

into its own data. Since then, however, genome projects have used only the whole-genome shotgun approach.

High-resolution sequence maps showing the complete order of nucleotides can be produced in two ways. The hierarchical shotgun sequencing approach generates overlapping BAC clones to generate a minimal tiling path. The whole-genome shotgun strategy shears the genome randomly into segments of known length; these are then assembled by a computer program into chromosomal strings.

10.2 Major Insights from the Human and Model Organism Genome Sequences

In addition to promoting new analytical approaches, the complete sequence of the human genome has provided striking new insights into the architecture, gene organization, structural elements, and evolution of chromosomes. The project has also profoundly changed the practice of biology, genetics, and genomics. We now describe some of the main lessons and surprises.

The human genome project has advanced gene finding and analysis

The genome sequencing achievements to date have expedited gene-finding and gene-function analyses in several ways. First, the identification of genes in one organism's genome facilitates identification by sequence homology of genes in a second organism. If the second organism's genome sequence is available, its genes can be identified by a computer search. If the second organism's genome is not available and the two genomes are sufficiently similar, PCR primers from the first organism's genome (if sufficiently similar to the second organism's sequences) can be used to identify genes in the second organism's genome.

Second, the comparisons of all the genes within and between organisms has shown that many of the genes are paralogous or orthologous to one another. **Orthologous** genes are genes in two different species that arose from the same gene in the species' common ancestor. By contrast, **paralogous** genes arise by duplication within a single species, often within the same chromosome. Hence, knowledge of how a gene functions in one organism may help us understand its function in a second organism.

Third, the complete genome sequences have revealed that exons often encode discrete **protein domains,** or discrete functional units. Genes with multiple exons encode multiple protein domains analogous to the cars of a train. Each train is composed of many different cars, and each kind of car (engine, flat car, dining car, caboose) has a discrete function. Different trains may carry different combinations of cars and thus execute different functions. Similarly, many genes are composed of distinct exons that encode discrete protein domains. Each gene may express different combinations of domain-encoding regions by the shuffling, addition, or deletion of exons. Through these genetic mechanisms, protein architecture, defined by combinations of domains, may change with evolution.

Figure 10.7 which shows a series of domains associated with different *transcription factors,* illustrates the idea of different domains and the shifting of domain

Figure 10.7 How the domains and architectures of transcription factors have expanded in specific lineages.
(a) Specific families of transcription factors have expanded in the worm (nematode), fly (*Drosophila*), and human proteomes. (A proteome is the collection of all proteins present in an organism or individual cell type.) The diagram shows the approximate numbers of each domain identified in each of the three species. **(b)** Samples of transcription factor architectures found in all animals (ancient architectures), in only fruit flies and humans, and uniquely in one lineage. (See website at www.mhhe.com/hartwell4: Chapter 10 for definitions and explanations of abbreviations.)

architecture across the species. As mentioned in Chapter 8, transcription factors are proteins that bind to DNA promoters and other control regions, and differing domains enable transcription factors to bind with different DNA sequences and also to interact uniquely with cofactors. The specific domains of a protein are associated with particular functions and provide insights into what the protein does. Biologists may guess at the function of a new protein (or the gene that encodes it) by analogy, after searching for the protein's sequence in a database of all known domains.

Fourth, the genome sequence has established ready access to the identification of human polymorphisms, and the genomewide genetic map has made it possible to correlate some of the many DNA polymorphisms and their associated genes with predispositions to disease and interesting aspects of physiology (genetic mapping is described in the following chapter).

Finally, comparisons between sequenced genomes will more readily allow researchers to assemble the sequence fragments of an appropriately related, newly sequenced genome into its chromosomal strings. For example, the mouse and human genomes, which diverged 85 million years ago, exhibit striking similarities in genes as well as their conserved order on the chromosomes. Indeed, the mouse and human genomes exhibit approximately 180 homologous blocks of chromosomal sequence, ranging in size from 24 kb to 90.5 Mb—for an average of 17.6 Mb (**Fig. 10.8**). Such blocks of linked loci are called **syntenic blocks.** The orders of these blocks, as determined from their chromosomal linkage relationships, are totally different in the two organisms. It is as if one genome had been cut into 180 pieces of varying size and then randomly assembled into the other genome. Within each of the human syntenic blocks is information useful for assembling the corresponding homologous mouse sequences, and vice versa. *Conserved synteny,* in which the same two or more loci are linked in different species, also exists between the human and puffer fish genomes, which diverged more than 400 million years ago. In this case, though, the syntenic blocks are relatively small—averaging about 10 kb in length.

Thus, as these few examples show, successful sequence analysis of the human and model organism genomes has changed the strategies for biology, genomics, and medicine.

The human genome contains approximately 25,000 genes

The first surprise to emerge from the human genome sequence was the discovery of just 25,000 genes, a much lower number than expected. A back-of-the-envelope calculation done at the initiation of the Human Genome

Figure 10.8 Conserved segments or syntenic blocks in the human and mouse genomes. Human chromosomes, with segments containing at least two genes whose order is conserved in the mouse genome; the segments appear as *color blocks.* Each color corresponds to a particular mouse chromosome. Centromeres; subcentromeric heterochromatin of chromosomes 1, 9, and 16; and the repetitive short arms of 13, 14, 15, 21, and 22 are in *black.*

Human chromosomes

Mouse chromosome key

Project had suggested that there might be 100,000 human genes—approximately 1 gene every 30 kb. This has not proven to be the case; although the human genome has more genes than the genomes of the simpler model organisms, it has not nearly as many as one would expect from the increased complexity (see Table 10.2). This means that mechanisms other than the expression of different germline genes must help generate metazoan (multicellular animal) complexity.

Many proteins contain discrete functional domains that, as described earlier, can be joined in many different orders by addition, deletion, or shuffling (**Fig. 10.9**). The number and order of a protein's domains constitute its **domain architecture.** Although the human organism has only a modest increase in the total number of protein domains over

Figure 10.9 Examples of domain accretion in chromatin proteins. Domain assemblies in various lineages **(a–c)** are shown using schematic representations of domain architectures (not to scale). *Asterisks* indicate the mobile domains that have participated in the accretion. Species in which a domain architecture has been identified are indicated *above* the diagrams (Y, yeast; W, worm; F, fly; V, vertebrate). Protein names are *below* the diagrams.

a	AT hook motif
Ba	bromo-associated homology motif
Br	Bromo
C	Cysteine triad motif associated with Msl-2 and SET
Ch	Chromodomain
EP1/EP2	Enhancer of polycomb domains 1 and 2
Me	DNA methylase/Hrx-associated DNA-binding zinc finger
Sa	Sant
SET	Chromatin protein methyltransferase
sja	SET-JOR-associated domain
SW12	Superfamily II helicase/ATPase
Znf	Zinc finger

the model organisms, it has evolved many new gene arrangements that alter domain architecture, thus creating a far more complex repertoire of proteins (**Fig. 10.10**).

Human proteins may be modified by more than 400 different chemical reactions, each capable of altering the proteins' functions. Thus, the typical human cell might have perhaps 20,000 different types of mRNAs and perhaps 1 million different proteins. Humans can make more protein modifications than their simple model-organism counterparts.

> Comparison of genomes has shown a much greater conservation of sequence than would be expected on the basis of organism complexity or external differences. The roughly 25,000 human genes have many counterparts among the genes of other organisms, which implies that mechanisms other than simple genetic variation account for organism differences.

The genome contains distinct types of gene organization

The organization of genes is strikingly different across the genome. Examples of different types of gene organization include gene families, gene-rich regions, and gene-poor

Figure 10.10 Number of distinct domain architectures in four eukaryotic genomes. The number of architectures is split into three cellular environments: intracellular, extracellular, and transmembrane.

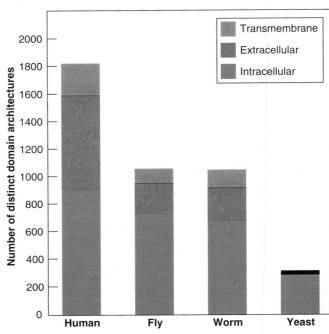

deserts. A fundamental unanswered question is whether these different organizations have biological meaning.

Gene families

Closely related genes that are members of multigene families abound throughout the genome. Such families may be clustered together on one chromosome or dispersed on several chromosomes. Examples of gene families include the genes that encode histones, hemoglobins, immunoglobins, actins, collagens, and heat-shock proteins. We described the hemoglobin-encoding globin gene family on pp. 322–325 of Chapter 9. Here we take a brief look at the human olfactory receptor (OR) multigene family, which has about 1000 members that evolved in two ways. In the first, one OR gene underwent multiple duplications to create roughly 20 copies, or a family of approximately 20 paralogs. These family members, which were originally identical, then diverged to paralogs that were quite distinct from one another. Next, a massive duplication event created 30 different families from the original 20-paralog family. In this massive event, the entire family, or portions of it, duplicated and translocated to about 30 sites, or clusters, around the genome. Each of the 30 sites contains all or a portion of the 20 or so paralogs of the original OR family (**Fig. 10.11**). Interestingly, the equivalent paralogs in each of the 30 clusters—for example, paralog 3 at all 30 sites—are more closely related to each other than to other paralogs, say 2 or 7, in the same cluster. In a second mode of evolution, a single OR gene recently duplicated to generate a gene family of mostly similar paralogs. This is the class I family depicted in medium blue in Fig. 10.11.

Perhaps the expansion of olfactory receptor genes reflects an evolutionary response to the selective pressures for a more acute and discriminating sense of smell in mammals and other vertebrates. However, when our more recent hominoid ancestors evolved three-color vision and a more sophisticated ability to process sound, a keen sense of smell was no longer important for human survival. As a result, mutations that eliminate OR function or delete whole OR genes have not been negatively or positively selected, resulting in a large degree of polymorphism among people, in terms of numbers of active OR genes. Differences of 100 genes or more are not uncommon, and give rise to large differences in the abilities of individuals to distinguish odors.

Gene-rich regions

Some chromosomal regions are densely packed with genes. For example, the 700 kb class III region of the major histocompatibility complex on chromosome 6 contains 60 genes encoding many diverse functions (**Fig. 10.12**). Only one is a pseudogene. This is the most gene-rich region of the human genome; 70% of the DNA in this region is transcribed. Moreover, the region has a high G C content, 54%, versus a genomewide average of 45%. High G C content is also seen in other gene-rich areas and is associated with the light regions (interbands) in karyotypes. Why are these genes so densely packed? Is there a functional explanation or is it a reflection of the chance events that shape chromosomal architecture? These questions remain to be answered.

Gene deserts

The current human genome draft contains 82 gene deserts, which are chromosomal regions containing a megabase or more of DNA with no identifiable genes. Deserts span 144 Mb, or 3% of the genome. The largest desert is 4.1 Mb in length.

One explanation for the existence of gene deserts is that they contain genes that are difficult to identify. An example is the class of genes called *big genes*. A big gene is a single gene whose nuclear transcript spans 500 kb or more of chromosomal DNA. The largest of the big genes is the gene for dystrophin, which spans 2.3 Mb. One hundred twenty-four big genes encompassing 112 Mb of chromosomal DNA have been defined to date. Interestingly, many big genes have modest-sized mRNAs; the exons encoding these RNAs typically encompass about 1% of the total chromosomal gene region in which they occur. This means the exons are widely scattered across large regions composed mainly of introns, and thus they are extremely difficult to find by computational methods alone. Full-length cDNA sequences are often essential for the delineation of exon/intron structures in big genes. But because big genes are synthesized very slowly, their synthesis cannot be completed in rapidly dividing cells. A large fraction of the big genes are expressed in neurons, which do not divide.

Once again, several intriguing questions arise: Do gene-rich or gene-poor areas have functional significance, or do these different chromosomal organizations represent random fluctuations in evolutionary events? Similarly, do big genes provide some selective advantage, or does their existence reflect chance events that reshaped the chromosomal architecture at the genomic level?

> Gene families consist of closely related genes that encode similar products. Gene-rich regions contain a high number of functional genes. Gene deserts are chromosome areas containing a large amount of DNA in which no genes have been identified; it may be that these deserts contain "big genes" that have large introns or are synthesized slowly.

Combinatorial strategies may lead to gene amplification and diversity

Combinatorial amplification results from the potential for combining a set of basic elements in many different ways. A simple slot machine, for example, may contain 3 wheels, each carrying 7 different symbols; from its 21 basic elements ($7 + 7 + 7$), it can generate 343 different combinations (7^3, or $7 \times 7 \times 7$). In biology, combinatorial amplification occurs at both the DNA and RNA levels.

Figure 10.11 Olfactory receptor (OR) gene families. ORs are depicted as *squares*, colored by family (*see key*). All members of the class I family are colored equally. Unclassified ORs are indicated in *light gray*. *Framed squares* denote intact or functional genes. ORs to the *left* of each chromosome indicate single genes, and those to the *right* are in clusters of two or more. The largest cluster on chromosome 11 is shown split to fit on the page.

Figure 10.12 Class III region of the human major histocompatibility complex. This region contains 60 genes and is 700 kb in length.

Figure 10.13 A schematic diagram of the human (β) T-cell receptor gene family. The variable (antigen recognition) gene is composed of three elements: V, D, and J. During T-cell development, any D may join with any J. Any V may join with any D-J.

Combinatorial strategies at the DNA level

Antibody and T-cell receptor genes, as one example, are encoded by a multiplicity of gene segments (**Fig. 10.13**). The human T-cell receptor family has 45 functional variable (V) gene segments, two functional diversity (D) gene segments, and 11 functional joining (J) gene segments. In an individual T cell, any D element may first join to any J element by deletion of the intervening DNA. This joined D-J element may, in turn, join to any V element—once again by deletion of the intervening DNA—to generate a complete V-D-J gene. This combinatorial process can generate 990 different V-D-J genes ($45 \times 2 \times 11 = 990$), although in a given T cell, only one such functional rearrangement occurs. Thus, from 58 gene elements ($45 + 2 + 11$), a combinatorial joining mechanism can generate 990 V-D-J genes.

T cells, have receptors capable of interacting with foreign molecular structures, which are termed antigens. These cells are driven by contact with antigens to divide and expand their numbers 1000-fold or more. This antigen-triggered expansion by mitosis to a clone of genetically identical cells is a key part of every immune response. The particular combinatorial gene rearrangements in a few of the original population of T cells produce T-cell receptors more precisely fitted to the antigen. Binding with the antigen then triggers the clonal expansion of the cells that carry the tightly fitting receptors, amplifying the useful combinatorial information. As a result, the specificity and strength of the immune response increases.

Figure 10.14 The organization of the three neurexin genes. Each gene has two promoters (α and β) to initiate mRNA synthesis and five sites at which alternative RNA splicing can occur. The *blue rectangles* indicate exons affected by alternative splicing. Numbers at the top of the figure designate exons.

Neurexin Statistics			
Gene	Length in Human	Length in Puffer Fish	Number of Potential Alternative Splice Variants in Human
NRXN1	1112 kb	>163 kb	292
NRXN2	117 kb	unknown	194
NRXN3	1692 kb	>181 kb	1764

Combinatorial strategies at the RNA level

The splicing together of RNA exons in different orders is another way in which combinatorial strategies can increase information and generate diversity. Further diversity results from the initiation of transcription at distinct promoter regions, which create transcripts with different numbers of exons.

The three neurexin genes illustrate both of these combinatorial RNA strategies (**Fig. 10.14**). Each neurexin gene contains two promoter regions (producing α and β mRNAs) and five sites at which alternative splicing can occur. Together, these three genes can probably generate more than 2000 alternatively spliced forms of mRNA.

Key questions include how many of the splice variants encode distinct functional proteins (rather than proteins with the same function), and whether different variants represent different addresses for telling neurons where to go during embryonic development.

Genome sequence studies affirm evolution from a common ancestor

The availability of complete genomic sequences has created an opportunity to analyze large numbers of gene products (mRNAs, proteins) in the context of specific cell types or in the context of the changing patterns of gene expression during the activation of developmental or physiological pathways.

Preliminary analyses support the conclusion of earlier molecular studies that the basic cellular mechanisms of all living organisms have remarkably similar genetic components. This observation, in turn, supports the idea that we and other living organisms are all descendants of a single, fortuitous life-producing biochemistry. The similarity of basic genetic components also affirms that the analysis of appropriate biological systems in model organisms can provide fundamental insights into how the corresponding human systems function.

> Genetic diversity in some cases can be generated by combinatorial amplification, in which a small number of elements are combined to produce a great variety of protein products, or exons of mRNAs are spliced in a number of different ways to produce a variety of transcripts. Sequence similarities support a common ancestor for all living organisms.

10.3 Global Analysis of Genes and Their mRNAs

The scientific challenge of the Human Genome Project initiated a revolution in the development of technologies to analyze both the genome itself and the biochemical machinery that interacts with the genome to carry out its function.

The Human Genome Project has given us the complete sequences of a variety of genomes. The next step is to carry out global analyses of these basic data to gain a more complete understanding of the information in the genome.

The need for global genomic analysis has driven the development of powerful high-throughput platforms that enable researchers to generate the information necessary to carry out large-scale, automated searches of global databases. In this context, a *platform* denotes all the components needed for an automated acquisition of a set of data. A high-throughput genomic platform might include automated instrumentation to prepare DNA fragments for sequencing, an automated sequencer to carry out the sequencing, and a set of computational tools to capture and store the information obtained from sequencing.

We now describe some of the main instruments developed for large-scale genomic analyses. In our discussion of these tools, we use *genomics* to mean the global analysis of chromosomal and RNA features (such as sequence, genetic markers, mRNAs).

DNA sequencers and DNA arrays are high-throughput instruments

Two high-throughput technologies have played a key role in genomic platforms: the DNA sequencer and DNA microarrays, including oligonucleotide arrays.

DNA sequencing

The first generation automated DNA sequencer employed the dideoxy (Sanger) sequencing strategy described in detail on pp. 314–317 of Chapter 9. The automated format is a three-step process (**Fig. 10.15**), which we briefly summarize.

Step 1 A complementary DNA strand of an unknown sequence is synthesized to serve as a template. The four chain-terminating dideoxy bases are then used in separate synthesis reactions at concentrations that ensure that 0.5% of the growing chains are stopped at each G, C, A, and T across the sequence. The primers for each of these four reactions are labeled with one of four fluorescent dyes to distinguish the fragments, based on the terminal dideoxy nucleotide.

Step 2 The four different sets of color-coded fragments are pooled, and then the mixture is separated by electrophoresis that can distinguish fragments differing by a single base.

Step 3 The fluorescence of each fragment identifies its terminal nucleotide. For example, all fragments ending in A fluoresce red, while those ending in T fluoresce yellow.

The sequencing instruments described in section 10.4 can analyze 96 or, more recently, 384 DNA fragments at a time. Moreover, several large sequencing centers have created sequencing production lines in which the production of DNA fragments for sequencing has been semiautomated, and the capture and quality assessment of the DNA sequence data have been fully automated. New technologies allow the sequencing of 100 billion bp in 96 hours.

Figure 10.15 Sanger sequencing scheme.

(a) Each reaction contains (1) the unknown template DNA cloned in a single-strand sequencing vector, (2) a primer oligonucleotide complementary to a region of the vector near the 3′ end of the unknown DNA, (3) a DNA polymerase, (4) all four deoxynucleotide triphosphates (dNTPs), and (5) one dideoxynucleotide triphosphate (ddNTP). The detection label (·) is shown attached to the 5′ end of the primer. **(b)** Schematic depictions of the gel electrophoresis detection system used in DNA sequencing. Real-time detection of bands from four sequencing reactions, each using a different-colored label, run in a single gel track. **(c)** Data from DNA sequencing experiments, which is delivered as superimposed four-color traces. Data shown correspond to the same region of the vector as that in (a). **(d)** Commercial implementation employing fluorescence scanning of slab electrophoresis gel.

New DNA sequencing strategies using highly parallel simultaneous analyses (which sequence simultaneously millions of DNA fragments) now permit the rapid and inexpensive sequencing of individual human genomes.

DNA microarrays

A DNA array is a large set of DNA fragments displayed on a solid support. To make a DNA microarray, researchers either synthesize DNA fragments encoding portions of individual genes at selected sites on a solid support or "spot" (that is, deposit) presynthesized DNA fragments at precise locations on the solid support (Fig. 10.16). They then hybridize a complex mixture of fluorescent or radio-labeled DNA or RNA fragments (for example, mRNAs or cDNAs) with the array of anchored fragments to quantitatively analyze the levels of expression of individual genes represented on the array. In this

manner, researchers can analyze tens of thousands of gene-expression patterns.

The mixture of mRNAs or cDNAs to be analyzed is labeled with fluorescent dyes and hybridized. The level of fluorescence in a single DNA spot is proportional to the level of gene expression. A researcher can use microarrays to simultaneously analyze two different cDNA (or RNA) samples taken from one kind of cell in two different states or from two cell types. To distinguish the samples, each is labeled with a different-colored dye (**Fig. 10.17a**). It is possible to measure the levels of the two dyes for each spot on the array to determine patterns of gene expression in the two different cell states or cell types (Fig. 10.17b). The differences in gene expression can be detected only if they vary by a factor of two or more. This technology is relatively inexpensive compared to the third type of array.

Figure 10.16 An oligonucleotide array. The oligonucleotides are covalently linked to the glass or silicon. Typically, the oligonucleotides range in size from 20 to 60 bp.

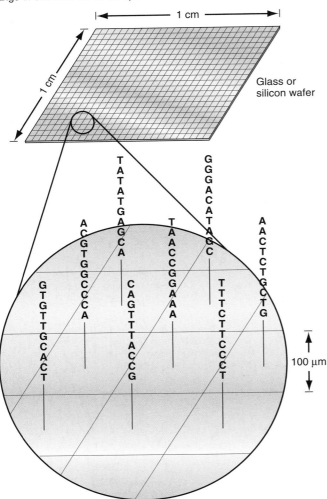

Figure 10.17 Two-color DNA microarrays. (a) Two separate cDNA samples, one from normal yeast, the other from a mutated yeast, are labeled with red and green fluorescent dyes and hybridized to a PCR microarray. When both labeled samples hybridize to a PCR product, a *yellow* color is produced. The *red* hybridizations represent mRNAs (cDNAs) overexpressed in the mutant, and the *green* hybridizations represent mRNAs overexpressed in the normal yeast. Black squares contain a PCR product that fails to hybridize with either cDNA. **(b)** The entire yeast genome of ≈6000 genes is represented on this DNA microarray.

(a)

(b)

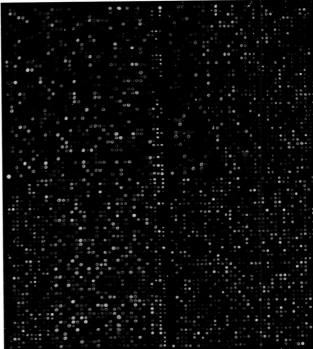

Oligonucleotide arrays

This type of DNA array involves the synthesis or spotting of oligonucleotides at densities of 1 million or more on glass slides. An **oligonucleotide** is a short segment of DNA or RNA that is chemically synthesized to precise specifications. Oligonucleotides are usually 20–60 nucleotides in length. The Affymetrix oligonucleotide array can carry up to about 6 million oligonucleotides on a single glass support, making it possible to analyze more than 1.5 million SNPs simultaneously (*SNPs,* or *single nucleotide polymorphisms,* are described in detail in the following chapter).

One approach to scaling up the density of oligonucleotide arrays comes from the application of optic fiber technology. It is possible to create 50,000 wells in the end of an optical fiber 1 mm in diameter (**Fig. 10.18**). Fifty thousand beads, each with a different 25-nucleotide sequence can be placed in these wells and used to interrogate a target sample, either for SNPs or patterns of gene expression. Because current instruments employ 96 optical fibers, they can carry out

Figure 10.18 An optical fiber approach to DNA array analyses (see the text for details).

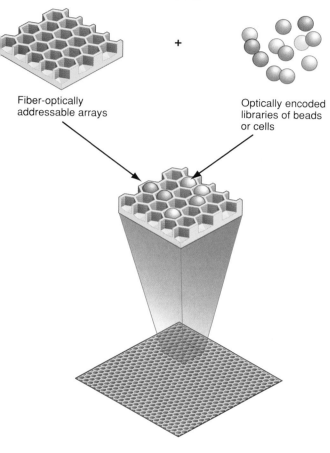

Fiber-optically
addressable arrays

Optically encoded
libraries of beads
or cells

lose to 5 million measurements per cycle of analysis (50,000, $\times$ 5 $\times$ 10^4 $\times$ 96 = 4,700,000). These optical arrays can nalyze more than 1 million SNPs per day.

Development of high-throughput technologies such as DNA sequencers and DNA microarrays, including oligonucleotide arrays, has revolutionized the speed with which genomic sequences can be produced. As time and material costs decrease, production of individual genomes becomes more possible.

Genomic researchers have developed strategies for utilizing platforms with mRNAs

he instruments just described are the analytic centers of gh-throughput platforms. As mentioned earlier, these atforms include the automated preparation of the samples be analyzed, the analytic instruments themselves, and utomated software for capturing and assessing the quality the global data sets gathered. We now describe how nomic researchers use the tools in selected platforms.

Researchers employ three types of DNA sequencing to determine the quantities of different mRNAs in a mixture. They have used the automated DNA sequencer, for example, to generate more than 6 million human **expressed sequence tags (ESTs),** which are single-sequence runs of about 600 to 1000 bp in length on cDNA inserts. They have produced these ESTs from hundreds of different cell types.

More recently, investigators have developed a technique termed **serial analysis of gene expression,** or **SAGE.** With SAGE, they can synthesize small cDNA tags about 15 bp in length from the 3′ ends of mRNA and link these small tags together into 1000 bp DNA that can then be sequenced. In principle, each 1000 bp DNA string contains 15 bp tags from roughly 67 different genes (15 $\times$ 67 = $\approx$1000). The sequence analyses of thousands of these linked 15 bp tags permit a quantitative estimate of the mRNAs present in the original cell type.

Finally, the very recent **massively parallel signature sequence (MPSS)** technique appears to be the most powerful approach to quantitatively defining the transcriptomes of individual cell types (**Fig. 10.19**). A **transcriptome** is the population of mRNAs expressed in a single cell or cell type. MPSS is the only technique that readily (and cost effectively) allows the routine identification of most of a cell's rarely expressed mRNAs (fewer than 10 copies expressed per cell). The MPSS approach could, for example, take a cDNA library of 1 million clones and amplify each clone with a unique PCR tag so that the products from each clone can be attached to a single nylon bead (Fig. 10.19). The million beads are displayed in a flow cell, and then the million different sequences are simultaneously sequenced with fluorescent reporter groups to generate 1 million sequence tags of 17–20 bp. If the genome of the organism whose cell type was used to make the cDNA library has been sequenced (so that all or most of the genes have been identified), then the MPSS technique can provide a precise quantitative measure of most of the mRNA types in the cell down to those from genes expressed in only a single copy. This sensitivity is significant because many biologically important genes are expressed at very low levels (less than 50 copies per cell). The typical mammalian cell has perhaps 300,000 transcripts representing 20,000 different mRNAs. Ninety percent of the mRNAs are expressed at levels of less than 100 copies per cell.

The DNA array approaches, particularly the microarray and oligonucleotide arrays, also permit a semiquantitative analysis of patterns of gene expression. Two-color microarray analyses have been particularly useful in comparing different tissue or cell types (for example, normal versus cancerous). Most DNA arrays, however, do not accurately detect mRNAs expressed at less than 50 copies per cell.

Genomicists have applied the same sophisticated tools to mRNA studies, facilitating analysis of transcripts even when very few copies of a transcript are produced.

Figure 10.19 Lynx Therapeutics sequencing strategy of multiple parallel signature sequencing (MPSS). The text describes how this recently introduced technique for quantitatively defining the composition of a cell's transcriptome is used.

20 cycles of proprietary base-by-base sequencing

1 million beads

1 million beads arranged in a monolayer

Each of a million beads provides a 20-base-pair signature sequence

	Signature sequence	Number of beads
1	GATCAATCGGACTTGTCGAA	2
2	GATCGTGCATCAGCAGTACT	53
3	GATCCGATACAGCTTTGGGC	212
4	GATCTATGGGTATAGTCGAG	349
5	GATCCAGCGTTTGGTGCTTG	417
6	GATCCCAGCAAGATAACAGC	561
7	GATCCTCCTGTCTCACATGT	672
8	GATCACTTCTCTCATTAACA	702
9	GATCTACAGAACTCGGTGAG	814
.		
.		
30,285	GATCGGACCGAATCGACTAT	2,935

10.4 Global Analysis of Proteomes

From the draft sequence of the human genome, investigators predicted about 25,000 protein-coding genes. The collective translation of all protein-coding genes into protein is termed the **proteome.** The human proteome contains *homologs*—in this context, proteins that are related by evolutionary descent—for 61% of the fruit fly proteome, 43% of the worm proteome, and 46% of the yeast proteome.

Proteomic analyses have revealed that there are about 1200 gene families containing two or more members, of which 92 (7%) are vertebrate-specific; these vertebrate-specific families encode proteins active in immunity, other types of defense, and the nervous system. Analysts have also found a striking increase in the complexity of the proteome from yeast to humans.

As shown in earlier sections, global technologies make possible the comprehensive, large-scale study of the components of biological systems. Here we discuss high-throughput platforms for the acquisition and measurement of proteomic data, including amino acid sequence data and the amount, modifications, and compartmentalization of all the proteins in a cell or organism.

Proteome analysis is highly complex

The analysis of proteomes is more complex and challenging than the analysis of genomes for two reasons. First, the range of protein expression in cells is enormous: from one copy to 10^6 copies/cell. Because currently no equivalent of PCR exists for the amplification of interesting proteins, the tools of protein analysis need to function across concentration differences spanning six orders of magnitude. Second, proteins in complex mixtures have many different features that need to be identified and characterized. These include

- the gene(s) encoding each protein;
- chemical modifications to the polypeptide;
- levels of expression in particular cell types, which change across developmental stages or physiological responses;

- covalent modifications to proteins (for example, phosphorylation, glycosylation);
- interactions with other proteins, macromolecules, or small molecules;
- compartmentalization within the cell—for example, in the nucleus, the cytoplasm, or on the cell surface;
- state of activation of the protein;
- proteins' half-lives;
- proteins' three-dimensional structure; and
- the relationship between their structure and function.

Proteins are dynamic molecules with constantly changing concentrations, chemical modifications, interactions, and cellular locations. The ability to analyze variations in all the features of proteins is important to an understanding of how they function in the systems in which they participate.

A mass spectrometer allows identification of components in complex mixtures

The mass spectrometer, an instrument that measures the masses of a wide variety of molecules, can analyze proteins that can be enriched to a certain level of abundance. The sensitivity of mass spectrometers is continually increasing, so they can be used to analyze more and more proteins from complex mixtures such as cells or blood. For our purposes, interesting molecules include small proteins, peptides, oligonucleotides, lipids, carbohydrates, small RNAs, and other molecules.

How the mass spectrometer works

The mass spectrometer requires that molecules can be ionized and transferred to a vacuum. The spectrometer determines the masses by measuring the molecules' migration rates in an electric field (small masses migrate more rapidly than large masses). Because mass spectrometry can measure the masses of small molecules more accurately than large ones, proteins or protein mixtures are often converted into smaller peptide fragments by a proteolytic enzyme such as trypsin.

Mass spectrometers consist of three components: (1) a source of ionization, which turns peptides of a single protein or a mixture of proteins, for example, into ions; (2) a mass analyzer, which separates the ion fragments according to their mass-to-charge ratio (m/z); and (3) a detector, which measures separation times or distances and produces a graphic representation of the results (**Fig. 10.20**).

Using different combinations of ionization sources and mass analyzers, commercial mass spectrometers can accurately measure the masses of peptides and small proteins. They can also sequence the peptides by further fragmentation and mass measurement of the smaller derivative peptides. An instrument known as the *ion trap tandem spectrometer* separates different-sized fragments in a first

Figure 10.20 Mass spectrometer. The mass spectrometer consists of three components: (1) an ionization source, (2) a mass analyzer, and (3) a detector. The text explains the function of each component.

Mass Spectrometer

mass spectrometer, selects fragments for further fragmentation by collision with ions, and then measures the masses of the resulting peptide fragments in a second mass spectrometer. In this manner, it can sequence the amino acids in peptides. The mass spectrometer is thus a powerful instrument for identifying and sequencing peptide fragments from proteins in complex mixtures.

Identifying proteins in complex mixtures

The mass spectrometer has become a powerful tool for identifying the protein components of proteomes. Once the protein sequences of the 25,000 or so gene sequences of the human genome are known, researchers can computationally determine the mass of each individual protein as well as the mass of the peptides derived from it by enzymatic cleavage. The realization that the proteins of a complex mixture can be proteolytically cleaved and then identified from mass determinations of their individual peptides has given proteomics an enormous boost.

The process of identification is as follows. First, cells of a particular type are purified. In the next step, proteins are extracted from the cells and digested with trypsin, a protease that cleaves polypeptide chains at arginine and lysine residues. The peptides resulting from treatment with trypsin, known as *tryptic peptides,* are partially fractionated on a *reverse phase column:* a column separating peptides based on their hydrophobicity, that is, their ability to repel water. Successive aliquots from the column are introduced into the mass spectrometer to obtain mass measurements of the partially fractionated tryptic peptides. In an alternative approach, the proteins can be separated by two-dimensional gel electrophoresis (separation by size in one dimension and by charge in the second), and the protein spots can be cut out from the gel and digested with trypsin. The resulting tryptic peptides are then injected into the mass spectrometer (**Fig. 10.21**). In every yeast cell, for example, there are potentially 6000 gene-encoded proteins and approximately 350,000 tryptic peptides.

Most of these peptides have unique masses that are recorded in a database. A computer software program can compare the mass of each peptide experimentally analyzed in a mass spectrometer against the database of

Figure 10.21 A strategy using two-dimensional gels and mass spectrometry to identify proteins in complex mixtures and the genes that encode them. A two-dimensional gel separates proteins by size and charge. Individual spots can be extracted from the gel, digested with trypsin to produce peptides, and analyzed in a tandem mass spectrometer. The first mass spectrometer in this instrument (Q1) separates the peptide fragments (MS base peak); one fragment (*orange*) is then moved to the collision cell (Q2) and fragmented into components, which can be analyzed in the second mass spectrometer (Q3). Researchers can compare the mass spectrum against a databases of theoretical fragments to identify peptides and proteins and, by extrapolation, the genes that encode them.

theoretical peptide masses for the proteins encoded by the genome. This database has been computationally determined through the identification of all the genes in a specific genome, followed by the determination of genes that encode the proteins from which particular tryptic peptides have been derived. A single mass spectrometry run can assign hundreds of peptide fragments to the genes that encode them.

Mass spectrometry allows identification of peptide samples that have been separated according to mass and ionic charge. These may then be stored in a database. A tandem mass spectrometer refines the technique by isolating a fragment from the first analysis, fragmenting it further, and then analyzing it again.

Protein concentration changes in different cell or tissue states can be analyzed

A technique called *isotope analysis,* which employs prepared reagents known as *isotope-coded affinity tags (ICAT),* permits researchers to analyze the changing patterns of protein expression in two different cellular states. The ICAT reagent has three components:

1. a biotin tag (biotin is a molecule that binds tightly to avidin molecules, and this binding provides a means for purifying proteins or peptides of interest);

2. a linker to which eight hydrogens or eight deuteriums can be attached to create light (hydrogen) or

Figure 10.22 The isotope-coded affinity tag (ICAT) approach to quantifying complex protein mixtures from two different states. (a) The isotope-coded affinity tag reagent (described in the text). **(b)** The strategy for labeling the proteins of two cell types with the light and heavy reagents (also described in the text). The *green circles* indicate covalent linkage of the heavy ICAT reagent (with deuterium) from part (a) to cysteines in proteins from cancer cells. The *yellow squares* indicate covalent linkage of the light ICAT reagent (with hydrogen) from part (a) to cysteines in proteins from normal cells.

heavy (deuterium) chemical isotope forms (differing by 8 mass units);

. a chemical group that reacts with the thiol (—SH) group of cysteine amino acids and thus attaches the ICAT reagent to all cysteines in a protein or peptide (**Fig. 10.22a**).

In one example of this isotope analysis technique, ormal cells are labeled with the light isotope reagent and ncerous counterparts with the heavy one (**Fig. 10.22b**). ter equal quantities of the normal and cancerous cells ~~e~~ mixed together, their proteins are purified and digested th trypsin, and the cysteine-ICAT-labeled peptides are rified by affinity chromatography that binds all biotin-~~r~~eled peptides, while all other peptides flow right ~~r~~ough the column. The biotin-labeled peptides are then

fractionated on a reverse phase column, and successive aliquots of the biotin-labeled fractionated peptides are analyzed in two ways in the mass spectrometer. First, as shown in Fig. 10.22b, the areas under the curves of the isotope pairs of peptides (hydrogen/deuterium) are determined. These areas are proportional to the concentrations of the peptides (and, by extension, the proteins) expressed in the two cell types. Second, after further fragmentation in the mass spectrometer, the peptide pairs are analyzed to determine their amino acid sequences. With these sequences in hand, the gene that encodes the protein can be determined from the database table of the masses of tryptic fragments. The ICAT technique is thus similar to the two-color microarray studies: The ICAT quantifies proteins, whereas the microarrays quantify mRNAs, from two different cellular states. Work is now underway to develop high-throughput platforms for measuring many other features of proteins, such as phosphorylation and activation.

> Isotope analysis utilizing isotope-coded affinity tags (ICATs) allows quantification of amounts of proteins a cell produces through labeling proteins with heavy and light isotopes. In this way differences between cells in different states, such as normal and diseased, can be analyzed.

Two methods can identify protein-protein interactions

The ability to carry out global analyses of protein-protein interactions is critical to the description of protein networks. There are two commonly employed strategies for characterizing protein-protein interactions: (1) affinity capture combined with mass spectrometry and (2) yeast two-hybrid interactions.

Affinity capture/mass spectrometry

In this method, an antibody or other specifically interacting molecule is used to "pull down" one protein from a complex mixture (**Fig. 10.23**). The antibody or other specifically interacting molecule is called a *capture molecule*. The affinity-capture procedure also pulls down all proteins associated with the first protein. The complexes of pulled-down interacting proteins can then be identified in the mass spectrometer.

One global approach to analyzing protein-protein interactions is to attach a nucleic-acid sequence encoding a good affinity tag to the 5' or 3' end of a gene (for example, protein A, a bacterial cell wall protein that binds strongly to antibody molecules). When this tagged gene is integrated into the genome of the organism, the protein it encodes can be pulled down as just described. It is possible, for example, to so modify all 6000 yeast genes and construct 6000 strains, each with the same protein A tag attached to a different gene. Subsequent pull-down experiments with each protein can be carried out with just a single protein-capture agent. From the assembly of these multiple interactions, one can begin to shed light on the global network of all protein-protein interactions.

Protein arrays

Biologists can place small amounts of proteins in ordered arrays on silicon or glass surfaces similar to the way in which they construct the DNA arrays described earlier. Protein arrays can be used to investigate both the proteins' interactions with other proteins (or other macromolecules) and their potential for chemical modification. In one use, a set of proteins is arrayed to determine whether they are substrates for chemical modification such as phosphorylation

Figure 10.23 How to use affinity purification and mass spectrometry to identify protein interactions. First, use genetic engineering to label the problem of interest (see text). Next, prepare a cellular extract and isolate the protein complex by affinity purification. Finally, identify the interacting proteins in the complex by mass spectrometry.

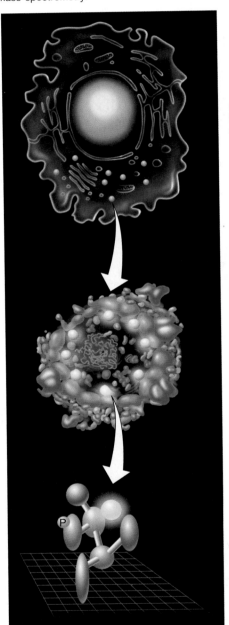

Single protein tagged in whole cell.

Cellular extract prepared.

Protein complex isolated by affinity purification.

Proteins in comple identified by mass spectrometry.

(**Fig. 10.24**). In a second example, a battery of specific an bodies is arrayed to determine whether the molecules the interact with are present in a given protein mixtu Antibody arrays can also be used to compare two differe cellular states to see whether the levels of individual pr teins change from one state to the other, similar to t ICAT method described earlier.

Figure 10.24 Protein array of different types of protein kinases. The two very intense spots at the top and bottom of the two left-hand columns are control protein kinases. **(a)** A spectral image of a protein chip with different protein kinases. The red and more intense white colors indicate the amount of protein present in each spot as identified by antibodies. **(b)** Picture of a photographic film of the same protein array indicating the radioactivity associated with each different kinase after a radioactive kinase substrate has been applied. These images show that protein chips can be used to identify the specific enzymatic activity of individual members of a related set of proteins.

a)

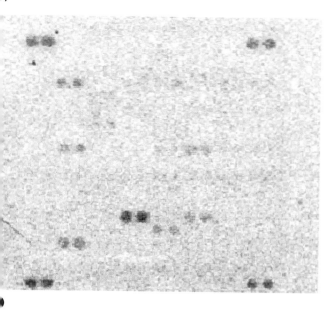
b)

Current limitations of protein chips are that they do not allow a global analysis of all the proteins in the proteome being studied (most chips have fewer than a few hundred proteins arrayed). In addition, the individual protein-capture components on the chip do not allow very precise quantification of the recognized proteins from the proteome. Projects are underway to make antibodies against all human proteins. Studies using these antibodies in conjunction with comprehensive protein arrays could quantify the expression patterns of most proteins in the proteomes under investigation.

> The affinity capture method utilizes antibodies to remove proteins of interest from a mixture so that they can then be analyzed by mass spectrometry. Protein arrays, similar to DNA arrays, also allow limited identification of protein interactions.

ChIP/chip analyses identify protein-DNA interactions

The ability to make global measurements of protein-DNA interactions is critical for the description of gene regulatory networks. The most widely used tool for these measurements is **chromatin immunoprecipitation (ChIP)** analyzed on a chip—abbreviated as *ChIP/chip analysis*. It employs a combination of genomic and proteomic techniques to measure the interactions of transcription factors (proteins) with their *cis*-control elements (DNA), or the interactions of complex protein machines, such as activator or repressor complexes, with their chromosome (DNA) binding sites.

The ChIP/chip technique, also known as *genome-wide localization,* can identify all the genomic sites at which a transcription factor expressed in a particular cell type may bind. The protocol, diagrammed in **Fig. 10.25,** works as follows.

1. Through genetic engineering, a DNA sequence encoding an antibody-binding-site peptide is added to the 5′ or 3′ end of the gene for the transcription factor under investigation. This modified gene is then transformed into the organism's genome; when expressed, the protein product of the gene will have the peptide tag at its N or C terminus.

2. Next, the chromatin is isolated from a cell type of interest, and the transcription factor is cross-linked to its corresponding binding sites by a small reversible cross-linking chemical.

3. The DNA of the chromatin is then fragmented into small pieces (300–500 base pairs in length), and the antibody against the peptide tag is added to the fragmented chromatin. The antibody binds to the tagged transcription factor and thus isolates the transcription factor as well as the DNA to which it is cross-linked.

4. All the cross-links are then reversed, and both ends of the purified transcription-factor-binding DNA fragments are attached to PCR primer sequences.

5. The specific DNA binding sites are then amplified and labeled with a red fluorescent dye. A control procedure lacking the modified transcription factor gene follows the protocol just described, and the PCR-amplified control DNA fragments are labeled with a green fluorescent dye.

6. DNA or oligonucleotide arrays are prepared that contain the potential DNA sequences of all sites at which *cis*-control elements may be encoded: 5', 3', and within the introns of each gene whose *cis*-control regions are to be studied. (Ideally, one would like to study all the genes of the genome at the same time.)

7. The experimental and control samples are mixed, then hybridized against noncoding DNA or oligonucleotide arrays.

The ratio of red to green dye is determined for each DNA fragment on the array. High red ratios indicate DNA fragments to which the corresponding transcription factor has bound (that is, the *cis*-control DNA has been enriched in the experimental PCR amplifications). By repeating this process for each of the transcription factors expressed in a cell, one can obtain a global map of the *cis*-control elements to which the transcription factors bind.

> Protein-DNA interactions occur during transcription and other cellular processes. ChIP/chip analysis allows investigators to find all the sites in a genome where a transcription factor can bind, helping to clarify cellular controls.

Figure 10.25 Diagram of the ChIP/chip process. (a) A DNA sequence encoding an antibody binding site is attached to one end of a transcription factor gene, which is expressed in the appropriate cell type. The expressed protein (*yellow* with *orange* peptide tag) is allowed to bind to all of its cognate *cis*-control elements and is then covalently cross-linked to these DNA sites. **(b)** The DNA is sheared into fragments 300–500 bp in length, and these fragments are purified using the specific antibody (*blue*) as a marker. **(c)** PCR amplification linkers (*aqua*) are now put on both ends of these DNA fragments, and they are amplified incorporating a *red* dye **(d, right side)**. In the control, investigators leave out the cross-linking and incorporate a *green* dye into the amplified DNA **(c and d, left side). (e)** The amplified control and experimental DNAs are mixed and hybridized to a DNA array carrying all the appropriate non-coding DNAs to which the transcription factor might bind. The color ratios of the individual DNA spots on the chip are analyzed; a high red-to-green ratio indicates the presence of a *cis*-control element that binds to the transcription factor under study.

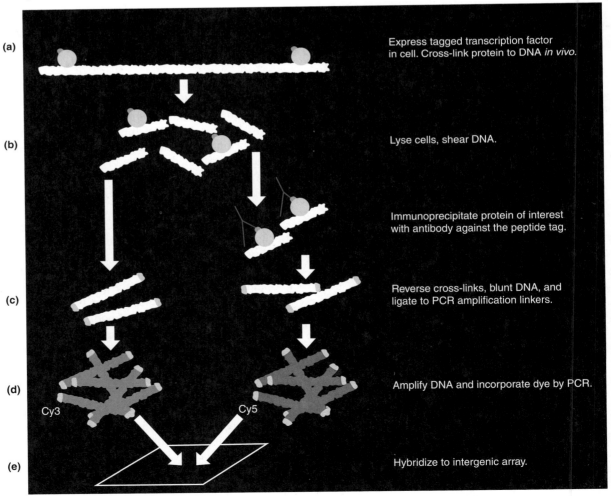

(a) Express tagged transcription factor in cell. Cross-link protein to DNA *in vivo*.

(b) Lyse cells, shear DNA.

Immunoprecipitate protein of interest with antibody against the peptide tag.

(c) Reverse cross-links, blunt DNA, and ligate to PCR amplification linkers.

(d) Amplify DNA and incorporate dye by PCR.

Cy3   Cy5

(e) Hybridize to intergenic array.

10.5 Repercussions of the Human Genome Project and High-Throughput Technology

The genome sequences of humans and model organisms have transformed all of biology. Knowledge of these sequences enables us to identify and readily access most human genes, and the ability to do this greatly facilitates our understanding of their functions. We can also use the genome sequences to search for the control elements of each gene, which help regulate the gene's expression (see Chapters 15, 16, and 17).

High-throughput platforms have transformed research methods

For each organism of interest, researchers would like to use the high-throughput platforms to accomplish the following tasks:

Sequence the organism's genome.
Define quantitatively the transcriptomes and proteomes in each cell type.
Delineate the nature of proteome interactions in various cell types.
Analyze other features of the proteome, such as the location of proteins, their state and level of activation, their half-life, and their three-dimensional structure.

For each organism, geneticists would also like to develop strains from different genetic manipulations—for example, separate knockout strains for each gene of the genome. In addition, the global production of mutants is important because one cannot determine the consequences of different levels of mRNA or protein activity from the all-or-none knockout mutations. Investigators would also like to be able to express each protein from an organism to study it individually or in combination with other proteins.

High-throughput platforms can also be applied to experimental genetic and environmental manipulations of organisms or cells. Yeast researchers, for example, have used knockout strains and global protein interaction data to study a variety of biological systems, including the cell cycle. And medical researchers have carried out microarray analyses of tissues from patients with leukemia, prostate cancer, breast cancer, and melanoma in comparison with the corresponding normal tissues. These analyses have revealed molecular markers that allow phenotypically similar cancers to be separated into distinct groups. This indicates that the cancers probably result from different cellular defects, suggesting that prognoses may vary with a particular defect and may require more specialized treatments.

It is now possible to sequence individual human, other animal, and plant genomes rapidly and inexpensively.

As a result, we will be able to identify not only the control elements of all genes but also the transcription factors that bind to those elements and reveal the complex gene regulatory networks of individual organisms. Thus, from the digital information of individual genomes, we will be able to decipher the logic of life for each species. This capacity will help transform the practice of medicine, moving it from a reactive to a predictive, preventive, and personalized mode.

Great potential exists for predictive/preventive medicine

The potential for predictive/preventive medicine depends on access to whole-genome sequences. One goal is to improve technologies to the point where an individual human genome sequence will cost less than $1000, and many people will be able to have their genomes sequenced. The inexpensive sequences will serve as one basis of predictive medicine because they will provide access to the DNA polymorphisms underlying human variability.

Although most polymorphisms fall outside of genes and thus do little to change human phenotypes, some are responsible for differences in normal physiology, and others predispose to disease. For example, a single defective copy of the breast cancer 1 gene (*BRCA1*), causes 70% of the women who inherit it to be afflicted with breast cancer by the age of 60. Why only 70%? Either environmental factors operate in concert with the defective gene, or other modifying, disease-predisposing genes are present only 70% of the time. In either case, a prediction can be made about the future likelihood of disease for individuals carrying the defective gene. In time, physicians will be able to scan the genomes of the young and provide a probabilistic projection of what the future may hold with regard to a wide variety of diseases. Of course, being able to predict a disease without being able to cure or prevent it leaves physicians in a very uncomfortable position. As the techniques of systems biology mature, scientists hope to be able to learn how to circumvent the limitations of these defective genes—with, for example, novel drugs, environmental controls, or other approaches such as stem cell transplants or gene therapy. Preventive measures may be designed to avoid or greatly delay the onset of the disease.

Social, ethical, and legal issues have no simple solutions

The ability to analyze the genomes of individual humans raises a host of pressing questions about the privacy of genetic information, limitations on the use of genetic testing, the patenting of DNA sequences, society's view of older people, the training of physicians, and the extent to which the human genetic engineer should seek to engineer himself or herself.

GENETICS AND SOCIETY

Patentability of DNA

Some people argue that genetic information, the naturally occurring raw material of life's evolution, is a common heritage that belongs to everyone. Yet since the mid-1970s, universities and biotechnology companies have sought patents on specific DNA sequences in virtually all types of genomes—plant, human, other animal, bacterial, viral, and plasmid.

Patent examiners evaluate the patentability of a product or process by three criteria: Is it *new*? Is it *nonobvious*? Is it *useful*? In the DNA arena, the courts have made the following interpretations of patent law. Raw materials of nature, such as wild-type DNA in a living organism, are not novel and thus are not patentable; modified products, such as bacterial DNA altered by a synthetic mutation or human DNA in a mouse genome, are novel and thus eligible for patents by the novelty criterion. DNA-based processes that produce a novel material, such as clones of a gene (consisting of a DNA construct in a vector), are also patentable. Publication in a scientific journal makes an item, such as a DNA sequence, obvious and thus unpatentable per se; but a specific use of a published sequence may be nonobvious and thus patentable. A well-defined use might be a particular test for a genetic aberration or a particular process for the manufacture of a therapeutic agent.

Different countries apply the basic tenets of patent law in different ways. In the United States, the purified form of a gene or protein is patentable because genes and proteins do not exist in nature in purified form. In England, a naturally occurring gene sequence is not patentable no matter what form it is in. And in France, the code on intellectual property declares unpatentable "the human body, its elements and products as well as knowledge of the partial or total structure of a human gene."

The rationale for granting patents is to encourage innovation—the invention of useful contributions to society—by providing a time-limited monopoly to protect an invention from imitation. This commercial protection is given in exchange for the complete disclosure of the information related to a product or process. In fact, in pursuing a patent, a company protects its interests by making available as much information as possible about the modified product or process. Patents protect use for profit; they do not interfere with research or other noncommercial uses of the information in the patent.

Currently, much debate is taking place over the application of patent criteria, originally developed for mechanical or chemical inventions, to life-forms or materials derived from them. This debate identifies several areas of concern.

Openness Versus Secrecy

A company putting a great deal of money into the research and development of what it hopes will be a patentable gene therapy may withhold publication of its data or publish only partial results until its patent application is in the pipeline.

For example, in the 1980s, before the discovery of the cystic fibrosis gene, one gene diagnostics company published an article about markers for the *CF* gene but, in an effort to protect their work, did not include the fact that those markers were on chromosome 7. As it happens, other groups subsequently found closer markers and then the gene. But the question remains regarding to what extent commercial considerations interfere with free exchange of ideas, and if so, whether anything can or should be done about it.

Profitability Versus the Social Good

Most companies consider potential profitability as the basis for pursuing research and development. Some people wonder whether they should also factor into the equation concerns about serving the poor (who cannot pay much for drugs or therapies) and the relatively few patients suffering from uncommon diseases. For example, about 25 million people in Africa are infected with HIV, the virus that causes AIDS. In the United States and Europe, AIDS can be managed by triple drug therapy—the simultaneous administration of three drugs that attack AIDS with different mechanisms—but this therapy costs more than $12,000 per year. Most infected individuals in Africa cannot afford the treatment.

India has started to manufacture generic AIDS drugs costing just a few dollars per day, roughly $1100 per year. India can manufacture these drugs inexpensively because the very costly research to identify promising compounds and develop them into drugs was paid for by European and American pharmaceutical companies. In fact, India is violating drug-company patents when it sells the AIDS drugs inexpensively in Africa. Millions of infected people in Africa, however, could never receive appropriate treatment for AIDS without the inexpensive generic drugs manufactured in India. The terrible dilemma faced is the ongoing need for additional research, for which companies must pay, contrasted with the need of suffering people to receive care for their illnesses.

Development and Funding of Socially Useful Research Applications

Because companies must pour large sums of money into developing DNA-based drugs or therapies, testing them on large numbers of people, and bringing them to market, many researchers—at both universities and commercial enterprises—maintain that the survival of biotechnology companies, particularly small ones, depends on patent protection. Without the possibility of a patent, they argue, companies may not be able to afford to use knowledge of, for example, the *CF* gene and the transmembrane conductance regulator it encodes to develop therapies that may ease and extend the lives of thousands of CF sufferers. And yet, many of the patents providing the basis for development and marketing are granted on inventions made in university laboratories; and the investigators in some of these laboratories are nonprofit recipients of federal grants that are ultimately funded by taxpayers. Most government agencies allow such patents because governments lack the considerable additional funds needed to develop research ideas for the marketplace.

Thus, the availability of purified DNA, especially specific stretches of the human genome, raises several issues that the framers of patent law could not foresee. Vigorous public debate will help scientists, businesspeople, ethicists, and lawmakers to distill some of the answers.

Because of the complexity of these controversial issues, we have presented individual topics in the Genetics and Society essays found throughout this book. In this chapter's essay, "Patentability of DNA," we consider who owns the information being revealed by research and in what ways that information may legally—and ethically—be used. Other social and ethical issues include confidentiality, privacy, and genetic diagnosis and screening.

Another consideration is the impact of longevity that may be brought about through improved predictive/preventive medicine. With more people living productively into their nineties and beyond, societies may need to rethink philosophies of retirement, Social Security, and access to medical care.

Many preventative or remedial measures constitute **somatic gene therapy** in which medical practitioners compensate for a faulty gene by inserting a replacement gene into the affected tissue where the gene is expressed. Somatic gene therapy causes biochemical and physiological changes in the genetically modified tissue or tissues that die with the individual. A potential therapy for cystic fibrosis, for example, consists in inserting a wild-type *CFTR* gene into lung cells. This type of genetic engineering is not different in kind from drug therapies aimed at correcting a particular physiological deficiency (for example, the insulin injections aimed at treating diabetes). The alterations resulting from somatic gene therapy affect only the somatic cells of the individual undergoing the therapy and cannot be transmitted to offspring.

Most of the controversy surrounding genetic engineering stems from the potential for **germ-line gene therapy:** modifications of the human germ line. Germ-line gene therapy produces changes in germ cells that are passed on to progeny. Ethical concerns focus on what is and is not appropriate. Should, for example, parents be able to eliminate a cancer-predisposing gene in their unborn child? Should they be allowed to alter the child's potential for obesity or longevity? Should they have the option of choosing the child's eye color? (See the Genetics and Society box in Chapter 11 for more on this subject.)

Many geneticists and bioethicists support the idea of somatic gene therapy but oppose germ-line therapy. At the same time, they urge serious and open discussion of the issues before perfection of the technology overtakes our ability to control its use.

> While new technologies allow greater research and medical possibilities than ever before, ethical questions remain to be resolved. Somatic gene therapy may allow individuals to survive otherwise debilitating diseases. Germ-line gene therapy is far more controversial.

Connections

One of the triumphs of modern genetics has been the determination of the complete sequence of the human genome and the genomes of many model organisms. With powerful new "shotgun" strategies for sequencing large genomes, genomicists have sequenced more than 250 different microbe, plant, and animal genomes. The genome projects now underway in laboratories around the world will eventually add hundreds of additional genomes to this list.

The high-throughput DNA sequencing platforms, developed by the Human Genome Project have catalyzed the emergence of similar platforms for analyzing mRNA and proteins. Based on these tools, analyses have provided insights into the architecture and evolution of genomes and proteomes. The genetics parts lists made available by the genome sequences are transforming the practice of biology and medicine.

The human genome defines the human species. Indeed, every individual person carries a diploid genome that is 99.9% identical to that carried by every other individual. But the flip side of a 99.9% identity is a 0.1% nonidentity that distinguishes people (other than identical twins) from each other. This 0.1% difference translates into 6 million DNA sequence differences, or polymorphisms, that are responsible for all of the inherited ways in which individuals differ from one another. Of critical interest to medical researchers are the specific DNA polymorphisms that either directly alter or indirectly mark the genes that cause or predispose to disease. In Chapter 11 on genome-wide variation we discuss how researchers identify and use DNA polymorphisms to uncover disease-causing genes and other genes of interest in humans and other species. The discussion includes an examination of complex genetic traits, which arise from interactions among multiple genes and the environment.

ESSENTIAL CONCEPTS

1. Long-range physical maps chart the features of chromosomes. Fluorescent *in situ* hybridization, or FISH, locates a cloned locus to a particular band on a particular chromosome.

2. Long-range sequence maps, compiled from the sequences of subclones, provide a readout of every nucleotide in each chromosome. The subclones are derived either from previously mapped

large insert clones (hierarchical shotgun approach) or directly from the genome (whole-genome shotgun approach).

3. A variety of major insights have emerged from analyses of human and model organism genomes. The number of human genes, approximately 25,000, is surprisingly low, and an organism's complexity is not an indicator of the number of genes its DNA carries. Many gene sequences have been conserved over evolutionary time, allowing the possibility that gene function can be deduced from known functions of similar genes in other species.

4. The human genome exhibits clustering of genetic material in three ways: gene families, in which many genes encode similar proteins; gene-rich regions that are densely packed with genes; and gene deserts in which large stretches of DNA are not associated with any identifiable gene.

5. Combinatorial strategies at the DNA level and RNA level allow production of highly diversified gene products; for example, the specific antigen receptors of T cells, and the alternative splicing patterns of exons associated with the neurexin genes.

6. Comparison of genomes allows investigators to infer evolutionary relationships as well as the function of genes across species. The DNA sequences of microbes, plants, and animals all employ the same genetic code and show a remarkable similarity among many basic biological systems. This affirms the idea that all present life descended from a single common ancestor.

7. The Human Genome Project has catalyzed the development of the DNA sequencer and DNA microarrays for genomics studies. These instruments have been integrated into high-throughput

platforms for DNA sequencing and genotyping, as well as for mRNA (transcriptome) analysis.

8. The term proteome refers collectively to all products of translation of the protein-coding genome. High-throughput platforms have been adapted to proteomic studies. The mass spectrometer in conjunction with fractionation methods has allowed analysis of the amino acid sequences of proteins.

9. Isotope analysis utilizing isotope-coded affinity tags (ICATs) has enabled the study of how protein concentration changes in two different cellular or tissue states, such as normal versus cancerous.

10. Affinity capture, in which an antibody is used to capture and pull down a protein from a complex mixture, is one way to approach analysis of protein-protein interactions. The pulled-down proteins can then be separated by mass spectrometry. Protein arrays, constructed similarly to DNA arrays, can also be probed with tagged molecules to determine binding affinity between proteins.

11. To analyze protein-DNA interactions, a combination technique of chromatin immunoprecipitation (ChIP) analyzed on an array (chip) can identify all specific transcription factor binding sites in a genome.

12. The Human Genome Project has brought about tremendous changes in approaches to biology and medicine. Predictive medicine may allow researchers to correlate polymorphisms with disease predisposition and to make health-history predictions for each individual. Preventive medicine may allow identification of defective genes and facilitate development of ways to avoid their limitations with drugs, diet, gene therapy, or stem cell therapy. The potential of predictive/preventive medicine raises social, ethical, and legal questions for which there are no easy answers.

On Our Website | www.mhhe.com/hartwell4

Annotated Suggested Readings and Links to Other Websites

- Historical papers on the origins of the Human Genome Project
- Historical and contemporary papers on the technologies of the Human Genome Project
- Historical and contemporary papers on the conclusions drawn from the Human Genome Project

- Links to publicly available sequence data and other genomic information
- Historical and contemporary papers on the ethical, social, and legal implications of the Human Genome Project

Specialized Topics

- The first two classic papers on the Human Genome Project

I. A physical map of overlapping clones (a contig) was available for an area of a human chromosome containing three genes (and part of a fourth gene) that are transcribed within ovarian tumor tissue. The restriction map of the region is shown; tick marks above the line indicate *Bam*H1 restriction sites, while those below the line indicate *Xho*I sites. Sizes of DNA fragments between adjacent restriction sites are given in kilobases. Individual restriction fragments were purified, made radioactive, and used as probes for Northern blots of poly-A-containing RNA derived from ovarian tumors. In a *Northern blot* (described in Fig. 11.20), mRNAs are analyzed just as DNA fragments are in a Southern blot (see Chapter 9). The poly-A-containing mixture of mRNAs from a particular cell type is subjected to electrophoresis—separating the mRNAs according to size (smaller mRNA migrate more rapidly than larger ones). The mRNAs are then transferred from the gel to a nitrocellulose filter and a radio-labeled probe for a particular gene (or gene fragment) is hybridized against the mRNAs on the filter. If size standards are also run, the presence and size of particular mRNAs can be established. The resulting autoradiograms are presented below the restriction map. Using these data, characterize the four genes within the contig in the following ways:

a. What is the length of the mRNA for each of the three complete genes?

b. What is the minimum length of the primary transcript for the largest of these RNAs?

c. What is the minimum number of exons for each gene?

d. What is the minimum number of introns for each gene?

Answer

This problem requires an understanding of primary and processed transcripts and the analysis of RNAs using Northern hybridization.

a. The bands on the Northern blots that hybridize with the probes represent the mRNAs from this region. The three mRNAs corresponding to the genes in this region are *1.1, 2.4,* and *6.8 kb* in length. The 4.3 kb transcript comes from a gene

that is only partly contained in the DNA used as a probe since the one DNA fragment that hybridizes is only 2.0 kb in length.

b. The bands on the Northern blot represent processed transcripts (introns have been removed). Primary mRNAs are made by copying from contiguous DNA sequences, including those regions that will be removed by splicing. The minimum length of a primary transcript is based on the sizes of the restriction fragments that hybridize with the RNAs and any intervening fragments. *For the 6.8 kb largest mRNA, the minimum size is 2.8 + 1.6 + 1.4 + 3.1 + 2.6 + 2.9 + 2.2 + 0.5 + 4.4 kb, or 21.5 kb.* We cannot say from these data whether transcription begins before the 2.8 kb fragment or extends beyond the 4.4 kb fragment.

c./d. The minimum number of exons is determined by counting the number of hybridizing fragments or groups of contiguous fragments. This is a minimum number because any of the fragments could contain more than one exon. The nonhybridizing fragments that separate these must contain introns.

Transcript	Minimum number of exons	Minimum number of introns
1.1 kb	one exon	none
2.4 kb	two exons	one
6.8 kb	four exons	three

II. Reverse transcriptase, the enzyme used to synthesize cDNA starting with mRNA as a template, often falls off the template before completely copying the mRNA. When screening for a cDNA clone of a gene, it is therefore not uncommon to isolate partial cDNA clones. What comparison could you make experimentally that would indicate if you had isolated a plasmid clone containing a partial cDNA?

Answer

For this problem, consider the two alternatives: you have the complete cDNA clone or you have a partial cDNA clone. What would be the differences that you could detect experimentally? The cDNA must be as long as its corresponding mRNA to be full length. You need to find out what the full length of the message is to do the comparison. The way to *measure the length of mRNA is to run a Northern gel and hybridize with the cDNA as a probe.* (Another alternative would be to hybridize a fragment from near the 5' end of the gene to your clone. This would require that you have a fragment that you know is from the 5' end of the gene.

Problems

Interactive Web Exercises

We highlight here two resources maintained by the National Center for Biotechnology Information (NCBI). The first is Map Viewer, which is a graphical representation of the entire human genome. By navigating through Map Viewer, you will acquire a feeling for the way in which genes are organized on human chromosomes. The second resource is BLAST, a program which enables investigators to find DNAs, RNAs, or proteins homologous to any nucleic acid or protein for which nucleotide or amino acid sequence information is available. To access this material, visit our website at www.mhhe.com/hartwell4, go to Chapter 10, and click on "Interactive Web Exercises."

Vocabulary

1. For each of the terms in the left column, choose the best matching phrase in the right column.

a. sequence tagged sites (STSs)
1. a map showing the order of cloned inserts of DNA

b. whole-genome shotgun sequencing
2. fragments of DNA on a chip

c. DNA array
3. a genome sequencing strategy that avoids physical mapping

d. alternative RNA splicing
4. a polymorphic single-base site

e. physical map
5. the joining together of the exons of a gene in different combinations

f. SNP
6. unique DNA sequences that serve as molecular markers

Section 10.1

2. Would it be possible to construct a complete physical map of the human genome (assuming a 3 Gb size) with 15,000 BAC clones each with a 200 kb insert? Why or why not?

3. To make a set of clones more suitable for the analysis of DNA sequence, a series of cosmid clones was prepared by digesting a BAC clone and subcloning the resulting restriction fragments. The restriction patterns of the inserted fragments are shown next. Arrange these four cosmids into a physical map, showing the order of the clones and the overlap between them.

4. In an alternative approach to that described in Problem 4, a cosmid library was probed with an insert from a BAC, and 22 cosmids were obtained. All but two of the cosmids could be arranged as an overlapping group (a contig). This set of cosmids covered the length of the BAC insert. What explanation can you offer for the two cosmids that did not fit into this contig? Why did these hybridize with the BAC probe?

5. During the course of the genome project for the rhesus monkey *Macaca mulatta*, 5 BAC clones (A–E) forming a single contig were obtained. Researchers determined a short (≈500 bp) sequence of monkey DNA from each of the two ends of the BAC clones (that is, from where the monkey genomic DNA was joined to the BAC vector). The scientists converted these sequences into sequence tagged sites (STSs) by making PCR primers that could amplify the 500 bp of monkey DNA if were present in any DNA sample. The table below shows which STSs were found in each of the 5 BACs; each clone of course has the two STSs corresponding to the sequenced monkey DNA at each end.

BAC clone	End STSs	Other STSs
A	1 2	4 5 7 10
B	3 4	2 9
C	5 6	1 8
D	7 8	1 5
E	9 10	2 4

a. Why is it very efficient to determine the sequence of monkey DNA at locations where it is joined the BAC vector?

b. Diagram a physical map of this region consistent with the data, indicating the relative order of the BAC clones and the location of the STSs.

c. If you wanted to determine the DNA sequence of the entire contig, it would be advantageous to work with the minimal tiling path of the BAC clones. Why Diagram the minimal tiling path consistent with the data in the table.

d. Estimate the size of the contig in kb.

6. In the course of sequencing a genome, a computer trying to assemble the following six DNA sequences into contigs:

```
5′ CAAATAGCAGCAAATTACAGCAATATGAAG 3′
5′ AAAATGCCCTAAAGGAAATGAGATTTTTAA 3′
5′ TGATCTCTTCATATTGCTGTAATTTGCTGC 3′
5′ GTAGTATCTCCTTTTAAAAATCTCATTTCC 3′
5′ CAATATGAAGAGATCATACAGTCCACTGAA 3′
5′ TCTCATTTCCTTTAGGGCATTTTCAAATTC 3′
```

How many contigs are represented by this set of DNA sequences, and what is the sequence of each contig

7. Repetitive DNA sequences present a challenge to genome projects. Why is this so? What types of repetitive sequences are most problematic? How can hierarchical shotgun and whole-genome shotgun sequencing strategies deal with this problem?

8. It is often difficult to find genome-unique PCR primers in certain regions of the genome. Offer two explanations.

9. What are two potential difficulties with the whole-genome shotgun sequencing strategy?

10. Figure 10.4b on p. 339 shows a fluorescence *in situ* hybridization (FISH) analysis that reveals the position in the human genome of DNA sequences homologous to a particular probe.
    a. Suppose you made two probes, one of which fluoresces in red and the other in green. Estimate how far apart the corresponding sequences on the chromosomes have to be so that you could accurately resolve the order of these sequences along the same chromosome. Assume that the size of the FISH signal is typical for this type of experiment, and that the chromosome containing the homologous sequences is of average size in the human genome.
    b. Since the publication of the human genome sequence, human geneticists have done fewer FISH experiments than in the past. Explain why. For what purposes would FISH still be useful today?

11. What are the advantages of the FISH protocol over linkage mapping for the initial characterization of the chromosomal location of a gene?

12. A clear limitation to gene mapping in humans is that family sizes are small, so it is very difficult to collate enough data to get accurate recombination frequencies. A technique that circumvents this problem begins with the purification of DNA from single sperm cells. (Remember that recombination occurs during meiosis. Analysis of a population of sperm provides a large data set for linkage studies.) The DNA from single sperm cells can be used for polymerase chain reaction (PCR) studies. The PCR reactions can be run such that a PCR primer will not hybridize to DNA if there is a single-nucleotide difference between the sequence of

the primer and the template DNA to be analyzed. A PCR product will be formed only if both primers hybridize to the template.

A series of three pairs of PCR primers were synthesized according to DNA sequences from human genomic clones. The alpha primers amplify a fragment 100 bp long; the beta primers produce a 200 bp product; the delta primers produce a 400 bp product. Twenty-five sperm obtained from one man were subjected to PCR analysis with these three pairs of primers simultaneously. Refer to the figure at the bottom of this page.
    a. Is this man homozygous for any nucleotide polymorphism detected by this method? If so, which one?
    b. Determine the genetic map information you can glean from this data.

Section 10.2

13. Give two different reasons for the much higher ratio of total DNA to DNA that encodes proteins in the human genome compared to bacterial genomes.

14. Using a cDNA library, you isolated two different cDNA clones that hybridized with your probe for a nerve growth factor gene. The beginning and ending sequences of the clones are the same but the middle sequence is different. How can you explain the different cDNAs?

15. What sequence information about a gene is lacking in a cDNA library?

16. A restriction map of part of the *Drosophila* X chromosome has been determined; it is presented here. Messenger RNA from *Drosophila* adults was purified, fractionated on agarose gels according to size, and then transferred to nitrocellulose filters. Radioactive recombinant DNAs corresponding to fragments A–G were hybridized to identical copies of the nitrocellulose filters containing the fractionated mRNAs. Using the map information, indicate the region of the DNA that must be transcribed to form each of three primary transcripts, which are then processed into the three mRNAs observed. Indicate where exons and introns occur in relation to the restriction fragments.

Probe: G F E D C B A

17. The maps of human chromosomes in males and females indicate that the centimorgan distances between genes is different in the two sexes.
    a. What could account for this difference in distances?
    b. Do you think the physical distances between genes in males and females would differ also? Why or why not?

18. List three independent techniques you could use to identify DNA sequences encoding human genes within a cloned genomic region.

19. Discuss three observations that suggest not all repeat sequences are junk.

20. An interesting phenomenon found in vertebrate DNA is the existence of pseudogenes, nonfunctional copies of a gene found elsewhere in the genome. Pseudogenes appear to be double-stranded DNA copies of mature mRNA inserted into the chromosome. What sequence information would provide a clue(s) that the source of these pseudogenes is cDNA?

21. List an advantage of each of the following model organisms for the analysis of gene function. Give an example of the type of gene you might choose to analyze in each of these model organisms.
    a. yeast (*S. cerevisiae*)
    b. nematodes (*C. elegans*)
    c. mouse (*M. musculus*)

22. With new information from the Human Genome Project, many new genes will be identified for which the function is not known.
    a. What features of the DNA sequence might help you determine the function of a newly identified gene?
    b. What are two other types of analysis that would help you learn more about a new gene?

23. a. If you found a zinc-finger domain (which facilitates DNA binding) in a newly identified gene, what hypothesis would you make about the gene's function?
    b. In another gene, what would a high percentage of similarity throughout the gene with a previously identified gene in the same organism suggest about the origin of the gene?

24. You sequence the genomes of four different organisms and compare their sequences over a short region as shown below.

    5′ AGGTATATAATTTGCG 3′
    5′ CAATATAAAACCCTAC 3′
    5′ GCGTATAAAAGAGCTA 3′
    5′ TTATATATAAAGAAGT 3′

    a. Determine the consensus sequence common to the four regions above.
    b. Why would you want to define the consensus sequence? How would you decide whether the four sequences above were worth comparing to define a consensus?
    c. How could you use this general strategy for defining a consensus sequence to determine which amino acids of a protein are most critical for its function?

25. The human genome has been sequenced, but we still don't have an accurate count of the number of genes. Why not?

26. Chimpanzees have a set of hemoglobin genes very similar to the set in humans (shown in Fig. 9.20 on p. 324). For example, the genomes of both species have α1, α2, β, Gγ, Aγ, δ, ε, and ζ genes.
    a. Of the human and chimpanzee hemoglobin genes, which would be considered homologous? Which paralogous? Which orthologous?
    b. When comparing genomes, geneticists would usually like to know which genes are the most likely to perform similar if not identical functions in different species. This determination can be somewhat complicated in the case of gene families. Would paralogous genes or orthologous genes be more likely to be functionally equivalent? Explain.
    c. Which gene would have the greatest degree of nucleotide homology to the human β gene: the chimpanzee β gene, or the human γ gene? Explain.
    d. Rationalize the pattern of hemoglobin genes in the two species with the existence of duplication and divergence events among the hemoglobin genes depicted in Figure 9.20 on p. 324.

27. A *cladogram* is a branching diagram (a "Tree of Life") used to illustrate evolutionary relationships. The endpoints of the branches represent present-day species or genes or proteins; the branch points tell whe

these species or molecules diverged from common ancestral forms.

a. How would a cladogram of gene sequences discriminate whether a particular gene had been laterally transferred (say from bacteria to humans) or vertically inherited over a long period of time from one generation to the next?

b. If lateral transfer were involved, how might you be able to tell roughly when in the course of evolution the transfer had occurred?

c. How could you recognize if a gene was somehow lost from the genome of a particular species?

28. From an expression library, you isolated a clone and made an antibody to the protein produced by the cloned gene. When the antibody was used to stain a preparation of a mouse embryo, the protein localized to the brain. Northern analysis showed that there were three mRNA transcripts from the gene present in the brain. Two of these mRNAs were also present in tissues other than the brain. Propose a hypothesis to explain the presence of RNAs in many tissues but protein only in the brain.

29. Complete genome sequences indicate that the human genome has roughly 25,000–30,000 genes, and the worm (nematode) genome has 19,000 genes. Explain how the human genome can encode a creature enormously more complex than the worm with at most only one-third more genes in its genome.

Section 10.3

30. The following factors pose technical challenges for the design of gene therapy experiments. Suggest ways to get around these problems.

a. large gene size in eukaryotes (up to 100 kb of DNA in the genome)

b. the need to get genes expressed in specific tissues

31. Consider a microarray experiment similar to the one shown in Fig. 10.17 on p. 350, in which each square represents a PCR-amplified fragment of a different

human gene, and the red-labeled probe is cDNA from a human lung tumor while the green-labeled probe is cDNA from normal lung tissue.

a. How would you interpret results in which the fluorescence signal was black? Green? Red? Yellow?

b. If you were searching for an anticancer drug that would inactivate a protein whose activity contributes to cancer, which of the genes represented on the microarray encode proteins you would most likely chose as a potential target for such a drug?

32. A region of the genome from two individuals is amplified by PCR so that the PCR products from one individual are labeled with rhodamine (which fluoresces in red), while the PCR products from the other person are labeled with fluorescein (which fluoresces in green). These PCR products are mixed and hybridized to an oligonucleotide microarray with the following results.

The oligonucleotides on the array are:

```
M1:  5′  ACTTACCGAGAGAACCTGCG  3′
M2:  5′  ACTGACCGAGAGAGCCTGCG  3′
M3:  5′  ACTTACCGAGAGAGCCTGCG  3′
M4:  5′  ACTCACCGAGAGACCCTGCG  3′
M5:  5′  ACTCACCGAGAGATCCTGCG  3′
M6:  5′  ACTGACCGAGAGAACCTGCG  3′
```

a. As accurately as possible, describe the genotypes of the two individuals.

b. Why would you encounter ambiguity in assigning genotypes to these two particular individuals if you sequenced the PCR products directly, rather than by hybridizing them to an oligonucleotide microarray as above?

c. In what way would the oligonucleotide microarray approach be valuable as a diagnostic tool for human genetic diseases?

CHAPTER 11

Genome-Wide Variation and Trait Analysis

An eighteenth-century painting depicting the 64 offspring of the ninth Sultan of Yogyakarta and his 13 wives. In this family tree, boys are depicted as fruit, girls as leaves. The two fruits emerging from a single stem on the right indicate twins. The painting is currently located in the Sultan's Palace inside the central walled-in city (Kraton) of Yogyakarta (on the island of Java in present-day Indonesia).

A couple whose firstborn suffers from cystic fibrosis learns from the medical diagnosis of that child's symptoms that both parents are carriers of a recessive disease-producing mutation. Together they run a 25% risk of having a second child exhibiting this life-threatening hereditary condition. In the early 1990s, one such couple did not want to take that chance and, after genetic counseling, decided to try an experimental protocol: *in vitro* fertilization combined with the direct detection *in vitro* of the embryo's genotype, before its placement in the mother's womb.

The procedure took less than a week. At the start, a team of medical workers, including an obstetrician and a reproductive biologist, obtained 10 eggs from the woman and fertilized them with sperm from the man. Three days later, after the fertilized eggs had undergone several mitotic divisions to generate embryos with 6–10 cells, a research assistant used micropipettes to remove one cell from each embryo (**Fig. 11.1**). Because embryos that split naturally at this stage can develop into healthy identical twins, the removal of a single cell would not prevent normal development.

Next, the research assistant used PCR (see Fig. 9.16 on p. 320) to amplify from each isolated cell a specific DNA segment in each homolog of chromosome 7 containing the site of the most common mutation within the gene responsible for cystic fibrosis (the *CFTR* gene). They then used wild-type and mutant CFTR probes to detect the genotype of the cells, and by inference, of each embryo.

On the same day that the embryos were biopsied and genotyped, the doctor, in consultation with the parents, selected for placement in the mother's womb two embryos of known genotype. Of the two embryos they chose, one was a heterozygous carrier, the other a homozygote for the normal allele. The use of two embryos improves the chances of at least one implantation and is a part of many *in vitro* fertilization procedures. As it happened, only the embryo carrying two normal alleles of the *CFTR* gene implanted into the woman's uterus.

CHAPTER OUTLINE

- 11.1 Genetic Variation Among Individual Genomes
- 11.2 Single Nucleotide Polymorphisms (SNPs) and Small-Scale-Length Variations
- 11.3 Deletions or Duplications of a DNA Region
- 11.4 Positional Cloning: From DNA Markers to Disease-Causing Genes
- 11.5 Complex Traits
- 11.6 Genome-Wide Association Studies

Nine months later, the mother gave birth to a healthy 7 lb 3 oz baby girl. When evaluated by a pediatrician at her four-week checkup, the infant daughter was found to be completely normal in both physical and mental development. At the same time, testing at an independent laboratory confirmed that neither of her homologous chromosome 7s carried the *CFTR* mutation.

In this chapter, we examine how geneticists use an array of molecular tools to detect DNA differences among individuals. The techniques are sensitive enough to operate on single hair follicles and even single cells from human embryos.

The ability to detect genotype directly at the DNA level has far-reaching consequences. It provides geneticists with tools for mapping and identifying the genes responsible for human diseases that, like the cystic fibrosis gene, were previously defined only by their effect on phenotype. Once the genes and their variant alleles are identified DNA genotyping can help predict the probability of future disease—*in vitro, in utero,* or after birth—or reveal the presence of a silent recessive disease allele in a carrier who shows no evidence of disease. With the use of high density DNA microarrays, researchers and clinicians can rapidly and cheaply determine genotypes at over a million locations throughout a person's genome. The application of whole genome analysis to thousands of individuals who have also been evaluated clinically also gives human geneticists the power to uncover common DNA variants that contribute to extremely complex traits, including diabetes and heart disease.

Our discussion of these novel genetic technologies and applications suggests two general themes. First, the ability to distinguish genotypic differences of all kinds extends our concept of a locus and the alleles that define it. Second, techniques for direct detection of genotype provide access to genetic details about human individuals never before available. Who should have access to this information, and how should it be used?

Figure 11.1 Preimplantation embryo diagnosis. Plucking one cell from an eight-cell embryo for the direct detection of genotype.

1. Maturation of multiple oocytes is stimulated with injections of FSH (follicle stimulating hormone) and other hormones.

2. An ultrasound probe allows the physician to visualize ripe follicles on the surface of the ovary. The egg retrieval needle is inserted through the rear wall of the vagina and into each ovarian follicle to recover eggs.

3. Ten individual eggs are placed into separate wells of a sample plate and fertilized with sperm. Incubation at 37°C for three days allows several rounds of cell division.

4. After three days, six of the embryos have undergone normal development to the 6–10 cell stage. A single cell is removed from each one.

5. PCR is used to amplify the DNA of the sample cell (see Chapter 10).

6. Upon completion of the reaction, each sample is divided into two portions.

Ovary
Retrieval needle (not seen)
Ultrasound probe
Egg collection tube
Ovary
Ripe follicles

Blot DNA portions to filter

Hybridize with ASO for normal *CF* allele.

Hybridize with ASO for mutant *CF* allele.

7. Diagnosis

	Cell 1	Cell 2*	Cell 3	Cell 4*	Cell 5	Cell 6
Normal ASO	○	●	○	●	●	○
Mutant ASO	●	○	●	●	○	●

* Cells from embryos later transplanted into uterus

11.1 Genetic Variation Among Individual Genomes

Although Darwin's theory of natural selection predated the rediscovery of Mendel's Laws, these two pillars of modern biology—genetics and evolution—were separate intellectual fields without any obvious connection. (Genetics and evolution were first brought together under the rubric of the "modern synthesis" in the 1940s.) Consequently, the first geneticists worked under the age-old conceptualization of a whole species as a unique and *discrete* entity. This view led to the assumption that an "ideal specimen" of any particular species would carry species-specific "wild-type" alleles at each of the genes in its genome. Alleles that were not wild-type were considered mutant. But mutant alleles could only be recognized indirectly as the causative agents of mutant phenotypes.

Extensive allelic variation distinguishes individuals within a species

The first crack in the wild-type/mutant allele dichotomy came during the 1950s and 1960s with the application of gel electrophoresis to study the chemical properties of specified proteins. The results obtained from a variety of species from *Drosophila* to humans were consistent and striking—presumed "wild-type" individuals of the same species frequently produced different variant forms of proteins, encoded by variant alleles. A locus with two or more alleles that are each present in more than 1% of a species' members is considered to be **polymorphic,** and the alleles of a polymorphic locus are called **genetic variants,** rather than wild-type or mutant.

With the advent of DNA cloning and sequencing, and with more recent forays into personal genome sequencing, the staggering degree to which individual human genomes differ from each other has become slowly uncovered. A direct comparison of the genomes of James Watson, codiscoverer of the DNA double helix, and J. Craig Venter, a pioneer of DNA sequencing, reveals 2,021,206 single nucleotide substitutions, of which 5015 cause changes in amino acid sequences of expressed proteins (**Fig. 11.2**). Pairwise comparisons of Watson's or Venter's genome to that of an anonymous Chinese man reveals similar differences. The genomes of the two men also differ by small additions or substractions of genetic material—deletions or insertions—at over 100,000 genomic sites, ranging in size from 2 to 38,896 bp.

Not only is there no such thing as a wild-type human genome, there is also no such thing as a wild-type human genome length. Polymorphic deletions, insertions,

and duplications result in genome lengths that differ by as much as 1% in healthy individuals.

The ability to distinguish genotypic differences of all kinds extends our concept of a locus and the alleles that define it. In the early days of genetic analysis, loci and genes were synonymous simply because nonfunctional regions of DNA were invisible (by definition) at the level of phenotype. By contrast, modern geneticists, able to look at genotype directly, can pick out genotypic differences in both coding and noncoding DNA regions on the basis of changes in DNA sequence alone. As a result, a **locus** is now considered to be any location in the genome that is defined by chromosomal coordinates for the convenience of researchers, irrespective of biological function. A DNA locus can contain multiple genes or no genes; it can be a

Figure 11.2 Pairwise comparison of three personal genomes. Single nucleotide substitutions in the genomes of J. Craig Venter, James D. Watson, and an anonymous Chinese man (YH). Numbers of unique nucleotide substitutions are shown in nonoverlapping portions of each circle. Variants shared by two of the three men are shown in the double overlap regions. The central three-way overlap indicates numbers of substitutions relative to the human reference sequence. **(a)** Differences across the whole genome. **(b)** Amino acid–changing substitutions only.

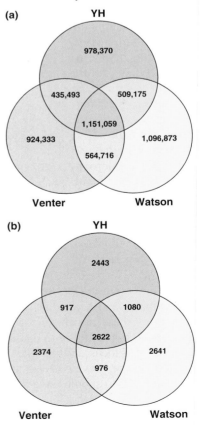

TABLE 11.1 | Categories of Genetic Variants

	Short Name	Size	Frequency	Total Loci Recorded	Method of Detection			
					DNA Microarray	PCR & Gel Electrophoresis	PCR & ASO Hybridization	DNA Sequence
Single nucleotide polymorphism	SNP	1 bp	1 kb	18,000,000	Yes		Yes	
Insertion/deletion	InDel	2–100 bp	10 kb	200,000	(Yes)	Yes		
Simple sequence repeat	SSR, microsatellite	3–200 bp	30 kb	100,000		Yes		
Copy number variation/copy number polymorphism	CNV/CNP	0.1–1,000 kb	3 Mb	8,600	Yes			
Complex variant			500 kb					Yes

single base pair or millions of base pairs, as long as it has a defined genomic location and length.

Along with a new definition of a locus comes a new definition of an allele. Since a locus can be any defined segment of DNA in the genome, an allele of that locus is any variation in the DNA sequence itself, even if it has no impact on the expression of any trait. Whether it is functional or not makes no difference in the manner that a locus is transmitted from one generation to the next. We will see that researchers can still use polymorphic non-functional loci as genetic markers to identify, locate, isolate, and follow the transmission of nearby genes.

Genetic variants are classified according to several criteria

For the purposes of genotyping, geneticists place polymorphic DNA loci into one of the five categories shown in Table 11.1 based on size, frequency within individual genomes, and the method used for their detection. The simplest and most generally useful class of genetic variants are the **single nucleotide polymorphisms** called **SNPs** ("snips"). SNPs are particular base positions in the genome where alternative letters of the DNA alphabet commonly distinguish some people from others.

Beyond the first category of SNPs, genetic variants arise in every size and complexity. For convenience, geneticists place them into one of four additional categories: (2) short deletions and insertions called **InDels** or **DIPs;** (3) regions of repeating two- or three-base-long units termed simple sequence repeats **(SSRs);** (4) large regions of duplication or deletion (copy number polymorphisms, **CNPs,** or copy number variants, **CNVs,** depending on their frequency of occurrence); and (5) a catch-all category of complex variants that don't fit into any other category. Although the borders between these classes are fuzzy, categories serve the purpose of orienting researchers to a sense of what a particular genetic variant looks like.

The original view of what constitutes a genetic locus has changed as modern technology has revealed the genome at the base-pair level. Widespread genetic variance exists among members of a species, even when the variations do not cause a phenotypic difference. Variations are characterized single nucleotide polymorphisms, short deletions and insertions, simple sequence repeats, and copy number polymorphisms.

11.2 SNPs and Small-Scale-Length Variations

The simplest type of DNA polymorphism is the single-base SNP, which arises from a rare mistake in replication or due to a mutagenic chemical (**Fig. 11.3**). SNPs account for the vast majority of the total variation that exists between human genomes, occurring on average once every 1000 bases in any pairwise comparison. The per-base mutation rate is less than one in 30 million per generation, which is so low that in nearly all cases, each individual SNP can be traced back to a genomic change that occurred once in a single ancestral genome. This also means that those people who did not inherit the variant allele have a more ancient allele that was probably present long before the human species took form.

The origin of human SNPs is determined by comparison to other species

Geneticists can take advantage of the close relationship between the human and chimpanzee genomes to distinguish between the original chimp-shared allele and the derived allele (**Fig. 11.3c**). With a comparison of the two genomes, it is possible to identify which of the two alleles at a human

Figure 11.3 Single nucleotide polymorphisms. (a) SNPs are single-base-pair polymorphisms. Geneticists routinely represent genome sequences as the single strand with a 5′ direction toward the start position of the chromosome. **(b)** SNP genotypes are indicated with a two-letter notation. **(c)** A comparison of two human genomic sequences to the chimp sequence indicates positions where single-base changes have occurred since divergence of species. **(d)** The NCBI Sequence Viewer and the UCSC Genome Browser were used to interrogate a 400 kb region of chromosome 7 (from 116,700,001 to 117,100,000) that contains three genes, including *CFTR*, and a small unnamed pseudogene. Three tracks of single nucleotide polymorphisms (SNPs) are shown. Two were read from the personal genomes of Watson and Venter. The third track shows the positions of all SNPs that have been uncovered in sequences from European subjects.

(a)

Allele	Genome	Single-Strand Notation
1	AGCTCTGATAC TCGAGACTATG	AGCTCTGATAC
2	AGCTCCGATAC TCGAGGCTATG	AGCTCCGATAC

(b)

Genotype	Notation
Homozygous T	TT
Heterozygous T	TC
Homozygous C	CC

(c)

Human 1   TTGAC**G**TATAAATGATCTTTATAT**T**TTCAGAAGTC

Human 2   TTGAC**G**TATAAATGATCTTTATAT**C**TTCAGAAGTC

Chimp   TTGAC**A**TATAAATGATCTTTATAT**C**TTCAGAAGTC

(d)

SNP locus is the original version that was present in the common chimp-human ancestor. In the example shown, two single-base changes have occurred in this small genomic region since the divergence of the two species. One is shared by all human genomes and is, thus, not polymorphic.

The second base change was from a C in the common chimp-human ancestor to a T in the ancestor of some people but not others. This means that if you and a friend share an allele at an anonymous SNP locus, you both got that allele from the same ancestor (who may have lived thousands or even hundreds of thousands of years ago). The fact that every random pair of human beings on the planet shares many unlinked SNP alleles indicates recent common ancestry for all people.

SNP distributions

Although SNPs in coding sequences can alter the amino acid sequence of a gene product and have a direct impact on phenotype, the vast majority of SNPs appear to be functionally silent. The reason is illustrated with the 400 kb genomic region in **Fig. 11.3d.** This particular region is denser than average in transcription units with three functional genes that include the cystic fibrosis transmembrane receptor (*CFTR*), which can mutate to cause cystic fibrosis. But the actual number of base pairs used for protein coding in all three genes is only 6945 which is less than 2% of the total. Even if we add in the additional base pairs involved in gene regulation and splicing, over 95% still remains in the nonfunctional category.

No evolutionary advantage or disadvantage is presen for mutations at these noncoding, nonregulatory loci Thus, single-base mutations that occur at nonfunctiona sites will not be selected against, and although most ar lost just by chance, some will remain and gain frequenc in a population. But as described earlier, some do alte coding regions, and some of those are likely to have phenotypic effect. Functional SNPs will be subject t selective pressures like other functional mutations.

Human SNPs

Although it would be possible, in theory, for SNPs t exist at a billion or more genomic sites, the predicte number of common human SNPs is much lower for rea sons that will be fully elucidated later in the chapter. T date, the analysis of thousands of human genomes has le to the identification of approximately 18 million SNP which is likely to represent the majority of those that actu ally exist. In Fig. 11.3d, you can see the distribution c all known SNPs across the 400 kb CFTR region.

Most SNP variation among people is confined to limited number of positions. This result is seen mos clearly in a comparison of the two most fully validate whole-genome sequences of individual persons: Jame Watson and Craig Venter. Approximately 3.3 millio SNPs were identified that distinguish the two individual (as predicted for an average pairwise SNP frequency c once per kilobase). Of the total SNPs found, 82% an 85%, respectively, are listed in the SNP database (dbSNI at NCBI. These two results are remarkably consistent with each other and prior predictions.

In Fig. 11.3 is a display of the SNP differences observed in a comparison of the personal genomes of Watson or Venter against the genome represented in the human reference sequence. You can also get a sense of the similarity of the Watson and Venter genomes to each other. In some large blocks of genome (for example, 116,740 K to 116,830 K), differences of either man with the reference genome are sparse and unique. In these blocks, Watson and Venter are no more related to each other than either is to the reference sequence.

A 20 kb block of genome centering on position 116,880 shows a very different three-way relationship in which Watson and Venter carry the same SNP alleles which differ substantially from the reference sequence. The block patterns of SNP similarity and dissimilarity provide the foundation for genome-wide associations studies discussed later in this chapter.

Some SNPs that do not have a direct effect on phenotype lie so close to a disease gene or other genes influencing significant phenotypic differences (such as positive or negative responses to a particular medication) that they can serve as DNA markers: specific DNA loci with identifiable variations. Medical researchers can use such markers to identify and follow phenotypic differences in groups of people.

> SNPs are the simplest and most frequent type of stable genetic variation. In a comparison of any two unrelated haploid human genomes, alternative SNP alleles will be found, on average, once in every 1000 base pairs.

SNPs can be genotyped with several different molecular methods

Because alleles of a SNP locus are well-defined, single-base changes in DNA sequence, they can be distinguished by a variety of molecular biology protocols that operate upon, or resolve, specific DNA sequences. These protocols include restriction enzyme digestion, gel electrophoresis, Southern blotting, PCR, allele-specific oligonucleotide hybridization, and DNA microarrays.

Southern blot analysis of restriction site–altering SNPs

A small proportion of SNPs by chance eliminate or create a restriction site recognized by a restriction enzyme. When this happens, researchers can use the restriction enzyme to distinguish between the two alleles. Consider, for example, the SNP shown in **Fig. 11.4.** A single-base change from A in allele 1 to G in allele 2 (using single-strand notation) determines the presence or absence of an *Eco*RI restriction site.

Prior to the last decade, a Southern blot was the tool of choice for detecting a SNP-caused restriction site poly-

Figure 11.4 Restriction site–altering SNPs detected by Southern blots. (a) A SNP can create a restriction site polymorphism at an *Eco*RI site. The two SNP alleles will produce different-sized restriction fragments. **(b)** Southern blot analysis and hybridization with the probe can distinguish among the three possible genotypes at this SNP locus.

morphism (see Fig. 9.15 on p. 318). In the Southern blot protocol, genomic DNA from the test samples is treated with *Eco*RI, the digested DNA is separated by gel electrophoresis and then transferred to a filter paper. The resulting Southern blot is hybridized with a DNA probe obtained from the region between the polymorphic restriction site and an adjacent nonpolymorphic restriction site.

The length of the genomic restriction fragment that hybridizes to the probe reveals which version of the polymorphic restriction site is present. The probe in Fig. 11.3 detects a 3 kb restriction fragment in DNA with SNP allele 1 and a 5 kb restriction fragment in DNA with SNP allele 2. Because the different SNP alleles, when analyzed in this way, change the size of the hybridizing restriction fragment detected on the Southern blot, this type of polymorphism is called a restriction fragment length polymorphism, or RFLP.

PCR analysis of restriction site–altering SNPs

Restriction site polymorphisms can be detected much more quickly and cheaply with a PCR-based protocol that also requires much less material than Southern blot analysis. This protocol has three steps: (1) amplification by PCR of a several hundred base-pair region encompassing the SNP; (2) exposure of the PCR products to the appropriate restriction enzyme; and (3) evaluation of the samples by gel electrophoresis and ethidium bromide staining, followed by a reading of the size of the DNA fragments off the gel.

We illustrate this experimental approach with a solution to the real-life problem of detecting the mutation at the β-globin locus that is responsible for sickle-cell anemia. Sickle-cell anemia occurs, as we have seen, when a person carries two copies of a mutant form of the *HBB* gene with a single-base substitution that replaces an A with a T and changes the encoded amino acid from glutamic acid to valine (see section 9.7). The normal allele is called *A,* and the sickle-cell allele *S.* Since the sickle-cell mutation also by chance destroys the recognition site of the restriction enzyme *Mst*II (**Fig. 11.5a**), it is possible to use PCR and restriction enzyme digestion to detect the mutant allele.

Suppose a carrier couple (both of genotype *AS*) have a child with sickle-cell anemia (genotype *SS*) and want to know the genotype of the fetus they have recently conceived. Through amniocentesis, their doctor recovers fetal cells from the pregnant woman's womb. He or she next subjects the genomic DNA in this sample, as well as in samples from both parents and the first child, to PCR amplification with primers complementary to sequences on either side of the sickle-cell mutation (Fig. 11.5a). The doctor then mixes the restriction enzyme *Mst*II with the PCR products and separates the resulting DNA fragments according to size by gel electrophoresis. It is easy to distinguish DNA from the normal allele—which is digested into two fragments by *Mst*II—from the indigestible DNA of the mutant allele. **Figure 11.5b** shows the results: The fetus is *AA,* so the younger sibling will neither have sickle-cell anemia nor carry the sickle-cell trait.

Detection of any SNP with allele-specific oligonucleotide hybridization

Most SNP variants do not alter restriction sites. Fortunately, however, they can be detected by a protocol that exploits differences in hybridization between short oligonucleotide probes with either no mismatch or one mismatch to a genomic sequence containing a SNP.

Only with very short probes—oligonucleotides containing around 40 bases—can single-base changes provide a

Figure 11.5 Detection of the sickle cell–causing SNP with PCR. (a) The normal (*A*) and sickle-cell (*S*) alleles at the β-globin locus differ by a single base-pair substitution that changes glutamic acid (Glu) to valine (Val) in the protein product. The base-pair change also eliminates the restriction site *Mst*II. **(b)** PCR amplification of the region containing this SNP, with the primers shown, produces a 500 bp product. Exposure of the normal PCR product to *Mst*II digests this DNA fragment into two smaller fragments of 200 and 300 bp in size; exposure of the mutant PCR product to the restriction enzyme has no effect. Three possible genotypes can be distinguished

large enough difference to be readily detected. The reason is that for very small DNA molecules—those composed of no more than 60 bp—the length of the molecule itself helps determine whether the double helix remains intact or falls apart. The effective length, and therefore the strength of the hydrogen-bond forces holding together the double helix of a short-probe/short-target DNA hybrid depends on the longest stretch that does not contain any mismatches. When the two strands do not match exactly there may not be enough weak hydrogen bonds in a row to hold them together.

If, for example, a 40-base probe hybridizes to a target strand that differs at a single base in the middle of the sequence, the effective length of the resulting double-strande

Figure 11.6 Short hybridization probes can distinguish single-base mismatches. (a) Researchers allow hybridization between a short 40-base probe and two different target sequences. (1) A perfect match between probe and target extends across all 40 bases. When the temperature rises, this hybrid has enough hydrogen bonds to remain intact. (2) With a single-base mismatch in the middle of the probe, the effective length of the probe-target hybrid is only 20 bases. When the temperature rises, this hybrid falls apart. **(b)** Researchers allow hybridization to occur with a probe of 100 bases. (1) A perfect match between a 50-base probe and its target bases achieves stability; any extension in the length of the match has no significant effect on temperature dissociation. (2) Thus, a 100 bp hybrid with one mismatched base is not easily distinguished from a 100 bp hybrid with a perfect match.

(a)   1. 21-base probe/target hybrid with no mismatches

Probe

Completely complementary target strand

Raise temperature

2. 21-base probe/target hybrid with middle mismatch

Mismatch at base 11

Raise temperature

(b)   1. 50-base probe/target hybrid with no mismatches

Probe

Target strand

Raise temperature

2. 100-base probe/target hybrid with one mismatch

Mismatch

Raise temperature

hybrids is only 20 bp. Since a 20 bp hybrid is significantly less stable than a 40 bp hybrid, one can devise hybridization conditions to select between them—for example, by choosing temperatures under which the perfect hybrids will remain intact, while the imperfect hybrids will not (**Fig. 11.6a**). By comparison, molecules longer than 60 bp can maintain their double helix conformation even with intermittent mismatches. Once a critical number of hydrogen bonds required for double helix stability is achieved, any further increase in the number of these bonds makes no difference (**Fig. 11.6b**). Short oligonucleotides of 30–40 bases that hybridize to only one of the two alleles at a SNP locus under appropriate conditions are known as **allele-specific oligonucleotides**, or **ASOs**.

Detection of millions of SNPs simultaneously with DNA microarrays

Rapid advances in DNA microarray (or chip) manufacturing technology, as described in Chapters 1 and 10, have led to an exponential rise in capacity along with a dramatic decrease in the cost per single chip analysis. Standard microarrays produced by several companies detect SNP alleles at over 1 million loci for a cost of several hundred dollars per sample, at the time of this writing, which works out to a per-SNP genotyping cost that is a small fraction of a penny.

International cooperation among geneticists has allowed the development of a standardized SNP nomenclature system and a freely accessible public database (http://www.ncbi.nlm.nih.gov/projects/SNP/) where SNP information is compiled. Anyone can now purchase a SNP chip analysis of their own personal genome from several direct-to-consumer companies. With SNP results in hand, consumers can now perform their own comparisons to see what secrets their genomes hold. **Figure 11.7** provides an example of text output from dbSNP for all SNP loci within the coding regions of the first four *CFTR* exons.

Automated technology allows millions of SNPs to be detected simultaneously. Hybridization, PCR amplification, and the Southern blot technique can allow comparison and identification of individual SNPs.

Figure 11.7 Known SNP loci and alleles in the first four exons of the *CFTR* gene. Only SNP loci within the coding regions of the first four CFTR exons are shown. Many more SNPs are located in the introns between these exons. Transcript (mRNA) and codon (Protein) addresses are indicated for each SNP along with position within each codon. Both alleles of each SNP locus are indicated. No function is provided for the alleles that appear in the human reference sequence.

	Position			Allele		Variant Function	SNP ID	Allele Frequency
	mRNA	Protein	Codon	Base	Amino Acid			
Exon_1	133	1				start codon		
	156	8	3	A	Lys [K]	synonymous	rs1800071	N.D.
		8	3	G	Lys [K]			
	163	11	1	A	Ile [I]	missense	rs1800072	N.D.
		11	1	G	Val [V]			
Exon_2	204	24	3	A	Leu [L]	synonymous	rs55773134	N.D.
		24	3	G	Leu [L]			
	223	31	1	T	Cys [C]	missense	rs1800073	0.014
		31	1	C	Arg [R]			
	263	44	2	T	Val [V]	missense	rs1800074	N.D.
		44	2	A	Asp [D]			
Exon_3	345	71	3	C	Asn [N]	synonymous	rs1800075	N.D.
		71	3	T	Asn [N]			
	356	75	2	A	Gln [Q]	missense	rs1800076	0.012
		75	2	G	Arg [R]			
Exon_4	485	118	2	C	Ser [S]	frameshift	rs35871908	N.D.
		118	2	-/C	Ser [S]			
	492	120	3	A	Ala [A]	synonymous	rs1800077	N.D.
		120	3	G	Ala [A]			
	545	138	2	C	Pro [P]	missense	rs1800078	N.D.
		138	2	T	Leu [L]			
	575	148	2	C	Thr [T]	missense	rs35516286	0.026
		148	2	T	Ile [I]			

Genetic variation can be caused by subtraction or addition of short sequences

The DNA changes in this category are the result of mutagenic events that expand or contract the length of a DNA region by deleting, duplicating, or inserting genetic material into chromosomes. These changes in genomic length can range in size from one base pair to multiple megabases. In this section, we address genetic variants of just one or a few base pairs. In the next section, we will discuss larger duplications and deletions. In Chapter 13, we will present a general discussion of deletions, duplications, and insertions, as well as chromosome-scale aberrations in genomic content.

Deletion-insertion polymorphisms (DIPs)

Short insertions or deletions of genetic material that are typically one or a few base pairs in length represent the second most common form of genetic variation in the human genome. These variants are referred to as InDels or DIPs. A direct comparison of the Venter whole-genome sequence to that of the human reference sequence detects 292,102 DIPs ranging in length from one base pair to 571 base pairs, with a steep decline in relative frequency in relation to length (**Fig. 11.8a**).

A visual sense of the density and distribution of DIPs relative to SNPs and SSRs (discussed in the next section) can be attained in a view of the 400 kb genomic region around *CFTR* shown in **Fig. 11.8b.** While SNP loci occur with a frequency of about one per kilobase, DIPs are distributed at a frequency of about one in every 10 kb of DNA.

The 75% of DIPs that are one or two base pairs in length can be detected on DNA microarrays alongside SNPs, with allele-specific oligonucleotide probes that match the presence or absence of the base pairs. Large DIPs display more of a size differential between alleles and are amenable to detection by PCR and gel electrophoresis as detailed next for SSRs.

Simple sequence repeats (SSRs)

The genomes of humans and other complex organisms are loaded with loci defined by simple sequence repeats (SSRs). The most common repeating units are one-, two-, or three-base sequences repeated in tandem 15–100 times. Examples of SSRs are AAAAAAAAAAAAAAA or CACACACACACACACACACA (see pp. 340–341 of

Figure 11.8 Genetic variants defined by changes in DNA length. (a) Size distribution of InDel variations detected between the human reference genome and the Venter genome. **(b)** Distribution of SNPs, DIPs (InDels), and SSR variants in the *CFTR* region.

Chapter 10). In the mammalian genome, the CA-repeat SSR occurs on average once in every 30,000 bp.

SSRs arise spontaneously from random events that initially produce a short repeated sequence with four to five repeat units. Once a short SSR mutates into existence, however, it can expand into a longer sequence by the process shown in **Fig. 11.9.** Unlike SNPs—which are biallelic and do not change after the mutational event that gave rise to them—individual SSR loci often mutate into multiple alleles.

Research shows that faulty DNA replication is the main mutational mechanism (Fig. 11.9). Because the same short homologous unit (CA, for example) is repeated over and over again, DNA polymerase may develop a stutter during replication; that is, it may slip and make a second copy of the same dinucleotide, or skip over a dinucleotide. SSRs are thus highly polymorphic in the number of repeats they carry, with many alleles distinguishable at each SSR locus.

New alleles arise at SSR loci at an average rate of 10^3 per locus per gamete (that is, one in every thousand gametes). This frequency is much greater than the single nucleotide mutation rate of 10^9 and results in a large amount of SSR variation among unrelated individuals within a population. At the same time, the rate of SSR mutation is low enough that changes usually do not occur within a few generations of even a large family; because of this, SSRs can serve as relatively stable, highly polymorphic DNA markers in linkage studies of human families, other animals, and plants.

Genotyping of short length variants

Small variations in the actual size of a locus can be directly and easily distinguished by gel electrophoresis as illustrated in **Fig. 11.10.** You begin by using a pair of primers complementary to sequences on either side of the actual length polymorphism to amplify by PCR the locus from an individual's DNA. You then subject the PCR products to gel electrophoresis to separate DNA fragments according to their size. After staining with ethidium bromide, each allele shows up as a specific band.

A single researcher can use this protocol to genotype hundreds of samples in a single day, without any specialized equipment (other than the apparatus necessary for PCR and gel electrophoresis). The protocol can also be automated using fluorescently tagged primers and electrophoresis in the same apparatus that is used for automated DNA sequencing (see Fig. 9.18 on p. 321). In Chapter 13, we present an in-depth look at the general category of deletions, duplications, and insertions. Here we focus our attention on the special categories of short length variants.

The most useful SSRs for genotyping consist of 2 or 3 bp units repeated 15–100 times in a row. These SSRs are highly polymorphic, with multiple alleles that differ in 2 or 3 bp unit increments. All of the multiple alleles can be detected as different-sized PCR products (Fig. 11.10).

SSRs played a crucial role in the development of linkage maps across the genomes of mice, humans, and other species. The reasons for their widespread use include their frequent appearance in all vertebrate genomes and their extensive polymorphism.

SSRs and disease

A small number of genes naturally contain SSR sequences with triplet repeat units within their coding regions. The propensity of the SSR sequences to change in size from one generation to the next can produce mutant alleles with

Figure 11.9 Simple sequence repeats (SSRs) are highly polymorphic because of their potential for faulty replication. (a) An SSR consisting of 15 tandem repeats of the CA dinucleotide sequence. **(b)** Replication of the strands by DNA polymerase moving in the 5-to-3 direction. **(c)** Pauses can occur if the required nucleotides are, by chance, not in the vicinity of the polymerase. **(d)** When the required nucleotides become available, the newly synthesized strand reanneals to the template and acts as a primer for further replication. But the new strand may be out of register such that the polymerase begins by adding one or more nucleotides across from a part of the template strand that has already been replicated. **(e)** The resulting DNA molecule will have one or more identical repeats in the newly synthesized strand. DNA repair processes then adjust the template strand to make it the same length as the newly synthesized strand.

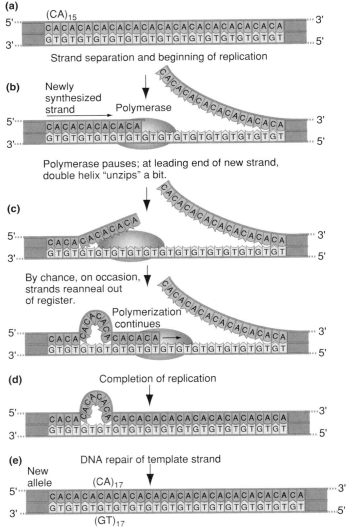

Figure 11.10 Detection of simple sequence repeat (SSR) polymorphisms by PCR and gel electrophoresis. (a) SSR alleles differ in length. Left and right primers are devised based on sequences that flank the SSR locus. **(b)** Genomic DNA is amplified by PCR with primers specific for the SSR locus. **(c)** Gel electrophoresis and ethidium bromide staining distinguish the alleles from each other. **(d)** SSRs are often highly polymorphic with many different alleles present in a population.

(a) Determine sequences flanking microsatellites.

(b) Amplify alleles by PCR.

(c) Analyze PCR products by gel electrophoresis.

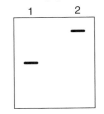

(d) Example of population with three alleles

Six diploid genotypes are present in this population.

Figure 11.11 Mutations at the Huntington disease locus are caused by expansion of a triplet repeat microsatellite in a coding region. (a) Near the 5′ end of the coding region is a repeating triplet sequence that codes for a string of glutamines. **(b)** Different alleles at the *HD* locus have different numbers of repeating units. Fewer than 34 repeats gives a normal phenotype. As the number of repeats increases beyond 42, the onset of the disease is earlier.

(a) Basic structure of the *HD* gene's coding region

Each triplet encodes glutamine.

(b) Some alleles at the *HD* locus

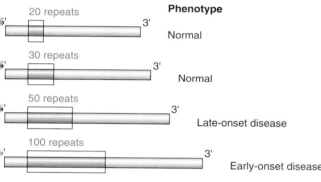

rastic effects on phenotype. One example of a disease in this category is Huntington disease (HD).

Huntington disease is transmitted as an autosomal dominant mutation. Over 30,000 Americans show one or more symptoms of the disease—involuntary, jerky movements; unsteady gait; mood swings; personality changes; slurred speech; impaired judgment. An additional 150,000 have an affected parent, which gives them a 50:50 chance of carrying and expressing the dominant condition themselves as they age. Although symptoms usually show up between the ages of 30 and 50, the first signs of the disease have appeared in people as young as 2 and as old as 83. Some people with a family history of HD would like to know their genotype before deciding whether to have a family.

In 1993, after 10 years of intensive research, investigators identified and cloned the *HD* gene. With the gene in hand, they were able to uncover the unusual mutation that causes the disease (**Fig. 11.11a**). Unlike the vast majority of disease mutations, which result from base-pair changes or the elimination of genetic information, HD is caused by too much genetic information: an expansion of a CAG trinucleotide repeat in the coding sequence, which translates into a string of glutamine amino acids.

It is possible to detect *HD* alleles directly with the same size-based PCR procedure used to detect other SSR

alleles. The normal allele contains up to 34 repeats while disease causing alleles carry 42 or more. In general, the greater the number of repeats, the earlier the age of disease onset (**Fig. 11.11b**). Those who inherit a disease allele invariably get the disease if they live long enough. Thus, although expressivity, which depends on the number of triplet repeats, is variable, penetrance is complete. Several other diseases caused by triplet repeat expansion have been uncovered, including a variety of neurological disorders, and the fragile X syndrome described in the Genetics and Society box on pp. 208–209 in Chapter 7.

> Short-sequence insertions and deletions include deletion-insertion polymorphisms (DIPs) and simple sequence repeats (SSRs). These may be detected and analyzed with PCR followed by electrophoresis. SSRs consisting of triplet repeats that expand with successive DNA replications can be responsible for genetic diseases.

11.3 Deletions or Duplications of a DNA Region

Earlier we mentioned that a fourth category of DNA variants consists of duplications or deletions. Included in this category are the short copy number repeats (minisatellites), which are useful for DNA fingerprinting, and the large-scale duplications and deletions referred to as copy number polymorphisms (CNPs) and copy number variants (CNVs).

Short copy number repeats are ideal for DNA fingerprinting

In distinguishing between individuals on the basis of DNA, one of the most useful methods is the comparison of minisatellites.

Minisatellites

Minisatellites are a subcategory of DNA length polymorphisms that are at the low end of the broader CNP category. They are defined arbitrarily as repeats having a unit size in the range of 500 bp to 20 kb. The real power of minisatellites lies in the fact that particular minisatellite sequences often occur at a small number of different genomic loci. With restriction enzyme digestion, gel electrophoresis, and Southern blot hybridization using a cross-hybridizing minisatellite probe, researchers can look simultaneously at allelic variation at these multiple unlinked loci (**Fig. 11.12**). (This strategy wouldn't work for microsatellites because their core mono-, di-, or trinucleotide sequences are each present thousands of times in the genome.)

How many loci would you have to examine to be certain that two DNA samples come from the same individual (or identical twins) and no one else? A simple calculation

Figure 11.12 Minisatellite analysis provides a broad comparison of whole genomes. (a) Two individuals each carry two alleles at three loci containing the same minisatellite repeating unit sequence. The *arrows* indicate a restriction site recognized by a particular restriction enzyme. Notice that minisatellite lengths are different both among alleles at a locus and among different loci. **(b)** After restriction enzyme digestion, gel electrophoresis, Southern blotting, and hybridization to the minisatellite probe, researchers can obtain an autoradiograph of the type shown here for four individuals.

(a) Digest DNA with restriction enzyme that does not cut inside minisatellite.

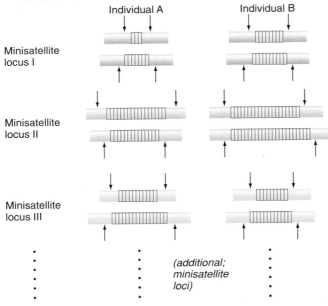

(b) Run DNA samples on a gel. Perform Southern blotting. Hybridize with probe containing minisatellite sequence.

shows that the probability of two unrelated individuals having identical genotypes at a locus with two equally prevalent alleles is 37.5%—quite a high probability. However, the chance that the same two individuals will be identical at 10 such loci, all unlinked, is only 0.375^{10}, or 0.005%—quite a low probability. The result of 0.005% means there is 1 chance in 20,000 that the two will by chance have the same genotype at 10 unlinked loci. By extension, if you simultaneously detect genotype at 24 unlinked two-allele loci, the chance of two individuals being the same at all 24 drops to 0.375^{24}, or 1 in 17 billion. Since the total human population is less than 8 billion, there is virtually no chance that two individuals (who are not identical twins) would have the same genotype at all 24 loci. In short, a relatively small number of loci are sufficient to produce a combination genotype pattern that, like a traditional fingerprint, will be unique for each individual (or pair of identical twins) within the species.

How minisatellite comparison generates DNA fingerprints

In 1985, Alec Jeffreys and coworkers made two key findings: Each minisatellite locus is highly polymorphic; and many minisatellites occur at multiple sites (usually between 2 and 50) scattered around the genome. As a result, they realized, minisatellite probes would be perfect reagents for obtaining a **DNA fingerprint:** a pattern produced by the simultaneous detection of genotype at a group of unlinked highly polymorphic loci.

The most useful minisatellite families have 10–20 members per genome. This range of numbers is small enough to allow the resolution of all the loci as individual bands on an autoradiograph, but large enough to provide true fingerprint information. If one fingerprint is not sufficient to resolve the relationship between two different DNA samples, investigators can always obtain data from two, three, or even more minisatellite families.

Figure 11.13 illustrates an interesting example of the utility of DNA fingerprinting. In 1997, scientists from the Roslin Institute in Scotland announced that they had cloned a sheep by injecting a diploid nucleus from an adult udder cell (grown in culture) into an unfertilized egg whose own genetic material had been removed. Initially, many scientists were skeptical of this result and thought that "Dolly" might actually be the result of a fertilization between some contaminating sperm and the egg. If this were the case, Dolly's genome would be unique. Instead, the results of the fingerprint analysis shown in Fig. 11.13 demonstrated that Dolly's DNA fingerprint was identical to that of the adult udder cell used to clone her. This established beyond a doubt that her genome was indeed a clone of that cell's DNA.

The uses of DNA fingerprinting

DNA fingerprints are a powerful tool for forensic analysis. Prosecutors and defense attorneys alike use them to show the likelihood of a suspect's presence at the scene of a crime.

Figure 11.13 DNA fingerprint analysis confirmed that Dolly was cloned from an adult udder cell. Genomic DNA samples were prepared from the donor udder cells (U), from the cell culture prepared from the udder cells (C), from Dolly's blood cells (D), and from control sheep 1–12. The DNA fingerprints of the 12 control sheep are all different from each other and from the cells involved in the Dolly experiment. Dolly's DNA fingerprint is identical to the fingerprints of both the udder cells and the derived cell culture. This result provides very strong evidence that Dolly is a clone of the ewe that donated the udder cells.

150 other men unjustly convicted of rape or murder have been released from jail thanks to DNA fingerprint analysis.

Also in 1993, the courts for the first time accepted plant DNA as evidence in a murder trial. The defendant, accused of killing a woman whose body was found abandoned in the Arizona desert, owned a pickup truck. When police searched the back of the truck, they found a few seed pods from a Palo Verde tree. The county sheriff's department asked a molecular geneticist if there was any way to match the pods to an individual tree at the scene of the crime. DNA fingerprinting was used to compare the pods recovered from the bed of the pickup truck with a variety of Palo Verde trees. Only one match was found, and it was to the tree located at the site of the crime. Although this evidence does not prove the defendant was at the scene of the crime, it strongly suggests that the defendant's truck was there.

More recently, DNA fingerprints demonstrated that skeletal remains unearthed at Ekaterinburg in the Ural Mountains of Russia belonged to Czar Nicholas II and his family, who were murdered in 1918 during the Bolshevik revolution. Geneticists established the relationship by comparing DNA from the excavated bones with samples obtained from a number of living relatives of the Romanov family, including Prince Philip, Duke of Edinburgh. This information disproved the claim of Anna Anderson that she was the Grand Duchess Anastasia; in three independent analyses, her DNA (obtained from hair and from biopsy samples removed during an examination for cancer years before her death in 1984) did not match that of members of the Romanov line—living or dead.

> Modern genetic analysis enables quick comparison of minisatellites—short repeats of 500 bp to 1 kp found at a relatively small number of genomic loci. Analysis of minisatellite genotypes at 10 to 24 of these loci is the basis for DNA fingerprinting, which can be applied to identification of individuals.

Large-scale deletions and duplications commonly differentiate human genomes

With advances in DNA microarray technology, it became possible to scan individual genomes for the presence of deletions and duplications that were large enough to cover one or more whole genes. Several research groups took advantage of this new technological capability to investigate the possibility that relatively large genomic alterations of this type might be responsible for severe mental diseases that were clearly heritable but had resisted previous attempts at genetic localization.

Identification of CNPs and CNVs

Researchers unexpectedly discovered an extensive degree of polymorphism within their control (nondiseased) population

to prove the innocence of someone falsely accused. In [o]ne case, a man arrested on rape charges in 1981 had blood [ty]pe alleles that matched those of cells in the semen found [in] the victim. The crude blood-typing tests available at that [ti]me did not have the resolving power to prove that the [se]men definitely came from the accused. But after the victim [pi]cked the accused out of a lineup, the prosecution used the [te]st results as evidence to help obtain a conviction. Eleven [ye]ars later, a defense lawyer filed an appeal based on the [fin]ding that DNA fingerprints of the semen obtained from [th]e victim and from cells of the convicted man were differ[en]t. With this evidence, the court reversed its decision and [in] 1993, set the convicted man free. Since that time, over for the deletion or duplication of relatively large blocks of genetic material that can measure up to 1 Mb in length without causing disease. This category of genetic variants is referred to as **copy number variants (CNVs)** or **copy number polymorphisms (CNPs),** depending on whether their frequency in the population is less than or greater than 1%. For ease of description, the CNV term will be used to encompass both CNVs and CNPs when they are grouped together.

Unlike SNPs, CNVs can be detected through microarray analysis even if they have not been observed previously. The Affymetrix 6.0 DNA microarray is designed specifically to allow detection of CNVs with several hundred thousand nonpolymorphic oligonucleotide probes (NPOs), which are spaced uniformly across the genome. CNVs are detected as an increase or decrease in hybridization—for duplications and deletions respectively—across a contiguous set of NPOs (**Fig. 11.14a**).

Surprisingly to geneticists, CNVs turn out to be quite common both in their distribution across the genome and in their frequency of occurrence within human populations (**Fig. 11.14b**). Over 6000 CNV loci have been identified, and

pairwise comparison of any two genomes typically identifies a different allele for several hundred. Over 99% of all CNVs are derived from inheritance rather than new mutation.

Copy number variation in the olfactory receptor (*OR*) gene family

One example of copy number variants (CNVs) is the olfactory receptor (*OR*) gene family, which is composed of several hundreds to thousands of members that provide animals with the ability to smell a diverse array of odors. A typical mouse genome carrys 1400 *OR* genes distributed at numerous chromosomal sites. But a keen sense of smell is no longer as important for human survival. As a result, *OR* genes can be lost without consequence, and people typically carry less than a thousand genes. However, individuals vary widely around the mean.

Figure 11.15a shows the variation in copy number among 60 people at 11 representative *OR* loci. One locus, *OR4K2*, varies in copy number from two to six in different genomes, while seven of the eleven loci are completely missing from some individuals. All together, some people can have

(a)

Samples / Probe order

10.06   10.07   10.08   10.09

Figure 11.14 Chromosomal locations of CNPs or CNVs identified in multiple individuals. (a) Results of DNA microarray analysis performed on 88 samples, lined up in rows, for adjacent probes across a region of chromosome 4. Each column portrays the intensity of hybridization for a particular probe. Red indicates low intensity and yellow high intensity. Several samples display evidence of a deletion across the same 15 kb genomic region. **(b)** Representation of a human karyotype. Blue and green bars represent the locations of CNVs and CNPs identified as of June 2009.

(b)

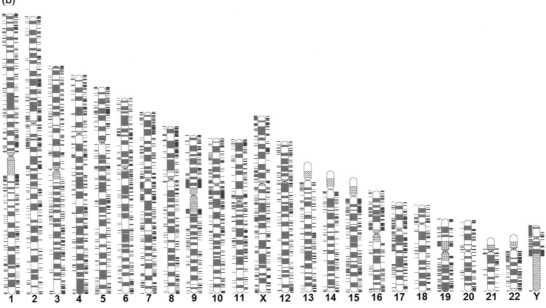

1 2 3 4 5 6 7 8 9 10 11 X 12 13 14 15 16 17 18 19 20 21 22 Y

Figure 11.15 CNVs with an effect on phenotype. (a) Olfactory receptor genes. **(b)** CNVs with a causative role in mental disease.

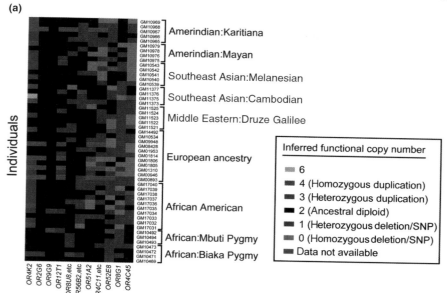

(a)

(b)

| Chromosomal Location | | | | Total CNVs | Type | Number of People | | Diseases |
Chr	Start	Stop	Length			Diseased	Controls	
chr15	27,015,263	30,650,000	3,634,737	19	loss	19	0	Schizophrenia
chr15	18,376,200	30,756,771	12,380,571	58	gain	45	13	Autism, mental retardation, schizophrenia, controls
chr22	17,014,900	19,993,127	2,978,227	31	loss	31	0	Autism, mental retardation, schizophrenia
chr22	17,200,000	21,546,762	4,346,762	14	gain	9	5	Autism, schizophrenia, controls
chr1	142,540,000	146,059,433	3,519,433	27	loss	24	3	Autism, schizophrenia, controls
chr1	142,800,580	146,009,436	3,208,856	15	gain	12	3	Autism, mental retardation, schizophrenia, controls
chr22	45,144,027	49,509,153	4,365,126	4	loss	4	0	Autism
chr22	47,572,875	48,323,417	750,542	6	gain	5	1	Autism, schizophrenia, controls
chr16	29,470,951	30,252,473	781,522	11	loss	8	3	Autism, controls
chr16	29,474,810	30,235,818	761,008	7	gain	6	1	Autism, schizophrenia
chr17	14,000,000	15,421,835	1,421,835	7	loss	6	1	Autism, schizophrenia, controls
chr17	12,650,000	15,540,000	2,890,000	5	gain	4	1	Autism, mental retardation, schizophrenia, controls
chr16	60,141,700	61,581,600	1,439,900	4	loss	4	0	Autism
chr11	78,120,000	85,610,000	7,490,000	3	loss	3	0	Autism, mental retardation, schizophrenia
chr2	184,270,000	186,892,000	2,622,000	3	gain	3	0	Autism
chr15	82,573,421	83,631,697	1,058,276	4	loss	4	0	Autism, schizophrenia
chr9	206456	1599250	1,392,794	3	gain	3	0	Autism, schizophrenia
chr3	197,179,156	198,842,299	1,663,143	3	loss	3	0	Schizophrenia
chr16	21,693,739	22,611,363	917,624	5	loss	5	0	Autism, schizophrenia
chr16	80,737,839	82,208,451	1,470,612	4	gain	4	0	Autism, schizophrenia

hundreds of *OR* genes more than others do, resulting in large differences in the abilities of people to distinguish odors.

Copy number variation and mental disease

Serious psychiatric diseases can be devastating to the lives of individuals and their families. Together, the five most frequent of these occur in 5% of the population (schizophrenia, bipolar I, bipolar II, autism, and autism spectrum disorder [ASD]). Recent results have demonstrated that, contrary to past conventional wisdom, the potentiation of these diseases is 100% or close to it—this means that the disease always has a genetic cause, even if the genetic aberration doesn't always cause the disease. Nevertheless, until recently geneticists struggled to come up with reducible associations of specific genes with these diseases.

Although most CNVs appear not to be associated with strong phenotypic effects, the exceptions are stark. In general, long deletions and duplications—over a megabase in length anywhere in the genome—increase the risk of psychiatric disease to a level of 30%. And in particular, CNVs that cover a number of specific genomic regions have been directly associated with autism, schizophrenia, or mental retardation, as indicated in **Fig. 11.15b**.

The association of individual SNPs with diseases and traits is usually demonstrable only through large-scale whole-genome-association studies, discussed below. In contrast, the disease-causing potential of a newly discovered CNV can often be evaluated immediately by looking at the NCBI database to determine whether critical genes have been deleted or duplicated. If, for example, a gene with an essential role in brain development or function is deleted or disrupted on one chromosome of a healthy women, and the same gene is deleted or disrupted in her reproductive partner, there is a 25% risk of giving birth to a child who has no copies of the essential gene and is likely to be mentally disabled or strongly predisposed to mental illness.

In simply determining relatedness with DNA fingerprinting, the location of a locus on a chromosome is unimportant. Geneticists are interested in chromosomal position, however, particularly where disease phenotypes and other inherited differences are concerned. The next section describes techniques for studying positional effects.

> Large-scale deletions and duplications are surprisingly common in the human genome. CNPs and CNVs are present normally in some systems, and they have been implicated in certain diseases, notably mental conditions.

11.4 Positional Cloning: From DNA Markers to Disease-Causing Genes

A knowledge of the chromosomal location of individual DNA markers can be of great use to geneticists who want to determine the chromosomal location of genes responsible for disease phenotypes and other inherited differences among people, animals, and plants. The chromosomal positions of DNA markers linked to genes defined by phenotype alone can serve as a basis for cloning those genes in a process called *positional cloning*.

In a few cases, a causative gene can be discovered without mapping

Medical researchers learned from the analysis of pedigrees like the one shown in **Fig. 11.16a** that hemophilia A is an X-linked recessive trait governed by a single gene. Geneticists were able to make an educated guess at the biochemical function of the responsible gene. The function of the wild-type hemophilia A gene, they proposed, is production of a normal clotting factor; mutations that inactivate this factor produce hemophilia A.

Once molecular investigators worked out the details of the blood-clotting cascade (**Fig. 11.16b**), they could look for clotting factors in normal individuals that were absent in hemophiliacs (**Fig. 11.16c**). In this way, they identified a protein known as factor VIII. They next determined the amino acid sequence of factor VIII and used the genetic code to predict the nucleotide sequence of the corresponding gene. This information allowed them to develop a degenerate oligonucleotide probe that could identify clones of the factor VIII gene (now called the *F8* gene) within genomic libraries (**Fig. 11.16d**). When they sequenced this gene from people suffering from hemophilia A, they found mutations with an absolute correlation to the disease phenotype and thereby verified the gene as the causative agent of the disease.

Of the thousands of genes responsible for known human genetic diseases, only a small number can be identified in the manner just outlined. Much more often, making an educated guess about the protein altered by the disease allele is difficult.

Cystic fibrosis, for example, is a recessive autosoma genetic condition inherited by 1 child in every 2500 born from two parents of European descent. But because the trait is recessive, the frequency of unaffected carriers in the population is much greater, about 1 in every 36 people. Many carriers come from families where the disease has never appeared, and so the first birth of a child with the disease can come as a complete shock. Children with the disease have a variety of symptoms arising from abnormally viscous secretions in the lungs, pancreas, sweat glands, and several other tissues. Even with modern medical treatments that combat some symptoms of the disease, most cystic fibrosis patients die before the age of 30.

Unfortunately, the gross symptoms of cystic fibrosis did not provide insight into the underlying molecular cause of the disease. Hundreds of proteins contribute to the process of cell secretion, and most of these were still unidentified in the 1980s. Without a way to determine

Figure 11.16 How geneticists identified and cloned the hemophilia A gene. (a) A pedigree of the royal family descended from Queen Victoria. This family tree uses the standard pedigree symbols. **(b)** The blood-clotting cascade. Vessel damage induces a cascade of enzymatic events that convert inactive factors to active factors. The cascade results in the transformation of fibrinogen to fibrin and the formation of a clot. **(c)** Blood tests can determine whether an active form of each factor involved in the clotting cascade is present. The results of such analyses show that many hemophiliacs, such as those found in Queen Victoria's pedigree, lack an active factor VIII in their blood. **(d)** Researchers purified factor VIII, determined its amino acid sequence, used this information to infer all possible degenerate coding sequences, constructed oligonucleotides for a region with minimal degeneracy, probed a genomic library with these oligonucleotides, and obtained genomic clones of the *F8* gene.

(c) Analysis of presence or absence of blood-clotting factors

	Wild-type	
Factors	**person**	**Hemophiliac**
XII	+	+
XI	+	+
IX	+	+
VIII	+	−
X	+	+
V	+	+
Prothrombin	+	+
Fibrinogen	+	+

which one is defective in cystic fibrosis, investigators had no simple way to work their way from gene function to the protein's DNA coding sequence.

In positional cloning, linkage analysis with DNA markers helps identify disease genes

The challenge for identifying the defects associated with most human hereditary diseases is no biochemical data helps to guide researchers to the genes. Without such data, the standard approach is to combine linkage analysis (as described in Chapter 5) with the use of DNA markers described earlier in this chapter to localize the human disease gene to a specific region of chromosomal DNA. Then other techniques can determine which gene—among the small number in this region—contains mutations that correlate with the disease phenotype. This entire protocol is called **positional cloning.**

You learned in Chapter 5 that a simple two-point cross can demonstrate linkage if the two loci under analysis lie close enough together on the same chromosome that the rate of recombination is significantly less than the 50% expected with independent assortment. You also saw that the frequency of recombination between the two loci provides a direct measure of the distance separating them, as recorded in centimorgans (cM), or map units (m.u.). (Geneticists studying humans, mice, and other mammals use the centimorgan unit of measure, which we adopt in this chapter.) Finally, you learned that it is possible to integrate multiple pairs of linked loci into a "linkage group" by performing many different two- or three-point crosses with overlapping sets of loci. The **linkage maps** constructed from these crosses depict the distances between loci as well as the order in which they occur on a chromosome.

With the use of SNPs and other polymorphic DNA markers discussed in this chapter, rather than markers defined by phenotype, there is no limit to the number of loci that can be mapped in a single cross or extended human family. In place of a traditional three-point cross, it becomes possible to perform linkage analysis combining thousands or hundreds of thousands of DNA loci with the disease locus of interest. If genetic linkage can be demonstrated between a disease trait and one or more previously mapped DNA markers, then the gene responsible for the trait must lie in the same subchromosomal region as those DNA markers.

Discovery of a DNA marker that shows linkage to the disease locus is the first goal of positional cloning. For traits expressed in plants or small animals, it is a simple matter to set up a single testcross for the production of hundreds of offspring that can be easily analyzed to identify the map position of the trait in question. For human traits such as disease phenotypes, directed breeding is not a possibility. Instead, until recently, researchers had no other choice but to try to find many different extended families—each with a large number of children—in which some individuals express the mutant phenotype and others do not.

The mapping of a human disease locus begins with the genotyping of all members of the disease-carrying families for a series of DNA markers ideally spaced along each chromosome.

Because the human genome has been sequenced, you already know the chromosomal positions of all DNA markers. The only unknown map position is that of the disease locus. You can thus view a thousand and one-point linkage analysis as 1000 separate two-point crosses, each one a test for linkage between an individual DNA marker and the disease locus. If the number of genotyped individuals is sufficiently large, a simply inherited Mendelian disease locus must show linkage to one or more of these markers. Finding linkage to at least one marker of known position will place the disease locus in a particular subregion of a particular chromosome (**Fig. 11.17a**).

Figure 11.17 Positional cloning: From phenotype to chromosomal location to guilty gene. (a) Diagram of a human chromosome with four markers—M1, M2, M3, and M4—used in the linkage analysis of a disease phenotype. Each marker provides "linkage coverage" of a portion of the chromosome. This suggests that the gene responsible for the disease lies between those markers. **(b)** With this information, an investigator could type additional markers that lie between M1 and M2 to position the disease locus with higher resolution. **(c)** Looking for candidate genes. Analysis of the region between recombination sites that define the smallest area within which the disease locus can lie should reveal the presence of candidate genes. **(d)** Finding the correct candidate through comparisons of the structure and expression of each candidate gene in many diseased and nondiseased individuals.

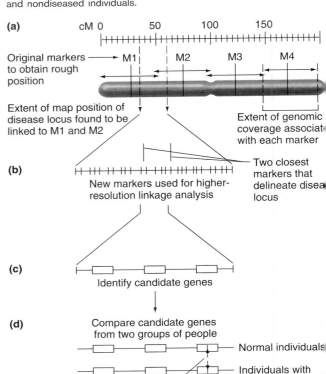

Figure 11.18 Detection of linkage between the DNA marker G8 and a locus responsible for Huntington disease (HD) was the first step in the cloning of the *HD* gene. Portion of a large Venezuelan pedigree affected by HD, or Huntington disease. For living members of the pedigree, alleles at the G8 marker locus are indicated (A, B, C, and D). It is easy to see the cotransmission of marker alleles with the mutant and wild-type alleles at the *HD* locus. Pedigree analysis shows that the *HD* locus is within 5 cM of the G8 marker.

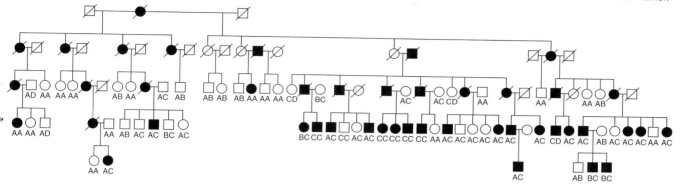

In 1984, the Huntington disease (*HD*) locus became the first human disease gene to be successfully mapped by positional cloning. **Figure 11.18** shows the five-generation, 104-member family pedigree used to demonstrate linkage between a previously mapped DNA marker named G8 and the *HD* locus. Preliminary linkage between the *HD* locus and the G8 marker placed the disease gene on human chromosome 4. Further linkage analysis then narrowed down the map position of *HD* to less than 1000 kb.

In some genetic diseases, affected loci can be identified through inference and by working backward from a defective protein to the DNA sequence in question. Positional cloning allows mapping of disease alleles through comparison with thousands of markers of known position, narrowing the region of the disease locus.

11.5 Complex Traits

In humans, only a small fraction of disease traits follow the simple Mendelian pattern of single-gene inheritance seen in cystic fibrosis, Huntington disease, and hemo-philia A. Most common characteristics of human appearance, such as height, skin color, the shape of the face, hair type, and many essential measures of human physiology have a more complex pattern of inheritance, as described initially in Chapter 3.

We now review the chief causes of complex inheritance and describe the problems they pose for the linkage mapping and positional cloning protocols described so far for single-gene traits (**Table 11.2**). We then explain how researchers adapt the procedures for analyzing single-gene traits to the more difficult task of identifying, mapping, and characterizing the genes that contribute to complex traits.

With incomplete penetrance, a mutant genotype does not always cause a mutant phenotype

All cancers have a genetic basis; that is, they are the result of mutations in genes that regulate cell proliferation (see Chapter 17 for details). Most of these mutations occur in somatic tissues and are *not* inherited. Cancers arising in

	TABLE 11.2	Complexities That Alter Traditional Mendelian Ratios	
Category of Complexity	**Problem in Observed Relationship Between Genotype and Phenotype**	**Changes Necessitated in Mapping Strategy**
Incomplete penetrance	Disease genotype can occur in an individual who does not express the disease phenotype	Eliminate nondiseased individuals from analysis
Phenocopy	Disease phenotype can be expressed by an individual who does not have the disease genotype	Limit studies to families that show evidence for inheritance of the trait
Genetic heterogeneity	In different families, different disease genotypes are responsible for the same disease phenotype	Divide complete set of disease-transmitting families into subgroups (based on various parameters such as average age of onset) and perform linkage analysis separately on each subgroup
Polygenic determination	Mutant alleles at more than one locus influence expression of the disease phenotype in a single individual	To search for complex patterns of association between the disease trait and multiple DNA markers

Figure 11.19 Incomplete penetrance and genetic heterogeneity in the inheritance of breast cancer. Both pedigrees in this figure show evidence of the transmission of a dominant mutation with incomplete penetrance that causes breast cancer. Linkage analysis shows that the mutation in the first pedigree resides on chromosome 17, whereas the mutation in the second pedigree is on chromosome 13. The first family is segregating a mutant *BRCA1* allele, while the second family is segregating a mutant *BRCA2* allele.

this way are termed *sporadic* and account for 90% of all breast cancers. A correlation has been found between sporadic breast cancer and several environmental factors, including alcohol consumption. By contrast, about 10% of women with breast cancer have inherited an allele that predisposes them to this condition, as suggested by the observation that their mothers and aunts have a higher than normal incidence of breast cancer as well.

Medical investigators used a positional cloning protocol to map and clone the *BRCA1* (BReast CAncer 1) gene, one of several genes that can cause breast cancer. Significantly, only 66% of women who carry a mutant allele at the *BRCA1* locus develop breast cancer by the age of 55. As seen in the first pedigree in **Fig. 11.19**, it is possible for a mother to carry a mutant *BRCA1* allele and remain disease-free, while her daughter becomes afflicted with the disease. Thus, although the mutant *BRCA1* allele predisposes a woman to breast cancer, it does not guarantee that the disease phenotype will occur; that is, it is not completely penetrant. By comparison, a disease such as sickle-cell anemia, in which a mutant genotype always causes a mutant phenotype, is completely penetrant.

The causes of incomplete penetrance vary from trait to trait and from individual to individual. With breast cancer, it seems that chance plays the largest role in determining which predisposed individuals get the disease—through the accumulation of secondary somatic mutations. With heart disease, the individual's environment—especially diet and amount of exercise—plays a large role in determining whether a predisposing genotype results in a mutant phenotype, and if so, at what age.

Incomplete penetrance hampers linkage mapping an positional cloning for one main reason: Individuals wh do not express a mutant phenotype may nevertheless carr a mutant genotype. The simplest solution to this problem is to exclude all nondiseased individuals from the analysis With age-dependent traits like breast cancer and Huntingto disease, such exclusion has meant that in disease-carryin families, the majority of children and adults under the ag of 40 could not be included in the analysis. As a resul many more families were required for the studies that le to the mapping and cloning of the genes associated wit both diseases.

With variable expressivity, individuals exhibit different degrees of expressior of a mutant trait

Variation in gene expression may be in age of onset, ph notypic severity, or any other measurable paramete Variable expressivity does not normally interfere wit genetic analysis, because geneticists can use any degr of mutant phenotype as evidence for the presence of mutant allele.

Phenocopy describes a disease phenotype that occurs in the absence of any inherited, predisposing mutation

The observation that 3% of women who do not carr mutation at the *BRCA1* locus or have any family histo of the disease still develop breast cancer by age 55 suggests that the disease can arise entirely from one or more somatic mutations in the breast cells themselves. This form of the disease is considered a **phenocopy** because it is indistinguishable from the inherited form of the disease yet is not caused by an inherited mutant genotype. The percentage of women who develop phenocopy breast cancer rises to 8% by age 80.

We have seen that researchers focus on families with a history of disease to map predisposing alleles. If a small but significant fraction of women who develop the disease carry wild-type alleles, the correlation between the inheritance of the disease locus (or a locus-linked marker) and expression of the disease will diminish. Phenocopies thus make it more difficult to map disease-causing loci.

With genetic heterogeneity, mutations at more than one locus cause the same phenotype

Sometimes it is possible to use sophisticated diagnostic techniques to separate what appears to be a single disease into a set of related diseases caused by mutations in different genes. For example, researchers can distinguish insulin-dependent from insulin-independent diabetes on the basis of their different physiological origins. However, even when the limit of disease subdivision has been reached, what appears to be a homogeneous phenotype may still arise from genetic heterogeneity. The seemingly simple disease of thalassemia is a case in point. Mutations in either the α-globin gene or the β-globin gene can cause the same phenotype: severe reduction or elimination of the functional hemoglobin molecules produced in red blood cell precursors.

Genetic heterogeneity complicates attempts to map disease-causing loci in the following way. Although individual human families usually segregate only a single mutation responsible for a rare disease, most families do not have enough members to provide sufficient data for determining linkage. For this reason, linkage studies in humans almost always combine data from multiple families. But if a disease is heterogeneous, a marker linked to the disease locus in one family may assort independently from a different disease locus in a second family. When data from the two families are combined, the calculated probability of linkage between the marker and the initial disease locus would drop below that obtained with the first family alone.

Genetic heterogeneity is suspected whenever a comprehensive analysis of many families, each with several affected members, fails to map a locus responsible for the disease trait. In such a case, investigators try to divide the complete set of disease-transmitting families into subsets—based on any of several phenotypic parameters—and then combine only the families in each subset for linkage analysis. For example, when researchers combined the data from a large set of breast-cancer-prone families, they found no evidence of linkage to any marker. But when they selected a subset of the families in which the average age of disease onset was less than 47 years, they obtained strong evidence for a disease locus on chromosome 17, named *BRCA1* (Fig. 11.19). It is now clear that mutations in *BRCA1* cause the onset of breast cancer at an earlier age than predisposing alleles at other loci.

Classification of families into early-onset and late-onset groups may be helpful with any trait showing age-dependent expression. With traits for which classification by age of onset fails to produce evidence of linkage, classification by other variables, such as severity of the expressed phenotype, may prove helpful.

Once researchers have identified a first locus responsible for a disease, they can use DNA markers at that locus to determine whether it is responsible for the disease in other families with a disease history. A process of elimination may identify a subset of families that must inherit the disease because of a predisposing allele at a different locus or loci. This type of testing and elimination identified a group of families in which *BRCA1* could not be the locus predisposing women to breast cancer. The combined data from these non-*BRCA1* families revealed a second breast cancer locus, on chromosome 13, named *BRCA2* (Fig. 11.19). Mutations at *BRCA1* or *BRCA2* account for many inherited breast cancers, but not all. As of 2005, at least one, and probably more, breast cancer loci were yet to be discovered.

Polygenic inheritance occurs when two or more genes interact in expression of a phenotype

So far, we have examined ways in which diseases caused by mutations in a single gene are associated with complex patterns of inheritance. But as we saw in Chapter 3, many traits arise from the interaction between two or more genes. Some such polygenic traits are discrete: They either show up or they don't. The occurrence of a heart attack, or myocardial infarction, is a discrete polygenic trait. Other polygenic traits are quantitative: They vary over a continuous range of measurement, from one extreme through the normal range to the opposite extreme. Blood sugar levels, cholesterol levels, and depression are examples of quantitative traits. Loci that influence the expression of such quantitative traits are known as **quantitative trait loci,** or **QTLs.** Although extreme values of QTL expression are considered abnormal, the border between normal and abnormal is arbitrary.

Virtually an unlimited number of transmission patterns are possible for polygenic traits. A completely penetrant discrete trait may require mutations at multiple loci to cause the abnormal phenotype. With other discrete polygenic traits, penetrance may increase as the number of mutant loci increases. With quantitative polygenic traits, the measured degree of expression (expressivity) may vary with the number of mutant loci present in the individual or with the degree to which different mutations at a single locus alter the level of polypeptide production.

Many other factors can complicate the analysis of polygenic traits. Some members of a set of interacting polygenic loci may make a disproportionately large (or small) contribution to the penetrance or expressivity of the trait. Mutations at some loci in a set may be recessive, while mutations at other loci are dominant or codominant. Some traits may arise from a mixture of polygenic and heterogeneous components. For example, one form of a disease may be caused by mutations at loci A, B, C, and D; a second form, by mutations at B and E; and a third form, by a single mutation at F. The more complex the inheritance pattern of a trait, the more difficult it is to identify the loci involved.

> Complex traits are hard to pin down with linkage mapping and positional cloning because of ambiguity in disease effects. Penetrance and expressivity may make it difficult to distinguish a potential disease genotype from a healthy one. In some cases, a disease arises from phenocopy rather than from inheritance, so that pedigrees do not indicate transmitted alleles. Finally, traits affected by mutations in more than a single gene, or that result from interactions of several genes, make loci identification a daunting task.

11.6 Genome-Wide Association Studies

The guiding principle of traditional disease-gene discovery is conceptually quite simple. First, identify one or several large families in which a disease of interest is inherited by some offspring but not others. Second, with the use of DNA markers spread across the genome, independently determine which copies of each chromosome region have been inherited by each family member. Finally, search for a significant correlation between disease transmission and a particular marked region of a chromosome. If a genetic correlation is uncovered, use the tools of molecular biology to zero in on the guilty gene.

The vast majority of genetically influenced attributes that distinguish one person from another result from complex interactions among different variant forms of multiple genes, however. The expression of most complex genetic traits is also influenced by nongenetic factors such as diet, other aspects of a person's lifestyle, and the "noise" inherent in biological systems. Because human environments are variable and not subject to control by scientists, nongenetic influences on the translation of genotype into phenotype can be substantial.

Family-based pedigree studies are inadequate to reveal complex-trait genes

Although DNA-based pedigree analysis has been used successfully in the identification of genes involved in a variety of monogenic traits, its power to identify more complex genetic associations is severely limited for several reasons. First, the study of each new trait requires scientists to perform a new round of tedious and costly tests of individual DNA markers in each subject. Second, by definition, inheritance of a complex trait is only partially correlated with the inheritance of any single gene. Evidence for a partial correlation requires a larger sample size than is needed when a correlation is absolute. The most useful data for genetic mapping comes from the analysis of multiple siblings, but in modern societies human parents typically have only a few children. Pedigree mapping and identification of genes involved in a complex trait would require analysis of families with hundreds or thousands of members that express the trait under investigation.

In the United States, where a majority of disease-gene discovery projects have been conducted, most people cannot trace their ancestors back more than a few generations, and the largest families, extending to second or third cousins, consist of a few hundred living subjects at most. Subject panels of this size were fine for identifying genes associated with simply inherited, all-or-none diseases, but they fail to provide sufficient data to identify weaker multiple-gene correlations typical for common diseases.

The Icelandic geneticist Kari Stefansson decided to solve this problem by taking aim at the largest well-documented extended family that he knew—which was actually, his own. Nearly all of the 300,000 citizens of Iceland, like Stefansson, can trace their ancestors back through detailed, public genealogical records, to the Vikings who settled this desolate European island over a thousand years ago. Stefansson convinced the Icelandic government to provide DeCODE Genetics with exclusive access to the health records of its citizenry in return for bringing investment capital and hundreds of high-tech jobs to the capital of Reykjavik.

DeCODE made rapid progress in identifying genes associated with 28 common diseases, including glaucoma, schizophrenia, diabetes, heart disease, prostate cancer, hypertension, and stroke, among others. In some cases, such as glaucoma and prostate cancer, DeCODE's findings could lead to diagnostic tests for identifying people at risk of developing disease. In other instances, such schizophrenia, gene identifications have led to immediate insight about the cause of disease, which could lead to future therapies.

Buoyed by Stefansson's success, other geneticists were eager to perform large-scale family studies, yet few had similar access to ancient genealogical records. Gene "mapping" is based on the fact that long segments of chromosomes are transmitted in blocks from parents to children. Conventional wisdom held that unrelated families carried unrelated gene variants that were separately responsible for the expression of heritable characteristics. If this were true, geneticists outside Iceland might never have had the power to identify causative genes and alleles.

Haplotyping allows the world population to be seen as one giant pedigree

And then serendipity struck with an amazing discovery. With DNA microarray analysis of SNPs in the genomes of many people, geneticists were able to detect and decipher the remnants of distant family relationships among individuals in all human populations. What primarily distinguishes so-called "unrelated" people from each other is not unique variants or alleles, but rather, unique combinations of common SNP alleles along extended regions of genome. Fragments of genomes carried by our distant ancestors can be observed as blocks of DNA called **haplotypes** that are shared by many "unrelated" people, who are actually distant relatives.

A haplotype is created over evolutionary time by the accumulation of SNP variants, one by one, in a region of DNA that has been inherited intact over many generations, extending back thousands or tens of thousands of years. Indeed, for the purposes of genetic analysis and prediction, all 6 billion people can be treated as members of a single extended family with major branches located on each of the inhabited continents. In essence, we all carry ancestral genetic whispers of humanity's evolutionary past.

Haplotypes can be viewed as extended versions of alleles. Previously we learned that most of the genetic variation in the global human population is confined to a limited number of SNP loci, each of which can appear as

Figure 11.20 Whole-genome association study of body mass index (BMI). (a) *P* values for all SNPs tested for association with BMI across all chromosomes. Each dot represents a single SNP test. The higher the dot, the lower *p* value. **(b)** Fine-scale mapping resolution of two BMI-associated regions.

one of two possible DNA bases. Allelic haplotypes are distinguished from each other at every SNP in a chromosomal region that may cover multiple genes. As a result of the common human heritage, haplotypes can be shared in their entirety by many "unrelated" people throughout the world. In many regions of the genome, 95% or more of the existing diversity is defined by just 5 to 10 alternative haplotypes.

Because of the haplotype structure of the human genome, scientists can use information from a limited number of SNP loci to profile an entire human genome. A haplotype, containing dozens or hundreds of SNP alleles, can be tagged with just a few well-chosen "tag SNPs." A nearly complete whole-genome profile of any individual person can be obtained with the use of a DNA microarray that distinguishes genotypes at just 500,000 tag SNPs.

This conceptual breakthrough alone would not have been enough to transform human genetics if the process of DNA marker typing remained as tedious as it had been just a few years ago. But DNA microarrays have allowed the development of a technology for simultaneously screening large numbers of SNPs. Over the last decade, chip capacity has more than doubled every year, and in 2007, it crossed a threshold of 500,000 SNPs. Automated data analysis of large test populations screened with these high-capacity chips led to a flood of SNP-trait associations, and a new era of "genome-wide" genetics was born.

The massive data from genome-wide studies can be sifted for gene-disease correlations

The application of SNP chip genotyping to large populations of people for the purpose of discovering genetic associations between particular SNPs and traits is referred to as a **genome-wide association study,** or GWAS. Since the first GWAS publication in 2007, SNPs have been identified that are tightly linked to, and sometimes play causative roles, in a broad range of common diseases

Figure 11.21 Genes associated with common complex traits in GWAS.

Social and Ethical Issues Surrounding Preimplantation Genetic Diagnosis

- In 1990, preimplantation genetic diagnosis (PGD) was successfully used to screen embryos for regions of the Y chromosome. The goal was to select for female embryos in order to avoid X-linked genetic disorders (including X-linked mental retardation).
- In 1992, clinicians used PGD to select for an embryo that did not carry two copies of the mutant cystic fibrosis allele.
- In 1998, physicians at the Genetics and *In Vitro* Fertilization (IVF) Institute in Fairfax, Virginia, reported the use of Microsort™, a technology to separate sperm cells containing X chromosomes from sperm cells containing Y chromosomes for the purpose of sex selection.
- In 1999, a British medical ethics board approved use of double PGD screen for selection of an embryo that would develop into a child who would not have Fanconi anemia, but would have an HLA genotype match with a diseased sibling. Born in August 2000 and named Adam Nash, this child would become a transplantation donor for the sibling who had Fanconi anemia. With this procedure, the term "savior siblings" was coined.
- In 2004, two London fertility clinics applied for licenses to use PGD to screen embryos for mutations at the *BRCA1* gene that increase the risk of developing breast cancer.

Nations and groups around the world have responded in different ways to the issues generated by the new reproductive technologies. For example, in 1994, France and Norway passed legislation that limits genetic testing to situations in which the results are medically therapeutic; these laws prohibit the use of genetic testing for sex selection and normal trait enhancement. In contrast, in 2001, the governing board of the American Society for Reproductive Medicine—the major organization representing fertility doctors in the United States—decided that preimplantation sex selection is acceptable when parents already have a child of one sex and want to have another of the opposite sex. And as of 2005, U.S. women could still sell their eggs to the highest bidder in 48 states. Advertisements in some college newspapers offered up to $50,000 for eggs from women who met highly selective criteria of height, appearance, SAT scores, and grades. In all countries of Western Europe, as well as Australia and Canada, egg selling is forbidden.

The range of responses to the issues generated by the new reproductive technologies shows a diversity of approach based in part on national culture and history. It also reflects international apprehension about the potential for misuse and abuse of the new technologies. Here are some of the main concerns.

Which Genetic Variants Should Be Screened?

The couple in our opening story whose firstborn suffered from cystic fibrosis faced a medical problem. PGD could help them have a second child unaffected by the disease. With no cure at present for CF and no therapy that allows for CF-affected people to look forward to a life of normal health or length, this is an example of medically therapeutic screening. Governmental and professional committees in most industrialized countries permit PGD for this purpose, although Germany and Japan ban any use of preimplantation genetic testing for any purpose. And even in countries where PGD is permitted, there is opposition from people who hold a religious belief that all human embryos—even those at the earliest stages of development—have a right to life. Others object to PGD because they think people shouldn't have a right to interfere with the natural process of allele segregation, even if nature selects a lethal childhood disease.

How Should the Tests Be Carried Out?

The couple screening for CF began by consulting a genetic counselor and then worked with medical practitioners associated with a university laboratory. Most geneticists agree that counseling before a procedure should foster an open discussion of all the issues (including the possibility that, in the case of CF, the tests might give false negatives) and that long-term follow-up should be part of the process. PGD itself, like other forms of genetic testing, should be carried out by highly trained personnel in licensed laboratories that are subject to standards and review.

Who Should Have Access to the Technology?

The cost of *in vitro* fertilization and PGD testing averaged $15,000 in the U.S. in 2008. Should the government provide tests for people who cannot afford them? How should society decide this issue? (A related discussion of access to medical technology appears in the Genetics and Society box on pp. 32–33 of Chapter 2.)

Should Parents Have the Right to Make Any Genetic Decision?

If, for instance, parents decide to forgo PGD and then have a child affected by a genetic disease, should they bear all financial responsibility for the child's care, or does society have an obligation to assist with medical treatment? On the other hand, how should physicians handle a request from prospective parents who wish to select against alleles responsible for minor diseases like myopia (nearsightedness) or late-onset diseases like Huntington disease or Alzheimer's disease? What about selection for alleles that provide a child with a relative advantage such as complete resistance to infection by HIV? (Such resistance is inherited naturally by about 10% of individuals in some populations.)

Who Should Have Access to Test Results?

The parents and eventually the child? The parents, the child, and certain community institutions, such as schools? Some combination of these plus commercial enterprises, such as insurance companies and places of employment? (We discuss these same questions of privacy in relation to other types of genetic testing in the Genetics and Society boxes in Chapters 2 and 3.)

What Constitutes a Person?

Cultural and religious beliefs, rather than scientific knowledge, are the basis for answers to this question. Some people see PGD as an alternative to abortion that allows a couple to make a decision before pregnancy begins. Others argue that even at the eight-cell stage, a microscopic preimplantation embryo is the equivalent of a human being, and rejection of an embryo is equivalent to killing a human being. The difference between these two positions is in part the result of different religious beliefs about the moral significance of embryonic cells.

Although there are no simple solutions to these complex issues, geneticists around the globe agree on the need for continuous open discussion and oversight of the development of new reproductive technologies.

including type 1 and type 2 diabetes; schizophrenia; bipolar disorder; glaucoma; inflammatory bowel disease; rheumatoid arthritis; hypertension; restless legs syndrome; susceptibility to gallstone formation; lupus; multiple sclerosis; coronary heart disease; colorectal, prostate, and breast cancer; and the pace at which HIV infection causes full-blown AIDS. With more and more biomedical research groups taking advantage of commercially available DNA chips, equipment, and software, every imaginable human attribute is being investigated for SNP associations. New SNP-trait associations are being published on a daily basis, and earlier associations are being refined and expanded by correlating larger sets of SNPs to more narrowly defined subtraits.

The open source genome

Two aspects of the genome-wide profiling approach to gene discovery are critical to its enormous success. First, essentially every published research finding is based on SNPs defined by a standardized open source system of nomenclature. Second, all newly obtained information about human genes and associated traits, along with numerous software tools used for analysis, is deposited in freely available, public databases maintained by the National Center for Bioinformatics (NCBI) and other institutes at the National Institutes of Health. Consequently, bioinformaticians can compare any newly obtained, individual genome-wide profile against the compendium of banked data to determine a broad range of heritable characteristics. In a metaphorical sense, it is possible to "Google" the genome.

Currently, NCBI hosts 29 interlinked databases. Most relevant to a GWAS program are "dbSNP," a comprehensive database of all identified human SNPs (14,708,752 identified with 6,573,789 validated, as of 11/22/2008; (http://www.ncbi.nlm.nih.gov/SNP/get_html.cgi ?whichHtml=overview): "dbGap," a relational database of the results obtained in genome-wide association studies with the use of DNA microarrays to identify relationships between specific SNPs and specific diseases or nondisease traits (http://www.ncbi.nlm.nih.gov/sites/entrez?db=gap); and "OMIM," an online compendium of annotated records with detailed descriptions of each heritable human trait and gene that has been characterized (19,097 records, to date; [http://www.ncbi.nlm.nih.gov/Omim/mimstats .html]). NCBI has created numerous software tools, researchers can build upon, to query and retrieve online genetic data automatically for specialized uses. NCBI datasets provide the foundation for other important, open-access NIH-based and offsite data consolidation efforts focused on particular research problems or efforts. Three that focus on established associations between genes and traits are the Genetic Association Database (GAD) maintained by the National Institute on Aging (http://geneticassociationdb.nih.gov/), the Human Genome

Epidemiology navigator maintained by the Center for Disease Control (http://hugenavigator.net/), and the Catalog of Published Genome-Wide Association Studies (http://www.genome.gov/gwastudies/) maintained by the National Human Genome Research Institute. Among the most important consolidators of genetic and genomic data is the UCSC Genome Browser, which provides a graphical interface to view specific associations between traits and SNPs.

The GWAS methodology

The genome-wide association study (GWAS) approach to gene mapping is computationally intensive but conceptually simple. As a first step, DNA microarrays are used to obtain whole-genome profiles for each member of a test population consisting of thousands or tens of thousands of people. Each individual is also observed or tested for expression of one or more traits of interest to investigators. Finally, uses the genotype results for tag SNP at time, to separate the test population into three genotypic groups. The determines whether the subpopulations differ, on average, in trait expression. This computational sequence is repeated independently for each tag SNP and each trait. The vast majority of the tag SNPs will not be associated with differences in trait expression. But the experiment is successful, a small number will show an association.

GWAS analyses are more broadly applicable and provide greater power and resolution than traditional pedigree analyses. Unlike all previous methods of gene mapping, genome-wide approaches do not depend on the analysis of closely related family members. There is no limit to the number of human subjects that can be included in a GWA test population. Once DNA microarray results are obtained, the same test population can be studied for genetic associations. The GWA approach can be used to map and identify trait-associated genes that follow any pattern of inheritance, simple or complex.

The first broad-based GWA study, published June 2007, included 17,000 British test subjects and resulted in the identification of 24 independent genetic loci associated with seven common diseases, including type 2 diabetes. Between 2007 and 2008, dozens GWAS analyses have uncovered genetic variants over 150 genes with roles in 50 common diseases and traits, and additional associations are being reported every month.

Type 2 diabetes is a prototype for exploring the power of the GWA approach. From 2007 to 2008, dozens additional GWA studies of type 2 diabetes in European, Asian, or African populations led to the reproducible identification of 20 separate tagged haplotypes with influence on the disease.

Once a tagged haplotype is found to be associated with diabetes, a more detailed study of SNPs and other variants in the region leads to the identification of the precise DNA sequence that is responsible. The specific role played by this sequence in the function of a particular gene can be deciphered. This knowledge provides better insight into the disease and potential therapies to overcome it. Each individual diabetes-related gene influences disease risk by a small amount, but when multiple risk genes appear together in the same genome, risk increases substantially. One remarkable finding of GWA results obtained for diverse populations

is that the same disease-causing variants are present universally, although at different frequencies in different parts of the world.

> The discovery of GWAS as a way of viewing the entire human population as an "extended" family pedigree has revolutionized the evaluation of disease genotypes. Identification of contributing genes may allow refinements of treatment options and adjustments to individual cases.

Connections

In Chapter 9, we described the new tools of biotechnology and bioinformatics that enable geneticists to interpret the DNA sequence in individual genomes. In Chapter 10, we explained how these technologies generate huge amounts of data that can be used to obtain descriptions of the complete expression of genomes into transcripts and proteins.

In this chapter, we have examined how researchers apply the molecular tools to the direct analysis of genotype at the DNA level. Health professionals can use direct genotyping to diagnose hereditary disease; forensic experts can use it to determine the identity and degree of relatedness of DNA samples. Finally, researchers can use direct

genotyping to identify and characterize the genes responsible for any inherited trait that differs in its expression among individuals within a population. With these new approaches, the human species has become a superb system for genetic analysis.

Biologists are fully aware, however, that a static list of genes cannot describe life. Rather, life is a dynamic system of molecular interactions and information processing. The study of these dynamic processes at the level of an organism or discrete biological systems is called "systems biology." In Chapter 12, we explore the experimental methods used by systems biologists and the insight into life provided by these approaches.

ESSENTIAL CONCEPTS

1. Using a variety of tools of biotechnology, researchers have detected enormous variation in nearly all animals and plants. When two or more alleles exist at a DNA locus, the locus is polymorphic, and the variations themselves are DNA polymorphisms. Polymorphic DNA loci that are useful for genetic studies are known as DNA markers.

2. The four classes of DNA polymorphisms are single nucleotide polymorphisms, or SNPs; microsatellites; minisatellites; and deletions, duplications, and insertions in nonrepeat loci (InDels or DIPs).

3. Nucleotide substitutions occur at a predictable rate, which allows investigators to estimate points of evolutionary divergence between virtually any two species.

4. Several methods allow genotyping of SNPs: (1) Southern blot analysis of SNPs that eliminate or create a restriction site; (2) PCR analysis of the same type of SNPs; (3) allele-specific oligonucleotide hybridization to find any type of SNP; and

(4) DNA microarrays that allow identification of millions of SNPs at once.

5. Deletion and subtraction of short sequences also causes genetic variation. These include deletion-insertion polymorphisms (DIPs) and simple sequence repeats (SSRs). Automated PCR combined with gel electrophoresis can readily distinguish SSRs in the range of 15–300 repeats. SSRs are the cause of certain genetic diseases such as Huntington disease and fragile X syndrome.

6. Copy number variants (CNVs) and copy number polymorphisms (CNPs) are relatively large blocks of genetic material. Some of these have normal function or at least do not produce a detectable phenotypic variation, but others have been implicated in mental disease.

7. Positional cloning identifies the genes responsible for traits whose molecular cause is unknown. To localize a trait-affecting gene to a specific region of chromosomal DNA, researchers combine formal

linkage analysis with the use of DNA markers. Researchers catalog all possible candidate genes in a suspected genomic region to narrow the search.

8. To identify the one candidate gene that is responsible for the trait of interest, researchers compare groups of phenotypically normal and abnormal individuals. A finding that the gene's DNA sequence or transcript is altered in all individuals exhibiting the mutant trait is strong evidence that the candidate gene is responsible for the trait.

9. Most common, genetically determined trait variation among individuals results from complex interactions that exhibit non-Mendelian inheritance.

10. With incomplete penetrance, a mutant genotype does not always cause a mutant phenotype.

11. Mutant traits that arise in the absence of a mutant genotype are considered phenocopies.

12. Mutant traits caused by mutations at any one of two or more alternative loci exhibit genetic heterogeneity.

13. A phenotype controlled by alleles at multiple loci is termed a polygenic trait.

14. If different combinations of alleles cause quantifiable differences in a trait, the trait is a quantitative trait, and the loci involved are quantitative trait loci, or QTLs.

15. Genome wide association studies for mapping disease loci is not dependent on the analysis of genetic transmission of alleles from parent to child. Instead, the haplotype structure of a population of genomes is analyzed. The term *haplotype* refers to a specific combination of alleles at two or more DNA markers situated close together on the same chromosomal homolog. All individuals who carry a particular haplotype must have inherited it from the same ancestor.

On Our Website | www.mhhe.com/hartwell4

Annotated Suggested Readings and Links to Other Websites

- Polymorphism analysis
- Sex determination in mice
- DNA fingerprinting on Dolly

- The SNP consortium
- The HapMap project

Specialized Topics

- Positional cloning of the cystic fibrosis gene

Solved Problems

I. The figure shows the pedigree of a family in which a completely penetrant, autosomal dominant disease is transmitted through two generations, together with a corresponding Southern blot with individual pedigree samples digested with *Eco*RI and probed with a DNA fragment that detects a restriction fragment length polymorphism (RFLP). Do the data suggest the existence of genetic linkage between the RFLP locus and the disease locus? If so, what is the estimated genetic distance between the two loci?

Answer

To solve this problem, you need to understand how DNA polymorphisms can be followed through a pedigree and how they can be tested for linkage to a locus defined by phenotype alone. First, examine the Southern blot pattern to determine what the forms of the DNA polymorphism are. The two segregating DNA alleles in the pedigree are represented by RFLPs having sizes of 8 kb and 7 kb. Some individuals are heterozygous, carrying both restriction fragments; and some are homozygous with just the 8 kb fragment or the 7 kb fragment alone.

When two parents have one DNA allele in common, but are different at the second allele, it is possible for a child to inherit the common allele from either or both parents. If the child is homozygous for the allele, then he or she must have received it from both parents. But, if the child has just one copy of the common allele, exclusion analysis can be used to determine which parent had to be the one that transmitted. For example, children II-5, II-6, and II-7 have a 7

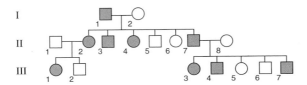

allele that could have come only from their father (I-1), because their mother doesn't carry this allele. By exclusion, their second allele—which is 8 kb—must have come from their mother, even though it is present in the genomes of both parents:

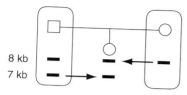

8 kb
7 kb

In the second generation set of siblings (II-2 through II-7), inheritance of the paternal 8 kb allele correlates with inheritance of the disease allele in five of six children: II-2, II-3, and II-4 inherit the paternal 8 kb allele along with the disease, and II-5 and II-6 do not receive the paternal 8 kb allele and do not exhibit the disease. The remaining child (II-7) exhibits the disease but inherited the 7 kb allele from his father. There are two possible explanations for this discrepant individual. First, the RFLP locus could be unlinked to the disease locus, and the six out of seven transmission correlation could be a chance event. Second, the loci could indeed be linked with the II-7 child representing a recombination event that brings the disease locus onto the same chromosome as the 7 kb allele.

To distinguish between these possibilities, you need to examine transmission to the third-generation children using the same logic but with different facts. First, in the third-generation family on the left, the diseased parent (II-2) is homozygous for the 8 kb RFLP allele, and thus, no useful data on linkage can be obtained from her children III-1 and III-2. But useful data can be obtained from the third-generation family on the right. If your hypothesis of linkage is correct, it should now be the 7 kb allele that is transmitted in correlation with the disease allele. Indeed, III-3, III-4, and III-7 receive a paternal 7 kb allele together with the disease allele, and III-5 and III-6 do not receive either the 7 kb allele or the disease allele.

When linkage data are combined from the entire pedigree, you find that there are 11 informative offspring. *In 10 of 11 cases, alleles at the disease locus show cotransmission with alleles at the RFLP locus.* This is evidence for linkage between the two loci. The recombination rate can be estimated as $1/11 = 0.09$, which translates into a genetic distance between the disease locus and the DNA marker of 9 cM. Further studies with additional families would be required to confirm this linkage.

II. A clear limitation to gene mapping in humans is that family sizes are small, so it is very difficult to collect enough data to get accurate recombination frequencies. A technique that circumvents this problem begins with the purification of DNA from single sperm cells. (Remember that recombination occurs during meiosis. Analysis of individual sperm in a large population can provide a large data set for linkage studies.) The DNA from single sperm cells can be used for SNP studies. Four pairs of primers were used for PCR amplification of four defined SNP loci from one man's somatic cells and from 21 single sperm that he provided for this research. Each of these primer pairs amplifies a different SNP locus referred to as A, B, C, and D. The four pairs of PCR primers were used simultaneously on each sample of DNA. Each of the amplified DNAs was divided into eight aliquots (identical subsamples), and these aliquots were denatured and spotted onto eight nitrocellulose membrane strips (vertically, as shown in the figure). Each of these strips was then hybridized with a different ASO (allele-specific oligonucleotide). There are two different ASOs for each SNP. For example, ASOs named A1 and A2 detect different alleles at SNP locus A. Black spots indicate that the amplified DNA hybridized to the ASO probe.

a. Based on the results shown, which SNP loci could be X-linked?

b. Which SNP loci could be on the Y chromosome?

c. Which SNP loci must be autosomal and homozygous?

d. Which SNP loci must be autosomal and heterozygous?

e. Do any SNP loci appear to be linked to each other?

f. Ignoring the results from sperm number 21, what is the distance between the two linked SNP loci?

g. How could you map the genomic region defined by SNP locus A?

h. What event could have given rise to sperm number 21?

Answer

For this problem, you need to understand how ASOs detect SNP alleles and the advantages and limitations of SNPs as DNA marker loci. An advantage of SNP analysis by PCR is that the technique is so sensitive that the single alleles present within individual sperm cells can be assayed. An ASO result is either positive or negative. If the result is positive (as indicated by a black dot of hybridization in this example), a tested somatic cell sample can be either homozygous or heterozygous for the corresponding ASO allele; a positive ASO result by itself doesn't distinguish between these possibilities. If the result is negative, the sample doesn't contain the ASO allele under analysis, but nothing can be said about the alleles (if any) that are present at the tested locus.

a. Half of the sperm cells will not have an X chromosome and would not be expected to show a positive result with any ASO for any X-linked SNP locus. The other half of the sperm cell will carry the same SNP allele. *Gene C shows this type of pattern.*

b. Similarly, a gene on the Y chromosome would be found in only half the sperm. Again, *gene C is a candidate for a Y-linked gene.*

c. If an individual is homozygous at an autosomal SNP locus, all the sperm from that individual will show hybridization to one ASO for that locus and not any other. *Locus A appears to be homozygous and autosomal.*

d. At a heterozygous SNP locus, one ASO will hybridize to approximately one-half of the sperm samples, and a second ASO will hybridize to those

samples that do not hybridize to the first ASO. *SNP loci B and D show this type of pattern.*

e. Alleles at linked loci will segregate together more than 50% of the time and would therefore end up in the same sperm. Alleles B1 and D2 are transmitted together more often than not, and the reciprocal alleles B2 and D1 are also transmitted together more often than not. *This result suggests that loci B and D are linked.*

f. Sperm 3, 9, and 18 show evidence of recombination between alleles at the B and D loci. Three out of 20, or 15%, are recombinant. *The distance between the B and D loci is therefore 15 cM.*

g. Since SNP locus A is homozygous in this individual, it can't be mapped in a linkage analysis. But, SNPs are found at an approximate rate of one in a thousand base pairs. *By sequencing several kilobases of genomic DNA around SNP locus A from this individual, you could identify a nearby SNP locus that is heterozygous and that could be mapped in a linkage analysis.*

h. *Sperm sample number 21 could accidentally have two sperm cells rather than one. It is also possible that a single sperm in this sample has accidentally received two copies of the chromosome that carries loci B and D through meiotic nondisjunction.*

Problems

Interactive Web Exercise

The National Center for Biotechnology Information (NCBI) brings together a variety of database resources providing information on the occurrence and impact of mutant alleles that cause mutant human phenotypes. The oldest of these resources is the Online Inheritance in Man (or OMIM), which came into existence long before the human genome project as a printed catalog of all known human diseases. This exercise will show you how to use the online version of OMIM (www.ncbi.nlm.nih.gov/entrez/query.fcgi?db=OMIM) to investigate the cystic fibrosis phenotypes caused by different mutations at the CFTR locus. The exercise will also demonstrate the use of NCBI's Single Nucleotide Polymorphism database as a tool for genotype analysis (http://www.ncbi.nlm.nih.gov/entrez/query.fcgi?db=Snp). To access this exercise, go to our website at www.mhhe.com/hartwell4 and click on Chapter 11 then "Interactive Web Exercise."

a. DNA polymorphism

b. haplotype

c. RFLP

d. ASO

e. SNP

f. DNA fingerprinting

g. minisatellite

h. locus

1. DNA element composed of tandemly repeated identical sequences

2. two different nucleotides appear at the same position in genomic DNA from different individuals

3. combination of alleles at multiple tightly linked loci that are transmitted together over many generations

4. location on a chromosome

5. a DNA sequence that occurs in two or more variant forms

6. a short oligonucleotide probe that will hybridize to only one allele at a chosen SNP locus

7. detection of genotype at a number of unlinked highly polymorphic loci using one probe

8. variation in the length of a restriction fragment detected by particular probe due to nucleotide changes at a restriction site

Vocabulary

1. Choose the phrase from the right column that best fits the term in the left column.

Section 11.1

2. What advantages do anonymous DNA markers afford for genetic mapping as opposed to traditional allelic markers

associated with visible phenotypes? What are the disadvantages of anonymous DNA markers for mapping?

3. Would you characterize the pattern of inheritance of anonymous DNA polymorphisms as recessive, dominant, incompletely dominant, or codominant?

4. Would you be more likely to find SNPs in the protein-coding or in the noncoding DNA of the human genome?

5. Mutations at microsatellite loci occur at a frequency of 1×10^{-3}, which is much higher than the rate of base substitutions at other loci.
a. What is the nature of microsatellite polymorphisms?
b. By what mechanism are these polymorphisms generated?
c. Minisatellites also mutate at a relatively high frequency. Do these mutations occur by the same or a different mechanism?

6. If you were comparing two closely-related but non-identical gene sequences from different individuals of the same species, how would you distinguish whether these sequences represented polymorphisms of a single gene or two different paralogous genes?

Section 11.2

7. Each of the following reagents can be used to detect SNP polymorphisms. Where is the polymorphism located in relation to the probe or primer DNA sequence used in each of these techniques?
a. allele-specific oligonucleotide (ASO)
b. primer-extension oligonucleotide
c. RFLP probe

8. An 18 bp deletion in the *PAX-3* gene causes Waardenburg syndrome (an autosomal dominant condition that is responsible for a small percentage of deafness in humans). What features of this mutation make it amenable to molecular analyses that could not be applied to detection of the mutation in the β-globlin gene responsible for sickle cell anemia?

9. Given the two allelic sequences shown here and the site at which a single-base polymorphism occurs (underlined in the sequence), what sequences would you use as oligonucleotide probes for ASO analysis of genotype by hybridization? (Assume that ASO probes are usually 19 bp in length.)

```
Allele 1:
5' GGCATTGCATGCTAACCCTATAAATGCGCTAGGCGTAGTTAGCTGGGAA
   TAAAAAGCT 3'
Allele 2:
5' GGCATTGCATGCTAACCCTATAAATGGGCTAGGCGTAGTTAGCTGGGAA
   TAAAAAGCT 3'
```

10. The ASO technique was used to determine the genotypes of 10 family members with regard to sickle-cell anemia, as shown here. Each pair of dots represents the

results of ASO analysis for the DNA from one person. The upper row represents hybridization with the normal oligonucleotide, and the lower row represents the results of hybridization using the mutant oligonucleotide. The three replications of the assay were incubated at 100°C (upper set), 90°C (middle set), and 80°C (lower set).
a. Why do the three replications of the same sample set look different?
b. What are the genotypes of the individuals?

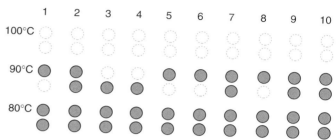

11. Angela and George have one child, and Angela has sickle-cell anemia. They want to have more children but do not want any of them to suffer from this disease. They also do not want to be in a position of having to abort a fetus, so they elect to have *in vitro* fertilization and embryo screening. Briefly list the steps they must take to accomplish this goal.

12. DNA fingerprinting can be used to settle cases concerning paternity. In the DNA fingerprint shown, the mother's DNA sample is in lane 1, the daughter is in lane 2, and two samples of men that could be the father are in lanes in 3 and 4. Can you determine from these data if one of the men must be the father?

13. The police discovered the body of a woman who had been brutally beaten and raped while working late in her office one evening. They suspected that one of her seven coworkers might be responsible for the crime. To test this possibility, they recovered semen from her vagina and used it to prepare a DNA sample. They also took DNA samples from each of her coworkers. All eight samples were subjected to DNA fingerprinting analysis based on restriction digestion, gel electrophoresis, Southern blotting, and probing with a minisatellite. The results are shown in the photo shown below.

Is any one of her coworkers likely to be the perpetrator of the crime? Which one? Estimate how likely it is that this particular person is the perpetrator rather than another person unknown to the authorities.

1   2   3   4   5   6   7   Crime
                              sample

14. Individuals homozygous for a point mutation, changing an A to a T, in the human β-globin gene develop sickle-cell anemia. The wild-type gene sequence over this region is shown here (the top strand is the RNA-like coding strand):

    5′ ATGGTGCACCTGACTCCTGAGGAG 3′
    3′ TACCACGTGGACTGAGGACTCCTC 5′

and the sickle-cell allele sequence is:

    5′ ATGGTGCACCTGACTCCTGTGGAG 3′
    3′ TACCACGTGGACTGAGGACACCTC 5′

Design a PCR-based strategy to distinguish the DNA from homozygous wild-type, heterozygous, and homozygous sickle-cell allele individuals. Your strategy should exploit the single A to T transversion and should produce an "all or none" response in which amplification will occur with particular sets of primers while no amplification will occur with other sets of primers.

15. The trinucleotide repeat region of the Huntington disease (*HD*) locus in six individuals is amplified by PCR and analyzed by gel electrophoresis as shown in the following figure; the numbers to the right indicate the sizes of the PCR products in bp. Each person whose DNA was analyzed has one affected parent.

   a. Which individuals are most likely to be affected by Huntington disease, and in which of these people is the onset of the disease likely to be earliest?

   b. Which individuals are least likely to be affected by the disease?

   c. Consider the two PCR primers used to amplify the trinucleotide repeat region. If the 5′-end of one of these primers is located 70 nucleotides upstream of the first CAG repeat, what is the maximum distance downstream of the last CAG repeat at which the 5′-end of the other primer could be found?

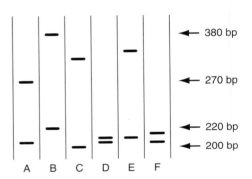

A   B   C   D   E   F

16. Sperm samples were taken from two men just beginning to show the effects of Huntington disease. Individual sperm from these samples were analyzed by PCR for the length of the trinucleotide repeat region in the *HD* gene. In the graphs that follow, the horizontal axes represent the number of CAG repeats in each sperm, and the vertical axes represent the fraction of total sperm of a particular size. The first graph shows the results for a man whose mutant *HD* allele (as measured in somatic cells) contained 62 CAG repeats; the man whose sperm were analyzed in the second graph had a mutant *HD* allele with 48 repeats.

   a. What is the approximate CAG repeat number in the HD^+ alleles from both patients?

   b. Assuming that these results indicate a trend, what can you conclude about the processes that give rise to mutant *HD* alleles? In what kinds of cells do these processes take place?

   c. How do these results explain why approximately 5–10% of Huntington disease patients have no family history of this condition?

   d. Predict the results if you performed this same PCR analysis on single blood cells from each of these patients instead of single sperm.

b. Which restriction fragment is associated with the disease mutation in the mother shown in the right pedigree?

c. If the male child from the left pedigree marries the female child from the right pedigree, what is the probability that their child will be diseased?

d. What is the probability their child will be a carrier?

18. The recessive disease cystic fibrosis displays extensive *allelic heterogeneity:* more than 800 different mutations of the *CFTR* gene have been shown to be associated with cystic fibrosis worldwide. Approximately 1 in 35 Americans is a carrier for some mutant allele of *CFTR*. One of these alleles, a deletion of three nucleotides that results in the loss of a single phenylalanine from the encoded protein, accounts for approximately 70% of the mutant alleles in populations of western European descent. With these facts in mind, is it feasible and worthwhile to mount a nationwide screening program for cystic fibrosis, and if so, how should this screening program be conducted?

17. A relatively frequent, completely penetrant recessive disease known as the foul mouth syndrome (FM) has been found to be due to a variety of mutations in the *FM* gene, which has recently been cloned. Analysis of Southern blots of human DNA cleaved with the enzyme *Hpa*I and probed with a radioactively labeled fragment of the *FM* gene has revealed that *Hpa*I does not cleave within the gene itself. However, the positions of *Hpa*I sites surrounding the gene vary among individuals, producing at least three RFLPs in the population: the sizes of the RFLP alleles are 13, 10, and 7kb. Shown here are two small pedigrees of families in which individuals with the disease are shaded in black. Below each pedigree symbol is the corresponding result obtained from the DNA sample in a Southern blot analysis with the FM probe.

Section 11.3

19. When a researcher begins to choose DNA markers for linkage analysis of a disease trait in a particular family, what are the first criteria used in this choice?

20. Imagine that you have identified a SNP marker that lies 1 cM away from a locus causing a rare hereditary autosomal dominant disease. You test additional nearby markers and find one that shows no recombination with the disease locus in the one large family that you have used for your linkage analysis. Furthermore, you discover that all afflicted individuals have a G base at this SNP on their mutant chromosomes, while all wild-type chromosomes have a T base at this SNP. You would like to think that you have discovered the disease locus and the causative mutation but realize you need to consider other possibilities.

a. What is another possible interpretation of the results?

b. How would you go about obtaining additional genetic information that could support or eliminate your hypothesis that the base-pair difference is responsible for the disease?

21. Approximately 3% of the population carries a mutant allele at the *CFTR* gene responsible for cystic fibrosis. New disease-causing mutations at this locus arise at a frequency of 1 in 10^4 gametes. A genetic counselor is examining a family in which both parents are known to be carriers for a *CFTR* mutation. Their first child was born with the disease, and the parents have come to the counselor to assess whether the new fetus inside the mother is also diseased, is a carrier, or is completely wild type at the *CF* locus. DNA samples

a. Which restriction fragment is associated with the disease mutation in the father shown in the left pedigree?

from each family member and the fetus are tested by PCR and gel electrophoresis for a microsatellite marker within one of the *CFTR* gene's introns. The following results are obtained:

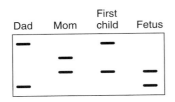

a. What is the probability that the child who will develop from this fetus will exhibit the disease?
b. If this child grows up and gets married, what is the probability that one of her children will be afflicted with the disease?

22. The pedigrees indicated here were obtained with three unrelated families whose members express the same completely penetrant disease caused by a dominant mutation that is linked at a distance of 10 cM from a marker locus with three alleles numbered 1, 2, and 3. The marker alleles present within each live genotype are indicated below the pedigree symbol. The phenotypes of the newly born labeled individuals—A, B, C, and D—are unknown. What is the probability of disease expression in each of these individuals?

23. One of the difficulties faced by human geneticists is that matings are not performed with a scientific goal in mind, so pedigrees may not always provide desired information. As an example, consider the following matings (W, X, Y, or Z). Which of these matings are informative and which non-informative for testing linkage between anonymous loci A and B? (A1 and A2 are different alleles of locus A, B1 and B2 are different alleles of locus B, etc.) Explain your answer for each mating.

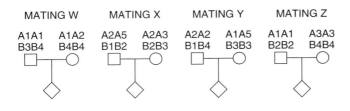

24. The next disease that you decide to tackle is Pinocchio syndrome, which causes the noses of afflicted individuals to grow larger when they tell a lie. You discover a family in which this disease is segregating as indicated in the following pedigree. You have reason to believe that a SNP locus called SNP1 is linked to the Pinocchio gene, and you test each individual in the family with ASOs that recognize allele 1 or allele 2 at this SNP locus with the genotyping results shown here.

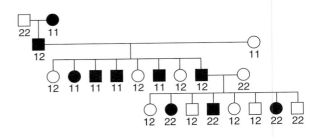

a. What is the most likely genetic basis for Pinocchio syndrome?
b. Is it likely or unlikely that the Pinocchio locus is linked to the SNP1 locus?
c. Sequence analysis shows the SNP1 locus actually resides in the middle of a coding region. How likely is it that this coding region is equivalent to the Pinocchio locus?

25. List three independent conceptual approaches for finding genes within a large cloned and sequenced genomic region.

26. Mice can be genetically engineered to express a hereditary disease that afflicts people. Strains of these mutant mice can provide biomedical scientists with a model for testing possible therapies.
a. What is the best strategy for creating a mouse model for a particular form of hypercholesterolemia that results from a mutant human gene that overexpresses a cholesterol-forming enzyme?
b. What is the best strategy for creating a mouse model for hemophilia?

27. A rare human disease leads to overgrowth of the heart without any other effect on the afflicted individual. Linkage analysis with DNA markers has been used to map the disease locus to a small chromosomal region. This region has been divided into five DNA fragments (named A through E) that are each labeled and used to probe Northern blots containing a single lane of RNA from one of three tissues—liver, heart, and muscle—taken from nondiseased cadavers. The results are shown here.

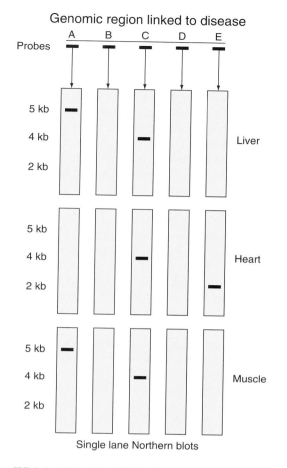

Single lane Northern blots

a. Which of the five DNA fragments is likely to contain a gene?

b. How many genes have been identified in this region by Northern blot analysis?

c. Is it possible that there are more genes in this region than those detected here?

d. Which of the five DNA fragments could possibly contain the gene responsible for this disease?

e. Which fragment is most likely to contain the gene?

f. What is your next step in testing this candidate gene as the causative factor for the disease?

Section 11.4

28. You have decided to study another disease trait that is very rare. You have searched far and wide to come up with an extended family in which a number of nonsibling individuals express the disease. The pedigree is as follows:

a. What is the most likely genetic basis for the disease?

b. Are there any individuals in the pedigree who *must* carry the disease mutation even though they don't express the disease trait? If so, list those individuals according to their generation number (in Roman numerals) and their number within the generation (counting from left to right across the entire pedigree).

29. You have decided to study another disease trait that is very rare. You have found an extended family in which a number of nonsibling individuals express the disease. One pair of identical twins are indicated with a horizontal line that joins both symbols together and with descent lines that join together at a vertex.

The pedigree is as follows:

a. What is the most likely genetic basis for the disease?

b. Are there any individuals in the pedigree who *must* carry the disease mutation even though they don't express the disease trait? If so, list those individuals according to their generation number (in Roman numerals) and their number within the generation (counting from left to right across the entire pedigree).

30. Among the most prevalent diseases that afflict human beings is heart disease, which can have a severe impact on quality of life as well as result in premature death. While heart disease mostly afflicts those who are older, 1% or 2% of people in their thirties, and even their twenties, suffer from this disease. There are genetic and environmental components to this disease. Use this information to answer the following questions.

a. What strategy might you use to choose families to participate in a linkage study of heart disease–causing genes?

b. Once you have cloned a gene that you believe plays a role in heart disease, how would you confirm this role?

Section 11.5

31. Human chromosome 6 has a region containing several closely-linked genes encoding cell surface proteins called human leukocyte antigens. Three of the genes in this region called *HLA-A*, *HLA-B*, and *HLA-C* are

highly polymorphic: About 25 alleles of *HLA-A*, 50 alleles of *HLA-B*, and 10 alleles of *HLA-C* are known.

a. How many different haplotypes for these three genes are possible in human populations?

b. How many diplotypes (that is, different pairs of haplotypes) are possible?

Now consider the inheritance of HLA alleles in the following family:

	HLA-A		HLA-C		HLA-B	
Father	A23	A25	C2	C4	B7	B35
Mother	A3	A24	C5	C9	B8	D44
Child #1	A24	A25	C4	C5	B7	B8
Child #2	A3	A23	C2	C9	B35	B44
Child #3	A23	A24	C2	C5	B8	B35
Child #4	A3	A25	C4	C9	B7	B44

c. Diagram the two haplotypes in the father and the two haplotypes in the mother. Because the genes are so closely linked, assume none of these children is the result of recombination events in the parents.

d. For tissue transplantation to succeed, it is best that the donated tissue has the same alleles of the three *HLA* genes as the recipient. What is the chance that the next child born to this family (child #5) would be able to serve as a bone marrow donor to child #1 (his sister) with no danger of rejection due to incompatibility between *HLA-A*, *HLA-B*, and *HLA-C* antigens?

32. Canavan disease is a recessive, severe neurodegenerative syndrome usually causing death by the age of 18 months.

The frequency of Canavan disease is particularly high in Jewish populations. In an effort to map the gene causing this condition, researchers looked at 10 SNPs (1–10) spaced at roughly 100 kb distances along chromosome 17 in 5 affected Jewish patients and 4 unaffected control Jewish individuals. In the table below, each row depicts a single haplotype. G, C, A, and T represent the actual nucleotide at the indicated SNP location.

a. Does the disease-causing mutation appear to be in linkage disequilibrium with any of the SNP alleles? If so, which ones?

b. Where is the most likely location for the Canavan disease gene? About how long is the region to which you can ascribe the gene?

c. How many independent mutations of the Canavan gene are suggested by these data?

d. Suppose that individuals 2–9 are Ashkenazic (whose ancestors lived in the Rhine river basin of Germany and France after the Jews were expelled from Judea in 70 A.D.) while individual 1 is Sephardic (a non-Ashkenazic Jew). Would these facts provide any information about the history of the mutations causing Canavan disease?

e. For mapping genes by haplotype association, why is it often helpful to focus on certain subpopulations? Does this strategy have any disadvantages?

f. Human chromosome 17 is an autosome, so each person contains two copies of each region along the chromosome. With this in mind, how could the researchers determine any individual haplotype, such as those shown in the table?

Patient	SNP1	SNP2	SNP3	SNP4	SNP5	SNP6	SNP7	SNP8	SNP9	SNP10
1	G	T	G	T	T	T	C	A	G	T
2	A	T	G	T	T	T	C	A	G	T
3	G	T	G	T	T	T	C	A	G	C
4	A	A	G	T	T	T	C	T	C	C
5	G	A	G	C	C	T	G	A	C	C
Control										
6	A	A	G	T	T	T	C	A	G	T
7	G	T	G	G	C	T	G	A	G	T
8	A	T	C	T	C	G	C	T	C	C
9	G	T	C	G	T	G	G	A	C	T

Chromosomal Rearrangements and Changes in Chromosome Number

Chromosomal rearrangements can be mapped with high precision on Drosophila *polytene chromosomes. The* red arrow *points to a very large transposable element that has inserted into one chromosome but is not present in the paired homologous wild-type chromosome* (black arrow).

During the early days of genome sequencing in the 1990s, studies comparing the human genome with that of the laboratory mouse (*Mus musculus*) revealed a surprising evolutionary paradox: At the DNA level, there is a close similarity of nucleotide sequence across hundreds of thousands of base pairs; but at the chromosomal level, mouse and human karyotypes bear little resemblance to each other. These early genomic analyses focused considerable effort on the sequencing of regions encompassing more than 2000 kb of mouse and human DNA containing a complex of genes that encode immune response proteins known as T-cell receptors. Comparisons of the corresponding mouse and human regions show that the nucleotide sequences of the T-cell receptor genes are similar (though not identical) in the two species, as are the order of the genes and the relative positions of a variety of noncoding sequences (of unknown function) along the chromosome. Comparisons of mouse and human Giemsa-stained karyotypes, however, reveal no conservation of banding patterns between the 20 mouse and 23 human chromosomes.

Data for resolving this apparent paradox emerged with the 2002 publication of the nearly complete mouse genome sequence, which researchers could compare with the human genome sequence completed a year earlier. The data showed that each mouse chromosome consists of pieces of different human chromosomes, and vice versa. For example, mouse chromosome 1 contains large blocks of sequences found on human chromosomes 1, 2, 5, 6, 8, 13, and 18 (portrayed in different colors in **Fig. 13.1**). These blocks represent **syntenic segments** in which the identity, order, and transcriptional direction of the genes are almost exactly the same in the two genomes. In principle, scientists could "reconstruct" the mouse genome by breaking the human genome into 342 fragments, each an average length of about 6 Mb, and pasting these fragments together in a different order. Figure 13.1 illustrates this process in detail for mouse chromosome 1; Fig. 10.8 on p. 343 shows the syntenic relationships between the entire mouse and human genomes at lower resolution. Because a 16 Mb fragment would occupy no more than one or two bands

Mouse Chromosome 1

Figure 13.1 Comparing the mouse and human genomes. Mouse chromosome 1 contains large blocks of sequences found on human chromosomes 1, 2, 5, 6, 8, 13, and 18 (portrayed in different colors). *Arrows* indicate the relative orientations of sequence blocks from the same human chromosome.

of a stained chromosome, this level of conservation is not visible in karyotypes. It does, however, show up in the sequence of a smaller genomic region, such as that encoding the T-cell receptors.

These findings contribute to our understanding of how complex life-forms evolved. Although mice and humans diverged from a common ancestor about 65 million years ago, the DNA sequence in many regions of the two genomes is very similar. It is thus possible to hypothesize that the mouse and human genomes evolved through a series of approximately 300 reshaping events during which the chromosomes broke apart and the resulting fragments resealed end to end in novel ways. After each event, the newly rearranged chromosomes somehow became fixed in the genome of the emerging species. Both nucleotide sequence differences and differences in genome organization thus contribute to dissimilarities between the species.

In this chapter, we examine two types of events that reshape genomes (1) **rearrangements,** which reorganize the DNA sequences within one or more chromosomes, and (2) changes in chromosome number involving losses or gains of entire chromosomes or sets of chromosomes (**Table 13.1**) Rearrangements and changes in chromosome number may affect gene activity or gene transmission by altering the position, order, or number of genes in a cell. Such alterations often, but not always, lead to a genetic imbalance that is harmful to the organism or its progeny.

We can identify two main themes underlying the observations of chromosomal changes. First, karyotypes generally remain constant within a species not because rearrangements and changes in chromosome number occur infrequently (they are, in fact, quite common), but because the genetic instabilities and imbalances produced by such changes usually place individual cells or organisms and their progeny at a selective disadvantage. Second, despite selection against chromosomal variations, related species almost always have different karyotypes, with closely related species (such as chimpanzees and humans) diverging by only a few rearrangements and more distantly related species (such as mice and humans) diverging by a larger number of rearrangements. These observations suggest there is significant correlation between karyotypic rearrangements and the evolution of new species.

13.1 Rearrangements of DNA Sequences

All chromosomal rearrangements alter DNA sequence. Some do so by removing or adding base pairs. Others relocate chromosomal regions without changing the number of base pairs they contain. This chapter focuses on heritable rearrangements that can be transmitted through the

germ line from one generation to the next, but it also explains that the genomes of somatic cells can undergo changes in nucleotide number or order. For example, the Fast Forward box "Programmed DNA Rearrangements and the Immune System" (pp. 432–433) describes how the normal development of the human immune system depends on noninherited, programmed rearrangements of the genome in somatic cells.

TABLE 13.1 | Chromosomal Rearrangements and Changes in Chromosome Number

Chromosomal Rearrangements

Before → **After**

Deletion: Removal of a segment of DNA

1 | 2 | 3 | 4 | 5 | 6 | 7 | 8 → 1 | 2 | 3 | 5 | 6 | 7 | 8

Duplication: Increase in the number of copies of a chromosomal region

1 | 2 | 3 | 4 | 5 | 6 | 7 | 8 → 1 | 2 | 3 | 2 | 3 | 4 | 5 | 6 | 7 | 8

Inversion: Half-circle rotation of a chromosomal region

1 | 2 | 3 | 4 | 5 | 6 | 7 | 8 (180 rotation) → 1 | 4 | 3 | 2 | 5 | 6 | 7 | 8

Translocations:

Nonreciprocal: Unequal exchanges between non-homologous chromosomes

1 | 2 | 3 | 4 | 5 | 6 | 7 | 8 / 12 | 13 | 14 | 15 | 16 | 17 | 18 → 12 | 13 | 4 | 5 | 6 | 7 | 8 / 14 | 15 | 16 | 17 | 18

Reciprocal: Parts of two nonhomologous chromosomes trade places

1 | 2 | 3 | 4 | 5 | 6 | 7 | 8 / 12 | 13 | 14 | 15 | 16 | 17 | 18 → 12 | 13 | 14 | 15 | 5 | 6 | 7 | 8 / 1 | 2 | 3 | 4 | 16 | 17 | 18

Transposition: Movement of short DNA segments from one position in the genome to another

1 | 2 | 3 | 4 | 5 | 6 | 7 | 8 → 1 | 2 | 4 | 5 | 6 | 3 | 7 | 8

Changes in Chromosome Number

Chromosomes 1, 2, and 3 (represented in different colors) are nonhomologous.

Euploidy: Cells that contain only complete sets of chromosomes

Diploidy (2*x*): Two copies of each homolog

Monoploidy (*x*): One copy of each homolog

Polyploidy: More than the normal diploid number of chromosome sets

Triploidy (3*x*): Three copies of each homolog

Tetraploidy (4*x*): Four copies of each homolog

Aneuploidy: Loss or gain of one or more chromosomes producing a chromosome number that is not an exact multiple of the haploid number

Monosomy (2*n* − 1)

Trisomy (2*n* + 1)

Tetrasomy (2*n* + 2)

Deletions remove material from the genome

We saw in Chapter 7 that **deletions** remove one or more contiguous base pairs of DNA from a chromosome. They may arise from errors in replication, from faulty meiotic or mitotic recombination, and from exposure to X-rays or other chromosome-damaging agents that break the DNA backbone

(**Fig. 13.2a**). Here we use the symbol *Del* to designate a chromosome that has sustained a deletion. However, many geneticists, particularly those working on *Drosophila,* prefer the term *deficiency* (abbreviated as *Df*) to deletion.

Small deletions often affect only one gene, whereas large deletions can generate chromosomes lacking tens or even hundreds of genes. In higher organisms, geneticists usually find it difficult to distinguish small deletions

FAST FORWARD

Programmed DNA Rearrangements and the Immune System

The human immune system is a marvel of specificity and diversity. It includes close to a trillion B lymphocytes, specialized white blood cells that make more than a billion different varieties of antibodies (also called *immunoglobulins*, or *Igs*). Each B cell, however, makes antibodies against only a single bacterial or viral protein (called an *antigen* in the context of the immune response). The binding of antibody to antigen helps the body attack and neutralize invading pathogens.

One intriguing question about antibody responses is, How can a genome containing only 20,000–30,000 (2–3×10^4) genes encode a billion (10^9) different types of antibodies? The answer is that programmed gene rearrangements, in conjunction with somatic mutations and the diverse pairing of polypeptides of different sizes, can generate roughly a billion binding specificities from a much smaller number of genes. To understand the mechanism of this diversity, it is necessary to know how antibodies are constructed and how B cells come to express the antibody-encoding genes determining specific antigen-binding sites.

The genetics of antibody formation produce specificity and diversity

All antibody molecules consist of a single copy or multiple copies of the same basic molecular unit. Four polypeptides make up this unit: two identical light chains, and two identical heavy chains. Each light chain is paired with a heavy chain (**Fig. A**). Each light

Figure A How antibody specificity emerges from molecular structure. Two heavy chains and two light chains held together by disulfide (–S–S–) bonds form the basic unit of an antibody molecule. Both heavy and light chains have variable (V) domains near their N termini, which associate to form the antigen-binding site. "Hypervariable" stretches of amino acids within the V domains vary extensively between antibody molecules. The remainder of each chain is composed of a C (constant) domain; that of the heavy chain has several subdomains (C_{H1}, hinge, C_{H2}, and C_{H3}).

and each heavy chain has a constant (C) domain and a variable (V) domain. The C domain of the heavy chain determines whether the antibody falls into one of five major classes (designated IgM, IgG, IgE, IgD, and IgA), which influence where and how an antibody functions. For example, IgM antibodies form early in an immune response and are anchored in the B-cell membrane; IgG antibodies emerge later and are secreted into the blood serum. The C domains of the light and heavy chains are not involved in determining the specificity of antibodies. Instead, the V domains of light and heavy chains come together to form the antigen-binding site, which defines an antibody's specificity.

The DNA for all domains of the heavy chain resides on chromosome 14 (**Fig. B**). This heavy-chain gene region consists of more than 100 V-encoding segments, each preceded by a promoter, several D (for diversity) segments, several J (for joining) segments, and nine C-encoding segments preceded by an enhancer (a short DNA segment that aids in the initiation of transcription by interacting with the promoter; see Chapter 16 for details). In all germ-line cells and in most somatic cells, including the cells destined to become B lymphocytes, these various gene segments lie far apart on the chromosome. During B-cell development, however, somatic rearrangements juxtapose random, individual V, D, and J segments together to form the particular variable region that will be transcribed. These rearrangements also place the newly formed variable region next to a C segment and its enhancer, and they further bring the promoter and enhancer into proximity, allowing transcription of the heavy-chain gene. RNA splicing removes the introns from the primary transcript, making a mature mRNA encoding a complete heavy-chain polypeptide.

The somatic rearrangements that shuffle the V, D, J, and C segments at random in each B cell permit expression of one, and only one, specific heavy chain. Without the rearrangements, antibody gene expression cannot occur. Random somatic rearrangements also generate the actual genes that will be expressed as light chains. The somatic rearrangements allowing the expression of antibodies thus generate enormous diversity of binding sites through the random selection and recombination of gene elements.

Several other mechanisms add to this diversity. First, each gene's DNA elements are joined imprecisely, which is perpetrated by cutting and splicing enzymes that sometimes trim DNA from or add nucleotides to the junctions of the segments they join. This imprecise joining helps create the hypervariable regions shown in Fig. A. Next, random somatic mutations in a rearranged gene's V region increase the variation of the antibody's V domain. Finally, in every B cell, two copies of a specific H chain that emerged from random DNA rearrangements combine with two copies of a specific L chain that also emerged from random DNA rearrangements to create molecules with a specific, unique binding site. The fact that any light chain can pair with any heavy chain exponentially increases the potential diversity of antibody types. For example, if there were 10^4 different light chains and 10^5 different heavy chains, there would be 10^9 possible combinations of the two.

Heavy-chain gene region

Heavy-chain gene expression

Figure B The heavy-chain gene region on chromosome 14. The DNA of germ-line cells (as well as all non-antibody-producing cells) contains more than 100 V_H segments, about 20 D segments, 6 J_H segments, and 9 C_H segments (*top*). Each V_H and C_H segment is composed of two or more exons, as seen in the alternate view of the same DNA on the next line. In B cells, somatic rearrangements bring together random, individual V_H, D, and J_H segments. The primary transcript made from the newly constructed heavy-chain gene is subsequently spliced into a mature mRNA. The μ heavy chain translated from this mRNA is the type of heavy chain found in IgM antibodies. Later in B-cell development, other rearrangements (*not shown*) connect the same V-D-J variable region to other C_H segments such as $C_δ$, allowing the synthesis of other antibody classes.

Mistakes by the enzymes that carry out antibody gene rearrangements can lead to cancer

RagI and RagII are enzymes that interact with DNA sequences in antibody genes to help catalyze the rearrangements just described. In carrying out their rearrangement activities, however, the enzymes sometimes make a mistake that results in a reciprocal translocation between human chromosomes 8 and 14. After this translocation, the enhancer of the chromosome 14 heavy-chain gene lies in the vicinity of the unrelated *c-myc* gene from chromosome 8. Under normal circumstances, *c-myc* generates a transcription factor that turns on other genes active in cell division, at the appropriate time and rate in the cell cycle. However, the translocated antibody-gene enhancer accelerates expression of *c-myc*, causing B cells containing the translocation to divide out of control. This uncontrolled B-cell division leads to a cancer known as Burkitt's lymphoma (**Fig. C**).

Thus, although programmed gene rearrangements contribute to the normal development of a healthy immune system, misfiring of the rearrangement mechanism can promote disease.

Chapter 20 describes the evolution of the gene families that encode antibodies and other immune system proteins.

Figure C Misguided translocations can help cause Burkitt's lymphoma. In DNA from this Burkitt's lymphoma patient, a translocation brings transcription of the *c-myc* gene (*green*) under the control of the enhancer adjacent to Cμ. As a result, B cells produce abnormally high levels of the c-myc protein. Apparently, the RagI and RagII enzymes have mistakenly connected a J_H segment to the *c-myc* gene from chromosome 8, instead of to a D segment.

Figure 13.2 Deletions: Origin and detection. (a) When a chromosome sustains two double-strand breaks, a deletion will result if the chromosomal fragments are not properly religated. **(b)** One way to detect deletions is by PCR. The two PCR primers shown will amplify a larger PCR product from wild-type DNA than from DNA with a deletion.

(a) DNA breakage may cause deletions.

X-rays break both strands of DNA

A B C D E F G → A B F G

Deletion of region *CDE*

C D E

(b) Detecting deletions using PCR

Wild-type PCR product

PCR primer 1 ⟶

5′
3′

3′
5′ Wild type

PCR primer 2

No deletion

Deleted DNA

PCR primer 1 ⟶

5′
3′

3′
5′ Deletion (Del)

PCR primer 2

Deletion PCR product

affecting only one gene from point mutations; they can resolve such distinctions only through analysis of the DNA itself. For example, deletions can result in smaller restriction fragments or polymerase chain reaction (PCR) products, whereas most point mutations would not cause such changes (**Fig. 13.2b**). Larger deletions are sometimes identifiable because they affect the expression of two or more adjacent genes. Very large deletions are visible at the relatively low resolution of a karyotype, showing up as the loss of one or more bands from a chromosome.

Lethal effects of homozygosity for a deletion

Because many of the genes in a genome are essential to an individual's survival, homozygotes (*Del/Del*) or hemizygotes (*Del/Y*) for most deletion-bearing chromosomes do not survive. In rare cases where the deleted chromosomal region is devoid of genes essential for viability, however, a deletion hemi- or homozygote may survive. For example, *Drosophila* males hemizygous for an 80 kb deletion including the *white* (*w*) gene survive perfectly well in the laboratory; lacking the w^+ allele required for red eye pigmentation, they have white eyes.

Detrimental effects of heterozygosity for a deletion

Usually, the only way an organism can survive a deletion of more than a few genes is if it carries a nondeleted wild-type homolog of the deleted chromosome. Such a *Del/+* individual is known as a *deletion heterozygote*. Nonetheless, the missing segment cannot be too large, as heterozygosity for very large deletions is almost always lethal. Even small deletions can be harmful in heterozygotes. Newborn humans heterozygous for a relatively small deletion from the short arm of chromosome 5 have *cri du chat* syndrome (from the French for "cry of the cat"), so named because the symptoms include an abnormal cry reminiscent of a mewing kitten. The syndrome also leads to mental retardation.

Why should heterozygosity for a deletion have harmful consequences when the *Del/+* individual has at least one wild-type copy of all of its genes? The answer is that changes in **gene dosage**—the number of times a given gene is present in the cell nucleus—can create a **genetic imbalance.** This imbalance in gene dosage alters the amount of a particular protein relative to all other proteins, and this alteration can have a variety of phenotypic effects. For some rare genes, the normal diploid level of gene expression is essential to individual survival; fewer than two copies of such a gene results in lethality. In *Drosophila*, a single dose of the locus known as *Triplolethal* (Tpl^+) is lethal in an otherwise diploid individual. For certain other genes, the phenotypic consequences of a decrease in gene dosage are noticeable but not catastrophic. For example, *Drosophila* containing only one copy of the wild-type *Notch* gene have visible wing abnormalities but otherwise seem to function normally (**Fig. 13.3**). In contrast with these unusual examples, diminishing the dosage of most genes produces no obvious change in phenotype. There is a catch, however. Although a single dose of any one gene may not cause substantial harm to the individual, the genetic imbalance resulting from a single dose of many genes at the same time can be lethal. Humans, for example, cannot survive, even as heterozygotes, with deletions that remove more than about 3% of any part of their haploid genome.

Another answer to the question of why heterozygosity for a deletion can be harmful is that with only one remaining wild-type copy of a gene, a cell is more vulnerable to subsequent mutation of that remaining copy. If the gene encodes a protein that helps control cell division, a cell without any wild-type protein may divide out of control and generate a tumor. Thus, individuals born heterozygous for certain deletions have a greatly increased risk of losing both copies of certain genes and developing cancer. One case in point is retinoblastoma (RB), the most malignant form of eye cancer, which was previously introduced in Chapter 5 (p. 148). Karyotypes of normal, noncancerous tissues from many people suffering from retinoblastoma reveal heterozygosity for deletions on chromosome 13.

Figure 13.3 Heterozygosity for deletions may have phenotypic consequences.
Flies carrying only one copy of the *Notch*⁺ gene instead of the normal two copies have abnormal wings.

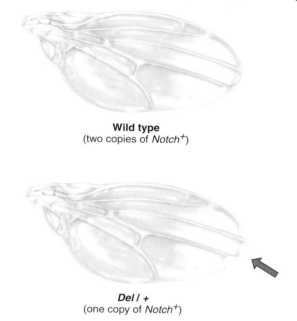

Wild type
(two copies of *Notch*⁺)

***Del*/ +**
(one copy of *Notch*⁺)

Cells from the retinal tumors of these same patients have a mutation in the remaining copy of the *RB* gene on the non-deleted chromosome 13. Chapter 17, "Somatic Mutation and the Genetics of Cancer," explains in detail how deletion of certain chromosomal regions greatly increases the risk of cancer and how researchers have used this knowledge to locate genes whose mutant forms cause cancer.

Effects of deletion heterozygosity on genetic map distances

Because recombination between maternal and paternal homologs can occur only at regions of similarity, map distances derived from genetic recombination frequencies in deletion heterozygotes will be aberrant. For example, no recombination is possible between genes *C, D,* and *E* in **Fig. 13.4** because the DNA in this region of the normal, nondeleted chromosome has nothing with which to recombine. In fact, during the pairing of homologs in prophase of meiosis I, the "orphaned" region of the nondeleted

Figure 13.4 Deletion loops form in the chromosomes of deletion heterozygotes.
During prophase of meiosis I, the nondeleted region of the normal chromosome has nothing with which to pair and forms a deletion loop. No recombination can occur within the deletion loop. In this simplified figure, each line represents two chromatids.

chromosome forms a **deletion loop**—an unpaired bulge of the normal chromosome that corresponds to the area deleted from the other homolog. The progeny of a *Del/+* heterozygote will always inherit the markers in a deletion loop as a unit (*C, D,* and *E* in Fig. 13.4). As a result, these genes cannot be separated by recombination, and the map distances between them, as determined by the phenotypic classes in the progeny of a *Del/+* individual, will be zero. In addition, the genetic distance between loci on either side of the deletion (such as between markers *B* and *F* in Fig. 13.4) will be shorter than expected because fewer crossovers can occur between them.

"Uncovering" genes in deletion heterozygotes

A deletion heterozygote is, in effect, a hemizygote for genes on the normal, nondeleted chromosome that are missing from the deleted chromosome. If the normal chromosome carries a mutant recessive allele of one of these genes, the individual will exhibit the mutant phenotype. This phenomenon is sometimes called **pseudodominance.** In *Drosophila,* for example, the *scarlet* (*st*) eye color mutation is recessive to wild type. However, an animal heterozygous for the *st* mutation and a deletion that removes the *scarlet* gene (*st/Del*) will have bright scarlet eyes, rather than wild-type, dark red eyes. In these circumstances, the deletion "uncovers" (that is, reveals) the phenotype of the recessive mutation (**Fig. 13.5**).

Geneticists can use pseudodominance to determine whether a deletion has removed a particular gene. If the phenotype of a recessive-allele/deletion heterozygote is mutant, the deletion has uncovered the mutated locus; the gene thus lies inside the region of deletion. In contrast, if the trait determined by the gene is wild type in these heterozygotes, the deletion has not uncovered the recessive allele, and the gene must lie outside the deleted region. You can consider this experiment as a complementation test between the mutation and the deletion: The uncovering of a mutant recessive phenotype demonstrates a lack of complementation because neither chromosome can supply wild-type gene function.

Using deletions to locate genes

Geneticists can use deletions that alter chromosomal banding patterns to map genes relative to specific regions

Figure 13.5 In deletion heterozygotes, pseudodominance shows that a deletion has removed a particular gene.
A fly of genotype *st/Del* displays the recessive scarlet eye color. The deletion has thus "uncovered" the scarlet (*st*) mutation.

Figure 13.6 Polytene chromosomes in the salivary glands of *Drosophila* larvae. (a) A drawing of the banding pattern seen in polytene chromosomes. The inset shows the relative size of normal mitotic chromosomes. Note that the homologous polytene chromosomes are paired along their lengths. **(b)** A hypothetical model showing how the 1024 chromatids of each polytene chromosome are aligned in register, with the chromatin in the bands being more condensed than the chromatin of the interbands.

(a) Banding pattern of *Drosophila* polytene chromosomes

(b) Alignment of chromatids in polytene chromosomes

chromosomes in these cells go through 10 rounds of replication without ever entering mitosis. As a result, the sister chromatids never separate, and each chromosome consists of $2^{10} (=1024)$ double helices. In addition, because the homologous chromosomes in the somatic cells of *Drosophila* remain tightly paired throughout interphase, pairs of homologs form a cable of double thickness containing 2048 double helices of DNA (1024 from each homolog). These giant chromosomes consisting of many identical chromatids lying in parallel register are called **polytene chromosomes (Fig. 13.6a).**

When stained and viewed in the light microscope, *Drosophila* polytene chromosomes have an irregular fine-grain banding pattern in which denser dark bands alternate with lighter interbands. The chromatin of each dark band is roughly 10 times more condensed than the chromatin of the lighter interbands **(Fig. 13.6b)**. Scientists do not yet understand the functional significance of bands and interbands. One possibility is that the bands represent units of transcriptional regulation containing genes activated at the same time. In any event, the precisely reproducible banding patterns of polytene chromosomes provide a detailed physical guide to gene mapping. *Drosophila* polytene chromosomes collectively carry about 5000 bands that range in size from 3 kb to approximately 150 kb; investigators designate these bands by numbers and letters of the alphabet.

Because homologous polytene chromosomes pair with each other, deletion loops form in the polytene chromosomes of deletion heterozygotes **(Fig. 13.7)**. Scientists can pinpoint the region of the deletion by noting which bands are present in the wild-type homolog but missing in the deletion. If researchers find that a small deletion removing only a few

Figure 13.7 Deletion loops also form in the paired polytene chromosomes of *Drosophila* deletion heterozygotes. The *thick arrow* points to the wild-type chromosome; the corresponding region is missing from the *Del* homolog.

of metaphase chromosomes. A deletion that results in the loss of one or more bands from a chromosome and also uncovers the recessive mutation of a particular gene places that gene within the missing chromosomal segment.

The greater the number of distinguishable bands in a chromosome, the greater the accuracy of gene localization by this strategy. For this reason, specialized giant chromosomes found in the salivary gland cells of *Drosophila* larvae are a prized mapping resource. The interphase

Figure 13.8 Using deletions to assign genes to bands on *Drosophila* polytene chromosomes. *Red bars* show the bands removed by various deletions; for example, *Df 258-45* eliminates bands 3B3–3C3. Complementation experiments determined whether these deletions uncovered the *white* (*w*), *roughest* (*rst*), or *facet* (*fa*) genes. For instance, *w/Df 258-45* females have white eyes, so the *w* gene is removed by this deletion. The *w* gene must lie within bands 3C2–3 (*green*) because that is the region common to the deletions that uncover *w*. Similarly, *rst* must be in bands 3C5–6 (*yellow*) and *fa* in band 3C7 (*purple*).

Regions of genes

Figure 13.9 *In situ* hybridization as a tool for locating genes at the molecular level. (a) *In situ* hybridization of a probe containing the *white* gene to a single band (3C2) near the tip of the wild-type *Drosophila* X chromosome. **(b)** A particular labeled probe hybridizes to the wild-type chromosome but not to the deletion chromosome in a *Df 258-45/+* heterozygote. The *Df 258-45* deletion thus lacks DNA homologous to the probe.

(a) *In situ* hybridization of the *white* gene to wild-type polytene chromosomes

(b) Characterizing deletions with *in situ* hybridization to polytene chromosomes

polytene chromosome bands uncovers a gene or that several overlapping larger deletions affect the same gene, they can assign the gene to one or a small number of bands, often representing less than 100 kb of DNA. **Figure 13.8** shows how geneticists used this strategy to assign three genes to regions containing only one or two polytene chromosome bands on the *Drosophila* X chromosome.

Geneticists can use deletions analyzed at even higher levels of resolution to help locate genes on cloned fragments of DNA. They must first determine whether a particular deletion uncovers a recessive allele of the gene of interest and then ascertain which DNA sequences are removed by the deletion. *In situ* hybridization provides a straightforward way to show whether a particular DNA sequence is part of a deletion. Suppose you are trying to determine whether a small segment of the *Drosophila* X chromosome in the vicinity of the *white* gene has been deleted. You could use purified DNA fragments as probes for *in situ* hybridization to polytene chromosomes prepared from female flies heterozygous for various deletions in this region of their X chromosomes. If a probe hybridizes to a *Del* chromosome, the deletion has not completely removed that particular fragment of DNA; lack of a hybridization signal on a *Del* chromosome, however, indicates that the fragment has been deleted (**Fig. 13.9**).

Geneticists can also localize deleted regions by asking whether particular bands are removed from human mitotic chromosomes, but because bands in these chromosomes that

contain less than 5 Mb of DNA cannot be detected visually, the resolution of this method is much lower than is possible with *Drosophila* polytene chromosomes. As the final section of this chapter on "Emergent Technologies: Beyond the Karyotype" illustrates, new techniques nonetheless allow human geneticists to determine the molecular extent of deletions in human chromosomes. Once this information is available, *in situ* hybridization to human mitotic chromosomes serves as a useful tool to diagnose whether individuals have genetic diseases associated with heterozygosity for particular deletions. **Figure 13.10** shows an application of this strategy to the diagnosis of DiGeorge syndrome, which accounts for approximately 5% of all congenital heart malformations.

Homozygosity or even heterozygosity for deletions can be lethal or harmful; the effects depend on the size of the deletion and the identity of the deleted genes. In deletion heterozygotes, deletions reveal or "uncover" recessive mutations on the intact homolog because the phenotype is no longer masked by the presence of a dominant wild-type allele. Geneticists can use these properties of deletions to map and identify genes.

Figure 13.10 Diagnosing DiGeorge syndrome by fluoresence *in situ* hybridization (FISH) to human metaphase chromosomes. The *green* signal is a control probe that identifies both chromosome 22's. The *red* signal is a fluorescent probe from region 22q11, which is deleted in one of the chromosome 22's in DiGeorge syndrome patients. These homologous metaphase chromosomes do not pair with each other and thus do not form a deletion loop.

Figure 13.11 Duplications: Structure, origin, and detection. (a) In tandem duplications, the repeated regions lie adjacent to each other in the same or in reverse order. In nontandem duplications, the two copies of the same region are separated. **(b)** In one scenario for duplication formation, X-rays break one chromosome twice and its homolog once. A fragment of the first chromosome inserts elsewhere on its homolog to produce a nontandem duplication. **(c)** Duplication loops form when chromosomes pair in duplication heterozygotes (*Dp/+*). During prophase I, the duplication loop can assume different configurations. A single line represents two chromatids in this simplified diagram.

(a) Types of duplications

(b) Chromosome breakage can produce duplications.

(c) Different kinds of duplication loops

Duplications add material to the genome

Duplications increase the number of copies of a particular chromosomal region. In **tandem duplications,** repeats of a region lie adjacent to each other, either in the same order or in reverse order (**Fig. 13.11a**). In **nontandem** (or *dispersed*) **duplications,** the two or more copies of a region are not adjacent to each other and may lie far apart on the same chromosome or on different chromosomes. Duplications arise by chromosomal breakage and faulty repair, unequal crossing-over, or errors in DNA replication (**Fig. 13.11b**). In this book, we use *Dp* as the symbol for a chromosome carrying a duplication.

Most duplications have no obvious phenotypic consequences and can be detected only by cytological or molecular means. Sufficiently large duplications, for example, show up as repeated bands in metaphase or polytene chromosomes. During the prophase of meiosis I in heterozygotes for such duplications (*Dp/+*), the repeated bands form a **duplication loop**—a bulge in the *Dp*-bearing chromosome that has no similar region with which to pair in the unduplicated normal homologous chromosome. Duplication loops can occur in several alternative configurations (**Fig. 13.11c**). Such loops also form in the polytene chromosomes of *Drosophila* duplication heterozygotes, where the pattern of the bands in the duplication loops is a repeat of that seen in the other copy of the same region elsewhere on the chromosome.

Phenotypic effects of duplications

Although duplications are much less likely to affect phenotype than are deletions of comparable size, some duplications do have phenotypic consequences for visible traits or for survival. Geneticists can use such phenotypes to identify individuals whose genomes contain the duplication. Duplications can produce a novel phenotype either by increasing the number of copies of a particular gene or set of genes, or by placing the genes bordering the duplication in a new chromosomal environment that alters the

Figure 13.12 The phenotypic consequences of duplications. (a) Duplication heterozygotes (Dp/+), have three copies of genes contained in the duplication. Flies with three copies of the Notch⁺ gene have aberrant wing veins. This phenotype differs from that caused by only one copy of Notch⁺ (see Fig. 13.3). (b) In *Drosophila*, three copies or one copy of Tpl⁺ are lethal.

(a) Duplication heterozygosity can cause visible phenotypes.

Wild-type wing:
two copies of *Notch⁺* gene

Three copies of *Notch⁺* gene

Aberrant wing veins

(b) For rare genes, survival requires exactly two copies.

Unequal crossing-over between duplications

In individuals homozygous for a tandem duplication (Dp/Dp), homologs carrying the duplications occasionally pair out of register during meiosis. **Unequal crossing-over,** that is, recombination resulting from such out-of-register pairing, generates gametes containing increases to three and reciprocal decreases to one in the number of copies of the duplicated region. In *Drosophila*, tandem duplication of several polytene bands near the X chromosome centromere produces the Bar phenotype of kidney-shaped eyes. *Drosophila* females homozygous for the Bar eye duplication produce mostly Bar eye progeny. Some progeny, however, have wild-type eyes, whereas other progeny have double-Bar eyes that are even smaller than Bar eyes (**Fig. 13.13**). The genetic explanation is that flies with wild-type eyes carry X chromosomes containing only one copy of the region in question, flies with Bar eyes have X chromosomes containing two copies of the region, and flies with double-Bar eyes have X chromosomes carrying three copies. Unequal crossing-over in females homozygous for double-Bar chromosomes can yield progeny with even more extreme phenotypes associated with four or five copies of the duplicated region. Duplications in homozygotes thus allow for the expansion

Figure 13.13 Unequal crossing-over can increase or decrease copy number. Duplication of the X chromosome polytene region 16A causes Bar eyes. Unequal pairing and crossing-over during meiosis in females homozygous for this duplication produce chromosomes that have either one copy of region 16A (conferring normal eyes) or three copies of 16A (causing the more abnormal double-Bar eyes).

expression. These phenotypic consequences often arise even in duplication heterozygotes (Dp/+). For example, *Drosophila* heterozygous for a duplication including the Notch⁺ gene have abnormal wings that signal the three copies of Notch⁺ (**Fig. 13.12a**); we have already seen that Del/+ flies with only one copy of the Notch⁺ gene have a different kind of wing abnormality (review Fig. 13.3). In another example from *Drosophila*, the locus known as *Triplolethal* (Tpl⁺) is lethal when present in one or three doses in an otherwise diploid individual (**Fig. 13.12b**). Thus, heterozygotes for a Tpl deletion (Del/+) or for a Tpl⁺ duplication (Dp/+) do not survive. Heterozygotes carrying one homolog deleted for the locus and the other homolog duplicated for the locus (Del/Dp) are viable because they have two copies of Tpl⁺.

Organisms are usually not so sensitive to additional copies of a single gene; but just as for large deletions, imbalances for the many genes included in a very large duplication have additive deleterious effects that jeopardize survival. In humans, heterozygosity for duplications covering more than 5% of the haploid genome is most often lethal.

Genotype of X chromosomes

Wild type — 16A

Bar — 16A | 16A

Double-Bar — 16A | 16A | 16A

Out-of-register pairing during meiosis in a Bar-eyed female

16A | 16A

16A | 16A

Gene copy number decreased

16A

Gene copy number increased

16A | 16A | 16A

Phenotype

Wild-type eye

Bar eye

Double-Bar eye

and contraction of the number of copies of a chromosomal region from one generation to the next.

A duplication heterozygote has three copies of a particular chromosomal region, even though the remainder of the genome is diploid. The resulting genetic imbalance can have harmful or even lethal effects, depending of the size of the duplication and the identity of the duplicated genes. Unequal crossing-over between homologous chromosomes bearing the same duplicated region can lead to increases and reciprocal decreases in the number of copies of that region.

Inversions reorganize the DNA sequence of a chromosome

The half-circle rotation of a chromosomal region known as an **inversion (In)** can occur when radiation produces two double-strand breaks in a chromosome's DNA. The breaks release a middle fragment, which may turn 180° before religation to the flanking chromosomal regions, resulting in an inversion (**Fig. 13.14a**). Inversions may also result from rare crossovers between related DNA sequences present in two positions on the same chromosome in inverted orientation (**Fig. 13.14b**), or they may arise by the action of transposable genetic elements (discussed later in this chapter). Inversions that include the centromere are **pericentric,** while inversions that exclude the centromere are **paracentric** (see Fig. 13.14a).

Phenotypic effects of inversions

Most inversions do not result in an abnormal phenotype, because even though they alter the order of genes along the chromosome, they do not add or remove DNA and therefore do not change the identity or number of genes. Geneticists can detect some inversions that do not affect phenotype, especially those that cause cytologically visible changes in banding patterns or those that suppress recombination in heterozygotes (as described later) and thereby change the expected results of linkage analysis. In natural populations, however, many inversions that do not affect phenotype go undetected.

If one end of an inversion lies within the DNA of a gene (**Fig. 13.14c**), a novel phenotype can occur. Inversion following an intragenic break separates the two parts of the gene, relocating one part to a distant region of the chromosome, while leaving the other part at its original site. Such a split disrupts the gene's function. If that function is essential to viability, the inversion acts as a recessive lethal mutation, and homozygotes for the inversion will not survive.

Inversions can also produce unusual phenotypes by moving genes residing near the inversion breakpoints to chromosomal environments that alter their normal expres-

Figure 13.14 Inversions: Origins, types, and phenotypic effects. (a) Inversions can arise when chromosome breakage produces a DNA segment that rotates 180° before it reattaches. When the rotated segment includes the centromere, the inversion is *pericentric;* when the rotated segment does not include the centromere, the inversion is *paracentric.* **(b)** If a chromosome has two copies of a sequence in reverse orientation, rare intrachromosomal recombination can give rise to an inversion. **(c)** An inversion can affect phenotype if it disrupts a gene. Here, the inversion $In(1)y^4$ inactivates the *y* (*yellow*) gene by dividing it in two.

(a) Chromosome breakage can produce inversions.

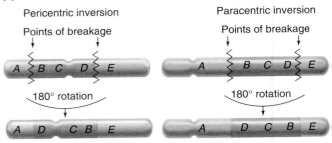

(b) Intrachromosomal recombination can also cause inversions.

(c) Inversions can disrupt gene function.

sion. For example, mutations in the *Antennapedia* gene of *Drosophila* that transform antennae into legs (review Fig. 8.31 on p. 279) are inversions that place the gene in a new regulatory environment, next to sequences that cause it to be transcribed in tissues where it would normally remain unexpressed. Inversions that reposition genes normally found in a chromosome's euchromatin to a position near a region of heterochromatin can also produce an unusual phenotype; spreading of the heterochromatin may inactivate the gene in some cells, leading to position-effect variegation, as discussed in Chapter 12 (see particularly Fig. 12.13 on p. 414).

Inversion heterozygosity and crossover suppression

Individuals heterozygous for an inversion $(In/+)$ are *inversion heterozygotes*. In such individuals, when the chromosome carrying the inversion pairs with its homolog at meiosis, formation of an **inversion loop** allows the tightest possible alignment of homologous regions. In an inversion loop, one chromosomal region rotates to conform to the similar region in the other homolog (**Fig. 13.15**). Crossing-over within an inversion loop produces aberrant recombinant chromatids whether the inversion is pericentric or paracentric.

If the inversion is pericentric and a single crossover occurs within the inversion loop, each recombinant chromatid will have a single centromere—the normal number—but will carry a duplication of one region and a deletion

Figure 13.15 Inversion loops form in inversion heterozygotes. To maximize pairing during prophase of meiosis I in an inversion heterozygote $(In/+)$, homologous regions form an inversion loop. (*Top*) Simplified diagram in which one line represents a pair of sister chromatids. (*Bottom*) Electron micrograph of an inversion loop during meiosis I in an $In/+$ mouse.

Inversion loop
formed during
meiosis

Normal
chromosome

Inverted
chromosome

of a different region (**Fig. 13.16a**). Gametes carrying these recombinant chromatids will have an abnormal dosage of some genes. After fertilization, zygotes created by the union of these abnormal gametes with normal gametes are likely to die because of genetic imbalance.

If the inversion is paracentric and a single crossover occurs within the inversion loop, the recombinant chromatids will be unbalanced not only in gene dosage but also in centromere number (**Fig. 13.16b**). One crossover product will be an **acentric fragment** lacking a centromere; whereas the reciprocal crossover product will be a **dicentric chromatid** with two centromeres. Because the acentric fragment without a centromere cannot attach to the spindle apparatus during the first meiotic division, the cell cannot package it into either of the daughter nuclei; as a result, this chromosome is lost and will not be included in a gamete. By contrast, at anaphase of meiosis I, opposing spindle forces pull the dicentric chromatid toward both spindle poles at the same time with such strength that the dicentric chromatid breaks at random positions along the chromosome. These broken chromosome fragments are deleted for many of their genes. This loss of the acentric fragment and breakage of the dicentric chromatid results in genetically unbalanced gametes, which at fertilization will produce lethally unbalanced zygotes that cannot develop beyond the earliest stages of embryonic development. Consequently, no recombinant progeny resulting from a crossover in a paracentric inversion loop survive. Any surviving progeny are nonrecombinants.

In summary, whether an inversion is pericentric or paracentric, crossing-over within the inversion loop of an inversion heterozygote has the same effect: formation of recombinant gametes that after fertilization prevent the zygote from developing. Because only gametes containing chromosomes that did not recombine within the inversion loop can yield viable progeny, inversions act as **crossover suppressors.** This does not mean that crossovers do not occur within inversion loops, but simply that there are no recombinants among the viable progeny of an inversion heterozygote.

Geneticists use crossover suppression to create **balancer chromosomes,** which contain multiple, overlapping inversions (both pericentric and paracentric), as well as a marker mutation that produces a visible dominant phenotype (**Fig. 13.17**). The viable progeny of a *Balancer/+* heterozygote will receive either the balancer or the chromosome of normal order $(+)$, but they cannot inherit a recombinant chromosome containing parts of both. Researchers can distinguish these two types of viable progeny by the presence or absence of the dominant marker phenotype. Geneticists often generate balancer heterozygotes to ensure that a chromosome of normal order, along with any mutations of interest it may carry, is transmitted to the next generation unchanged by recombination. To help create genetic stocks, the marker in

Figure 13.16 Why inversion heterozygotes produce few if any recombinant progeny. Throughout this figure, each line represents one chromatid, and different shades of *green* indicate the two homologous chromosomes. **(a)** The chromatids formed by recombination within the inversion loop of a pericentric inversion heterozygote are genetically unbalanced. **(b)** The chromatids formed by recombination within the inversion loop of a paracentric inversion heterozygote are not only genetically unbalanced but also contain two or no centromeres, instead of the normal one.

Figure 13.17 Balancer chromosomes are useful tools for genetic analysis. Balancer chromosomes carry both a dominant marker *D* as well as inversions (*brackets*) that prevent the balancer chromosome from recombining with an experimental chromosome carrying mutations of interest (*m₁* and *m₂*). A parent heterozygous for the balancer and experimental chromosomes will transmit either the balancer or the experimental chromosome, but not a recombinant chromosome, to its surviving progeny.

homozygotes. The *Drosophila* portrait (on our website a www.mhhe.com/hartwell4) discusses this and other signifi cant uses of balancer chromosomes in genetic analysis.

> Although inversions do not add or remove DNA, they can alter phenotype if they disrupt a gene or alter its expression. In inversion heterozygotes, recombination within the inversion loop yields genetically imbalanced gametes that produce nonviable zygotes. Geneticists can take advantage of this property to create balancer chromosomes that are useful in the production of genetic lines of known composition.

Translocations attach part of one chromosome to another chromosome

Translocations are large-scale mutations in which part o one chromosome becomes attached to a nonhomologou chromosome or in which parts of two different chromo somes trade places. This second type of translocation known as a **reciprocal translocation** (**Fig. 13.18a**). results when two breaks, one in each of two chromosome yield DNA fragments that do not religate to their chromo some of origin; rather, they switch places and becom attached to the other chromosome. Depending on the pos tions of the breaks and the sizes of the exchanged fragment the translocated chromosomes may be so different fro the original chromosomes that the translocation is visib in a cytological examination (**Fig. 13.18b**).

most balancer chromosomes not only causes a dominant visible phenotype, but it also acts as a recessive lethal muta-tion that prevents the survival of balancer chromosome

Figure 13.18 Reciprocal translocations are exchanges between nonhomologous chromosomes. (a) In a reciprocal translocation, the region gained by one chromosome is the region lost by the other chromosome. **(b)** Karyotype of a human genome containing a translocation. The two translocated chromosomes are stained both red *and* green (*arrows*). Two normal, non-translocated chromosomes are stained entirely red *or* entirely green (*arrowheads*), indicating that this person is heterozygous for the translocation.

(a) Two chromosome breaks can produce a reciprocal translocation.

(b) Chromosome painting reveals a reciprocal translocation.

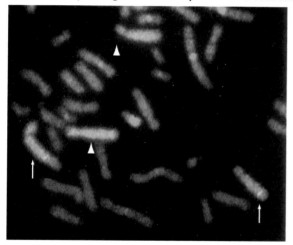

Robertsonian translocations are an important type of cytologically visible reciprocal translocations that arise from breaks at or near the centromeres of two acrocentric chromosomes (**Fig. 13.19**). The reciprocal exchange of broken parts generates one large metacentric chromosome and one very small chromosome containing few, if any, genes. This tiny chromosome may subsequently be lost from the organism. Robertsonian translocations are named after W. R. B. Robertson, who in 1911 was the first to suggest that during evolution, metacentric chromosomes may arise from the fusion of two acrocentrics.

Phenotypic effects of reciprocal translocations

Most individuals bearing reciprocal translocations are phenotypically normal because they have neither lost nor gained genetic material. As with inversions, however, if one of the translocation breakpoints occurs within a gene, that gene's function may change or be destroyed. Or if

Figure 13.19 Robertsonian translocations can reshape genomes. In a Robertsonian translocation, reciprocal exchanges between two acrocentric chromosomes generate a large metacentric chromosome and a very small chromosome. The latter may carry so few genes that it can be lost without ill effect.

the translocation places a gene normally found in the euchromatin of one chromosome near the heterochromatin of the other chromosome, normal expression of the gene may cease in some cells, giving rise to position-effect variegation (see Fig. 12.13 on p. 414).

Several kinds of cancer are associated with translocations in somatic cells. In normal cells, genes known as *protooncogenes* help control cell division. Translocations that relocate these genes can turn them into tumor-producing *oncogenes* whose protein products have an altered structure or level of expression that leads to runaway cell division. For example, in almost all patients with chronic myelogenous leukemia, a type of cancer caused by overproduction of certain white blood cells, the leukemic cells have a reciprocal translocation between chromosomes 9 and 22 (**Fig. 13.20**). The breakpoint in chromosome 9 occurs within an intron of a protooncogene called *c-abl;* the breakpoint in chromosome 22 occurs within an intron of the *bcr* gene. After the translocation, parts of the two genes are adjacent to one another. During transcription, the RNA-producing machinery runs these two genes together, creating a long primary transcript. After splicing, the mRNA is translated into a fused protein in which 25 amino acids at the N terminus of the *c-abl*-determined protein are replaced by about 600 amino acids from the *bcr*-determined protein. The activity of this fused protein releases the normal controls on cell division, leading to leukemia. (See the Fast Forward box on pp. 432–433 of this chapter for another example of a translocation-induced cancer called Burkitt's lymphoma.)

Medical practitioners can exploit the rearrangement of DNA sequences that accompany cancer-related translocations for diagnostic and therapeutic purposes. To confirm a diagnosis of myelogenous leukemia, for example, they first obtain a blood sample from the patient, and they then use a pair of PCR primers derived from opposite sides of the breakpoint—one synthesized from the appropriate part of chromosome 22, the other from chromosome 9—to

Figure 13.20 How a reciprocal translocation helps cause one kind of leukemia. **(a)** Uncontrolled divisions of large, dark-staining white blood cells in a leukemia patient (*right*) produce a higher ratio of white to red blood cells than that in a normal individual (*left*). **(b)** A reciprocal translocation between chromosomes 9 and 22 contributes to chronic myelogenous leukemia. This rearrangement makes an abnormal hybrid gene composed of part of the *c-abl* gene and part of the *bcr* gene. The hybrid gene encodes an abnormal fused protein that disrupts controls on cell division. *Black arrows* indicate PCR primers that will generate a PCR product only from DNA containing the hybrid gene.

(a) Leukemia patients have too many white blood cells.

Normal   Leukemic

(b) The genetic basis for chronic myelogenous leukemia

carry out a PCR on DNA from the blood cells. The PCR will amplify the region between the primers only if the DNA sample contains the translocation (**Fig. 13.20b**). To monitor the effects of chemotherapy, they again obtain a blood sample and extract genomic DNA from the white blood cells. If the sample contains even a few malignant cells, a PCR test with the same two primers will amplify the DNA translocation from those cells, indicating the need for more therapy. PCR thus becomes a sensitive assay for this type of leukemic cell.

Pharmaceutical researchers have recently exploited their understanding of the molecular nature of the translocation underlying chronic myelogenous leukemia to achieve a stunning breakthrough in the treatment of this cancer. The protein encoded by *c-abl* is a *protein tyrosine kinase,* an enzyme that adds phosphate groups to tyrosine amino acids on other proteins. This enzyme is an essential part

of the set of signals that dictate cell growth and division. Normal cells closely regulate the activity of the *c-abl* protein, blocking its function most of the time but activating it in response to stimulation by growth factors in the environment. By contrast, the fused protein encoded by *bcr/c-abl* in cells carrying the translocation is not amenable to regulation. It is always active, even in the absence of growth factor, and this leads to runaway cell division. Pharmaceutical companies have developed a drug called Gleevec® that specifically inhibits the enzymatic activity of the protein tyrosine kinase encoded by *bcr/c-abl*. In clinical trials, 98% of participants experienced a complete disappearance of leukemic blood cells and the return of normal white cells. This drug is now the standard treatment for chronic myelogenous leukemia and is a model for new types of cancer treatments that home in on cancer cells without hurting healthy ones.

Figure 13.21 The meiotic segregation of reciprocal translocations. In all parts of this figure, each bar or line represents one chromatid. **(a)** In a translocation homozygote (*T/T*), chromosomes segregate normally during meiosis I. **(b)** In a translocation heterozygote (*T/+*), the four relevant chromosomes assume a cruciform (crosslike) configuration to maximize pairing. The alleles of genes on chromosomes in the original order (*N1* and *N2*) are shown in lowercase; the alleles of these genes on the translocated chromosomes (*T1* and *T2*) are in uppercase letters. **(c)** Three segregation patterns are possible in a translocation heterozygote. Only the alternate segregation pattern gives rise to balanced gametes. **(d)** This semisterile ear of corn comes from a plant heterozygous for a reciprocal translocation. It has fewer kernels than normal because unbalanced ovules are aborted.

(a) Segregation in a translocation homozygote

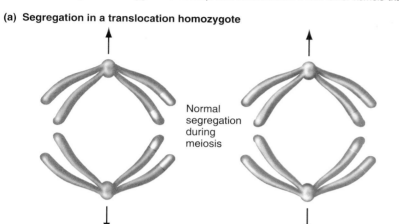

Normal segregation during meiosis

(b) Chromosome pairing in a translocation heterozygote

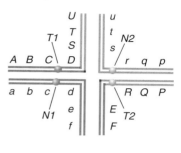

(c) Segregation in a translocation heterozygote

Segregation pattern	Alternate		Adjacent-1		Adjacent-2 (less frequent)	
	Balanced *N1 + N2*	Balanced *T1 + T2*	Unbalanced *T1 + N2*	Unbalanced *N1 + T2*	Unbalanced *N1 + T1*	Unbalanced *N2 + T2*
Gametes	a b c d e f	p q r s t u	A B C D S T U	P Q R E F	a b c d e f	A B C D S T U	p q r s t u	P Q R E F
Type of progeny when mated with normal *abcdefpqrstu* homozygote	*abcdef pqrstu*	*ABCDEF PQRSTU*	None surviving	None surviving	None surviving	None surviving

(d) Semisterility in corn

Diminished fertility and pseudolinkage in translocation heterozygotes

Translocations, like inversions, produce no significant genetic consequences in homozygotes if the breakpoints do not interfere with gene function. During meiosis in a translocation homozygote, chromosomes segregate normally according to Mendelian principles (**Fig. 13.21a**). Even though the genes have been rearranged, both haploid sets of chromosomes in the individual have the same arrangement. As a result, all chromosomes will find a single partner with which to pair at meiosis, and there will be no deleterious consequences for the progeny.

In translocation heterozygotes, however, certain patterns of chromosome segregation during meiosis produce genetically unbalanced gametes that at fertilization become deleterious to the zygote. In a translocation heterozygote, the two haploid sets of chromosomes do not carry the same arrangement of genetic information. As a result, during prophase of the first meiotic division, the translocated chromosomes and their normal homologs assume a crosslike configuration in which four chromosomes, rather than the normal two, pair to achieve a maximum of synapsis between similar regions (**Fig. 13.21b**). To keep track of the four chromosomes participating in this crosslike structure, we denote the chromosomes carrying translocated material with a *T* and the chromosomes with a normal order of genes with an *N*. Chromosomes *N1* and *T1* have homologous centromeres found in wild type on chromosome 1; *N2* and *T2* have centromeres found in wild type on chromosome 2.

During anaphase of meiosis I, the mechanisms that attach the spindle to the chromosomes in this crosslike configuration still usually ensure the disjunction of homologous centromeres, bringing homologous chromosomes to opposite spindle poles (that is, *T1* and *N1* go to opposite poles, as do *T2* and *N2*). Depending on the arrangement of the four chromosomes on the metaphase plate, this normal disjunction of homologs produces one of two equally likely patterns of segregation (**Fig. 13.21c**). In the **alternate segregation pattern,** the two translocation chromosomes (*T1* and *T2*) go to one pole, while the two normal chromosomes (*N1* and *N2*) move to the opposite pole. Both kinds of gametes resulting from this segregation (*T1, T2* and *N1, N2*) carry the correct haploid number of genes, and the zygotes formed by union of these gametes with a normal gamete will be viable. By contrast, in the **adjacent-1 segregation pattern,** homologous centromeres disjoin so that *T1* and *N2* go to one pole, while *N1* and *T2* go to the opposite pole. As a result, each gamete contains a large duplication (of the region found in both the normal and the translocated chromosome in that gamete) and a correspondingly large deletion (of the region found in neither of the chromosomes in that gamete), which make them genetically unbalanced. Zygotes formed by union of these gametes with a normal gamete are usually not viable.

Because of the unusual cruciform pairing configuration in translocation heterozygotes, nondisjunction of homologous centromeres occurs at a measurable but low rate. This nondisjunction produces an **adjacent-2 segregation pattern** in which the homologous centromeres *N1* and *T1* go to the same spindle pole, while the homologous centromeres *N2* and *T2* go to the other spindle pole (Fig. 13.21c). The resulting genetic imbalances are lethal after fertilization to the zygotes containing them.

Thus, of all the gametes generated by translocation heterozygotes, only those arising from alternate segregation, which account for slightly less than half the total, can produce viable progeny when crossed with individuals who do not carry the translocation. As a result, the fertility of most translocation heterozygotes, that is, their capacity for generating viable offspring, is diminished by at least 50%. This condition is known as **semisterility.** Corn plants illustrate the correlation between translocation heterozygosity and semisterility. The demise of genetically unbalanced ovules produces gaps in the ear where kernels would normally appear (**Fig. 13.21d**); in addition, genetically unbalanced pollen grains are abnormally small (not shown).

The semisterility of translocation heterozygotes undermines the potential of genes on the two translocated chromosomes to assort independently. Mendel's second law requires that all gametes resulting from both possible metaphase alignments of two chromosomal pairs produce viable progeny. But as we have seen, in a translocation heterozygote, only the alternate segregation pattern yields viable

progeny in outcrosses; the equally likely adjacent-1 pattern and the rare adjacent-2 pattern do not. Because of this, genes near the translocation breakpoints on the nonhomologous chromosomes participating in a reciprocal translocation exhibit **pseudolinkage:** They behave as if they are linked.

Figure 13.21c illustrates why pseudolinkage occurs in a translocation heterozygote. In the figure, lowercase *a b c d e f* represent the alleles of genes present on normal chromosome 1 (*N1*), and *p q r s t u* are the alleles of genes on a nonhomologous normal chromosome 2 (*N2*). The alleles of these genes on the translocated chromosomes *T1* and *T2* are in uppercase. In the absence of recombination, Mendel's law of independent assortment would predict that genes on two different chromosomes will appear in four types of gametes in equal frequencies; for example, *a p, A P, a P,* and *A p.* But alternate segregation, the only pattern that can give rise to viable progeny, produces only *a p* and *A P* gametes. Thus, in translocation heterozygotes such as these, the genes on the two nonhomologous chromosomes act as if they are linked to each other.

Translocations and gene mapping

In humans, approximately 1 of every 500 individuals is heterozygous for some kind of translocation. While most such people are phenotypically normal, their fertility is diminished because many of the zygotes they produce abort spontaneously. As we have seen, this semisterility results from genetic imbalances associated with gametes formed by adjacent-1 or adjacent-2 segregation patterns. But such genetic imbalances are not inevitably lethal to the zygotes. If the duplicated or deleted regions are very small, the imbalanced gametes generated by these modes of segregation may produce children.

An important example of this phenomenon is seen among individuals heterozygous for certain reciprocal translocations involving chromosome 21, such as the Robertsonian translocation shown in **Fig. 13.22.** These people are phenotypically normal but produce some gametes from the adjacent-1 segregation pattern that have two copies of a part of chromosome 21 near the tip of its long arm. At fertilization, if a gamete with the duplication unites with a normal gamete, the resulting child will have three copies of this region of chromosome 21. A few individuals affected by Down syndrome have, in this way, inherited a third copy of only a small part of chromosome 21. These individuals with **translocation Down syndrome** provide evidence that the entirety of chromosome 21 need not be present in three copies to generate the phenotype.

Geneticists are now mapping the chromosome 21 regions duplicated in translocation Down syndrome patients to find the one or more genes responsible for the syndrome. Although chromosome 21 is the smallest human autosome, it nevertheless contains an estimated 350 genes, most of them in the 43 million base pairs of its long arm. The mapping of genes relative to the breakpoints of one or more such translocations considerably simplifies the task of identifying those genes that in triplicate produce the

Figure 13.22 How translocation Down syndrome arises. In heterozygotes for a translocation involving chromosome 21, such as 14q21q (a Robertsonian translocation between chromosomes 21 and 14), adjacent-1 segregation can produce gametes with two copies of part of chromosome 21. If such a gamete unites with a normal gamete, the resulting zygote will have three copies of part of chromosome 21. Depending on which region of chromosome 21 is present in three copies, this tripling may cause Down syndrome. (In the original translocation heterozygote, the small, reciprocally translocated chromosome [14p21p] has been lost.)

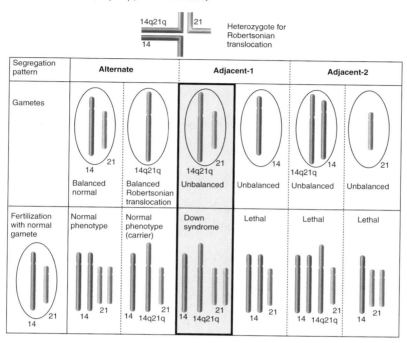

symptoms of Down syndrome. One way to locate which parts of chromosome 21 are responsible for Down syndrome is to obtain cloned chromosome 21 sequences from the Human Genome Project and then use these clones as FISH (fluorescence *in situ* hybridization) probes for the genome of the translocation Down syndrome patient. If the probe lights up the translocation chromosome as well as the two normal copies of chromosome 21, it identifies a region of the genome that is of potential importance to the syndrome.

In a reciprocal translocation, parts of two nonhomologous chromosomes trade places without any net loss or gain of DNA. As with inversions, reciprocal translocations can alter phenotype if they disrupt a gene or its expression. Translocation heterozygotes produce genetically imbalanced gametes from two of three possible meiotic segregation patterns; the result is semisterility and pseudolinkage.

13.2 Transposable Genetic Elements

Large deletions and duplications, as well as inversions and translocations, are major chromosomal reorganizations visible at the relatively low resolution of a karyotype. Small deletions and duplications are lesser chromosomal reorganizations that reshape genomes without any visible effect on karyotype. Another type of cytologically invisi-

ble sequence rearrangement with a significant genomic impact is **transposition:** the movement of small segments of DNA—entities known as **transposable elements (TEs)**—from one position in the genome to another.

Marcus Rhoades in the 1930s and Barbara McClintock in the 1950s inferred the existence of TEs from intricate genetic studies of corn. At first, the scientific community did not appreciate the importance of their work because their findings did not support the conclusion from classical recombination mapping that genes are located at fixed positions on chromosomes. Once the cloning of TEs made it possible to study them in detail, geneticists not only acknowledged their existence, but also discovered TEs in the genomes of virtually all organisms, from bacteria to humans. In 1983, Barbara McClintock received the Nobel Prize for her insightful studies on movable genetic elements (**Fig. 13.23**).

Molecular studies confirmed transposable element movement

Copia is a transposable element in *Drosophila*. If you examined the polytene chromosomes from two strains of flies isolated from different geographic locations, you would find in general that the chromosomes appear identical. A probe derived from the *white* gene for eye color, for example, would hybridize to a single site near the tip of the X chromosome in both strains (review Fig. 13.9a). However, a probe including the *copia* TE would hybridize to 30–50 sites scattered throughout the genome, and the positions of

Figure 13.23 Barbara McClintock: Discoverer of transposable elements.

in situ hybridization would not be the same in the two strains. Some sites would be identical in the two polytene sets, but others would be different (**Fig. 13.24**). These observations suggest that since the time the strains were separated geographically, the *copia* sequences have moved around (transposed) in different ways in the two genomes even though the genes have remained in fixed positions.

Any segment of DNA that evolves the ability to move from place to place within a genome is by definition a transposable element, regardless of its origin or function. TEs need not be sequences that do something for the organism; indeed, many scientists regard them primarily as "selfish" parasitic entities carrying only information that allows their self-perpetuation. Some TEs, however, appear to have evolved functions that help their host. In one interesting example, TEs maintain the length of *Drosophila* chromosomes. *Drosophila* telomeres, in contrast to those of most organisms, do not contain TTAGGG repeats that are extendable by the telomerase enzyme (see Fig. 12.19 on p. 419). Certain TEs in flies, however, combat the shortening of chromosome ends that accompanies

Figure 13.24 Transposable elements (TEs) can move to many locations in a genome. A probe for the *copia* TE hybridizes to multiple sites (*black bands* superimposed over the *blue* chromosomes) that differ in two different fly strains.

every cycle of replication by jumping with high frequency into DNA very near chromosome ends. As a result, chromosome size stays relatively constant.

Most transposable elements in nature range from 50 bp to approximately 10,000 bp (10 kb) in length. A particular TE can be present in a genome anywhere from one to hundreds of thousands of times. *Drosophila melanogaster,* for example, harbors approximately 80 different TEs, each an average of 5 kb in length, and each present an average of 50 times. These TEs constitute $80 \times 50 \times 5 = 20,000$ kb, or roughly 12.5% of the 160,000 kb *Drosophila* genome. Mammals carry two major classes of TEs: **LINEs,** or long interspersed elements; and **SINEs,** or short interspersed elements. The human genome contains approximately 20,000 copies of the main human LINE—*L1*—which is up to 6.4 kb in length. The human genome also carries 300,000 copies of the main human SINE—*Alu*—which is 0.28 kb in length (**Fig. 13.25a**). These two TEs alone thus constitute roughly 7% of the 3,000,000 kb human genome. Because some TEs exist in only one or a few closely related species, it is probable that some elements arise and then disappear rather frequently over evolutionary time. Chapter 20 describes the evolutionary origins of LINEs and SINEs.

Classification of TEs on the basis of how they move around the genome distinguishes two groups. **Retroposons** transpose via reverse transcription of an RNA intermediate. The *Drosophila copia* elements and the human SINEs and LINEs just described are retroposons. **Transposons** move their DNA directly without the requirement of an RNA intermediate. The genetic elements discovered by

Figure 13.25 TEs in human and corn genomes. (a) The human genome carries about 300,000 copies of the 0.28 kb *Alu* retroposon, the major human SINE. **(b)** Movements of a transposon mottles corn kernels when the transposon jumps into or out of genes that influence pigmentation.

(a) *Alu* **SINEs in the human genome**

0.28 kb *Alu* units: ≈300,000 found
dispersed throughout human genome
at ≈10 kb intervals

kb 0   10   20   30   40   50

(b) TEs cause mottling in corn.

arbara McClintock in corn responsible for mottling the ernels are transposons (**Fig. 13.25b**). Some biologists use ne term "transposon" in the broader sense to refer to all Es. In this book, we reserve it for the direct-movement lass of genetic elements, and we use "transposable elements TEs)" to indicate all DNA segments that move about in ne genome, regardless of the mechanism.

Studies in corn and *Drosophila* revealed the existence of transposable genetic elements (TEs): small segments of DNA that can move around, and accumulate in, the genome. TEs can be subdivided according to their mode of transposition. Retroposons move via RNA intermediates, whereas the DNA of transposons moves directly without first being transcribed into RNA.

Retroposons move via RNA intermediates

The transposition of a retroposon begins with its transcription by RNA polymerase into an RNA that encodes a reverse-transcriptase-like enzyme. This enzyme, like the reverse transcriptase made by the AIDS-causing HIV virus described in the Genetics and Society box on pp. 260–261 of Chapter 8, can copy RNA into a single strand of cDNA and then use that single DNA strand as a template for producing double-stranded cDNA. Many retroposons also encode polypeptides other than reverse transcriptase.

Some retroposons have a poly-A tail at the 3′ end of the RNA-like DNA strand, a configuration reminiscent of mRNA molecules (**Fig. 13.26a**). Other retroposons end

igure 13.26 Retroposons: Structure and movement. (a) Some retroposons have a poly-A tail at the end of the RNA-like DNA strand (*top*); ners are flanked on both sides by long terminal repeats (LTRs; *bottom*). (b) Researchers constructed a plasmid bearing a *Ty1* retroposon that contained an ron. When this plasmid was transformed into yeast cells, researchers could isolate new insertions of *Ty1* into yeast genomic DNA. The newly inserted *Ty1* I not have the intron, which implies that transposition involves splicing of a primary transcript to form an intronless mRNA. (c) The reverse-transcriptase-e enzyme synthesizes double-stranded retroposon cDNA in a series of steps. Insertion of this double-stranded cDNA into a new genomic location (*blue*) olves a staggered cleavage of the target site that leaves "sticky ends"; polymerization to fill in the sticky ends produces two copies of the 5 bp target site.

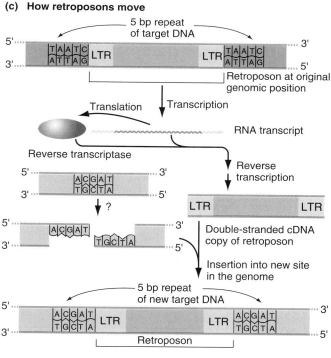

in *long terminal repeats* (*LTR*s): nucleotide sequences repeated in the same orientation at both ends of the element (Fig. 13.26a). The structure of this second type of retroposon is similar to the integrated DNA copies of RNA tumor viruses (known as retroviruses), suggesting that retroviruses evolved from this kind of retroposon, or vice versa. In support of this notion, researchers sometimes find retroposon transcripts enclosed in viruslike particles.

The structural parallels between retroposons, mRNAs, and retroviruses, as well as the fact that retroposons encode a reverse-transcriptase-like enzyme, prompted investigators to ask whether retroposons move around the genome via an RNA intermediate. Experiments in yeast helped confirm that they do. In one study, a copy of the *Ty1* retroposon found on a yeast plasmid contained an intron in one of its genes; after transposition into the yeast chromosome, however, the intron was not there (**Fig. 13.26b**). Because removal of introns occurs only during mRNA processing, researchers concluded that the *Ty1* retroposon passes through an RNA intermediate during transposition.

The mechanisms by which various retroposons move around the genome resemble each other in general outline but differ in detail. **Figure 13.26c** outlines what is known of the process for the better understood LTR-containing retroposons. As the figure illustrates, one outcome of transposition via an RNA intermediate is that the original copy of the retroposon remains in place while the new copy inserts in another location. With this mode of transmission, the number of copies can increase rapidly with time. Human LINEs and SINEs, for example, occur in tens of thousands or even hundreds of thousands of copies within the genome. Other retroposons, however, such as the *copia* elements found in *Drosophila*, do not proliferate so profusely and exist in much more moderate copy numbers of 30–50. Currently unknown mechanisms may account for these differences by regulating the rate of retroposon transcription or by limiting the number of copies through selection at the level of the whole organism.

> Retroposons encode a reverse transcriptase enzyme that copies processed retroposon RNA (without introns) into complementary DNA; this DNA can insert into a new location in the genome. Because movement of retroposons involves an RNA intermediate, the number of copies in the genome can potentially increase rapidly.

Movement of transposon DNA is catalyzed by transposase enzymes

A hallmark of transposons—TEs whose movement does not involve an RNA intermediate—is that their ends are inverted repeats of each other, that is, a sequence of base pairs at one end is present in mirror image at the

other end (**Fig. 13.27a**). The inverted repeat is usuall 10–200 bp long.

DNA between the transposon's inverted repeats com monly contains a gene encoding a transposase, a protei that catalyzes transposition through its recognition those repeats. As Fig. 13.27a illustrates, the steps result ing in transposition include excision of the transposo from its original genomic position and integration into new location. The double-stranded break at the transpo son's excision site is are repaired in different ways in di ferent cases. **Figure 13.27b** shows two of the possibilitie In *Drosophila*, after excision of a transposon known as *P element*, DNA exonucleases first widen the resulting ga and then repair it using either a sister chromatid or homologous chromosome as a template. If the templa contains the *P* element and DNA replication is complete accurate, repair will restore a *P* element to the positic from which it was excised; this will make it appear as the *P* element remained at its original location durir transposition (Fig. 13.27b, *left*). If the template does n contain a *P* element, the transposon will be lost from t original site after transposition (Fig. 13.27b, *right*).

Some strains of *D. melanogaster* are called "P strain because they harbor many copies of the *P* element; " strains" of the same species do not carry the *P* element all. Virtually all commonly used laboratory flies are strains, whereas many flies isolated from natural populatio since 1950 are P strains. Because Thomas Hunt Morgan a coworkers in the early part of the twentieth century isolat the flies that have proliferated into most current laborato strains, these observations suggest that *P* elements did n enter *D. melanogaster* genomes until around 1950. T prevalence of *P* elements in many contemporary natu populations attests to the rapidity with which transposab elements can spread once they enter a species' genome.

Interestingly, the mating of male flies from P strai with females from M strains causes a phenomenon call **hybrid dysgenesis,** which creates a series of defects inclu ing sterility of offspring, mutation, and chromosome brea age. One of the more interesting effects of hybrid dysgene: is to promote the movement of *P* elements to new positio in the genome. Because elevated levels of transposition c foster many kinds of genetic changes (described in the f lowing), some geneticists speculate that hybrid dysgenes like events involving various transposons in different speci had a strong impact on evolution. The *Drosophila* portr (on our website at www.mhhe.com/hartwell4) provides m information on the molecular mechanisms underlying hyb dysgenesis and the ways in which fly geneticists use t phenomenon to introduce new genes into *Drosophila*.

> Transposons encode transposase enzymes that recogniz the inverted repeats at the ends of the transposon DN/ These enzymes then catalyze the movement of the transpo sons without the involvement of an RNA intermediate.

Figure 13.27 Transposons: Structure and movement. (a) Most transposons contain inverted repeats at their ends (*light green; red arrows*) and encode a transposase enzyme that recognizes these inverted repeats. The transposase cuts at the borders between the transposon and adjacent genomic DNA, and it also helps the excised transposon integrate at a new site. **(b)** Transposase-catalyzed integration of *P* elements creates a duplication of 8 bp present at the new target site. A gap remains when transposons are excised from their original position. After exonucleases widen the gap, cells repair the gap using related DNA sequences as templates. Depending on whether the template contains or lacks a *P* element, the transposon will appear to remain or to be excised from its original location.

(a) Transposon structure

(b) How *P* element transposons move

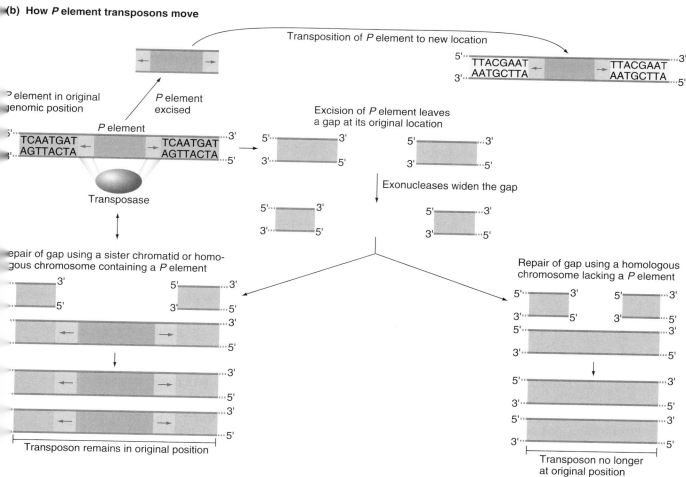

Genomes often contain defective copies of transposable elements

Many copies of TEs sustain deletions either as a result of the transposition process itself (for example, incomplete reverse transcription of a retroposon RNA) or as a result of events following transposition (for example, faulty repair of a site from which a *P* element was earlier excised). If a deletion removes the promoter needed for transcription of a retroposon, that copy of the element cannot generate the RNA intermediate for future movements. If the deletion removes one of the inverted repeats at one end of a transposon, transposase will be unable to catalyze transposition of that element. Such deletions create defective TEs unable to transpose again. Most SINEs and LINEs in the human genome are defective in this way.

Other types of deletions create defective elements that are unable to move on their own, but they can move if nondefective copies of the element elsewhere in the genome supply the deleted function. For example, a deletion inactivating the reverse transcriptase gene in a retroposon or the transposase gene in a transposon would "ground" that copy of the element at one genomic location if it is the only source of the essential enzyme in the genome. If reverse transcriptase or transposase were provided by other copies of the same element in the genome, however, the defective copy could move. Defective TEs that require the activity of nondeleted copies of the same TE for movement are called **nonautonomous elements;** the nondeleted copies that can move by themselves are **autonomous elements.**

> Deleted, defective copies of TEs that can still transpose are called nonautonomous elements. The movement of nonautonomous elements requires that the genome also contains nondefective copies (autonomous elements) that can supply reverse transcriptase or transposase enzymes.

Transposable elements can disrupt genes and alter genomes

Geneticists usually consider TEs to be segments of "selfish DNA" that exist for their own sake. However, the movement of TEs may have profound consequences for the organization and function of the genes and chromosomes of the organisms in which they are maintained.

Gene mutations caused by TEs

Insertion of a TE near or within a gene can affect gene expression and change phenotype. We now know that the wrinkled pea mutation first studied by Mendel resulted from insertion of a TE into the gene for a starch-branching enzyme. In *Drosophila,* a large percentage of spontaneous mutations, including the w^1 mutation discovered by T. H. Morgan in 1910, are caused by insertion of TEs (**Fig. 13.28**). Surprisingly, in light of the large numbers

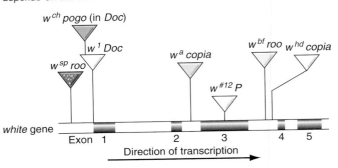

Figure 13.28 TEs can cause mutations on insertion into a gene. Many spontaneous mutations in the *white* gene of *Drosophila* arise from insertions of TEs such as *copia, roo, pogo,* or *Doc.* The resultant eye color phenotype (indicated by the color in the *triangles*) depends on the element involved and where in the *white* gene it inserts.

of LINEs and SINEs in human genomes, only a handful of mutant human phenotypes are known to result from insertion of TEs. Among these is a B-type hemophilia caused by *Alu* insertion into a gene encoding clotting factor IX; recall that *Alu* is the main human SINE.

A TE's effect on a gene depends on what the element is and where it inserts within or near the gene (Fig. 13.28). If an element lands within a protein-coding exon, the additional DNA may shift the reading frame or supply an in-frame stop codon that truncates the polypeptide. If the element falls in an intron, it could diminish the efficiency of splicing. Some of these inefficient splicing events might completely remove the element from the gene's primary transcript; this would still allow some—but less than normal—synthesis of functional polypeptide. TEs that land within exons or introns may also provide a transcription stop signal that prevents transcription of gene sequences downstream of the insertion site. Finally, insertions into regions that regulate transcription, such as promoters, can influence the amount of gene product made in particular tissues at particular times during development. Some transposons insert preferentially into the upstream regulatory regions of genes, and some even prefer specific types of genes, such as tRNA genes.

Chromosomal rearrangements caused by TEs

Retroposons and transposons can trigger spontaneous chromosomal rearrangements other than transpositions several ways. Sometimes, deletion or duplication of chromosomal material adjacent to the transposon occurs as a mistake during the transposition event itself. In another mechanism, if two copies of the same TE occupy near but not identical sites in homologous chromosomes, the two copies of the TE in heterozygotes carrying both types of homolog may pair with each other and cross over (**Fig. 13.29a**). The recombination resulting from this unequal crossover would produce one chromosome deleted for the region between the two TEs and a reciprocal homolog with a tandem duplication of the same region. The duplicati

Figure 13.29 How TEs generate chromosomal rearrangements and relocate genes. (a) If a TE (*pink*) is found in slightly different locations on homologous chromosomes (here on opposite sides of segment *B*), unequal crossing-over produces reciprocal deletions and duplications. **(b)** If two copies of a transposon are nearby on the same chromosome, transposase can recognize the outermost inverted repeats (IRs), creating a composite transposon that allows intervening genes such as *w⁺* (*red*) to jump to new locations.

a) Unequal crossing-over between TEs

b) Two transposons can form a large, composite transposon.

Composite transposon can move to new location.

associated with the *Bar* mutation in *Drosophila* (review Fig. 13.13) probably arose in this way.

Gene relocation due to transposition

When two copies of a transposon occur in nearby but not identical locations on the same chromosome, the inverted repeats of the transposons are positioned such that an inverted version of the sequence at the 5′ end of the copy to the left will exist at the 3′ end of the copy to its right (Fig. 13.29b). If transposase acts on this pair of inverted repeats during transposition, it allows the entire region between them to move as one giant transposon, mobilizing and relocating any genes the region contains. Some composite transposons, such as that pictured in the figure at the beginning of this chapter on p. 429, carry as much as 40 kb of DNA. In prokaryotes, the capacity of two TEs to relocate the intervening genes helps mediate the transfer of drug resistance between different strains or species of bacteria, as will be discussed in Chapter 14.

The movement of TEs has three main genetic consequences: (1) mutation of a gene due to TE insertion within or near the gene; (2) chromosomal rearrangements either caused by unequal crossing-over between copies of the same TE, or generated as a by-product of the transposition process; and (3) relocation of genes between two nearby transposons on the same chromosome.

13.3 Rearrangements and Evolution: A Speculative Comprehensive Example

We saw at the beginning of this chapter that roughly 300 chromosomal rearrangements could reshape the human genome to a form that resembles the mouse genome. Many of these rearrangements are transpositions and translocations that could construct a new chromosome from large blocks of sequences that were on different chromosomes in an ancestral organism. Figure 13.1 provides clear evidence that these reorganizations also include inversions. For example, mouse chromosome 1 contains two adjacent syntenic segments that are found in human chromosome 6, but in a reshuffled order, with one segment turned around 180° with respect to the other segment. Direct DNA sequence comparison of the mouse and human genomes further indicates that deletions, duplications, translocations and transpositions have occurred in one or the other lineage since humans and mice began to diverge from a common ancestor 65 million years ago.

The occurrence of these various rearrangements over evolutionary time suggests two things. First, although most chromosomal variations, including single-base changes and chromosomal rearrangements, are deleterious to an organism or its progeny, a few changes are either neutral or provide an advantage for survival and manage to become fixed in a population. Second, some rearrangements almost certainly contribute to the processes underlying speciation. Although we still do not know enough to understand how any particular rearrangement that distinguishes the human from the mouse genome may have provided a survival advantage or otherwise helped guide speciation, it is nonetheless useful to consider in a general way how chromosomal rearrangements might contribute to evolution.

Deletions A small deletion that moves a coding sequence of one gene next to a promoter or other regulatory element of an adjacent gene may rarely allow expression of a protein at a novel time in development or in a novel tissue. If the new time or place of expression is advantageous to the organism, the deletion might become established in the genome.

Duplications An organism cannot normally tolerate mutations in a gene essential to its survival, but duplication would provide two copies of the gene. If one copy remained intact to perform the essential function, the other would be free to evolve a new function. The genomes of most higher plants and animals, in fact, contain many **gene families**—sets of closely related genes with slightly different functions, that most likely arose from a succession of gene duplication events. In vertebrates, some *multigene families* have hundreds of members.

Inversions Suppose one region of a chromosome has three mutations that together greatly enhance the reproductive fitness of the organism. In heterozygotes where one homolog carries the mutations and the other does not, recombination could undo the beneficial linkage. If, however, the three mutations are part of an inversion, crossover suppression will ensure that they remain together as they spread through the population.

Translocations On the tiny volcanic island of Madeira off the coast of Portugal in the Atlantic Ocean, two populations of the common house mouse (*Mus musculus*) are in the process of becoming separate species because of translocations that have led to reproductive isolation. The mice live in a few narrow valleys separated by steep mountains. Geneticists have found that populations of mice on the two sides of these mountain barriers have very different sets of chromosomes because they have accumulated different sets of Robertsonian translocations (**Fig. 13.30**). Mice in one Madeira population, for example, have a diploid

number ($2n$) of 22 chromosomes, whereas mice in a different population on the island have 24; for most house mice throughout the world, $2n = 40$. (Recall from Fig. 13.19 that Robertsonian translocations can reduce chromosome number if the small chromosome that results from a translocation is lost.)

The hybrid offspring of matings between individuals of these two populations are completely sterile or infertile because chromosomal complements that are so different cannot properly segregate at meiosis. Thus reproductive isolation has reinforced the already established geographical isolation, and the two populations are close to becoming two separate species. What is remarkable about this example of speciation is that mice were introduced into Madeira by Portuguese settlers only in the fifteenth century. This means that the varied and complicated sets of Robertsonian translocations that contributed to speciation became fixed in the different populations in less than 600 years.

Transpositions Movement of TEs may cause novel mutations, a small proportion of which might be selected for because they are advantageous to the organism. TEs can also help generate potentially useful duplications and inversions.

> Rearrangements and transpositions alter DNA sequences and thus provide raw material for evolutionary change. Duplicated genes can diverge by mutation to acquire different functions. The reduced fertility of heterozygotes for inversions and translocations can contribute to reproductive isolation of populations and thus promote speciation.

13.4 Changes in Chromosome Number

We have seen that in peas, *Drosophila*, and humans, normal diploid individuals carry a $2n$ complement of chromosomes, where n is the number of chromosomes in the gametes. All the chromosomes in the haploid gametes of these diploid organisms are different from one another. In this section, we examine two types of departure from chromosomal diploidy found in eukaryotes: (1) aberrations in usually diploid species that generate cells or individuals whose genomes contain one to a few chromosomes more or less than the normal $2n$, for example, $2n + 1$ or $2n - 1$; and (2) species whose genomes contain complete but nondiploid sets of chromosomes, for example, $3n$ or $4n$.

Aneuploidy is the loss or gain of one or more chromosomes

Individuals whose chromosome number is not an exact multiple of the haploid number (n) for the species

Figure 13.30 Rapid chromosomal evolution in house mice on the island of Madeira. (a) Distribution of mouse populations with different sets of Robertsonian translocations (indicated by circles of different colors). **(b)** Karyotypes of female mice from two different populations. The karyotype I at the *top* is from the population shown with *red dots* in part (a); the karyotype II at the *bottom* is from the population indicated by *green dots*. Robertsonian translocations are indicated by numbers separated by a comma (for example, 2,19 is a Robertsonian translocation between chromosomes 2 and 19 of the standard mouse karyotype).

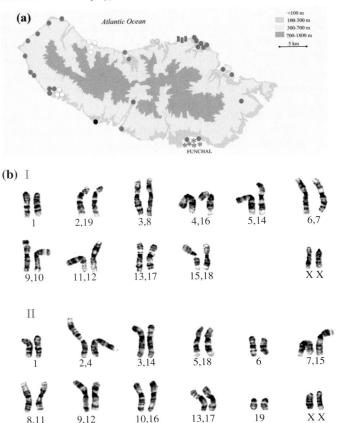

aneuploids (review Table 13.1 on p. 431). Individuals lacking one chromosome from the diploid number ($2n - 1$) are **monosomic,** whereas individuals having one chromosome in addition to the normal diploid set ($2n + 1$) are **trisomic.** Organisms with four copies of a particular chromosome ($2n + 2$) are **tetrasomic.**

Deleterious effects of aneuploidy for autosomes

Monosomy, trisomy, and other forms of aneuploidy create genetic imbalance that is usually deleterious to the organism. In humans, monosomy for any autosome is generally lethal, but medical geneticists have reported a few cases of monosomy for chromosome 21, one of the smallest human chromosomes. Although born with severe multiple abnormalities, these monosomic individuals survived for a short time beyond birth. Similarly, trisomies involving a human autosome are also highly deleterious. Individuals with trisomies for larger chromosomes, such as 1 and 2, are almost always aborted spontaneously early in pregnancy. Trisomy 18 causes Edwards syndrome, and trisomy 13 causes Patau syndrome; both phenotypes include gross developmental abnormalities that result in early death.

The most frequently observed human autosomal trisomy, trisomy 21, results in Down syndrome. As one of the shortest human autosomes, chromosome 21 contains only about 1.5% of the DNA in the human genome. Although there is considerable phenotypic variation among Down syndrome individuals, traits such as mental retardation and skeletal abnormalities are usually associated with the condition. Many Down syndrome babies die in their first year after birth from heart defects and increased susceptibility to infection. We saw earlier (in the discussion of translocations) that some people with Down syndrome have three copies of only part of, rather than the entire, chromosome 21. It is thus probable that genetic imbalance for only a few genes may be a sufficient cause of the condition. Unfortunately, as of late 2008, scientists had not yet been able to identify any of these genes unambiguously with a particular Down syndrome phenotype.

Dosage compensation through X-chromosome inactivation

Although the X chromosome is one of the longest human chromosomes and contains 5% of the DNA in the genome, individuals with X chromosome aneuploidy, such as XXY males, XO females, and XXX females, survive quite well compared with aneuploids for the larger autosomes. The explanation for this tolerance of X chromosome aneuploidy is that X-chromosome inactivation equalizes the expression of most X-linked genes in individuals with different numbers of X chromosomes.

As we saw in Chapter 12, X-chromosome inactivation represses expression of most genes on all but one X chromosome in a cell. As a result, even if the number of X chromosomes varies, the amount of protein generated by most X-linked genes remains constant. Human X-chromosome aneuploidies are nonetheless not without consequence. XXY men have *Klinefelter syndrome,* and XO women have *Turner syndrome.* The aneuploid individuals affected by these syndromes are usually infertile and display skeletal abnormalities, leading in the XXY men to unusually long limbs and in the women XO to unusually short stature.

If X inactivation were 100% effective, we would not expect to see even the relatively minor abnormalities of Klinefelter syndrome, because the number of functional X chromosomes—one—would be the same as in normal individuals. One explanation is that during X inactivation, several genes near the telomere and centromere of the short arm of the human X chromosome escape inactivation and thus remain active. As a result, XXY males make twice the amount of protein encoded by these few genes as XY males (**Fig. 13.31**).

The reverse of X inactivation is *X reactivation;* it occurs in the oogonia, the female germ-line cells that develop into the oocytes that undergo meiosis (review Fig. 4.17 on p. 100). Reactivation of the previously inactivated X chromosomes in the oogonia ensures that every mature ovum (the gamete) receives an active X. If X reactivation did not occur, half of a woman's eggs (those with inactive X chromosomes) would be incapable of supporting development after fertilization. The phenomenon of X reactivation in the oogonia might help explain the infertility of women with Turner syndrome. With X reactivation, oogonia in normal XX females have two functional doses of X chromosome genes; but the corresponding cells in XO Turner women have only one dose of the same genes and may thus undergo defective oogenesis.

Figure 13.31 Why aneuploidy for the X chromosome can have phenotypic consequences. X-chromosome inactivation does not affect all genes on the X chromosome. As a result, in XXY Klinefelter males, a few X chromosome genes are expressed inappropriately at twice their normal level.

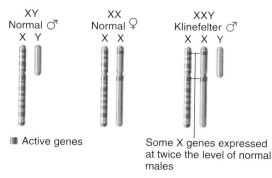

Meiotic nondisjunction

How does aneuploidy arise? Mistakes in chromosome segregation during meiosis produce aneuploids of different types, depending on when the mistakes occur. If homologous chromosomes do not separate (that is, do not disjoin) during the first meiotic division, two of the resulting haploid gametes will carry both homologs, and two will carry neither. Union of these gametes with normal gametes will produce aneuploid zygotes, half monosomic, half trisomic (**Fig. 13.32a,** *left*). By contrast, if meiotic nondisjunction occurs during meiosis II, only two of the four resulting gametes will be aneuploid (Fig. 13.32a, *right*).

Abnormal *n* + 1 gametes resulting from nondisjunction in a cell that is heterozygous for alleles on the nondisjoining chromosome will be heterozygous if the nondisjunction

happens in the first meiotic division, but they will be homozygous if the nondisjunction takes place in the second meiotic division. (We assume here that no recombination has occurred between the heterozygous gene in question and the centromere, as would be the case for genes closely linked to the centromere.) It is possible to use this distinction to determine when a particular nondisjunction occurred (Fig. 13.32a). The nondisjunction events that give rise to Down syndrome, for example, occur much more frequently in mothers (90%) than in fathers (10%). Interestingly, in women, such nondisjunction events occur more often during the first meiotic division (about 75% of the time) than during the second. By contrast, when the nondisjunction event leading to Down syndrome takes place in men, the reverse is true.

Figure 13.32 Aneuploidy is caused by problems in meiotic chromosome segregation. (a) If trisomic progeny inherit two different alleles (*A* and *a*) of a centromere-linked gene from one parent, the nondisjunction occurred in meiosis I (*left*). If the two alleles inherited from one parent are the same (*A* and *A;* or *a* and *a*), the nondisjunction occurred during meiosis II (*right*). **(b)** Because aneuploids carry chromosome that have no homolog with which to pair, aneuploid individuals frequently produce aneuploid progeny.

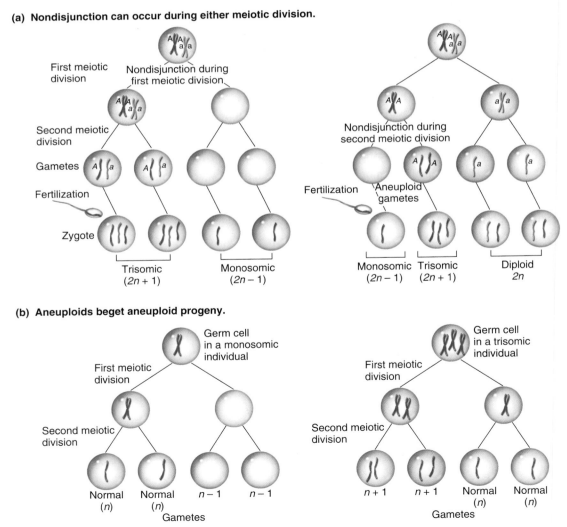

(a) **Nondisjunction can occur during either meiotic division.**

(b) **Aneuploids beget aneuploid progeny.**

Recently obtained data show that many meiotic nondisjunction events in humans result from problems in meiotic recombination. By tracking DNA markers, clinical investigators can establish whether recombination took place anywhere along chromosome 21 during meioses that created $n + 1$ gametes. In approximately one-half of Down syndrome cases caused by nondisjunction during the first meiotic division in the mother (that is, in about 35% of all Down syndrome cases), no recombination occurred between the homologous chromosome 21's in the defective meioses. This result makes sense because chiasmata, the structures associated with crossing-over, hold the maternal and paternal homologous chromosomes together in a bivalent at the metaphase plate of the first meiotic division (review Feature Figure 4.13 on pp. 94–95). In the absence of recombination and thus of chiasmata, there is no mechanism to ensure that the maternal and paternal chromosomes will go to opposite poles at anaphase I. The increase in the frequency of Down syndrome children that is associated with increasing maternal age may therefore reflect a decline in the effectiveness of the mother's machinery for meiotic recombination.

If an aneuploid individual survives and is fertile, the incidence of aneuploidy among his or her offspring will generally be extremely high. This is because half of the gametes produced by meiosis in a monosomic individual lack the chromosome in question, while half of the gametes produced in a trisomic individual have an additional copy of the chromosome (**Fig. 13.32b**).

Mitotic nondisjunction and chromosome loss

As a zygote divides many times to become a fully formed organism, mistakes in chromosome segregation during the mitotic divisions accompanying this development may, in rare instances, augment or diminish the complement of chromosomes in certain cells. In **mitotic nondisjunction,** the failure of two sister chromatids to separate during mitotic anaphase generates reciprocal trisomic and monosomic daughter cells (**Fig. 13.33a**). Other types of mistakes, such as a lagging chromatid not pulled to either spindle pole at mitotic anaphase, result in a **chromosome loss** that produces one monosomic and one diploid daughter cell (**Fig. 13.33b**).

In a multicellular organism, aneuploid cells arising from either mitotic nondisjunction or chromosome loss may survive and undergo further rounds of cell division, producing clones of cells with an abnormal chromosome count. Nondisjunction or chromosome loss occurring

Figure 13.33 Mistakes during mitosis can generate clones of aneuploid cells. Mitotic nondisjunction **(a)** or chromosome loss during mitosis **(b)** can create monosomic or trisomic cells that can divide to produce aneuploid clones. **(c)** If an X chromosome is lost during the first mitotic division of an XX *Drosophila* zygote, one daughter cell will be XX (female), while the other will be XO (male). Such an embryo will grow into a gynandromorph. Here, the zygote was $w^+ \ m^+ \ / \ w \ m$, so the XX half of the fly (*left*) has red eyes and normal wings; loss of the $w^+ \ m^+$ chromosome gives the XO half of the fly (*right*) white eyes (*w*), miniature wings (*m*), and a male-specific sex comb on the front leg.

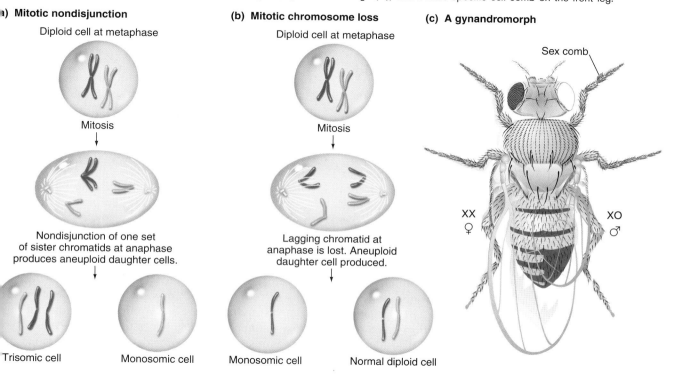

(a) Mitotic nondisjunction

Diploid cell at metaphase

Mitosis

Nondisjunction of one set of sister chromatids at anaphase produces aneuploid daughter cells.

Trisomic cell   Monosomic cell

(b) Mitotic chromosome loss

Diploid cell at metaphase

Mitosis

Lagging chromatid at anaphase is lost. Aneuploid daughter cell produced.

Monosomic cell   Normal diploid cell

(c) A gynandromorph

Sex comb

XX ♀   XO ♂

early in development will generate larger aneuploid clones than the same events occurring later in development. The side-by-side existence of aneuploid and normal tissues results in a **mosaic** organism whose phenotype depends on what tissue bears the aneuploidy, the number of aneuploid cells, and the specific genes on the aneuploid chromosome. Many examples of mosaicism involve the sex chromosomes. If an XX *Drosophila* female loses one of the X chromosomes during the first mitotic division after fertilization, the result is a **gynandromorph** composed of equal parts male and female tissue (**Fig. 13.33c**).

Interestingly, in humans, many Turner syndrome females are mosaics carrying some XX cells and some XO cells. These individuals began their development as XX zygotes, but with the loss of an X chromosome during the embryo's early mitotic divisions, they acquired a clone of XO cells. Similar mosaicism involving the autosomes also occurs. For example, physicians have recorded several cases of mild Down syndrome arising from mosaicism for trisomy 21. In people with Turner or Down mosaicism, the existence of some normal tissue appears to ameliorate the condition, with the individual's phenotype depending on the particular distribution of diploid versus aneuploid cells.

Aneuploidy for autosomes is usually deleterious, but organisms can better tolerate aneuploidy for sex chromosomes because of dosage compensation mechanisms such as X-chromosome inactivation. Rare events of meiotic nondisjunction can produce aneuploid gametes and thus aneuploid organisms. Rare mistakes in mitosis, including mitotic nondisjunction and chromosome loss, can generate a mosaic organism that has cells with different karyotypes.

Some euploid species are not diploid

In contrast to aneuploids, **euploid** cells contain only complete sets of chromosomes. Most euploid species are diploid, but some euploid species are **polyploids** that carry three or more complete sets of chromosomes (see Table 13.1 on p. 431). When speaking of polyploids, geneticists use the symbol x to indicate the **basic chromosome number,** that is, the number of different chromosomes that make up a single complete set. Triploid species, which have three complete sets of chromosomes are then $3x;$ tetraploid species with four complete sets of chromosomes are $4x;$ and so forth. For diploid species, x is identical to n—the number of chromosomes in the gametes—because each gamete contains a single complete set of chromosomes. This identity of $x = n$ does not, however, hold for polyploid species, as the following example illustrates. Commercially grown bread wheat has a total of 42 chromosomes: 6 nearly (but not wholly) identical sets each containing 7 different chromosomes. Bread

wheat is thus a hexaploid with a basic number of $x = 7$ and $6x = 42$. But each triploid gamete has one-half the total number of chromosomes, so $n = 21$. Thus, for bread wheat, x and n are not the same. Another form of euploidy, in addition to polyploidy, exists in **monoploid** (x) organisms, which have only one set of chromosomes.

Monoploidy and polyploidy are rarely observed in animals. Among the few examples of monoploidy are some species of ants and bees in which the males are monoploid, whereas the females are diploid. Males of these species develop *parthenogenetically* from unfertilized eggs. These monoploid males produce gametes through a modified meiosis that in some unknown fashion ensures distribution of all the chromosomes to the same daughter cell during meiosis I; the sister chromatids then separate normally during meiosis II. Polyploidy in animals normally exists only in species with unusual reproductive cycles, such as hermaphroditic earthworms, which carry both male and female reproductive organs, and goldfish, which are parthenogenetically tetraploid species. In *Drosophila,* it is possible, under special circumstances, to produce triploid and tetraploid females, but never males. In humans, polyploidy is always lethal, usually resulting in spontaneous abortion during the first trimester of pregnancy.

Monoploid organisms

Botanists can produce monoploid plants experimentally by special treatment of germ cells from diploid species that have completed meiosis and would normally develop into pollen. (Note that monoploid plants obtained in this manner can also be considered haploid because $x = n.$) The treated cells divide into a mass of tissue known as an *embryoid.* Subsequent exposure to plant hormones enables the embryoid to develop into a plant (**Fig. 13.34a**). Monoploid plants may also arise from rare spontaneous events in a large natural population. Most monoploid plants, no matter how they originate, are infertile. Because the chromosomes have no homologs with which to pair during meiosis I, they are distributed at random to the two spindle poles during this division. Rarely do all chromosomes go to the same pole, and if they do not, the resulting gametes are defective as they lack one or more chromosomes. The greater the number of chromosomes in the genome, the lower the likelihood of producing a gamete containing all of them.

Despite such gamete-generating problems, monoploid plants and tissues are of great value to plant breeders. They make it possible to visualize normally recessive traits directly, without crosses to achieve homozygosity. Plant researchers can also introduce mutations into individual monoploid cells; select for desirable phenotypes such as resistance to herbicides; and use hormone treatments to grow the selected cells into monoploid plants.

Figure 13.34 The creation and use of monoploid plants. (a) Under certain conditions, haploid pollen grains can grow into haploid embryoids. When treated with plant hormones, haploid embryoids grow into monoploid plants. **(b)** Researchers select monoploid cells for recessive traits such as herbicide resistance. They then grow the selected cells into a resistant embryoid, which (with hormone treatment) eventually becomes a mature, resistant monoploid plant. Treatment with colchicine doubles the chromosome number, creating diploid cells that can be grown in culture with hormones to make a homozygous herbicide-resistant diploid plant. **(c)** Colchicine treatment prevents formation of the mitotic spindle and also blocks cytokinesis, generating cells with twice the number of chromosomes. *Blue, red,* and *green* colors denote nonhomologous chromosomes.

(a) How to create a monoploid plant

Diploid plant

1. Haploid pollen grains are treated and plated onto agar.

2. Growth of haploid embryoids

3. Embryoids treated with plant hormones

4. Monoploid plant (usually sterile)

(b) Using monoploid plants to select for herbicide resistance

1. Monoploid plant sensitive to selective agent

2. Cell walls of somatic cells removed; cells exposed to mutagen; plated on agar containing selective agent

3. Cells with resistance mutation grow into resistant embryoids.

4. Resistant monoploid (sterile)

5. Treatment of somatic cells with colchicine

6. Cells become diploid

7. Cells can be grown into diploid homozygous resistant plant (fertile).

(c) Using colchicine to double chromosome numbers

Normal mitosis

n Metaphase   Anaphase   Two daughter cells (n)

Mitosis with colchicine treatment

n No spindle forms   No chromosome movement to poles of cell   One daughter cell ($2n$)

Fig. **13.34b**). They can then convert monoploids of their choice into homozygous diploid plants by treating tissue with *colchicine,* an alkaloid drug obtained from the autumn crocus. By binding to tubulin—the major protein component of the spindle—colchicine prevents formation of the spindle apparatus. In cells without a spindle, the sister chromatids cannot segregate after the centromere splits, so there is often a doubling of the chromosome set following treatment with colchicine (**Fig. 13.34c**). The resulting diploid cells can be grown into diploid plants that will express the desired phenotype and produce fertile gametes.

Figure 13.35 The genetics of triploidy. (a) Production of a triploid ($x = 3$) from fertilization of a monoploid gamete by a diploid gamete. Nonhomologous chromosomes are either *blue* or *red*. **(b)** Meiosis in a triploid produces unbalanced gametes because meiosis I produces two daughter cells with unequal numbers of any one type of chromosome. If x is large, balanced gametes with equal numbers of all the chromosomes are very rare.

(a) Formation of a triploid organism

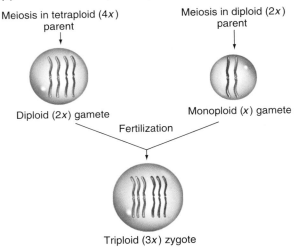

Meiosis in tetraploid ($4x$) parent

Meiosis in diploid ($2x$) parent

Diploid ($2x$) gamete

Monoploid (x) gamete

Fertilization

Triploid ($3x$) zygote

(b) Meiosis in a triploid organism

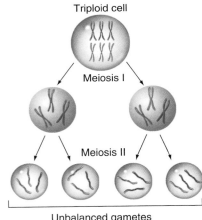

Triploid cell

Meiosis I

Meiosis II

Unbalanced gametes

Triploid organisms

Triploids ($3x$) result from the union of monoploid (x) and diploid ($2x$) gametes (**Fig. 13.35a**). The diploid gametes may be the products of meiosis in tetraploid ($4x$) germ cells, or they may be the products of rare spindle or cytokinesis failures during meiosis in a diploid.

Sexual reproduction in triploid organisms is extremely inefficient because meiosis produces mostly unbalanced gametes. During the first meiotic division in a triploid germ cell, three sets of chromosomes must segregate into two daughter cells; regardless of how the chromosomes align in pairs, there is no way to ensure that the resulting

gametes obtain a complete, balanced x or $2x$ complement of chromosomes. In most cases, at the end of anaphase I, two chromosomes of any one type move to one pole, while the remaining chromosome of the same type moves to the opposite pole. The products of such a meiosis have two copies of some chromosomes and one copy of others (**Fig. 13.35b**). If the number of chromosomes in the basic set is large, the chance of obtaining any balanced gametes at all is remote. Thus, fertilization with gametes from triploid individuals does not produce many viable offspring.

It is possible to propagate some triploid species, such as bananas and watermelons, through asexual reproduction. The fruits of triploid plants are seedless because the unbalanced gametes do not function properly in fertilization or, if fertilization occurs, the resultant zygote is so genetically unbalanced that it cannot develop. Either way, no seeds form. Like triploids, all polyploids with odd numbers of chromosome sets (such as $5x$ or $7x$) are sterile because they cannot reliably produce balanced gametes.

Tetraploidy and speciation

During mitosis, if the chromosomes in a diploid ($2x$) tissue fail to separate after replication, the resulting daughter cells will be tetraploid ($4x$; **Fig. 13.36a**). If such tetraploid cells arise in reproductive tissue, subsequent meioses will produce diploid gametes. Rare unions between diploid gametes produce tetraploid organisms. Self fertilization of a newly created tetraploid organism will produce an entirely new species, because crosses between the tetraploid and the original diploid organism will produce infertile triploids (review Fig. 13.35a). Tetraploids made in this fashion are **autopolyploids,** a kind of polyploid that derives all its chromosome sets from the same species.

Maintenance of a tetraploid species depends on the production of gametes with balanced sets of chromosomes. Most successful tetraploids have evolved mechanisms ensuring that the four copies of each group of homologs pair two by two to form two **bivalents**—pairs of synapsed homologous chromosomes (**Fig. 13.36b**). Because the chromosomes in each bivalent become attached to opposite spindle poles during meiosis I, meiosis regularly produces gametes carrying two complete sets of chromosomes. The mechanism requiring that each chromosome pair with only a single homolog suppresses other pairing possibilities, such as a 3:1, which cannot guarantee equivalent chromosome segregation.

Tetraploids, with four copies of every gene, generate unusual Mendelian ratios. For example, even if there are only two alleles of a gene (say, A and a), five different genotypes are possible: $A\,A\,A\,A$, $A\,A\,A\,a$, $A\,A\,a\,a$, $A\,a\,a\,a$ and $a\,a\,a\,a$. If the phenotype depends on the dosage of A

Figure 13.36 The genetics of tetraploidy. (a) Tetraploids arise from a failure of chromosomes to separate into two daughter cells during mitosis in a diploid. **(b)** In successful tetraploids, the pairing of chromosomes as bivalents generates genetically balanced gametes. **(c)** Gametes produced in an *A A a a* tetraploid heterozygous for two alleles of a centromere-linked gene, with orderly pairing of bivalents. The four chromosomes can pair to form two bivalents in three possible ways. For each pairing scheme, the chromosomes in the two pairs can assort in two different orientations. If all possibilities are equally likely, the expected genotype frequency in a population of gametes will be 1 (*A A*) : 4 (*A a*) : 1 (*a a*).

(a) Generation of tetraploid (4x) cells

Diploid (2x) interphase cell (x = 2)   Mitotic metaphase in 2x cell   Defective mitosis, chromosomes remain in same cell

Tetraploid (4x) cell

(b) Pairing of chromosomes as bivalents

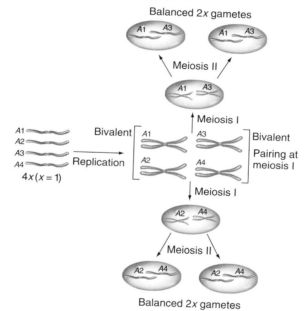

Balanced 2x gametes

A1 A3   A1 A3

Meiosis II

A1 A3

Meiosis I

A1   A3
Bivalent   Bivalent
A2   A4
Pairing at meiosis I

Replication

4x (x = 1)

Meiosis I

A2 A4

Meiosis II

A2 A4   A2 A4

Balanced 2x gametes

(c) Gametes formed by *A A a a* tetraploids

Chromosomes	Pairing			Gametes Produced by Random Spindle Attachment
1. _A_ 2. _A_	1 ↑A 2 ↓A 3 ↑a 4 ↓a	**or**	1 ↑A 2 ↓A 4 ↑a 3 ↓a	1 + 3 A a 1 + 4 A a **or** 2 + 4 A a 2 + 3 A a
3. _a_ 4. _a_	1 ↑A 3 ↓a 2 ↑A 4 ↓a	**or**	1 ↑A 3 ↓a 4 ↑a 2 ↓A	1 + 2 A A 1 + 4 A a **or** 3 + 4 a a 2 + 3 A a
	1 ↑A 4 ↓a 2 ↑A 3 ↓a	**or**	1 ↑A 4 ↓a 3 ↑a 2 ↓A	1 + 2 A A 1 + 3 A a **or** 3 + 4 a a 2 + 4 A a

Total:
2(*A A*) : 8(*A a*) : 2(*a a*)
= 1(*A A*) : 4(*A a*) : 1(*a a*)

then five phenotypes, each corresponding to one of the genotypes, will appear. The segregation of alleles during meiosis in a tetraploid is similarly complex. Consider an *A A a a* heterozygote in which the *A* gene is closely linked to the centromere, and the *A* allele is completely dominant. What are the chances of obtaining progeny with the recessive phenotype, generated by only the *a a a a* genotype? As **Fig. 13.36c** illustrates, if during meiosis I, the four chromosomes carrying the gene align at random in bivalents along the metaphase plate, the expected ratio of gametes is 2 (*A A*) : 8 (*A a*) : 2 (*a a*) = 1 (*A A*) : 4 (*A a*) : 1 (*a a*). The chance of obtaining *a a a a* progeny during self-fertilization is thus 1/6 × 1/6 = 1/36. In other words, because *A* is completely dominant, the ratio of dominant to recessive phenotypes, determined by the ratio of *A - - -* to *a a a a* genotypes is 35:1. The ratios will be different if the gene is not closely linked to the centromere or if the dominance relationship between the alleles is not so simple.

New levels of polyploidy can arise from the doubling of a polyploid genome. Such doubling occurs on rare occasions in nature; it also results from controlled treatment with colchicine or other drugs that disrupt the mitotic spindle. The doubling of a tetraploid genome yields an octaploid (8*x*). These higher-level polyploids created by successive rounds of genome doubling are autopolyploids because all of their chromosomes derive from a single species.

Polyploids in agriculture

Roughly one out of every three known species of flowering plants is a polyploid, and because polyploidy often increases plant size and vigor, many polyploid plants with edible parts have been selected for agricultural cultivation. Most commercially grown alfalfa, coffee, and peanuts are tetraploids (4*x*). MacIntosh apple and Bartlett pear trees that produce giant fruits are also tetraploids. Commercially grown strawberries are octaploids (8*x*) (**Fig. 13.37**). The evolutionary success of polyploid plant species may stem from the fact that polyploidy, like gene

duplication, provides additional copies of genes; while one copy continues to perform the original function, the others can evolve new functions. As you have seen, however, the fertility of polyploid species requires an even number of chromosome sets.

Polyploidy can arise not only from chromosome doubling, but also from crosses between members of two species, even if they have different numbers of chromosomes. Hybrids in which the chromosome sets come from two or more distinct, though related, species are known as **allopolyploids.** In crosses between octaploids and tetraploids, for example, fertilization unites tetraploid and diploid gametes to produce hexaploid progeny. Fertile allopolyploids arise only rarely, under special conditions, because chromosomes from the two species differ in shape, size, and number, so they cannot easily pair with each other. The resulting irregular segregation creates genetically unbalanced gametes such that the hybrid progeny will be sterile. Chromosomal doubling in germ cells, however, can restore fertility by creating a pairing partner for each chromosome. Organisms produced in this manner are termed **amphidiploids** if the two parental species were diploids; they contain two diploid genomes, each one derived from a different parent. As the following illustrations show, it is hard to predict the characteristics of an amphidiploid or other allopolyploids.

A cross between cabbages and radishes, for example, leads to the production of amphidiploids known as *Raphanobrassica*. The gametes of both parental species contain 9 chromosomes; the sterile F₁ hybrids have 18 chromosomes, none of which has a homolog. Chromosome doubling in the germ cells after treatment with colchicine, followed by union of two of the resulting gametes, produces a new species: a fertile *Raphanobrassica* amphidiploid carrying 36 chromosomes—a full complement of 18 (9 pairs) derived from cabbages and a full complement of 18 (9 pairs) derived from radishes. Unfortunately, this amphidiploid has the roots of a cabbage plant and leaves resembling those of a radish, so it is not agriculturally useful.

By contrast, crosses between tetraploid (or hexaploid) wheat and diploid rye have led to the creation of several allopolyploid hybrids with agriculturally desirable traits from both species (**Fig. 13.38**). Some of the hybrids combine the high yields of wheat with rye's ability to adapt to unfavorable environments. Others combine wheat's high level of protein with rye's high level of lysine; wheat protein does not contain very much of this amino acid, an essential ingredient in the human diet. The various hybrids between wheat and rye form a new crop known as *Triticale*. Some triticale strains produce nutritious grains that already appear in breads sold in health food stores. Plant breeders are currently assessing the usefulness of various triticale strains for large-scale agriculture.

Figure 13.37 Many polyploid plants are larger than their diploid counterparts. A comparison of octaploid (*left*) and diploid (*right*) strawberries.

Figure 13.38 Amphidiploids in agriculture. (a) Plant breeders cross wheat with rye to create allopolyploid *Triticale*. Because this strain of wheat is tetraploid, x_1 (the number of chromosomes in the basic wheat set) is one-half n_1 (the number of chromosomes in a wheat gamete). For diploid rye, $n_2 = x_2$. Note that the F_1 hybrid between wheat and rye is sterile because the rye chromosomes have no pairing partners. Doubling of chromosome numbers by colchicine treatment of the F_1 hybrid corrects this problem, allowing regular pairing. **(b)** A comparison of wheat, rye, and *Triticale* grain stalks.

(a)

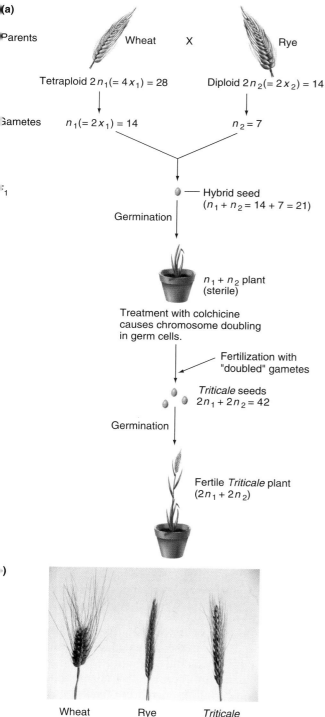

Parents — Wheat X Rye

Tetraploid $2n_1(= 4x_1) = 28$ Diploid $2n_2(= 2x_2) = 14$

Gametes $n_1(= 2x_1) = 14$ $n_2 = 7$

F_1

Hybrid seed
$(n_1 + n_2 = 14 + 7 = 21)$

Germination

$n_1 + n_2$ plant
(sterile)

Treatment with colchicine
causes chromosome doubling
in germ cells.

Fertilization with
"doubled" gametes

Triticale seeds
$2n_1 + 2n_2 = 42$

Germination

Fertile *Triticale* plant
$(2n_1 + 2n_2)$

(b)

Wheat   Rye   *Triticale*

Organisms with odd numbers of chromosome sets are generally infertile because during meiosis, some or all of their chromosomes do not have pairing partners. Chromosome doubling can produce new, fertile polyploid species of plants with even numbers of chromosome sets. In autopolyploids, all the chromosomes originally came from a single ancestral species, but in allopolyploids, the chromosomes were derived from two different ancestral species.

13.5 Emergent Technologies: Beyond the Karyotype

Two main problems occur when searching for chromosomal rearrangements and changes in chromosome number by karyotype analysis. First, it is a tedious procedure that depends on highly trained technicians to identify chromosomal alterations under the microscope. Because of the subjective nature of the analysis, mistakes can reduce the accuracy of results. Second, even in the hands of the best technicians, there is a limit to the viewing resolution. Even under optimal circumstances, it is not possible to detect deletions or duplications of less than 5 Mb in human karyotypes. Human populations no doubt have many chromosomes with as yet undetected smaller deletions or duplications.

To overcome the limitations of karyotype analysis, researchers have developed a microarray-based hybridization protocol that can scan the genome for deletions, duplications, and aneuploidy with much greater resolution, very high accuracy, and much greater throughput and without the need for a subjective determination of the result. The technique is called *comparative genomic hybridization (CGH)* or sometimes *virtual karyotyping.*

The protocol works as follows (**Fig. 13.39**). First, a series of 20,000 BAC clones with DNA inserts averaging 150 kb that collectively represent the entire human genome are spotted onto a microarray. These BAC clones were characterized in the course of the Human Genome Project. Next, genomic DNA from a control sample with a normal genome content is labeled with a yellow fluorescent dye, while the genomic DNA from the test sample is labeled with a red fluorescent dye. The two genomic DNA samples are mixed together in equal amounts, denatured, and applied to the microarray as a probe. After hybridization is complete and unhybridized material is washed away, the fluorescence emission from each microarray dot is analyzed automatically by a machine designed for this task.

If the genomic region probed with a particular BAC clone is present in two copies in the test sample, then the ratio of red to yellow dyes on that dot will be 1 : 1. However, if a particular genomic region is duplicated or deleted from one homolog in the test sample, the ratio of red to yellow will be 1.5 : 1 or 0.5 : 1, respectively. An example of this analysis is shown in Fig. 13.39.

Figure 13.39 Comparative Genomic Hybridization detects duplications, deletions, and aneuploidy. (a) BAC clones representing the human genome are spotted in order onto a microarray. **(b)** The genomic sample to be tested is labeled with one color dye (here, *red*), and the control genome sample is labeled with a second color dye (*yellow*). **(c)** The two samples are mixed together, denatured, and then incubated on the microarray. **(d)** Automated analysis of each spot on the microarray detects the ratio of the two dyed probes that hybridize. *Orange* indicates a 1 : 1 ratio; other colors indicate deletion (0.5 : 1 ratio; *yellow*) or duplication (1.5 : 1 ratio; *red*) of BAC clone sequences in the test sample.

CGH provides a powerful clinical tool to detect any type of aneuploidy or any deletion or duplication of 50 kb or more anywhere in the genome. Clinicians can use it in conjunction with amniocentesis or preimplantation genetic analysis. They can also use CGH to screen tissue biopsies for cancerous cells that have deleted or duplicated regio containing oncogenes or tumor suppressor genes. T technique thus holds great promise for the detection new genes that contribute to the genesis of cancer.

Connections

The detrimental consequences of most changes in chromosome organization and number cause considerable distress in humans (**Table 13.2**). Approximately 4 of every 1000 individuals has an abnormal phenotype associated with aberrant chromosome organization or number. Most of these abnormalities result from either aneuploidy for the X chromosome or trisomy 21. By comparison, abo 10 people per 1000 suffer from an inherited disease caus by a single-gene mutation.

The incidence of chromosomal abnormalities amo humans would be much larger were it not for the fact th many embryos or fetuses with abnormal karyotypes ab

TABLE 13.2	Aneuploidy in the Human Population	
Chromosomes	Syndrome	Frequency at Birth
Autosomes		
Trisomic 21	Down	1/700
Trisomic 13	Patau	1/5000
Trisomic 18	Edwards	1/10,000
Sex chromosomes, females		
XO, monosomic	Turner	1/5000
XXX, trisomic		
XXXX, tetrasomic		1/700
XXXXX, pentasomic		
Sex chromosomes, males		
XYY, trisomic	Normal	1/10,000
XXYY, tetrasomic		
XXXY, tetrasomic		
XXXXY, pentasomic	Klinefelter	1/500
XXXXXY, hexasomic		

About 0.4% of all babies born have a detectable chromosomal abnormality that generates a detrimental phenotype.

spontaneously early in pregnancy. Fully 15% to 20% of recognized pregnancies end with detectable spontaneous abortions; and half of the spontaneously aborted fetuses show chromosomal abnormalities, particularly trisomy, sex chromosome monosomy, and triploidy. These figures almost certainly underestimate the rate of spontaneous abortion caused by abnormal chromosomal variations, because embryos carrying aberrations for larger chromosomes, such as monosomy 2 or trisomy 5, may abort so early that the pregnancy goes unrecognized.

But despite all the negative effects of chromosomal rearrangements and changes in chromosome number, a few departures from normal genome organization survive to become instruments of evolution by natural selection.

As we see in the next chapter, chromosomal rearrangements occur in bacteria as well as in eukaryotic organisms. In bacteria, transposable elements catalyze many of the changes in chromosomal organization. Remarkably, the reshuffling of genes between different DNA molecules in the same cell catalyzes the transfer of genetic information from one bacterial cell to another.

ESSENTIAL CONCEPTS

1. Rearrangements reorganize the DNA sequences within genomes. The results are subject to natural selection, and thus rearrangements serve as instruments of evolution.

2. Deletions remove DNA from a chromosome. Homozygosity for a large deletion is usually lethal, but even heterozygosity for a large deletion can create a deleterious genetic imbalance. Deletions may uncover recessive mutations on the homologous chromosome and are thus useful for gene mapping.

3. Duplications add DNA to a chromosome. The additional copies of genes can be a major source of new genetic functions. Homozygosity or heterozygosity for duplications causes departures from normal gene dosage that are often harmful to the organism. Unequal crossing-over between duplicated regions expands or contracts the number of gene copies and may lead to multigene families.

4. Inversions alter the order, but not the number, of genes on a chromosome. They may produce novel phenotypes by disrupting the activity of genes near the rearrangement breakpoints. Inversion heterozygotes exhibit crossover suppression because progeny formed from recombinant gametes are genetically imbalanced.

5. In reciprocal translocations, parts of two chromosomes trade places without the loss or gain of chromosomal material. Translocations may modify the function of genes at or near the translocation breakpoints. Heterozygosity for translocations in the germ line results in semisterility and pseudolinkage.

6. Transposable elements (TEs) are short, mobile segments of DNA that reshape genomes by generating mutations, causing chromosomal rearrangements, and relocating genes.

7. Aneuploidy, the loss or gain of one or more chromosomes, creates a genetic imbalance. Mistakes in meiosis produce aneuploid gametes, whereas mistakes in mitosis generate aneuploid clones of cells. Autosomal aneuploidy is usually lethal. Sex chromosome aneuploidy is better tolerated because of dosage compensation mechanisms.

8. Euploid organisms contain complete sets of chromosomes. Organisms with three or more sets of chromosomes are polyploids. In autopolyploidy, all chromosome sets are derived from the same species; in allopolyploidy, chromosome sets come from two or more distinct, though related, species.

9. Monoploids (with only a single complete chromosome set) as well as polyploids containing odd numbers of chromosome sets are sterile because the chromosomes cannot pair properly during meiosis I.

10. Polyploids having even numbers of chromosome sets can be fertile if proper chromosome segregation occurs. Amphidiploids, which are allopolyploids produced by chromosome doubling of genomes derived from different diploid parental species, are often fertile and are sometimes useful in agriculture.

On Our Website   www.mhhe.com/hartwell4

Annotated Suggested Readings and Links to Other Websites

- Historical articles describing early investigations on chromosomal rearrangements, transposable elements, and variations in chromosome number

- Recent reviews and research articles on these topics, with special emphasis on the use of transposable elements as tools for molecular genetic analysis

- A database cataloging human chromosomal abnormalities that have been characterized by fluorescence *in situ* hybridization (FISH) and comparative genomic hybridization (CGH)

- Online maps comparing the organization of human chromosomes with those from mice and rats

---

Solved Problems

I. Male *Drosophila* from a true-breeding wild-type stock were irradiated with X-rays and then mated with females from a true-breeding stock carrying the following recessive mutations on the X chromosome: yellow body (*y*), crossveinless wings (*cv*), cut wings (*ct*), singed bristles (*sn*), and miniature wings (*m*). These markers are known to map in the order:

$$y - cv - ct - sn - m$$

Most of the female progeny of this cross were phenotypically wild type, but one female exhibited *ct* and *sn* phenotypes. When this exceptional *ct sn* female was mated with a male from the true-breeding wild-type stock, there were twice as many females as males among the progeny.

a. What is the nature of the X-ray-induced mutation present in the exceptional female?

b. Draw the X chromosomes present in the exceptional *ct sn* female as they would appear during pairing in meiosis.

c. What phenotypic classes would you expect to see among the progeny produced by mating the exceptional *ct sn* female with a normal male from a true-breeding wild-type stock? List males and females separately.

Answer

To answer this problem, you need to think first about the effects of different types of chromosomal mutations in order to deduce the nature of the mutation. Then you can evaluate the consequences of the mutation on inheritance.

a. Two observations indicate that X-rays induced a *deletion mutation*. The fact that two recessive mutations are phenotypically expressed in the exceptional female suggests that a deletion was present on one of her X chromosomes that uncovered the two mutant alleles (*ct* and *sn*) on the other X chromosome. Second, the finding that there were twice as many females as males among the progeny of the exceptional female is also consistent with a deletion mutation. Males who inherit the deletion-bearing X chromosome from their exceptional mother will be inviable (because other essential genes are located in the region that is now deleted), but some who inherit a nondeleted X chromosome will survive. On the other hand, all of the exceptional female's daughters will be viable: Even if they inherit a deleted X chromosome from their mother, they also receive a normal X chromosome from their father. As a result, there are half as many ma progeny as females from the cross of the exceptional female with a wild-type male.

b. During pairing, *the DNA in the normal (nondeleted) X chromosome will loop out* because there is no homologous region in the deletion chromosome. In the simplified drawing of meiosis I that follows, each line represents both chromatids comprising each homolog.

c. *All daughters of the exceptional female will be wild type* because the father contributes wild-type copies of all the genes. Each of the surviving sons must inherit a nondeleted X chromosome from the exceptional female. Some of these X chromosomes are produced from meioses in which no recombination occurred, but other X chromosomes are the products of recombination. *Males can have any of the genotypes listed here and therefore the corresponding phenotypes.* All contain the *ct sn* combination because no recombination between homologs is possible in this deleted region. Some of these genotypes require multiple crossovers during meiosis in the mother and will thus be relatively rare.

y	cv	ct	sn	m
+	+	ct	sn	+
+	cv	ct	sn	m
y	+	ct	sn	+
y	cv	ct	sn	+
+	+	ct	sn	m
+	cv	ct	sn	+
y	+	ct	sn	m

II. One of the X chromosomes in a particular *Drosophila* female had a normal order of genes but carried recessive alleles of the genes for yellow body color (*y*), vermilion eye color (*v*), and forked bristles (*f*), as well as the dominant X-linked Bar eye mutation (*B*). Her other X chromosome carried the wild-type alleles of all four genes, but the region including y^+, v^+, and f^+ (but not B^+) was inverted with respect to the normal order of genes. This female was crossed to a wild-type male in the cross diagrammed here.

The cross produced the following male offspring:

y	v	f	B	48
y^+	v^+	f^+	B^+	45
y	v	f	B^+	11
y^+	v^+	f^+	B	8
y	v^+	f	B	1
y^+	v	f^+	B^+	1

a. Why are there no male offspring with the allele combinations $y\ v\ f^+$, $y^+\ v^+\ f$, $y\ v^+\ f^+$, or $y^+\ v\ f$, (regardless of the allele of the Bar eye gene)?

b. What kinds of crossovers produced the $y\ v\ f\ B^+$ and $v^+\ y^+\ f^+\ B$ offspring? Can you determine any genetic distances from these classes of progeny?

c. What kinds of crossovers produced the $y^+\ v\ f^+\ B^+$ and $y\ v^+\ f\ B$ offspring?

Answer

To answer this question, you need to be able to draw and interpret pairing in inversion heterozygotes. Note that this inversion is paracentric.

a. During meiosis in an inversion heterozygote, a loop of the inverted region is formed when the homologous genes align. In the following simplified drawing, each line represents both chromatids comprising each homolog.

If a single crossover occurs within the inversion loop, a dicentric and an acentric chromosome are formed. Cells containing these types of chromosomes are not viable. The resulting allele combinations from such single crossovers are not recovered. The four phenotypic classes of missing male offspring would be formed by single crossovers between the *y* and *v* or between the *v* and *f* genes in the female inversion heterozygote and therefore are not recovered.

b. *The* y v f B$^+$ *and* y$^+$ v$^+$ f$^+$ B *offspring are the result of single crossover events outside of the inversion loop, between the end of the inversion (just to the right of* f *on the preceding diagram) and the* B *gene.* This region is approximately 16.7 m.u. in length (19 recombinants out of 114 total progeny).

c. *The* y$^+$ v f$^+$ B$^+$ *and* y v$^+$ f B *offspring would result from two crossover events within the inversion loop, one between the y and v genes and the other between the v and f genes. You should note that these could be either two-strand or three-strand double crossovers, but they could not be four-strand double crossovers.*

III. In maize trisomics, $n + 1$ pollen is not viable. If a dominant allele at the *B* locus produces purple color instead of the recessive phenotype bronze and a *B b b* trisomic plant is pollinated by a *B B b* plant, what proportion of the progeny produced will be trisomic and have a bronze phenotype?

Answer

To solve this problem, think about what is needed to produce trisomic bronze progeny: three *b* chromosomes in the zygote. The female parent would have to contribute two *b* alleles, because the $n + 1$ pollen from the male is not viable. What kinds of gametes could be generated by the trisomic *B b b* purple female parent, and in what proportion? To track all the possibilities, rewrite this genotype as $B\ b_1\ b_2$, even though b_1 and b_2 have identical effects on phenotype. In the trisomic female, there are three possible ways the chromosomes carrying these alleles could pair as bivalents during the first meiotic division so that they would segregate to opposite poles: *B* with b_1, *B* with b_2, and b_1 with b_2. In all three cases, the remaining chromosome could move to either pole. To tabulate the possibilities as a branching diagram:

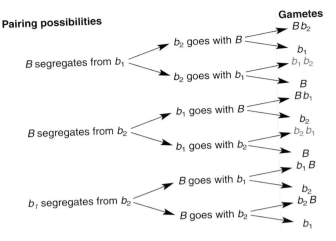

Pairing possibilities

Gametes

B segregates from b_1
- b_2 goes with B → $B b_2$ / b_1
- b_2 goes with b_1 → $b_1 b_2$ / B

B segregates from b_2
- b_1 goes with B → $B b_1$ / b_2
- b_1 goes with b_2 → $b_2 b_1$ / B

b_1 segregates from b_2
- B goes with b_1 → $b_1 B$ / b_2
- B goes with b_2 → $b_2 B$ / b_1

Of the 12 gamete classes produced by these different possible segregations, only the 2 classes written in red contain the two *b* alleles needed to generate the bronze (*b b b*) trisomic zygotes. There is thus a $2/12 = 1/6$ chance of obtaining such gametes.

Although segregation in the *B B b* male parent is equally complicated, remember that males cannot produce viable $n + 1$ pollen. The only surviving gametes would thus be *B* and *b*, in a ratio (2/3 *B* and 1/3 *b*) that must reflect their relative prevalence in the male parent genome. *The probability of obtaining trisomic bronze progeny from this cross is therefore the product of the individual probabilities of the appropriate* b b *gametes from the female parent (1/6) and* b *pollen from the male parent (1/3): 1/6 × 1/3 = 1/18.*

Problems

Vocabulary

1. For each of the terms in the left column, choose the best matching phrase in the right column.

   a. reciprocal translocation

   b. gynandromorph

   c. pericentric

   d. paracentric

   e. euploids

   f. polyploidy

   g. transposition

   h. aneuploids

   1. lacking one or more chromosomes or having one or more extra chromosomes

   2. movement of short DNA elements

   3. having more than two complete sets of chromosomes

   4. exact exchange of parts of two nonhomologous chromosomes

   5. excluding the centromere

   6. including the centromere

   7. having complete sets of chromosomes

   8. mosaic combination of male and female tissue

Section 13.1

2. For each of the following types of chromosomal aberrations, tell: (i) whether an organism heterozygous for the aberration will form any type of loop in the chromosomes during prophase I of meiosis; (ii) whether a chromosomal bridge can be formed during anaphase in a heterozygote, and if so, under what condition; (iii) whether an acentric fragment can be formed during anaphase I in a heterozygote, and if so, under what condition; (iv) whether the aberration can suppress meiotic recombination; and (v) whether the two chromosomal breaks responsible for the aberration occur on the same side or on opposite sides of a single centromere or if the two breaks occur on different chromosomes.

   a. reciprocal translocation

   b. paracentric inversion

   c. small tandem duplication

   d. Robertsonian translocation

   e. pericentric inversion

   f. large deletion

3. In flies that are heterozygous for either a deletion a duplication, there will be a looped-out region in preparation of polytene chromosomes. How cou you distinguish between a deletion or a duplicati using polytene chromosome analysis?

4. For the following types of chromosomal rearrangements, would it theoretically ever be possible to obtain a perfect reversion of the rearrangement? If so, would such revertants be found only rarely, or would they be relatively common?

a. a deletion of a region including five genes
b. a tandem duplication of a region including five genes
c. a pericentric inversion
d. a Robertsonian translocation
e. a mutation caused by a transposable element jumping into a protein-coding exon of a gene

5. Four strains of *Drosophila* were constructed in which one autosome contained recessive mutant alleles of the four genes *rolled eyes, thick legs, straw bristles,* and *apterous wings,* and the homologous autosome contained one of four different deletions (deletions 1–4). The phenotypes of the flies were as follows:

Deletion	Phenotype
1	rolled eyes, straw bristles
2	apterous wings, rolled eyes
3	thick legs, straw bristles
4	apterous wings

Whole-genome DNA was prepared from the flies. The DNA was digested to completion with the restriction enzyme *Bam*HI, run on an agarose gel, and transferred to nitrocellulose filters. The filters were then probed with a 20 kb cloned piece of wild-type genomic DNA obtained by partially digesting the plasmid clone with *Bam*HI (so the ends of the probe were *Bam*HI ends, but the piece was not digested into all the possible *Bam*HI fragments). The results of this whole-genome Southern blot are shown below. Dark bands indicate fragments present twice in the diploid genome; light bands indicate fragments present once in the genome.

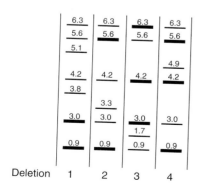

Deletion   1   2   3   4

a. Make a map of the *Bam*HI restriction sites in this 20 kb part of the wild-type *Drosophila* genome, indicating distances in kilobases between adjacent *Bam*HI sites. (*Hint:* The genomic DNA fragments in wild type are 6.3, 5.6, 4.2, 3.0, and 0.9 kb long.)
b. On your map, indicate the locations of the genes.

6. A diploid strain of yeast was made by mating a haploid strain with a genotype w^-, x^-, y^-, and z^- with a haploid strain of opposite mating type that is wild type for these four genes. The diploid strain was phenotypically wild type. Four different X-ray-induced diploid mutants with the following phenotypes were produced from this diploid yeast strain. Assume there is a single new mutation in each strain.

Strain 1	w^-	x^+	y^-	z^+
Strain 2	w^+	x^-	y^-	z^-
Strain 3	w^-	x^+	y^-	z^-
Strain 4	w^-	x^+	y^+	z^+

When these mutant diploid strains of yeast go through meiosis, each ascus is found to contain only two viable haploid spores.

a. What kind of mutations were induced by X-rays to make the listed diploid strains?
b. Why did two spores in each ascus die?
c. Are any of the genes *w, x, y,* or *z* located on the same chromosome?
d. Give the order of the genes that are found on the same chromosome.

7. Human chromosome 1 is a large, metacentric chromosome. A map of a cloned region from near the telomere of chromosome 1 is shown below. Three probe DNAs (A, B, and C) from this region were used for *in situ* hybridization to human mitotic metaphase chromosome squashes made with cells obtained from individuals with various genotypes. The breakpoints of chromosomal rearrangements in this region are indicated on the map. The black bars for deletions (*Del*) 1 and 2 represent DNA that is deleted. The breakpoints of inversions (*Inv*) 1 and 2 not shown in the figure are near but not at the centromere. For each of the following genotypes, draw chromosome 1 as it would appear after *in situ* hybridization. An example is shown in the following figure for hybridization of probe A to the two copies of chromosome 1 in wild type(+/+).

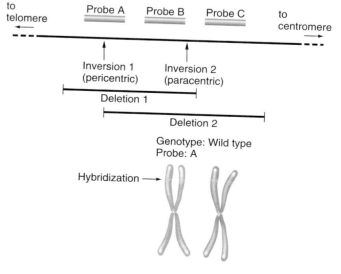

a. genotype: *Del1/Del2;* probe: B
b. genotype: *Del1/Del2;* probe: C
c. genotype: *Del1/ +;* probe: A
d. genotype: *Inv1/+;* probe: A
e. genotype: *Inv2/+;* probe: B
f. genotype: *Inv2/Inv2;* probe: C

8. A series of chromosomal mutations in *Drosophila* were used to map the *javelin* gene, which affects bristle shape, and *henna*, which affects eye pigmentation. Both the *javelin* and *henna* mutations are recessive. A diagram of region 65 of the *Drosophila* polytene chromosomes is shown here.

The chromosomal breakpoints for six chromosome rearrangements are indicated in the following table. (For example, deletion A has one breakpoint between bands A2 and A3 and the other between bands D2 and D3.)

Breakpoints in region 65

Deletions	A	A2–3;	D2–3
	B	C2–3;	E4–F1
	C	D2–3;	F4–5
	D	D4–E1;	F3–4

Breakpoints

Inversions	A	Band 65A6	Band 82A1
	B	Band 65B4	Band 98A3

Flies with a chromosome containing one of these six rearrangements (deletions or inversions) were mated to flies homozygous for both *javelin* and *henna*. The phenotypes of the heterozygous progeny (that is, *rearrangement/javelin, henna*) are shown here.

Phenotypes of F₁ flies

Deletions	A	javelin, henna
	B	henna
	C	wild type
	D	wild type
Inversions	A	javelin
	B	wild type

Using these data, what can you conclude about the cytogenetic location for the *javelin* and *henna* genes?

9. The partially recessive, X-linked z^1 mutation of the *Drosophila* gene *zeste* (*z*) can produce a yellow (zeste) eye color only in flies that have two or more copies of the wild-type *white* (*w*) gene. Using this property, tandem duplications of the w^+ gene called w^{+R} were identified. Males with the genotype $z^1 w^{+R}/Y$ thus have zeste eyes. These males were crossed to females

with the genotype $y z^1 w^{+R} spl/y^+ z^1 w^{+R} spl^+$. (These four genes are closely linked on the X chromosome, in the order given in the genotype, with the centromere to the right of all these genes: y = yellow bodies; y^+ = tan bodies; *spl* = split bristles; spl^+ = normal bristles.) Out of 81,540 male progeny of these females, the following exceptions were found:

Class A	2430 yellow bodies, zeste eyes, wild-type bristles
Class B	2394 tan bodies, zeste eyes, split bristles
Class C	23 yellow bodies, wild-type eyes, wild-type bristles
Class D	22 tan bodies, wild-type eyes, split bristles

a. What were the phenotypes of the remainder of the 81,540 males from the first cross?
b. What events gave rise to progeny of classes A and B?
c. What events gave rise to progeny of classes C and D?
d. On the basis of these experiments, what is the genetic distance between *y* and *spl*?

10. Genes *a* and *b* are 21 m.u. apart when mapped in highly inbred strain 1 of corn and 21 m.u. apart when mapped in highly inbred strain 2. But when the distance is mapped by testcrossing the F₁ progeny of a cross between strains 1 and 2, the two genes are only 1.5 m.u. apart. What arrangement of genes *a* and *b* and any potential rearrangement breakpoints could explain these results?

11. In the following group of figures, the *pink* lines indicate an area of a chromosome that is inverted relative to the normal (*black* line) order of genes. The diploid chromosome constitution of individuals 1–4 is shown Match the individuals with the appropriate statement(s that follow. More than one diagram may correspond to the following statements, and a diagram may be a correct answer for more than one question.

a. An inversion loop would form during meiosis I an in polytene chromosomes.
b. A single crossover involving the inverted region o one chromosome and the homologous region of th other chromosome would yield genetically imbalanced gametes.
c. A single crossover involving the inverted region one chromosome and the homologous region of t other chromosome would yield an acentric fragme
d. A single crossover involving the inverted regi yields four viable gametes.

12. Three strains of *Drosophila* (Bravo, X-ray, and Zorro) are obtained that are homozygous for three variant forms of a particular chromosome. When examined in salivary gland polytene chromosome spreads, all chromosomes have the same number of bands in all three strains. When genetic mapping is performed in the Bravo strain, the following map is obtained (distances in map units).

Bravo and X-ray flies are now mated to form Bravo/X-ray F_1 progeny, and Bravo flies are also mated with Zorro flies to form Bravo/Zorro F_1 progeny. In subsequent crosses, the following genetic distances were found to separate the various genes in the hybrids:

	Bravo/X-ray	Bravo/Zorro
a–b	5.2	5.2
b–c	6.8	0.7
c–d	0.2	<0.1
d–e	<0.1	<0.1
e–f	<0.1	<0.1
f–g	0.65	0.7
g–h	3.2	3.2

a. Make a map showing the relative order of genes *a* through *h* in the X-ray and Zorro strains. Do not show distances between genes.

b. In the original X-ray homozygotes, would the physical distance between genes *c* and *d* be greater than, less than, or approximately equal to the physical distance between these same genes in the original Bravo homozygotes?

c. In the original X-ray homozygotes, would the physical distance between genes *d* and *e* be greater than, less than, or approximately equal to the physical distance between these same genes in the original Bravo homozygotes?

13. Two yeast strains were mated and sporulated (allowed to carry out meiosis). One strain was a haploid with normal chromosomes and the linked genetic markers *ura3* (requires uracil for growth) and *arg9* (requires arginine for growth) surrounding their centromere. The other strain was wild type for the two markers (*URA3* and *ARG9*) but had an inversion in this region of the chromosome as shown here in *pink*:

During meiosis, several different kinds of crossover events could occur. For each of the following events, give the genotype and phenotype of the resulting four haploid spores. Assume that any chromosomal defi-

ciencies are lethal in haploid yeast. Do not consider crossovers between sister chromatids.

a. a single crossover outside the inverted region

b. a single crossover between *URA3* and the centromere

c. a double crossover involving the same two chromatids each time, where one crossover occurs between *URA3* and the centromere and the other occurs between *ARG9* and the centromere

14. Suppose a haploid yeast strain carrying two recessive linked markers *his4* and *leu2* was crossed with a strain that was wild type for *HIS4* and *LEU2* but had an inversion of this region of the chromosome as shown here in *blue*.

Several different kinds of crossover events could occur during meiosis in the resulting diploid. For each of the following events, state the genotype and phenotype of the resulting four haploid spores. Do not consider crossover events between chromatids attached to the same centromere.

a. a single crossover between the markers *HIS4* and *LEU2*

b. a double crossover involving the same chromatids each time, where both crossovers occur between the markers *HIS4* and *LEU2*

c. a single crossover between the centromere and the beginning of the inverted region

15. In the mating between two haploid yeast strains depicted in Problem 14, describe a scenario that would result in a tetratype ascus in which all four spores are viable.

16. During ascus formation in *Neurospora*, any ascospore with a chromosomal deletion dies and appears white in color. How many ascospores of the eight spores in the ascus would be white if the octad came from a cross of a wild-type strain with a strain of the opposite mating type carrying

a. a paracentric inversion, and no crossovers occurred between normal and inverted chromosomes?

b. a pericentric inversion, and a single crossover occurred in the inversion loop?

c. a paracentric inversion, and a single crossover occurred outside the inversion loop?

d. a reciprocal translocation, and an adjacent-1 segregation occurred with no crossovers between translocated chromosomes?

e. a reciprocal translocation, and alternate segregation occurred with no crossovers between translocated chromosomes?

f. a reciprocal translocation, and alternate segregation occurred with one crossover between translocated chromosomes (but not between the translocation breakpoint and the centromere of any chromosome)?

17. In the following figure, *black* and *pink* lines represent nonhomologous chromosomes. Which of the figures matches the descriptions below? More than one diagram may correspond to the statements, and a diagram may be a correct answer for more than one question.

a. gametes produced by a translocation heterozygote
b. gametes that could not be produced by a translocation heterozygote
c. genetically balanced gametes produced by a translocation heterozygote
d. genetically imbalanced gametes that can be produced (at any frequency) by a translocation heterozygote

18. In *Drosophila*, the gene for cinnabar eye color is on chromosome 2, and the gene for scarlet eye color is on chromosome 3. A fly homozygous for both recessive *cinnabar* and *scarlet* alleles (*cn/cn; st/st*) is white-eyed.
a. If male flies (containing chromosomes with the normal gene order) heterozygous for *cn* and *st* alleles are crossed to white-eyed females homozygous for the *cn* and *st* alleles, what are the expected phenotypes and their frequencies in the progeny?
b. One unusual male heterozygous for *cn* and *st* alleles, when crossed to a white-eyed female, produced only wild-type and white-eyed progeny. Explain the likely chromosomal constitution of this male.
c. When the wild-type F_1 females from the cross with the unusual male were backcrossed to normal *cn/cn; st/st* males, the following results were obtained:

wild type	45%
cinnabar	5%
scarlet	5%
white	45%

Diagram a genetic event at metaphase I that could produce the rare cinnabar or scarlet flies among the progeny of the wild-type F_1 females.

19. Semisterility in corn, as seen by unfilled ears with gaps due to abortion of approximately half the ovules, is an indication that the strain is a translocation heterozygote. The chromosomes involved in the translocation can be identified by crossing the translocation heterozygote to a strain homozygous recessive for a gene on the chromosome being tested. The ratio of phenotypic classes produced from crossing semisterile F_1 progeny back to a homozygous recessive plant indicates whether the gene is on one of the chromosomes involved in the translocation. For example, a semisterile strain could be crossed to a strain homozygous for the *yg* mutation on chromosome 9. (The mutant has yellow-green leaves instead of the wild-type green leaves.) The semisterile F_1 progeny would then be backcrossed to the homozygous *yg* mutant.
a. What types of progeny (fertile or semisterile, green or yellow-green) would you predict from the backcross of the F_1 to the homozygous *yg* mutant if the gene was not on one of the two chromosomes involved in the translocation?
b. What types of progeny (fertile or semisterile, green or yellow-green) would you predict from the backcross of the F_1 to the homozygous mutant if the *yg* gene is on one of the two chromosomes involved in the translocation?
c. If the *yg* gene is located on one of the chromosomes involved in the translocation, a few fertile, green progeny and a few semisterile, yellow-green progeny are produced. How could these relatively rare progeny classes arise? What genetic distance could you determine from the frequency of these rare progeny?

20. A proposed biological method for insect control involves the release of insects that could interfere with the fertility of the normal resident insects. One approach is to introduce sterile males to compete with the resident fertile males for matings. A disadvantage of this strategy is that the irradiated sterile males are not very robust and can have problems competing with the fertile males. An alternate approach that is being tried is to release laboratory-reared insects that are homozygous for several translocations. Explain how this strategy will work Be sure to mention which insects will be sterile.

21. A *Drosophila* male is heterozygous for a translocation between an autosome originally bearing the dominant mutation *Lyra* (shortened wings) and the Y chromosome; the other copy of the same autosome is *Lyra^+*. This male is now mated with a true-breeding wild-type female. What kinds of progeny would b obtained, and in what proportions?

22. a. Among the selfed progeny of a semisterile cor plant that is heterozygous for a reciprocal translcation, what ratio do you expect for progeny plant with normal fertility versus those showing sem sterility? In this problem, ignore the rare gamet produced by adjacent-2 segregation.
b. Among the selfed progeny of a particular semiste ile corn plant heterozygous for a reciprocal transl cation, the ratio of fertile to semisterile plants w 1:4. How can you explain this deviation from yo answer to part *a?*

23. Solved problem I on p. 195 of Chapter 6 shows the ge esis of a small chromosomal inversion. Assuming t 11 bp-long primers can be used for the polymerase ch reaction (even though ordinarily longer primers are needed), give the sequences of the two 11 bp primers that could be used to generate the longest PCR product that would indicate the presence of the inversion. (That is, this pair of primers would produce a PCR product from the genomic DNA of individuals with the inversion, but not from wild type genomic DNA.)

24. The figure below portrays human chromosome 21 in blue and chromosome 14 in red. The arrows represent the 5′-to-3′ orientations of various PCR primers. If primer A is one of the two primers used, what is the other primer you could employ to diagnose the presence of a Robertsonian translocation (14q21q) that might be involved in translocation Down syndrome? (That is, which numbered primer, in conjunction with primer A, would produce a PCR product from the genomic DNA of individuals with the translocation, but no PCR product from genomic DNA lacking the translocation?)

Section 13.2

25. The picture at the beginning of this chapter on p. 429 shows a polytene chromosome preparation from a fruit fly heterozygous for a chromosome carrying a very large composite transposon and a wild-type homolog. Suppose you had a probe made from wild-type DNA sequences that span the site into which the transposon is inserted. Diagram the pattern of *in situ* hybridization you would expect on the polytene chromosome preparation shown on p. 429.

26. Explain how transposable elements can cause movement of genes that are not part of the transposable element.

27. In the 1950s, Barbara McClintock found a transposable element in corn she called *Ds* (*Dissociator*). When inserted at a particular location, this element could often cause chromosomal breaks at that site, but these breaks occurred only in the presence of another unlinked genetic element she called *Ac* (*Activator*). She found further that in the presence of *Ac*, *Ds* could jump to other chromosomal locations. At some of these locations (and in the presence of *Ac*), *Ds* would now cause chromosomal breakage at the new position; at other positions, it appeared that *Ds* could cause new mutations that were unstable as shown by their patchy, variegated expression in kernels. Interestingly, the position of the *Ac* element seemed to be very different in various strains of corn. Explain these results in terms of our present-day understanding of transposons.

28. Gerasimova and colleagues in the former Soviet Union characterized a mutation in the *Drosophila* cut wing (*ct*) gene called ct^{MR2}, which is associated with the insertion of a transposable element called *gypsy*. This allele is very unstable: approximately 1 in 100 of the progeny of flies bearing ct^{MR2} show new *ct* variants. Some of these are ct^+ revertants, whereas others appear to be more severe alleles of *ct* with stronger effects on wing shape. When the ct^+ revertants themselves are mated, some of the ct^+ alleles appear to be stable (no new *ct* mutants appear), whereas others are highly unstable (many new mutations appear). What might explain the generation of stable and unstable ct^+ revertants as well as the stronger *ct* mutant alleles?

29. In sequencing a region of the human genome, you have come across a segment of about 200 A nucleotides. You suspect that the sequence preceding the A residues may have been moved here by a transposition event mediated by reverse transcriptase. If the adjacent sequence is in fact a retroposon, you might expect to find other copies in the genome. How could you determine if other copies of this DNA exist in the genome, and whether this DNA is indeed transposable?

30. The *Eco*RI restriction map of the region in which a coat-color gene in mice is located is presented in the following. The left-most *Eco*RI site is arbitrarily labeled 0 and the other distances in kilobases are given relative to this coordinate. Genomic DNA was prepared from one wild-type mouse and 10 mice homozygous for various mutant alleles. This genomic DNA is digested with *Eco*RI, fractionated on agarose gels, and then transferred to nitrocellulose filters. The filters were probed with the radioactive DNA fragment indicated by the *purple* bar, extending from coordinate 2.6 kb to coordinate 14.5. The resultant autoradiogram is shown schematically.

Assume that each of the mutations 1–10 is caused by one and only one of the events on the following list. Which event corresponds to which mutation?

a. a point mutation exactly at coordinate 6.8
b. a point mutation exactly at coordinate 6.9
c. a deletion between coordinates 10.1 and 10.4
d. a deletion between coordinates 6.7 and 7.0
e. insertion of a transposable element at coordinate 6.2

f. an inversion with breakpoints at coordinates 2.2 and 9.9

g. a reciprocal translocation with another chromosome with a breakpoint at coordinate 10.1

h. a reciprocal translocation with another chromosome with a breakpoint at coordinate 2.4

i. a tandem duplication of sequences between coordinates 7.2 and 9.2

j. a tandem duplication of sequences between coordinates 11.3 and 14.3

Section 13.3

31. In the figure at the bottom of the page, the top and bottom lines represent chromosomes 4 and 12 of the yeast *Saccharomyces cerevisiae* (*Scer 4* and *Scer 12*). Numbers refer to specific genes, and the red arrows represent the direction and extent of transcription. The middle line is the sequence of a region from chromosome 1 from a different, but related yeast species called *Klyuyveromyces waltii* (*Kwal 1*), with genes indicated in *light blue*. Homologies (close relationships in DNA sequence) are shown as lines joining chromosomes of the two species.
    a. What is the meaning of the two *K. waltii* genes filled in *dark purple?*
    b. Based on these data, formulate a hypothesis to explain the genesis of the part of the *S. cerevisiae* genome illustrated in the figure.

32. Two possible models have been proposed to explain the potential evolutionary advantage of gene duplications. In the first model, one of the two duplicated copies retains the same function as the ancestral gene, leaving the other copy to diverge through mutation to fulfill a new biochemical function. In the second model, both copies can diverge rapidly from the ancestral gene, so that both can acquire new properties. Considering your answer to Problem 31, and given that both the *S. cerevisiae* and *K. waltii* genomes have been completely sequenced, how could you determine which of these two models better represents the course of evolution?

Section 13.4

33. The number of chromosomes in the somatic cells of several oat varieties (*Avena* species) are: sand oats

(*Avena strigosa*)—14; slender wild oats (*Avena barata*)—28; and cultivated oats (*Avena sativa*)—42.
    a. What is the basic chromosome number (x) in *Avena?*
    b. What is the ploidy for each of the different species?
    c. What is the number of chromosomes in the gametes produced by each of these oat varieties?
    d. What is the n number of chromosomes in each species?

34. Common red clover, *Trifolium pratense,* is a diploid with 14 chromosomes per somatic cell. What would be the somatic chromosome number of
    a. a trisomic variant of this species?
    b. a monosomic variant of this species?
    c. a triploid variant of this species?
    d. an autotetraploid variant?

35. Somatic cells in organisms of a particular diploid plant species normally have 14 chromosomes. The chromosomes in the gametes are numbered from 1 through 7. Rarely, zygotes are formed that contain more or fewer than 14 chromosomes. For each of the zygotes below, (i) state whether the chromosome complement is euploid or aneuploid; (ii) provide terms that describe the individual's genetic makeup as accurately as possible; and (iii) state whether or not the individual will likely develop through the embryonic stages to make an adult plant, and if so, whether or not this plant will be fertile.
    a. 11 22 33 44 5 66 77
    b. 111 22 33 44 555 66 77
    c. 111 222 333 444 555 666 777
    d. 1111 2222 3333 4444 5555 6666 7777

36. Genomes A, B, and C all have basic chromosome numbers (x) of nine. These genomes were originally derived from plant species that had diverged from each other sufficiently far back in the evolutionary past that the chromosomes from one genome can no longer pair with the chromosomes from any other genome. For plants with the following kinds of euploid chromosome complements, (i) state the number of chromosomes in the organism; (ii) provide terms that describe the individual's genetic makeup as accurately as possible; (iii) state whether or not it is likely that this plant will be fertile, and if so, give the number of chromosomes (n) in the gametes.
    a. AABBC
    b. BBBB

c. CCC
d. BBCC
e. ABC
f. AABBCC

37. Fred and Mary have a child with Down syndrome. A probe derived from chromosome 21 was used to identify RFLPs in Fred, Mary, and the child (darker bands indicate signals of twice the intensity). Explain what kind of nondisjunction events must have occurred to produce the child if the child's RFLP pattern looked like that in lanes A, B, C, or D of the following figure:

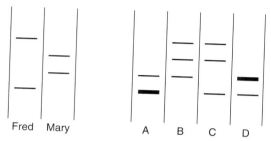

38. *Uniparental disomy* is a rare phenomenon in which only one of the parents of a child with a recessive disorder is a carrier for that trait; the other parent is homozygous normal. By analyzing DNA polymorphisms, it is clear that the child received both mutant alleles from the carrier parent but did not receive any copy of the gene from the other parent.

a. Diagram at least two ways in which uniparental disomy could arise. (*Hint:* These mechanisms all require more than one error in cell division, explaining why uniparental disomy is so rare.) Is there any way to distinguish between these mechanisms to explain any particular case of uniparental disomy?

b. How might the phenomenon of uniparental disomy explain rare cases in which girls are affected with rare X-linked recessive disorders but have unaffected fathers, or other cases in which an X-linked recessive disorder is transmitted from father to son?

c. If you were a human geneticist and believed one of your patients had a disease syndrome caused by uniparental disomy, how could you establish that the cause was not instead mitotic recombination early in the patient's development from a zygote?

39. Human geneticists interested in the effects of abnormalities in chromosome number often karyotype tissue obtained from spontaneous abortions. About 35% of these samples show autosomal trisomies, but only about 3% of the samples display autosomal monosomies. Based on the kinds of errors that can give rise to aneuploidy, would you expect that the frequencies of autosomal trisomy and autosomal monosomy should be more equal? Why or why not? If you think the frequencies should be more equal, how can you explain the large excess of trisomies as opposed to monosomies?

40. Among adults with Turner syndrome, it has been found that a very high proportion are genetic mosaics. These are of two types: In some individuals, the majority of cells are 45, XO, but a minority of cells are 46, XX. In other Turner individuals, the majority of cells are 45, XO, but a minority of cells are 46, XY. Explain how these somatic mosaics could arise.

41. The *Drosophila* chromosome 4 is extremely small; there is virtually no recombination between genes on this chromosome. You have available three differently marked chromosome 4's: one has a recessive allele of the gene *eyeless* (*ey*), causing very small eyes; one has a recessive allele of the *cubitus interruptus* (*ci*) gene, which causes disruptions in the veins on the wings; and the third carries the recessive alleles of both genes. *Drosophila* adults can survive with two or three, but not with one or four, copies of chromosome 4.

a. How could you use these three chromosomes to find *Drosophila* mutants with defective meioses causing an elevated rate of nondisjunction?

b. Would your technique allow you to discriminate nondisjunction occurring during the first meiotic division from nondisjunction occurring during the second meiotic division?

c. What progeny would you expect if a fly recognizably formed from a gamete produced by nondisjunction were testcrossed to a fly homozygous for a chromosome 4 carrying both *ey* and *ci?*

d. Geneticists have isolated so-called *compound 4th chromosomes* in which two entire chromosome 4's are attached to the same centromere. How can such chromosomes be used to identify mutations causing increased meiotic nondisjunction? Are there any advantages relative to the method you described in part *a?*

42. In *Neurospora*, *his2* mutants require the amino acid histidine for growth, and *lys4* mutants require the amino acid lysine. The two genes are on the same arm of the same chromosome, in the order

centromere - *his2* - *lys4*.

A *his2* mutant is mated with a *lys4* mutant. Draw all of the possible ordered asci that could result from meioses in which the following events occurred, accounting for the nutritional requirements for each ascospore. Ascospores without any copy of a chromosome will abort and die, turning white in the process.

a. a single crossover between the centromere and *his2*
b. a single crossover between *his2* and *lys4*
c. nondisjunction during the first meiotic division
d. nondisjunction during the second meiotic division
e. a single crossover between the centromere and *his2*, followed by nondisjunction during the first meiotic division
f. a single crossover between *his2* and *lys4*, followed by nondisjunction during the first meiotic division

43. You have haploid tobacco cells in culture and have made transgenic cells that are resistant to herbicide. What would you do to obtain a diploid cell line that could be used to generate a new fertile herbicide-resistant plant?

44. An allotetraploid species has a genome composed of two ancestral genomes, A and B, each of which have a basic chromosome number (x) of seven. In this species, the two copies of each chromosome of each ancestral genome pair only with each other during meiosis. Resistance to a pathogen that attacks the foliage of the plant is controlled by a dominant allele at the F locus. The recessive alleles F^a and F^b confer sensitivity to the pathogen, but the dominant resistance alleles present in the two genomes have slightly different effects. Plants with at least one F^A allele are resistant to races 1 and 2 of the pathogen regardless of the genotype in the B genome, and plants with at least one F^B allele are resistant to races 1 and 3 of the pathogen regardless of the genotype in the A genome. What proportion of the self-progeny of an $F^A F^a F^B F^b$ plant will be resistant to all three races of the pathogen?

45. Using karyotype analysis, how could you distinguish between autopolyploids and allopolyploids?

46. Chromosomes normally associate during meiosis I as bivalents (a pair of synapsed homologous chromosomes) because chromosome pairing involves the synapsis of the corresponding regions of two homologous chromosomes. However, Fig. 13.21b on p. 445 shows that in a heterozygote for a reciprocal translocation, chromosomes pair as quadrivalents (that is, four chromosomes are associated with each other).

Quadrivalents can form in other ways: For example, in some autotetraploid species, chromosomes can pair as quadrivalents rather than as bivalents.
a. How could quadrivalents actually form in these autotetraploids, given that chromosomal regions synapse in pairs? To answer this question, diagram such a quadrivalent.
b. How can these autotetraploid species generate euploid gametes if the chromosomes pair as quadrivalents rather than bivalents?
c. Could quadrivalents form in an amphidiploid species? Discuss.

Section 13.5

47. The accompanying figure shows a virtual karyotype obtained from a line of tumor cells derived from a human leukemia. The left-to-right direction for each chromosome corresponds to the orientation of that chromosome from the telomere of the small arm to the telomere of the long arm. Every colored dot corresponds to a different short region of the chromosome analyzed by a microarray technique similar to that shown in Fig. 13.39 on p. 464.
a. Do the data indicate the existence of aneuploidy or any chromosomal rearrangements within the genome of the tumor cell?
b. What do you think you would see if you did a virtual karyotype of a cell line derived from normal, nonleukemic cells from the same person?
c. Are there any kinds of chromosomal rearrangements that could not be detected by this virtual karyotyping method?
d. What do these data say about genes that might be responsible for the leukemia?
e. Do these data tell us anything about the dosage of genes needed for the viability of individual cells?

15

Gene Regulation in Prokaryotes

Among the many types of bacteria that thrive in sewage water is the species *Vibrio cholerae,* the cause of the life-threatening diarrheal disease cholera. The last worldwide cholera pandemic began in 1961. Today, cholera is nearly absent from areas of the globe where secure sanitation systems are in place, but epidemics of the disease still devastate human populations in regions where sewage treatment and water purification programs are inadequate or nonexistent.

When a person drinks water contaminated by a disease-causing *V. cholerae,* the bacteria enter the digestive tract. Soon after, the bacteria encounter the "perilous" environment of the stomach, whose acidity kills the majority of them. The bacteria respond to this hostile environment by curtailing production of several proteins they will use later but do not need for passage through the stomach. Only a large initial *V. cholerae* population ensures that at least a small group of cells will survive to exit the stomach and enter the small intestine.

Upon arrival in the small intestine, these survivors come face to face with a thick mucus that coats their ultimate target—the intestinal epithelial cells. To penetrate this protective mucous layer, the *V. cholerae* cells navigate by chemotaxis and by using flagella (**Fig. 15.1**). They also make and secrete proteases that ease their passage by degrading the protein component of mucus.

When the bacteria at last reach their destination, they stop fabricating flagellin (the chief protein component of flagella) and begin production of several virulence proteins, including a pilus (by which they attach to epithelial cells of the small intestine) and a potent toxin that is the actual agent of cholera. Mutant bacteria that produce no toxin do not generate symptoms of disease.

The toxin secreted by cholera bacteria causes chloride ions (Cl$^-$) to leak from the intestinal cells. To reestablish the osmotic balance, these same cells secrete water. Symptoms of this ionic disruption and fluid flow are watery diarrhea and severe dehydration, which can lead to death within a few hours. The most effective life-saving therapy is oral rehydration: administration of an electrolyte solution consisting of glucose, table salt (NaCl), sodium bicarbonate (NaHCO$_3$), and potassium chloride (KCl) dissolved in purified water. Once toxin production is in full swing, antibiotics without oral rehydration are of little benefit.

The story of *V. cholerae* infection illustrates two key aspects of the life of a unicellular prokaryote: direct contact with their external environment and the ability

Lac *repressor protein* (violet) *binds to specific sites in the DNA to turn off expression of the* lac *operon in* E. coli. *Lac* repressor *is a tetramer with two subunits binding to each of two operator sites 93 bases apart, causing a loop* (blue *and* green) *to form in the DNA. This model also shows where the CRP protein* (dark blue) *binds to* lac *DNA.*

CHAPTER OUTLINE

- 15.1 Overview of Prokaryotic Gene Regulation
- 15.2 The Regulation of Gene Transcription
- 15.3 Attenuation of Gene Expression: Termination of Transcription
- 15.4 Global Regulatory Mechanisms
- 15.5 A Comprehensive Example: The Regulation of Virulence Genes in *V. cholerae*

Figure 15.1 *V. cholerae* **bacteria.** *V. cholerae* invade cells in the intestine.

to respond to changes in that environment by changes in gene expression. This coordinated control of gene expression in a bacterial cell is an example of **prokaryotic gene regulation,** the subject of this chapter. Prokaryotes regulate gene expression by activating, increasing, diminishing, or preventing the transcription and translation of specific genes or groups of genes. *V. cholerae* bacteria that have entered a human host respond to rapid changes in external conditions in part by diminishing or abolishing the production of proteins not required for survival (thereby conserving energy and nutrients) and in part by initiating or increasing synthesis of proteins required in new environments (such as proteases when they contact mucus, and toxin and other virulence proteins in the vicinity of intestinal epithelial cells). Bacteria attune their gene-function controls in a coordinated way. These cells do not waste energy making unneeded proteins. In fact, many aspects of prokaryotic gene regulation enable bacterial cells to conserve energy by distinguishing housekeeping proteins that are synthesized continuously from proteins required only in specific situations.

One overarching theme emerges from our discussion. In unicellular organisms like bacteria, the regulatory mechanisms that turn genes on and off in response to environmental conditions enable the organisms to adapt and survive in a constantly changing world.

15.1 Overview of Prokaryotic Gene Regulation

We saw in Chapter 8 that *gene expression* is the production of proteins according to instructions encoded in DNA. During gene expression, the information in DNA is transcribed into RNA, and the RNA message is translated into a string of amino acids.

RNA polymerase is the key enzyme for transcription

To begin the process of gene expression in prokaryotes, RNA polymerase transcribes a gene's DNA into RNA. RNA polymerase participates in all three phases of transcription: initiation, elongation, and termination. Initiation requires a special subunit of RNA polymerase—the sigma (σ) subunit—in addition to the two alpha (α), one beta (β), and one beta prime (β') subunits that make up the core enzyme (**Fig. 15.2**). When bound to the core enzyme, the σ subunit recognizes and binds specific DNA sequences at the promoter; in its free form, σ does not bind DNA because the σ DNA-binding site is obscured by its own C-terminal tail. The full RNA polymerase—core enzyme plus σ—when bound to the promoter, functions as a complex that both initiates transcription by unwinding the DNA and begins polymerization of bases complementary to the DNA template strand.

The switch from initiation to elongation requires the movement of RNA polymerase away from the promoter and the release of σ. Elongation continues until the RNA polymerase encounters a signal in the RNA sequence that triggers termination (Fig. 15.2). Two types of termination signals are found in prokaryotes: Rho dependent and Rho independent. In Rho-dependent termination, a protein factor called Rho (ρ) recognizes a sequence in the newly transcribed mRNA and terminates transcription by binding the RNA and pulling it away from the RNA polymerase enzyme. In Rho-independent termination, a sequence of about 20 bases in the RNA, with a run of 6 or more U at the end, forms a secondary structure, known as a *stem loop,* that serves as a signal for the release of RNA polymerase from the completed RNA.

Translation in prokaryotes begins before transcription ends

Because there is no membrane enclosing the bacterial chromosome, translation of the RNA message into a polypeptide can begin while mRNA is still being transcribed. Ribosomes bind to special initiation sites at the 5' end of the reading RNA frame while transcription of downstream regions of the RNA is still in progress. Signals for the initiation and termination of translation are distinct from signals for the initiation and termination of transcription. Because prokaryotic mRNAs are often polycistronic, that is, contain the information of several genes, ribosomes can initiate translation at several positions along a single mRNA molecule. Fig. 8.25 on pp. 270–271 for a review of how ribosomes, tRNAs, and translation factors mediate the initiation

Figure 15.2 Role of RNA polymerase. The core RNA polymerase enzyme plus sigma factor bind to a promoter sequence to initiate transcription. RNA polymerase then moves along the DNA to elongate the transcript, leaving sigma factor behind. Transcription terminates when rho factor recognizes a sequence on the mRNA or a stem loop (Rho-independent signal) forms in the mRNA, causing release of the enzyme and message.

ongation, and termination phases of mRNA translation
produce a polypeptide that grows from its N terminus
its C terminus, according to instructions embodied in
e sequence of mRNA codons.

egulation of expression can
ccur at many steps

any levels of control determine the amount of a particu-
r polypeptide in a bacterial cell at any one time. Some
ntrols affect an aspect of transcription: the binding of
NA polymerase to the promoter, the shift from transcrip-
onal initiation to elongation, or the release of the mRNA
the termination of transcription. Other controls are post-
nscriptional and determine the stability of the mRNA
er its synthesis, the efficiency with which ribosomes
cognize the various translational initiation sites along the
RNA, or the stability of the polypeptide product.

As we see next, the critical step in the regulation of most
cterial genes is the binding of RNA polymerase to DNA at
promoter. The other potential points of control, while some-
es important in the expression of certain genes, serve
re often to fine-tune the amount of protein produced.

prokaryotes, RNA polymerase is the key enzyme in tran-
cription. Translation begins before transcription ends in
ese organisms, and regulation of gene expression can
ccur at many different points in this process.

15.2 The Regulation
of Gene Transcription

Researchers delineated the principles of gene regulation
in prokaryotes through studies of various metabolic pathways in *Escherichia coli*. In this section, we focus our
attention on regulation of the lactose utilization genes in
E. coli because genetic and molecular experimentation in
this system established a fundamental principle of gene
regulation: The binding of regulatory proteins to DNA
targets controls transcription. The DNA binding of these
regulatory proteins either inhibits or enhances the effectiveness of RNA polymerase in initiating transcription. In our
discussion, we consider the inhibition of RNA polymerase
activity as "negative regulation" and the enhancement of
RNA polymerase activity as "positive regulation."

E. coli's utilization of lactose provides
a model system of gene regulation

Proliferating *E. coli* can use any one of several sugars as
a source of carbon and energy. If given a choice, however,
they prefer glucose. *E. coli* grown in medium containing
both glucose and lactose, for example, will deplete the
glucose before gearing up to utilize lactose.

Lactose is a complex sugar composed of two mono-
saccharides: glucose and galactose. A membrane protein,

lac permease, transports lactose in the medium into the *E. coli* cell. There, the enzyme β-galactosidase splits the lactose into galactose and glucose (**Fig. 15.3**).

Induction of gene expression by lactose

The two proteins lac permease and β-galactosidase, both required for lactose utilization, are present at very low levels in cells grown without lactose. The addition of lactose to the bacterial medium induces a 1000-fold increase in the production of these proteins. The process by which a specific molecule stimulates synthesis of a given protein is known as **induction.** The molecule responsible for stimulating production of the protein is called the **inducer.** In the regulatory system under consideration, lactose modified to a derivative known as allolactose is the inducer of the genes for lactose utilization.

How lactose in the medium induces the simultaneous expression of the proteins required for its utilization was the subject of a major research effort in the 1950s and 1960s—a period some refer to as the golden era of bacterial genetics.

The research advantages of the lactose system in *E. coli*

Lactose utilization in *E. coli* was a wise choice as a model for studying gene expression. The possibility of culturing large numbers of the bacteria made it easy to isolate rare mutants. Once isolated, the mutations responsible for the altered phenotypes could be located by mapping techniques. Another advantage was that the lactose utilization genes are not essential for survival because the bacteria can grow

using glucose as a carbon source. In addition, there is a striking 1000-fold difference between lactose utilization protein levels in induced and uninduced cells. This make it easy to see the difference between the mutant and wild type states, and it also allows the identification of mutant that have partial—not just all-or-none—effects.

The ability to measure levels of expression was critica for many of these experiments. To this end, chemists synthe sized compounds other than lactose, such as *o*-nitropheny galactoside (ONPG), that could be split by β-galactosidas into products that were easy to assay. One product of ONPG splitting has a yellow color, whose intensity is proportiona to the amount of product made and thus reflects the leve of activity of the β-galactosidase enzyme. A spectrophoton eter can easily measure the amount of cleaved yellow prod uct in a sample. Another substrate of the β-galactosidas enzyme that produces a color change upon cleavage X-Gal, whose cleavage produces a blue substance; as w have seen, X-Gal is often used to indicate whether a piec of DNA has been cloned into plasmid vectors containi parts of the β-galactosidase gene (see Fig. 9.7 on p. 300)

The operon theory explains how a single substance can regulate several clustered genes

Jacques Monod (**Fig. 15.4**), a man of diverse interests, wa catalyst for research on the regulation of lactose utilizatio A political activist and a chief of French Resistance ope ations during World War II, he was also a fine musici and esteemed writer on the philosophy of science. Mon led a research effort centered at the Pasteur Institute in Pa where scientists from around the world came to study enzy induction. Results from many genetic studies led Mon and his close collaborator François Jacob to propose a mo of gene regulation known as the **operon theory,** which su gested that a single signal can simultaneously regulate expression of several genes that are clustered together o chromosome and involved in the same process. They reaso that because these genes form a cluster, they can

Figure 15.3 Lactose utilization in an *E. coli* cell. Lactose passes through the membranes of the cell via an opening formed by the lactose permease protein. Inside the cell, β-galactosidase splits lactose into galactose and glucose.

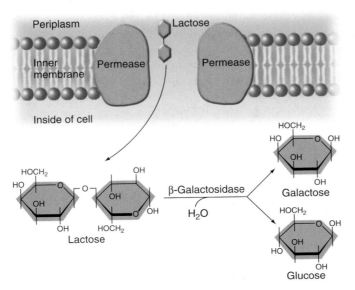

Figure 15.4 Jacques Monod. A key scientist in discovering principles of gene regulation, Jacques Monod was also a talented musician, philosopher, and political activist.

FEATURE FIGURE 15.5

The Lactose Operon in *E. coli*

(a)

(b) Repression

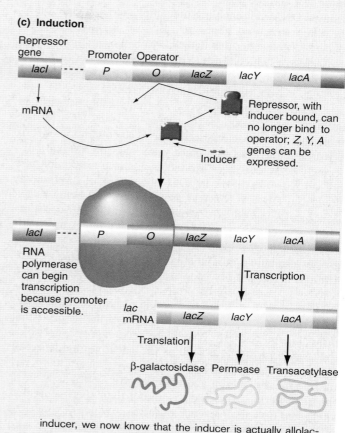

(c) Induction

a. The players

The coordination of various elements enables bacteria to utilize lactose in an energy-efficient way. These elements include

1. A closely linked cluster of three structural genes—*lacZ*, *lacY*, and *lacA*—that encode the enzymes active in splitting lactose into glucose and galactose.
2. A promoter site, from which RNA polymerase initiates transcription of a polycistronic mRNA. The promoter acts in *cis*, affecting the expression of only downstream structural *lac* genes on the same DNA molecule.
3. A *cis*-acting DNA operator site lying very near the *lac* operon promoter on the same DNA molecule.
   The three structural genes together with the promoter and the operator constitute the *lac operon*.
4. A *trans*-acting repressor that can bind to the operator; the repressor is encoded by the *lacI* gene, which is separate from the operon and is unregulated. After synthesis, the repressor diffuses through the cytoplasm and binds with its target.
5. An inducer that prevents the repressor's binding to the operator. Although early experimenters thought lactose was the

inducer, we now know that the inducer is actually allolactose, a molecule derived from and thus related to lactose.

How the Players Interact to Regulate the Lactose-Utilization Genes

b. Repression

In the absence of lactose, the repressor binds to the DNA of the operator, and this binding prevents transcription. The repressor thus serves as a negative regulatory element.

c. Induction

1. When lactose is present, allolactose, an inducer derived from the sugar, binds to the repressor. This binding changes the shape of the repressor, making it unable to bind to the operator.
2. With the release of the repressor from the operator, RNA polymerase gains access to the *lac* operon promoter and initiates transcription of the three lactose-utilization genes into a single polycistronic mRNA.

anscribed together into a single mRNA, and thus anything at regulates the transcription of this mRNA will affect all e genes in the cluster. Clusters of genes regulated in this ay are called **operons.** We first summarize the theory elf and then describe key experiments that influenced

Jacob and Monod's thinking, as well as data that supported components of their theory.

Figure 15.5 presents the players in the theory and how they interact to achieve the coordinate regulation of the genes for lactose utilization. As shown, the structural genes (*lacZ*, *lacY*, and *lacA*) encoding proteins needed for lactose utilization, together with two regulatory elements—the promoter (*P*) and the operator (*O*)—make up the **lac operon:** a single DNA unit enabling the simultaneous regulation of the three structural genes in response to environmental changes. Molecules that interact with the operon include the repressor, which binds to the operon's operator, and the inducer, which when present, binds to the repressor and prevents it from binding to the operator.

Jacob and Monod's theory was remarkable because the authors were working with a very abstract sense of the molecules in the bacterial cell: The Watson-Crick model of DNA structure was only eight years old, mRNA had only recently been identified, and the details of transcription had not yet been described. In 1961, the details of information flow from DNA to RNA to protein were still being established and knowledge of protein roles in the cell was limited. For example, although Monod was a biochemist with a special interest in allostery and its effects, the repressor itself was a purely conceptual construct; at the time of publication, it had not yet been isolated, and it was unknown whether it was RNA or protein. Jacob and Monod thus made a major leap in understanding to propose the theory.

We now know that a key concept of the theory—that proteins bind to DNA to regulate gene expression—holds true for the positive as well as the negative regulation of the *lac* operon. It also applies to many prokaryotic genes outside the *lac* operon and to eukaryotic genes as well. In the next section, we look at some of the experiments that suggested how the presence of lactose induces expression of the genes required for its own utilization.

> In induction, a molecule (inducer) stimulates production of a protein. In *E. coli*, three structural genes, *lacZ*, *lacY*, and *lacA* encode proteins for utilizing lactose; these plus the promoter and operator make up the *lac* operon, a single unit in which the genes are regulated simultaneously. The inducer in this system is allolactose, which forms when lactose is present.

Genetic analysis identifies the roles of the *lac* genes

In proposing the operon theory, Jacob and Monod took enzyme induction, which most of their contemporaries considered a biochemical problem, and used genetic analysis to develop a molecular model explaining how environmental changes could provoke changes in gene activity. On the way to developing the operon theory of gene regulation, Monod and his collaborators isolated many different Lac⁻ mutants, that is, bacterial cells unable to utilize lactose.

Complementation analysis

Using complementation analysis, the researchers showed that the cells' inability to break down lactose resulted from

Figure 15.6 Lactose utilization genes in *E. coli*. Three genes, *lacZ*, *lacY*, and *lacA*, are involved in lactose metabolism in *E. coli*.

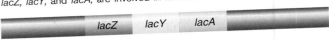

mutations in two genes: *lacZ*, which encodes β-galactosidase, and *lacY*, which encodes lac permease. They also discovered a third *lac* gene, *lacA*, which encodes a transacetylase enzyme that adds an acetyl (CH₃CO) group to lactose and other β-galactoside sugars. Genetic mapping showed that the three genes appear on the bacterial chromosome in a tightly linked cluster, in the order *lacZ-lacY-lacA* (**Fig. 15.6**). Because the *lacA* gene product is not required for the breakdown of lactose, most studies of lactose utilization have focused on *lacZ* and *lacY*.

Evidence for a repressor protein

Mutations in another gene named *lacI* produce **constitutive mutants** that synthesize β-galactosidase and lac permease even in the absence of lactose. *Constitutive mutants* synthesize certain enzymes irrespective of environmental conditions. The existence of these constitutive mutants suggested that *lacI* encodes a negative regulator, or **repressor.** Cells would need such a repressor to prevent expression of *lacY* and *lacZ* in the absence of inducer. In constitutive mutants, however, a mutation in the *lacI* gene generates a defect in the repressor protein that prevents it from carrying out this negative regulatory function.

The historic PaJaMo experiment—named after Arthur Pardee (a third collaborator), Jacob, and Monod—provided further evidence that *lacI* indeed encodes this hypothetical negative regulator of the *lac* genes. Matings in which the chromosomal DNA of a donor cell is transferred into a recipient cell served as the basis of the PaJaMo study. The researchers transferred the *lacI⁺* and *lacZ⁺* alleles into cytoplasm devoid of LacI and LacZ proteins in a medium containing no lactose (**Fig. 15.7**). Shortly after the transfer of the *lacI⁺* and *lacZ⁺* genes, the researchers detected synthesis of β-galactosidase. Within about an hour, the synthesis stopped.

Pardee, Jacob, and Monod interpreted these results as follows. When the donor DNA is first transferred to the recipient, there is no repressor (LacI protein) in the cytoplasm because the recipient cell's chromosome is *lacI⁻*. In the absence of repressor, the *lacY* and *lacZ* genes are expressed. Over time, however, the host cell begins to make the LacI repressor protein from the *lacI⁺* gene introduced by the mating and expression is again repressed.

On the basis of the described experiments, Monod and company proposed that the repressor protein prevents further transcription of *lacY* and *lacZ* by binding to a hypothetical **operator site:** a DNA sequence near the promoter of the lactose-utilization genes. They suggested that the binding of repressor to this operator site blocks the promoter and occurs only when lactose is not present in the medium.

Figure 15.7 The PaJaMo experiment. When DNA carrying *lacI⁺ lacZ⁺* genes was introduced into a *lacI⁻ lacZ⁻* cell, β-galactosidase was synthesized from the introduced *lacZ⁺* gene initially, but as repressor (made from the introduced *lacI⁺* copy of the gene) accumulates, the synthesis of β-galactosidase stops and only residual β-galactosidase is seen. If inducer is added (*dotted line*), the synthesis of β-galactosidase resumes.

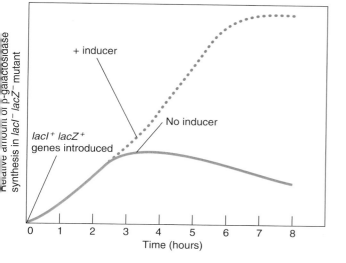

How the inducer acts to trigger enzyme synthesis

In the final step of the PaJaMo experiment, the researchers added the lactose inducer to the culture medium. With this addition, the synthesis of β-galactosidase resumed.

Their interpretation of this result was that the inducer binds to the repressor. This binding changes the shape of the repressor so that it can no longer bind to DNA. When the inducer is removed from the environment, the repressor, free of inducer, reverts to its DNA-bindable shape. Proteins that undergo reversible changes in conformation when bound to another molecule are called **allosteric proteins.** The binding of inducer to repressor causes an allosteric effect that abolishes the repressor's ability to bind the operator. In this sequence of events, the inducer is an effector molecule that releases repression without itself binding to the DNA.

A repressor with an inducer attached cannot bind to the DNA of the operator, whereas a repressor without an inducer attached can. When the repressor is bound to the operator, RNA polymerase cannot recognize the promoter, so transcription does not occur.

The repressor's two distinct binding domains

If the repressor protein interacts with both the operator and the inducer, what outcome would you predict for mutations that disrupt one of these interactions without affecting the other? Biochemical studies showed that the constitutive *lacI⁻* mutations we discussed earlier produce

Figure 15.8 Repressor mutant (*lacI⁻*). In the *lacI⁻* mutants, the repressor cannot bind to the operator site and therefore cannot repress the operon.

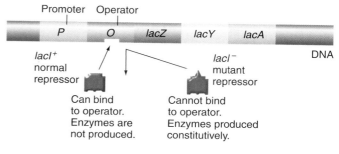

Figure 15.9 Superrepressor mutant *lacIˢ*. In superrepressor mutants, LacIˢ bind to operator but cannot bind inducer, so the repressor cannot be removed from the operator and genes are continually repressed.

defects in the repressor's ability to bind DNA (**Fig. 15.8**). A different type of *lacI* mutant cannot undergo induction. Researchers designate the noninducible mutations as *lacIˢ* or superrepressor (**Fig. 15.9**). The *lacIˢ* mutants, although they cannot bind inducer, can still bind to DNA and repress transcription of the operon.

The mapping of large numbers of these two types of mutations by DNA sequencing has shown that *lacI⁻* missense mutations, which generate proteins incapable of binding DNA, are clustered in the codons that determine the amino (N) terminus of the repressor, while the *lacIˢ* mutations, which generate proteins incapable of binding inducer, cause amino acid alterations throughout much of the rest of the repressor. Subsequent structural analyses of the repressor protein confirmed what these mutational analyses suggest: The repressor protein has at least two separate domains, one that binds to DNA, another that binds inducer (**Fig. 15.10**).

The repressor has separate regions, or domains, correlating with two functions that were uncovered through mutations. Defects in either domain, as well as the presence or absence of the inducer, can affect repressor function.

Operator mutants

While mutations in the DNA-binding domain of the repressor can erase repressor activity, mutations that alter the specific nucleotide sequence of the operator recognized by the repressor can have the same effect (**Fig. 15.11**). When mutations

Figure 15.10 Domains of repressor protein. X-ray crystallographic data enable the construction of a model of repressor structure that shows a region to which operator DNA binds and another region to which inducer binds.

DNA-binding domain

N terminus

Inducer-binding domain

C terminus

Figure 15.11 Operator mutants. The repressor cannot recognize the altered DNA sequence in the *lacO^c* mutant site, so it cannot bind and repress the operon.

Mutant operator (*o^c*)

| P | O | lacZ | lacY | lacA |

Nucleotide sequence is changed

Repressor cannot recognize and bind to operator. *lac* enzymes are synthesized constitutively.

change the nucleotide sequence of the operator, the repressor is unable to recognize and bind to the site; the resulting phenotype is the constitutive synthesis of the lactose-utilization proteins. Researchers have isolated constitutive mutants whose genetic defects map to the *lac* operator site, which is adjacent to the *lacZ* and *lacY* genes. They call the constitutive operator DNA alterations *lacO^c* mutations.

Proteins act in *trans*, DNA sites act in *cis*

How can one distinguish the constitutive operator (*lacO^c*) mutants from the previously described constitutive *lacI^-* mutants, considering that both prevent repression? The answer is found in a *cis/trans* test.

Elements that act in ***trans*** can diffuse through the cytoplasm and act at target DNA sites on any DNA molecule in the cell. Elements that act in ***cis*** can influence only the expression of adjacent genes on the same DNA molecule. Studies of partial diploids in which a second copy of the *lac* genes was introduced helped distinguish mutations in the operator site (*lacO^c*), which act in *cis,* from mutations in *lacI*, which encodes a protein that acts in *trans*.

The partial diploids were made using F′ plasmids that carry a few chromosomal bacterial genes. When F′ *lac* plasmids are present in a bacterium, the cell has two copies of the lactose-utilization genes—one on the plasmid and one on the bacterial chromosome. Using F′ *lac* plasmids, Monod's group could create bacterial strains with diverse combinations of regulatory (*lacO^c* and *lacI*) and structural-gene (*lacZ* and *lacY*) mutations. The phenotype of these partially diploid cells allowed Monod and his collaborators to determine whether particular constitutive mutations were in the genes that produce diffusible, *trans*-acting proteins or at *cis*-acting DNA sites that affect only genes on the same molecule.

In one experiment, Monod and colleagues used a *lacI^- Z^+* bacterial strain that was constitutive for β-galactosidase production because it could not synthesize repressor (**Fig. 15.12**). The introduction of an F′ *lacI^+ Z^-* plasmid into this strain created a partial diploid that was phenotypically wild type with respect to β-galactosidase expression: both repressible in the absence of lactose and inducible in its presence. Its capacity for repression and subsequent induction indicated that *lacI^+* is dominant to *lacI^-* and that the LacI protein produced from the *lacI^+* gene on the plasmid can bind to the operator on the bacterial chromosome. Thus, the product of the *lacI* gene is a *trans*-acting protein able to diffuse inside the cell and bind to any operator site it encounters, regardless of the chromosomal location of the operator.

In a second experiment, introduction of a *lacI^s* plasmid into a *lacI^+* strain of bacteria that was both repressible and inducible created bacteria that were still repressible but were no longer inducible (**Fig. 15.13**). This effect occurred because the mutant LacI^s repressor, while still able to bind to the operator, could no longer bind inducer. The noninducible repressor was dominant to the wild-type repressor because after awhile, the mutant repressor, unable to bind inducer, occupied all the operator sites and blocked all *lac* gene transcription in the cell.

Figure 15.12 *LacI^+* protein acts in *trans*. Repressor protein, made from the *lacI^+* gene on the plasmid, can diffuse in the cytoplasm and bind to the operator on the chromosome as well as the operator on the plasmid.

F′ *lacI^+ o^+ Z^-* plasmid in *lacI^- o^+ Z^+* bacteria

Active repressor protein

lacI^+
o^+
lacZ^-

lacI^- o^+ lacZ^+

Inactive repressor

Bacterial chromosome

Inducible synthesis but *lacZ^-* does not code for active protein.

Plasmid

Inducible synthesis from chromosome copy.

Figure 15.13 *LacI^s* **protein acts in *trans*.** The superrepressor encoded by lacI^s on the plasmid diffuses and binds to operators on both the plasmid and chromosome to repress the *lac* operon even if the inducer is present.

F' *lacI^s Z^-* plasmid in *lacI^+ Z^+* bacteria

lacI^s mutant encodes a diffusible element that acts in *trans*.

In a third set of experiments, the researchers used *lacI^+ lacO^c lacZ^+* bacteria that were constitutive for lactose utilization because the wild-type repressor they produced could not bind to the altered operator (**Fig. 15.14**). Introduction of an F' *lacI^+ lacO^+ lacZ^-* plasmid did not change this state of affairs—the cells remained constitutive for β-galactosidase production. The explanation is that the *lacO^+* operator on the plasmid had no effect on the *lacZ^+* gene on the chromosome DNA because the operator DNA acts only in *cis*. Because it was able to influence gene expression only of the *lacZ^-* gene on its own DNA molecule, the wild-type operator on the plasmid could not override the mutant chromosomal operator to allow repression of genes on the bacterial chromosome.

A general rule derived from these experiments is that if a gene encodes a diffusible element—usually a protein—that can bind to target sites on any DNA molecule in the cell, whichever allele of the gene is dominant will override any other allele of that gene in the cell (and therefore act in *trans*). If a mutation is *cis*-acting, it affects only the

Figure 15.14 *lacO^c* **acts in *cis*.** The *lacO^c* constitutive mutation affects only the operon of which it is a part. In this cell, only the chromosomal copy will be expressed constitutively.

F' *lacI^+ o^+ lacZ^-* plasmid in *lacI^+ o^c lacZ^+* bacteria

Active repressors

lacI^+ o^c lacZ^+

Inducible but *lacZ^-* doesn't code for active protein.

Constitutive synthesis from chromosome copy.

expression of adjacent genes on the same DNA molecule; it does this by altering a DNA site, such as a protein-binding site, rather than by altering a protein-encoding gene.

Coordinate expression of *lac* genes as a single mRNA

Many of the experiments that led to an understanding of the *lac* genes focused on the expression of *lacZ* because the level of β-galactosidase is easy to measure. But Monod and coworkers also showed that the repression and induction of *lacY* and *lacA* occur in tandem with the repression and induction of *lacZ*.

Observation of the coordinate expression of the genes for lactose utilization led to the proposal that the three genes are transcribed as part of the same polycistronic mRNA. Although researchers in the 1960s hypothesized that RNA was the intermediate between DNA and protein, they had not yet demonstrated the existence of such an intermediary for any gene. In the 1970s, however, biochemical studies showed that RNA polymerase initiates transcription of the tightly linked *lac* gene cluster from a single promoter. During transcription, the polymerase produces a single polycistronic mRNA containing the *lac* gene information in the order 5'-*lacZ-lacY-lacA*-3'. As a result, mutations in the promoter (which must be located just upstream of *lacZ*) affect the transcription of all three genes.

The *lacO^c* constitutive operator has the same effect as the *lacI^-* constitutive mutant. These can be distinguished by the *cis/trans* test: An altered protein acts in *trans*, whereas an altered operator sequence acts in *cis*. Experiments in the 1970s verified that the *lac* genes are transcribed as a cluster that has a single promoter.

Operons can also be regulated by positive controls

In focusing on the repression and subsequent induction of the genes for lactose utilization, the Jacob and Monod model did not address a key question: Why do *E. coli* grown in a medium containing both glucose and lactose not produce high levels of lac proteins? We know that glucose is a better carbon source and should be used preferentially, but how is this achieved? If the lactose is present, why doesn't it act as an inducer? Answers to these questions emerged from molecular studies carried out long after publication of the theory. These studies showed that transcriptional initiation at the *lac* operon is a complex event. In addition to the release of repression, initiation depends on a positive regulator protein that assists RNA polymerase in the start-up of transcription. Without this assist, the polymerase does not open up the double helix very efficiently. As we see next, the presence of glucose indirectly blocks the function of this positive regulator.

Positive regulation of the *lac* operon by the CRP protein

Inside bacterial cells, the small nucleotide known as cAMP (cyclic adenosine monophosphate) binds to a protein called cAMP receptor protein, or CRP. The binding of cAMP to CRP enables CRP to bind to DNA in the regulatory region of the *lac* operon, and this DNA binding of CRP increases the ability of RNA polymerase to transcribe the *lac* genes (**Fig. 15.15**). Thus, CRP functions as a positive regulator that enhances the transcriptional activity of RNA polymerase at the *lac* promoter, while cAMP is an effector whose binding to CRP enables CRP to bind to DNA near the promoter and carry out its regulatory function.

Glucose indirectly controls the amount of cAMP in the cell by decreasing the activity of adenyl cyclase, the enzyme that converts ATP into cAMP. Thus, when glucose is present, the level of cAMP remains low; when glucose is absent, cAMP synthesis increases. As a result, when glucose is present in the culture medium, there is little cAMP available to bind to CRP and therefore little induction of the *lac* operon, even if lactose is present in the culture medium. The overall effect of glucose in preventing *lac* gene transcription is known as **catabolite repression,** because the presence of a preferred catabolite (glucose) represses transcription of the operon.

In addition to functioning as a positive regulator of the *lac* operon, the CRP–cAMP complex increases transcription in several other catabolic gene systems, including the *gal* operon (whose protein products help break down the sugar galactose) and the *ara* operon (contributing to the breakdown of the sugar arabinose). As you would expect, these other catabolic operons are also sensitive to the presence of glucose, exhibiting a low level of expression when glucose is present and cAMP is in short supply. Mutations in the gene encoding CRP that alter the DNA-binding domain of the protein reduce transcription of the *lac* and other catabolic operons. The binding of the CRP–cAMP complex is an example of a global regulatory strategy in response to limited glucose in the environment.

Positive regulation of the *araBAD* operon by AraC

There are several instances where positive regulators increase transcription of genes in only one pathway. AraC for example, is a positive regulatory protein specific for all the arabinose genes involved in the breakdown of the sugar arabinose. Three arabinose structural genes, *araB, araA,* and *araD,* appearing on the chromosome in that order, constitute an operon (*araBAD*) that is regulated as a single transcription unit. Like the genes for lactose utilization, the arabinose genes are induced when their substrate (arabinose) is present. Evidence that the AraC protein is a positive regulator of the *araBAD* operon came from studies in which *araC⁻* mutants did not express high levels of these three arabinose genes in either the presence or absence of arabinose (**Fig. 15.16**). The mutations were recessive loss-of-function mutations. When the loss of function of a regulatory protein results in little or no expression of the regulated genes, the protein must be a positive regulator. (By contrast, loss of function of a negative regulator causes constitutive production of the operon's gene products.)

> Positive regulators can be identified when their loss-of-function mutations lead to little or no expression of the regulated genes. Positive regulation occurs when CRP, formed when glucose is absent, enhances the transcriptional activity of RNA polymerase at the *lac* promoter and the promoters of many other catabolic operons. As another example, the AraC protein increases transcription of arabinose genes in the *araBAD* operon.

Figure 15.15 Positive regulation by CRP–cAMP. High-level expression of the *lac* operon requires that a positive regulator, the CRP–cAMP complex, be bound to the promoter region.

Inducer is bound to repressor; doesn't inhibit expression of *lac* genes, but high-level expression also needs positive regulator complex, CRP–cAMP.

Positive regulation: CRP bound to cAMP can bind to DNA and promote expression of *lac* structural genes.

CRP monomers

Catabolite repression: Glucose decreases availability of adenyl cyclase and reduces availability of cAMP for binding to CRP.

Figure 15.16 AraC is a positive regulator. Expression of the arabinose genes in *E. coli* requires the AraC protein to be bound next to the promoter. In an *araC⁻* mutant, the defective protein cannot bind, and RNA polymerase will not transcribe the genes.

(a) *araC⁺*

Arabinose

araO   RNA polymerase

araI₁   araI₂   Promoter   araB   araA   araD

Transcription of *araBAD*

(b) *araC⁻*

araO

Promoter   araB   araA   araD

No transcription of *araBAD*

How DNA-binding proteins control initiation of operon transcription: A summary

In bacteria, the initiation of transcription by RNA polymerase is under the control of regulatory genes whose products bind to specific DNA sequences in the vicinity of the promoter. The binding of negative regulatory proteins prevents the initiation of transcription; the binding of positive regulators assists the initiation of transcription. Regulation of the *lac* operon depends on at least two proteins: the repressor (a negative regulator) and CRP (a positive regulator). Maximum induction of the *lac* operon occurs in media containing lactose but lacking glucose. Under these conditions, the repressor binds inducer and becomes unable to bind to the operator, while CRP complexed with cAMP binds to a site near the promoter to assist RNA polymerase in the initiation of transcription.

Operons that function in the breakdown of other sugars are also under the control of negative and positive regulators. Transcription of the arabinose operon, for example, which is induced in the presence of arabinose, receives a boost from two positive regulators: the CRP–cAMP complex and AraC.

Thus, proteins that bind to DNA affect RNA polymerase's ability to transcribe a gene. The activity of multiple regulators that respond to different cues increases the range of gene regulation.

Further studies reveal more about regulatory proteins and sites

With the development of cloning, DNA sequencing, and techniques for analyzing protein-DNA interactions in the 1970s, researchers increased their ability to isolate specific macromolecules, determine the structure of each molecule, and analyze the interactions between molecules.

In 1966, scientists purified the *lac* repressor protein and determined that it is a tetramer of four identical *lacI*-encoded subunits, with each subunit containing an inducer-binding domain as well as a domain that recognizes and binds to DNA. (Note that we use the term "domains" for the functional parts of proteins but the term "sites" for the DNA sequences with which a protein's DNA-binding domain interacts.)

A radioactively labeled repressor protein and a bacterial virus DNA that contained the *lac* operon were used to show that the repressor binds to operator DNA. When researchers combined the labeled protein and viral DNA and centrifuged the mixture in a glycerol gradient, the radioactive protein cosedimented with the DNA (**Fig. 15.17**). If the viral DNA contained a *lac* operon that had a *lacO^c* mutation, the protein did not cosediment with the DNA, because it could not bind to the altered operator site. Subsequent sequence analysis of the isolated DNA revealed that the *lac* operator

Figure 15.17 The *lac* repressor binds to operator DNA. A radioactive tag is attached to the *lac* repressor protein so it can be followed in the experiment. **(a)** When repressor protein from *lacI^+* cells was purified and mixed with DNA containing the *lac* operator (on bacterial virus DNA), the protein cosedimented with the DNA. **(b)** When wild-type repressor was mixed with DNA containing a mutant operator site, no radioactivity sedimented with the DNA.

is about 26 bp in length, and it includes the first nucleotides used as a template for the mRNA.

Helix-turn-helix proteins

We can predict a protein's secondary structures—such as α helices and β sheets—by comparing the amino acid sequence of a newly isolated protein with sequences of proteins whose secondary structures have already been determined by X-ray crystallography. Several of the polypeptides that make up repressor proteins, including the subunits of the *lac* repressor, have the identifiable feature of two α-helical regions separated by a turn in the protein structure. This helix-turn-helix (HTH) motif in the protein fits well into the major groove of the DNA. One of the α helices in an HTH carries amino acids that recognize and interact with a specific DNA sequence of nucleotides; thus, each HTH has a specificity for DNA binding based on its sequence of amino acids (**Fig. 15.18**).

To examine specificity of protein recognition, scientists used cloned DNA to construct made-to-order mutations in the gene encoding the repressor of a bacterial virus known as 434. The 434 repressor binds to DNA of the 434 viral DNA that has integrated into the bacterial genome and prevents transcription and production of viral particles. After predicting that a region of the α helix of the 434 repressor recognizes the DNA of its specific operator site, researchers altered the DNA sequence of the gene

Figure 15.18 DNA recognition sequences by helix-turn-helix motif. A protein motif that has the shape of a helix-turn-helix (*helixes shown here inside a cylindrical shape*) fits into the major groove of the DNA helix. Specific amino acids within the helical region of the protein recognize a particular base sequence in the DNA.

Recognition helix

region encoding this α helix so that it now encoded most of the amino acids in the corresponding α helix of the repressor for another bacterial virus P22 (**Fig. 15.19**). The resulting hybrid 434-P22 repressor protein, encoded by the altered gene, contained a P22 α helix that recognized the P22 operator *in vivo*. Binding of the hybrid repressor to the P22 prophage DNA operator region that had integrated into the bacterial host genome shut down transcription of most P22 viral proteins and prevented subsequent infection by the P22 virus. This experiment showed that specific amino acids in this α helix determine the binding specificity of the repressor protein. The P22-like α helix in the hybrid protein is sufficient to convert the binding specificity of the 434 repressor to that of the P22 repressor.

The HTH motif is found in hundreds of DNA-binding proteins. Surprisingly, more than 20 different DNA-binding proteins in bacteria are very similar to the LacI repressor, not only in the HTH DNA-binding domain but throughout much of the protein. This group of repressors is known as the LacI repressor family of proteins. Their structural simi-

larity suggests that they evolved from a common ancestral gene whose duplication and divergence produced a family of transcriptional repressor proteins with similar overall structures but unique recognition regions. The uniqueness of their DNA-recognition regions means that they interact with different operators to regulate different groups of genes.

Rotational symmetry of binding sites

In the 1970s, geneticists studying gene regulation developed new *in vitro* techniques to determine where regulatory proteins bind to the DNA. Purified proteins that bind to fragments of DNA protect the region to which they bind from digestion by enzymes such as DNase that break the phosphodiester bonds between nucleotides. If a sample of DNA, labeled at one end of one strand and bound by a purified protein, is partially digested with DNase I, the enzyme will cleave phosphodiester bonds in at least some DNA molecules in the sample, except for those phosphodiester bonds that are in regions protected by the bound protein. Gel electrophoresis of the DNA and autoradiography reveals bands at positions corresponding to the cleavage between each base, except in the region where bound protein protected the DNA. Portions of the gel without bands are thus "footprints," indicating the nucleotides of the DNA fragment that were protected by the DNA-binding protein (**Fig. 15.20**).

Identified in this way, many of the DNA sequences to which a negative or positive regulator protein bind exhibit rotational symmetry; that is, their two DNA strands have an almost identical sequence when read in the 5'-to-3' direction on both strands (these sequences are usually not perfect palindromes). An example of such symmetry is in the *lac* operon's CRP-binding site whose sequence is

$$5'\ \text{TGTGAGTTAGCTCACA}\ 3'$$

$$3'\ \text{ACACTCAATCGAGTGT}\ 5'$$

Figure 15.19 Changing amino acids in recognition sequence. The amino acids inside the recognition helix for phages 434 and P22 and for the hybrid 434-P22 repressor. The amino acids shown in *red* in the hybrid repressor helix section are ones that were modified to be like those of the P22 repressor.

Figure 15.20 DNase footprint shows where proteins bind. DNase footprint establishes the region to which a protein binds. A partial digestion with DNase I produces a series of fragments. If a protein is bound to DNA, DNase cannot digest at sites covered by the protein. Gel electrophoresis of digested products shows which products were not generated and indicates where the protein binds.

Multiple subunits in regulatory proteins

Most regulatory proteins that bind to DNA exist as oligomers composed of two to four polypeptide subunits. The regulatory proteins, which are present in very low numbers in the cell, gain an advantage from this multimeric form. Because each polypeptide subunit of an oligomer has a DNA-binding domain, an assembled oligomer has multiple DNA-binding domains. If the sites to which an oligomeric protein can bind are clustered in a gene's regulatory region, many contacts can be established between the protein and the regulatory region. By increasing the stability of protein-DNA interactions, these multiple binding domains collectively produce the strength of binding necessary to maintain repression or activate transcription.

Many regulatory proteins contain helix-turn-helix (HTH) motifs that allow them to fit into the major groove on DNA, where one of the helixes can recognize a nucleotide sequence. Often these sequences exhibit a symmetry when read in either direction. Most regulatory proteins are also oligomeric, so that the assembled oligomer has multiple binding domains, allowing many contacts.

CRP and *lac* repressor binding

The CRP protein binds to DNA as a dimer at a sequence with rotational symmetry, with one monomer of CRP binding to each side of the sequence (**Fig. 15.21**). Thus, CRP-binding sites (such as the site in the *lac* operon whose sequence was just shown) actually consist of two recognition sequences, each able to bind one subunit of the CRP dimer.

The *lac* repressor exists as a tetramer with each of its four subunits containing a DNA-binding HTH motif. This tetramer binds to two operators located far apart on the DNA, with each operator containing two recognition sequences. The binding of the tetrameric repressor to the two operators causes a loop of DNA to form between the two operator sites (**Fig. 15.22**); formation of the

Figure 15.21 CRP–cAMP dimer. CRP–cAMP binds as a dimer to a regulatory region.

Figure 15.22 *lac* repressor tetramer binds to two sites. The *lac* repressor is a tetramer. For simplicity we previously showed a single repressor object binding to one operator site, but in reality, there are two identical LacI subunits that bind to each operator site. Two of the subunits bind to the sequence in one operator site (O_1), and the other two subunits bind to a second operator (either O_2 or O_3).

O_2 or O_3

O_1

loop, in turn, facilitates the two-position binding. There are actually three operator sites in the *lac* operon to which the repressor can bind: O_1 (the site originally identified by *lacO^c* mutations), O_2, and O_3. Site O_1 has the strongest binding affinity for the repressor, and two subunits of the tetramer always bind at this site. The other two subunits bind at either O_2 or O_3. The distance between operator sites—multiples of 10 bases—allows repressor binding to the same side of the helix and thus formation of the loop.

Mutations in *either* O_2 *or* O_3 have very little effect on repression. By contrast, mutations in *both* O_2 *and* O_3 make repression 50 times less effective. The conclusion is that for maximal repression, all four of the repressor's subunits must bind DNA simultaneously. Binding at four recognition sequences (in two operator sites) increases the stability of the protein-DNA interactions. In fact, the DNA binding of the *lac* repressor is so efficient that only 10 repressor tetramers per cell are sufficient to maintain repression.

DNA looping and the mechanism of AraC action

Looping first came to light in work on AraC, the regulatory protein that helps control the arabinose operon described previously. AraC functions as a dimer. As we have seen, in the presence of the inducer arabinose, AraC is a positive regulator that helps initiate transcription of the *araBAD* operon. Unexpectedly, in the absence of arabinose, AraC acts as a repressor. In this capacity, the AraC dimer binds to two sites—*araO* and *araI*—that are 194 nucleotide pairs apart (**Fig. 15.23**). In one set of experiments analyzing the binding to two sites with concomitant looping of DNA, researchers altered the distance between *araO* and *araI* by inserting several base pairs. The introduction of 11 or 31 bp—alterations that are close to integral changes in the number of turns of the double helix (a full turn of the helix = 10.5 bp)—had little effect on repression. The introduction of 5, 15, or 24 bp, however, noticeably reduced repression. These results suggest that the orientation of the binding sites

Figure 15.23 AraC acts as both a repressor and an activator. The AraC protein can bind to sites *araI₁*, *araI₂*, and *araO*. **(a)** When no arabinose is present, the binding of AraC to *araO* and the *araI₁* sites causes looping of the DNA and prevents RNA polymerase from transcribing the genes. **(b)** When arabinose (inducer) is present, AraC binds to *araI₁* and *araI₂* but not to *araO*. RNA polymerase interacts with AraC at the *araI* sites and transcribes the genes.

(a) No arabinose present

AraC dimer binding at both *araO* and *araI* sites. No *araBAD* genes are transcribed.

araO

Ara C

Ara C

araI₁ *araI₂* Promoter *araB* *araA* *araD*

araI

(b) Arabinose present

Arabinose

araO

RNA polymerase

Ara C   Ara C

araI₁ *araI₂* Promoter *araB* *araA* *araD*

is a significant variable; only when two sites have an orientation that puts them on the same side of the helix can a dimer bind simultaneously to both and cause formation of a DNA loop.

What enables the AraC dimer to function as both an activator and a repressor? The answer most likely involves allostery and AraC's different binding affinities for recognition sequences at *araI* and *araO*. The *araI* site contains two recognition sequences (*araI₁* and *araI₂*) to which AraC can bind; the *araO* site contains one recognition sequence. The AraC dimer is an allosteric protein whose structure changes with the binding of inducer (arabinose). One hypothesis of how this allosteric change alters function is that in the absence of arabinose, the size and shape of the protein unbound to inducer allow the AraC dimer to bind to two recognition sequences—*araO* and one of the two sites within *araI*—at the same time; this double binding prevents AraC from binding in a way that would enable it to assist RNA polymerase in the initiation of transcription. When arabinose is present, binding to the inducer changes the shape of the AraC dimer. In this inducer-bound conformation, the regulatory molecule does not bind to *araI* and *araO* at the same time; instead, the inducer–dimer complex binds exclusively to recognition sequences in *araI* (Fig. 15.16b). When bound to DNA at only this site, AraC's positive regulatory domain is free to interact with RNA polymerase and increase transcription.

Figure 15.24 Regulatory protein binding sites overlap. The *lac* repressor bound to the operator prevents RNA polymerase from binding. The binding sites for RNA polymerase and repressor (determined by DNase digestion experiments) show that there is overlap between the two sites.

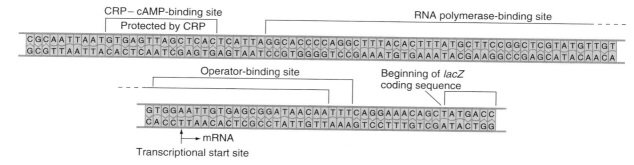

Regulatory proteins and RNA polymerase

Many negative regulators, such as the *lac* repressor, prevent initiation by blocking the functional binding of RNA polymerase. For example, the O_1 operator site to which the *lac* repressor tightly binds consists of 27 nucleotides centered 11 bp downstream from the transcriptional start site. The operator thus includes part of the region where RNA polymerase has to bind to initiate transcription (**Fig. 15.24**). When repressor is bound to the operator, its presence on the DNA prevents RNA polymerase from binding in the way needed to initiate transcription.

Positive regulators, by contrast, usually establish a physical contact with RNA polymerase that enhances the enzyme's ability to initiate transcription (**Fig. 15.25**). For several positive regulators, researchers have identified points of contact between the regulator and the α, β, or σ subunits of RNA polymerase. Although RNA polymerase will bind to a promoter in the absence of a positive regulator, it is less likely to unwind DNA and begin polymerization than when it receives assistance from a positive regulator.

Negative regulators, such as the tetrameric *lac* repressor, prevent initiation by blocking RNA polymerase's binding to the initiator. Positive regulators, such as CRP, enhance initiation through physical contact with RNA polymerase. AraC can act as a positive regulator or as a repressor; it has different binding affinities in the presence or absence of arabinose.

Fusion of a *lacZ* gene to regulatory regions as a reporter allows functional assessments

Extensive molecular knowledge of the *lacZ* gene and assays to measure its expression have enabled its use as a "reporter" gene in the study of a large variety of regulatory regions in both prokaryotes and eukaryotes. A **reporter**

Figure 15.25 CRP-cAMP interaction. The CRP–cAMP complex contacts RNA polymerase directly to help in transcription initiation.

gene is a protein-encoding gene whose expression in the cell is quantifiable by sensitive and reliable techniques of protein detection.

Measuring gene expression

Fusion of the coding region of the reporter gene to *cis*-acting regulatory regions (including promoters and operators) of other genes creates a DNA molecule that enables researchers to assess the activity of the regulatory elements by monitoring the amount of reporter gene product appearing in the cell. For example, with the fusion of gene *X*'s regulatory region to the *lacZ* gene, one can assess the activity of the regulatory elements of gene *X* by monitoring the level of β-galactosidase expression. With this fusion molecule, conditions that induce expression of gene *X* will generate β-galactosidase (**Fig. 15.26**).

Identifying regulatory sites

The use of reporter genes makes it possible to identify the DNA sites necessary for regulation as well as the genes and signals involved in that regulation. For example, you could mutate gene *X*'s control region *in vitro* and then transform the gene *X-lacZ* fusion molecule back into bacterial cells and look for mutations that disrupt a particular aspect of control (as measured by

Figure 15.26 *lacZ* gene fused to regulatory region. The *lacZ* structural gene can be fused to a regulatory region of gene *X*. Expression of β-galactosidase will be dependent on signals in the regulatory region to which *lacZ* is fused.

Fusion used to perform genetic studies of the regulatory region of gene *X*.

lacZ expression is under control of gene *X* regulatory region.

β-galactosidase

levels of *lacZ*); this protocol would identify *cis*-acting sites important for the regulation. Or, you could mutate the bacteria themselves and then introduce a reporter fusion molecule into the mutated cells and look for changes in level of *lacZ* expression as measured by blue or white colony color; this protocol would identify *trans*-acting genes.

Identifying sets of genes regulated by the same stimulus

Reporter fusion molecules not only provide the basis for analyzing the regulation of one specific gene, they also make it possible to identify many genes regulated by the same stimulus. To this end, researchers can use transposition to insert the *lacZ* gene without its regulatory region at various sites around the bacterial chromosome. Introducing the *lacZ* reporter into a population of cells generates a collection of *E. coli* cells, some of which contain *lacZ* fused to genes and their regulatory regions. On exposure of this collection to a stimulus such as UV light, the cells containing *lacZ* fused to the regulatory regions of genes induced by UV light will produce β-galactosidase (**Fig. 15.27**). Researchers identified a set of genes activated by exposure to DNA-damaging agents by this method.

Controlling gene expression

In addition to using *lacZ* as a reporter gene, geneticists studying gene regulation can use their extensive knowledge of the *lac* operon regulatory region to construct recombinant molecules carrying genes whose expression can be controlled. For example, by fusing the *lac* operon control DNA to a human gene expressed in *E. coli*, they could cause overproduction of the human protein in response to an induction cue. The ability to control expression of a foreign gene is important because it provides a way to ensure that protein production is not turned on until cells have proliferated to a high density. The culture will thus contain many cells making the desired foreign protein; and even if the protein has deleterious effects on

Figure 15.27 *lacZ* introduced into a population of *E. coli* cells. Creating a collection of *lacZ* insertions in the chromosome. The *lacZ* gene without its promoter integrates randomly around the chromosome. If *lacZ* integrates within a gene in the orientation of transcription, *lacZ* expression will be controlled by that gene's regulatory region. The library of clones created can be screened to identify insertions in genes regulated by a common signal.

+ *lacZ* gene fragment

Collection (library) of *E. coli* cells each with *lacZ* inserted at a different chromosome location (and therefore fused to regulatory regions of different genes).

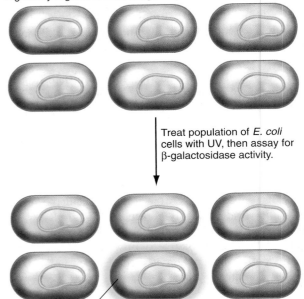

Treat population of *E. coli* cells with UV, then assay for β-galactosidase activity.

This cell exhibits expression of β-galactosidase after UV treatment. Gene to which *lacZ* is fused is regulated by UV light.

the growth of *E. coli*, the culture can still grow to high density before addition of the inducer. The production in *E. coli* of human proteins, such as human growth hormone, human insulin, and other pharmacologically useful proteins, is based on this strategy (**Fig. 15.28**).

A reporter gene is a protein-encoding gene that has been fused to other genes as an insertion. The presence or absence of its product can then be used as a reliable indicator (reporter) of expression of those genes. *lacZ* fusions have been widely used to study gene expression.

Figure 15.28 Use of fusions to overproduce a gene product. (a) The *lac* regulatory region can be fused to gene *X* to control expression of genes. **(b)** The gene encoding human growth hormone is cloned next to the *lac* control region and transformed into *E. coli*. Conditions that induce *lac* expression will cause expression of growth hormone that can be purified from the cells.

(a)

Expression of gene *X* under control of *lac* regulatory system (inducible by lactose or analogs)

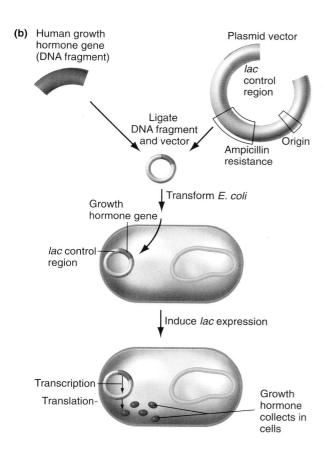

15.3 Attenuation of Gene Expression: Termination of Transcription

In bacteria, the multiple genes of both catabolic and anabolic pathways are clustered together and coregulated in operons. We have seen that regulators of the catabolic *lac* and *ara* operons respond to the presence of lactose or arabinose, respectively, by inducing gene expression. By contrast, regulators of anabolic operons respond to the presence of the pathway's end product by shutting down the genes of the operon that encode proteins needed to manufacture the end product.

There are many anabolic bacterial operons involved in the synthesis of amino acids. A well-studied example is the *E. coli* tryptophan (*trp*) operon, a group of five structural genes—*trpE, trpD, trpC, trpB,* and *trpA*—required for construction of the amino acid tryptophan. Maximal expression of the *trp* genes occurs when tryptophan is absent from the growth medium.

Tryptophan activates a repressor of the *trp* operon

The *trp* operon is regulated by a protein repressor that is the product of the *trpR* gene. In contrast to the *lac* operon, where lactose functions as an inducer that prevents the repressor from binding to the operator, tryptophan functions as a **corepressor:** an effector molecule whose binding to the actual TrpR repressor protein allows the negative regulator to bind to DNA and inhibit transcription of the genes in the operon. The binding of tryptophan to the TrpR repressor causes an allosteric alteration in the repressor's shape, and only with this alteration can the TrpR protein bind to the operator site (**Fig. 15.29**). Mutations in the *trpR* gene that change either the protein's tryptophan-binding domain or its DNA-binding domain destroy the TrpR repressor's ability to bind DNA, and they result in the constitutive expression of the *trp* genes even when tryptophan is present in the growth medium.

Figure 15.29 Tryptophan acts as a corepressor. (a) When tryptophan is available, it binds to the *trp* repressor, causing the molecule to change shape so that the repressor can bind to the operator of the *trp* operon and repress transcription. **(b)** When tryptophan is not available, the repressor cannot bind to the operator, and the tryptophan biosynthetic genes are expressed.

(a) Tryptophan present

(b) Tryptophan not present

TABLE 15.1	Expression of *trp* Operon in *trpR⁺* and *trpR⁻* Strains	
	With Tryptophan* (%)	**Without Tryptophan** (%)
TrpR⁺	8	100
TrpR⁻	33	100

*In the growth medium

The TrpR-mediated repression of the *trp* operon is critical, but it is only one of the regulatory components controlling expression of the *trp* genes in *E. coli*.

Termination of transcription fine-tunes regulation of the *trp* operon

One would expect *trpR⁻* mutants to show constitutive expression of their *trp* genes. With or without tryptophan in the medium, if there is no repressor to bind at the operator, RNA polymerase would have uninterrupted access to the *trp* promoter. Surprisingly, studies show that the *trp* genes of *trpR⁻* mutants are not completely de-repressed (that is, turned on) when tryptophan is present in the growth medium. As **Table 15.1** shows, the removal of tryptophan from a medium in which *trpR⁻* mutants are growing causes expression of the *trp* genes to increase threefold. What control mechanism is responsible for this repressor-independent change in *trp* operon expression?

Alternative transcripts, different outcomes

In a series of elegant experiments analyzing transcription of the *trp* operon, Charles Yanofsky and coworkers found that initiation at the *trp* promoter can produce two alternative transcripts (Fig. 15.29 and **Fig. 15.30a**). Sometimes initiation at the promoter leads to transcription of a truncated mRNA about 140 bases long from a short DNA region immediately preceding the first *trp* structural gene (*trpE*); this pregene DNA region is called a **leader sequence,** and the RNA transcribed from it is the *RNA leader*. At other times, transcription continues beyond the end of the leader sequence to produce a full operon-length transcript. In analyzing why some mRNAs terminate before they can transcribe the structural *trp* genes, while others do not, the researchers discovered **attenuation:** control of gene expression by premature termination of transcription. Whether or not transcription terminates prematurely depends on how the translation machinery reads the secondary structure of the RNA leader.

Figure 15.30 Attenuation in the tryptophan operon of *E. coli*. (a) Stem loops form by complementary base pairing in the *trp* leader RNA. Two different secondary structures are possible in the mRNA from the *trp* operon. Stem loops using complementary base pairs between regions 1 and 2 will enable the formation also of the stem-loop 3–4, which is a termination signal for RNA polymerase. Base pairing between regions 2 and 3 leads to a stem loop that prevents formation of stem-loop 3–4. In the early portion of the transcript, there are two codons for tryptophan. (b) When tryptophan is present, the ribosome follows quickly along the transcript, preventing stem-loop 2–3 from forming. Stem-loop 3–4 can form and transcription is terminated. (c) If tryptophan is absent, the ribosome stalls at the *trp* codons, allowing formation of stem-loop 2–3, preventing stem-loop 3–4 formation. Transcription continues.

(a)
Alternate stem-loop structures

(b)
Tryptophan present

(c)
Tryptophan not present

The RNA leader can fold into two different stable conformations, each one based on the complementarity of bases in the same molecule of RNA. The first structure contains two stem-loop structures with regions 1 and 2 associated by base pairing and regions 3 and 4 similarly associated by base pairing. When the transcriptional machinery "sees" the 3–4 stem-loop configuration, which has seven U's at the end, it stops transcription, producing a short, "attenuated" RNA. The alternative RNA structure forms by base pairing between regions 2 and 3. In this conformation, the leader RNA does not display the 3–4 stem-loop termination signal, and as a result, the transcription machinery reads right through it to produce a full-length transcript that includes the structural-gene sequences.

How a small region of the leader determines the outcome

The early translation of a short portion of the RNA leader (while transcription of the rest of the leader is still taking place) determines which of the two alternative RNA structures forms. That key portion of the RNA leader includes a short open reading frame containing 14 codons, 2 of which are *trp* codons (**Fig. 15.30b**). When tryptophan is present, the ribosome moves quickly past the *trp* codons in the RNA leader and proceeds to the end of the leader's codons, allowing formation of the stem-loop 3–4 structure and preventing formation of the alternative RNA structure. As we have seen, this 3–4 RNA structure causes the termination of transcription and hence the attenuation (that is, lessening) of *trp* gene expression. In the absence of tryptophan, the ribosome stalls at the two *trp* codons in the RNA leader because of the lack of charged tRNA^{Trp} in the cell. The 2–3 stem-loop structure depicted in **Fig. 15.30c** is then able to form, and its formation prevents formation of the 3–4 stem-loop RNA structure recognized by the transcriptional terminator. As a result, transcription proceeds through the leader into the structural genes.

How do we know these secondary RNA structures exist *in vivo* and that the translation of the leader RNA plays a significant role in their formation? Several experiments support this model of attenuation. First, deletion of the complete leader sequence results in the loss of control by attenuation; in *trpR⁻* mutants that also do not contain the leader sequence, there is no difference in *trp* expression with or without tryptophan in the medium. This double mutant makes the *trp* biosynthetic enzymes constitutively at maximal levels. Second, mutations that weaken the stems of the RNA stem-loop secondary structures alter regulation, but they can be compensated for by a second-site mutation that restores base pairing. Third, mutations that change the RNA terminator structure increase the readthrough of transcription and thus enhance gene expression. Finally, mutations of the translation-initiating AUG codon that prevent translation of the leader sequence produce an increase in the amount of short transcript, as predicted from the model.

Why has such a complex system evolved in the regulation of the *trp* operon and other biosynthetic pathways? Whereas the TrpR repressor shuts off transcription in the presence of tryptophan and allows it in the amino acid's absence, the attenuation mechanism provides a way to fine-tune this off/on switch. It allows the cell to sense the level of tryptophan by "reading" the level of charged tRNA^{Trp} and to adjust the level of *trp* mRNA accordingly. In *E. coli,* systems for regulation by attenuation similar to that observed for tryptophan exist for several other amino acid biosynthetic operons, including histidine, phenylalanine, threonine, and leucine.

The attenuation mechanism is unique to prokaryotes because only in cells without a membrane-enclosed nucleus can the expression machinery couple transcription and translation. The opportunity for some aspect of the translational apparatus to directly affect the outcome of transcription does not exist in eukaryotes.

> The *trp* operon illustrates the attentuation of gene expression as a result of the presence of its substrate. Fine-tuning is provided by stalling of transcription at a leader sequence. Only prokaryotes can take advantage of this mechanism because they couple transcription and translation.

15.4 Global Regulatory Mechanisms

Dramatic shifts in environmental conditions can trigger the expression of sets of genes or operons dispersed around the chromosome. The absence of glucose, we have already seen, increases the expression of several catabolic operons that are at least partially controlled by a common factor, the CRP–cAMP complex. A group of genes whose expression is regulated by the same regulatory proteins is called a **regulon.** Another example of such global regulation is *E. coli*'s response to heat shock, which results from exposure to extremely high temperatures (up to 45°C).

An alternative sigma (σ) factor mediates *E. coli*'s global response to heat shock

At high temperatures, most proteins denature or aggregate, or both. In *E. coli,* exposure to high temperature induces the expression of several proteins that alleviate heat-shock-related damage. The induced proteins include those that recognize and degrade aberrant proteins as well as so-called *chaperone proteins,* which assist in the refolding of other proteins and also prevent their aggregation.

E. coli's induction of the proteins that combat heat shock is a highly conserved stress response. Organisms as

Figure 15.31 Sigma factor recognition sequences.
Base sequences recognized by σ^{32} and σ^{70}. (The N indicates that any base can be found at this position.)

σ^{70} recognizes this promoter sequence.

| T T G A C A | 16–18 bp | T A T A A T |

σ^{32} recognizes this promoter sequence.

| C T T G A A | 13–15 bp | C C C C A T N T |

different as bacteria, flies, and plants induce similar proteins, notably the chaperones, in response to high temperatures.

Conditional mutants and the global mechanism

Conditional lethal *E. coli* mutants in which high temperatures do not induce transcription of the heat-shock genes provided critical evidence for the global regulatory mechanism. These conditional lethal mutants have a defect in the *rpoH* gene that encodes an alternate RNA polymerase sigma factor known as σ^{32}. The normal housekeeping sigma factor, σ^{70}, is active in the cell under normal physiological conditions. By contrast, the alternative σ^{32} can function at high temperatures; it also recognizes different promoter sequences than those recognized by σ^{70}. Genes induced by heat shock contain nucleotide sequences in their promoters that are recognized by σ^{32} (**Fig. 15.31**). σ^{32} mediates the heat-shock response by binding to the core RNA polymerase, thereby allowing the polymerase to initiate transcription of the genes encoding the heat-shock proteins. The RNA polymerase σ^{32} holoenzyme is relatively resistant to heat inactivation compared to the heat-sensitive σ^{70}-dependent RNA polymerase. As a result, when temperatures rise, genes with a σ^{32} promoter undergo transcription, while genes with a σ^{70} promoter do not.

Levels of the σ^{32} protein and the σ^{32} RNA polymerase holoenzyme increase immediately after heat shock. Several factors cause this increase in σ^{32} activity, including

- An increase in the transcription of the *rpoH* gene.
- An increase in the translation of σ^{32} mRNA stemming from greater stability of the *rpoH* mRNA.
- An increase in the stability and activity of the σ^{32} protein. Chaperones DnaJ/K bind to and inhibit σ^{32} under normal physiological conditions. When the temperature rises, these proteins bind to the large number of cellular proteins that become denatured, leaving σ^{32} free to associate with RNA polymerase.
- The inactivity of σ^{70} at high temperatures. Because of this inactivity, σ^{70} does not compete with σ^{32} in forming the RNA polymerase holoenzyme.

How alternative sigma factors are transcribed at high temperatures

Given that high temperatures render σ^{70} inactive, what enables the transcription of σ^{32} during heat shock? The

Figure 15.32 Alternate sigma factor in the heat-shock response. At high temperature, the *rpoH* gene (encoding σ^{32}) is transcribed. The σ^{32} interacts with RNA polymerase and transcribes the heat-shock genes.

rpoH gene, which encodes σ^{32}, has a promoter sequence that is recognized by σ^{70} and used for transcription at lower temperatures. However, at high temperatures, another sigma factor, σ^{24}, recognizes a different promoter sequence at *rpoH* and transcribes the *rpoH* gene from that promoter (**Fig. 15.32**). Although σ^{24} is always present in the cell, its own transcription (mediated by the σ^{24} holoenzyme) increases with heat shock and the appearance of denatured proteins.

The RpoS sigma factor

Another sigma factor, RpoS, that is active during many different stress conditions is also activated during heat shock. The RpoS protein was originally identified as a sigma factor that becomes active as growth of *E. coli* slows. The *rpoS* gene is transcribed throughout growth in *E. coli*, but translation is inhibited during normal growth. A secondary structure forms in the long leader sequence of the *rpoS* mRNA and blocks access of the message to the ribosome for translation (**Fig. 15.33**). When *E. coli* is under stress (lack of nutrients, heat shock, or other stresses), a small RNA, *dsrA*, that has complementarity to 20 nucleotides of the *rpoS* mRNA binds to the message, preventing the secondary structure from forming, thereby allowing translation to occur. Thus the gene encoding the *rpoS* gene, the product of which acts to regulate transcription, is regulated at the translation step in gene expression.

Global regulation by alternative sigma factors

The induction of new sets of genes in many different bacteria is often achieved in bacteria by the turn of alternate sigma factors. By coordinating the transcription of sets of genes in response to cues from the environment, the alternate sigma factors contribute to the control of such complex processes as sporulation, the synthesis of flagella, and nitrogen fixation (See the Genetics and Society box "Nitrogen Fixation and Gene Regulation" on pp. 540–541).

Genome analysis reveals that the genomes of bacterial species contain several related but slightly different sigma factor genes. For example, the bacterium *Bacillus*

Figure 15.33 Translational control of *rpoS*. (a) Translation of *rpoS* mRNA is blocked by secondary structure (base pairing) that occurs in the RNA. **(b)** *dsrA* RNA brown base pairs with *rpoS* RNA, freeing the translation start site.

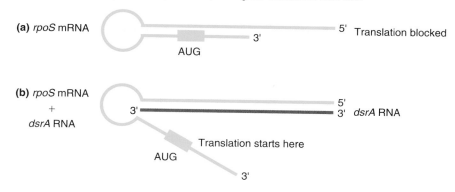

subtilis, under the adverse conditions of nutrient deprivation (such as nitrogen or carbon starvation), uses a cascade of sigma factors, induced in a temporal order, to turn on successive sets of genes needed to form spores. With the proper expression of these genes, the bacterial cell becomes a metabolically inert spore able to withstand heat, aridity, extreme cold, toxic chemicals, and radiation.

Sudden environmental changes can trigger gene expression, as is shown by the heat-shock proteins of *E. coli.* Alternative sigma factors are present that can recognize different promoter sequences and complex with the core RNA polymerase as the temperature rises. Many bacterial species have evolved similar strategies for dealing with environmental change.

Microarrays provide a tool for studying genes regulated in a global response

Microarrays are an important new tool for microbial geneticists studying cellular responses to changing environmental conditions. The cellular responses to these conditions often involve a global change in gene expression that is measurable by microarray analysis of mRNA isolated from cultures of cells grown under different conditions.

For example, to study changes in gene expression when lactose is substituted for glucose in the extrinsic environment (growth medium), scientists grow one culture of *E. coli* in medium containing glucose as a carbon source and another culture in medium containing lactose as a carbon source. They then isolate RNA from each culture and synthesize labeled DNA complementary to the collection of RNAs from the two different cultures.

By comparing the hybridization of the two sets of cDNAs to microarrays containing oligonucleotide spots for each *E. coli* gene, they can see which genes are turned on and which are turned off. In the lactose-treated cells, one would expect to see an increase in the mRNA of the lactose operon genes and therefore an increase in hybridization to the *lacZ, Y,* and *A* gene spots on the microarray.

Experiments using DNA arrays to compare the gene expression patterns of cells grown in media containing as their carbon source glucose, glycerol, succinate, or alanine provide an interesting glimpse into the cellular response to poorer energy sources. The cells grown on glycerol, succinate, or alanine not only turned on the few genes specifically required to use the poorer carbon source, but they also turned on a hierarchy of large sets of additional genes. Cells grown on glycerol or succinate showed increased expression of 40 genes; cells grown on alanine turned on 188 genes, including the set of 40 that were expressed in the glycerol- and succinate-grown cultures. These 40 genes included those of the stress response as well as those of the CRP regulon. Recall that when glucose is not present, cAMP levels rise, and the CRP–cAMP complex binds and increases expression of other genes, including several catabolic genes.

Unexpectedly, the cells grown on poorer carbon sources also turned on genes encoding proteins for motility and for the transport of many compounds in addition to the compound in their medium. The cellular response to carbon sources other than glucose seems to be the expression of genes that allow the cell to search out and use any alternative energy source. Motility genes, for example, might be turned on to allow the cell to move about in search of food. Another global transcription change is that RNA polymerase transcribes rRNA at a lower rate in the cells with poorer carbon sources, because these cells channel their energy into the search for and use of an alternative carbon source.

Nitrogen Fixation and Gene Regulation

Nitrogen, an essential component of amino acids, chlorophylls, and nucleic acids, is a growth-limiting plant nutrient—the more nitrogen available, the faster most plants grow. However, although gaseous nitrogen (N_2) makes up 78% of earth's atmosphere, plants cannot use nitrogen in this form. They can use only nitrogen that has been *fixed,* that is, converted to ammonia (NH_3) or another nitrogen-containing compound.

Plants obtain fixed nitrogen from three main sources: (1) the decayed organic matter in soils, which releases nitrate and ammonium; (2) the activity of nitrogen-fixing bacteria, which fix atmospheric N_2 into ammonium and other biologically available forms of nitrogen; and (3) inorganic nitrogen fertilizers. The last 50 years has seen a 10-fold increase in the application of inorganic fertilizer. This excessive use of fertilizer has produced runoff that increases the mineral content of rivers and coastal waters, which has led to algal blooms and a depletion of oxygen in aquatic ecosystems.

In an attempt to reduce the amount of inorganic fertilizers used in agriculture, many scientists are studying how bacteria fix nitrogen. Several types of bacteria are agents of nitrogen fixation. These bacteria may be free-living cells (such as those in the genus *Klebsiella*) or plant symbionts (such as those in the genus *Rhizobium*). Of the many symbiotic rhizobial species, each one is able to form a working relationship with only one or a few plants, mainly legumes like peas, beans, and alfalfa. For hundreds of centuries, farmers made practical use of the nitrogen-fixing abilities of rhizobial bacteria via the rotation of crops.

Bacteria–Plant Interactions Lead to Nitrogen Fixation

In the symbiotic relationship that develops between *R. meliloti,* a small heterotrophic nitrogen-fixing bacterium, and alfalfa, bacterial genes produce the enzymatic machinery for nitrogen fixation, while the plants provide a low-oxygen environment that allows the nitrogen-fixation enzymes to function. A series of communications between plant and bacteria lead to dramatic changes in both the anatomy of the plant and the structure of the bacteria that enable symbiosis.

Alfalfa's secretion of flavonoids triggers the events leading to nitrogen fixation. *R. meliloti* responds to this environmental signal by expressing *nodulation (nod)* genes, whose protein products are enzymes active in the synthesis of liposaccharides known as Nod factors. Release of the Nod factors from the rhizobial cells elicits a curling of root hairs and cell division in the meristem, which lead to the formation of root nodules in the alfalfa plant **(Fig. A)**. The bacteria now navigate by chemotaxis to the alfalfa host nodules and penetrate the host's root cortex with the help of a gelatinous filament secreted by the plant itself.

Once inside the plant, the *R. meliloti* enter root cells, where they divide and differentiate into *bacteroids,* cells that produce nitrogenase, an enzyme complex that catalyzes the conversion of N_2 to NH_3. The host plant monitors the concentration of oxygen in the area of the nodule where the bacteroids thrive to ensure that it is much lower than in the surrounding plant cells or soil. A nearly anaerobic environment in the nodule is crucial to the survival and function of nitrogenase. The alfalfa plant uses the nitrogen fixed by *R. meliloti* as its source of nitrogen and, in return, provides the bacteria with photosynthetic products and amino acids.

The Genetic Components and Mechanisms That Mediate Nitrogen Fixation in Rhizobial Bacteria

The steps of nodule formation and nitrogen fixation just outlined require the coordinated expression of at least three types

Mutants allow the study of more specific response mechanisms

The experiments previously described, although they enhanced understanding of how genetics controls bacterial physiology, were not specific enough to reveal changes in gene expression related only to the change from glucose to an alternative carbon source. Environmental changes often produce a general physiological reaction, and to get around this experimental difficulty, investigators use bacterial strains with mutations in specific genes—namely, the regulatory genes that serve as the main on/off switch for numerous genes in the pathway they are analyzing. Instead of treating cells to two different growth conditions and measuring RNA levels under the different conditions, they use microarrays to compare RNA levels in a wild-type culture to RNA levels in a culture of cells containing a mutation in the key regulatory gene. Note that the two cultures can be grown under the same environmental conditions because the mutation itself simulates a different condition. For example, a *lacI⁻* cell behaves as if lactose is in the medium, even if the mutant is grown in a glucose medium.

Microbiologists have successfully identified genes that *E. coli* expresses specifically in response to nitrogen limitation. Under the best of circumstances, *E. coli* uses ammonia as its source of nitrogen. A lack of ammonia in the external environment, however, activates a master control gene called *ntrC.* The NtrC protein, in turn, activates many genes whose expression enables *E. coli* to use sources of nitrogen other than ammonia.

Researchers identified many of the genes activated by nitrogen limitation through molecular analyses. To carry out a more comprehensive analysis, however, they compared RNA levels of all *E. coli* genes in a cell containing a null mutation in *ntrC* to RNA levels in a mutant strain that produced a greater than normal amount of the NtrC protein. The resulting microarray data confirmed a finding from earlier studies that the *glnA* gene, which encodes glutamine synthetase, is regulated by NtrC. A second, very striking finding from the microarray analysis was that about 2% of the *E. coli* genome is under NtrC control

Figure A *R. meliloti's* release of Nod factors induces the formation of root nodules in alfalfa. Nod⁻ mutants cannot form nodules.

Nod⁻   Nod⁺

Nodules ──○

of *R. meliloti* genes: *nod* genes, which elicit the early steps of nodule formation; *fix* genes, which contribute to the development and metabolism of bacteroids and are essential to nitrogen fixation; and *nif* genes, which encode the polypeptide subunits of the nitrogenase complex. The FixL protein in the membrane senses the O_2 concentration and activates the transcription factor FixJ, which then turns on expression of other *fix* genes as well as *nifA*. The *nif* genes carry a special type of promoter that RNA polymerase recognizes only when the polymerase is associated with a specific σ factor called σ^{54} factor.

Figure B How environmental signals influence the expression of *nif* genes in *R. meliloti.* Low oxygen activates the *nif* genes via RNA polymerase associated with a σ^{54} factor. A regulatory cascade promotes expression of the *nifA* gene only under appropriate conditions. Pluses and minuses indicate the turning on or off of genes.

Low O_2

FixL ⊕→ FixJ

⊕↙   ↘⊕

fix genes   *nifA* gene

↓

NifA *nif* genes

↓

Nitrogenase complex

High O_2

FixK

↓⊖

nifA gene

Initiation of transcription at the σ^{54}-dependent promoters of the *nif* genes depends on NifA, an activator protein responsive to environmental signals that reflect the concentration of oxygen **(Fig. B)**.

This brief description of the process of nitrogen fixation by *R. meliloti* gives some idea of the complex layering of gene regulation that ensures nitrogen fixation moves forward under favorable conditions but comes to a halt under conditions of too much oxygen. The coordinate expression of these bacterial genes contributes to these bacterial species' ability to respond to environmental signals and become nitrogen-generating symbionts in their host plants.

Arranging the spots on microarrays in the order in which the genes occur in the genome makes it easier to identify coregulated adjacent genes that might form an operon.

This type of microarray analysis has revealed several additional genes that are regulated by NtrC. The additional genes are involved in the scavenging of proteins and nitrogen through the transport of nitrogen-containing compounds from the cell wall into the cell and the breakdown of amino acids. NtrC's regulation of these genes has been confirmed by other types of analysis. Microarrays have thus provided an avenue for uncovering changes in gene expression that investigators can confirm and expand on through other methodologies.

Mutations in regulatory genes combined with microarray analysis allow a further refinement of findings about genes that operate under stress. The environmental conditions can be kept the same in such experiments because the mutation effectively creates the stress environment for the substance in question.

Computer analysis can identify regulatory proteins and their DNA binding sites

A goal in the postgenomic era is to identify the complete set of proteins that regulate transcription in an organism, as well as their DNA binding sites and the genes they regulate. This information will help researchers discover molecular targets for controlling cell proliferation and the production of harmful or helpful metabolites; it will also make it possible to model how a cell works. A first step in uncovering the regulatory machinery in bacteria is to identify operons. It is easy to correlate genomic DNA sequence with potential open reading frames, but how can you find genes that are cotranscribed? Because operons have a single promoter for several genes, you can look at clusters of genes that have promoter sequences before the first but not the subsequent genes. You can also look for genes with almost no separation between them. Cotranscribed genes have little space between them in the genome because no nucleotides are needed to regulate the expression of each gene separately. Computer experts have developed algorithms that search for one promoter for several closely spaced genes, as well as for transcription termination signals. While not perfect, these algorithms appear to be good operon predictors because known operons are among the results. The predictions can be further assessed by comparative species analysis. With genes that are cotranscribed and regulated as an operon in one species, a homologous set of adjacent genes in another species is also likely to be cotranscribed as an operon. As with all *in silico* analyses, predictions made with computational tools should be tested experimentally.

Genes encoding regulatory proteins can be identified in the genome by searching for sequences encoding DNA binding motifs, such as HTH. Of 314 putative regulator proteins identified by the presence of transcription factor domains in *E. coli,* 248 contained the HTH motif. Comparative genomic analyses by computer can help identify the genes that encode these regulatory proteins.

When a set of coregulated genes is present in different species, the proteins that regulate these genes are often conserved, as are their DNA binding sites. Researchers can use information from organisms such as *E. coli,* in which extensive genetic and biochemical analyses have defined regulatory pathways, to discover regulatory components in less well understood bacteria.

> Although computerized searches of genomes can reveal potential DNA sites for regulatory proteins, these must be verified experimentally. Nevertheless, computer analysis provides a starting point for further research.

15.5 A Comprehensive Example: The Regulation of Virulence Genes in *V. cholerae*

The principles and mechanisms of gene regulation in *E. coli* apply to gene regulation in other prokaryotics as well, including the bacteria *V. cholerae,* which we described at the beginning of this chapter. As we saw, these bacterial agents of cholera are able to sense changes in their environment and transmit signals about those changes to regulators. These regulators then initiate, enhance, diminish, or repress the expression of various genes as the bacteria pass through the stomach, colonize the intestine, and finally produce a toxin. Of particular interest to epidemiologists and medical practitioners seeking to prevent or treat the symptoms of cholera are the genes bestowing virulence.

lacZ reporters help identify regulators of toxin production

To understand the regulation of the genes for virulence, researchers first cloned the two genes that encode the polypeptide subunits of cholera toxin: *ctxA* and *ctxB,* which are transcribed and regulated together as an operon. They next made a *ctxA-lacZ* reporter gene fusion molecule that could detect changes in regulation of the operon through changes in levels of β-galactosidase expression. *LacZ* would be expressed and β-galactosidase produced when the cholera toxin promoter was being used, and no β-galactosidase would be produced when the promoter was shut off. They then cut *V. cholerae* genomic DNA into pieces and cloned these into a vector that would replicate in *E. coli.* With the construction of these tools, they were able to perform experiments in *E. coli* cells, which are more amenable than *V. cholerae* to some types of genetic manipulation.

To isolate a gene that regulates expression of the *ctx* operon, they transformed *E. coli* cells already containing the *ctxA-lacZ* fusion molecule with clones containing *V. cholerae* DNA. A clone that contains a gene encoding a positive cholera toxin regulatory protein should turn on expression of the *lacZ* fusion molecule in *E. coli.* Clones that turned on expression contained the regulatory *toxR* gene, which encodes a membrane protein (ToxR) with an N-terminal end in the cytoplasm and a C-terminal end in the periplasm (the space between the inner and outer membranes of the bacterium). In *V. cholerae,* *toxR⁻* mutants do not induce virulence, and the *toxR⁻* mutation is recessive as you would predict of a positive regulator.

Different fusions reveal genes regulated by ToxR and ToxT

To determine what genes ToxR regulates other than those in the *ctx* operon, researchers fused the *toxR* gene to a constitutive promoter, and they introduced this fusion molecule into a collection of *V. cholerae* strains in which copies of the *lacZ* gene had randomly inserted around the chromosome. Those colonies expressing β-galactosidase (as shown by the blue color resulting from the splitting of the X-Gal substrate) contained *lacZ* genes adjacent to a promoter region regulated by *toxR.*

In *V. cholerae,* these *lacZ* fusion genes must have been regulated by ToxR (at least indirectly) because all bacteria in the study contained the *toxR* gene fused to a constitutive promoter and thus were constitutive synthesizers of ToxR. However, when transferred into *E. coli,* this collection of genes was not regulated by ToxR. Something required to make these genes respond to ToxR was present in the *V. cholerae* genome but was missing in *E. coli.* The lack of direct regulation by ToxR in *E. coli* triggered a search that culminated in the identification of an intermediate regulatory gene named *toxT.* The ToxT protein is a transcriptional activator that carries out its function by binding to the promoters of many genes, including *ctx* and the other virulence genes. While either ToxR or ToxT can activate the *ctx* genes that produce toxin, ToxT alone activates the additional virulence genes, which encode pili and other proteins that enable the bacteria to colonize the small intestine.

ToxT is a major regulator of several virulence genes, but how is it regulated? Mutations in the *tcpP* gene lead to loss of ToxT transcription, as do mutations in *toxR.* Analyses of the promoter region of *toxT* showed that TcpP binds to the *toxT* promoter close to the transcription start point, while ToxR binds further upstream. This upstream binding suggests that ToxR helps recruit the TcpP protein to the promoter, where TcpP acts as the positive regulator of *toxT.* Both ToxR and TcpP are membrane bound, with the N terminal region in the cytoplasm available to bind to DNA and the C terminus in the periplasmic space able to receive environmental signals about the location of the bacterium in the body. Expression of cholera toxin and the pilus is induced when the bacteria have reached the intestine after passing through the bile-laden stomach. Information about the environment is probably transmitted through the activation of *tcpP,* as the transcription of this gene is temperature- and pH-dependent. By comparison, *toxR* is transcribed independently of both temperature and pH.

A model of virulence regulation includes a cascade of regulators

On the basis of these studies, researchers proposed the following model (**Fig. 15.34**):

- ToxR is a positive regulator of the *ctx* genes and acts as an auxiliary factor in the regulation of ToxT.
- ToxT is a positive regulator of the many virulence genes that make up the virulence regulon in *V. cholerae.*
- Maximal transcription of *toxT* requires the TcpP regulator, with assistance from ToxR.
- The sensing of environmental change is a part of the regulator gene activation process that is mediated by TcpP.

Experiments in which investigators monitored gene expression in the animal (mouse) disease model for *V. cholerae* confirmed the requirement of ToxR as a posi-

Figure 15.34 Model for how *V. cholerae* regulates genes for virulence. In the cytoplasm, ToxR interacts with promoter of the *ctxA* and *ctxB* genes. ToxR and TcpP both bind to the *toxT* gene. ToxT in turn regulates the expression of many other virulence genes.

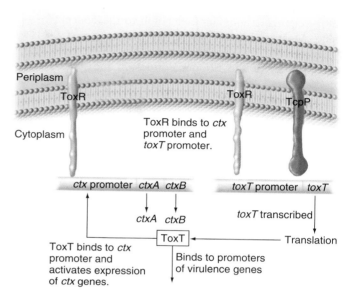

tive regulator of *ctxA* expression during pathogenesis in the animal. In these animal studies, when *V. cholerae* strains containing the *ctx* reporter gene fusion were injected into mice, expression of *ctxA-lacZ* occurred in the *toxR*⁺ strain but not in the *toxR*⁻ mutant. Interestingly, in the mouse model, the specifics of some of the other regulatory pathways for the *V. cholerae* pathogenesis genes did not coincide with the results obtained from the isolated bacterial cultures. From these studies, we can conclude that studying gene expression in pathogenic strains in culture, where it is easier to manipulate genes and measure their expression, provides a valuable first analysis. Once the potential regulators and pathways have been identified, experiments to detect gene expression during pathogenesis in model animal systems provide critical tests of the models.

Several intriguing questions remain about the regulatory system that controls the expression of the virulence genes in *V. cholerae.* What is the signal that makes the cholera bacteria stop swimming and start to colonize (that is, adhere to the cells of) the small intestine? What molecular events differentiate swimming and colonization? Why is there a cascade (ToxR, ToxT) of regulatory factors?

Answers to these questions will help scientists complete the picture of how *V. cholerae* generate disease. With a better understanding of pathogenesis, they will be able to devise more effective treatments for cholera as well as measures to prevent it.

Connections

Regulation in prokaryotes depends on the binding of regulatory proteins to specific DNA segments in the vicinity of a gene or group of genes. The existence of these regulatory elements adds another notch to the concept of the gene. Most geneticists would say that a gene consists of the nucleotides that specify amino acids in the gene's protein product or the ribonucleotides in the gene's RNA product, as well as the regulatory elements that influence the gene's transcription.

Some of the ways in which bacteria regulate their genes are available to eukaryotes as well. For example,

both types of organisms can use diffusible regulatory proteins to start or stop transcription. By contrast, eukaryotes cannot regulate transcription by the attenuation mechanism described for the *trp* operon because their nuclear membrane prevents access to the growing transcript by the translational machinery. However, eukaryotic cells, with their larger genomes, have evolved many other mechanisms of gene regulation that go beyond those found in prokaryotic systems. In Chapter 16, we examine the special regulatory needs of eukaryotes and some of the solutions they have evolved.

ESSENTIAL CONCEPTS

1. Most mechanisms of gene regulation in prokaryotes block or enhance the initiation of transcription. Later steps in gene expression are potential targets for fine-tuning the amount of gene products that accumulate in cells.

2. In the lac operon model proposed by Jacob and Monod, the binding of a repressor protein (encoded by the *lacI* gene) to the DNA *operator* prevents transcription of the structural genes *lacZ, lacY,* and *lacA* in the absence of the inducer lactose. When lactose is present, its binding to the repressor induces expression of the structural genes by causing the repressor to change its shape and lose its ability to bind to the operator.

3. A critical, general principle emerges from the *lac* operon studies: Regulatory genes usually encode *trans*-acting regulatory proteins that interact with *cis*-acting regulatory DNA elements located near the promoter (such as the operator). Negative regulatory proteins prevent or diminish the rate of transcription, while positive regulatory proteins enhance transcription.

4. Many types of coordinated gene regulation result from the clustering of genes into operons that are transcribed into a single polycistronic mRNA from a single promoter.

5. The binding of repressor proteins to operators can be influenced by either inducers (as for

the *lac* repressor) or corepressors (as for the *trp* operon).

6. Catabolite repression regulates certain catabolic operons by preventing the CRP protein, a positive regulator, from binding to the operons' promoter region in the presence of high concentrations of glucose.

7. Many regulatory proteins, both positive and negative, contain a helix-turn-helix motif, function as oligomers that bind to more than one DNA site, and interact with RNA polymerase to prevent or assist its function.

8. Attenuation, a form of fine-tuning for operons involved in the biosynthesis of amino acids, is based on premature termination of mRNA transcription. The termination, in turn, is determined by the intracellular concentration of tRNAs charged with the amino acid produced by the enzyme products of the structural genes in the operon.

9. Cells can express different sets of genes at different times or under different conditions by using alternative sigma factors or by producing novel RNA polymerases that recognize different classes of promoters.

10. DNA sequences from many bacterial species are raw data that can be analyzed computationally to identify regulatory features in the bacterial genome.

On Our Website   www.mhhe.com/hartwell4

Annotated Suggested Readings and Links to Other Websites

- Landmark papers on the lactose operon in *E. coli*

- Recent papers on the use of microarrays to understand gene regulation

- Recent papers on regulation of *V. cholerae* pathogenesis genes

Solved Problems

I. In the galactose operon in *E. coli,* a repressor, encoded by the *galR* gene, binds to an operator site, *O,* to regulate expression of three structural genes, *galE, galT,* and *galK.* Expression is induced by the presence of galactose in the media. For each of the strains listed, would the cell show constitutive, inducible, or no expression of each of the structural genes? (Assume that *galR⁻* is a loss of function mutation.)

a. $galR^- galO^+ galE^+ galT^+ galK^+$

b. $galR^+ galO^c galE^+ galT^+ galK^+$

c. $galR^- galO^+ galE^+ galT^+ galK^- /$
$galR^+ galO^+ galE^- galT^+ galK^+$

d. $galR^- galO^c galE^+ galT^+ galK^- /$
$galR^+ galO^+ galE^- galT^+ galK^+$

Answer

This problem requires an understanding of how regulatory sites and proteins that bind to regulatory sites behave. To predict expression in these strains, look at each copy of the operon individually, and then assess what effect alleles present in the other copy of the operon could have on the expression. After doing that for each copy of the operon, combine the results.

a. The *galR* gene encodes a repressor, so the lack of a *GalR* gene product would lead to constitutive expression of the *galE, T,* and *K.*

b. The *galO^c* mutation is an operator site mutation. By analogy with the *lac* operon, the designation *galO^c* indicates that repressor cannot bind and there is constitutive expression of *galE, T,* and *K.*

c. The first copy of the operon listed has a *galR⁻* mutation. Alone, this would lead to constitutive synthesis *galE* and *galT.* (*galK* is mutant, so there will not be constitutive expression of this gene.) The other copy is wild type for the *galR* gene, so it produces a repressor that can act in *trans* on both copies of the operon, overriding the effect of the *galR⁻* mutation. Overall, there will be *inducible expression of the three* gal *genes.*

d. The first copy of the operon contains a *galO^c* mutation, leading to constitutive synthesis of *galE* and *galT.* The other copy has a wild-type operator, so it is inducible, but neither operator has effects on the other copy of the operon. The net result is constitutive *galE* and *galT* and inducible *galK* expression.

II. The *araI* site is required for induction of *araBAD.* *I⁻* mutants do not express *araBAD.* In an *I⁻* mutant, a second mutation arose that resulted in constitutive arabinose synthesis. A Southern blot using a probe from the regulatory region and early part of the *araB* gene showed a very different set of restriction fragments than were seen in the starting strain. Based on the altered restriction pattern and constitutive expression, propose a hypothesis about the nature of the second mutation.

Answer

To answer this question, you need to consider how changes in restriction patterns could arise, what effects they could have, and what is necessary to get expression. The fact that the experiment began with a strain that lacked the inducing site, *I,* and that there is constitutive synthesis mean that the normal regulation is lacking. Constitutive synthesis could result from a *deletion that fused the* araBAD *genes to another promoter* (one that is on under the growth conditions used). A deletion would lead to a different pattern of restriction fragments that could be observed in the Southern hybridization analysis.

III. Bacteriophage λ, after infecting *E. coli,* can take one of two routes. It will either produce many progeny that are released by lysis of the cell (lytic growth), or the phage DNA will integrate into the chromosome because transcription from the major phage promoters of the phage will have been shut down. The repressor protein cI, encoded by phage λ, binds to two operator regions to shut down expression, and, therefore, no phages are produced. Mutations in the *cI* gene that destroy the binding ability of the repressor lead to the lytic type of life cycle exclusively; that is, all cells infected by the phage will burst and release progeny phages. Another type of mutation gives the same phenotype-lytic growth only. Such mutations, called λ*vir,* arise at a much lower frequency than the *cI* mutations (about 1 in 10^{12} compared with 1 in 10^6 for *cI* mutants). What do you think these mutations are, and why are they less frequent than *cI* mutations?

Answer

This problem requires an understanding of the types of regulatory mutations that can affect negative regulation. The lack of negative regulation (by *cI*) in the life cycle leads to the lytic cycle of growth only. Such mutations could be either in the gene encoding the negative regulator or in the site to which the repressor binds. You were told that the *cI* mutations are defects in the gene encoding the repressor. The λ*vir* mutations could be mutations in the site to which the repressor binds, but because the repressor has to bind to two sites, *there must be two mutations in a* λvir *mutant. Therefore, these would arise less frequently* (at a frequency predicted for two independent mutational events combined: 1 in 10^6 × 1 in 10^6, or 1 in 10^{12}).

Problems

Interactive Web Exercise

SWISS-PROT is a central resource of annotated protein sequences. Our website at www.mhhe.com/hartwell4 contains a brief exercise in which you use this resource to explore families of bacterial transcription factors; once at the website, go to Chapter 15 and click on "Interactive Web Exercise."

Vocabulary

1. For each of the terms in the left column, choose the best matching phrase in the right column.

   a. induction   1. glucose prevents expression of catabolic operons

   b. repressor   2. protein undergoes a reversible conformational change

   c. operator   3. often fused to regulatory regions of genes whose expression is being monitored

   d. allostery   4. stimulation of protein synthesis by a specific molecule

   e. operon   5. site to which repressor binds

   f. catabolite repression   6. gene regulation involving premature termination of transcription

   g. reporter gene   7. group of genes transcribed into one mRNA

   h. attenuation   8. negative regulator

Section 15.1

2. The following statement occurs early in this chapter: ". . . the critical step in the regulation of most bacterial genes is the binding of RNA polymerase to DNA at the promoter." Why might it be advantageous for bacteria to regulate the expression of their genes at this step?

3. One of the main lessons of this chapter is that several bacterial genes are often transcribed from a single promoter into a large multigene transcript. The region of DNA containing the set of genes that are cotranscribed, along with all of the regulatory elements that control the expression of these genes, is called an *operon*.
   a. Which of the mechanisms in the list below could explain differences in the levels of the mRNAs for different operons?
   b. Which of the mechanisms in the list below could explain differences in the levels of the protein products of different genes in the same operon?
      i. Different promoters might have different DNA sequences.
      ii. Different promoters might be recognized by different types of RNA polymerase.
      iii. The secondary structures of mRNAs might differ so as to influence the rate at which they are degraded by ribonucleases.
      iv. In an operon, some genes are farther away from the promoter than other genes.
      v. The translational initiation sequences at the beginning of different open reading frames in an operon might result in different efficiencies of translation.
      vi. Proteins encoded by different genes in an operon might have different stabilities.

4. All mutations that abolish function of the Rho termination protein in *E. coli* are conditional mutations. What does this tell you about the *rho* gene?

Section 15.2

5. The promoter of an operon is the site to which RNA polymerase binds to begin transcription. Some base changes in the promoter result in a mutant site to which RNA polymerase cannot bind. Would you expect mutations in the promoter that prevent binding of RNA polymerase to act in *trans* on another copy of the operon on a plasmid in the cell, or only in *cis* on the copy immediately adjacent to the mutated site?

6. You are studying an operon containing three genes that are cotranscribed in the order *hupF, hupH,* and *hupG*. Diagram the mRNA for this operon, showing the location of the 5'- and 3'-ends, all open reading frames, translational start sites, stop codons, transcription termination signals, and any regions that might be in the mRNA but not serve any of these functions.

7. You have isolated a protein that binds to DNA in the region upstream of the promoter sequence of the *sy* gene. If this protein is a positive regulator, which o the following would be true?
   a. Loss-of-function mutations in the gene encodin the DNA-binding protein would cause constitutiv expression.
   b. Loss-of-function mutations in the gene encodin the DNA-binding protein would result in little or n expression.

8. You have isolated two different mutants (*reg1* an *reg2*) causing constitutive expression of the *em* operon (*emu1 emu2*). One mutant contains a defe in a DNA-binding site, and the other has a loss-o function defect in the gene encoding a protein th binds to the site.
   a. Is the DNA-binding protein a positive or negati regulator of gene expression?
   b. To determine which mutant has a defect in t site and which one has a mutation in the bindi

protein, you decide to do an analysis using F′ plasmids. Assuming you can assay levels of the Emu1 and Emu2 proteins, what results do you predict for the two strains (*i* and *ii*) (see descriptions below) if *reg2* encodes the regulatory protein and *reg1* is the regulatory site?

   i. F' $reg1^-$ $reg2^+$ $emu1^-$ $emu2^+$/$reg1^+$ $reg2^+$ $emu1^+$ $emu2^-$

   ii. F' $reg1^+$ $reg2^-$ $emu1^-$ $emu2^+$/$reg1^+$ $reg2^+$ $emu1^+$ $emu2^-$

c. What results do you predict for the two strains (*i* and *ii*) if *reg1* encodes the regulatory protein and *reg2* is the regulatory site?

9. Bacteriophage λ, after infecting a cell, can integrate into the chromosome of the cell if the repressor protein, cI, binds to and shuts down phage transcription immediately. (A strain containing a bacteriophage integrated in the chromosome is called a lysogen.) The alternative fate is the production of many more viruses and lysis of the cell. In a mating, a donor strain that is a lysogen was crossed with a lysogenic recipient cell and no phages were produced. However, when the lysogen donor strain transferred its DNA to a nonlysogenic recipient cell, the recipient cell burst, releasing a new generation of phages. Why did mating with a nonlysogenic cell result in phage growth and release but infection of a lysogenic recipient did not?

10. Mutants were isolated in which the constitutive phenotype of a missense *lacI* mutation was suppressed. That is, the operon was now inducible. These mapped to the operon but were not in the *lacI* gene. What could these mutations be?

11. For each of the *E. coli* strains containing the *lac* operon alleles listed, indicate whether the strain is inducible, constitutive, or unable to express β-galactosidase and permease.

a. I^+ O^+ Z^- Y^+/I^+ O^c Z^+ Y^+
b. I^+ O^+ Z^+ Y^+/I^- O^c Z^+ Y^-
c. I^+ O^+ Z^- Y^+/I^- O^c Z^+ Y^-
d. I^-P^- O^+ Z^+ Y^- /I^+ P^+ O^c Z^- Y^+
e. I^s O^+ Z^+ Y^+ /I^- O^+ Z^+ Y^-

12. For each of the growth conditions listed, what proteins would be bound to *lac* operon DNA? (Do not include RNA polymerase.)

a. glucose
b. glucose + lactose
c. lactose

13. For each of the following mutant *E. coli* strains, plot a 30-minute time course of concentration of β-galactosidase, permease, and acetylase enzymes grown under the following conditions. For the first 10 minutes, no lactose is present; at 10′ lactose becomes the sole carbon source. Plot concentration on the y-axis, time on the x-axis. (Don't worry about the exact units for each protein on the y-axis.)

a. I^- P^+ O^+ Z^+ Y^+ A^+ /I^+ P^+ O^+ Z^- Y^+ A^+
b. I^- P^+ O^c Z^+ Y^+ A^- /I^+ P^+ O^+ Z^- Y^+ A^+
c. I^s P^+ O^+ Z^+ Y^+ A^+ /I^- P^+ O^+ Z^- Y^+ A^+
d. I^- P^- O^+ Z^+ Y^+ A^+ /I^- P^+ O^+ Z^+ Y^- A^+
e. I^- P^+ O^+ Z^- Y^+ A^+ /I^- P^- O^c Z^+ Y^- A^+

14. Maltose utilization in *E. coli* requires the proteins encoded by genes in three different operons. One operon includes the genes *malE, malF,* and *malG;* the second includes *malK* and *lamB;* and the genes in the third operon are *malP* and *malQ*. The MalT protein is a positive regulator that regulates the expression of all three operons; expression of the *malT* gene itself is catabolite sensitive.

a. What phenotype would you expect to result from a loss-of-function mutation in the *malT* gene?

b. Do you expect the three maltose operons to contain binding sites for CRP (cAMP receptor protein)? Why or why not?

In order to infect *E. coli,* bacteriophage λ binds to the maltose transport protein LamB (also known as the λ receptor protein) that is found in the outer membrane of the bacterial cell. The synthesis of LamB is induced by maltose in the medium via expression of the MalT protein, as described above.

c. List the culture conditions under which wild-type *E. coli* cells would be sensitive to infection by bacteriophage λ.

d. *E. coli* cells that are resistant to infection by bacteriophage λ have been isolated. List the types of mutations in the maltose regulon that λ-resistant mutants could contain.

15. Clones of three adjacent genes involved in arginine biosynthesis have been isolated from a bacterium. If these three genes together make up an operon, what result do you expect when you use the DNA from each of these genes as probes in a Northern analysis? What result do you expect if the three genes do not make up an operon?

16. Given the following data, explain which strains and growth conditions are important for reaching the following conclusions.

a. Arabinose induces coordinate expression of the *araBAD* genes (encoding kinase, isomerase, and epimerase).

b. The *araC* gene encodes a positive regulator of *araBAD* expression.

Genotype	Arabinose in medium	Kinase	Isomerase	Epimerase
1. C^+ B^+ A^+ D^+	no	−	−	−
2. C^+ B^+ A^+ D^+	yes	+	+	+
3. C^- B^+ A^+ D^+	no	−	−	−
4. C^- B^+ A^+ D^+	yes	−	−	−

17. Seven *E. coli* mutants were isolated. The activity of the enzyme β-galactosidase produced by cells containing each mutation alone or in combination with other mutations was measured when the cells were grown in medium supplemented with different carbon sources.

	Glycerol	Lactose	Lactose + Glucose
Wild type	0	1000	10
Mutant 1	0	10	10
Mutant 2	0	10	10
Mutant 3	0	0	0
Mutant 4	0	0	0
Mutant 5	1000	1000	10
Mutant 6	1000	1000	10
Mutant 7	0	1000	10
F' *lac* from mutant 1/ mutant 3	0	1000	10
F' *lac* from mutant 2/ mutant 3	0	10	10
Mutants 3 + 7	0	1000	10
Mutants 4 + 7	0	0	0
Mutants 5 + 7	0	1000	10
Mutants 6 + 7	1000	1000	10

Assume that each of the seven mutations is one and only one of the genetic lesions in the following list. Identify the type of alteration each mutation represents.
a. superrepressor
b. operator deletion
c. nonsense (amber) suppressor tRNA gene (assume that the suppressor tRNA is 100% efficient in suppressing amber mutations)
d. defective CRP–cAMP binding site
e. nonsense (amber) mutation in the β-galactosidase gene
f. nonsense (amber) mutation in the repressor gene
g. defective *crp* gene (encoding the CRP protein)

18. Cells containing mutations in the *crp* gene (encoding the positive regulator CRP) are Lac⁻, Mal⁻, Gal⁻, etc. To find suppressors of the *crp* mutation, cells were screened to find those that were both Lac⁺ and Mal⁺.
a. What types of suppressors would you expect to get using this screen compared with a screen for Lac⁺ only?
b. All suppressors isolated were mutant in the gene for the α-subunit of RNA polymerase. What hypothesis could you propose based on this analysis?

19. Six strains of *E. coli* (mutants 1–6) that had one of the following mutations affecting the *lac* operon were isolated.
   i. deletion of *lacY*
   ii. *lacOᶜ* mutation

iii. missense mutation in *lacZ*
iv. inversion of the *lac* operon (but not an inversion of the *lacI* gene)
v. superrepressor mutation
vi. inversion of *lacZ, Y,* and *A* but not *lacI, P, O*
a. Which of these mutations would prevent the strain from utilizing lactose?

b. The entire *lac* operon (including the *lacI* gene and its promoter) from each of the six *E. coli* strains was cloned into a plasmid vector containing an ampicillin resistance gene. Each recombinant plasmid was transformed into each of the six strains to create partial diploids. In analysis of these strains, mutant 1 was found to carry a deletion of *lacY*, so this strain corresponds to mutation i in the list above. Which of the other types of mutations would be expected to complement mutant 1 in these partial diploids so as to allow lactose utilization?
c. In the analysis described in part b, each strain was plated on ampicillin media in which lactose is the only carbon source. (Ampicillin was included to ensure maintenance of the plasmid.) Growth of the transformants is scored below (a + sign = growth, a − sign = no growth). Synthesis of β-galactosidase and permease are required for growth on this medium. Results of this merodiploid analysis are shown here. Which mutant bacterial strain (1–6) contained each of the alterations (i–vi) listed previously?

	1	2	3	4	5
1	−	+	−	+	−
2	+	−	−	+	−
3	−	−	−	+	−
4	+	+	+	+	−
5	−	−	−	−	−
6	+	+	+	+	+

20. The following data (top of p. 549) are from a DNase footprinting experiment in which either RNA polymerase or a repressor protein was added to a labeled DNA fragment, and then the complex was digested with DNaseI. DNA sequencing reactions were also performed on the same DNA so the bases that were protected by proteins binding could be identified. (Notice that DNaseI does not cut after each base in the DNA fragment.)
a. What is the sequence of the DNA in this fragment?
b. Mark on the sequence the region where the repressor binds.
c. Mark on the sequence the region where RNA polymerase binds.

DNase treated

No protein   + repressor   + RNA polymerase

DNA sequencing reactions

G   A   T   C

21. a. The original constitutive operator mutations in the *lac* operon were all base changes in O_1. Why do you think mutations in O_2 or O_3 were not isolated in these screens?

b. Explain how a mutagen that causes small insertions could produce an O^c mutation.

c. Would the O^c mutation described above in part *b* be sensitive to lacI^s? Why or why not?

22. In an effort to determine the location of an operator site for a negatively regulated gene, you have made a series of deletions within the regulatory region. The extent of each deletion is shown by the line underneath the sequence, and the resulting expression from the operon (*i* = inducible; *c* = constitutive; − = no expression is also indicated).

```
. . . GGATCTTAGCCGGCTAACATGATAAATATAA . . .
. . . CCTAGAATCGGCCGATTGTACTATTTATATT . . .
i    ————————
−    —————————————————————————
c    ——————————————————————
−    —————————————————————————————
c    —————————
```

a. What can you conclude from these data about the location of the operator site?

b. Why do you think deletions 2 and 4 show no expression?

23. An operon fusion consists of a regulatory region cloned next to the coding region of the genes of an operon. A gene fusion consists of a regulatory region of a gene such as *lacZ* and the DNA encoding the first amino acids of the β-galactosidase protein cloned next to the coding region of another gene. What additional feature do you have to consider to create a functional gene fusion that is not necessary for an operon fusion?

Section 15.3

24. a. How many ribosomes are required (at a minimum) for the translation of *trpE* and *trpC* from a single transcript of the *trp* operon?

b. How would you expect deletion of the two tryptophan codons in the RNA leader to affect expression of the *trpE* and *trpC* genes?

25. The following is a sequence of the leader region of the *his* operon mRNA in *Salmonella typhimurium*. What bases in this sequence could cause a ribosome to pause when histidine is limiting (that is, when there is very little of it) in the medium?

5′ AUGACACGCGUUCAAUUUAAACACCACCAUCAUCACCAUCA
UCCUGACUAGUCUUUCAGGC 3′

26. For each of the *E. coli* strains that follow, indicate the effect of the genotype on expression of the *trpE* and *trpC* genes in the presence and absence of tryptophan. (In the wild type [R^+ P^+ O^+ *att*$^+$ *trpC*$^+$], *trpC* and *trpE* are fully repressed in the presence of tryptophan and are fully induced in the absence of tryptophan.)

R = repressor gene; R^n product cannot bind tryptophan; R^- product cannot bind operator

O = operator; O^- cannot bind repressor

att = attenuator; *att*$^-$ is a deletion of the attenuator

P = promoter; P^- is a deletion of the *trp* operon promoter

trpE$^-$ and *trpC*$^-$ are null (loss-of-function) mutations

a. R^+ P^- O^+ *att*$^+$ *trpE*$^+$ *trpC*$^+$

b. R^- P^+ O^+ *att*$^+$ *trpE*$^+$ *trpC*$^+$

c. R^n P^+O^+ *att*$^+$ *trpE*$^+$ *trpC*$^+$

d. R^- P^+ O^+ *att*$^-$ *trpE*$^+$ *trpC*$^+$

e. R^+ P^+ O^- *att*$^+$ *trpE*$^+$ *trpC*$^-$ / R^- P^+ O^+ *att*$^+$ *trpE*$^-$ *trpC*$^+$

f. R^+ P^- O^+ *att*$^+$ *trpE*$^+$ *trpC*$^-$ / R^- P^+ O^+ *att*$^+$ *trpE*$^-$ *trpC*$^+$

g. R^+ P^+ O^- *att*$^-$ *trpE*$^+$ *trpC*$^-$ / R^- P^+ O^- *att*$^+$ *trpE*$^-$ *trpC*$^+$

27. A molecular geneticist is investigating an operon by measuring the amount of expression of the four structural genes (*A, B, C,* and *D*) produced in wild-type and mutant bacterial cells after the addition of compound Z to a minimal medium. An additional protein (E) is of very small size (less than 20 amino acids) and cannot be measured by the same analytical system employed for the other proteins. Several of the mutations are nonsense mutations that have an effect on the genes transcribed after them in the operon. In addition to stopping translation of the gene in which the mutations lie, these so-called *nonsense polar mutations* prevent the expression of genes downstream of the mutation. (For example, in the *lac* operon, some *lacZ* nonsense mutations can result in no expression of *lacY* and *lacA*.) The investigator has also obtained mutations in two other sites, *F* and *G*, closely linked to *A–D*. The graphs shown are all semilogarithmic. The percentage of maximal possible expression for a particular protein is plotted on the y-axis, while the x-axis coordinate is time. Compound Z is added at the point specified by the arrow.

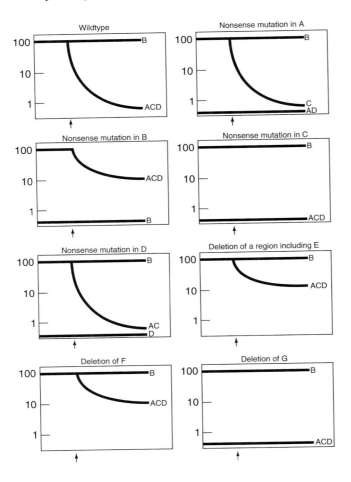

a. Is this operon likely to be involved in a pathway of biosynthesis or a pathway of degradation? Is the operon inducible or repressible?

b. For each of the conditions graphed, state if genes A–D are constitutive, completely repressible, partly repressible, or not expressed.

c. Construct a map of this operon. Indicate the relative positions of genes *A, B, C, D,* and *E* as well as the sites *F* and *G*. List possible functions for all the genes and sites. (Possible functions for the genes and sites *A–G:* promoter, operator, enzyme structural gene, CRP-binding site, *crp* gene, attenuator region. This list is not necessarily all inclusive.)

28. The previous problem (#27) introduced the concept of polar mutations in bacterial operons: nonsense mutations in a "proximal" gene nearer the promoter of the operon can abolish the expression of a "distal" gene in the same operon that is farther from the promoter. Essentially all polar mutations are nonsense mutations; missense mutations do not have this property.

a. Suggest a model to explain why nonsense but not missense mutations might exhibit polarity.

b. Interestingly, in strains that simultaneously carry a polar mutation and a nonsense suppressor mutation in a tRNA gene, the expression both of the gene with the nonsense mutation and of the distal genes in the operon can be restored. However, in strains with both a polar mutation and a loss-of-function mutation in the gene encoding the Rho transcription termination factor, expression of the distal genes can be restored but that of the gene with the nonsense mutation cannot. How might these results influence your model for the underlying cause of polarity?

Section 15.4

29. Many genes whose expression is turned on by DNA damage have been isolated. Loss of function mutations in the *lexA* gene leads to expression of many of these genes, even when there has been no DNA damage. Would you hypothesize that LexA protein is a positive or negative regulator? Why?

30. In 2005, Frederick Blattner and his colleagues found that *E. coli* have a global transcriptional program that helps them "forage" for better sources of carbon. Many genes, including genes needed for bacterial motility, are turned on in response to poorer carbon sources so that the bacteria can search for better nutrition. You now want to search for genes that regulate this response. How could you use *lacZ* fusions to try to identify such regulatory genes?

31. To find genes that are turned on or off in response to changes in osmolarity (the total concentration of solutes in solution), you grow a culture of *E. coli* in medium with high osmolarity and another culture in medium with low osmolarity. You now want to perform a DNA microarray analysis.

a. What would you use as your probe(s) for the DNA array analysis?

b. What nucleic acids would you spot on the DNA array? How many spots should the DNA array contain?

c. It is possible that osmotic changes may induce a general stress response that may be seen with other stresses as well (for example, heat-shock). How could you distinguish the genes that might be involved in a general stress response from those that are specific for the osmolarity change?

32. Figure A on p. 551 shows the results of a recent microarray analysis measuring the relative abundance of mRNAs for all of the genes of bacteriophage T4 as

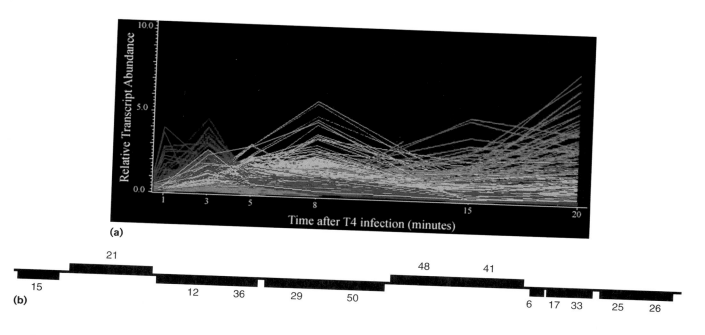

(a)

(b)

function of time after the infection of *E. coli* cells. The genes can be subdivided into three main classes: early genes (*blue*) transcribed almost immediately after infection, middle genes (*green*) transcribed somewhat later, and late genes (*red*) transcribed later still. Figure B depicts a 10 kb region of the 170 kb T4 genome showing the extent of several genes, each indicated by a number and classified by the same color scheme. Boxes above the black line indicate genes transcribed from left to right, while those below the line indicate genes transcribed in the opposite direction.

a. What is the minimal number of promoters in the 10 kb region depicted in Figure B? Which genes could be transcribed as part of the same operon(s)?

b. The *e* gene of bacteriophage T4 encodes an enzyme called endolysin, which helps lyse the *E. coli* host cell to release progeny bacteriophage particles. Would you expect *e* to be an early, middle, or late class gene? Explain your reasoning.

3. Several T4 genes participate in regulating the bacteriophage T4 life cycle described in the preceding problem (#32) and in Figures A and B above. The product

of the *motA* gene is a protein that binds to DNA near the promoters for middle genes, enabling the *E. coli* RNA polymerase core enzyme to recognize these promoters. The gene *asiA* encodes an "anti-σ factor" that associates with *E. coli* σ^{70} and disrupts its function. The protein encoded by *regA* is a ribonuclease that specifically destroys early mRNAs. T4 gene *55*'s product is a σ factor required for recognition of late promoters by the *E. coli* RNA polymerase core enzyme.

a. Of the genes described above (*motA, asiA, regA,* and *55*), which are likely to be early, middle, or late?

b. What class of T4 genes (early, middle, late) has promoters recognized by the *E. coli* σ^{70} RNA polymerase holoenzyme?

c. What happens to the transcription of genes in the host *E. coli* chromosome as T4 infection progresses?

d. Predict the results of loss-of-function mutations in the *motA, asiA,* and *55* genes on the transcription of early, middle, and late mRNAs as well as the mRNAs for host *E. coli* genes.

e. What aspect of Figure A is explained by the function of the RegA ribonuclease?

Gene Regulation in Eukaryotes

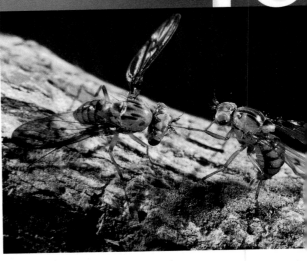

A Drosophila *male (right center) courting a female (on the left).*

When a *Drosophila* male courts a *Drosophila* female, he sings a species-specific song and dances an ancient dance. If successful, his instinctive behaviors culminate in mating. The male senses a female's presence by visual and tactile cues as well as by the pheromones she produces. After orienting himself at a precise angle with respect to his prospective mate, he taps his partner's abdomen with his foreleg and then performs his song by stretching out his wings and vibrating them at a set frequency; when the song is over, he begins to follow the female. If she is unreceptive (perhaps because she has recently mated with another male), she will run away, but if she is receptive, she will let him overtake her. When he does, he licks her genitals with his proboscis, curls his abdomen, mounts the female, and copulates with her for about 20 minutes.

Various mutations in a gene called *fruitless* produce behavioral changes that prevent the male from mating properly. Some mutant alleles alter the song to an unfamiliar melody. Others diminish the male's ability to distinguish females from males; male flies with this mutation court each other. Still others reduce the male's ability to court either sex. Finally, some mutations create lethal null alleles that cause male flies to die just before they emerge from the pupal case, showing that the *fruitless* gene has other functions in addition to its effects on courtship and mating.

Cloned in 1996, *fruitless* is a large gene—roughly 150 kb in length—encoding a product that can regulate transcription at multiple promoters. Some forms of the fruitless protein are sex-specific, appearing only in males or only in females. Other fruitless proteins are expressed at low levels in many kinds of cells in both sexes.

The male version of the fruitless protein, although very similar to the female protein, has an extra 101 amino acids at its N terminus, and this addition almost certainly determines the observed differences in male and female behavior. Remarkably, the male-specific fruitless mRNA is synthesized in only a few hundred of the tens of thousands of neurons that make up the male *Drosophila*'s nervous system. Most of these *fruitless*-expressing cells are located near motor neurons that control either wing movements (and thus possibly the song) or abdominal movements (and thus possibly the abdominal curling that immediately precedes mating). Work on the *Drosophila fruitless* gene has provided strong evidence that differences in gene expression, and not just differences in alleles, can directly influence complex behaviors.

In this chapter, we see that **eukaryotic gene regulation**—the control of gene expression in the cells of eukaryotes—depends on an array of interacting regulatory elements that turn genes on and off in the right places at the right times. During the embryonic development of multicellular eukaryotic organisms such as *Drosophila* or humans, gene regulation controls not only the elaboration of sex-related characteristics and behaviors but also the differentiation of tissues and organs, as well as the precise positioning of these tissues and organs. Some of the regulatory elements are specific DNA sequences in the vicinity of the gene to be regulated; others are DNA-binding proteins encoded by genes located elsewhere in the genome; and still others are micro-RNA molecules (miRNAs) that use the specificity of base paring to down-regulate, or curtail, specific gene expression after transcription.

In contrast to the theme of environmental adaptation found in the unicellular prokaryotes, the theme in multicellular eukaryotes appears to be maintenance of homeostasis of the organism. But even in unicellular eukaryotes, the mechanisms of regulation are different from those of prokaryotes. In eukaryotic gene regulation, we see a larger, more complex set of interactions than is found in prokaryotes, although some basic principles are shared between them. In addition, since many of the biological functions in multicellular organisms arise from the regulated interactions of large networks of genes, and each gene in a network has multiple potential points of regulation, the possibilities for regulatory refinement are enormous.

16.1 Overview of Eukaryotic Gene Regulation

As you explore the intricacies of eukaryotic gene regulation, bear in mind the key similarities and differences between eukaryotes and prokaryotes (**Table 16.1**). In both types of cells, transcriptional regulation can occur through the attachment of DNA-binding proteins to specific DNA sequences that are in the vicinity of the transcription unit itself; and several polypeptide motifs appear in many DNA-binding proteins in prokaryotes and eukaryotes.

However, additional levels of complexity are both necessary and possible for controlling expression in eukaryotes for several reasons.

- Eukaryotic genomes contain far more DNA than do those of prokaryotes, making it challenging for proteins to locate binding sequences.
- Chromatin structure makes DNA unavailable to transcription machinery.
- Additional RNA processing events occur.
- Transcription occurs in the nucleus, but translation takes place in the cytoplasm.

TABLE 16.1 Key Regulatory Differences Between Eukaryotes and Prokaryotes		
Characteristic	**Prokaryote**	**Eukaryote**
Control of transcription through specific DNA-binding proteins	Yes	Yes
Re-utilization of same DNA-binding motifs by different DNA-binding proteins	Yes	Yes
Activator proteins	Yes	Yes
Repressor proteins	Yes	Yes
Specificity of binding to DNA by regulatory protein	Specific	Highly specific
Affinity of binding	Strong	Very strong
Role played by chromatin structure	No	Yes
Coordinate control achieved with operons	Yes	Rare
Differential splicing	No	Yes
Attenuation	Yes	No
mRNA processing	No	Yes
Differential polyadenylation	No	Yes
Differential transport of RNA from nucleus to cytoplasm	No	Yes

In addition to these basic differences between eukaryotes and prokaryotes, multicellular eukaryotes must be able to use gene regulation to control cellular differentiation and the complex interactions of various types of differentiated cells within tissues and organs. Molecular biologists have traditionally assumed that eukaryotic gene expression was regulated predominantly at the point of transcriptional initiation. However there are many more steps in the process leading to an active product beyond transcription initiation. Recall that gene expression is defined by the production of an active gene product (**Fig. 16.1**). Transcript processing (including splicing), export of mRNA from the nucleus, translatability of the message, localization of the protein product in specific organelles in the cell, and modifications to the protein are all activities that can be regulated and that affect the amount of final active product.

With the discovery of alternative splicing in the late 1970s, followed by the progressive appreciation that post-transcriptional mechanisms are powerful means for gene activity control, the view that transcription was the primary process regulating gene expression radically changed. As a result, modern models for gene activity control visualize a complex and highly dynamic gene expression network within which the different biochemical machines responsible for transcription, splicing, and other molecular processes share some components and are therefore

tightly coupled. In spite of all this, it is still true that important decisions concerning the amount of gene product in the cell are made during the initiation of transcription, when RNA polymerase starts to make a primary transcript, or RNA copy, of a gene's template strand.

16.2 Control of Transcription Initiation

Three types of RNA polymerases transcribe genes in eukaryotes. RNA polymerase I (pol I) transcribes genes that encode the major RNA components of ribosomes (rRNAs). RNA polymerase II (pol II) transcribes genes that encode all proteins and micro-RNAs. RNA polymerase III (pol III) transcribes genes that encode the tRNAs as well as certain other, small RNA molecules. We focus on the major transcription activity that produces proteins: pol II transcription.

RNA polymerase II transcribes all protein-encoding genes

During transcription in eukaryotes, RNA polymerase II catalyzes the synthesis of a single-stranded RNA molecule—known as the primary transcript—that is complementary in base sequence to a gene's DNA template strand.

Most of the primary transcripts produced by pol II undergo further processing to generate mRNAs (see Fig. 8.14 on p. 262). During mRNA formation, introns are spliced out. In addition, ribonuclease cleaves pol II–transcribed primary transcripts to form a new 3′ end, to which the enzyme poly-A polymerase adds a poly-A tail; and the chemical modification of the 5′ end of the transcript produces a "5′GTP cap," which protects the molecule from degradation.

Measurements of mRNA and protein levels in eukaryotic cells have revealed that, usually, the more mRNA of a gene that accumulates in the cell, the greater the production of that gene's protein product; however, in many cases this correlation is not perfect because regulatory mechanisms affect RNA processing and translation.

The *cis*-acting regulatory regions: Promoters and enhancers

Although each of the regulatory regions of the thousands of pol II–transcribed genes in a eukaryotic genome is unique, they all contain two kinds of essential DNA sequences. The **promoter** is always very close to the gene's protein-coding region. It includes an initiation site, where transcription begins. The initiation site is most often a "TATA box, consisting of roughly seven nucleotides of the sequence T–A–T–A–(A or T)–A–(A or T), but it can also be an "initiator" box that is located downstream of the initiation

Figure 16.1 Gene expression in eukaryotes. Gene expression involves transcription and mRNA processing in the nucleus, then translation and modifications in the cytoplasm to produce an active protein.

Figure 16.2 *cis*-acting elements. *cis*-acting regulatory elements are regions of DNA sequence that lie nearby on the same DNA molecule as the gene they control. Promoter elements typically lie directly adjacent to the gene that they control. Enhancers that regulate expression can sometimes lie thousands of base pairs away from a gene.

***cis*-acting elements**

site. Binding of RNA polymerase to the TATA or initiation box allows a basal level of transcription (**Fig. 16.2**). **Enhancers** are regulatory sites that can be quite distant—up to tens of thousands of nucleotides away—from the promoter. Binding of proteins to enhancers augments or represses basal levels of transcription.

Identifying promoters and enhancers

The sequences that make up the promoter and enhancer sites for specific genes are identified using reporter gene fusions, as described in Chapter 15. Recall that reporter constructs are DNA molecules synthesized in the laboratory to contain a gene's postulated regulatory region, but with a "reporter" coding region inserted in place of the gene's own coding region (**Fig. 16.3a**). Investigators can systematically identify promoters and enhancers by altering reporter constructs through *in vitro* mutagenesis across a presumed regulatory region and then reintroducing the reporter constructs into the genome by transformation. Cells transformed with the reporter construct "report" the presence or absence of regulatory elements.

In assembling a reporter construct for this purpose, scientists replace the coding region of the gene whose regulation they are studying with the coding region of an easily identifiable product (the "reporter"), such as β-galactosidase or green fluorescent protein (GFP). (Recall that β-galactosidase produces a blue color in the presence of

a substrate known as X-Gal [review Fig. 9.7]; similarly, GFP fluoresces green when exposed to light of a particular wavelength.) Reporter constructs are particularly valuable for looking at mutations that affect gene expression rather than the amino acid composition of the gene's polypeptide product. Mutations that alter the amount of reporter synthesized help define the elements necessary for a gene's regulation (**Fig. 16.3b**).

> In contrast to prokaryotes, eukaryotes have three RNA polymerases. All transcription of genes that yield proteins is performed by RNA polymerase II (pol II). The *cis*-acting regulatory regions include promoters, which are found near the coding region and contain an initiation site, and enhancers, which may be distant and act to increase or repress the basal level of transcription.

The *trans*-acting proteins control transcription initiation

The binding of proteins to a gene's promoter and enhancer (or enhancers) controls the rates of transcriptional initiation. Different types of proteins bind to each of the *cis*-acting regulatory regions: *Basal factors* bind to the promoter; *activators* and *repressors* bind to the enhancers (**Fig. 16.4**). Additional regulatory proteins may interact with these regulators bound to sites on the DNA. The proteins that regulate transcription initiation are collectively known as transcription factors.

Figure 16.4 *trans*-acting factors. *trans*-acting genetic elements encode products called transcription factors that interact with *cis*-acting elements, either directly through DNA binding or indirectly through protein-protein interactions.

***trans*-acting gene products**

Figure 16.3 Identifying *cis*-acting sites. (a) A fusion between a gene's regulatory region and the GFP gene provides an easy way to monitor levels of transcription. **(b)** Base changes (mutations) that reduce transcription (and therefore the level of green fluorescent protein) identify regulatory sites.

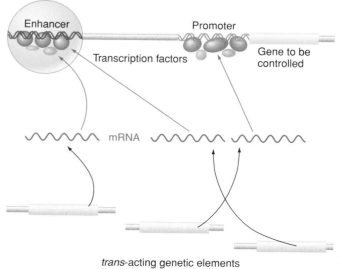

trans-acting genetic elements

Figure 16.5 Identifying *trans*-acting factors. (a) *trans*-acting factors bind to regulatory regions (enhancers) to increase transcription. **(b)** A *trans*-acting mutation that reduces transcription identifies a regulatory protein.

Figure 16.6 Basal factors bind to promoters of all protein-encoding genes. Schematic representation of the binding of the TATA box–binding protein (TBP) to the promoter DNA, the binding of two TBP-associated factors (TAFs) to TBP, and the binding of RNA polymerase (pol II) to these basal factors.

Just as with *cis*-acting regions, *trans*-acting elements can be identified using reporter gene fusions (**Fig. 16.5**). Mutations that alter the level of expression of a reporter, and that map far from the target gene or reporter construct, are likely to reside in *trans*-acting elements. Biochemical procedures can be used to isolate proteins that bind *in vitro* to *cis*-acting DNA sequences. Once researchers identify a *trans*-acting element, they can clone it for further study.

Basal factors

Basal factors assist the binding of RNA polymerase II to the promoter and the initiation of a low level of transcription called basal transcription (from which the basal factors get their name). The key component of the basal factor complex that forms on most promoters is the TATA box–binding protein, or **TBP** (so named because it binds to the TATA box described previously). The TBP is essential to the initiation of transcription from all class II genes that have a TATA box in their promoter. TBP associates with several other basal factors called TBP-associated factors, or **TAFs** (**Fig. 16.6**). The complex of basal factors binds to the proximal promoter in an ordered pathway of assembly. Once the complex has formed, basal transcription is initiated. Researchers have determined the structure of the TBP-TAF complex on the DNA at the TATA box and find there is a sharp bend in the DNA at the TATA box, induced by TBP.

The primary sequence and three-dimensional structure of the basal factors are highly conserved in all eukaryotes, from yeast to humans. This level of evolutionary conservation in sequence and structure underlies a high level of functional conservation across the eukaryotes, which has in turn facilitated the biochemical purification of some of these factors. For example, researchers isolated yeast

TBP—the first basal factor to be purified—through its ability to substitute for mammalian TBP *in vitro*.

Activators

Although similar sets of basal factors bind to all the promoters of the tens of thousands of genes in the eukaryotic genome, a cell can transcribe different genes into widely varying amounts of mRNA. This enormous range of transcriptional regulation occurs through the binding of different transcription factors to enhancer elements associated with different genes. When regulatory transcription factors bind to an enhancer element, they can interact directly or indirectly with basal factors at the promoter in a three-dimensional protein/DNA complex to cause an increase in transcriptional activity (**Fig. 16.7**). Due to their ability to increase transcriptional activity, these factors are called **activators.** Researchers have already identified hundreds of eukaryotic activators, and it is likely that each eukaryotic genome encodes several thousand of them. At the mechanistic level, transcriptional activator proteins bound at their target sites on DNA can increase RNA synthesis via three different, but not mutually exclusive, systems:

1. They could stimulate the "recruitment" of the basic transcription machinery (such as the RNA polymerase itself and/or some of its associated factors) to core promoter sequences by directly interacting with the components of this machinery;
2. They could stimulate the activity of the basal factors already bound to the promoter; and
3. Activators could facilitate the changes in chromatin structure that allow higher transcription levels.

Figure 16.7 Binding to enhancers increases transcriptional levels. In the presence of basal factors alone bound to the promoter, low levels of transcription occur. The binding of activator proteins to an enhancer element leads to an increase in transcription beyond the basal level.

Figure 16.8 Activator protein domains. Common motifs found in activator proteins include the helix-loop-helix, helix-turn-helix, and zinc-fingers.

Domains within Activators To carry out their function on selected subsets of genes (and not to all genes), transcriptional activator proteins must (a) bind to enhancer DNA in a sequence-specific way—and after binding, they must (b) be able to interact with other proteins to activate transcription. Two structural domains within the activator protein—the DNA-binding domain and the transcription-activator domain—mediate these two biochemical functions.

A rather small number of protein motifs appear over and over again in the DNA-binding domains of many different activator proteins (**Fig. 16.8**). The best characterized of these motifs are the helix-loop-helix and the helix-turn-helix conformations, which are also found in prokaryotic regulators and the zinc-finger motif, found mostly in eukaryotes. The general function of each of these motifs is to promote binding to the DNA double helix. The proteins fit within or interact within the major groove of DNA. Subtle differences in amino acid sequence among activators can specify high-affinity binding to different DNA sequences associated with different enhancer elements.

Some activators have a third domain that is responsive to specific signals from the environment. An example of activators with this type of domain are the steroid hormone receptors (**Fig. 16.9**). Each receptor has a domain that is unique for a particular steroid. The binding of this steroid causes an allosteric change that greatly increases the affinity of the DNA-binding domain of the protein for its target enhancer sequence. Once bound, the hormone-receptor

complex activates transcription of its target genes. In the absence of hormone, DNA binding does not occur, and target genes remain unactivated—that is, transcribed only at basal rates. A steroid hormone gene regulation system allows one organ in the human body (a hormone-producing gland) to control gene activity in other organs. There are no universal features of signal response domains.

Figure 16.9 Steroid hormone receptors. Some activator domains are themselves activated into a DNA-binding conformation through allosteric changes caused by the binding of a steroid hormone molecule to another domain within the activator protein.

Proteins and other molecules that play a role in transcriptional activation without binding directly to DNA are called **coactivators.** The hormone component of a DNA-bound hormone-receptor activation complex is one example of a coactivator. One of the most important protein coactivators is a large multiprotein complex composed of 25–30 proteins called Mediator. The Mediator is considered a central link within the enhancer–pol II promoter pathway. Mediator does not bind to DNA but serves as essential molecular bridge between the promoter and enhancer for many of the pol II promoters in all eukaryotic organisms (Fig. 16.7).

Formation of Dimers As in prokaryotes, many transcription regulators are multimeric proteins. Molecular analyses indicate that many eukaryotic transcription factors are homomers (that is, multimeric proteins composed of identical subunits) or heteromers (multimeric proteins composed of nonidentical subunits; review Fig. 7.27 on p. 230). Among the best-characterized transcription factors of this type is Jun, which can form dimers (multimers composed of two subunits) with either itself or with another protein called Fos (**Fig. 16.10**). The Jun-Jun dimers are *homodimers;* the Jun-Fos dimers are *heterodimers* and each of these dimers recognizes different enhancer sequences.

Dimerization occurs through yet another transcription factor domain, the **dimerization domain,** which is specialized for specific polypeptide-to-polypeptide interactions. As with other transcription factor domains, certain motifs recur in dimerization domains. One of the most common is the leucine zipper motif (**Fig. 16.11**), an amino

acid sequence that twirls into an α helix with leucine residues protruding at regular intervals. The motif received its name from the propensity of one leucine zipper motif to interlock like a zipper with a leucine zipper motif on another polypeptide. The ability of two leucine zippers to interlock depends on the specific amino acids that lie between the leucines.

The Jun and Fos polypeptides both contain leucine zippers in their dimerization domains. A Jun leucine zipper can interact with another Jun leucine zipper or with a Fos leucine zipper. But the Fos leucine zipper *cannot* interact with its own kind to form a homodimer. Neither Jun nor Fos alone can bind DNA, so neither can act as a transcription factor as a monomer. Thus the Jun-Fos transcription factor system can produce only two types of transcription factors: Jun-Jun proteins or Jun-Fos proteins. Both bind to the same enhancer elements, but with different affinities.

The ability to form heterodimers greatly increases the number of potential regulatory transcription complexes a cell can assemble from a set number of gene products. In theory, 100 polypeptides could combine in different ways to form 5000 different transcription factors; with 500 polypeptides, the number jumps to 125,000.

Repressors

Some transcription factors suppress the activation of transcription caused by activator proteins. Any transcription factor that has this effect is considered a **repressor.** Different repressors act in different ways. Some compete with activator proteins for binding to the same enhancer (**Fig. 16.12a**). When a repressor binds to an enhancer, it blocks the activator's access to the same sequence. The Myc-Max system described in the following section provides an example of this type of activator-repressor competition.

Some repressors operate without binding DNA at all. Instead, in a mechanism called *quenching,* they bind directly to a specific activator (**Fig. 16.12b**). In one type of quenching, a repressor binds to and blocks the DNA-binding region of an activator, thereby preventing the activator from attaching to its enhancer. In another type of quenching, a repressor binds to and blocks the activation domain of an activator. These blocked activators still bind to their enhancers, but once bound, they are unable to carry out activation. Quenching polypeptides that operate in this manner are termed **corepressors.** Just like coactivators, corepressors associate indirectly with enhancers through their interaction with DNA-binding proteins.

The repression resulting from both activator-repressor competition and quenching reduces activation, but it has no effect on basal transcription. As in prokaryotes, however, some eukaryotic repressors act directly on the promoter to eliminate almost all transcriptional activity. They can do this by binding to DNA sequences very close to

Figure 16.10 Jun-Jun and Jun-Fos dimers. Homodimers contain two identical polypeptides whereas heterodimers contain two different polypeptides.

Homodimer
(Jun - Jun)

Heterodimer
(Jun - Fos)

Figure 16.11 Leucine zipper. A common peptide motif present within dimerization domains is the leucine zipper.

Leucine zipper

Dimerization domain

DNA-binding domain

Figure 16.12 Repressor proteins act through competition or quenching. (a) Some repressor proteins act by *competing* for the same enhancer elements as activator proteins. But repressor proteins have no activation domain, so when they bind to enhancers, no activation of transcription can occur. **(b)** A second class of repressors act by binding directly to the activator proteins themselves to *quench* activation in one of two ways. Type I quenching is achieved when the repressor prevents the activator from reaching the enhancer. Type II quenching is achieved when the activator can bind to the enhancer, but the repressor prevents the activation domain from binding to basal proteins.

(a) Competition for binding between repressor and activator proteins

Binding of repressor to enhancer blocks binding of activator.

(b) Quenching

Type I: Repressor binds to and blocks the DNA-binding region of an activator.

DNA-binding domain is blocked. Activator cannot bind to enhancer.

Type II: Repressor binds to and blocks the activation domain of an activator.

Activator can bind to enhancer, but cannot carry out activation.

Figure 16.13 The same transcription factors can play different roles in different cells. (a) In haploid α yeast cells, the α2 factor acts to silence the set of "a" genes. **(b)** In α/a diploid yeast cells, the α2 factor dimerizes with the a1 factor and acts to silence the set of haploid-specific genes.

(a) Haploid α cell

"a" genes are silenced

Haploid-specific genes are active

(b) Diploid α /a cell

"a" genes are silenced

Binding of α2 and a1 alters repressor's DNA-binding specificity. Haploid-specific genes are silenced; diploid state is maintained.

the promoter and thereby blocking RNA polymerase's access to the promoter. Or they can bind to DNA sequences further from the promoter and then reach over and contact the basal factor complex at the promoter, causing the DNA between the enhancer and promoter to loop out and allow contact between the repressor and the basal factor complex. This second mechanism also denies RNA polymerase access to the promoter and reduces transcription below the basal level.

Whether a transcription factor acts as an activator or repressor, or has no effect at all, depends not only on the cell type in which it is expressed but also on the gene it is regulating. This is one reason why all *cis*-acting elements bound by either activators or repressors are referred to as enhancers, even though some may actually repress transcription when associated with the appropriate protein.

The specificity of transcription factors can be altered by other molecules in the cell. One example of this phe-

nomenon is observed with the yeast α2 repressor, which helps determine the mating type of *a* cell. Yeast cells can be either haploid or diploid, and haploid cells come in two mating types: α and *a*. In *a* cells, the α2 repressor binds to enhancers that control the activity of a set of *a*-determining genes, whose expression would make the cell type *a*. The binding of the α2 repressor to these *a*-determining genes is one step in the generation of α cells (**Fig. 16.13a**). In diploid yeast cells, however, the same α2 repressor plays an additional role. In such cells, expression of the polypeptide known as a1 occurs; the binding of a1 to the α2 repressor alters the repressor's DNA-binding specificity such that α2/a1 now binds to enhancers associated with a set of haploid-specific genes, repressing the expression of those genes (In diploid cells α2 alone still represses the *a* genes.) (**Fig. 16.13b**). To summarize, in diploid cells, the α2 repressor maintains the diploid state by repressing haploid-specific genes.

The *trans*-acting proteins include basal factors that bind to promoters, and activators and repressors that bind to enhancers. Basal factors are responsible for a basal transcription level. Activators have a number of binding domains, and binding at one or more of these domains can change its conformation and thus its affinity to enhancers. Repressors suppress the action of activators by competing for binding at the enhancer or by binding directly with the activator.

The Myc-Max mechanism can activate or repress transcription

The Myc-Max transcription factor system is one in which dimer structure and concentrations of subunits determine whether transcription is activated or repressed. Through the identification of mutations affecting *myc* gene expression in one class of lymphocytes, researchers showed that *myc* plays a critical role in the regulation of cell proliferation. This class of lymphocytes is responsible for Burkitt's lymphoma, a form of cancer. Genetic data suggested that the Myc protein is a transcription factor, but biochemists could find no evidence for this function *in vitro*. Their experiments revealed that even though the Myc polypeptide contains both a helix-loop-helix (HLH) motif and a leucine zipper, it cannot bind to DNA or form homodimers. The apparent contradiction between genetic and biochemical results stymied the scientists who first associated mutations in the *myc* gene with Burkitt's lymphoma and other forms of cancer.

The discovery of the *max* gene product helped resolve this dilemma. Like Myc, Max contains an HLH motif and a leucine zipper (**Fig. 16.14**). Moreover, both Myc and Max contain another, more recently defined DNA-binding motif called a "basic motif" (because it contains mostly basic amino acids). Unlike Myc, however, the Max polypeptide can form homodimers. When one mixes Max with Myc, heterodimers of the two polypeptides form.

The Myc polypeptide contains an activation domain, but when the molecule is on its own, it cannot bind DNA and thus cannot serve as an activator. The Max polypeptide, on the other hand, can form homodimers and can bind DNA when present without Myc—but Max has no activation domain, so it cannot function as an activator even when it does bind to DNA (**Fig. 16.15a**). Only when Myc and Max come together in a heterodimer do both DNA binding and Myc-directed activation become possible, and a transcriptional activator is born. Myc-Max

heterodimers and Max-Max homodimers both bind to the same enhancer sequences associated with multiple genes that contribute to cell proliferation. (**Fig. 16.15b**) The binding of a heterodimer results in transcriptional activation, whereas the binding of a homodimer results in transcriptional repression.

One final characteristic of this system is that Myc polypeptides have a much higher affinity for Max polypeptides than Max has for itself. Thus, when Myc and Max are in solution together, the predominant dimer is the heterodimer. With this extensive background, we are ready to see how the cell uses the Myc-Max system to respond rapidly to signals that tell it to proliferate or stop proliferating.

The *max* gene is expressed in all cells at all times, but because its protein product does not carry an activation domain, Max-Max homodimers, when bound to enhancer DNA, inhibit transcription and therefore inhibit cell proliferation. By contrast, the *myc* gene is not universally expressed; the Myc polypeptide is normally synthesized in cells undergoing proliferation but not in cells at rest.

As soon as a cell expresses its *myc* gene, virtually all its Max-Max homodimers convert to Myc-Max heterodimers that bind to the enhancers previously bound by the

Figure 16.15 Myc-Max system of activation and repression. (a) Gene repression results when a cell makes only the Max polypeptide. **(b)** Gene activation occurs when a cell makes both Myc and Max.

(a) Expression of Max monomer alone

(b) Expression of Myc and Max

Figure 16.14 Comparative structures of Myc and Max. Linear illustration of the Myc and Max polypeptides and the locations of different domains. The Myc polypeptide has an activation domain, whereas the Max polypeptide does not. Both polypeptides have a DNA-binding domain with a basic amino acid motif and a dimerization domain with adjacent helix-loop-helix (HLH) and leucine zipper (LZ) motifs.

homodimers. Because the heterodimers include the Myc activation domain, the binding of Myc-Max complexes induces the expression of genes required for cell proliferation. Although researchers have not yet characterized all the genes activated by the Myc-Max dimer, they know that the genes guide the cell through its mitotic cycle. Thus, each cell in which *myc* is active divides to produce two daughter cells.

> The Myc-Max system provides a rapid genetic switch for regulating cell division during the cell proliferation and terminal differentiation phases of development. When myc is expressed, Myc-Max heterodimers immediately form, serving as transcription activators.

Complex regulatory regions enable fine-tuning of gene expression

In complex multicellular organisms, a large percentage of genes are devoted to transcriptional regulation. Of the estimated 20,000–30,000 genes in the human genome, scientists estimate that about 2000 genes encode transcription regulatory proteins. Each gene can have many proteins that regulate its expression, but each regulatory protein may act on many different genes. The number of possible combinations of regulators is staggering and provides the flexibility important for differentiation of cells and development in multicellular eukaryotes. Gene regulation is not just a matter of turning genes on and off, however. It also entails fine-tuning the precise level of transcription—higher or lower in different cells, and higher or lower in cells of the same tissue but at different stages of development. It also includes mechanisms that allow each cell to modify its program of gene activity in response to constantly changing signals from its neighbors. Organisms accomplish the orchestration of transcription from each of tens of thousands of genes through *cis*-acting regulatory regions that are often far more complex than those we have so far described.

Enhancers and enhanceosomes

A regulatory region may contain a dozen or more enhancer elements, each with the ability to bind different activators and repressors, with varying affinities. At any moment, there may be dozens of transcription factors in the cell whose affinities for DNA or other polypeptides are being modulated by binding to hormones or other molecules. Different sets of these transcription factors compete for different enhancers within the regulatory region. And different sets of coactivators and corepressors compete with each other for binding to different activators or repressors. The biochemical integration of all this information yields a precise level of transcriptional activation or repression.

The term **enhanceosome** is used to describe a multimeric complex of proteins and other small molecules associated with an enhancer element (see Fig. 16.4); the multimeric complex of proteins can include activators, coactivators, and other types of transcription factors known as repressors and corepressors. Slight changes in a cell's environment can dispatch signal molecules that cause changes in the balance of transcription factors or in their relative affinities for DNA or for each other. These changes, in turn, lead to the assembly of an altered enhanceosome, which recalibrates gene activity. In short, a large, exquisitely controlled machinery determines the level of primary transcript produced.

Control of the *string* gene in *Drosophila*

The enhancer regions of some class II genes are very large, containing multiple elements that make possible the fine-tuned regulation of a gene. This is particularly true for those genes in multicellular eukaryotes that must be expressed in many different tissues. The *string* gene in *Drosophila* is an example. The gene encodes a protein that activates the fourteenth mitosis of embryonic development. This fourteenth mitosis begins just after membranes simultaneously form around the roughly 6000 nuclei of the giant syncytium that resulted from the first 13 mitoses. What is interesting about the fourteenth mitosis is that cells in different areas, or domains, of the embryo enter this division at different times in an intricate but reproducible temporal pattern (**Fig. 16.16a**). Thus, although the cells of each domain go through a fourteenth nuclear division, the time at which that mitosis takes place is different for different domains.

Remarkably, the cells within each domain simultaneously express the *string* gene just before they enter mitosis; in fact, expression of the *string* gene induces their entry into the mitotic cycle. In *string* mutants, all embryonic cells arrest in the G_2 stage of cycle 14 and never undergo mitosis. A roughly 35 kb region upstream of the *Drosophila string* gene contains binding sites for many transcription factors known to regulate formation of the *Drosophila* body pattern (**Fig. 16.16b**). The complex interaction of these factors ensures that the *string* gene is turned on in the cells of each embryonic domain at the correct time.

> An enhanceosome is a large complex of proteins associated with an enhancer; its many components can undergo molecular alteration to fine-tune transcription according to the cell's needs and the environment. The *string* gene in *Drosophila* is an example of how transcription can be timed by binding of different transcription factors to coincide with cell proliferation during development.

Figure 16.16 *Drosophila string* **gene enhancer. (a)** *Colors* indicate individual mitotic domains during the fourteenth cell cycle of the fruit fly embryo. The cells within each domain divide synchronously, but different domains initiate their divisions at different times. Both lateral and cross-sectional views of the embryo are shown. **(b)** Proteins that bind to the enhancer region in each of these developmental mitotic domains to turn on *string* at the appropriate time are indicated (CNS: central nervous system; PNS: peripheral nervous system).

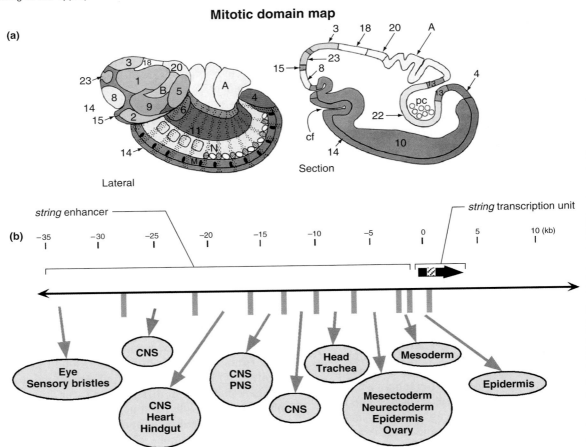

16.3 Chromatin Structure and Epigenetic Effects

In Chapter 12 you learned that the DNA of eukaryotic genomes does not float freely in the nucleus but is packaged into chromatin. The basic repeating structural unit of chromatin is the nucleosome, which consists of a ball of histone proteins (two each of H2A, H2B, H3, and H4) around which is wrapped approximately 160 bp of DNA.

In vitro experiments show that basal factors and RNA polymerase readily bind to promoters on naked DNA and initiate high levels of transcription in the absence of activator proteins (**Fig. 16.17a**). One significant function of chromatin, then, is the reduction of transcription from all genes to a very low level (**Fig. 16.17b**). In contrast to transcriptional modulation in prokaryotes, which requires active repression through the binding of repressors to *cis*-acting elements, the normal structure of chromatin in eukaryotes is sufficient by itself to maintain transcriptional activity at the minimal, basal level. In essence, the nucleosomes may sequester promoters, such that they are inaccessible to RNA polymerase and transcription factors.

Altered chromatin structure can cause changes in gene expression and therefore phenotypic changes in a cell or an organism. These changes may be inherited from one generation to the next. These changes are not due to changes in the DNA sequence, but are modifications of the genomic blueprint and are know as **epigenetic** changes.

Histone tails may be chemically modified

Recall that the N-terminal tails of histones H3 and H4 can be modified in one of several ways, including methylation and acetylation, phosphorylation, ubiquitination, and more. Histone N-terminal tails extend outward from the nucleosome, and they can therefore influence interaction with other nucleosomes as well as with regulatory factors. These histone tail modifications can affect higher-order chromatin structures.

Figure 16.17 Chromatin reduces transcription. (a) DNA molecules containing a promoter and an associated gene can be purified away from chromatin proteins *in vitro*. The addition of basal factors and RNA polymerase to this purified DNA induces high levels of transcription. **(b)** Within the eukaryotic nucleus, DNA is present within chromatin. Promoter regions are generally sequestered within the nucleosome and only rarely bind to basal factors and RNA polymerase. Thus, the chromatin structure maintains basal transcription at very low levels.

(a) Naked promoter binds RNA polymerase and basal factors.

(b) Chromatin reduces binding to basal factors and RNA pol II to very low levels.

Modifications of histones have been closely linked to transcriptional regulation and are required for many biological processes, including the differentiation of pluripotent stem cells into specific tissue lineages. For instance, some transcription factors can establish histone modifications around selected loci in embryonic stem cells, and thus determine lineage-specific gene expression patterns. Thus, histone covalent modifications seem to have crucial roles for the establishment of genetic programs during development.

Methylation of DNA can also control transcription

Methylation of DNA—the addition of a methyl (CH_3) group—is another common modification associated with transcription changes. Methylation occurs at the fifth carbon of the cytosine base in a CpG dinucleotide pair (see Fig. 6.9a on p. 169).

It is possible to determine the state of methylation of a DNA region by using two restriction enzymes that both cleave at a sequence containing a CG dinucleotide but that have different sensitivities to the methylation of the DNA substrate. For example, *Hpa*II and *Msp*I both cleave at CCGG, but *Hpa*II does not cleave if the middle C of this site is methylated; in contrast, *Msp*I can cleave regardless (**Fig. 16.18**). Thus, by digesting genomic DNA with *Hpa*II and *Msp*I and using a specific DNA probe on a Southern blot, you can determine whether a given CCGG sequence is methylated. Although methylation is associated with transcription silencing, we know it cannot be the only mechanism, because some organisms that show silencing, such as yeast, do not contain methylated DNA.

Figure 16.18 Determining methylation state of DNA. A determination of the methylation status of a DNA region can be made using a pair of restriction enzymes that both recognize the same base sequence, with one being able to digest methylated DNA, while the other can't. In this example, the restriction site is CCGG, and the enzymes are *Msp*I, which can digest both methylated and unmethylated sites, and *Hpa*II, which cannot digest methylated sites. If a methylated site is present between two unmethylated sites, *Hpa*II digestion will leave a larger fragment than *Msp*I. After electrophoresis and Southern blot analysis with a probe that hybridizes to a sequence on one side of the methylated site, there will be a clearly observable difference in band size.

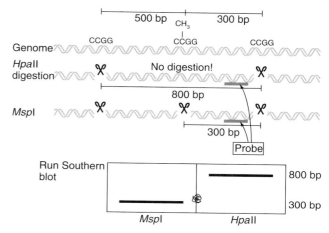

The remodeling of chromatin mediates activation of transcription

Nucleosomes can be repositioned or bumped off the DNA to expose promoter sequences and other regulatory sequences, thereby allowing high levels of transcription. This activity, known as *chromatin remodeling,* is characteristic of some of the transcriptional activators. Proteins associated together that carry out this function are called remodeling complexes (**Fig. 16.19**). The freed DNA becomes much more accessible to basal transcription factors, to RNA polymerase, and probably to enhancer binding transcription factors allowing them to interact with DNA sequences to affect transcription.

Chromosomal regions from which the nucleosomes have been eliminated are experimentally recognizable

Figure 16.19 Chromatin remodeling. Chromatin remodeling can expose the promoter region. Remodeling proteins cause specific nucleosomes to unravel in specific cells at specific times during differentiation or development. Exposed promoter regions more readily bind basal factors.

Chromatin remodeling can expose promoter.

through their hypersensitivity to the enzyme DNase. When one scans a chromosome with the enzyme for the presence of **DNase hypersensitive (DH) sites,** the sites show up at the 5′ ends of genes that are either undergoing transcription or are being prepared for transcription in a later step of cellular differentiation (see Fig. 12.13). For example, DH sites appear at the 5′ end of the β-globin gene in human stem cells that are precursors to the hematopoietic cells in which the gene will be activated, but not in cells from other differentiative pathways.

Remodeling by SWI-SNF

Remodeling of chromatin is one way in which gene expression changes occur. One of the best-studied remodeling complexes involves the SWI-SNF proteins in yeast. These proteins form a multisubunit complex that disrupts chromatin structure by removing or repositioning nucleosomes. The resulting chromatin decompaction gives basal factors much greater access to promoter regions, and consequently, transcription rapidly accelerates (**Fig. 16.20**). The SWI-SNF complexes use the energy of ATP hydrolysis to alter nucleosome positioning relative to a segment of DNA.

In *Drosophila,* mutations in the gene encoding the ATPase subunit of the SWI-SNF complex impair transcription by RNA polymerase II suggesting a general role of these remodeling complexes in gene activation. Human cells contain related multisubunit protein complexes that also influence nucleosome position or structure, suggesting that this particular nucleosome-disrupting machinery has been conserved throughout evolution. The SWI-SNF protein complex represents just one of the many that help remodel chromatin at specific chromosomal locations in specific cells at particular points of development.

Hypercondensation of chromatin

As described in Chapter 12, many regions of eukaryotic chromosomes, including parts of centromeres and telomeres and all of Barr bodies, are highly condensed into heterochromatic DNA. As a result, most of the genes contained

Figure 16.20 SWI-SNF remodeler. The SWI-SNF protein complex is a well-characterized remodeling apparatus that functions within yeast cells to expose promoter regions to basal factors, RNA polymerase, and transcriptional activation.

SWI-SNF remodeling complex

The SWI-SNF multisubunit destabilizes chromatin structure and gives transcription machinery access to the promoter.

Figure 16.21 Condensed chromatin. Normal chromatin in standard nucleosome conformation can be converted into tightly packed heterochromatin with the addition of methyl groups to a series of cytosine bases within a local DNA region.

in heterochromatin are transcriptionally inactive or silenced (**Fig. 16.21**). We know that the heterochromatic regions are characterized by specific methylation on a lysine in histone H3 and also by methylation of the CpG dinucleotides in DNA.

The heterochromatic state is inherited from one cell generation to the next—a characteristic of an *epigenetic* phenomenon. Epigenetic modifications have phenotypic consequences that are inherited, but without a change in the DNA sequence. Examples described in earlier chapters included X inactivation and position-effect variegation in *Drosophila*. In X chromosome inactivation, alleles on one chromosome are not expressed, and this can have phenotypic consequences.

Let's look at a specific example in which a human female is heterozygous for the anhidrotic ectodermal dysplasia gene (on the X chromosome), which is required for sweat gland development as well as development of other ectoderm-associated tissues and organs. All cells in the female have the same genotype, but in some cells, the wild-type allele is on the inactivated X chromosome, exposing the mutant phenotype. The phenotype changes without a change in genotype, and this change is inherited in subsequent cell divisions. Therefore, an affected woman may have areas of skin that contain sweat glands while other areas do not, depending on the point at which the X chromosome with the wild-type gene became inactivated.

Insight into the mechanism of silencing comes from studies of mutations that give rise to sterility in yeast. Recall that yeast cells come in two mating types—α and a—and the α2 gene product represses certain a-determining genes. The chromosomal locus of the α2 gene is known as MAT (for <u>ma</u>ting <u>t</u>ype). In normally mating yeast cells, there are two additional copies of the MAT locus called HML and HMR; located near the telomeres on each arm of chromosome III, these loci are transcriptionally silent. Mutations that reduce or destroy silencing at these loci cause sterility because they allow the simultaneous expression of α and a information. The resulting cells, which behave as diploids, do not mate.

Analysis of these mutations identified the family of *SIR* genes. The SIR polypeptide products associate to

Figure 16.22 Silencing by SIR complex. The SIR complex of polypeptides can bind to basal factors associated with the promoters of the *HML* and *HMR* genes. This binding, in turn, causes the SIR complex to interact with the histones H3 and H4 present in downstream nucleosomes associated with the gene itself. The result is the complete silencing of transcription.

SIR complex binds to basal factors and interacts with H3 and H4 components of histones.

form a *trans*-acting complex that mediates silencing by acting at *cis*-acting sites near HML and HMR. Null mutations that eliminate the activity of any *SIR* gene or mutations that delete a exacting site abolish silencing. The SIR complex binds to other polypeptides, and these larger complexes interact with histones H3 and H4 (**Fig. 16.22**). These interactions with the histones establish a silenced chromosomal domain that remains hidden from the activators and repressors of transcription.

> Alterations to chromatin structure can control transcription. These include additions of chemical groups to histone tails, methylation of DNA at cytosine bases, removal or repositioning of nucleosomes, and hypercondensation of chromatin such as occurs with the Barr body. Some are epigenetic effects passed on from one cell generation to the next.

Genomic imprinting results from transcriptional silencing

A major tenet of Mendelian genetics is that the parental origin of an allele—whether it comes from the mother or the father—does not affect its function in the F_1 generation. For the vast majority of genes in plants and animals, this principle still holds true today. Surprisingly, however, experiments and pedigree analyses have uncovered convincing evidence of exceptions to this general rule for some genes in mammals.

The phenomenon in which the expression pattern of a gene depends on the parent that transmits it is known as **genomic imprinting.** In most cases of genomic imprinting, the copy of a gene inherited from one parent is transcriptionally inactive in all or most of the tissues in which the copy from the other parent is active. The term "imprinting" signifies that whatever silences the maternal or paternal copy of an imprinted gene is not encoded in its DNA

sequence; rather the "silencer" exercises its effect through some epigenetic alteration of the DNA or chromatin during gametogenesis. With the development of molecular tools able to distinguish between transcripts of a gene from either parental homolog, geneticists observed that expression of a small number of genes—scattered around the genome, but often found in clusters—depends on whether the copy of the gene comes from the female parent or the male parent. The silencing effect is epigenetic and does not involve a change in DNA sequence.

An understanding of the mechanism behind imprinted genes came from studies of the transmission of a deletion in the chromosome 7 insulin-like growth factor gene (*Igf2*) in mice. Mice inheriting the deletion from the paternal side were small, whereas mice inheriting the same deletion from the maternal side were normal size. The simplest explanation of these results is based on a model in which the *Igf2* gene copy inherited from the mother is normally silenced (**Fig. 16.23a** on pp. 566–567). Thus, a deletion inherited from the mother produces no phenotypic effect because the maternal allele is not expressed anyway. If the deletion comes from the father, however, it produces a phenotypic effect because the animal is now unable to make any IGF2 products.

A hypothesis for how this imprint can be maintained from one generation to the next is that the pattern of methylation can be transmitted during DNA replication, with the presence of a methyl group on one strand of a newly synthesized double helix signaling methylase enzymes to add a methyl group to the other strand. For imprinted genes, the imprint is reset during meiosis and passed on to the next generation.

Insulators

Although the biochemical mechanism of genomic imprinting is not yet completely understood, one important component is the methylation of cytosines in CG dinucleotides within the imprinted region (**Fig. 16.23b**). The methylated C's silence the gene or genes in the region by preventing RNA polymerase and other transcription factors from gaining access to the DNA. The methylation pattern is not transient as a response to a short-term stimulus, but is stably inherited.

Further insight into the mechanism of *Igf2* imprinting came from the surprising finding that *H19*, found just 70 kb downstream of *Igf2*, is also imprinted, but in the opposite way. With *H19*, the copy inherited from the father is silenced and the copy inherited from the mother is active in normal mice. A model of how imprinting works at both *H19* and *Igf2* is based on detailed biochemical and genetic studies of a 100 kb region encompassing both genes. Researchers identified an enhancer region downstream of the *H19* gene that can interact with promoters for both genes (**Fig. 16.23c**). In the region between the two genes lies another type of transcriptional regulation element called an **insulator.** When an insulator becomes functional, it stops communication

FEATURE FIGURE 16.23

Genomic Imprinting

(a) Deletion of *Igf2* causes mutant phenotype only when transmitted by father.

M – maternal chromosome
P – paternal chromosome

Deletion inherited from mother
Normal levels of *Igf2* expression
Normal size

Deletion inherited from father
No active *Igf2*
Small size

The phenotypic effect of an *Igf2* deletion is determined by the parent transmitting the mutant locus. This parent-of-origin effect can be demonstrated in the two-generation cross illustrated here.

(b) Methylation of complementary strands of DNA

Nonmethylated homolog

Methylated homolog

Replication
Mitosis
Cell division

New CH₃ groups

Methylase recognizes methyl group on one strand of the helix and then adds a methyl group to the other strand.

An epigenetic state of DNA methylation can be maintained across cell generations. This is accomplished by the activity of DNA methylases that recognize methyl groups on one strand of a double helix and respond by methylating the opposite strand.

(c) Methylation of paternally inherited *H19* promoter

Reciprocal parent-of-origin expression occurs with the *Igf2–H19* gene pair. Only the unmethylated insulator between the two genes can bind to the protein CTCF. On the maternal chromosome, the enhancer only has access to the *H19* promoter. On the paternal chromosome, methylation occurs only at the insulator and the *H19* promoter (indicated with darkened circles). This serves the double purpose of blocking transcription of *H19* and allowing access of the enhancer to *Igf2*. In mouse embryos lacking methylase, the paternal chromosome behaves biochemically like the maternal chromosome.

(d) The resetting of genomic imprints during meiosis

Follow the transmission of a pair of homologous chromosomes (homolog 1 from the mother and homolog 2 from the father) from gametes through fertilization and the development of female and male progeny, to meiosis and the creation of a new set of gametes. Maternally imprinted genes are shown in red, paternally imprinted genes in black. The cellular machinery erases the old imprints and establishes new ones in germs cells during meiosis. Note that in the second generation, one of the chromosomes in both egg (homolog 2) and sperm (homolog 1) will be differently imprinted than the way it was in the first generation.

(e) Genomic imprinting and human disease

Paternal imprinting

In each pedigree, affected individuals (represented by filled-in, orange circles and squares) are heterozygotes for a deletion removing a gene that has either a paternal or a maternal imprint. In these pedigrees, a dotted symbol indicates individuals carrying a deleted chromosome but not displaying the mutant phenotype.

Maternal imprinting

between enhancers on one side of it and promoters on the other side. Insulators exist throughout the genome, limiting the chromatin region over which an enhancer can operate. Without insulators, enhancers could wreak havoc in a cell by turning on genes at DNA distances of hundreds of kilobases.

In the *Igf2-H19* region, the insulator DNA becomes functional by binding a protein called CTCF. The binding normally occurs on the maternal chromosome. As a result, the enhancer element on the maternal chromosome can interact only with the promoter of *H19;* this interaction, of course, turns on the *H19* gene. In such a situation, the *Igf2* gene remains unexpressed. On the paternal chromosome, by contrast, both the insulator and the *H19* promoter are methylated. Because methylation of the insulator prevents the binding of CTCF, the insulator is not functional; and without a functional insulator, the enhancer downstream of *H19* can reach over a great distance to activate transcription from the *Igf2* promoter. In addition, methylation of the *H19* promoter suppresses transcription of the paternal *H19* gene. Imprinting of the paternal chromosome by methylation thus turns on transcription of *Igf2* and prevents transcription of *H19.*

This epigenetic imprint remains throughout the life of the mammal, but it is erased and regenerated during each passage of the gene through the germ line into the next generation (**Fig. 16.23d**). Some genes receive an imprint in the maternal germ line; others receive it in the paternal germ line. For each gene subject to this effect, imprinting occurs in either the maternal or paternal line, never in both.

Inheritance pattern of imprinted genes

Before the late 1980s, clinical geneticists were accustomed to seeing sex-linked differences in inherited phenotypes related to the sex of the affected individual. With imprinting, however, it is the sex of the parent carrying a mutant allele that counts, and not the sex of the individual inheriting the mutation. After the discovery of imprinting in mice, medical geneticists reanalyzed human pedigrees and determined retrospectively that what appeared to be instances of incomplete penetrance were actually manifestations of imprinting (**Fig. 16.23e**). An inactivating mutation in a maternally imprinted gene could pass unnoticed from mother to daughter for many generations (because the maternally derived gene copy is inactive due to imprinting). If, however, the mutation passed from mother to son, the son would have a normal phenotype (having received an active wild-type allele from his father), but the son's children, both boys and girls, would each have a 50% chance of receiving a mutant paternal allele and therefore expressing the mutant phenotype resulting from the absence of any gene activity.

Evidence for imprinting as a contributing factor now exists for a variety of human developmental disorders, including the related pair of syndromes known as Prader-Willi syndrome and Angelman syndrome. Children with Prader-Willi syndrome have small hands and feet, underdeveloped gonads and genitalia, a short stature, and mental retardation; they are also compulsive overeaters and obese. Children affected by Angelman syndrome have red cheeks, a large jaw, a large mouth with a prominent tongue, and a happy disposition accompanied by excessive laughing; they also show severe mental and motor retardation. Both syndromes are often associated with small deletions in the q11–13 region of chromosome 15. When the deletions are inherited from the father, the child develops Prader-Willi syndrome; when the deletions come from the mother, the child has Angelman syndrome.

The explanation for this phenomenon is that at least two genes in the region of these deletions are differently imprinted. One gene is maternally imprinted: Children receiving a deleted chromosome from their father and a wild-type (nondeleted) chromosome with an imprinted copy of this gene from their mother exhibit Prader-Willi syndrome because the imprinted, wild-type gene is inactivated. In the case of Angelman syndrome, a different gene in the same region is paternally imprinted: Children receiving a deleted chromosome from their mother and wild-type, imprinted gene from their father develop this syndrome.

> Imprinting appears to be accomplished largely by DNA methylation during gametogenesis. In some cases, a functionalized insulator region between two genes selectively interferes with transcription of one or the other of the genes. Some cases of incomplete penetrance have been found to result from imprinting. The inheritance pattern may resemble that of sex-linked alleles, but with generation skipping.

16.4 Regulation After Transcription

Gene regulation can take place at any point in the process of gene expression. So far we have mainly discussed the mechanisms that influence rates of transcription; some other systems regulate posttranscriptional events—these include RNA splicing; RNA stability; RNA localization; protein synthesis, stability, and localization. The regulation of all these processes relies on regulatory proteins as well as on small RNAs.

RNA splicing helps regulate gene expression

One surprise at the completion of genome projects for several complex organisms was that the number of genes was lower than originally anticipated. And yet, multicellular organisms require a large number of proteins for development and for physiological functions of different cell types, tissues, and organs. One way to generate more diversity of proteins to fulfill different needs is to splice primary transcripts into distinct mRNAS that produce different proteins. Alternative splicing is a common feature in eukaryotes and contributes to the mechanisms for regulating gene expression (review Fig. 8.18).

One example where we understand the players in regulating RNA splicing and the importance of alternative splicing is found in the regulation of the *Sxl* gene in *Drosophila*. As you will see in the comprehensive example at the end of this chapter, transcription factors in very early female (XX) embryos activate the expression of a key gene called *Sxl* through a promoter called the early promoter (P_e). The cellular machinery splices the resulting transcript to create an mRNA that is translated into the Sxl protein, which is essential to the female-specific developmental program. The *Sxl* gene is not transcribed in early male (XY) embryos, so these embryos do not make the Sxl protein (**Fig. 16.24a**).

Later in development, the transcription factors activating the *Sxl* early promoter in females disappear; but to develop as females, these animals still need the Sxl protein. How can they still make the Sxl protein they need? The answer is that later in embryogenesis, the *Sxl* gene in both males and females is transcribed from another promoter—the late promoter (P_L) (**Fig. 16.24b**). In males, splicing of the primary *Sxl* transcript generates an RNA that includes an exon (exon 3) containing a stop codon in its reading frame. As a result, this RNA in males is not productive—it does not generate any Sxl protein. In females, however, the Sxl protein previously produced by transcription from the early promoter influences the splicing of the primary transcript initiated at the late promoter. When the earlier-made Sxl protein binds to the later-transcribed RNA, this binding alters the splicing pathway such that exon 3 is no longer part of the final mRNA. Without exon 3, the mRNA is productive—that is, it can be translated to make more Sxl protein. Thus, a small amount of Sxl protein synthesized very early in development establishes a positive feedback loop that ensures more fabrication of Sxl protein later in development.

> Alternative splicing allows transcripts to be combined in different ways, increasing the variety of proteins a genome may produce. Splicing also serves to regulate gene expression by restricting or allowing certain combinations of transcripts.

Some small RNAs are responsible for RNA interference

In the first five years of the twenty-first century, a new family of gene regulators was discovered in the form of small specialized RNAs that prevent the expression of specific genes through complementary base pairing. Several classes of small regulatory RNAs have now been described, including **micro-RNAs (miRNAs)** and **small interfering RNAs (siRNAs).** New families of small RNAs continue to be discovered, making some of the divisions between classes ever more diffuse. Each small

Figure 16.24 Differential RNA splicing in *Drosophila* development. (a) In the early female—but not the male—*Drosophila* embryo, transcriptional activators initiate transcription from the P_e promoter of *Sxl* to produce an mRNA that encodes the Sxl protein. **(b)** Later in development, transcriptional activators that bind the P_L promoter are produced in both male and female animals. When the Sxl protein is present, as it is in females, it causes the splicing apparatus to skip over this exon and splice exon 2 directly to exon 4. The resulting RNA molecule has an intact coding sequence and can be translated into more Sxl protein. This results in a feedback loop that maintains the presence of Sxl protein in females but not in males.

(a) Early embryo

(b) Sxl protein regulates the splicing of its mRNA

RNA class is generated through distinct pathways, leading to the production of RNAs of slightly different length but always within the range of 21–30 nucleotides.

To exert their functions, each small RNA class requires distinct members of the Argonaute/Piwi protein family with which they form ribonucleoprotein complexes. The complexes are able to recognize nucleic acid targets with perfect or partial complementary. These small RNAs primarily regulate gene activity at the posttranscriptional level through the regulation of RNA stability or translation, but some recent reports suggest that they may also act at the transcriptional level—for instance, by affecting chromatin structure.

Why were these very important regulators not recognized until recently? The answer probably lies in the intrinsic properties of these molecules. For example, because of their reduced size, they are easily missed by most standard biochemical RNA analysis methods; their short length also makes them very poor targets for inactivation through classical genetic approaches. In addition, given that many miRNAs appear to be able to compensate for each other's function—a phenomenon known as *genetic redundancy*—conventional genetic screens have often failed to expose the biological significance of losing individual small RNAs. The first two miRNAs (*lin-4* and *let-7*) were discovered by genetic experiments in the worm *Caenorhabditis elegans*. Shortly afterward, siRNAs were found in animals, plants, and fungi as key molecular mediators of a phenomenon known as sequence-specific gene silencing, or RNA interference (RNAi). This discovery by Andrew Fire and Craig Mello gained them the Nobel Prize in Physiology or Medicine in 2006.

miRNAs

The miRNA pathway is responsible for the posttranscriptional regulation of many mRNAs via translational repression or enhancement of miRNA turnover. In animals, one of the most abundant small RNAs are the miRNAs. They are on average 20–23 nucleotides in length and usually have a uridine (U) at their 5′ end. Plants have on average 120 miRNA-encoding genes, invertebrate animals about 150, and humans close to 500, which show complex temporal and spatial expression patterns during development. Recently, miRNAs have also been identified in some viruses and green algae, indicating their broad phylogenetic distribution.

Most miRNAs are transcribed by RNA polymerase II from noncoding DNA regions that generate short dsRNA hairpins (**Fig. 16.25**). In animal cells, the endoribonuclease Drosha excises the miRNA stem loops from the primary

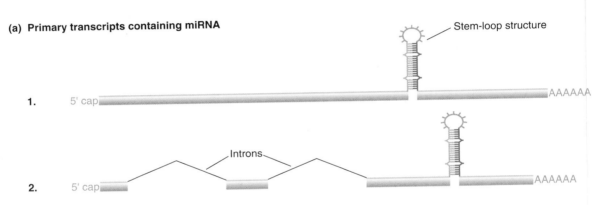

(a) Primary transcripts containing miRNA

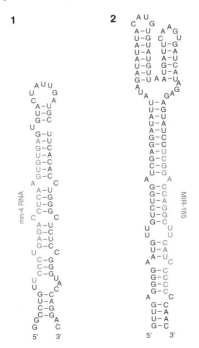

(b) Predicted pri-miRNA stem loops

Figure 16.25 micro-RNA-containing genes.
(a) Most primary (pri-) miRNA transcripts do not contain an open reading frame, but some miRNAs are present within the introns of protein-coding mRNAs, as shown in the second example. **(b)** Ribonucleotide sequences and predicted duplex structures of stem loops in different pri-miRNA transcripts. Example 1 is from *C. elegans;* nearly identical homologs of these stem-loop structures have been found in other animals, including flies and mammals. Example 2 is from the plant *Arabidopsis;* a nearly identical homolog has been uncovered in rice and other plants.

Source: Part (a) is created by Lee Silver; Part (b) is extracted directly from figure 1 of MicroRNAs: Genomics, Biogenesis, Mechanism, and Function; David P. Bartel; CELL, 23 January 2004, Pages 281–297.

Figure 16.26 miRNA processing. Immediately after transcription, micro-RNA-containing primary transcripts (pri-miRNAs) are recognized by the nuclear enzyme Drosha, which crops out pre-miRNA stem-loop structures from the larger RNA. The pre-miRNAs undergo active transport from the nucleus into the cytoplasm where they are recognized by the enzyme Dicer. Dicer reduces the pre-miRNA into a short-lived miRNA:miRNA* duplex, which is released and picked up by an RNA-induced silencing complex (RISC). RISC eliminates the miRNA* strand from the duplex and becomes a functional and highly specific miRISC.

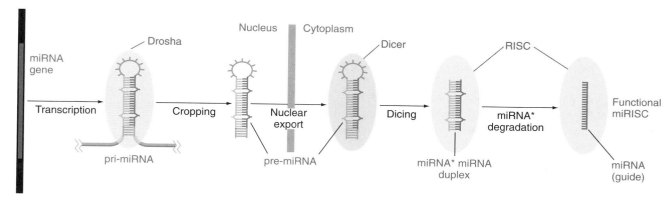

transcript (pri-miRNA) while it is still in the nucleus, releasing an approximately 70 base RNA intermediate (pre-miRNA) (**Fig. 16.26**). The pre-miRNA is actively exported to the cytoplasm by a protein complex. Once in the cytoplasm, the pre-miRNA is subsequently processed by the RNAse Dicer to produce a mature miRNA in the form of a double-stranded intermediate. One of the strands in these double-stranded miRNA intermediates—the "guide" strand—is incorporated into ribonucleoprotein complexes that are often referred to as miRNA-induced silencing complexes (miRISCs). The other strand, usually termed miRNA*, is degraded.

The ribonucleotide complexes (miRISCs) containing miRNAs mediate diverse functions depending on the par-

ticular Argonaute protein they possess, and on the extent of sequence complementarity between the guide miRNA and the target sequences in mRNA 3′ untranslated regions (3′UTRs) (**Fig. 16.27**). miRNA complexes with perfect complementarity between guide and target RNA cause mRNA cleavage. With less complementarity, the mechanism is often some type of inhibition of translation. The mechanisms used by miRNAs to regulate translational activity are still not fully understood. Recent work shows that miRNAs are able to repress protein expression in at least four distinct manners: (1) cotranslational protein degradation, (2) inhibition of translation elongation, (3) premature termination of translation (i.e., ribosome "drop-off"), and (4) inhibition of translation initiation.

Figure 16.27 Mechanism of interference. The miRISC can down-regulate gene expression through two different modes of action that are both based on specific binding to a target mRNA. 1. If the miRNA and its target mRNA contain perfectly complementary sequences, miRISC cleaves the mRNA. The two cleavage products are no longer protected from RNase and are rapidly degraded. 2. If the miRNA and its target mRNA have only partial complementarity, cleavage does not occur. However, the miRISC remains bound to its target and represses its movement across ribosomes. This mode of down-regulation is less efficient than cleavage.

siRNAs

In the siRNA pathway, dsRNAs are either produced by transcription of both strands of an endogenous DNA sequence in the genome, or arise from an exogenous source such as a virus. These dsRNAs are the pri-RNAs that are processed by Dicer, and the resulting ssRNA can interfere with expression of a gene containing the complementary sequence. This pathway may also protect the cell from invading dsRNAs produced by viruses by destroying those RNAs.

The siRNA pathway is responsible for detecting exogenous double-stranded RNAs (dsRNAs) and destroying any transcripts derived from the invading RNA, as well as from cellular dsRNA transcripts generated by transcription of both a sense and antisense strand of a gene. In plants, many siRNAs of viral and viroid origin are detected. The plant can destroy RNAs of these invading particles using the siRNA pathway.

Researchers have found the siRNA pathway to be a useful mechanism to selectively shut off expression of targeted genes. To study the function of a specific gene or the effect of loss of the selected gene product, researchers introduce dsRNA of that gene into the cell and expression of the endogenous gene is shut off or knocked down (Fig. A). The double-stranded siRNA is again composed of a guide RNA and a sense strand. The guide RNA will bind to complementary transcripts and mediate mRNA cleavage as with miRNAs. Researchers are excited about the possibility of using RNA interference to treat diseases, and this is detailed in the Tools of Genetics box on pp. 574–575.

> Small RNAs include a number of subclasses, and more are being discovered. Among these, micro-RNAs (miRNAs) are incorporated into RNA-induced silencing complexes (miRISCs) that act to repress translation. Small interfering RNAs (siRNAs) detect and destroy foreign double-stranded RNAs.

Other posttranscriptional regulators include half-life indicators and localization markers

The amount of protein made in a cell is affected by the amount of mRNA present. Initiation of transcription and mechanisms to inhibit translation can affect the final outcome, but stability of the mRNA is also important. mRNA contains information about its half-life in the 3′ and 5′ untranslated regions (UTRs). Specific proteins (as well as the miRNAs described earlier) can bind in the 3′UTR to stabilize mRNA or to cause more rapid degradation.

mRNA also contains information about its localization after leaving the nucleus. Some RNAs must be localized to specific regions where they will be translated at

appropriate times, when other factors are present with which they interact. This is especially true in large cells, such as neurons or fertilized eggs, that have polarization of functions.

Proteins may also be modified after translation

The action of a gene is reflected in the activity of its protein product, and a number of posttranslational modifications, including ubiquitination and phosphorylation, affect protein function. Many of these modifications occur extremely rapidly compared to the time it takes to activate gene transcription and accumulate sufficient protein product for use in a particular process, or to deactivate transcription and await the slow disappearance of a protein product. Thus, cells often rely on posttranslational modification in situations that require a rapid response.

Cells have many enzyme systems that destroy proteins. In one of these systems, ubiquitin—a small, highly conserved protein—functions as a marker. The covalent attachment of chains of ubiquitin to other proteins marks the ubiquitinized proteins for degradation by a large multienzyme complex known as the *proteosome*.

Phosporylation and dephosphorylation often occur in cascades. That is, one protein, after being phosphorylated, is then able to phosphorylate other proteins, which phosphorylate the next protein in the cascade, and so on. Such reactions are found in the transmission of a signal across the cell membranes and eventually to the nucleus (described in detail in Chapter 17).

Another example involving phosphorylation as a regulator of activity is in a process known as *sensitization;* many tissues exposed to hormones for a long time lose their ability to respond to the hormone. An example is the exposure of heart muscle to the stress hormone epinephrine (**Fig. 16.28** on p. 573). Binding of epinephrine to β-adrenergic receptors, located in the plasma membrane of heart muscle cells, normally increases the rate at which the heart contracts. But after several hours of continuous exposure to epinephrine, the heart muscle cells no longer respond in this way. Their sensitization is due to phosphorylation of the β-adrenergic receptors. The phosphorylation does not affect a receptor's ability to bind epinephrine, but it does prevent the receptor from transmitting the hormone signal into the heart muscle cells. The phosphorylation itself depends in large part on the activity of kinase (phosphate-adding) enzymes that phosphorylate the β-adrenergic receptor only when the receptor is bound to epinephrine. With the removal of epinephrine from the heart tissue, the kinases no longer act on the receptors, and phosphatase enzymes remove any phosphates already on them. The removal of phosphate from the β-adrenergic receptors eventually restores the heart muscle's ability to respond to new doses of epinephrine

Figure 16.28 Phosphorylation and desensitization.

Covalent phosphorylation of the β-adrenergic receptor has no effect on its binding to epinephrine, but it blocks its downstream function of modulating heart rate.

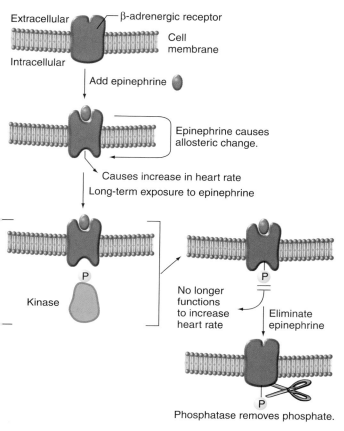

Phosphatase removes phosphate.

Posttranslation modifications may regulate protein function. Ubiquitination targets proteins for breakdown via proteosomes. Phosphorylation and dephosphorylation are responsible for cascade reactions such as occur in signal transmission, and they also play a role in sensitization of tissues to hormonal signals.

Computer analyses can reveal regulatory mechanisms

Just as with prokaryotes, computer analysis has allowed insight into regulatory mechanisms of eukaryotes. Molecular biologists and biochemists are not yet able to unravel the details of complex regulatory networks, but their knowledge of them increases every day. In addition, the recent emergence of bioinformatics—a field of science in which biology, computer science, and information technology merge to form a single discipline—promises to facilitate the understanding of complex transcriptional programs.

For example, modern computer programs translate putative open reading frames into *in silico* proteins and recognize motifs within the proteins, such as zinc-finger motifs. These motifs suggest the proteins are transcription factors, and further biochemical analyses can confirm this designation. Sites on *in silico* translated proteins suggest specific posttranslational modifications that could occur and may be important for function.

Possible transcriptional regulatory sites are identified by a global analysis called *phylogenetic footprinting*. In this analysis, genomic sequences of closely related species are compared to find DNA sequences outside of coding regions that are highly conserved between closely related species. Because noncoding DNA is not usually highly conserved, those sequences that have been conserved suggest important functions such as gene regulation.

Other global analysis of the genome used to analyze transcription factors include the ChIP technology (Chapter 10). Proteins are cross-linked to DNA *in vivo* and the chromosomal DNA is fragmented. The fragments are treated with antibody (Ab) that recognizes a specific transcription factor. The DNA sequence that is precipitated with the Ab, and transcription factor can be determined by hybridization to a DNA array or directly sequenced.

A similar process, using the ChIP technology, is being used to identify chromatin patterns and modifications throughout the genome. An Ab that recognizes a specific modification to a histone protein or recognizes a protein that binds to altered chromatin precipitates the protein and its associated DNA. Using this technique, a profile of chromatin modifications can be generated for different types of cells or at different times in development. These approaches are part of the emerging field of epigenomics—the understanding at the global level the changes in chromatin structure.

16.5 A Comprehensive Example: Sex Determination in *Drosophila*

Male and female *Drosophila* exhibit many sex-specific differences in morphology, biochemistry, behavior, and function of the germ line (**Fig. 16.29** on p. 576). By examining the phenotypes of flies with different chromosomal constitutions, researchers confirmed that the ratio of X to autosomal chromosomes (X:A) helps determine sex, fertility, and viability (**Table 16.2** on p. 576). They then carried out genetic experiments that showed that the X:A ratio influences sex through three independent pathways: One determines whether the flies look and act like males or females; another determines whether germ cells develop as eggs or sperm; and a third produces dosage compensation through doubling the rate of transcription of X-linked genes in males. (Note that this strategy of dosage compensation is just the opposite of that seen in mammals, where the inactivation of one X chromosome

TOOLS OF GENETICS

RNA Interference and Treatment of Disease

The recent discovery of RNA interference (RNAi) as a natural process of gene regulation in all eukaryotic cells suggests a new approach toward the development of therapies to combat disease. The general idea is to co-opt the existing cellular RNAi machinery into working with laboratory-designed siRNA molecules that target specific mRNAs from the disease-causing gene for destruction through the mechanism shown in **Fig. A.1** and **A.2**. Among the diseases researchers are currently targeting for RNAi therapy are incurable conditions such Huntington disease, ALS (amyotrophic lateral sclerosis), AIDS, and a variety of cancers. Investigators are also targeting conditions such as hypertension and hypercholesterolemia, for which current treatments are not specific enough.

The first step in the development of an RNAi therapy involves the design, construction, and experimental validation of an siRNA that can function inside living cells to eliminate disease-causing *target transcripts,* while not affecting the transcripts of any other gene. A well-designed siRNA contains a 21–23 base-long **antisense** sequence that is perfectly complementary to a unique sequence within the target transcript. This antisense sequence must be contained within a longer RNA strand that is itself part of a duplex with a complementary **sense** strand. The duplex structure and extended RNA length are required to allow recognition and binding by Dicer—the first cytoplasmic enzyme in the RNAi processing pathway—which trims the siRNA and passes it on to RISC.

With an automated oligonucleotide synthesizer, researchers can generate a large set of target-specific duplex RNA molecules. These duplex RNAs also have variations in the sequences adjacent to the antisense sequences. Experiments conducted on tissue culture cells can be used to identify which particular siRNAs have the desired properties of high activity and target specificity.

Moving from a therapeutic RNAi model that works well in tissue culture to one that is effective in whole animals—and eventually people—requires the development of a delivery strategy that (1) protects the siRNA sequence from degradation before it reaches cells carrying target transcripts, and (2) guides the siRNA sequence across the plasma membrane into those cells. Naked RNA molecules are not well suited for either task: They are rapidly degraded by RNases present in all bodily fluids, and their negatively charged phosphate groups prevent ready entry into the hydrophobic core of the plasma membrane.

Hans-Peter Vornlocher and his group from Kulmbach, Germany, developed a chemical strategy for overcoming siRNA delivery problems in a mouse model for hypercholesterolemia, a condition caused by excess low-density lipoproteins (LDLs) in blood serum. The liver protein apolipoprotein B (apoB) functions only in LDL biogenesis and thus presents an excellent target for the development of an LDL-specific RNAi therapy. In tissue culture experiments. Vornlocher and colleagues identified an siRNA with high activity and specificity for mouse apoB transcripts. They then synthesized the two strands of the siRNA, but rather than using them directly, they created chemical modifications at the 5′ and 3′ ends of both strands, as illustrated in Fig. A.2. The modified siRNA product could not be recognized by serum RNases, which do their work by digesting naked RNA from one end or the other.

Vornlocher's second chemical trick was to employ the lipid cholesterol as the chemical entity that was attached to the 3′ end of the sense strand in the siRNA duplex. Cholesterol not only protects one end of the RNA from degradation but also tends to incorporate itself into plasma membranes, which facilitates the passage of its siRNA cargo into the cell proper. Evidence that this strategy can actually work in a living animal was obtained after injection of the specially modified anti-apoB siRNA into the tail veins of normal mice. Within 24 hours, their serum LDL levels had fallen by over 50%. This remarkable result serves as a proof-of-principle for the use of chemical-based siRNA delivery systems in the development of RNAi therapies for treating chronic human diseases.

So far, the effectiveness of RNAi therapies has been demonstrated only in experimental animals. Although the results are very encouraging, these therapies are not yet ready for use in people. To develop human therapies, researchers must design siRNAs that work in human cells and then conduct full-scale clinical trials to ensure the effectiveness and safety of each RNAi protocol.

Figure A The development of RNAi therapy (1) An automated oligonucleotide synthesizer is used to create the antisense and sense strands of a potential siRNA molecule. (2) The two strands are chemically modified at their 5′ and 3′ ends and then brought together to form an siRNA duplex, which is injected into experimental animals. This chemical modification includes attachment of a cholesterol molecule to the 3′ end of the sense strand. The cholesterol group incorporates itself into the plasma membrane of cells and facilities entry of the whole siRNA duplex. In the cytoplasm, the RNAi enzyme dicer recognizes the siRNA, cleaves off its ends, and passes it to RISC. The siRNA-loaded RISC attaches to target mRNA transcripts and destroys them. The RISC complex is then recycled to attack further target mRNAs.

1. *In vitro* synthesis of siRNA

2. Chemically modified siRNA delivery

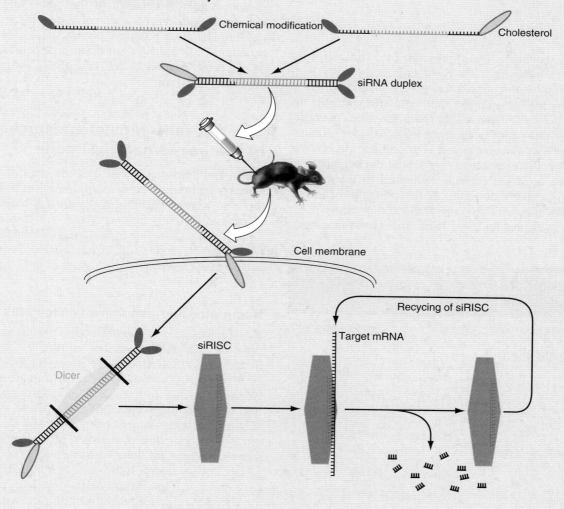

Figure 16.29 Sex-specific traits in *Drosophila*. Objects or traits shown in *blue* are specific to males. Objects or traits shown in *red* are specific to females. Objects or traits shown in *green* are found in different forms in the two sexes.

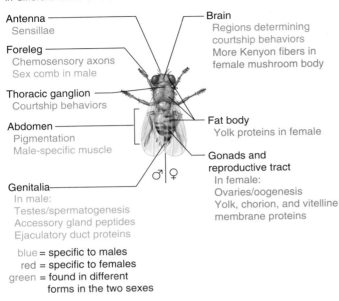

Antenna
  Sensillae

Foreleg
  Chemosensory axons
  Sex comb in male

Thoracic ganglion
  Courtship behaviors

Abdomen
  Pigmentation
  Male-specific muscle

Genitalia
  In male:
  Testes/spermatogenesis
  Accessory gland peptides
  Ejaculatory duct proteins

Brain
  Regions determining
  courtship behaviors
  More Kenyon fibers in
  female mushroom body

Fat body
  Yolk proteins in female

Gonads and
reproductive tract
  In female:
  Ovaries/oogenesis
  Yolk, chorion, and vitelline
  membrane proteins

♂ ♀

blue = specific to males
red = specific to females
green = found in different
        forms in the two sexes

TABLE 16.3	*Drosophila* Mutations That Affect the Two Sexes Differently	
Mutation	**Phenotype of XY**	**Phenotype of XX**
Sx^{fl}*	Male	Dead
Sxl^{ML}**	Dead	Female
transformer (*tra*)	Male	Male (sterile)
doublesex (*dsx*)	Intersex	Intersex
fruitless	Male with aberrant courtship behavior	Female

*Sx^{fl} is a recessive mutation of *Sex lethal*.
**Sxl^{ML} is a dominant mutation of *Sex lethal*.

in females equalizes the expression of X-linked genes with that in males.)

To simplify this discussion of sex determination in *Drosophila,* we focus on the first-mentioned pathway: the determination of somatic sexual characteristics. An understanding of this pathway emerged from analyses of mutations affecting particular sexual characteristics in one sex or the other. For example, as we saw at the beginning of the chapter, XY flies carrying mutations in the *fruitless* gene (*fru*) exhibit aberrant male courtship behavior, whereas XX flies with the same *fruitless* mutations appear to behave as normal females. **Table 16.3** shows that muta-

TABLE 16.2	How Chromosomal Constitution Affects Phenotype in *Drosophila*	
Sex Chromosomes	**X:A**	**Sex Phenotype**
Autosomal Diploids		
XO	0.5	Male (sterile)
XY	0.5	Male
XX	1.0	Female
XXY	1.0	Female
Autosomal Triploids		
XXX	1.0	Female
XYY	0.33	Male
XXY	0.66	Intersex

tions in other genes also affect the two sexes differently. Clarification of how these mutations influence somatic sex determination came from a combination of genetic experiments (studying, for example, whether one mutation in a double mutant is epistatic to the other) and molecular biology experiments (in which investigators cloned mutant and normal gene products for analysis). Through such experiments, *Drosophila* geneticists dissected various stages of sex determination to delineate the following complex regulatory network.

The X:A ratio regulates expression of the *sex-lethal* (*Sxl*) gene

Recall from Chapter 4 that it is the ratio of X chromosomes to autosomes (A) that determines sex in *Drosophila.* Since in normal diploids, there are two copies of each autosome, the X:A ratio is $2/2 = 1.0$ in a normal XX female and $1/2 = 0.5$ in a normal XY male. In short, when the X:A ratio is 1.0, females develop; when the ratio is 0.5, males develop.

Numerator and denominator elements

Key factors of sex determination are helix-loop-helix proteins encoded by genes on the X chromosome. Sisterless-A (Sis-A) and sisterless-B (Sis-B) are two such proteins. Referred to as *numerator elements,* these two proteins monitor the X:A ratio through the formation of homodimers containing two of the same kind of subunit, or heterodimers containing two different subunits. The homodimers consists of two numerator elements, whereas the heterodimers are composed of one numerator element and one denominator element. *Denominator elements* are helix-loop-helix proteins that are encoded by genes on autosomes. Because the number of X chromosomes determines the ratio of numerator

Figure 16.30 The X:A ratio determines the expression of *Sxl*.

Numerator elements are produced by the X chromosome at a slightly higher level than denominator elements are produced by autosomes. When the X:A ratio is 1 (in females), there are too many numerator elements to be occupied by denominators, and those not sequestered can form homodimers, which act as activators of the *Sxl* gene. When the X:A ratio is 1/2 (in males), there are fewer numerators than denominators, and all the numerators become sequestered.

omodimers to numerator/denominator heterodimers, ne homodimers of numerator elements provide a measure of the X:A ratio (**Fig. 16.30**).

The observation that in flies with a greater number of umerator homodimers, transcription of the *Sxl* gene ccurs early in development suggests that numerator subnit homodimers may function as transcription factors at turn on *Sxl*. In this hypothesis, the association of nominator subunits with numerator subunits sequesters e numerator elements in inactive heterodimers that annot activate transcription. Females produce enough umerator subunits, however, that some remain unbound denominator elements. Homodimers formed from these e numerator elements act as transcriptional activators

of *Sxl* at the P_e promoter early in development. Males, by contrast, carry only half as many X-encoded numerator subunits; thus, the abundant denominator proteins tie up all the numerator elements, and as a result, there are no free numerator elements in males to turn on the P_e promoter of the *Sxl* gene.

Although this model is likely to be an oversimplification, it suggests how different X:A ratios might activate and repress transcription of the *Sxl* gene.

The action of the Sxl protein in females

The Sxl protein produced early in the development of female embryos participates later in an autoregulatory feedback loop as just described (review Fig. 16.24). In this self-regulating system, the Sxl protein catalyzes the synthesis of more of itself through RNA splicing of the P_L-initiated transcript, which results in a productive mRNA. By contrast, in males where there is no transcription of *Sxl* early in development, activation of the P_L promoter later in embryonic development results in an unproductive *Sxl* transcript containing a stop codon near the beginning of the message. Because no Sxl protein is present to splice out the problem stop codon, this unproductive transcript is not translated to protein—and males thus have no Sxl protein at any point in development.

The effects of *Sxl* mutations

Recessive *Sxl* mutations that produce nonfunctional gene products have no effect in XY males, but they are lethal in XX females (see Table 16.3). The reason is that males, which do not normally express the *Sxl* gene, do not miss its functional product, but females, which depend on the Sxl protein for sex determination, do. The absence of the Sxl protein in females allows the aberrant expression of certain male-specific dosage-compensation genes that increase transcription of genes on the X chromosome—and the hypertranscription of these X-linked genes on two X chromosomes in mutant females proves lethal.

By comparison, rare dominant *Sxl* mutations that allow production of Sxl protein even in XY embryos are without effect in females but lethal to males. In these mutants, the *Sxl* gene product indirectly represses transcription of genes that males need to express for dosage compensation. Without the products of these male-specific dosage-compensation genes, males cannot hypertranscribe X-linked genes and thus do not have enough X-linked gene products to survive.

The Sxl protein triggers a cascade of splicing

In addition to splicing its own transcript, the Sxl protein influences the splicing of RNAs transcribed from other genes. Among these is the *transformer* (*tra*) gene. In the

Figure 16.31 Regulation by alternate splicing. (a) The presence of *Sxl* alters the splicing of *tra* mRNA. Female transcripts produce functional Tra protein, while male transcripts have a truncated open reading frame and are unable to produce Tra. **(b)** Tra protein, in turn, plays a role in altering the splicing pattern of the *dsx* mRNA. A different Dsx product results in males (Dsx-M) rather than in females (Dsx-F).

(a) *tra* **splicing**
Results of *tra* splicing when Sxl protein is present (♀)

(b) *dsx* **splicing**
Results of splicing when *tra* is present (♀)

Results of splicing when *tra* is absent (♂)

Figure 16.32 Male- and female-specific forms of Dsx protein. Dsx-F acts as a transcriptional activator, whereas Dsx-M acts as a transcriptional repressor.

presence of the Sxl protein, the *tra* primary transcript undergoes productive splicing that produces an mRNA translatable to a functional protein. In the absence of Sxl protein, the splicing of the *tra* transcript results in a non-functional protein (**Fig. 16.31a**).

The cascade continues. The functional Tra protein synthesized only in females, along with another protein encoded by the *tra2* gene (which is transcribed in both males and females), influences the splicing of the *double-sex* (*dsx*) gene's primary transcript. This splicing pathway results in the production of a female-specific Dsx protein called Dsx-F. In males, where there is no Tra protein, the splicing of the *dsx* primary transcript produces the related, but different, Dsx-M protein (**Fig. 16.31b**). The N-terminal parts of the Dsx-F and Dsx-M proteins are the same, but the C-terminal parts of the proteins are different.

The Dsx-F and Dsx-M proteins control development of somatic sexual characteristics

Although both Dsx-F and Dsx-M function as transcription factors, they have opposite effects. In conjunction with the protein encoded by the *intersex* (*ix*) gene, Dsx-F functions mainly as a repressor that prevents the transcription of genes whose expression would generate the somatic sexual characteristics of males. Dsx-M, which works independently of the intersex protein, accomplishes the

opposite: the activation of genes for the somatic sexual characteristics of males and the repression of genes that determine female somatic sexual characteristics.

Interestingly, the two Dsx proteins can bind to the same enhancer elements, but their binding produces opposite outcomes (**Fig. 16.32**). For example, both bind to an enhancer upstream of the promoter for the *YP1* gene, which encodes a yolk protein; females make this protein in their fat body organs and then transfer it to developing eggs. The binding of Dsx-F stimulates transcription of the *YP1* gene in females; the binding of Dsx-M to the same enhancer region inactivates transcription of *YP1* in males, working in conjunction with other transcription factors.

Mutations in *dsx* affect both sexes because in both males and females, the production of Dsx protein represses certain genes specific to development of the opposite sex. Null mutations in *dsx* that make it impossible to produce either functional Dsx-F or Dsx-M result in intersexes that cannot repress either certain male-specific or certain female-specific genes.

The Tra and Tra-2 proteins also help regulate expression of the *fruitless* gene

We saw at the beginning of this chapter that the courting song and dance of male *Drosophila* are among the sexual behaviors under the control of the *fruitless* (*fru*) gene. As it turns out, the *fru* primary transcript is another regulatory target of the Tra and Tra2 splicing factors (**Fig. 16.33**). In females, whose cells make both Tra and Tra2 proteins, splicing of the *fru* transcript produces an mRNA that encodes a protein we refer to as Fru-F. In males, whose cells carry no Tra protein, alternative splicing of the *fru* transcript generates a related Fru-M protein with 10 additional amino acids at its N terminus. As we mentioned at the beginning of this chapter, these additional

Figure 16.33 The primary *fru* RNA transcript is made in both sexes.
Splicing occurs unhindered in males to produce an mRNA, which is translated into the Fru-M protein product. But tra protein (present only in females) causes alternative splicing of the *fru* transcript to produce an alternative mRNA, which encodes an alternative protein product Fru-F.

repress genes whose sex-specific products help generate courting behaviors.

The sex-specific products of *fru* appear in only a few cells in the nervous system, and the location of these neurons is significant. Some are in regions known to help regulate the courtship song; others are in areas that process chemosensory information from the antennae (perhaps in neurons that receive pheromone signals); still others are in regions that control abdominal movements (suggesting how *fruitless* may influence the male's curling of the abdomen during mating). To understand precisely how changes in gene expression in these few cells control sexual behaviors, *Drosophila* researchers are now trying to discover which genes are the targets of transcriptional regulation by the fruitless protein.

> Sex determination in *Drosophila* illustrates several kinds of gene regulation. X-encoded numerators and autosome-encoded denominators allow assessment of the "femaleness" of a fly, leading to activation of *Sxl* transcription in early female embryos. The Sxl protein then acts as a splicing factor to perpetuate its synthesis in females. Additional splicing cascades result in female- and male-specific versions of Dsx proteins that determine sexual characteristics and behavior.

almost certainly determine some of the observed differences between male and female behavior. Because both Fru-F and Fru-M have the zinc-finger motifs characteristic of transcription factors, they probably activate and

Connections

Multiple controls regulate gene activity and function from imprinting, to chromatin remodeling, to the initiation of transcription, to the processing of RNA transcripts to RNA interference, to the chemical modification of final gene products. At the outset, the regulation of transcription occurs through the interaction of *cis*-acting DNA regions and a variety of transcription factors.

Accurate regulation of gene function is crucial for proper control of development and of the cell cycle.

Indeed, a critical network of *cis*-acting control regions, *trans*-acting factors, and protein modifications promotes cell growth, DNA replication, and cell division in response to certain environmental signals, and also delays these events in response to other signals, such as DNA damage. In Chapter 17, we describe the regulatory network controlling the cell cycle in normal cells and explain how mutations that disrupt one or more aspects of that network can result in cancer.

ESSENTIAL CONCEPTS

1. Transcriptional initiation is a critical point in the regulation of gene activity. Analyses of mutations that affect a gene's function without changing the sequence of its product provided insight into this level of regulation. Through these mutations, researchers defined *cis*-acting DNA regulatory elements and *trans*-acting transcription factors.

2. Two types of *cis*-acting regulatory regions—promoters and enhancers—are associated with genes transcribed by RNA polymerase II. The promoters are located at the 5′ end of the gene they influence. Basal factors bind to promoters to allow a low, nonspecific basal level of gene transcription. The enhancers have a more variable location in relation to the genes they control.

3. The association of transcription factors with enhancer elements can modulate levels of transcriptional initiation. Activation is mediated by transcription factors called activators, which bind to enhancers. Activators can interact with basal

factors at the promoter to increase transcription above the basal level. Repressors can compete with activators for enhancer binding or quench the ability of activators to carry out their function. Activators and repressors that bind directly to DNA often form homodimers and/or heterodimers, which can be a prerequisite for them to function as transcription factors.

4. The unraveling of the DNA in chromatin is an initial step in activation. Hypercompaction of chromatin domains causes transcriptional silencing by blocking access to the promoter and enhancers of a gene and thereby preventing its activation even in the presence of activator proteins.

5. Genomic imprinting is an example of epigenetic control over gene expression. Imprinting operates on the copy of a gene received from one parent but not the other. DNA methylation plays a role in the maintenance of imprinting from one mammalian somatic cell generation to the next.

6. Although the regulation of most genes depends primarily on controls over transcription, in some cases, further regulation down the path to protein production also plays a role. Modulation of gene function can occur through changes in RNA splicing, RNA interference, changes in the efficiency of translation, and chemical modification of the gene product.

On Our Website   www.mhhe.com/hartwell4

- Recent papers on mechanisms of gene regulation.
- Recent papers on epigenetic regulation.

Solved Problems

I. You are studying expression of a gene whose protein product is made after UV irradiation. You cloned the gene and made antibody to the protein.
  a. If expression is regulated by turning on transcription after UV exposure, what results would you predict from hybridizing a DNA probe to RNA isolated from cells before and after UV irradiation (Northern analysis) and from incubating the antibody to proteins isolated from cells before and after UV treatment (Western analysis)?
  b. If expression is regulated by preventing translation, what results would you predict from doing similar Northern and Western analyses?

Answer

To answer this question, you need to consider the consequences of transcriptional and translational regulation on expression and think through what happens experimentally in Northern and Western analyses.
  a. If a gene is transcriptionally regulated, the mRNA will not be present in cells that were not exposed to UV. *There will be no hybridizing band in the Northern analysis of mRNA from unexposed cells. The mRNA will be present in cells that have been treated with UV, and there will be a hybridizing*

band. Similarly, the protein will only be found i[n] cells that were exposed to UV, and the antibod[y] will bind to its protein target only in the protei[n] preparation from exposed cells.
  b. If expression is regulated at the translation ste[p,] mRNA will be present in the cells whether the[y] have been exposed to UV or not. *Hybridizin[g] bands will be found in both RNA samples. The pro tein will be present only in those cells that wer[e] exposed to UV, so signal will be seen only in th[e] exposed preparation.*

II. The retinoic acid receptor (RAR) is a transcriptio[n] factor that is similar to steroid hormone receptor[s.] The substance (ligand) that binds to this receptor [is] retinoic acid. One of the genes whose transcriptio[n] is activated by retinoic acid binding to the recept[or] is *myoD*. The diagram at the end of this proble[m] shows a schematic of the RAR protein produced b[y] a gene into which two different 12-base oligonucle otides had been inserted in the sequences encodi[ng] sites indicated by a–m. For constructs encodi[ng] a–e, oligonucleotide 1 (TTAATTAATTAA) w[as] inserted into the *RAR* gene. For constructs encodi[ng] f–m, oligonucleotide 2 (CCGGCCGGCCGG) w[as] inserted into the gene. Each mutant protein w[as] tested for its ability to bind retinoic acid, bind

DNA, and activate transcription of *myoD* gene. Results are tabulated as follows; the insertion site associated with each mutant protein is indicated with the appropriate letter on the polypeptide map.

Mutant	Retinoic acid binding	DNA binding	Transcriptional activation
a	−	−	−
b	−	−	−
c	−	−	−
d	−	+	+
e	+	+	+
f	+	+	+
g	+	+	−
h	+	+	−
i	+	−	−
j	+	−	−
k	−	+	+
l	−	+	+
m	+	+	+

a. What is the effect of inserting oligonucleotide 1 anywhere in the protein?
b. What is the effect of inserting oligonucleotide 2 anywhere in the protein?
c. Indicate the three protein domains on a copy of the preceding drawing.

Answer

This question involves the concepts of domains within proteins and use of the genetic code to understand effects of oligonucleotide insertions.

a. Oligonucleotide 1 contains a stop codon in any of its three reading frames. This means it will *cause termination of translation of the protein wherever it is inserted.*

b. Oligonucleotide 2 does not contain any stop codons and so will *just add amino acids to the protein.* Because there are 12 bases in the oligonucleotide, it will not change the reading frame of the protein. *Insertion of the oligonucleotide can disrupt the function of a site in which it inserts.*

c. Looking at the data overall, notice that all mutants that are defective in DNA binding are also defective in transcriptional activation, as would be expected for a transcription factor that binds to DNA. The mutants that will be informative about the transcriptional activation domain are those that do not have a DNA-binding defect. Inserts a, b, and c using oligonucleotide 1, which truncates

the protein at the site of insertion, are defective in all three activities. The protein must be made at least as far as point d before DNA binding or transcription activation are seen. These two activities must lie before d. Truncation at d is negative for retinoic acid binding, but the truncation at e does bind to retinoic acid. The retinoic acid–binding activity must lie before e. Using the oligonucleotide 2 set of insertions, transcriptional activation was disrupted by insertions at sites g and h, indicating that this region is part of the transcriptional domain; i and j insertions disrupted the DNA binding; and k and l insertions disrupted the retinoic acid binding. The minimal endpoints of domains as determined from these data are summarized in the following schematic.

III. A cDNA clone that you isolated using pituitary gland mRNA from mice was used as a probe against a blot containing RNAs from embryonic heart (EH), adult heart (AH), embryonic pituitary (EP), adult pituitary (AP), and testis (T). The results of the hybridization are shown here.

a. What would you conclude about this gene based on the result with AH RNA?
b. How would you explain the result with testis RNA?

Answer

This problem requires an understanding of RNA and transcription.

a. No RNA from adult heart (AH) hybridized with the probe, indicating that the *gene is not transcribed in this tissue.*

b. *A different-sized RNA is seen in the testis sample.* This could be due to *alternate splicing of the transcript or a different start site* in testis compared to other tissues.

Problems

Vocabulary

1. For each of the terms in the left column, choose the best matching phrase in the right column.

   a. basal factors
   b. transcriptional silencing
   c. activators
   d. imprinting
   e. RNAi
   f. coactivators
   g. homomers
   h. heteromers
   i. ubiquitination

   1. marks a protein for degradation
   2. pattern of expression is dependent on which parent transmitted the allele
   3. multimers of nonidentical subunits
   4. heterochromatin
   5. multimers of identical subunits
   6. bind to enhancers
   7. bind to promoters
   8. bind to activators
   9. prevents or reduces gene expression post transcriptionally

Section 16.1

2. Does each of the following types of gene regulation occur in eukaryotes only? in prokaryotes only? in both prokaryotes and eukaryotes?
   a. differential splicing
   b. positive regulation
   c. chromatin compaction
   d. attenuation
   e. negative regulation

3. List five events other than transcription initation that can affect the type or amount of active protein produced in a cell.

Section 16.2

4. Which eukaryotic RNA polymerase (RNA pol I, pol II, or pol III) transcribes which genes?
   a. tRNAs
   b. mRNAs
   c. rRNAs
   d. miRNAs

5. Which of the following types of fusion gene would you use for which purpose? (The slash indicates the fusion, and the parts of each type of fusion are given in the order in which they would occur.)

   Types of fusions:
   a. random mouse sequences/*lacZ* gene
   b. mouse metallothionein promoter/a mouse gene

   Uses:
   i. to identify genes turned on in neurons
   ii. to turn on expression of a gene by including the metal Zn in the diet

6. You isolated a gene expressed in differentiated neurons in mice. You then fused the upstream DNA and beginning of the gene to *lacZ* (reporter gene) so that you could monitor expression. Different fragments (shown as *dark lines* in the following figure) were cloned next to the *lacZ* gene that lacked a promoter. The clones were introduced into neurons in tissue culture to monitor expression. From the results that follow, which region contains the promoter and which contains an enhancer?

7. In yeast, the GAL4 protein binds to DNA to activate transcription of GAL7 or GAL10. GAL80 represses expression by binding to GAL4 protein and preventing it from binding to DNA. In which gene(s) should you be able to isolate galactose constitutive mutations, and in each case, what characteristics of the protein would the mutation disrupt?

8. A single enhancer site regulates expression of three adjacent genes *GAL1*, *GAL7*, and *GAL10*, but the genes are not cotranscribed as one mRNA. How could you show experimentally that each gene is transcribed separately?

9. Which of the listed motifs is associated with DNA binding, transcription activation, or dimer formation?
   a. zinc finger
   b. helix-loop-helix
   c. leucine zipper
   d. acidic region
   e. helix-turn-helix

10. How could you make a library of genes expressed during sporulation in yeast?

11. *MyoD* is a transcriptional activator that turns on the expression of several muscle-specific genes in human cells. The *Id* gene product inhibits *MyoD* action. How could you determine if *Id* acts by quenching *MyoD* or by blocking access to the enhancer? What differences would you expect to see experimentally?

12. a. Assume that two transcription factors are required for expression of the blue pigmentation genes in pansies. (Without the pigment, the flowers are white.) What phenotypic ratios would you expect

b. Now assume that either transcription factor is sufficient to get blue color. What phenotypic ratios would you expect from crossing strains heterozygous for each of the genes encoding these transcription factors?

Section 16.3

13. a. You want to create a genetic construct that will express the β-galactosidase enzyme encoded by E. coli's lacZ gene in Drosophila. In addition to the lacZ coding sequence, what DNA element(s) must you include in order to express this protein in flies if the construct could somehow become integrated into the Drosophila genome? Where should such DNA element(s) be located?

b. In making your construct, you place inverted repeats found at the ends of a particular type of transposable element on either side of the lacZ coding region and all of the DNA elements required by the answer to part a. Since all the DNA sequences located between these inverted repeats can move from place to place in the Drosophila genome, it is possible to generate many different fly strains, each with the construct integrated at a different location in the genome. You treat animals from each strain with a chemical that turns blue in the presence of β-galactosidase. Animals from different strains show different patterns: some show blue staining in the head, others in the thorax, some show no blue color, etc. Explain these results and describe a potential use of your construct.

14. In the previous problem (#13), you identified a region that is likely to behave as an enhancer. What experiments could you perform to verify that these DNA sequences indeed share all the characteristics of an enhancer?

15. What experimental evidence indicates that chromatin structure acts to reduce basal levels of transcription?

16. Which of the following would be suggested by a DNase hypersensitive site?
a. No transcription occurs in this region of the chromosome.
b. The chromatin is in a more open state than a region without the hypersensitive site.
c. Transcription terminates at this site.

17. You isolated nuclei from liver cells, treated them with increasing amounts of DNase-I, stopped the reactions, and isolated the DNA from each sample. You next treated the DNAs with the restriction enzyme EagI, electrophoresed the DNAs, transferred them to a blot, and hybridized the blot with a probe from the gene you are studying. With no DNase-I treatment, there was a 20 kb EagI fragment that hybridized with your probe.

With trace amounts of DNase-I, two bands of 16 and 4 kb were present. The same DNase-I treatment of DNA from muscle cells produced only a 20 kb fragment. What does this result tell you about the region of DNA?

18. From Northern analysis, you find that the ADAG gene is expressed only in the brain. You examine expression in glial and neuronal cell lines (two types of cells in the brain) and find that only glial cells make ADAG mRNA. No one has characterized the cis- or trans-acting elements required for glial specific expression, so you decide to do so. You make a set of deletions in the regulatory region and fuse these to the lacZ gene so you can easily monitor the expression after introducing the clones into tissue culture cells derived from a glial tumor. Deletions beginning at a site upstream of the gene and extending to base −85 (with the transcription start site considered −1 and bases prior to the start having negative designations) still retain full activity, but a deletion to −75 leaves only 1% of the original activity.
a. What do these findings tell you?

You now mix a DNA fragment from this region that is labeled with ^{32}P at the 5′-end of one strand with a purified glial-specific transcription factor. You perform a DNase-I footprinting experiment (as described in Figure 12.13 on p. 414), and obtain the results tabulated below. Lane 1 shows the DNase-I reaction of the labeled DNA alone, Lane 2 is the reaction involving the mixture of DNA and protein. You also analyze the DNA sequence of the same DNA fragment on the same gel.

b. What is the sequence of the segment containing the binding site(s) for the glial-specific transcription factor?
c. Additional evidence indicates that the glial-specific factor binds to DNA as a dimer, and each monomer binds the same target sequence. Identify the likely binding sites for the two monomers.

19. Match the gene expression phenomenon with molecular components that modulate each.

a. transcriptional silencing   1. insulator

b. imprinting   2. heterochromatin

c. restricting the range of enhancer activity   3. TBF, TAFs

d. basal transcription   4. methylation

20. Epigenetic changes that are inherited from one generation to the next can involve which of the following?
a. Methylation of histones
b. Methylation of DNA
c. Change in DNA sequence

21. Prader-Willi syndrome is caused by a mutation in a maternally imprinted gene. Answer the following questions as true or false, assuming that the trait is 100% penetrant.
a. Half of the sons of affected males will show the syndrome.
b. Half of the daughters of affected males will show the syndrome.
c. Half of the sons of affected females will show the syndrome.
d. Half of the daughters of affected females will show the syndrome.

22. A boy expresses a mutant phenotype because he has received a mutation in a paternally imprinted gene. From which parent did the boy inherit the mutant allele?

23. The *IGF-2R* gene is autosomal and maternally imprinted. Copies of the gene received from the mother are not expressed, but copies received from the father are expressed. You have found two alleles of this gene that encode two different forms of the IGF-2R protein distinguishable by gel electrophoresis. One allele encodes a 60K blood protein; the other allele encodes a 50K blood protein. In an analysis of blood proteins from a couple named Bill and Joan, you find only the 60K protein in Joan's blood and only the 50K protein in Bill's blood. You then look at their children, Jill and Bill Jr. Jill is producing only the 50K protein, while Bill Jr. is producing only the 60K protein.
a. With these data alone, what can you say about the *IGF-2R* genotype of Bill Sr. and Joan?
b. Bill Jr. and a woman named Sara have two children, Pat and Tim. Pat produces only the 60K protein and Tim produces only the 50K protein. With the accumulated data, what can you now say about the genotypes of Joan and Bill Sr.?

24. Assume that the disease illustrated with the pedigree below is due to expression of a rare allele of an autosomal gene that is a paternally imprinted. What would

you predict is the genotype of individuals (a) I-1, (b) II-1, and (c) III-2?

25. Follow the expression of a paternally imprinted gene through three generations. Indicate whether the copy of the gene from the male in generation I is expressed in the germ cells and somatic cells of the individuals listed.

a. generation I male (I-2) germ cells
b. generation II daughter (II-2): somatic cells
c. generation II daughter (II-2): germ cells
d. generation II son (II-3): somatic cells
e. generation II son (II-3): germ cells
f. generation III grandson (III-1): somatic cells
g. generation III grandson (III-1): germ cells

Section 16.4

26. Excluding the possible rare polycistronic message, how can a single mRNA molecule in a eukaryotic cell produce several different proteins?

27. What events occur during processing of a primary transcript?

28. You are studying muscle cells and have found a protein that is only made in this tissue. The data here are from analysis of RNA (Northern blot) using a DNA probe from the gene and analysis of protein (Western blot) using antibody directed against the protein. Is the gene transcriptionally or translationally regulated?

RNA analysis | Protein analysis

Muscle cell RNA | Nerve cell RNA | Skin cell RNA | Muscle cell protein | Nerve cell protein | Skin cell prote

29. The *hunchback* gene, one of the genes necessary for setting up the dorsal-ventral axis of the *Drosophila* embryo, is translationally regulated. The position of the coding region within the transcript is known, and there is additional sequence beyond the coding region at the 5′ and 3′ ends of the mRNA. How could you determine if the sequences at the 5′ or 3′ or both ends are necessary for proper regulation of translation?

30. You isolated a cDNA from skin cells, and when you hybridized that cDNA as a probe with a blot containing mRNAs from skin cells and nerve cells you saw a 1.2 and a 1.3 kb fragment, respectively. How could you explain the different-sized cDNAs?

31. From Northern and Western hybridization, you know that the mRNA and protein produced by a tissue-specific gene are present in brain, liver, and fat cells, but you detect an enzymatic activity associated with this protein only in fat cells. Provide an explanation for this phenomenon.

32. Modern-day geneticists are very excited by the prospect of using RNA interference as a way to find genes involved in various biological processes, such as mitosis or the development of specific body parts like the pancreatic cells that make insulin.
 a. How would you perform an RNAi-based screen to find genes involved in these processes?
 b. What is the advantage of doing an RNAi-based screen as opposed to a classical genetic screen involving mutagens?
 c. What are the disadvantages of performing an RNAi-based screen?

33. You are studying a strain of transgenic mice that express an *E. coli lacZ* reporter gene under the control of *cis*-acting regulatory elements that normally control an interesting gene needed for the early development of mice. Previous evidence from Northern blots indicates that mRNA for the gene of interest can be identified between days 8.5 and 10.5 of gestation. In your strain, staining for β-galactosidase (the protein product of *lacZ*) can be seen from about day 8.75 until at least day 12.

 a. Explain the discrepancy between mRNA and protein expression.
 b. Would you expect β-galactosidase protein expression to indicate more accurately the normal onset of activity for this gene, or the normal cessation of this gene's activity? Explain.

Section 16.5

34. The *Drosophila* gene *Sex lethal (Sxl)* is very deserving of its name. Certain alleles have no effect on XY animals, but cause XX animals to die early in development. Other alleles have no effect on XX animals, but XY animals with these alleles die early in development. Thus, some *Sxl* alleles are lethal to females, while others are lethal to males.
 a. Would you expect a null mutation in *Sxl* to cause lethality in males or in females? What about a constitutively active *Sxl* mutation?
 b. Why do *Sxl* alleles of either type cause lethality in a specific sex?

The gene *transformer (tra)* gets its name from "sexual transformation," since some *tra* alleles can change XX animals into sterile males, while other *tra* alleles can change XY animals into normal-appearing females.
 c. Which of these sex transformations would be caused by null alleles of *tra* and which would be caused by constituitively active alleles of *tra?*
 d. XX animals carrying particular alleles of *tra* develop as males, but they are sterile. Why?
 e. In contrast with *Sxl,* null *tra* mutations do not cause lethality either in XX or in XY animals. However, the Sxl protein regulates the production of the Tra protein. Why then do all *tra* mutant animals survive?
 f. Predict the consequences of null mutations in *tra-2* on XX and XY animals.
 g. XY males carrying loss-of-function mutations in the *fruitless (fru)* gene display aberrant courtship behavior. Would you predict that either XX or XY animals with wild-type alleles of *fru* but loss-of-function mutations of *tra* would also court abnormally?

Somatic Mutation and the Genetics of Cancer

Killer cells surround a large cancer cell. Note the extended cellular processes of the cancer cell.

We saw in Chapter 7 that a great variety of mutations can occur during the replication and segregation of DNA including single base changes, deletions of many bases, inversions, and insertions, as well as translocations between chromosomes. Although these events are rare per gene and per cell division, there are many genes in each cell and many cell divisions (about 10^{13}) between the fertilization of the egg cell and the production of an adult human individual. This means that all cells have some mutations, although not all of them necessarily affect the functions of genes. The mutations that occur between the formation of the fertilized egg and the production of the germ cells are the substrates upon which evolution acts by selecting for advantageous changes and selecting against deleterious ones.

What about the mutations that occur in the somatic cells of the organism? Because these do not appear in the germ cells, they are not transmitted to the next generation. Can they affect the individual in which they occur? If the mutation led to a nonfunctional cell then it might have little or no consequence because there are so many other cells in the tissue or organism that could compensate. But some mutations lead to abnormal cellular behavior, and these changes could affect health. Indeed cancer is usually the result of mutations that occur during the division of somatic cells.

Most of us give little thought to the life-sustaining cycle of cell death and renewal in somatic cells, because despite the continuous comings and goings of our body's cells, we generally remain the same shape and size. But the appearance of an abnormal growth or a set of symptoms diagnosed as cancer startles us into the realization that we take for granted the intricate checks and balances that control cell division and behavior. These controls enable all cells of the body to function as part of a tightly organized, cooperative society. Cancer results when some cells divide out of control and eventually acquire the ability to spread beyond their prescribed boundaries. Although there are many types of cancer, they all result from excessive and inaccurate cellular proliferation (**Fig. 17.1**). Thus, the body's ability to regulate cell division is a foundation of health.

In this chapter, we describe how mutations cause cancer. We then examine the genes and gene products that control normal cell proliferation, including molecules that control the machinery of cell division, molecules that integrate the repair of DNA damage with progression through the cell cycle, and molecules that relay messages about whether conditions are right for cell division.

Two unifying themes can be inferred from our study of cancer. First, cancer is ultimately a disease of the genes: The multiple phenotypes collectively referred

CHAPTER OUTLINE

- 17.1 Overview: Initiation of Division
- 17.2 Cancer: A Failure of Control over Cell Division
- 17.3 The Normal Control of Cell Division

to as cancer all result from mutations in genes that regulate a cell's passage through the cycle of growth and division. Chemicals in the environment that raise the rate of gene mutation increase the probability of cancer incidence. Second, cancer differs in two ways from cystic fibrosis, Huntington disease, and other genetic conditions caused by the inheritance of one or two copies of a single defective gene: (1) although some people inherit mutations that predispose them to cancer, most mutations that lead to cancer occur in the somatic cells of one tissue; and (2) multiple mutations in an array of genes must accumulate over time in the clonal descendants of a single cell before the cancer phenotype appears. By contrast, the mutations that cause cystic fibrosis and Huntington disease are transmitted through the germ line; thus, the mutant alleles of one particular gene appearing in all cells of all somatic tissues cause the disease in an affected individual.

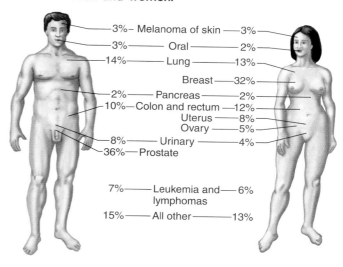

Figure 17.1 The relative percentages of new cancers in the United States that occur at different sites in the bodies of men and women.

17.1 Overview: Initiation of Division

How do cells know when to divide? To function according to the needs of the body as a whole, cells depend on signals sent from one tissue to another. These signals tell them whether to divide, metabolize (that is, make the products they are programmed to make) or die. The two basic types of signals are extracellular signals and cell-bound signals.

Extracellular signals in the form of steroids, peptides, and proteins act over long or short distances and are collectively known as hormones (**Fig. 17.2a**). The thyroid-stimulating hormone (TSH) produced by the brain's pituitary gland, for example, travels through the bloodstream to the thyroid gland, where it stimulates cells to produce another hormone, thyroxine, which in turn increases metabolic rate.

Cell-bound signals, such as the histocompatibility proteins that, like fingerprints, distinguish an individual's cells from all foreign cells and molecules, require direct contact between cells for transmission (**Fig. 17.2b**). The macrophages, helper T cells, and antibody-producing B cells of the immune system communicate via cell-bound signals about the presence of viral particles, bacteria, and toxins.

Each signaling system has four components

Although the details can be complex depending on the individual system, both types of signaling systems have four molecular components that control cell division.

- **Growth factors.** These factors are extracellular hormones or cell-bound signals that stimulate or inhibit cell proliferation. Most growth factors deliver their message to specific receptors embedded in the membrane of the receiving cell (**Fig. 17.3a**).
- The **receptors** are proteins that have three parts: a signal-binding site outside the cell, a transmembrane segment that passes through the cell membrane, and an intracellular domain that relays the signal (that is, the binding of growth factor) to proteins inside the cell's cytoplasm.
- These cytoplasmic proteins are known as **signal transducers.** They are responsible for relaying the signal inside the cell.
- The final link is usually a **transcription factor** that activates the expression of specific genes in the nucleus, either to promote or to inhibit cell proliferation (**Fig. 17.3b** and **c**). These factors were described in detail in Chapter 16.

Molecular interactions relay a signal

Binding of a growth factor to its specific receptor elicits a cascade of biochemical reactions inside the cell, often involving a large number of molecules. Each molecule in the cascade transmits the receptor's binding-of-messenger signal by activating or inhibiting another molecule. The activation and inhibition of intracellular targets after growth-factor binding is called **signal transduction.**

One example of a signal transduction system includes the product of the *RAS* gene (**Fig. 17.3d**). The RAS

Figure 17.2 Extracellular signals can diffuse from one cell to another or be delivered by cell-to-cell contact. (a) The pituitary gland produces thyroid-stimulating hormone (TSH) that moves through the circulation to the thyroid gland, which produces another hormone, thyroxine, that acts on many cells throughout the body. (b) A killer T cell recognizes its target cell by direct cell-to-cell contact.

(a)

Pituitary gland

Secretory cell

TSH molecules produced by pituitary travel through bloodstream to thyroid.

TSH molecule

Receptor site on thyroid cell surfaces

Thyroid

Thyroxine

Thyroid cells produce thyroxine, which increases metabolic rate.

(b)

Virus particle

These are T-cell receptors for histo-compatibility protein and for virus protein.

Host cell

T cell

Antigen

T cell binds to histo-compatibility-antigen complex.

Infected cell is destroyed by T cell.

Figure 17.3 Many hormones transmit signals into cells through receptors that span the cellular membrane. (a) Hormones bind to a specific cell surface receptor. The extracellular surface of the receptor transmits a signal to the intracellular domain of the receptor, which, in turn, interacts with other signaling molecules in the cell either to stimulate growth (b) or to inhibit growth (c). The RAS protein is an intracellular signaling molecule that is induced to exchange a bound GDP (inactive) for a bound GTP (active) when a growth factor binds to the cellular receptor with which RAS interacts (d).

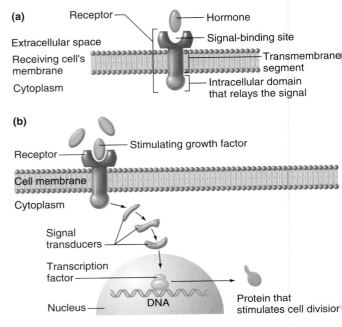

(a)

Receptor

Hormone

Signal-binding site

Extracellular space

Receiving cell's membrane

Transmembrane segment

Cytoplasm

Intracellular domain that relays the signal

(b)

Stimulating growth factor

Receptor

Cell membrane

Cytoplasm

Signal transducers

Transcription factor

Nucleus

DNA

Protein that stimulates cell division

(c)

Inhibiting growth factor

Receptor

Signal transducers

Transcription factor

DNA

Protein that blocks cell from dividing

(d)

Receptor

Growth factor

RAS

RAS inactive when bound to GDP

GDP

RAS active when bound to GTP

RAS

GTP

MAP kinase cascade

Transcription factor

Proliferation

protein is a molecular switch that exists in two forms: an inactive form in which it is bound to guanosine diphosphate (RAS-GDP), and an active form in which it is bound to guanosine triphosphate (RAS-GTP). Once a growth factor activates a receptor, the receptor "flicks the RAS switch" to active by exchanging GDP for GTP. Next, RAS-GTP activates a series of three protein kinases, and this trio, known as a **MAP kinase cascade,** activates a transcription factor.

The proteins in a signal transduction system are like the neurons in a nerve fiber: Each one serves as a link in a message-relay chain. In deciding whether or not to divide, the cell, like the brain, combines messages from many signal transduction systems and adjusts its behavior in response to the integrated information.

> Initiation of cell division involves either extracellular signals or cell-bound signals. Both systems comprise four general molecular components: growth factors, receptors, signal transducers, and transcription factors that promote DNA replication.

17.2 Cancer: A Failure of Control over Cell Division

An understanding of the molecular basis of cell-cycle regulation sheds light on the life-threatening proliferative disease of cancer. The many genes contributing to the normal control of cell proliferation through the different molecular components are all subject to mutations.

Accumulation of mutations results in the cancer phenotype

Cancer biologists now believe that most cancers result from the accumulation of many mutations during the proliferation of somatic cells. When enough mutations accumulate in genes controlling proliferation and other processes within a single clone of cells, that clone overgrows the normal cells that surround it, disseminates through the bloodstream to other parts of the body, and forms a life-threatening tumor, or cancer. (In this chapter, we use the term "tumor" to designate cancerous tissue and the term "growth" to designate a benign mass.) Epidemiological data, clinical studies, and experimental analyses of a range of cell types in a variety of species provide evidence for this gene-based view of cancer.

Cellular abnormalities

Theodor Boveri, one of the architects of the chromosome theory of inheritance, observed as early as 1914 that cells excised from malignant tumors have abnormal chromosomes. By the 1970s, when new staining techniques and improved equipment made it possible to distinguish each of the 23 different chromosome pairs in the human genome by their specific banding patterns, investigators noted that many different chromosomal abnormalities appear in tumor cells. Using tools developed in the 1980s, geneticists confirmed that most tumor cells exhibit karyotypic instability.

Figure 17.4 shows the main characteristics that distinguish tumor cells from normal cells. The cancer phenotype includes uncontrolled cell growth, genomic and karyotypic instability, the potential for immortality, and the ability to invade and disrupt local and distant tissues. Although no one cancer cell necessarily manifests all the phenotypic changes illustrated in Fig. 17.4, each cancer cell displays a number of them.

Multiple mutations leading to conversion

The large catalog of phenotypic changes seen in tumor cells suggests that many mutations in a number of genes are necessary to convert a normal cell into a cancerous cell. DNA sequencing of tumor cells has revealed thousands of mutations in each tumor, but how many actually contribute to the cancer phenotype is unclear because most of these mutations are different in different tumors of the same type. The number of genes in which mutations can fuel the progression to cancer is probably quite large—at least 100 and possibly several hundred. To study mutations associated with cancer, researchers initially identify and isolate a mutation of interest by linkage analysis of markers, traditional genetic mapping to a chromosome, and positional cloning (all techniques described in Chapter 11). It is possible to test in mice whether a mutation in a single gene associated with cancer is sufficient to induce a tumor. If the mutation acts in a dominant fashion, researchers insert a copy of the mutant allele into the mouse genome of a fertilized egg; if the mutation is recessive, they delete one copy of the homologous gene from the early embryonic mouse genome and then breed animals homozygous for the deletion.

In gene transfer experiments where a dominant cancer-causing mutation was inserted into a mouse genome under the control of a breast-cell-specific promoter, the transgenic mice produced a few breast tumors (**Fig. 17.5a**). Doubly transgenic mice made by breeding these transgenic mice carrying one mutated gene with transgenic mice carrying a different mutated gene implicated in cancer generated more tumors earlier. Even in these mice, however, only a small percentage of the transformed cells proliferated abnormally to form a tumor. These results support the idea that it takes several mutations in different genes to produce a cancer.

Studies of recessive mutations in the *p53* gene point to the same conclusion. Mice with both copies of the *p53* gene deleted from their genome develop relatively normally. The *p53* mutant mice, however, have shortened life spans and get a variety of tumors more frequently than wild-type mice (**Fig. 17.5b**). This experiment shows that the *p53* gene is not essential for development or for normal cell function, but it does play a role in preventing tumor formation. Consequently, deleting both copies of the wild-type gene from all of a mouse's cells does not convert every cell to a tumor cell, but it does increase the probability that at least one cell will become cancerous. The conclusion is that mutations in *p53* are just one of the many genetic changes that may occur in a cell to produce cancer.

Clonal proliferation

Examination of cells from women heterozygous for X-linked alleles provides evidence that cancer originates in a single somatic cell (**Fig. 17.6**). Although the random inactivation of one of the two X chromosomes in each cell of a female means that individual cells express only one of the two X-linked alleles, in small samples of normal somatic tissues, one usually finds both alleles expressed. The reason is that most somatic tissues are constructed from many clones of cells.

In contrast to normal tissue, tumors from females invariably express only one allele of an X-linked gene (review the discussion of X inactivation on p. 455 of Chapter 13). This finding suggests that the cells of each

(Text continues on p. 593)

FEATURE FIGURE 17.4

Phenotypic Changes That Distinguish Tumor Cells from Normal Cells

MOST NORMAL CELLS   **MANY CANCER CELLS**

a.1 — **Autocrine stimulation** — Absent / Present

a.2 — **Contact inhibition** — Present / Absent

a.3 — **Cell death** — Irradiation → Cell death (Present) / Irradiation (Absent)

a.4 — **Gap junctions** — Present / Absent

a. Changes that produce uncontrolled cell growth

1. *Autocrine stimulation.* Most cells "decide" whether or not to divide only after receiving signals from neighboring cells. Many tumor cells, by contrast, make their own stimulatory signals, in a process known as autocrine stimulation, or they have become insensitive to negative signals.

2. *Loss of contact inhibition.* Normal cells stop dividing when they come in contact with one another, as evidenced by the fact that normal cell types that grow in culture form sheets one cell thick. Tumor cells, in contrast, climb all over each other to produce piles that are many cells thick. This change contributes to the disordered array of cells seen in tumors.

3. *Loss of cell death.* Normal cells die when starved of growth factors or when exposed to agents that damage them. Programmed cell death (apoptosis) is activated by the expression of certain genes in the cell; it is probably a safeguard against the early stages of cancer. Most cancer cells are much more resistant than normal cells to programmed cell death.

4. *Loss of gap junctions.* Normal cells connect to their neighbors by small pores, or gap junctions, in their membranes. The gap junctions permit the transfer of small molecules that may be important in controlling cell growth. Most tumor cells have lost these channels of communication.

b.1

Replication

Mismatch created by
DNA polymerase

Normal cell —
corrected by
mismatch repair

Mismatch
not corrected
in cancer cell

Replication

Replication

Mutation

b. Changes that produce genomic and karyotypic instability

1. *Defects in the DNA replication machinery.* Cancer arises most often in cells that have lost the ability to reproduce their genomes faithfully. You saw in Chapters 6 and 7 that cells have elaborate systems for repairing DNA damage; these systems include the enzymatic machinery for mismatch repair and the repair of damage caused by radiation or ultraviolet light. Work on yeast and bacteria has shown that mutant organisms defective in DNA repair have enormously increased rates of mutation. These increased mutation rates often lead to cancer in multicellular organisms.

b.2

2. *Increased rate of chromosomal aberrations.* Tumor-cell karyotypes often carry gross rearrangements, including broken chromosomes, with some of the pieces rejoined to other chromosomes; multiple copies of individual chromosomes, rather than the normal two; and deletions of large chromosomal segments and of whole chromosomes. Studies have confirmed that the fidelity of chromosome reproduction is greatly diminished in tumor cells. Normal fibroblast cells, for example, have an undetectable rate of gene amplification (an increase in the number of copies of a gene), whereas tumor cells have amplification rates as high as 1 in 100 cells.

Probably only a small fraction of these chromosomal rearrangements lead to cancer; for example, tumors from solid tissues typically carry many chromosomal rearrangements, but most of these aberrations do not recur in all tumors. A few rearrangements, however, regularly appear in specific tumor types. Examples include the translocation between chromosomes 8 and 14 found in patients with certain kinds of lymphoma and the translocation between chromosomes 9 and 22 found in certain types of leukemias (see Fig. 14.20 on p. 492).

(Continued)

FEATURE FIGURE 17.4 (Continued)

c. Changes that produce a potential for immortality

1. *Loss of limitations on the number of cell divisions.* Most normal cells (except for the rare stem cells) die spontaneously after a specifiable number of cell divisions. Tumor cells, by contrast, can divide indefinitely.
2. *Ability to grow in culture.* Cells derived from tumor cells usually grow readily in culture, making cancerous cell lines available for study. Normal cells do not grow well in culture.

3. *Restoration of telomerase activity (not shown).* Most normal human somatic cells do not express the enzyme telomerase, and this lack of telomerase expression prevents them from replicating the repeated sequences in the telomeres at the ends of their chromosomes, contributing to cell aging and death (see Chapter 12, pp. 418–420). Tumor cells have the ability to express telomerase, a feature that most likely contributes to their immortality.

c.1   Most normal cells / Immortality / Many cancer cells

Cumulative cell number — Number of passages

c.2   Growth in soft agar

No cell growth — Cell growth

d. Changes that enable a tumor to disrupt local tissue and invade distant tissues

1. *The ability to metastasize.* Normal cells stay within rigidly defined boundaries. Tumor cells, by comparison, often acquire the capacity to invade surrounding tissues and eventually to travel through the bloodstream to colonize distant tissues. Metastasis—the invasion of other tissues—is a complicated behavior requiring many genetic changes.
2. *Angiogenesis.* Once the adult human body has developed, new blood vessels do not normally form except to heal a wound. Tumor cells, however, secrete substances that cause blood vessels to grow toward them. The new vessels serve as supply lines through which the tumor can tap new sources of nutrients and as escape routes through which tumor cells can metastasize.
3. *Evasion of immune surveillance (not shown).* The human immune system may recognize cancer cells as foreign and attack them, thereby helping to eliminate tumors even before they become large enough for clinical detection. As evidence, cancer patients often have antibodies and/or killer T cells directed against their cancer cells. Successful tumor cells, however, somehow develop the ability to evade detection by the immune system.

d.1 Metastasis

Tumor cells — Basement membrane

d.2 Angiogenesis

Blood vesse

Figure 17.5 The percent of mice still alive as a function of age. (a) The activated *myc* oncogene produces tumors more slowly than the *ras* oncogene. Mice containing both oncogenes develop tumors even faster than mice with *ras*. **(b)** Homozygous *p53⁺* mice rarely get life-threatening tumors, whereas those heterozygous for a *p53⁻* mutation develop tumors late in life. Mice homozygous for the *p53⁻* mutation develop tumors early in life.

Figure 17.6 Polymorphic enzymes encoded by the X chromosome reveal the clonal origin of tumors. Each individual cell in a female expresses only one form of a polymorphic X-linked gene because of X-chromosome inactivation. A patch of tissue will usually contain both types of cells. If single cells are grown into a clone, they exhibit one or the other enzyme form. A tumor also exhibits only one form, demonstrating that it arose from a single cell. The two allelic forms of the gene's protein product are distinguished by electrophoresis.

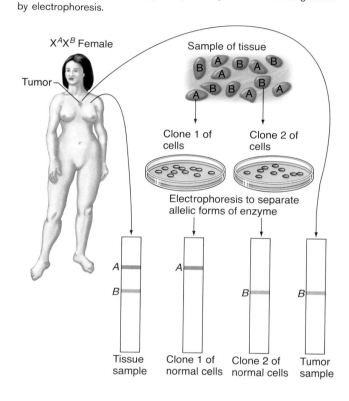

umor are the clonal descendants of a single somatic cell hat sustained a rare mutation.

The role of environmental mutagens

Several epidemiological surveys support the hypothesis that most cancers arise by chance in somatic cells during their division and differentiation from fertilized egg to adult. The mutations that produce these cancers are not inherited through the germ line in a dominant or recessive pattern; rather, they arise sporadically in a population as a result of chemicals or viruses in the environment. The evidence is as follows.

First, the degree of concordance for cancers of the same type among first-degree relatives, such as sisters and brothers or even identical twins, is low for most forms of

cancer in the population as a whole (we discuss specific exceptions later). If one sibling or twin gets a cancer, the other usually does not.

Second, although rates for the incidence of specific cancers vary worldwide (**Table 17.1**), when populations migrate from one place to another, their profile of cancer incidence becomes more like that of the people indigenous to the new location. The change in cancer profile often takes decades, suggesting that the environment acts over a long period of time to induce the cancer.

Third, epidemiological studies have established that numerous environmental agents increase the likelihood of cancer, and many of these agents are mutagens. These mutagens include cancer-causing viruses, some of which carry mutant forms of normal genes that control cell proliferation, as well as cigarette smoke. People who smoke for many years have a higher risk of lung cancer than people who do not smoke, and their risk increases with the number of cigarettes and the length of time they smoke.

TABLE 17.1 The Incidence of Some Common Cancers Varies Between Countries

Site of Origin of Cancer	High-Incidence Population		Low-Incidence Population	
	Location	Incidence*	Location	Incidence*
Lung	USA (New Orleans, blacks)	110	India (Chennai)	5.8
Breast	Hawaii (Hawaiians)	94	Israel (non-Jews)	14.0
Prostate	USA (Atlanta, blacks)	91	China (Tianjin)	1.3
Cervix	Brazil (Recife)	83	Israel (non-Jews)	3.0
Stomach	Japan (Nagasaki)	82	Kuwait (Kuwaitis)	3.7
Liver	China (Shanghai)	34	Canada (Nova Scotia)	0.7
Colon	USA (Connecticut, whites)	34	India (Chennai)	1.8
Melanoma	Australia (Queensland)	31	Japan (Osaka)	0.2
Nasopharynx	Hong Kong	30	UK (southwestern)	0.3
Esophagus	France (Calvados)	30	Romania (urban Cluj)	1.1
Bladder	Switzerland (Basel)	28	India (Nagpur)	1.7
Ovary	New Zealand (Polynesian Islanders)	26	Kuwait (Kuwaitis)	3.3
Pancreas	USA (Los Angeles, Koreans)	16	India (Pune)	1.5
Lip	Canada (Newfoundland)	15	Japan (Osaka)	0.1

*Incidence indicates number of new cases per year per 100,000 population, adjusted for a standardized population age distribution (so as to eliminate effects due merely to differences of population age distribution). Figures for cancers of breast, cervix, and ovary are for women; other figures are for men. Adapted from V. T. DeVita, S. Hellman, and S. A. Rosenberg (eds.), *Cancer: Principles and Practice of Oncology,* 4th ed. Philadelphia: Lippincott, 1993; based on data from C. Muir et al., *Cancer Incidence in Five Continents,* Vol. 5. Lyon: International Agency for Research on Cancer, 1987.

Cancer development over time

The data on lung cancer show that decades elapse between the time a population begins smoking and the time that lung cancer begins increasing. In the United States, cancer incidence in men rose dramatically after 1940, roughly two decades after men began frequent smoking; women did not begin frequent smoking until several decades after men, and lung cancer incidence in women did not begin its dramatic increase until after 1960 (**Fig. 17.7a**).

Epidemiological data also show that the incidence of cancer rises with age. The prevalence of cancer in older people supports the idea that cancer develops over time as well as the idea that the accumulation of many mutations in the clonal descendants of a somatic cell fuels the progression from normal to cancerous. If you assume that the rate of accumulation of cancer-causing mutations is constant over a lifetime, the slope of a logarithmic curve plotting cancer incidence against age is a measure of the number of mutations required for cancer (**Fig. 17.7b**). Interestingly, the data for many types of tumors generate a similar curve in which the evolution of cancer requires 6–10 mutations. Thus, the correlation between cancer incidence and aging, as well as the time lag between exposure to carcinogens and the appearance of tumors, suggests that the mutations that produce cancer accumulate over time. However, this simple interpretation is only part of the picture because cells increase their mutation rate at some point during their progression to cancer.

Cancers that run in families

In some families, a specific type of cancer recurs in many members, indicating the inheritance of a predisposition through the germ line. Retinoblastoma is an example of this type of cancer (see the Genetics and Society box on p. 148 of Chapter 5). Half the individuals in families affected by retinoblastoma inherit a mutation in the *RB* gene from one parent. Because all their somatic cells carry one defective copy of the gene, a mutation in the single remaining wild-type copy of the *RB* gene in the cells that proliferate to produce the retina predisposes these cells to develop retinal cancer (**Fig. 17.8**). People who do not inherit a mutation in the *RB* gene need to experience a mutation in both copies of the gene in the same cell to develop cancer; this type of double hit is very rare. Interestingly, for nearly all common types of cancer that occur sporadically in a population, rare families can be found that exhibit an inherited predisposition to that cancer.

Figure 17.7 Lung cancer death rates and incidence of cancer with age. **(a)** Lung cancer death rates in the United States during the twentieth century began increasing rapidly for men in the 1940s and for women in the 1960s. This reflects the fact that smoking became prevalent among men about 20 years before it did among women. **(b)** The incidence of most cancers shows a dramatic increase with age, a result thought to reflect the accumulation of mutations in somatic cells.

(a)

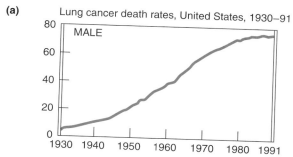

Lung cancer death rates, United States, 1930–91

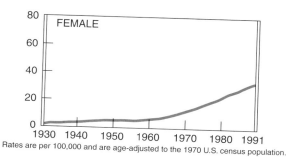

Rates are per 100,000 and are age-adjusted to the 1970 U.S. census population.

(b)

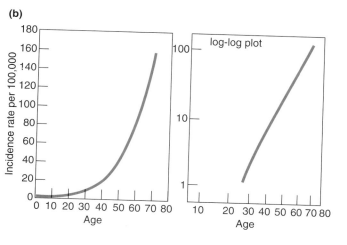

Figure 17.9 summarizes the sequence of events, as scientists now understand them, that ultimately lead to a malignant cell.

Cancer cells arise from multiple mutations occurring over time in a single cell that then produces a clone of malignant cells. Environmental mutagens are responsible for most cancers; inheritance of certain mutations predisposes some families to development of specific cancers.

Figure 17.8 Individuals who inherit one copy of the *RB⁻* allele are prone to cancer of the retina. During the proliferation of retinal cells, the *RB⁺* allele is lost or mutated, and cancers grow out of the *RB⁻/RB⁻* clone of cells.

Figure 17.9 Cancer is thought to arise by successive mutations in a clone of proliferating cells.

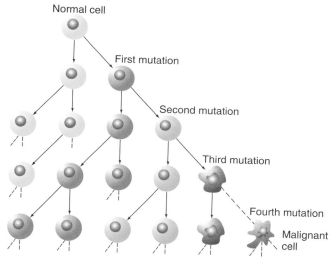

Mutations create dominant oncogenic alleles or recessive tumor-suppressor alleles

Research has not only revealed that cancer results from multiple genetic changes in the clonal descendants of one cell, it has also established that the mutations found in tumors are of two general types: those that improperly activate genes (for example, the genes responsible for promoting cell proliferation) and those that improperly inactivate genes (for example, the genes responsible for preventing excessive cell proliferation).

The mutant alleles that lead to cancer are referred to as **cancer genes,** but the term "genes" is a misnomer. All cancer genes are, in fact, mutant alleles of normal genes. When present in all or a subset of cells within an organism, these mutant alleles predispose the individual to develop

Figure 17.10 Cancer-producing mutations occur in two forms. (a) Dominant mutations generate oncogenes that exhibit abnormal activity or produce an excessive amount of protein. **(b)** Recessive mutations produce altered tumor suppressors that usually generate little or no phenotype when heterozygous with a wild-type allele, but that affect cell proliferation when a second mutation inactivates the wild-type allele.

(a) Dominant oncogene

Mutated gene → Abnormal or excessive protein

With one abnormal gene activated mutant protein is expressed.

Normal gene

Excessive cell proliferation

(b) Mutant tumor-supressor gene

Mutated gene → No protein or inactive protein

With one mutated gene normal protein is still expressed.

Normal gene → Normal protein

Normal cell proliferation

Both genes mutated
No protein or inactive protein

With two mutated genes no normal protein is expressed.

No protein or inactive protein

Excessive cell proliferation

cancer over a lifetime. Mutant alleles that act dominantly are known as **oncogenes;** in a diploid cell, one mutant oncogenic allele is sufficient to alter the cell phenotype (**Fig. 17.10a**). Mutant alleles that act recessively are known as mutant tumor-suppressor genes; in a diploid cell, both copies of a tumor-suppressor gene must be mutant to make the cell abnormal (**Fig. 17.10b**).

Increased cell proliferation from oncogenes

Two approaches to identifying oncogenes are the study of tumor-causing viruses and the study of tumor DNA itself.

Tumor viruses are useful tools for studying cancer-causing genes, first because they carry very few genes themselves, and second because they infect and change cultured cells to tumor cells, which makes it possible to study them *in vitro*. A large number of the viruses that generate tumors in animals are retroviruses whose RNA genome, upon infecting a cell, is copied to cDNA, which then integrates into the host chromosome (review the Genetics and Society box in Chapter 8 on pp. 260–261). Later, during excision from the host chromosome, the virus can pick up copies of host genes. These normal genes change to abnormally activated oncogenes either through mutations that occur during viral propagation or through their placement near powerful promoters and enhancers in the viral genome (**Fig. 17.11a**). The oncogenes carried by tumor-producing viruses are thus mutated versions of normal host cell genes. The wild-type genes

that become oncogenes upon mutation are known as **proto-oncogenes.** When a virus carrying one or more oncogenes infects a cell, the oncogenes cause abnormal proliferation that can lead to the accumulation of more mutations and eventually to cancer. The analysis of tumor-causing retroviruses led to the discovery of oncogenes in a variety of species (**Table 17.2**).

Some DNA viruses also carry oncogenes. An example is the human papillomavirus (HPV). HPV infection of a woman's cervical cells is probably the first step in the development of cervical cancer. The papillomavirus carries at least two oncogenes capable of transforming appropriate recipient cells in culture: *E6* and *E7*. The E6 and E7 proteins bind to and inactivate the normal products of the *p53* and *RB* genes. In addition, only those HPV subtypes whose E6 and E7 proteins bind p53 and RB proteins are associated with cervical cancer in women. Progression of HPV-initiated cells to cancer requires additional mutations in genes not yet identified.

Scientists also identify oncogenes by isolating DNA from tumor cells and exposing noncancerous cells in culture to this tumor DNA. Some tumor DNA transforms cultured cells into cells capable of producing tumors (**Fig. 17.11b**). For example, the DNA responsible for the transformation of mouse cells by human tumor DNA can be identified by reisolating the human DNA from the transformed mouse cells with probes for the short interspersed elements known as Alu sequences. These sequences appear only in the human genome (see Fig. 14.25a on p. 494). The oncogenes identified in this way, like those

Figure 17.11 Two methods to isolate oncogenes. (a) Retroviruses that cause cancer carry a mutant or overexpressed copy of a cellular growth-promoting gene. If the genome of a retrovirus integrates into the host chromosome near a proto-oncogene, the cellular gene may be packaged with the viral genome when the virus leaves the cell. **(b)** DNA isolated from some human cancers is able to transform mouse cells into cancer cells. These cells are found to contain a human oncogene. **(c)** The *RAS* oncogene, a mutant form of the *RAS* proto-oncogene, produces a protein that becomes locked into the GTP-activated form.

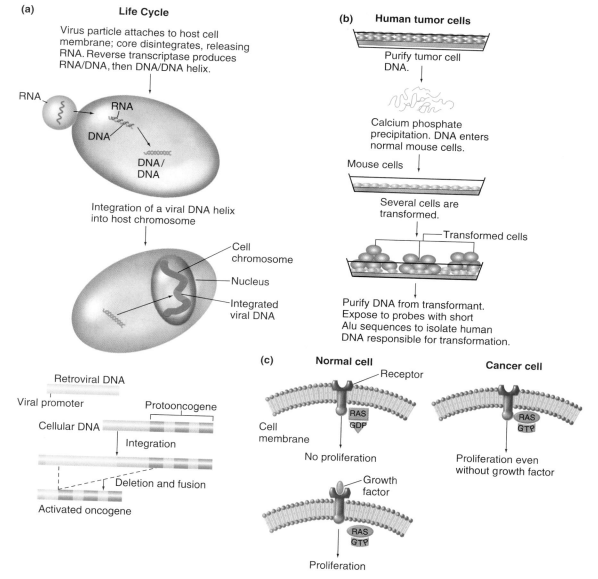

discovered in studies of tumor viruses, are oncogenic alleles of normal cellular genes that have mutated to abnormally active forms.

Sometimes the two approaches have identified the same oncogene, for example, *RAS*. The oncogenic forms of the *RAS* gene generate proteins that are always (or constitutively) in the GTP-activated form; therefore, whether or not growth factor is present, a cell carrying a *RAS* oncogene receives signals to divide (**Fig. 17.11c**). Like mutated *RAS*, many oncogenes continuously turn on one or more of a cell's many signal transduction systems. They do this by encoding receptors, signal transmitters,

and transcription factors that are active with or without growth factor (**Table 17.3**).

Enhanced mutation potential in proliferating cells

Like the oncogenic *RAS* gene, many of the oncogenes so far identified affect cell-signaling pathways that tell a cell whether or not to divide. The importance of these genes in generating cancer is not just that they cause cells to proliferate, because an increase in proliferation alone, without other changes, generates benign growths that are not life

TABLE 17.2	Retroviruses and Their Associated Oncogenes*		
Virus	**Species**	**Tumor**	**Oncogene**
Rous sarcoma	Chicken	Sarcoma	*src*
Harvey murine sarcoma	Rat	Sarcoma and erthyroleukemia	*H-ras*
Kristen murine sarcoma	Rat	Sarcoma and erthyroleukemia	*K-ras*
Moloney murine sarcoma	Mouse	Sarcoma	*mos*
FBJ murine osteosarcoma	Mouse	Chondrosarcoma	*fos*
Simian sarcoma	Monkey	Sarcoma	*sis*
Feline sarcoma	Cat	Sarcoma	*sis*
Avian sarcoma	Chicken	Fibrosarcoma	*jun*
Avian myelocytomatosis	Chicken	Carcinoma, sarcoma, and myleocytoma	*myc*
Ableson leukemia	Mouse	B-cell lymphoma	*abl*

*Retroviruses identified as causative agents of tumors in animals contain oncogenes that were derived from a cellular gene. Adapted from Lewin, *Genetics*, 1e, Oxford University Press, Inc. by permission.

TABLE 17.3	Oncogenes Are Members of Signal Transduction Systems*		
Name of Oncogene	**Tumor Associations**	**Mechanism of Activation**	**Properties of Gene Product**
hst	Stomach carcinoma	Rearrangement	Growth factor
erb-B	Mammary carcinoma, glioblastoma	Amplification	Growth factor receptor
trk	Papillary thyroid carcinomas	Rearrangement	Growth factor receptor
Ha-ras	Bladder carcinoma	Point mutation	GDP/GTP binding signaling protein
raf	Stomach carcinoma	Rearrangement	Cytoplasmic serine/threonine kinase
myc	Lymphomas, carcinomas	Amplification, chromosomal translocation	Nuclear transcription factor

*The roles of several oncogene products that are members of the signal transduction pathway and the ways in which they get activated in human cells are shown.

threatening and can be removed by surgery. Rather, increased proliferation provides a large clone of cells within which further mutations can occur, and these further mutations may eventually lead to malignancy. The more cells that exist in a clone, the more likely that rare mutations will occur in the clone—which already has the potential for rapidly propagating them. Although not all cancer-causing genes are dominant oncogenes, oncogenic mutations have been the easiest to identify for technical reasons.

Increased cell proliferation from mutant tumor-suppressor alleles

Mutant tumor-suppressor genes are recessive alleles of genes whose normal alleles help put cell division on hold, whether in terminally differentiated cells or in cells with DNA damage. Targets for tumor-suppressor mutations include *RB*, *p53*, and *p16*. One wild-type copy of these genes apparently produces enough protein to regulate cell division; the loss of both wild-type copies releases a brake on proliferation (see Fig. 17.10b). Researchers have identified dozens of tumor-suppressor genes through the genomic analysis of families with an inherited predisposition to

specific types of cancer or through the analysis of specific chromosomal regions that are reproducibly deleted in certain tumor types.

Retinoblastoma provides an example of this identification process. A cancer of the color-perceiving cone cells in the retina, retinoblastoma is one of several cancers inherited in a dominant fashion in human families (**Fig. 17.12a**). Roughly half the children of a parent with retinoblastoma develop the disease. Retinoblastoma tumors are easy to diagnose and remove before they become invasive. As you saw in Chapter 14, karyotypes of normal, noncancerous tissues from many people suffering from retinoblastoma reveal heterozygosity for deletions in the long arm of chromosome 13; that is, the patients carry one normal and one partially deleted copy of 13q. Karyotypes of the cancerous retinal cells from some of these same patients show homozygosity for the same chromosome 13 deletions that are heterozygous in the noncancerous cells (**Fig. 17.12b**). Although the deletions vary in size and position from patient to patient, they all remove band 13q14.

These observations indicate that band 13q14 includes a gene whose removal contributes to the development of retinoblastoma. *RB* is the symbol for this gene. The

Figure 17.12 The retinoblastoma tumor-suppressor gene. (a) A child with a retinoblastoma tumor in the left eye. **(b)** The *RB⁻* gene is inherited through the germ line as an autosomal recessive mutation. Subsequent changes to the *RB⁺* allele during somatic divisions generate a clone of cells homozygous or hemizygous for the *RB⁻* allele.

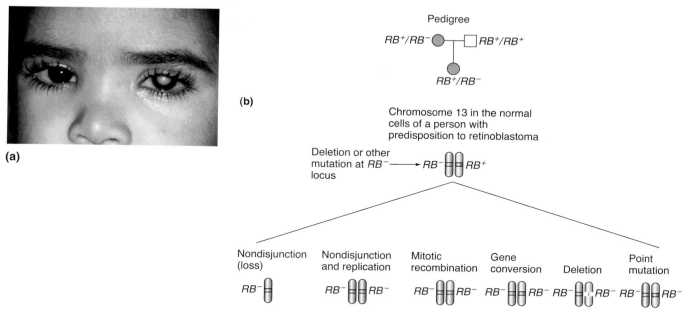

(a)

(b)

heterozygous cells in a patient's normal tissues carry one copy of the gene's wild-type allele (*RB⁺*), and this one copy prevents the cells from becoming cancerous. Tumor cells homozygous for the deletion, however, do not carry any copies of *RB⁺*, and without it, they begin to divide out of control.

Geneticists used their understanding of retinoblastoma inheritance to find the *RB* gene. They cloned DNA carrying the gene by looking for DNA sequences in band 13q14 that were lost in all of the deletions associated with the hereditary condition. They then identified the gene by characterizing a very small deletion that affected only one transcriptional unit—the *RB* gene itself. Analysis of the gene's function showed that it encodes a protein involved (along with many other proteins) in regulating the cell cycle. *RB* thus fits our definition of a tumor-suppressor gene: The protein it determines helps prevent cells from becoming cancerous. Cancer can arise when cells heterozygous for an *RB* deletion lose the remaining copy of the gene.

This picture of the genetics of retinoblastoma raises a perplexing question: How can the retinoblastoma trait be inherited in a dominant fashion if a deletion of the *RB* gene is recessive to the wild-type *RB* allele? At the level of the organism, *RB* deletions are dominant because of the strong likelihood that in at least one of the hundreds of thousands of retinal cells heterozygous for the deletion, a subsequent genetic event will disable the single remaining *RB* allele, resulting in a mutant cell with no functional tumor-suppressor gene. This one cell then multiplies out of control, eventually generating a clone

of cancerous cells (see the Genetics and Society box on p. 148 of Chapter 5).

Geneticists first recognized the recessive *RB* mutation that leads to retinoblastoma through the genomic analysis of families inheriting a predisposition to the cancer. More recently, they noted that both copies of the *p16* gene on chromosome 9 are deleted in roughly 75% of all melanomas (a malignant skin cancer) and in approximately 85% of all gliomas (the most common form of brain cancer). The *p16* gene encodes a protein that binds to and inactivates CDK4. In another example, observations of deletions of both copies of a specific region of chromosome 18 in all colon cancers led to identification of the *DCC* (deleted in colorectal cancer) gene.

Many tumor-suppressor mutations occur in genes that control the cell cycle and, with it, the accuracy of genomic replication. It is important to distinguish mutations that determine how the cell cycle is completed from mutations in genes that control proliferation. Alterations in genes that control proliferation result in an enlarged clone of cells, but aside from their increase in number, these cells—if they sustain no further mutations—are normal and thus form a benign growth. By contrast, mutations in genes that control the cell cycle can alter the accuracy with which a cell reproduces its genome. The resulting mutant cells can produce offspring with many more mutations than occur in normal cells, and this increase in the frequency of mutation vastly increases the probability that the cascade of mutations necessary to produce the phenotypic changes of tumor cells will occur.

TABLE 17.4	Mutant Alleles of These Tumor-Suppressor Genes Decrease the Accuracy of Cell Reproduction*	
Gene	**Normal Function of Gene (if known), or Disease Syndrome Resulting from Mutation**	**Function of Normal Protein Product**
p53	Controls G_1-to-S checkpoint	Transcription factor
RB	Controls G_1-to-S transition	Inhibits a transcription factor
ATM	Controls G_1-to-S phase, and G_2-to-M checkpoint	DNA-dependent protein kinase
BS	Recombinational repair of DNA damage	DNA/RNA ligase
XP	Excision of DNA damage	Several enzymes
hMSH2, hmLH1	Correction of base-pair matches	Several enzymes
FA	Fanconi anemia	Unknown
BRCA1	Repair of DNA breaks	Unknown
BRCA2	Repair of DNA breaks	Unknown

*Many tumor-suppressor genes have been associated with a specific function in the cell cycle necessary for accuracy of cell division.

Because cancer arises in cells that have lost the ability to reproduce their genomes faithfully, it seems reasonable to conclude that a cell's primary safeguard against cancer lies in maintaining the integrity of its genome. Cells have extensive, elaborate systems for repairing damage to their DNA, as described in Chapter 7. Mutants with a defective system have mutation rates several orders of magnitude greater than wild-type cells. In the l990s, cancer researchers discovered that some people with a hereditary predisposition to colon cancer are heterozygous for a mutation that inactivates a gene required for the normal functioning of the mismatch repair system; the cancers that develop in these individuals consist of cells that have lost the single remaining wild-type allele. This mismatch repair gene thus behaves like a classical tumor-suppressor gene. Presumably, the greatly increased mutation rate in a homozygous cell that has lost both wild-type alleles makes it easier for progeny cells to accumulate the large number of mutations necessary to produce a cancer cell. Why these cancers develop mainly in the colon rather than in other tissues is not clear. **Table 17.4** describes several other tumor-suppressor genes that affect the accuracy of cell division.

In the section that follows, we take a closer look at the details of the cell cycle—the process by which a somatic cell grows and divides.

Accumulated oncogenic and tumor-suppressor mutations produce cells with grossly altered genomes that proliferate both excessively and inaccurately. Dominant mutations to proto-oncogenes, producing oncogenes, may activate proteins that promote cell proliferation, while mutations in tumor-suppressor genes remove the brakes from cell division. Mutations that disable or disrupt DNA repair systems act to increase the mutational rate as errors accumulate with each round of division.

17.3 The Normal Control of Cell Division

A variety of genes and proteins control the events of the cell cycle. These genes and proteins allow progression to the next stage of the cycle when all is well, but they cause the cellular machinery to slow down when damage to the genome or to the machinery itself requires repair. We now describe the molecules that control cell division.

Cyclins and cyclin-dependent kinases ensure proper timing and sequence of events

Cell division, as you learned in Chapter 4, requires the duplication of chromosomes and other cellular components as well as the precise partitioning of the duplicated elements to two daughter cells. During this complicated process, the cell coordinates the function of hundreds of different proteins. To see how the cell orchestrates the events of cell division, we first review the stages of the cell cycle and then look at some of the proteins that control progression through that cycle.

The four phases of the cell cycle: G_1, S, G_2, and M

To review the cell cycle briefly, G_1 is the "gap" period between the end of mitosis and the DNA synthesis that precedes the next mitosis (**Fig. 17.13**). During G_1, the cell grows in size, imports materials to the nucleus, and prepares in other ways for DNA replication. S is the period of DNA synthesis, or replication. G_2 is the "gap" between DNA synthesis and mitosis. During G_2, the cell prepares for division. M, the phase of mitosis, includes the break down of the nuclear membrane, the condensation of the

Figure 17.13 The cell cycle is the series of events that transpire between one cell division and the next. After division, a cell begins in the G_1 phase, progresses into S phase, where the chromosomes replicate, to the G_2 phase, and to the M phase, where replicated sister chromosomes segregate to daughter cells. In M phase, the nuclear membrane breaks down, centrosomes form the poles of the spindle, and microtubules construct a scaffold on which chromosomes migrate.

G_1: Cell grows in size, prepares for DNA replication

Centrosome
Cell membrane
DNA
Nuclear membrane

S: DNA replication

Daughter cells

G_2: Cell prepares for division

Spindle pole
Condensed chromosome
Mitotic spindle

M: Mitosis
1. Breakdown of nuclear membrane
2. Condensation of chromosomes
3. Attachment of chromosomes to mitotic spindles

chromosomes, their attachment to the mitotic spindle, and the segregation of chromosomes to the two poles; at the completion of mitosis, the cell divides by cytokinesis.

During M, the cell must coordinate the activities of a variety of proteins: those that cause chromosome condensation (see Chapters 4 and 13), tubulins that polymerize to form the mitotic spindle on which the chromosomes move, motor proteins in the kinetochores that power chromosome movement, proteins that dissolve and re-form the nuclear membrane at the beginning and end of mitosis, and others.

Discovery of kinases in yeasts

The budding yeast *Saccharomyces cerevisiae* and the fission yeast *Schizosaccharomyces pombe* have been instrumental in identifying the genes that control cell division. Several properties of both yeast species make them particularly useful for this study. First, both can grow as haploid or diploid organisms. As a result, recessive mutations can be identified in the haploid cells, and then diploid cells can be constructed containing two mutations. These can be allowed to proliferate, and the resulting cell

populations tested to determine the number of complementation groups defined by the mutations.

The budding yeast *S. cerevisiae* has yet another property that facilitates cell-cycle analysis. At the beginning of the cell cycle, toward the end of G_1, a new daughter cell arises as a bud on the surface of the mother cell. As the mother cell progresses through the division cycle, the bud grows in size; it is small during S phase and large during mitosis. Bud size thus serves as a marker of progress through the cell cycle (**Fig. 17.14a**). One can order cells in an asynchronously cycling population according to position in the

Figure 17.14 A cell-cycle mutant of yeast. Cells of a temperature-sensitive mutant growing at the permissive temperature **(a)** display buds of all sizes. After incubation at the restrictive temperature **(b)**, the same cells have arrested—all with a large bud. Cells that are early in the cell cycle at the time of the temperature shift arrest in the first cell cycle; these cells have the small buds in (a). Cells that are later in the cell cycle finish the first cell cycle and arrest in the second, producing clumps with two large-budded cells.

(a)

(b)

cell cycle by observing the relative sizes of their buds. A normal population of growing yeast cells contains nonbudding cells as well as cells with buds of all sizes.

Isolation of Cell-Cycle Mutants. Mutations that interfere with the cell cycle are lethal; and because cell proliferation depends on successive repeats of the cell cycle, a mutant unable to complete the cell cycle cannot grow into a population of cells (**Fig. 17.14b**). Researchers have obtained cell-cycle-defective mutants by isolating cells with temperature-sensitive mutations (see the Fast Forward box on p. 232 of Chapter 7). In these mutants, a protein needed for cell division functions normally at a low permissive temperature, but it loses function at a higher restrictive temperature. At the permissive temperature, the mutants grow nearly normally, producing a population of cells for study. A shift to the restrictive temperature causes the temperature-sensitive protein in the mutant population to become nonfunctional; researchers can then study the consequences of its loss.

To isolate temperature-sensitive mutations, investigators expose haploid cells to a mutagen and then plate them at the permissive temperature, allowing them to form colonies (**Fig. 17.15**). After the colonies grow up, each from

Figure 17.15 The isolation of temperature-sensitive mutants of yeast. Mutations are induced in a culture of haploid cells by exposure to a chemical mutagen. The treated cells are distributed onto solid medium. Each cell proliferates to a colony (clone) of cells, passing on the mutation. Replicas of the colonies are imprinted onto solid medium. One is grown at the permissive temperature (22°C), one at the restrictive temperature (36°C). Colonies that grow on the former, but not the latter, carry a temperature-sensitive mutation.

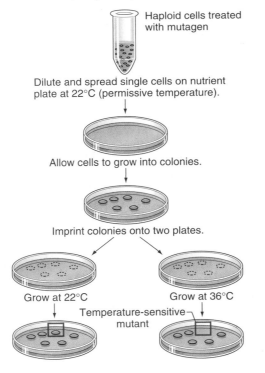

Haploid cells treated with mutagen

Dilute and spread single cells on nutrient plate at 22°C (permissive temperature).

Allow cells to grow into colonies.

Imprint colonies onto two plates.

Grow at 22°C   Grow at 36°C

Temperature-sensitive mutant

a single mutant cell, the experimenters use replica plating to imprint them on two plates. They incubate one plate at the permissive temperature and the other plate at the restrictive temperature. Cells that have sustained a temperature-sensitive mutation grow at the permissive temperature but not at the restrictive temperature.

Analysis of Cell-Cycle Mutants. With this protocol, researchers have isolated thousands of temperature-sensitive mutations. These mutations could occur in any gene required for cell reproduction. Genes of particular interest are those whose protein product functions at only one stage in the cell cycle. Such mutants were identified in *S. cerevisiae* by observing in the light microscope the shape and behavior of cells shifted from the permissive to the restrictive temperatures (see Fig. 17.14). A population of cells growing at the permissive temperature includes unbudded cells as well as cells with the full range of bud sizes. After a cell-cycle mutant has grown at the restrictive temperature for about two cycles, however, the cells have a uniform appearance. In the mutant population shown in Fig. 17.14, for example, all cells have a single large bud. Moreover, the nuclei (not visible in the figure) are uniformly located at a position between the mother cell and the daughter cell, as if beginning to divide. This uniformity identifies a particular cell-cycle mutant. Other cell-cycle mutants would arrest with different but also uniform morphologies, for example, with all unbudded cells. Thus, mutants that acquire a uniform bud-related morphology at the restrictive temperature are each defective at one stage of the cell cycle.

Further examination of cells transferred from permissive to restrictive temperatures illustrates another property of cell-cycle mutants—a requirement for the normal gene product at a particular stage of the cell cycle. Note that some of the cells in Fig. 17.14 formed one cell with a large bud at the restrictive temperature, while others formed two cells, each with a large bud. Note also that the former group all had smaller buds than the latter group at the time of the shift to the restrictive temperature. This observation indicates that cells early in the cell cycle at the moment of temperature shift arrested division in the first cell cycle, while those later in the cell cycle at the time of temperature shift finished the first cycle and became arrested only in the second cell cycle. The point at which a cell acquires the ability to complete a cell cycle is the moment at which the temperature-sensitive protein has fulfilled its function in that cycle.

By analyzing the morphology of buds on cells shifted from permissive to restrictive temperatures and using other methods, yeast geneticists have identified over 100 cell-cycle genes (**Table 17.5**). The significance of the *CDC28* gene in particular became apparent when geneticists identified related genes in other organisms. They found, for example, that the *CDC2* gene in fission yeast controls a step of commitment in that cell. They also learned that in extracts of *Xenopus laevis* (African clawed frog) embryos, the activity

TABLE 17.5	**Some Important Cell-Cycle and DNA Repair Genes**
Genes	**Gene Products and Their Function**
CDKs	Enzymes known as cyclin-dependent protein kinases that control the activity of other proteins by phosphorylating them
CDC28	A CDK discovered in the yeast *Saccharomyces cerevisiae* that controls several steps in the *S. cerevisiae* cell cycle
CDC2	A CDK discovered in the yeast *Schizosaccharomyces pombe* that controls several steps in the *S. pombe* cell cycle; also the designation for a particular CDK in mammalian cells
CDK4	A CDK of mammalian cells important for the G_1-to-S transition
CDK2	A CDK of mammalian cells important for the G_1-to-S transition
cyclins	Proteins that are necessary for and influence the activity of CDKs
cyclinD	A cyclin of mammalian cells important for the G_1-to-S transition
cyclinE	A cyclin of mammalian cells important for the G_1-to-S transition
cyclinA	A cyclin of mammalian cells important for S phase
cyclinB	A cyclin of mammalian cells important for the G_2-to-M transition
E2F	A transcription factor of mammalian cells important for the G_1-to-S transition
RB	A mammalian protein that inhibits E2F
p21	A protein of mammalian cells that inhibits CDK activity
p16	A protein of mammalian cells that inhibits CDK activity
p53	A transcription factor of mammalian cells that activates transcription of DNA repair genes as well as transcription of *p21*
RAD9	A protein that inhibits the G_2-to-M transition of *S. cerevisiae* in response to DNA damage
E6	A protein of the HPV virus that inhibits p53
E7	A protein of the HPV virus that inhibits Rb

of a protein known as MPF (for maturation-promoting factor) controls the rapid early divisions. Sequences of the cloned budding and fission yeast genes revealed that they encode **protein kinases,** enzymes that add phosphate groups to their protein substrates. The *Xenopus* MPF also turned out to be a protein kinase. Moreover, genetic swapping experiments showed that the budding yeast *CDC28* gene and the fission yeast *CDC2* gene can replace one another in either organism, demonstrating that they encode proteins that carry out the same activity; the same is true of the *Xenopus* MPF-encoding gene.

Thus, in three different organisms, genes that seem to be the central controlling element of the cell cycle encode functionally homologous protein kinases. Further work has shown that these kinases are **cyclin-dependent kinases (CDKs);** that is, they require another protein known as a **cyclin** for their activity.

The role of cyclin-dependent kinases

The CDKs are a family of kinases that regulate the transition from G_1 to S and from G_2 to M through phosphorylations that activate or inactivate target proteins. As mentioned, CDKs function only after associating with a cyclin. The cyclin portion of a CDK–cyclin complex specifies which set of proteins a particular CDK phosphorylates; the CDK portion of the complex then performs the phosphorylation (**Fig. 17.16a**). One CDK–cyclin complex, for example, activates target proteins required for DNA replication at the onset of the S phase, whereas another CDK–cyclin activates proteins necessary for chromosome condensation and segregation at the begin-

ning of the M phase. The cyclins that guide the CDK phosphorylations appear on cue at each phase of the cell cycle. After they associate with the appropriate CDKs and

Figure 17.16 The cyclin-dependent kinases (CDK) control the cell cycle by phosphorylating other proteins. (a) A CDK combines with a cyclin and acquires the capacity to phosphorylate other proteins. Phosphorylation of a protein can either inactivate or activate it. **(b)** CDK phosphorylation of the nuclear structure proteins, lamins, is responsible for the dissolution of the nuclear membrane at mitosis.

point out the proper protein targets, they then disappear to make way for the succeeding set of cyclins. The cycle of precisely timed cyclin appearances and disappearances is the result of two mechanisms: gene regulation that turns on and off the synthesis of particular cyclins, and regulated protein degradation that removes the cyclins. As an example, consider the action of one CDK on the **nuclear lamins,** a group of proteins that underlie the inner surface of the nuclear membrane (**Fig. 17.16b**). The nuclear lamins probably provide structural support for the nucleus and possibly provide sites for the assembly of proteins that function in DNA replication, transcription, RNA transport, and chromosome structure. During most of the cell cycle, the lamins form an insoluble structural matrix. At mitosis, however, the lamins become soluble, and this solubility allows dissolution of the nuclear membrane into vesicles. Lamin solubility requires phosphorylation; mutant lamins that resist phosphorylation do not become soluble at mitosis. Thus, one critical mitotic event—dissolution of the nuclear membrane—is most likely triggered by CDK phosphorylation of nuclear lamins.

Genetic studies of yeast provided much of the evidence that CDK–cyclin complexes are key controlling agents in all eukaryotic cell cycles. In one series of studies, geneticists used yeast mutants that carry defective CDKs or cyclins to find the corresponding human genes (**Fig. 17.17**) and to show that the human CDKs and cyclins can function in yeast in place of the native proteins.

Control of the G$_1$-to-S transition

Cell-cycle investigators have identified many of the molecular events controlling the transition from G$_1$ to S in human cells by analogy with similar events in the cell cycle of yeast. From their analyses, they have pieced together the following scenario.

- The first CDK–cyclin complexes to appear during G$_1$ in humans are CDK4–cyclinD and CDK2–cyclinE (**Fig. 17.18**). These complexes initiate the transition to S by a programmed succession of specific phosphorylations, among which are phosphorylations of the protein product of the retinoblastoma (*RB*) gene.
- Unphosphorylated Rb protein inhibits a transcription factor, E2F. Phosphorylated Rb no longer inhibits E2F.

Rb phosphorylation thus indirectly activates DNA synthesis by releasing the brakes on E2F and thereby allowing it to activate the transcription of genes necessary for DNA synthesis.

Control of the G$_2$-to-M transition

Human cells appear to make the transition from G$_2$ to mitosis much as the well-studied cells of the yeast *S. pombe* accomplish the same transition.

- In the yeast, a CDK known as CDC2 (the second C replaces the K for historical reasons) forms a complex with cyclinB. Both the CDC2 kinase and cyclinB

Figure 17.17 Mutant yeast permit the cloning of a human CDK gene. A culture of yeast cells containing a temperature-sensitive mutation in the CDK gene was transformed with a library composed of human cDNA cloned into a yeast centromere-containing (CEN) vector. The transformed yeast cells were spread on solid medium at the restrictive temperature. Only the rare transformants with a functional copy of the human CDK gene were able to grow.

Figure 17.18 CDKs mediate the transition from the G$_1$ to the S phase of the cell cycle. In human cells, CDK4 complexed to cyclinD, and CDK2 complexed to cyclinE, phosphorylate the Rb protein, causing it to dissociate from, and activate, the E2F transcription factor. E2F stimulates transcription of many genes needed for DNA replication. At the transition into S phase, cyclinD is destroyed, cyclinA is synthesized, and the CDK2–cyclinA complex activates DNA replication.

Figure 17.19 CDK activity in yeast is controlled by phosphorylation and dephosphorylation. The CDC2 protein complexed with cyclinB is inactivated prior to mitosis through phosphorylation by a specific kinase and then activated at the onset of mitosis through dephosphorylation by a specific phosphatase.

are present throughout G_2, but phosphorylation of a specific tyrosine residue on the cyclin-dependent kinase (by another protein kinase) keeps it inactive.

- When the time comes to initiate mitosis, a phosphatase enzyme removes the phosphate group from the CDC2 tyrosine; this removal activates the CDK, and the cell enters mitosis (**Fig. 17.19**).

Cell-cycle control: A summary

We now have some insight into how a cell is able to replicate its DNA at one time in the cell cycle and segregate its chromosomes at another. The two different phases of the cell cycle are governed by different kinase activities.

During S phase, a CDK is complexed with a cyclin that is specific to S phase. In this complex, it phosphorylates many proteins that lead to a cascade of protein synthesis and activation, and the newly synthesized proteins provide hundreds of activities required for DNA replication. During M phase, a different CDK is complexed with a cyclin specific for M phase. Its activity in this complex leads to the synthesis and activation of hundreds of proteins needed for mitosis. In summary, CDKs and cyclins together set the "state" of the cell: S phase or M phase.

How does the cell change from one state to the other? Among the cellular processes activated by CDKs are those that irreversibly destroy key regulatory proteins, including the cyclins. Thus, as the cell enters either S phase or M phase, it sets in place the end of each phase by removing cyclins and many other proteins whose activities must be limited to either S or M phase.

Just as attachment of a phosphate group activates or deactivates proteins, the covalent attachment of a

ubiquitin tag marks proteins for degradation. During S phase, activation of a group of proteins called SCF occurs. The activated SCF adds ubiquitin to proteins such as the S-phase cyclins. During M phase, activation of a group of proteins called APC takes place, and the activated APC adds ubiquitin to proteins such as the M-phase cyclins. Proteins tagged with ubiquitin are rapidly degraded by the cell in the large multiprotein complex, the proteosome. Thus, the cell cycle has an intrinsic ratchetlike mechanism, ensuring that activation of one phase (S or M) leads inevitably to the irreversible end of that phase and elimination of any proteins that could interfere with the next phase.

The discovery of cyclins and cyclin-dependent kinases through experiments with cell-cycle mutants in yeasts have provided insight into the control of cell division. Highly specific cyclins, produced at key points in the cell's cycle, bind with particular CDKs and lead to specialized protein activation. Cyclins produced for one phase are irreversibly marked for destruction at the end of that phase, ensuring that the processes go in only one direction.

Cell-cycle checkpoints ensure genomic stability

Damage to a cell's genome, whether caused by environmental agents or random errors of the cellular machinery as it attempts to replicate and segregate the chromosomes, can cause serious problems for the cell. Damage to the cell-cycle machinery can also cause problems. It is therefore not surprising that elaborate mechanisms have evolved to arrest the cell cycle while repair takes place. These additional controls are called checkpoints because they check the integrity of the genome and cell-cycle machinery before allowing the cell to continue to the next phase of the cell cycle.

The G_1-to-S checkpoint

When radiation or chemical mutagens damage DNA during G_1, DNA replication is postponed. This postponement allows time for DNA repair before the cell proceeds to DNA synthesis. Replication of the unrepaired DNA could exacerbate the damage; for example, replication over a single-strand nick or gap would produce a double-strand break. In mammals, cells exposed to ionizing radiation or UV light during G_1 delay entry into S phase by activating the *p53 pathway* (**Fig. 17.20a**). p53 is a transcription factor that induces expression of DNA repair genes as well as expression of the CDK inhibitor known as p21. Like other CDK inhibitors, p21 binds to CDK–cyclin complexes and inhibits their activity; specifically,

Figure 17.20 Cellular responses to DNA damage. (a) DNA damage activates the p53 transcription factor, which, in turn, induces expression of the *p21* gene. The p21 protein inhibits CDK activity, producing an arrest of the cell cycle in the G_1 phase. **(b)** Tumor cells exhibit amplified regions of DNA, unlike normal cells, that can appear as homogeneously staining regions (HSRs) within a chromosome or as double minutes, small pieces of extrachromosomal DNA. **(c)** When the *p53* gene is mutated in cancers, *p21* expression is not induced, cell-cycle progress is not arrested, and cells replicate damaged DNA, producing DNA double-strand breaks from single-strand nicks or gaps. **(d)** DNA damage in normal cells often leads to apoptosis.

(a) Transcription factor p53 activated by UV or ionizing radiation

p53 → Induces expression of CDK inhibitor, p21 → p21

Induces expression of DNA repair genes

p21 inhibits activity of CDK4–cyclinD complexes.

CDK4 / CyclinD

Rb remains unphosphorylated and E2F is inhibited, preventing entry into S phase of cell cycle.

E2F Rb

(c) p53 is mutated.

Single-strand break

Mutant — p53

p21

DNA replication

Double-strand break

Chromosome rearrangements

Defective G_1-to-S checkpoint. Replication proceeds: p53 inactive and p21 not induced.

Mutant p53 can't induce functional p21, so cell enters S phase.

(d) Apoptosis

DNA degraded

Nucleus condenses; cell may be devoured by surrounding cells.

(b) Tumor cells

HSR

Double minutes

p21 prevents entry into S by inhibiting the activity of CDK4–cyclinD complexes.

Mutations in *p53* disrupt the G_1-to-S checkpoint. One sign of this disruption is a propensity for gene amplification: an increase from the normal two copies to hundreds of copies of a gene. This amplification is visible under the microscope, appearing as an enlarged area within a chromosome known as a *homogeneously staining region* (HSR) or as small chromosome-like bodies (called **double minutes**) that lack centromeres and telomeres (**Fig. 17.20b**). Normal human cells do not generate gene amplification in culture, but *p53* mutants exhibit high rates of such amplification; *p53* mutants also exhibit many types of chromosome rearrangements. The explanation is as fol-

lows. Cells carrying mutations in the *p53* gene most likely have a defective G_1-to-S checkpoint that allows the replication of single-strand nicks. This replication produces double-strand breaks, which, in turn, lead to chromosome rearrangements. Some of the rearrangements generate gene amplification (**Fig. 17.20c**).

Wild-type cells able to produce functional p53 not only arrest in G_1 in the presence of DNA damage; if the damage is great enough, they also "commit suicide" in a process known as **programmed cell death (PCD)** or **apoptosis.** During apoptosis, the cellular DNA is degraded, and the nucleus condenses. The cell may then be devoured by neighboring cells or by phagocytes (**Fig. 17.20d**). Programmed cell death and the protein

Figure 17.21 Checkpoints acting at the G₂-to-M cell-cycle transition or during M phase. (a) DNA damage, particularly double-strand breaks, induce a signal that inhibits CDK activity, preventing entry into mitosis. **(b)** Spindle damage resulting from the failure of a chromosome to attach to the mitotic spindle generates a signal that inhibits CDK activity and thereby prevents the metaphase-to-anaphase transition.

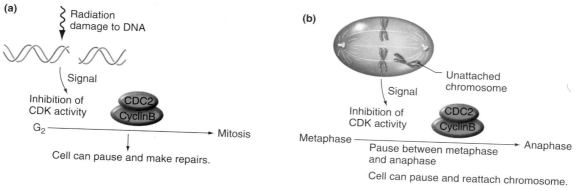

that regulate it—including those that are part of the p53 pathway—appear in multicellular animals from round-worms to humans. It makes sense for multicellular organisms to have a mechanism for eliminating cells that have sustained chromosomal damage. The survival and repro-duction of such cells could generate cancers.

The G₂-to-M checkpoint

Damage to DNA during G₂ delays mitosis, allowing time for repair before chromosome segregation (**Fig. 17.21a**). Researchers have identified many genes in mammalian and yeast cells that mediate this control. One of these genes is *RAD9*. Whereas wild-type yeast cells can pause to repair as many as 100 double-strand breaks before entering mitosis, *RAD9* mutants fail to arrest in G₂ and die as a result of any double-strand breaks that were not repaired before mitosis.

A spindle checkpoint in M

During mitosis, one checkpoint oversees formation of the mitotic spindle and proper engagement of all pairs of sister chromatids (**Fig. 17.21b**). Observations of liv-ing cells reveal that as chromosomes condense and attach to the spindle, sometimes a single chromosome fails to attach at the expected time. When this happens, the cell does not initiate sister chromatid separation or anaphase chromosome movement until the lagging chromosome attaches to the spindle. Other studies show that in yeast cells exposed to an inhibitor that prevents assembly of a functional spindle, sister chromatids remain firmly attached.

These observations suggest the presence of a check-point that prevents chromosome segregation until all chro-mosomes are properly attached to the spindle. Mutations that eliminate the surveillance of chromosome behavior

during mitosis have helped researchers identify several genes in yeast responsible for this checkpoint.

The necessity of checkpoints

Checkpoints are not essential for cell division. In fact, experiments in mice and other animals demonstrate that mutant cells with one or more defective checkpoints are viable and divide at a normal rate. These mutant cells, however, are much more vulnerable to DNA damage than normal cells.

Knowledge of how checkpoints work hand in hand with repair processes clarifies how checkpoints help prevent transmission of three types of genomic instability (described in Chapter 13): chromosome aberrations; aneuploidy (the loss or gain of one or more chromo-somes); and changes in ploidy, for example, from 2n to 4n (**Fig. 17.22**). Single-strand nicks resulting from oxida-tive or other types of DNA damage are probably fairly common. A cell normally repairs such nicks to DNA in G₁ before it enters S phase. If the checkpoint coordinat-ing this repair fails to function, however, the copying of single-strand breaks during replication would produce double-strand breaks that could lead to chromosome rearrangements. Chromosome loss or gain can occur if a chromosome fails to attach properly to the spindle. Nor-mally, the M-phase spindle checkpoint recognizes such fail-ures and prevents the initiation of anaphase until the cell has fixed the problem. Cells without a functional checkpoint produce daughter cells carrying too few or too many chromosomes.

Finally, changes in ploidy can occur if a cell begins S phase before completing mitosis or if a cell fails to repli-cate or to properly segregate its microtubule-organizing centers, or centrosomes. Checkpoints also recognize these errors, ensuring integration of the centrosome cycle with DNA replication and the formation and function of the mitotic spindle.

(a)

(b)

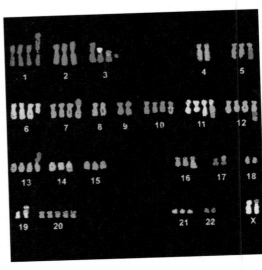

Figure 17.22 Three classes of error lead to aneuploidy in tumor cells. (a) Spindle errors can segregate chromosomes incorrectly, resulting in whole chromosome aneuploidy; DNA replication and/or repair damage can lead to chromosome aberrations; centrosome errors can result in changes in cell ploidy. **(b)** "Chromosome painting" techniques use fluorescent dyes attached to chromosomal DNA sequences. An appropriate choice of dyes and probes can cause each normal chromosome or chromosome arm to appear relatively homogeneous with a unique color (*top*), while cancer cell chromosomes reveal many rearrangements and whole chromosome changes (*bottom*).

Checkpoints at G_1-to-S and G_2-to-M, along with a spindle checkpoint, help to ensure that cells repair DNA damage or spindle attachments before replication and division proceeds. Normally, cells that do not pass a checkpoint undergo apoptosis.

Summary: The accumulation of oncogenic and tumor-suppressor mutations produces cancer cells with grossly altered genomes

Cancer-causing mutations disrupt the normal controls that create a balance between activation and inhibition of cell division. Dominant mutations that change proto-oncogenes to oncogenes may overactivate expression of proteins that promote proliferation. Recessive mutations in tumor-suppressor genes may release the brakes that keep cells from proliferating. Both types of mutations may tip the balance toward excessive and inaccurate cell proliferation.

Mutations that disable one part of a cell's elaborate DNA repair system increase its mutation rate and thus its likelihood of becoming cancerous. Although no single mutation converts a normal cell to a cancer cell, if a cell has a mutation in one gene that predisposes to cancer, that cell has a higher than normal probability of becoming cancerous because it is already one step along the way. The early mutations in a cell's progression from normal to cancerous may lead to increased proliferation and affect the accuracy of cellular reproduction, allowing the accumulation of several mutations. Other subsequent or simultaneous mutations may enable the abnormally and inaccurately proliferating cells of

GENETICS AND SOCIETY

The Uses of Genetic Testing in Predicting and Treating Cancer

Genetic tests for mutations in proto-oncogenes and tumor-suppressor genes can reveal whether a person has a higher probability of getting cancer at some point in his or her lifetime than a person without the mutations. But of those with an increased risk, some will develop cancer and some will not. Although a person who inherits one of these mutations is pushed one step along the road to cancer, other mutations must occur in one clone of cells by chance; nongenetic factors, such as exposure to radiation, influence whether the additional mutations occur. Given this situation, what good is it to learn from a genetic test that you have an increased probability of getting cancer sometime in your life?

Predictive testing is useful if the means of medical surveillance make it possible to detect the cancer to which a mutation predisposes at an early stage. Thus, testing for a genetic predisposition to skin, breast, or colon cancers can often lead to increased cancer-specific testing to detect cancers in their earliest stages. A person whose genetic test shows a predisposition to colon cancer, for example, could undergo a colonoscopy each year. If one of these colon exams discloses a small cancer, doctors could remove it by surgery or treat it by other means. Predictive testing is not yet useful for some cancers such as pancreatic cancer, because as yet no way to detect small tumors of the pancreas exists. By the time this cancer is identified it has almost always reached an aggressive state and metastasized to other tissues.

Once a cancer has been diagnosed, genetic testing of tumor cells can provide information for making a prognosis and determining a course of therapy. Completion of the Human Genome Project has opened up new possibilities for identifying and tracking the effects on survival of specific cancer-cell mutations. Indeed, comparative microarray analyses (see Chapter 10) of cancerous and normal tissues have revealed molecular

markers for leukemia, prostate cancer, breast cancer, and melanoma. These markers make it possible to separate phenotypically similar cancers into distinct groups that probably arose in different ways, have different prognoses, and require different treatments.

With breast cancer, for example, if a person has a small tumor (less than 2 cm in diameter) that has not spread to the lymph nodes, surgical removal and follow-up radiation (sometimes in conjunction with chemotherapy) usually give the patient a good chance of overcoming the cancer. However, if the tumor cells carry mutations in the *p53* gene, the prognosis is poorer, because breast tumors with absent or mutated p53 proteins tend to resist treatment with radiation and many anticancer drugs. In contrast, large, fast-growing tumors that have already metastasized may respond well to a recently developed drug named Herceptin—but only if their cells carry a mutation in the *HER2/neu* proto-oncogene. *HER2/neu* encodes a human epidermal growth factor receptor that helps control how cells grow, divide, and repair themselves. Breast cancers with a mutated *HER2/neu* are very aggressive and more likely to recur than some other types of breast cancer. Herceptin, an antibody-based drug, shrinks and even gets rid of *HER2/neu*-positive breast cancers that have spread; it also shrinks medium to large tumors in the breast tissue itself and reduces the risk of recurrence.

Tests to help determine the course of therapy are currently possible for only a few cancers in which specific mutations have been linked to specific prognoses. However, with the application of new genomic and proteomic tools, the number and scope of such tests will increase, which in conjunction with more precisely targeted drugs, will enable doctors to hone their diagnoses and tailor their treatments for individual cancer patients.

---

ingle lineage to avoid programmed cell death, evade he immune system, increase formation of blood vessels upplying the abnormal clone, alter the proteins that ontrol tissue architecture, and invade nearby or distant issues (that is, metastasize). Environmental factors such

as radiation and mutagenic chemicals cause most of the mutations that result in cancer, but rare inherited defects can contribute the first step (see the Genetics and Society box "The Uses of Genetic Testing in Predicting and Treating Cancer").

Connections

he existence of numerous controls in cell-cycle pathways uggests that evolution has erected many barriers in multcellular animals to the uncontrolled reproduction of selfish" cells. At the same time, the hundreds of genes ontributing to normal cell-cycle regulation provide hunreds of targets for cancer-producing mutations.

Variations on the theme of cell-cycle regulation play a key role in the development of eukaryotic organisms. In *Drosophila,* for example, after fertilization, nuclear division occurs without cell division for the first 13 cycles; during these cycles, the nuclei go through many rapid S and M phases without any intervening G_1 or G_2 (**Fig. 17.23**).

In cycles 10–13, the synthesis and degradation of cyclinB regulates mitosis. Sometime during cycles 14–16, a G_2 phase appears, and distinct patches of cells with different-length cycles become evident within the embryo. The differences in cycle time between the different cell types are the result of variable G_2 phases. Late in G_2, *CDC25* activates cyclin-dependent kinases to control the timing of mitosis. Many tissues stop dividing at cycle 16, but a few continue. In the still-dividing cells, a G_1 phase appears. Some of these cells will arrest in G_1 during larval growth, only to start dividing again in response to signals relayed during metamorphosis, when the larva changes into adult form.

In Chapter 18, we present the basic principles of development and describe how biologists have used genetic analysis in various model organisms to examine development at the cellular and molecular levels.

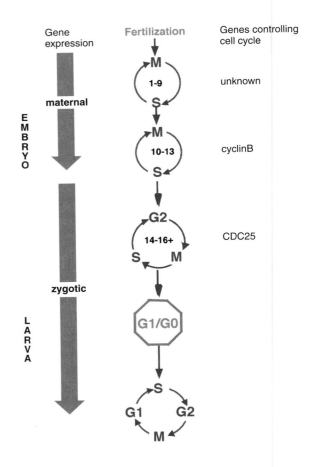

Figure 17.23 Regulation of the cell-cycle changes during *Drosophila* development. Each step of development has built-in regulators that act as barriers to uncontrolled reproduction of "selfish" cells. Some of these regulators, such as cyclinB and CDC25, are known; others have not yet been identified.

ESSENTIAL CONCEPTS

1. The genes and proteins of various signal transduction systems relay signals about whether or not to enter the cell cycle. The four molecular components of these systems include growth factors, receptors for these factors, intracellular transducers that continue the signal, and transcription factors that begin DNA replication.

2. Cancer is a genetic disease resulting from the growth of a clone of mutant cells. A cell requires many mutations to become cancerous. Exposure to environmental mutagens probably generates most of these mutations.

3. Many mutations that lead to cancer jeopardize cell-cycle regulation. Mutations in growth factors, receptors, and other elements of signal transduction pathways can release cells from control by the signals normally required for proliferation.

Mutations in CDKs and the proteins that control them may also lead to inappropriate proliferation or genomic instability. The latter may permit rapid evolution of abnormal tumor cells. Mutations in DNA repair and checkpoint controls lead to genomic instability and, often, to loss of the surveillance system that kills aberrant cells by apoptosis.

4. Several genetic pathways help control cell division. The inhibition or activation of CDKs inhibits or activates G_1-to-S and G_2-to-M transitions. The measured synthesis and degradation of different cyclins guides CDKs to the appropriate targets at the appropriate times. Checkpoints that integrate repair of chromosomal damage with events of the cell cycle minimize the replication of damaged DNA.

Annotated Suggested Readings and Links to Other Websites

- Key papers on the molecular genetics of cell-cycle regulation
- Classic papers on the genetics of cancer

Specialized Topics

- Comprehensive example of the genetics of brain cancer

Solved Problems

I. The addition of growth factors to tissue culture cells stimulates cell division. A number of candidate drugs can be tested for their ability to stop this stimulation of cell division. What do you think the target of these drugs could be?

Answer

This question concerns the regulation of cell division. Growth factors are made by one cell and bind to receptors of another cell to stimulate the cell division cycle. *A drug that binds to receptors* would block access and prevent growth factors from binding. Alternatively, *the drug could bind to the growth factor,* thereby preventing its interaction with the receptor. (These are the most obvious targets. If you are familiar with the signal transduction pathway inside the cell, you might also propose that proteins in this pathway could be targets for drug development.)

II. The *p53* gene has been cloned, and you are using it to analyze DNA in patients in which *p53* defects are involved in the development of their tumors. DNA samples were obtained from normal and tumor tissue of three different cancer patients, digested with *Bam*HI, electrophoresed on an agarose gel, and transferred to filter paper that was probed with a labeled *p53* fragment. Each of the patients inherited a *p53* mutation.

Thin bands indicate half the DNA content of thick bands. DNA from an individual who did not inherit a *p53* mutation is shown in the lane labeled wild type. All wild-type alleles in this study produce the same three fragments. Assuming the model of *p53* acting as a tumor-suppressor gene is correct and that *p53* defects

are involved in each of these cancer patients, how would you describe the genetic makeup of the *p53* gene in the normal and tumor tissue of each of the three patients?

Answer

This question requires knowledge of tumor-suppressor genes. The wild-type *p53* region (as seen in the "wild-type" individual) has three hybridizing bands. Because *p53* is a tumor suppressor, it is recessive at the cellular level, and both copies must be defective in the tumor cells. No observable changes are apparent in patient 1, so this patient must have inherited a point mutation in *p53,* and in the tumor cells, the second copy would also contain a small mutation, thereby inactivating both copies of *p53* in the tumor. In patient 2, a point mutation must have been inherited. In the tumor, the whole region containing *p53* was deleted from the wild-type copy (thereby removing the second copy of the gene), as seen by the loss of restriction fragments. In patient 3, a mutation is evident in one copy of gene from the altered restriction pattern, and in the tumor, the wild-type copy of the gene was deleted (probably by gene conversion since the tumor has two mutant copies of the gene).

III. The CDC28 protein of budding yeast *S. cerevisiae* and the CDC2 protein of fission yeast *S. pombe* are protein kinases required at the "start" of the cell cycle. The genes for both proteins were identified by mutational analysis (temperature-sensitive mutations in each gene cause cell cycle arrest), and both genes have been cloned. How could you determine if one could substitute for the other functionally? (Be sure to mention sources of DNA and genotypes involved.)

Answer

The *CDC28* gene of *S. cerevisiae* could be cloned into a vector and transformed into a temperature-sensitive *cdc2* mutant of *S. pombe.* If *CDC28* has the same role (function) as *CDC2,* the transformed cell will now grow and divide at nonpermissive temperatures. Conversely, a clone of the *CDC2* gene of *S. pombe* could be cloned into a vector able to transform a temperature-sensitive *cdc28* mutant of *S. cerevisiae.* If *CDC2* of *S. pombe* can substitute for *CDC28* of *S. cerevisiae,* the transformed cells would grow and divide at nonpermissive temperatures.

Problems

Interactive Web Exercise

The National Cancer Institute has gathered information and data about normal, precancerous, and cancerous cells at a site called the Cancer Genome Anatomy Project (CGAP). Our website at www.mhhe.com/hartwell4 contains a brief exercise to introduce you to the use of CGAP. Once at our site, go to Chapter 17 and click on "Interactive Web Exercise."

Vocabulary

1. For each of the terms in the left column, choose the best matching phrase in the right column.

   a. growth factor   1. mutations in these genes are dominant for cancer formation

   b. tumor-suppressor genes   2. programmed cell death

   c. cyclin-dependent protein kinases   3. series of steps by which a message is transmitted

   d. apoptosis   4. proteins that are active cyclically during the cell cycle

   e. oncogenes   5. control progress in the cell cycle in response to DNA damage

   f. receptor   6. mutations in these genes are recessive at the cellular level for cancer formation

   g. signal transduction   7. signals a cell to leave G_0 and enter G_1

   h. checkpoints   8. cell-cycle enzymes that phosphorylate proteins

   i. cyclins   9. protein that binds a hormone

Section 17.1

2. Molecules outside and inside the cell regulate the cell cycle, making it start or stop.
   a. What is an example of an external molecule?
   b. What is an example of a molecule inside the cell that is involved in cell cycle regulation?

3. a. Would you expect a cell to continue or stop dividing at a nonpermissive high temperature if you had isolated a temperature-sensitive *RAS* mutant that remained fixed in the GTP-bound form at nonpermissive temperature?
   b. What would you expect if you had a temperature-sensitive mutant in which *RAS* stayed in the GDP-bound form at high temperature?

4. Put the following steps in the correct ordered sequence.
   a. kinase cascade
   b. activation of a transcription factor
   c. hormone binds receptor
   d. expression of target genes in the nucleus
   e. RAS molecular switch

Section 17.2

5. Mouse tissue culture cells infected with the SV40 virus lose normal growth control and become transformed. If transformed cells are transferred into mice, they grow into tumors. The SV40 protein responsible for this transformation is called T antigen. T antigen has been found to associate with the cellular protein p53. If the *p53* gene fused to a high-level expression promoter is transfected into tissue culture cells, the cells are no longer transformed by infection by SV40.
   a. Propose a hypothesis to explain how the high expression of *p53* saves the cells from transformation by T antigen.
   b. You have decided to examine the functional domains of the p53 protein by mutagenizing the cDNA, fusing it to the high-level promoter, and transfecting into cells. Results are shown in the following table. How would you explain the effects of mutations 1 and 2 on p53 function?
   c. What is the effect of mutation 3 on p53 function?

p53 construct	Morphology	
	Noninfected cells	SV40-infected cells
None	Normal	Transformed
Wild type	Normal	Normal
Mutation 1	Normal	Transformed
Mutation 2	Normal	Transformed
Mutation 3	Normal	Normal

6. What are four characteristics of the cancer phenotype

7. Amplification of DNA sequences in *p53* mutants can be visualized using electron microscopy.
   a. Using a different technique, how could you detect amplification of a specific sequence?
   b. How could you detect gross rearrangements (>10 Mb of chromosomal DNA?

8. Some germ-line mutations predispose to cancer, yet often environmental factors (chemicals, exposure to radiation) are considered major risks for developing cancer. Are these conflicting views of the cause of cancer or can they be reconciled?

9. The incidence of colon cancer in the United States 30 times higher than it is in India. Differences in diet and/or genetic differences between the two populations may contribute to these statistics. How would you assess the role of each of these factors?

10. Put the following steps in the order appropriate for the positional cloning of *BRCA1*, a gene involved predisposition to breast cancer.
    a. Locate transcripts corresponding to the DNA.
    b. Use the physical map to get clones.

c. Determine the tissues in which the transcripts are present.

d. Look for homologous DNA in other organisms.

e. Determine linkage to RFLPs and other molecular markers.

f. Sequence the DNA from affected individuals.

11. Because mutations occur in the development of cancer, researchers suspected that defects in DNA repair machinery might lead to a predisposition to cancer. Place the following steps in appropriate order for following a candidate gene approach to determine if defects in mismatch repair genes lead to cancer.

a. Use molecular markers near the homologous gene to determine if the candidate gene is linked to a predisposition phenotype.

b. Isolate a human homolog of a yeast mismatch repair gene.

c. Compare the DNA sequence of the mismatch repair gene of affected and unaffected persons in a family with predispositions.

d. Determine the map location of the human homolog of the yeast mismatch gene.

12. Which of the following events is unlikely to be associated with cancer?

a. mutations of a cellular proto-oncogene in a normal diploid cell

b. chromosomal translocations with breakpoints near a cellular proto-oncogene

c. deletion of a cellular proto-oncogene

d. mitotic nondisjunction in a cell carrying a deletion of a tumor-suppressor gene

e. incorporation of a cellular oncogene into a retrovirus chromosome

13. You have decided to study genetic factors associated with colon cancer. An extended family from Morocco in which the disease presents itself in a large percentage of family members at a very early age has come to your attention. (The pedigree is shown below.) In this family, individuals either get colon cancer before the age of 16, or they don't get it at all.

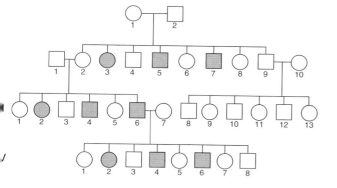

a. Based on the information you have been given, what evidence, if any, suggests an inherited contribution to the development of this disease?

b. You decide to take a medical history of all of the 36 people indicated in the pedigree and discover that a very large percentage drink a special coffee on a daily basis, while the others do not. The only ones who don't drink coffee are individuals numbered I-1, II-2, II-4, II-9, III-7, III-13, IV-1, and IV-3. Could the drinking of this special coffee possibly play a role in colon cancer? Explain your answer.

14. To further understand the basis for colon cancer, you find a family from the United States in which two members also get the disease before the age of 16. If there were a dominant inherited mutation segregating in this family, which of the individual(s) would you predict had the mutation in their colon cells but did not develop the disease?

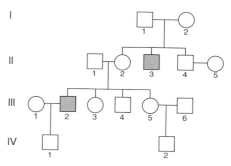

15. You suspect that a very specific point mutation in the *p53* gene is responsible for the majority of *p53* mutations found associated with tumors. Which combination of these techniques would you be most likely to use in developing a simple assay for predictive testing?

a. polymerase chain reaction with oligonucleotide primers flanking the mutation

b. restriction enzyme digestion followed by Southern blot

c. RNA isolation followed by Northern blot

d. hybridization with allele-specific oligonucleotides

16. A female patient 19 years old is diagnosed with chronic myelogenous leukemia (CML), whose symptoms are anemia and internal bleeding due to a massive buildup of leukemic white blood cells. Karyotype analysis shows that the leukemic cells of this patient are heterozygous for a reciprocal translocation involving chromosomes 9 and 22. However, none of the normal, nonleukemic cells of this patient contain the translocation. Which of the following statements is true and which is false?

a. The translocation results in the inactivation (loss-of-function) of a tumor-suppressor gene.

b. The translocation results in the inactivation (loss-of-function) of an oncogene.

c. There is a 50% chance that any child of this patient will have CML.

d. This patient is a somatic mosaic in terms of the karyotype.

e. DNA extracted from leukemic cells of this patient, if taken up by normal mouse tissue culture cells, could potentially transform the mouse cells into cells capable of causing tumors.

f. The normal function of the affected tumor-suppressor gene or proto-oncogene at the translocation breakpoint could potentially block the function of the cyclin proteins that drive the cell cycle forward.

g. This woman is heterozygous for an X-linked gene; the two alleles encode two distinguishable variant forms of the protein product of the gene. If you looked at different normal cells from different parts of her body, some would express exclusively one variant form of the protein, and other normal cells would express exclusively the other variant form.

h. If you examined different leukemic cells from this patient for the protein described in part *g*, all would express the same variant form of the protein.

i. Two rare events must have occurred to disrupt both copies of the tumor-suppressor gene or proto-oncogene at the translocation breakpoint in the leukemic cells.

j. A possible treatment of the leukemia would involve a drug that would turn on the expression of the tumor-suppressor gene or proto-oncogene at the translocation breakpoint in the leukemic cells.

17. Describe a molecular test to determine if chemotherapy given to the patient described in Problem 16 was completely successful. That is, devise a method to make sure that the patient's blood is now free of leukemic cells.

18. A generic signaling cascade is shown in the following figure. A growth factor (GF) binds to a growth factor receptor, activating the kinase function of an intracellular domain of the growth factor receptor. One substrate of the growth factor receptor kinase is another kinase, kinase A, that has enzymatic activity only when it is itself phosphorylated by the growth factor receptor kinase. Activated kinase A adds phosphate to a transcription factor. When it is unphosphorylated, the transcription factor is inactive and stays in the cytoplasm. When it is phosphorylated by kinase A, the transcription factor moves into the nucleus and helps turn on the transcription of a *mitosis factor* gene whose product stimulates cells to divide.

a. The following list contains the names of the genes encoding the corresponding proteins. Which of these could potentially act as a proto-oncogene? Which might be a tumor-suppressor gene?

    i. *growth factor*

    ii. *growth factor receptor*

    iii. *kinase A*

    iv. *transcription factor*

    v. *mitosis factor*

Though it is not pictured, the cell in the preceding figure also has a phosphatase, an enzyme that removes phosphates from proteins—in this case, from the transcription factor. This phosphatase is itself regulated by kinase A.

b. What would you expect to be the effect when kinase A adds a phosphate group to the phosphatase? Would this activate the phosphatase enzyme or inhibit it? Explain.

c. Is the *phosphatase* gene likely to be a proto-oncogene or a tumor-suppressor gene?

d. Several mutations are listed below. For each, indicate whether the mutation would lead to excessive cell growth or decreased cell growth if the cell were either homozygous for the mutation or heterozygous for the mutation and a wild-type allele. Assume that 50% of the normal activity of all these genes is sufficient for normal cell growth.

    i. A null mutation in the *phosphatase* gene

    ii. A null mutation in the *transcription factor* gene

    iii. A null mutation in the *kinase A* gene

    iv. A null mutation in the *growth factor receptor* gene

    v. A mutation that causes production of a constitutively active growth factor receptor whose kinase function is active even in the absence of the growth factor

    vi. A mutation that causes production of a constitutively active kinase A

vii. A reciprocal translocation that places the *transcription factor* gene downstream of a very strong promoter

viii. A mutation that prevents phosphorylation of the *phosphatase* gene

ix. A mutation that causes the production of a phosphatase that acts as if it is always phosphorylated

19. Are genome and karyotype instabilities consequences or causes of cancer?

20. Neurofibromatosis type 1 (NF1; also known as von Recklinghausen disease) is an inherited dominant disorder. The phenotype usually involves the production of many skin neurofibromas (benign tumors of the fibrous cells that cover the nerves).

a. Is it likely that *NF1* is a tumor-suppressor gene or an oncogene?

b. Are the *NF1* neurofibromatosis-causing mutations that are inherited by affected children from affected parents likely to be loss-of-function or gain-of-function mutations?

c. Neurofibromin, the protein product of *NF1*, has been found to be associated with the RAS protein. RAS is involved in the transduction of extracellular signals from growth factors. The active form of RAS (the form initiating the signal transduction cascade causing proliferation) is complexed with GTP; the inactive form of RAS is complexed with GDP. Would the wild-type neurofibromin protein favor the formation of RAS-GTP or RAS-GDP?

d. Which of the following events in a normal cell from an individual inheriting a neurofibromatosis-causing allele could cause the descendents of that cell to grow into a neurofibroma?

i. A second point mutation in the allele of *NF1* inherited from the afflicted parent.

ii. A point mutation in the allele of *NF1* inherited from the normal parent.

iii. A large deletion that removes the *NF1* gene from the chromosome inherited from the afflicted parent.

iv. A large deletion that removes the *NF1* gene from the chromosome inherited from the normal parent.

v. Mitotic chromosomal nondisjunction or chromosome loss.

vi. Mitotic recombination in the region between the *NF1* gene and the centromere of the chromosome carrying *NF1*

vii. Mitotic recombination in the region between the *NF1* gene and the telomere of the chromosome carrying *NF1*

e. The *American Journal of Medical Genetics* published a report in 1999 that certain patients with neurofibromatosis type I who had an affected parent also inherited specific facial anomalies from that parent. Formulate a succinct hypothesis to explain why these patients inherit this additional phenotype, but most other patients with inherited neurofibromatosis I do not.

f. There is a much rarer form of NF1 called segmental NF1. In this form of the disease, neither parent of the patient has any clinical sign of the disease. The tumors in the patient are restricted to one part of the body, like the right leg. Suggest an explanation for the genesis of segmental NF1 and why it is restricted to one part of the body.

Section 17.3

21. During which phase(s) of the cell cycle would the following enzymes or proteins be most active?

a. tubulins in the spindle fibers

b. centromere motor

c. DNA polymerase

d. CDC28 of *S. cerevisiae* or CDC2 of *S. pombe*

22. Conditional mutations are useful for genetic analysis of essential processes. For example, temperature-sensitive cell-cycle mutations in yeast do not divide at 37°C (nonpermissive temperature) but will divide at 30°C. An alternative type of conditional mutation is a cold-sensitive mutation in which the nonpermissive temperature is low (23°C). List the steps you would go through to isolate cold-sensitive cell-cycle mutants of yeast.

23. Many temperature-sensitive yeast mutants that showed defects in the cell cycle were isolated in the 1970s. The mutants that arrested at the unbudded stage were mated with each other to do a complementation analysis. A + sign on the chart indicates that the resulting diploids grew at the high (nonpermissive) temperature. How many complementation groups (that is, how many genes) are represented by these mutants?

	1	2	3	4	5	6	7	8	9
1	−	+	+	−	−	+	+	+	+
2	+	−	+	+	+	+	+	−	+
3	+	+	−	+	+	−	−	+	+
4	−	+	+	−	−	+	+	+	−
5	−	+	+	−	−	+	+	+	+
6	+	+	−	+	+	−	−	+	−
7	+	+	−	+	+	−	−	+	−
8	+	−	+	+	+	+	+	−	+
9	+	+	−	+	+	−	−	+	−

24. In 1951 a woman named Henrietta Lacks died of cervical cancer. Just before she died a piece of her tumor was taken and put into culture in a laboratory in an attempt to induce the cells to grow *in vitro*. The attempt succeeded, and the resulting cell line (known as HeLa cells) is still used today in laboratories around the world for studies of various aspects of cell biology. In the cell cycle of typical HeLa cells, G_1 lasts about 11 hours, S lasts about 8 hours, G_2 lasts 4 hours, and mitosis (M) takes about 1 hour.

   a. Cultured cells do not typically grow synchronously. That is, the individual cells in a culture are randomly distributed throughout the cell cycle. If you looked through the microscope at a sample of HeLa cells, in approximately what proportion of them would you expect the chromosomes to be visible? (The cells do not split apart completely after cytokinesis, and each joined double cell should be counted as one.)

   b. Approximately what proportion would be in interphase?

25. The activity of key cell-cycle regulatory proteins is cyclical, appearing only when needed. What are three ways by which a cell can achieve this cyclical nature of protein activity?

26. True or false?

   a. CDKs phosphorylate proteins in the absence of cyclins.

   b. Degradation of cyclins is required for the cell cycle to proceed.

   c. CDKs are involved in checking for aberrant cell-cycle events.

27. Checkpoints occur at several different times during the cell cycle to check that the DNA content of the cell has not been damaged or altered. Match the defect in a checkpoint with the consequences of that defective checkpoint.

Defective checkpoint	Consequences of defect in checkpoint
a. G_1 to S	1. aneuploidy
b. G_2 to M	2. single-strand nicks get replicated and amplification occurs
c. M	3. unrepaired double-strand breaks result in broken chromosomes

28. Draw a diagram illustrating the accumulation of S phase and M phase cyclins during the cell cycle. When are SCF and APC (the protein complexes that add ubiquitin to S phase and M phase cyclins, respectively) activated?

29. One of the hallmarks of mitotic anaphase is the separation of sister chromatids. Sister chromatids are held together by a protein complex called "cohesin." Based on your answer to Problem 28, propose a mechanism that would allow sister chromatids to separate during anaphase. How might your proposed mechanism also explain the M phase checkpoint that prevents sister chromatid separation until all the chromosomes have connected properly to the mitotic spindle?

Using Genetics to Study Development

A young patient with polydactyly, a genetically caused developmental defect that produces extra toes and/or fingers.

The union of a human sperm and egg (**Fig. 18.1a**) initiates the amazing process of development in which a single cell—the fertilized egg—divides by mitosis into trillions of genetically identical cells. These cells differentiate from each other during embryonic development to form hundreds of different cell types. Cells of various types assemble into wondrously complex yet carefully structured systems of organs, including two eyes, a heart, two lungs, and an intricate nervous system. Within a period of three months, the human embryo develops into a fetus whose form anticipates that of the baby who will be born six months later (**Fig. 18.1b**). At birth, the baby is already capable of crying, breathing, and eating; and the infant's development does not stop there. New cells form and differentiate throughout a person's growth, maturation, and even senescence.

Biologists now accept that genes direct the cellular behaviors underlying development, but as recently as the 1940s, this idea was controversial. Many embryologists could not understand how cells with identical chromosome sets, and thus the same genes, could form so many different types of cells if genes were the major determinants of development. As we now know, the answer to this riddle is very simple: Not all genes are "turned on" in all tissues. Cells regulate the expression of their genes so that each gene's protein product appears only when and where it is needed. Two central challenges for scientists studying development are to identify which genes are critical for the development of particular cell types or organs; and to figure out how these genes work together to ensure that each is expressed at the right time, in the right place, and in the right amount.

Biologists who use genetics to study how the fertilized egg of a multicellular organism becomes an adult are called **developmental geneticists.** Like other geneticists, they analyze mutations; in this case, mutations that produce developmental abnormalities. An understanding of such mutations helps clarify how normal genes control cell growth, cell communication, and the emergence of specialized cells, tissues, and organs.

Given the great diversity of the 6 billion humans on our planet, it is not hard to find rare individuals carrying mutations that alter their development. For example, pedigree analysis shows that one form of *polydactyly* (hands or feet with more than five fingers or toes) is inherited in families as a simple Mendelian autosomal dominant trait (see photograph on this page). There are, however, significant ethical and practical limitations on the study of developmental genetics in humans. These

CHAPTER OUTLINE

- 18.1 Model Organisms: Prototypes for Developmental Genetics
- 18.2 Using Mutations to Dissect Development
- 18.3 Analysis of Developmental Pathways
- 18.4 A Comprehensive Example: Body-Plan Development in *Drosophila*
- 18.5 How Genes Help Control Development

Figure 18.1 Human development. Fertilization of an egg by a sperm **(a)** creates a zygote, which undergoes many rounds of division and cell differentiation to produce a fetus **(b)** by the end of the first trimester of pregnancy.

(a) Fertilization

(b) A human fetus three months after fertilzation

Figure 18.2 Mutations in *Drosophila* genes can affect early development. Wild-type embryo (*top*); embryo homozygous for a mutation in a gene called *ftz* (*bottom*). The mutant embryo has fewer body segments than normal.

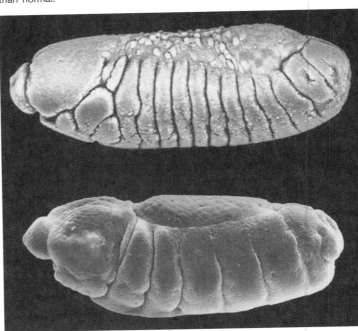

include taboos on the deliberate production of mutants, on the experimental manipulation of affected individuals, and on forced matings between individuals with various abnormalities. But one important limitation is not so obvious: Mutations that disrupt the earliest (and to some, the most interesting) stages of development almost always cause the spontaneous abortion of the affected embryo or fetus, often before the mother knows she is pregnant.

As a result, most modern developmental geneticists, even those whose primary interest is in human development, study mutations affecting the development of model organisms more amenable to experimentation. In *Drosophila,* for example, only a few dozen genes guide the formation of the early embryo's segmented body plan. Mutations in some of these genes eliminate specific body segments **(Fig. 18.2)**. Once the embryo has divided into segments that will become parts of the head, thorax, and abdomen, the activation and inactivation of different sets of genes direct the development of specialized organs, such as wings and legs, in each segment.

We examine in this chapter how the single cell of the fertilized egg, or zygote, differentiates into hundreds of cell types. It is impossible to present this complex topic in depth in a single textbook chapter. What we provide here is an overview of the experimental strategies scientists have used to examine this question, along with a synopsis of the major results they have obtained. We can discern two key themes in our exploration of genetics and development. One is that, surprisingly, many genes that control development have been highly conserved through evolution. Thus, for example, the study of a process in *Drosophila* can shed light on events that occur during the development of other animals, including humans. A second theme is that genes themselves are not the only determinants of development, because signals that pass between cells, or from the environment to the cells, can strongly influence how these genes function.

18.1 Model Organisms: Prototypes for Developmental Genetics

Throughout the twentieth century, developmental geneticists concentrated their research efforts on a small number of organisms that sampled a range of species from different phyla. The organisms that have contributed most to our understanding of development include the following:

- the yeast *Saccharomyces cerevisiae*
- the plant *Arabidopsis thaliana*
- the fruit fly *Drosophila melanogaster*
- the nematode (roundworm) *Caenorhabditis elegans*
- the mouse *Mus musculus*

Although we focus here on these five eukaryotic organisms, some researchers have made major findings in other model systems, such as corn and the zebra fish. Even prokaryotic organisms and viruses have provided paradigms for tackling certain developmental problems in eukaryotes.

Why study these model organisms?

The five model organisms we discuss in this chapter and in the genetic portraits on our website (www.mhhe.com/hartwell4) are easy to cultivate and rapidly produce large numbers of progeny. Geneticists can thus find rare mutations and study their segregation and behavior through successive generations. Each organism has attracted a dedicated cadre of researchers who share information, mutants, and other reagents. Stock centers maintain these mutants and make them available to the whole community of geneticists. Recently, each model organism's genome has been completely sequenced, and the results have been collated and annotated on computer databases. The completion of these genome projects makes it much easier for geneticists to identify genes whose alteration by mutation produces a phenotypic effect on the organism's development.

In addition to these shared advantages, each model organism also possesses idiosyncratic features that make it valuable for particular types of genetic or developmental analyses. Take yeast, for example. Although *S. cerevisiae* is a single-celled eukaryote, yeast cells signal to each other and differentiate into two mating types using variations of processes involved in the development of multicellular eukaryotes. Because *S. cerevisiae* cells can grow as haploids or diploids, researchers can identify extremely rare mutations in very large populations of haploid cells and then combine mutations in diploid cells for complementation analysis. In another example, the roundworm *C. elegans* is transparent (**Fig. 18.3**) and contains an

Figure 18.3 The transparency of *C. elegans* facilitates study of the worm's development.

invariant number of somatic cells as an adult—959 in the female/hermaphrodite and 1031 in the male. Because of these unusual properties, researchers can discern the lineage of every cell as the fertilized egg develops into the multicellular adult.

All living forms are related . . .

In the last 150 years, biologists have come to realize that life-forms are related on many levels. For example, the cells of all eukaryotic organisms have many features in common that are recognizable in the light or electron microscope, such as a nucleus and mitochondria. Moreover, the metabolic pathways by which cells make or degrade organic molecules are virtually identical in all living organisms, and almost all cells use the same genetic code to synthesize proteins. The relatedness of organisms is even visible at the level of the amino acid sequence of individual proteins. For example, over roughly 2 billion years, evolution has conserved the sequence of the histone protein H4, so the H4 proteins of widely divergent species are identical at all but a few amino acids. Most other proteins are not as invariant as H4, but nonetheless, scientists can often trace the evolutionary descent of a protein through the amino acid similarities of its homologs in various species.

Of particular importance to this chapter is the conservation of many basic strategies of development in all multicellular eukaryotes, even in organisms with body plans that look quite different. A graphic example is seen in studies of the genetic control of eye development in fruit flies, mice, and humans. *Drosophila* homozygous for mutations of the *eyeless* (*ey*) gene have either no eyes at all or, at best, very small eyes (**Fig. 18.4a**). Mutations in the *Pax-6* gene in mice (**Fig. 18.4b**) and the *Aniridia* gene in humans also reduce or totally abolish eye formation.

Figure 18.4 The *eyeless/Pax-6* gene is critical for eye development. **(a)** Hypomorphic or null mutations of the *eyeless* gene reduce the size of eyes or completely abolish them in adult flies. **(b)** Mutations in the homologous mouse *Pax-6* gene also reduce or abolish eye development. *Top:* wild-type mouse fetus. *Bottom: Pax-6* mutant fetus.

(a)

(b)

When researchers cloned the *ey, Pax-6,* and *Aniridia* genes, they found that the amino acid sequences of all three encoded proteins were closely related. This result was surprising because the eyes of vertebrates and insects are so dissimilar: Insect eyes are composed of many facets called ommatidia, whereas the vertebrate eye is a single camera-like organ (see Fig. 1.9 on p. 6). Biologists had thus long assumed that the two types of eyes evolved independently. However, the homology of *ey, Pax-6,* and *Aniridia* suggests instead that the eyes of insects and vertebrates evolved from a single prototypical light-sensing organ whose development required a gene ancestral to *ey* and its mouse and human homologs.

. . . Yet all species are unique

Although the conservation of developmental pathways makes it tempting to conclude that humans are simply large fruit flies, this is obviously not true. Evolution is not only conservative, but it is also innovative. Organisms sometimes use disparate strategies to accomplish the same developmental goal.

One example is the difference between the two-cell embryos that form in *C. elegans* and humans upon completion of the first mitotic division in the zygote. If one of the two cells is removed or destroyed in a *C. elegans* embryo at this stage, a complete nematode cannot develop. Because each of the two cells has already received a different set of molecular instructions to guide development, the descendents of one of the cells can differentiate into only certain cell types, and the descendent of the other cell into other types. The situation is very different in humans: If the two embryonic cells are separated from each other, two complete individuals (identical twins) will develop. In fact, as we saw in Fig. 11.1 on p. 369, removal of a cell from a 6-cell to 10-cell human embryo has no effect on the development of the remainder of the embryo.

An intrinsic difference exists, therefore, in the way worm and human embryos develop at these early stages. As soon as the *C. elegans* embryo has been formed by mitosis, each cell has already been assigned a specific fate; this pattern of development is often called **mosaic determination.** In contrast, the cells of a human embryo can alter or "regulate" their fates according to the environment, for example, to make up for missing cells; this is called **regulative determination.**

Genetic studies of development in model organisms often provide key information that can be generalized to all eukaryotes. These studies can also illustrate how evolution has molded the action of conserved genes to produce diverse developmental programs in different species.

18.2 Using Mutations to Dissect Development

Because proteins are the basic elements of cellular function, biologists can try to understand development by defining the roles played by individual proteins. To do this, they eliminate all copies of a single type of protein from a cell or organism and determine the consequences. From these consequences, they can often infer the function of the normal protein in normal development.

Genetics makes this experimental strategy possible. All an investigator has to do is isolate a mutant cell or organism with a specific, inactivated gene. Such mutants are usually found in the course of genetic screens to look for animals whose development is aberrant in interesting ways. A mutant with an altered gene will lack the wild-type protein encoded by that gene. Careful analysis of the mutant phenotype can then pinpoint what the protein does in development. As you will see, this basic strategy, although not the only way researchers can harness genetics to study development, is almost always the first and most important step.

Once a gene affecting a developmental process has been identified by a mutation, geneticists try to isolate many additional mutant alleles of that gene. If the mutations affect the function of the corresponding protein in a different way, studies of the phenotypes associated with the various mutations may shed light on the diverse roles the protein plays in the organism. The appendix *Genetic Tools for the Analysis of Development* (on our website) discusses in detail the types of genetic screens that researchers can perform to identify genes that are important to development and different kinds of alleles of these genes.

Loss-of-function mutations reveal genes required for normal development

Most mutations are loss-of-function mutations: They disrupt gene function by altering the amino acid sequence (and thus the three-dimensional structure) of the protein product or by interfering with any step of gene expression (transcription, translation, or RNA processing). As a result, such mutations give rise to proteins with diminished (or no) biochemical activity; or they decrease (or stop) production of an otherwise normal protein. We describe four kinds of loss-of-function mutations.

Null mutations

The best way to draw legitimate conclusions about the importance of a protein in development is to study an organism that completely lacks the function provided by that protein. In an analogy, if you tried to ride a bicycle with no chain, you might conclude that the chain is required to move the wheels. If, however, you tried to ride a bicycle whose chain had a damaged link (the equivalent of a partially defective protein) such that the bicycle would move but respond only erratically to your peddling, you might conclude that the chain is not critical to wheel movement and instead affords the cyclist some control over wheel movement. In Chapter 7, we saw that mutations that remove all function act as *null alleles* and that such null alleles are usually (but not always) recessive to wild-type alleles.

It is unfortunately not always easy or even possible to find null mutations in a genetic screen, even if mutagens are employed to increase the mutation rate. However, at least in some model organisms, scientists can use targeted mutagenesis to construct animals bearing null mutations in genes suspected of playing a critical role in

development. The idea is to take a cloned gene, use recombinant DNA techniques to destroy its function, and then replace the wild-type gene in the genome with the inactivated cloned copy.

Knockout mice provide key examples of this kind of targeted mutagenesis (**Fig. 18.5**). The formation of knockout mice depends on the existence of **embryonic stem (ES) cells,** which are undifferentiated cells, originally derived from early embryos, that can grow in cell culture and remain undifferentiated. If these cultured cells are injected into a different early embryo, they can contribute to any and all of the tissues in the mouse that develops from that embryo. (See the Genetics and Society box on pp. 623–624 for a discussion of "Stem Cells and Human Cloning.")

To generate knockout mice, scientists first disrupt the cloned gene of interest by inserting foreign DNA into the middle of the gene. They then treat a culture of ES cells with the altered gene. Some of the cells will "take up" the altered cloned gene, and in a small fraction of these cells, homologous recombination will allow the altered gene to replace the original gene (Fig. 18.5). Researchers can use one of several strategies to select those rare ES cells in which homologous recombination has occurred. These cells, now containing a null allele in place of a wild-type allele, are allowed to multiply in cell culture, and some of the resulting cells are injected into mouse embryos. Mice with tissues carrying the mutation are then used to begin a series of matings that culminate in the generation of animals homozygous for the null knockout mutation. The article *Mus Musculus: Genetic Portrait of the House Mouse* on our website discusses in more detail the protocols for creating knockout mice.

Hypomorphic mutations

Although the use of null mutations allows investigators to infer the most straightforward explanations for the function of the wild-type protein in development, there are situations in which it is actually more desirable to have a partial loss-of-function (*hypomorphic*) mutant allele. The reason is that many molecules function at multiple times in development. For example, the *wingless* (*wg*) gene in *Drosophila* is needed both for the formation of a proper embryo early in development and for the formation of an adult wing much later in development. An animal homozygous for a null allele of *wg* will die during embryogenesis. Because the animal dies before the wings form, you could not infer from this homozygote that the gene also functions to generate wing structures. In contrast, flies homozygous for a certain hypomorphic allele of the *wg* gene survive to adulthood, but they have no wings. Observing the effects of this allele alone, you would conclude that the gene is involved in wing formation, but you could not infer its role in early development. This example illustrates the importance of obtaining several different mutant alleles of a gene whose function you wish to study.

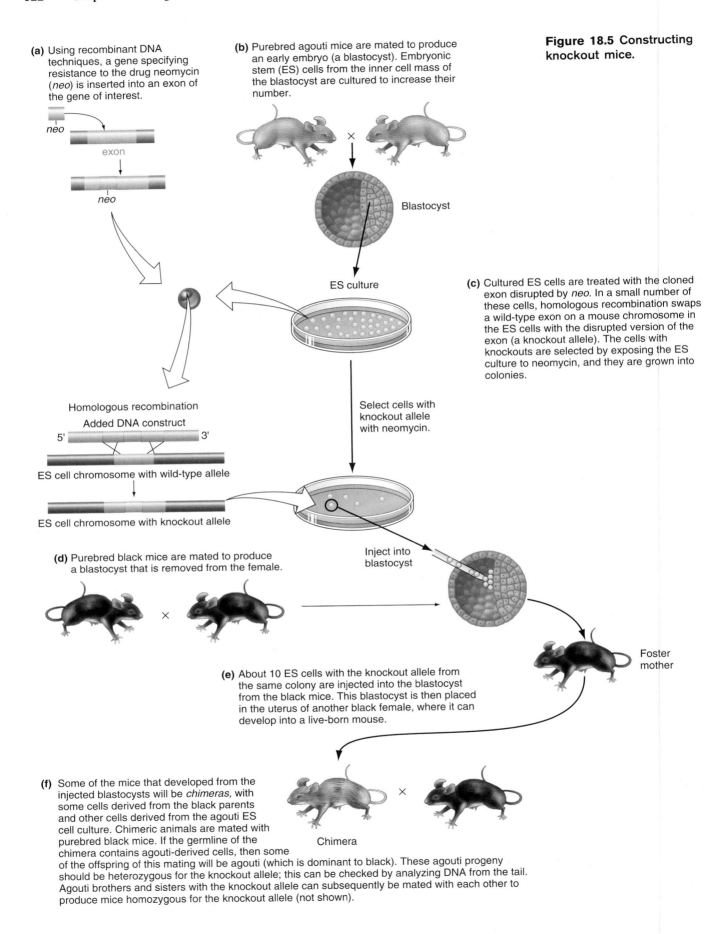

(a) Using recombinant DNA techniques, a gene specifying resistance to the drug neomycin (*neo*) is inserted into an exon of the gene of interest.

neo

exon

neo

(b) Purebred agouti mice are mated to produce an early embryo (a blastocyst). Embryonic stem (ES) cells from the inner cell mass of the blastocyst are cultured to increase their number.

Blastocyst

ES culture

Figure 18.5 Constructing knockout mice.

(c) Cultured ES cells are treated with the cloned exon disrupted by *neo*. In a small number of these cells, homologous recombination swaps a wild-type exon on a mouse chromosome in the ES cells with the disrupted version of the exon (a knockout allele). The cells with knockouts are selected by exposing the ES culture to neomycin, and they are grown into colonies.

Homologous recombination

Added DNA construct

5'   3'

ES cell chromosome with wild-type allele

ES cell chromosome with knockout allele

Select cells with knockout allele with neomycin.

(d) Purebred black mice are mated to produce a blastocyst that is removed from the female.

Inject into blastocyst

Foster mother

(e) About 10 ES cells with the knockout allele from the same colony are injected into the blastocyst from the black mice. This blastocyst is then placed in the uterus of another black female, where it can develop into a live-born mouse.

(f) Some of the mice that developed from the injected blastocysts will be *chimeras,* with some cells derived from the black parents and other cells derived from the agouti ES cell culture. Chimeric animals are mated with purebred black mice. If the germline of the chimera contains agouti-derived cells, then some

Chimera

of the offspring of this mating will be agouti (which is dominant to black). These agouti progeny should be heterozygous for the knockout allele; this can be checked by analyzing DNA from the tail. Agouti brothers and sisters with the knockout allele can subsequently be mated with each other to produce mice homozygous for the knockout allele (not shown).

Stem Cells and Human Cloning

Stem cells are relatively undifferentiated cells that have the ability to divide indefinitely. Among their progeny are more stem cells as well as fully differentiated cells that eventually cease dividing. *Embryonic stem (ES) cells,* which are obtained from the undifferentiated inner-mass cells of a blastocyst (an early-stage embryo), are *pluripotent.* Their progeny can develop into many different cell types in the body. *Adult stem cells,* which are involved in tissue renewal and repair and are found in specific locations in the body, are *multipotent:* They can give rise only to specific types of cells. For example, hematopoietic stem cells in the bone marrow give rise to an array of red and white blood cells.

Although many investigators value embryonic stem cells because of their pluripotency, research with human embryonic stem cells is controversial because in order to start a stem cell culture, a blastocyst must be destroyed. Medical research with adult stem cells is relatively noncontroversial because these cells can be harvested from a patient's own tissues. However, adult stem cells have significant limitations. They are present in only minute quantities and are thus difficult to isolate, and they can give rise to only certain kinds of differentiated cells.

For medical researchers, the greatest excitement surrounding the use of embryonic stem cells is the potential for human **therapeutic cloning** to replace lost or damaged tissues. In a protocol known as *somatic cell nuclear transfer,* researchers create a cloned embryo by taking the nucleus of a somatic cell from one individual and inserting it into an egg cell whose own nucleus has been removed (**Fig. A**). This hybrid egg is then stimulated to begin embryonic divisions by treatment with electricity or certain ions. The embryo is not allowed to develop to term; instead, it is cultured for about five days in a petri plate to the blastocyst stage, at which point the ES cells in the inner cell mass are collected and placed in culture. The cultured ES cells can be induced to differentiate into many kinds of cells that might be of therapeutic value, such as nerve cells to treat Parkinson disease (Fig. A). One of the major advantages of therapeutic cloning is that the ES cells and the differentiated cells derived from them are genetically identical to the patient's own cells. Thus, there should be little chance of tissue rejection when these cells are transplanted into the patient's body.

Therapeutic cloning, which is specifically intended to produce stem cells for the treatment of ailing patients, must not be confused with **reproductive cloning,** a type of cloning designed to make genetically identical complete organisms. The idea here is to create a cloned embryo by the same method just described for therapeutic cloning. In this case, however, the embryo is implanted into the uterus of a foster mother and allowed to develop to term (Fig. A). Reproductive cloning has been successfully

Figure A Reproductive cloning and therapeutic cloning. Both procedures begin with the fusion of a somatic cell nucleus and an enucleated egg, producing a hybrid egg that divides in culture into an early embryo. In reproductive cloning, this embryo is implanted into a surrogate mother and allowed to develop until birth. In therapeutic cloning, the early embryo develops in culture to the blastocyst stage, when the embryonic stem (ES) cells are harvested. These ES cells can be induced to differentiate into various cell types.

Donor supplies unfertilized eggs.

Tissue cell donor

Egg cell

Cells from animal to be cloned are maintained in culture so they do not divide.

Enucleated egg

Somatic cell

Nucleus is removed.

Nucleus fuses with egg after electric current is applied.

Reproductive Cloning

The hybrid embryo grows for seven days.

Embryo is implanted into surrogate mother.

Cloned animal

Embryo grows into blastocyst.

Blastocyst

Therapeutic Cloning

ES cells removed and placed in culture.

ES cell culture

ES cell differentiation induced.

Nerve cells

Pancreatic cells

(Continued)

performed in several mammalian species, such as sheep and cats, but many cloned animals exhibit puzzling developmental defects such as obesity. No country or group of scientists has yet condoned the reproductive cloning of humans.

The ethical controversy over embryonic stem cell research arises from the destruction of the blastocyst when the ES cells are harvested for therapeutic cloning. To most opponents of abortion, this is believed to be the destruction of a human life, whether the embryo was cloned or whether it was left over from *in vitro* fertilization attempts and would eventually be discarded. President George W. Bush shared these concerns and in 2001 limited federal funding for ES cell research to ES cell lines that had already been established by that time. In early 2009, President Barack Obama

announced his intention to lift many of these restrictions. However, at the time of this writing (in mid-2009), it is not yet clear what methodologies employing ES cells will be eligible for federal funding.

Ironically, decisions in the United States may have only a limited impact on the progress of human stem cell research worldwide, given that other countries have had a more permissive environment for this kind of work. Future scientific developments may eventually also make the ES cell controversy in the United States moot. For example, considerable progress has been reported on techniques to "reprogram" adult stem cells or even adult somatic cells to behave more like pluripotent ES cells. The next few years should help clarify the scientific and political issues surrounding the potential for stem-cell-based therapies.

Conditional mutations

Another way to study genes with effects on diverse developmental processes is to isolate *conditional mutations* that cause a loss of function only under special circumstances. The most commonly studied type of conditional mutation, the temperature-sensitive mutation, produces a protein that is functional at a lower, *permissive temperature* but defective at a higher, *restrictive temperature*. In contrast, the protein product of the wild-type allele functions at both temperatures. It is best if the conditional mutation produces completely nonfunctional proteins at the restrictive temperature, but it is sometimes difficult to determine whether the resulting protein is completely nonfunctional or remains partly functional.

Temperature-sensitive mutations have one main experimental advantage. They make it possible to raise an animal at the permissive temperature (which allows the early stages of development to proceed normally) and then to increase the temperature to assess the importance of the gene product at later developmental stages. **Figure 18.6** shows a temperature-shift analysis of a mutant strain of *C. elegans* carrying a temperature-sensitive lethal allele of the *zyg-9* gene, which helps determine the basic polarity of the early embryo. This temperature-shift study established that the ZYG-9 protein is required only in a very narrow window of about 15 minutes during the period between fertilization and the completion of the first mitotic division. If the protein is inactivated at any time outside the 15-minute window, development is normal.

Dominant-negative mutations

Most loss-of-function mutations have recessive effects because heterozygotes have about 50% of the gene function of wild-type homozygotes, and this level of gene function is sufficient for a normal phenotype. There are two exceptions to this rule. First, as discussed in Chapter 8, for a small number of developmentally important genes, one wild-type copy is insufficient for normal development. The mutant allele will thus be dominant to wild type; this

Figure 18.6 Time-of-function analysis. *C. elegans* embryos from mothers homozygous for a temperature-sensitive allele of the *zyg-9* gene develop properly if they are subjected to a short pulse of high temperature starting at any of the times indicated by the *green circles*. They develop incorrectly and subsequently die only if the high temperature begins at one of the times indicated by the *red circles*. (Each circle represents an experiment with one embryo.) These data show that the ZYG-9 protein is needed only during a 15-minute window of development.

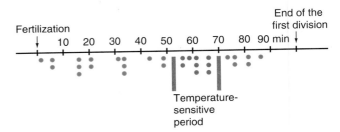

type of dominance is called **haploinsufficiency.** A second situation in which a loss-of-function mutation can have a dominant effect occurs with so-called **dominant-negative mutants.** Here, the inactive protein encoded by a mutant allele "poisons" or otherwise counteracts the function of the protein encoded by the wild-type allele. Figure 8.31 on p. 279 illustrates one of several ways in which this can occur: In a multimeric protein, the presence of one abnormal subunit might block the function of the protein even if the protein's other subunits are wild type.

Dominant-negative mutations can be particularly valuable when researchers suspect that a gene has an impact on development but they have not yet found a loss-of-function mutation in the gene to test their hypotheses. In such a situation, it is sometimes possible to engineer a dominant-negative mutant transgene *in vitro,* and then introduce this transgene back into a wild-type organism. In an interesting example of this technology, one research group made a dominant-negative fibroblast growth factor receptor (FGFR) in mice. These receptors are normally found on the surface membranes of many

Figure 18.7 Engineering a dominant-negative mutation in a mouse fibroblast growth factor receptor (FGFR) gene.
(a) A dimer of fibroblast growth factor (FGF) binds two FGFR molecules in the cell membrane. As a result, the protein kinase domains of the two FGFRs phosphorylate (add a phosphate group to) each other; they also phosphorylate and dimerize two STAT molecules, which initiates a signal necessary for development. **(b)** A truncated mutant soluble form of FGFR can bind to FGF, preventing it from binding to normal FGFR in the cell membrane. **(c)** Phenotypic effects. *Top:* wild-type mouse limb. *Bottom:* limb from a mouse engineered to contain the dominant-negative version of the *FGFR* gene shown in part (b). Note the poor development of the digits in the mutant mouse (*insets*).

cell types (**Fig. 18.7a**). One part of the receptor molecule faces the outside of the cell, where it can bind to a molecule called fibroblast growth factor (FGF). FGF is a **ligand:** a molecule involved in cell-to-cell communication that is produced by the cell sending the signal. Binding of the ligand to a receiving cell's receptor alters the behavior of that cell. The binding of FGF to the extracellular part of FGFR causes several changes in the receptor, including the dimerization of two FGFR subunits and the activation of a kinase in each subunit that adds a phosphate group to the other subunit. This reciprocal phosphorylation, in turn, initiates a complicated intracellular signaling mechanism that changes the receiving cell's developmental fate.

To make a dominant-negative FGFR mutant, the investigators synthesized a gene that gives rise to an abnormal form of the receptor. This mutant receptor cannot localize to the cell membrane and is instead secreted out of the cell. The researchers reasoned that the secreted form of FGFR would bind to FGF and thereby prevent the ligand from reaching the normal membrane-bound FGFR (**Fig. 18.7b**). When they injected their engineered transgene into early mouse embryos, they observed a number of defects, including problems in limb development (**Fig. 18.7c**). These results demonstrated that FGF signaling contributes to the developmental pathway leading to normal limbs.

Loss-of-function mutations allow researchers to assess the effects of reduced activity or complete absence of a gene product. Null mutations (knockouts) reveal the earliest developmental processes influenced by the gene. Hypomorphic or conditional mutations allow evaluation of a gene's importance later in development. Dominant-negative mutations are useful when loss-of-function mutations have not yet been found.

RNA interference disrupts gene function without mutations

The genetic screens performed to find mutations in developmentally important genes require a considerable investment of effort and are often subject to unanticipated difficulties. As a result, geneticists have so far identified mutations in only a subset of the genes that play a role in development. But within the last several years, researchers have been able to employ a new strategy to deplete the protein products of specific genes from developing organisms. This strategy, which makes use of *RNA interference* (*RNAi*), is based on the following discovery.

When cells ingest or are injected with double-stranded RNA (dsRNA) corresponding to the sequence of a gene's mRNA, the intracellular presence of the dsRNA triggers the degradation of the corresponding mRNA into short fragments. In the absence of intact mRNA, the cell cannot synthesize the protein. The details of RNAi are just being worked out, but it appears that many kinds of cells have enzymes that degrade long dsRNAs into shorter dsRNAs roughly 21 nucleotides in length. These shorter dsRNAs then serve as templates for the degradation of homologous mRNAs into similar 21 bp fragments (see Chapter 16 as well as the *C. elegans* portrait on our website).

To employ this RNAi strategy, researchers first synthesize a dsRNA and then deliver it into the cells of a developing organism. They usually carry out the dsRNA synthesis *in vitro*. For example, they clone a cDNA corresponding to a gene's mRNA into a plasmid vector such that the cDNA is located between strong promoters (**Fig. 18.8a**). They next use purified DNA from the recombinant clone as a template for transcribing the cDNA. The addition of RNA polymerase and the four nucleotide triphosphates (ATP, CTP, GTP, and UTP) initiates transcription, which then proceeds in both directions and produces RNAs from both strands of the cDNA. These complementary RNA strands can anneal together to form dsRNA.

There are several methods for getting the dsRNA into developing animals, including injection of dsRNA into the body cavity or soaking the animal in a dsRNA-containing solution. Investigators working with *C. elegans* can simply feed larvae with *E. coli* cells that contain a plasmid like the one shown in Fig. 18.8a. RNA polymerase within the *E. coli* cells containing such a plasmid will synthesize the desired dsRNA, which is then taken up by *C. elegans* larval cells as the bacteria are digested in the worm's gut.

Figure 18.8b shows an RNAi experiment in which the dsRNA corresponded to the mRNA for a *C. elegans* gene called *par-1*. The result of this dsRNA treatment was an abnormal vulva (the structure through which fertilized eggs are released) that protruded outside of the animal. Though worm researchers already knew that *par-1* functions very early in development to help establish the anterior-posterior axis of the animal, the results shown in Fig. 18.8b showed that the gene also functions later in development in the patterning of the vulva.

RNA interference is an extremely useful technique for creating a phenocopy that mimics a loss-of-function mutation. However, a phenocopy is not a true, heritable mutation; thus, RNAi-based protein depletion is not passed from generation to generation. Another slight drawback of the RNAi method is that results may vary because they depend on the relative level of dsRNA uptake. Consequently, even if the results of an RNAi experiment provide clues to a developmentally interesting gene's function, it is usually desirable to obtain and study a classical, heritable mutation in the gene as well.

Figure 18.8 RNA interference (RNAi): A new tool for studying development. (a) How to make double-stranded RNA (dsRNA). A cDNA is cloned between two promoters, allowing transcription from both cDNA template strands. Complementary RNA transcripts will anneal with each other to make dsRNA. **(b)** Abnormal structure of the vulva in *C. elegans* treated with dsRNA for the *par-1* gene. *Top:* wild-type vulva. *Bottom:* protruding vulva in an animal treated with *par-1* dsRNA.

(a) Synthesis of dsRNA

(b) A result of *par-1* dsRNA treatment

Wild-type vulva

Abnormal vulva

RNA interference utilizes dsRNA to degrade a corresponding mRNA. Expression of dsRNA within cells, or transfer of dsRNA into an organism's cells by ingestion or injection, can generate loss-of-function phenotypes.

Gain-of-function mutations also identify genes important for development

Mutations that produce too much protein, or proteins with a new function not present in the wild-type protein, are **gain-of-function mutations.** The alleles resulting from gain-of-function mutations are often dominant to the wild-type allele, in contrast with the majority of loss-of-function alleles, which are recessive to wild type.

It is hard to understand unambiguously the role of a protein in development from a gain-of-function allele. The reason is that the mutation, rather than taking something away, adds something unusual to the organism, which might behave in an unpredictable way. Nevertheless, gain-of-function mutants can help identify developmentally important genes and clarify the roles they play in development. We now look at two kinds of gain-of-function mutations.

Mutations causing excessive gene activity

Such mutations are rare because they result only from highly specific changes in a gene, in contrast with loss-of-function mutations, which can disrupt gene function in many ways. Nonetheless, there are several ways in which mutations can lead to increased gene activity. One mechanism involves changes to promoters that make the promoters more accessible to transcription factors and RNA polymerase. Other possible scenarios are illustrated by various dominant mutations in *FGFR3,* one of the four genes in mice and humans that encode related yet distinct fibroblast growth factor receptors (review Fig. 18.7). Some of these mutations increase the affinity of the FGFR3 receptor protein for its ligand FGF, inappropriately turning on the developmental signal when the concentration of the FGF ligand would normally be too low to accomplish this. Other *FGFR3* mutations allow the developmental signal to be turned on in the absence of FGF. These mutations cause the constitutive (continuous) activation of the phosphate-group-adding kinase domain of FGFR3; they accomplish this by altering a part of the protein that normally blocks the kinase function in the absence of the ligand.

Interestingly, a single amino acid substitution in the FGFR3 protein is sufficient to cause a gain-of-function dominant phenotype through the constitutive activation of the kinase domain. This substitution causes achondroplasia, the most common form of short-limb dwarfism in humans. Researchers have recently engineered mice with exactly the same amino acid substitution in their homologous FGFR3 gene. Remarkably, this mutant gene produces

Figure 18.9 Achondroplastic dwarfism in the mouse.
(a) The dwarf mouse at the *right* is heterozygous for an *FGFR3* allele with the same amino acid change as that causing achondroplasia in humans. A control littermate is at the *left.* **(b)** Skeletal abnormalities in the dwarf mouse at the *top* include a shorter face, overgrowth of the incisor teeth (*arrowhead*), and improper connection of the head to the spine (*arrow*) as compared to a control littermate at the *bottom.*

(a)

(b)

what appears to be the same dominant dwarf phenotype seen in human achondroplasia (**Fig. 18.9**).

Mutations causing ectopic gene expression

Suppose you suspect that a particular protein plays an important role in initiating the development of some structure like the legs or eyes. If that were true, it might be possible that expression of this protein in tissues in which it is not normally made could lead to the development of legs or eyes in unusual locations in the animal. The expression of a gene at an abnormal place or time is called **ectopic gene expression.**

Rarely, spontaneous mutations cause ectopic expression of genes important to development. An interesting example of such a mutation occurred in *Drosophila* when a chromosomal inversion moved the *Antennapedia* gene (normally transcribed in tissues destined to become legs) next to a specific kind of enhancer, which turned the gene on in tissues normally destined to develop into antennae. Animals carrying this *Antennapedia* mutation have legs growing out of their heads in place of antennae (review Fig. 8.31 on p. 279). The phenotype of this ectopic mutant

Figure 18.10 Ectopic expression of the *eyeless* gene produces ectopic eye tissue. This fly carries a synthetic *eyeless* gene that is turned on inappropriately. As a result, eye tissue grows in unexpected places, such as at the end of the antennae and on the thorax above the wings.

Ectopic red
eye tissue

Ectopic red
eye tissue

shows that the wild-type protein encoded by *Antennapedia* plays a critical role in leg development.

Instead of relying on rare and unpredictable mutations that might cause ectopic gene expression, researchers can now use recombinant DNA technology to make such mutations in a systematic way. They can change the promoter of a cloned gene by adding enhancers or other elements that might cause it to be transcribed at inappropriate places or times, and then introduce this altered gene back into the organism's genome by transformation. One research group placed the *eyeless* gene of *Drosophila* (review Fig. 18.4a) under the control of a promoter for a "heat-shock" gene whose transcription in any tissue is turned on by higher than normal temperatures. Flies bearing this recombinant gene that were grown at high temperature made the *eyeless*-encoded protein throughout their bodies. These animals had eye tissue growing at many different locations, even on their wings and antennae (**Fig. 18.10**). This result demonstrates that the Eyeless protein is a master developmental switch that can activate a cellular program causing eye development.

Ectopic eyes also arise when the mouse *Pax-6* or the human *Aniridia* gene is expressed in *Drosophila* under the control of the same heat-shock gene promoter. This result means that both elements of the amino acid sequence and the actual function of this master switch have been conserved throughout animal evolution.

Gain-of-function mutations often produce dominant phenotypes that can provide clues about a gene's role in a developmental process. Some genes, when ectopically expressed in tissues different from their normal sites of action, can activate programs of development that alter cellular fates.

18.3 Analysis of Developmental Pathways

Once you have isolated a comprehensive set of mutations and identified as many as possible of the genes involved in the biological process of interest, the next step is to establish the functions performed by these genes. The ultimate aim of such studies is to discern a *developmental pathway:* a detailed description of how the products of these many genes interact and cooperate with each other to produce a particular outcome in development.

The action of each gene in a pathway must be characterized

Before looking at a complicated pathway as a whole, investigators must first learn as much as possible about each of the genes that comprise it. Specifically, details about the nature of the encoded protein, the location and timing of the gene's expression, the location of the protein product in the organism or in individual cells, and the developmental phenotypes associated with mutations in the gene all help scientists establish a theoretical framework to guide further analysis.

Nature of the encoded protein

With the completion of genome projects for key model organisms, researchers can often identify the mutant gene within a few months of finding the mutation. Once you know the nucleotide sequence of a gene, you automatically know the amino acid sequence of the protein it encodes. You can then use computer programs to search the amino acid sequence for motifs that offer clues to the protein's function. For example, computer programs can often predict whether a protein resembles known membrane-bound receptors, or whether a protein acts as a kinase that phosphorylates other proteins.

One motif seen in many proteins with developmental significance is the **homeodomain** (**Fig. 18.11**). It is found in the proteins encoded by the *eyeless/Pax6* and *Antennapedia* genes discussed earlier in this chapter. The homeodomain is a region of about 60 amino acids that is structurally related to the helix-turn-helix motif of many bacterial regulatory proteins. The homeodomain binds to specific DNA sequences, so its presence suggests that a protein might be a transcription factor.

Location and timing of gene expression

One way to answer the questions of where and when a gene is transcribed is to perform an RNA *in situ* hybridization experiment. To do this, you label cDNA sequences corresponding to the gene's mRNA and then use the

Figure 18.11 The homeodomain: A DNA-binding motif found in many transcription factors that regulate development. The amino acid backbone of a homeodomain (*yellow*) interacts with specific sequences in a DNA double helix (*red* and *blue*).

labeled cDNA as a probe for the mRNA on preparations of thinly sectioned tissues. Signals where the probe is retained indicate cells containing the gene's mRNA (**Fig. 18.12**). Defining the tissues in which the gene is expressed can help formulate hypotheses concerning the gene's role in development. For example, if a mutation in the gene

Figure 18.12 *In situ* hybridization locates cells expressing a gene of interest. This example shows that mRNA for the *Pax-6* gene (*yellow signals*) accumulates in the eye of a human fetus in the seventh week of gestation. Hybridization is specific to the developing neural retina (nr) and the developing eye lens above it.

affects the development of a tissue other than that in which the gene is transcribed, you might hypothesize that the gene encodes a signaling molecule like a hormone. Such molecules of cellular communication are made in one tissue but influence the fate of cells in other tissues that contain receptors for the hormone.

Location of the protein product

It is often technically easier to find and evaluate the tissues in which a gene is expressed by following the gene's protein product rather than by using RNA *in situ* hybridization to look for the gene's mRNA. In addition, an mRNA may be found in a tissue that doesn't contain the protein. This would point to the existence of regulatory controls that prevent translation of the mRNA. Finally, the intracellular localization of a protein often provides clues to its function. For example, concentration of the protein in the nucleus would be consistent with a role as a transcription factor.

Methods to follow a protein usually involve the generation of antibodies against parts of the protein. One way to do this is to use recombinant DNA techniques to construct a fused gene (**Fig. 18.13a**). In this construct, part of a cDNA for the gene of interest is cloned downstream of, and in the same reading frame as, part of a gene encoding a protein that can be made at high levels in bacteria. If you transform a plasmid containing this fused gene into *E. coli,* the bacterial cells will make large amounts of a **fusion protein** whose N-terminal amino acids are from the bacterial protein and whose C-terminal amino acids are from the eukaryotic developmental protein. If you inject this fusion protein into rabbits or other animals, they will synthesize antibodies against it. And once you label these antibodies with a fluorescent tag, you can track the tagged antibodies as they react with the corresponding protein of developmental interest in preparations of tissues and cells (**Fig. 18.13b**).

A new way to track a protein is to construct a gene encoding a tagged protein that will itself fluoresce. The idea, illustrated in **Fig. 18.13c,** is to synthesize an open reading frame that encodes not only the entire protein of interest, but also (at the protein's N or C terminus) the amino acids composing a naturally fluorescent protein from jellyfish called *green fluorescent protein (GFP)*. When this recombinant gene is reintroduced into the genome by transformation, the organism will make the GFP fusion protein in the same places and times it makes the normal untagged protein. Investigators can keep track of the fusion protein by following GFP fluorescence (**Fig. 18.13d**). A major advantage of this approach is that researchers can use it to follow a GFP-tagged protein in living cells or animals, which is generally not possible with tagged antibodies for technical reasons. With the GFP fusion protein, researchers can even record videos that reveal subtle changes in the location of the protein over time.

Figure 18.13 Using antibodies and GFP tagging to follow the localization of proteins. **(a)** This synthetic gene encodes a fusion protein that will be made at high levels when transformed into *E. coli* cells. Animals injected with purified fusion protein will make antibodies against the protein of interest. **(b)** A *Drosophila* "imaginal disc" is stained with antibodies against several proteins. Each antibody is tagged with a dye that fluoresces in a particular color. **(c)** Making a GFP-tagged protein. This recombinant gene encodes a fusion protein that contains GFP at its C terminus. **(d)** This mouse contains a GFP-labeled transgene expressed thoughout the skin; the entire mouse becomes fluorescent when illuminated with UV light as at the *bottom*. The same mouse is shown in normal light at the *top*.

(a) Fusion protein gene in *E. coli*

(b) A tissue stained with fluorescent antibodies

(c) Tagging a protein with GFP

(d) A mouse with a GFP-tagged transgene

Developmental phenotypes

Phenotypes may be evaluated in many ways to understand how a mutation impacts particular tissues and the development of the organism as a whole. For example, the morphology of mutant tissues can be examined with increasingly powerful microscopes, and the physiology of these tissues can be analyzed by various biochemical tests.

The importance of such investigations is underlined by the apparently simple question, "What cells or tissues are affected by the loss of gene function?" At first glance, it might seem that this question can be answered by the studies just described to define the location and timing of gene expression. That is, only the cells that make the protein would show the phenotypic effects of mutations that prevent that protein's synthesis. But this "obvious" solution is misleading because cells often communicate with each other to influence developmental decisions. In one simple example, if a gland synthesizes a hormone that

circulates through the blood, and the gland can no longer make the hormone, the phenotypic effects might not show up in the gland itself but rather in target cells elsewhere in the body that contain receptors for the hormone.

To address a variety of issues involving communication between cells, developmental geneticists construct **genetic mosaics:** organisms in which some cells (like those in the gland just described) have one genotype, whereas other cells (such as those in the hormone's target tissues) have a different genotype. Researchers can use several techniques to make such genetic mosaics. The technique chosen often depends on the species. *Drosophila* geneticists usually employ mitotic recombination; those working with *C. elegans* use methods based on the loss of small extra chromosomes during mitosis; and investigators studying mice mix embryonic cells from mutant and wild-type strains to make *chimeric mice* with two different cell types. **Chimeras** are genetic mosaics in which cells of different genotype originate from two different individuals. (For more species-specific details concerning the use of genetic mosaics, see the genetic portraits of flies, worms, and mice on our website [www.mhhe.com/hartwell4].)

Most mosaics are constructed with markers that allow investigators to differentiate between tissues with mutant and wild-type genotypes for the developmental gene. **Figure 18.14a** shows mosaic seedlings of the plant *Arabidopsis* in which blue tissue contains both a marker gene resulting in blue color and a wild-type gene called *AGAMOUS*⁺, whereas white tissue lacks the marker gene and is simultaneously mutant for *AGAMOUS*. **Figure 18.14b** diagrams how researchers used such marked mosaics to show that cells from a particular layer of undifferentiated cells (called L2) in the apical meristem send a signal needed for the proper differentiation of cells in a different layer (L1). This signal depends on the presence of a wild-type *AGAMOUS*⁺ allele in L2 cells. In other words, even *AGAMOUS*⁺ genotypically wild-type L1 cells develop abnormally if the adjacent L2 cells are mutant for this gene.

Figure 18.14 Mosaic analysis. (a) In these mosaic seedlings, *blue* tissue contains both a marker gene and the *AGAMOUS*⁺ gene, whereas *white* tissue contains neither (it is *AGAMOUS*⁻). **(b)** A signal from blue *AGAMOUS*⁺ L2 cells is needed for the proper differentiation of nearby L1 cells. If L2 cells lack the *AGAMOUS*⁺ gene (*white*), nearby L1 cells do not differentiate properly, even if they are themselves *AGAMOUS*⁺.

(a) Mosaic seedlings of *Arabidopsis*

(b) Using mosaics to study cell signaling

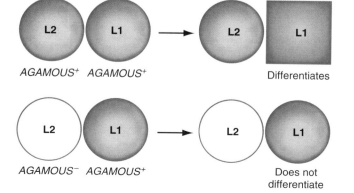

Careful analyses of protein structure, patterns of gene and protein expression, and phenotype provide clues about a gene's function in development. The construction of genetic mosaics is useful for determining whether the product of the gene influences the development of tissues other than those in which the gene is expressed.

The interactions of genes in a pathway must be determined

As you already know, genes do not work in isolation. Instead, complicated biological events demand the coordinated action of many genes. A full description of development from a genetic perspective thus requires not only the identification and analysis of the individual genes that contribute to development, but also the eventual elucidation of how the products of those genes work together.

It is generally easiest to focus first on the interaction of the genes in pairs: How does one gene influence the other, and vice versa? We mention here two of the most common approaches to answering this question. You will see other examples later in the chapter.

Analysis of how one gene affects the expression of another

Once you have defined the tissue distribution and intracellular location of one gene's mRNA or protein, you can ask how mutations in a different gene affect this distribution or localization. For example, consider the *wingless* and *vestigial* genes of *Drosophila*. Certain mutations in either gene result in the loss or reduction in size of the adult wings. The protein products of these genes are expressed only in small, overlapping subsets of the cells within tissues called "imaginal discs" that eventually develop into wings (**Fig. 18.15a**). Flies mutant for *wingless* not only fail to make the Wingless protein, but they also fail to produce the Vestigial protein in many of the cells where it would normally be found (**Fig. 18.15b**). This suggests that the expression of the *vestigial* gene in those cells is dependent upon *wingless* gene function in adjacent cells.

Analysis of double mutants

If two mutations define successive steps in a process, the double mutant will often arrest with the phenotype characteristic of the earliest block in the process; that is, the earlier-acting mutation is *epistatic* to the other. **Figure 18.16a** diagrams an analysis of two loss-of-function mutations in yeast that disrupt the secretion of molecules from the cell. Such secretion is important for many developmental events. The phenotype of the double mutant in this example makes sense. We would expect that a molecule needs to be loaded into secretory

Figure 18.15 A mutation in one gene can affect the expression of another gene. (a) A wild-type *Drosophila* wing imaginal disc stained for Wingless (Wg, *green*) and Vestigial (Vg, *red*) proteins. A thin band of cells expressing both Wg and Vg is *yellow*. **(b)** A *wingless* mutant wing disc stained as in (a). Not only is there no Wg protein, but Vg protein is made only in a narrow band about two cells wide, not in the broader region about 12 cells wide where it is normally made (as in part a).

(a)   **(b)**

vesicles before the fusion of these vesicles with the cell membrane allows the molecule to be secreted from a cell.

It would be incorrect, however, to conclude that an epistatic gene always governs an earlier step than the gene whose mutant phenotype is masked. In many pathways, the opposite is true. For example, in *C. elegans* the pathway leading to formation of the vulva includes three genes: *let-60, lin-45,* and *mek-2* (**Fig. 18.16b**). The LET-60 protein becomes activated in cells that receive an extracellular signal. Active LET-60 then activates the LIN-45 protein, which subsequently activates the MEK-2 protein; active MEK-2 protein leads through several steps to vulva formation. Gain-of-function *let-60* alleles cause the over-activation of LIN-45 protein, which in turn results in too much active MEK-2 protein, so the eventual phenotype is the formation of too many vulvas. Loss-of-function *mek-2* alleles have the opposite phenotype of no vulvas. Double mutant animals (with both the gain-of-function *let-60* allele and the loss-of-function *mek-2* allele) have no vulvas, so the *mek-2* mutation is epistatic, even though *let-60* encodes a protein that acts earlier in the process. This result makes sense because if there is no MEK-2 protein, the relative activity of LET-60 cannot affect vulva formation.

Epistasis, where the double mutant resembles either one of the single mutants, is only one of several possibilities for the phenotype of a double mutant. In some cases, mutations in one gene are counteracted by mutations in a second *suppressor gene,* so the phenotype of the double mutant is nearly wild type. In other cases, the effect of mutations in a gene might be worsened by the simultaneous presence of mutations in a different *enhancer gene.*

Whether double mutant analysis indicates epistasis, suppression, or enhancement, it is dangerous to interpret these results in isolation. Much more information is required. Are the mutations being analyzed loss-of-function or gain-of-function alleles? Does the blockage of each step in the pathway cause a different aberrant outcome, or does the whole pathway have a single output? Do the protein

products have recognizable biochemical roles—for example, as transcription factors, or kinases, or hormone receptors? Answering these questions helps illuminate gene interactions.

Commonly used techniques to explore how genes interact in developmental pathways include (1) determining whether mutations in one gene affect the timing or pattern of the expression of another gene, and (2) observing the phenotype of an individual with mutations in two genes (a double mutant). True understanding of a developmental pathway requires integrating the results of many kinds of analysis.

Figure 18.16 Double mutant analysis. (a) The product of gene *A* helps lead *red* molecules into small, round vesicles. The product of gene *B* allows vesicles to fuse with the cell membrane, causing secretion of the vesicles' contents. Mutations in gene *A* are epistatic to those in gene *B*. **(b)** In this signal transduction pathway for vulva formation, a mutation in the gene controlling a later step is epistatic to a mutation in a gene whose product acts earlier.

(a) Epistasis in the secretion pathway

(b) Epistasis in the pathway for vulva formation

18.4 A Comprehensive Example: Body-Plan Development in *Drosophila*

Studies on the genetic control of the basic body plan of *Drosophila* have revolutionized our understanding of development. Here, we focus on the aspect of this work that explains how the fly's body becomes differentiated and specialized along the *anterior-posterior (AP) axis,* the line running from the animal's head to its tail.

The research we describe was based on the observation that a fertilized *Drosophila* egg becomes subdivided into several clearly defined segments (review Fig. 18.2), each of which eventually has a specific appearance and function. Some segments become parts of the head, others parts of the thorax, and still others, parts of the abdomen. Scientists designed experiments to answer two fundamental questions about this segmentation. First, how does the developing animal establish the proper number of body segments? And second, how does each body segment "know" what kinds of structures it should form and what role it should play in the animal's biology? Results showed that very early in development, the action of a large group of genes, called the **segmentation genes,** subdivides the body into an array of essentially identical body segments. Later in development, the expression of a different set of genes, called **homeotic genes,** assigns a unique identity to each body segment.

Drosophila embryos become divided into segments

To understand how the segmentation and homeotic genes function, it is helpful to consider some of the basic events that take place in the first few hours of *Drosophila* development (**Fig. 18.17**). The egg is fertilized in the uterus as it is being laid, and the meiotic divisions of the oocyte nucleus, which had previously arrested in the metaphase of meiosis I, resume at this time. After fusion of the haploid male and female pronuclei, the diploid zygotic nucleus of the embryo undergoes 13 rounds of nuclear division at an extraordinarily rapid rate, with the average time of mitotic cycles 2 through 9 being only 8.5 minutes.

Nuclear division in early *Drosophila* embryos, unlike most mitoses, is not accompanied by cell division, so the early embryo becomes a multinucleate syncytium. During the first eight division cycles, the multiple nuclei are centrally located in the egg; during the ninth division, most

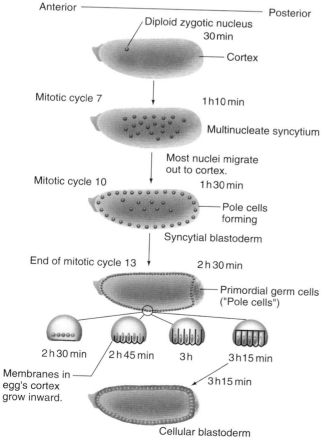

(a) The first three hours after fertilization

(b) Early embryonic stages in cross section

Figure 18.17 Early *Drosophila* development: From fertilization to cellular blastoderm. (a) The zygotic nucleus undergoes 13 very rapid mitotic divisions in a single syncytium. A few nuclei at the posterior end of the embryo become the germ-line *pole cells.* At the *syncytial blastoderm* stage, the egg surface is covered by a monolayer of nuclei. At the end of the thirteenth division cycle, cell membranes enclose the nuclei at the cortex into separate cells to produce a *cellular blastoderm.* **(b)** Photomicrographs of early embryonic stages stained with a fluorescent dye for DNA.

of the nuclei migrate out to the cortex—just under the surface of the embryo—to produce the **syncytial blastoderm.** During the tenth division, nuclei at the posterior pole of the egg are enclosed in membranes that invaginate from the egg cell membrane to form the first embryonic cells; these "pole cells" are the primordial germ cells. At the end of the thirteenth division cycle, about 6000 nuclei are present at the egg cortex.

During the interphase of the fourteenth cycle, membranes in the egg's cortex grow inward between these nuclei, creating an epithelial layer called the **cellular blastoderm** that is one cell deep (**Figs. 18.17 and 18.18a**). The embryo completes formation of the cellular blastoderm about 3 hours after fertilization. At the cellular blastoderm stage, no regional differences in cell shape or size are apparent (with the exception of the pole cells at the posterior end). Experiments in which blastoderm cells have been transplanted from one location to another, however, show that despite this morphological uniformity, the segmental identity of the cells has already been determined.

Consistent with this finding, molecular studies reveal that most segmentation and homeotic genes function during or even before the cellular blastoderm stage.

Immediately after cellularization, **gastrulation** and establishment of the embryonic germ layers begin. The *mesoderm* forms by invagination of a band of midventral cells that extends most of the length of the embryo. This infolding (the ventral furrow; **Fig. 18.18b**) produces an internal tube whose cells soon divide and migrate to produce a mesodermal layer. The *endoderm* forms by distinct invaginations anterior and posterior to the ventral furrow; one of these invaginations is the cephalic furrow seen in Fig. 18.18b. The cells of the endodermal infoldings migrate over the yolk to produce the gut. Finally, the nervous system arises from neuroblasts that segregate from bilateral zones of the ventral *ectoderm.*

The first visible signs of segmentation are periodic bulges in the mesoderm, which appear about 40 minutes after gastrulation begins. Within a few hours of gastrulation, the embryo is divided into clear-cut body segments

(a) Cellular blastoderm

(b) Gastrulation

(c) Segmentation

(d) Segment identity is preserved throughout development.

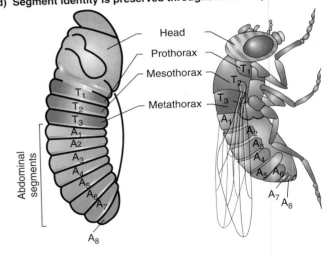

Figure 18.18 *Drosophila* development after formation of the cellular blastoderm. (a) Scanning electron micrograph of a cellular blastoderm. Individual cells are visible at the periphery of the embryo, and the pole cells at the posterior end can be distinguished (*arrow*). **(b)** A ventral view of some of the furrows that form during gastrulation, roughly 4 hours after fertilization: vf, ventral furrow; cf, cephalic furrow. **(c)** By 10 hours after fertilization, it is clear that the embryo is subdivided into segments. Ma, Mx, and Lb are the three head segments. CL, PC, O, and D refer to nonsegmented regions of the head. The three thoracic segments (labeled T_1, T_2, and T_3) are the prothorax, the mesothorax, and the metathorax, respectively, whereas the abdominal segments are labeled A_1-A_8. **(d)** The identities of embryonic segments (*left*) are preserved through the larval stages and are also retained through metamorphosis into the adult (*right*).

that will become the three head segments, three thoracic segments, and eight major abdominal segments of the larva (**Fig. 18.18c**). Even though the animal eventually undergoes metamorphosis to become an adult fly, the same basic body plan is conserved in the adult stage (**Fig. 18.18d**).

> The first rounds of mitosis in the *Drosophila* embryo produce a syncytial blastoderm. Cell membranes then grow around the thousands of nuclei under the embryonic surface, forming the cellular blastoderm. Some of these cells invaginate toward the middle of the embryo to make a gastrula. Although segmentation is first visible only after gastrulation, the genes responsible for segmentation function even earlier in development.

Segment number is first specified by maternal genes

Very little transcription of genes occurs in the embryonic nuclei between fertilization and the end of the 13 rapid syncytial divisions. Because of this near (but not total) absence of transcription, developmental biologists suspected that formation of the basic body plan initially requires **maternally supplied components** deposited by the mother into the egg during oogenesis. How could they identify the genes encoding these maternally supplied components? Christiane Nüsslein-Volhard and Eric Wieschaus realized that the embryonic phenotype determined by such genes does not depend on the embryo's own genotype; rather, it is determined by the genotype of the mother. They devised genetic screens to identify recessive mutations in maternal genes that influence embryonic development; these recessive mutations are often called **maternal-effect mutations.**

To carry out their screens, Nüsslein-Volhard and Wieschaus established individual balanced stocks for thousands of mutagen-treated chromosomes, and they then examined the phenotypes of embryos obtained from homozygous mutant mothers. They focused their attention on stocks in which homozygous mutant females were sterile, because they anticipated that the absence of maternally supplied components needed for the earliest stages of development would result in embryos so defective that they could never grow into adults. Through these large-scale screens, Nüsslein-Volhard and Wieschaus identified a large number of maternal genes that are required for the normal patterning of the body. For this and other contributions, they shared the Nobel Prize for Physiology or Medicine with Edward B. Lewis—whose work we describe later.

We focus here on two groups of the genes they found. One group is required for normal patterning of the embryo's anterior; the other is required mainly for normal posterior patterning. The genes in these two groups are the first genes activated in the process that determines segment number.

The finding that separate groups of maternal genes control anterior and posterior patterning is consistent with the conclusions of classical embryological experiments. Studies in which polar cytoplasm from the embryo's ends was transplanted, or in which preblastoderm embryos were separated into two halves by constriction of the embryo with a fine thread, suggested that the insect body axis is patterned during cleavage by the interaction of two signaling centers located at the anterior and posterior poles of the egg. In a specific model, Klaus Sander proposed that each pole of the egg produces a different substance, and that these substances form opposing gradients by diffusion. He suggested that the concentrations of these substances then determine the types of structures produced at each position along the body axis.

Molecular characterization of the maternal genes of the anterior and posterior groups indicates that the Sander model for body axis patterning is correct. Substances that define different cell fates in a concentration-dependent manner are known as **morphogens.**

Bicoid: The anterior morphogen

Embryos from mothers homozygous for null alleles of the *bicoid* (*bcd*) gene lack all head and thoracic structures. The protein product of *bcd* is a DNA-binding transcription factor whose transcript is localized near the anterior pole of the egg cytoplasm (**Fig. 18.19a**). Translation of the *bcd* transcripts takes place after fertilization. The newly made Bcd protein diffuses from its source at the pole to produce a high-to-low, anterior-to-posterior concentration gradient that extends over the anterior two-thirds of the embryo by the ninth division cycle (**Fig. 18.19b**). This gradient determines most aspects of head and thorax development.

One of the first lines of evidence that the Bcd protein functions as a morphogen came from experiments in which the maternal dosage of the *bcd* gene varied (**Fig. 18.19c**). Mothers that carried only one dose of the *bcd* gene instead of the normal diploid dose incorporated about half the normal amount of *bcd* RNA into their eggs. As a result, translation yielded less Bcd protein, and the Bcd gradient was shallower and shifted to the anterior. In these Bcd-deficient embryos, the thoracic segments developed from more anterior regions than normal, and less of the body was devoted to the head. The opposite effect occurred in mothers carrying extra doses of the *bcd* gene. These and other observations suggested that the level of Bcd protein is a key to the determination of head and thoracic fates in the embryo. Three other genes work with *bcd* in the anterior group of maternal genes; the function of the protein products of these three genes is to localize *bcd* transcripts to the egg's anterior pole.

The Bcd protein itself works in two ways: as a transcription factor that helps control the transcription of genes farther down the regulatory pathway, and as a translational repressor. The target of its repressor activity is the transcript

Figure 18.19 Bicoid is the anterior morphogen. (a) The *bicoid* (*bcd*) mRNA (visualized by *in situ* hybridization in *purple*) concentrates at the anterior tip of the embryo. **(b)** The Bicoid (Bcd) protein (seen by *green* antibody staining) is distributed in a gradient: high at the anterior end and trailing off toward the posterior. The Bcd protein (a transcription factor) accumulates in the nuclei of this syncytial blastoderm embryo. **(c)** The greater the maternal dosage of *bcd*+, the higher the concentration of Bcd in the embryo, and the more of the embryo that is devoted to anterior structures. Head structures will develop anterior of the head fold invagination; thoracic and abdominal structures posterior to it.

(a) Localization of *bicoid* mRNA

(b) A gradient of Bicoid protein

(c) Bicoid protein is a morphogen.

of the *caudal* (*cad*) gene, which also encodes a DNA-binding transcription factor. The *cad* transcripts are uniformly distributed in the egg before fertilization, but because of translational repression by the Bcd protein, translation of these transcripts produces a gradient of Cad protein that is complementary to the Bcd gradient. That is, there is a high concentration of Cad protein at the posterior end of the embryo and lower concentrations toward the anterior (**Fig. 18.20**). The Cad protein plays an important role in activating genes expressed later in the segmentation pathway to generate posterior structures.

Nanos: The primary posterior morphogen

The *nanos* (*nos*) RNA is localized to the posterior egg cytoplasm by proteins encoded by other posterior group maternal genes. Like *bcd* RNAs, *nos* transcripts are translated during the cleavage stages. After translation, diffusion produces a posterior-to-anterior Nos protein concentration gradient. The Nos protein, unlike the Bcd protein, is not a transcription factor; rather, the Nos protein functions only as a translational repressor. Its major target is the maternally supplied transcript of the *hunchback* (*hb*) gene, which is deposited in the egg during oogenesis and is uniformly distributed before fertilization.

For development to occur properly, the Hb protein (which is another transcription factor) must be present in a gradient with high concentrations at the embryo's anterior and low concentrations at the posterior. The Nos protein, which represses the translation of *hb* maternal mRNA and is present in a posterior-to-anterior concentration gradient, helps construct the anterior-to-posterior Hb gradient by lowering the concentration of the Hb protein toward the embryo's posterior pole (Fig. 18.20). The embryo also has a second mechanism for establishing the Hb protein gradient that functions somewhat later: It transcribes the *hb* gene from zygotic nuclei only in the anterior region (see following).

Maternal *bcd* and *nos* mRNAs are concentrated respectively near the anterior and posterior poles of *Drosophila* eggs. After fertilization, these mRNAs are translated into Bcd and Nos morphogens, which diffuse from the poles to form oppositely oriented gradients that pattern the anterior-to-posterior embryo axis. Bcd and Nos regulate translation of maternal *hb* and *cad* mRNAs, generating gradients of Hb and Cad proteins. Bcd, Hb, and Cad are transcription factors that control expression of later-functioning segmentation genes.

Figure 18.20 Distribution of the mRNA and protein products of maternal-effect genes within the early embryo. *Top:* In the oocyte prior to fertilization, *bicoid* (*bcd*) mRNA is concentrated near the anterior tip and *nanos* (*nos*) mRNA at the posterior tip, whereas maternally supplied *hunchback* (*hb*) and *caudal* (*cad*) mRNAs are uniformly distributed. *Bottom:* In early cleavage stage embryos, the Bicoid (Bcd) and Hunchback (Hb) proteins are found in concentration gradients high at the anterior and lower toward the posterior (A to P), whereas the Nanos (Nos) and Caudal (Cad) proteins are distributed in opposite P-to-A gradients.

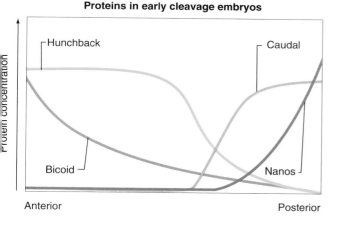

Segment number is further specified by zygotic genes

The maternally determined Bcd, Hb, and Cad protein gradients control the spatial expression of zygotic segmentation genes. Unlike the products of maternal genes, whose mRNAs are placed in the egg during oogenesis, the products of zygotic genes are transcribed and translated from DNA in the nuclei of embryonic cells descended from the original zygotic nucleus. The expression of zygotic segmentation genes begins in the syncytial blastoderm stage, a few division cycles before cellularization (roughly cycle 10).

Most of the zygotic segmentation genes were identified in a second mutant screen also carried out in the late 1970s by Christiane Nüsslein-Volhard and Eric Wieschaus. In this screen, the two *Drosophila* geneticists placed individual ethyl methane sulfonate (EMS)–mutagenized chromosomes into balanced stocks and then examined homozygous mutant embryos from these stocks for defects in the segmentation pattern of the embryo. These embryos were so aberrant that they were unable to grow into adults; thus, the mutations causing these defects would be classified as recessive lethals.

After screening several thousand such stocks for each of the *Drosophila* chromosomes, Nüsslein-Volhard and Wieschaus identified three classes of zygotic segmentation genes: gap genes (9 different genes); pair-rule genes (8 genes); and segment polarity genes (about 17 genes). These three classes of zygotic genes fit into a hierarchy of gene expression.

Gap genes

The gap genes are the first zygotic segmentation genes to be transcribed. Embryos homozygous for mutations in the gap genes show a gap in the segmentation pattern caused by an absence of particular segments that correspond to the position at which each gene is transcribed (**Fig. 18.21**).

How do the maternal transcription factor gradients ensure that the various gap genes are expressed in their broad zones at the proper position in the embryo? Part of the answer is that the binding sites in the promoter regions of the gap genes have different affinities for the maternal transcription factors. For example, some gap genes are activated by the Bcd protein (the anterior morphogen). Gap genes such as *hb* with low-affinity Bcd protein-binding sites are activated only in the most anterior regions, where the concentration of Bcd is at its highest; by contrast, genes with high-affinity sites have an activation range extending farther toward the posterior pole.

Another part of the answer is that the gap genes themselves encode transcription factors that can influence the expression of other gap genes. The *Krüppel* (*Kr*) gap gene, for example, appears to be turned off by high amounts of Hb protein at the anterior end of its band of expression; activated within its expression band by Bcd protein in conjunction with lower levels of Hb protein; and turned off at the posterior end of its expression zone by the products of the *knirps* (*kni*) gap gene (**Fig. 18.21c**). (Note that the *hb* gene is usually classified as a gap gene, despite the maternal supply of some *hb* RNA, because the protein translated from the transcripts of zygotic nuclei actually plays the more important role.)

Pair-rule genes

After the gap genes have divided the body axis into rough, generalized regions, activation of the pair-rule genes generates more sharply defined sections. These genes encode

(a) Zones of gap gene expression

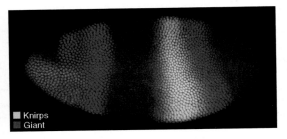

(b) Phenotypes caused by gap gene mutations

normal

Krüppel

hunchback

knirps

(c) Gap genes: a summary

Figure 18.21 Gap genes. (a) Zones of expression of four gap genes (*hunchback* [*hb*], *Krüppel* [*Kr*], *knirps* [*kni*], and *giant* [*gt*]) in late syncytial blastoderm embryos, as visualized with fluorescently labeled antibodies. **(b)** Defects in segmentation caused by mutations in selected gap genes, as seen in late embryos. Only the remaining thoracic and abdominal segments are labeled; the head segments at the anterior end are highly compressed and not labeled. **(c)** Mutation of a particular gap gene results in the loss of segments corresponding to the zone of expression of that gap gene in the embryo.

transcription factors that are expressed in seven stripes in preblastoderm and blastoderm embryos (**Fig. 18.22a**). The stripes have a two-segment periodicity; that is, there is one stripe for every two segments. Mutations in pair-rule genes cause the deletion of similar pattern elements from every alternate segment. For example, larvae mutant for *fushi tarazu* ("segment deficient" in Japanese) lack parts of abdominal segments A1, A3, A5, and A7 (see Fig. 18.2). Mutations in *even-skipped* cause loss of even-numbered abdominal segments.

There are two classes of pair-rule genes: primary and secondary. The striped expression pattern of the three primary pair-rule genes depends on the transcription factors encoded by the maternal genes and the zygotic gap genes. Specific elements within the upstream regulatory region of each pair-rule gene drive the expression of that pair-rule gene within a particular stripe. For example, as **Fig. 18.22b** and **c** shows, the DNA region responsible for driving the

expression of *even-skipped* (*eve*) in the second stripe contains multiple binding sites for the Bcd protein and the proteins encoded by the gap genes *Krüppel*, *giant* (*gt*), and *hb*. The transcription of *eve* in this stripe of the embryo is activated by Bcd and Hb, while it is repressed by Gt and Kr. Only in the stripe 2 region are Gt and Kr levels low enough and Bcd and Hb levels high enough to allow activation of the element driving *eve* expression.

In contrast with the primary pair-rule genes, the five pair-rule genes of the secondary class are controlled by interactions with transcription factors encoded by other pair-rule genes.

Segment polarity genes

Many segment polarity genes are expressed in stripes that are repeated with a single segment periodicity; that is, there is one stripe per segment (**Fig. 18.23a**). Mutations in segment polarity genes cause deletion of part of each segment, often accompanied by mirror-image duplication of the remaining parts. The segment polarity genes thus function to determine certain patterns that are repeated in each segment.

The regulatory system that directs the expression of segment polarity genes in a single stripe per segment is quite complex. In general, the transcription factors encoded by pair-rule genes initiate the pattern by directly regulating certain segment polarity genes. Interactions between various cell polarity genes then maintain this periodicity later in development. Significantly, activation of segment polarity genes occurs after cellularization of the embryo is complete, so the diffusion of transcription factors within the syncytium ceases to play a role. Instead, intrasegmental patterning is determined mostly by the diffusion of secreted proteins between cells.

Two of the segment polarity genes, *hedgehog* (*hh*) and *wingless* (*wg*), encode secreted proteins. These proteins, together with the transcription factor encoded by the *engrailed* (*en*) segment polarity gene, are responsible for many aspects of segmental patterning (**Fig. 18.23b**). A key component of this control is that a one-cell-wide stripe of cells secreting the Wg protein is adjacent to a stripe of cells expressing the En protein and secreting the Hh protein. The interface of these two types of cells is a self-reinforcing, reciprocal loop. The Wg protein secreted by the more anterior of the two adjacent stripes of cells is required for the continued expression of *hh* and *en* in the adjacent posterior stripe. The Hh protein secreted by the more posterior stripe of cells maintains expression of *wg* in the anterior stripe. Gradients of Wg and Hh proteins made from these adjacent stripes of cells control many aspects of patterning in the remainder of the segment. The products of both *wg* and *hh* appear to function as morphogens; that is, responding cells appear to adopt different fates depending on the concentration of Wg or Hh protein to which they are exposed.

Figure 18.22 Pair-rule genes. (a) Zones of expression of the proteins encoded by the pair-rule genes *fushi tarazu* (*ftz*) and *even-skipped* (*eve*) at the cellular blastoderm stage. Each gene is expressed in seven stripes. Eve stripe 2 is the second green stripe from the *left*. **(b)** The formation of Eve stripe 2 requires activation of *eve* transcription by the Bcd and Hb proteins and repression at its left and right ends by Gt and Kr proteins, respectively. **(c)** The 700 bp upstream regulatory region of the *eve* gene that directs the Eve second stripe contains multiple binding sites for the four proteins shown in part (b).

(a) Distribution of pair-rule gene products

Anterior

Posterior

- Even-skipped (Eve)
- Fushi tarazu (Ftz)

(b) Proteins regulating *eve* transcription

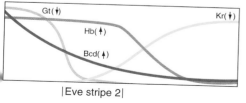

Gt(↓)　　　　　　　　　Kr(↓)

Hb(↑)

Bcd(↑)

|Eve stripe 2|

(c) Upstream regulatory region of *eve*

-1500 base pairs

-800

Kr　Gt　　　　Gt　Kr　　　　　Gt　Kr　　　Kr　Kr

Bcd　Bcd　　　　　　Bcd　　　　Bcd　　Hb　Bcd　　Hb　　Hb

Figure 18.23 Segment Polarity Genes. (a) Wild-type embryos express the segment polarity gene *engrailed* in 14 stripes. **(b)** The border between a segment's posterior and anterior compartments is governed by the *engrailed* (*en*), *wingless* (*wg*), and *hedgehog* (*hh*) segment polarity genes. Cells in posterior compartments express *en*. The En protein activates the transcription of the *hh* gene, which encodes a secreted protein ligand. Binding of this Hh protein to the Patched receptor in the adjacent anterior cell initiates a signal transduction pathway (through the Smo and Ci proteins) leading to the transcription of the *wg* gene. Wg is also a secreted protein that binds to a different receptor in the posterior cell, which is encoded by *frizzled*. Binding of the Wg protein to this receptor initiates a different signal transduction pathway (including the Dsh, Zw3, and Arm proteins) that stimulates the transcription of *en* and of *hh*. The result is a reciprocal loop stabilizing the alternate fates of adjacent cells at the border.

(a) Distribution of Engrailed protein

(b) Segment polarity genes establish compartment borders.

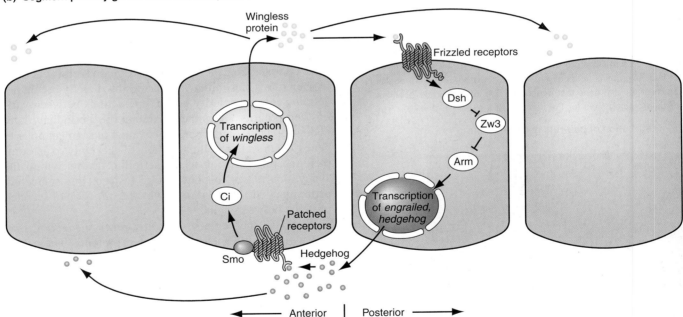

Other segment polarity genes encode proteins involved in **signal transduction pathways** initiated by the binding of Wg and Hh proteins to receptors on cell surfaces. Signal transduction pathways enable a signal received from a receptor on the cell's surface to be converted to a final intracellular regulatory response usually the activation or repression of particular target genes. The signal transduction pathways initiated by the Wg and Hh proteins determine the ability of cells in portions of each segment to differentiate into the particular cell types characteristic of those locations.

Homologs of the segment polarity genes are key players in many important patterning events in vertebrates. For example, the chicken *sonic hedgehog* gene (related to the fly *hh*) is critical for the initiation of the left-right asymmetry in the early chicken embryo as well as for the processes that determine the number and polarity of digits produced by the limb buds. The mammalian homolog of *sonic hedgehog* has the same conserved functions.

Summary of segment number specification

The pattern of expression for members of each class of segmentation genes is controlled either by genes higher

Figure 18.24 The genetic hierarchy leading to segmentation in *Drosophila*. (a) Genes in successively lower parts of the hierarchy are expressed in narrower bands within the embryos. **(b)** Mutations in segmentation genes cause the loss of segments that correspond to regions where the gene is expressed (*shown in yellow*). The denticle bands (*dark brown*) are features that help researchers identify the segments.

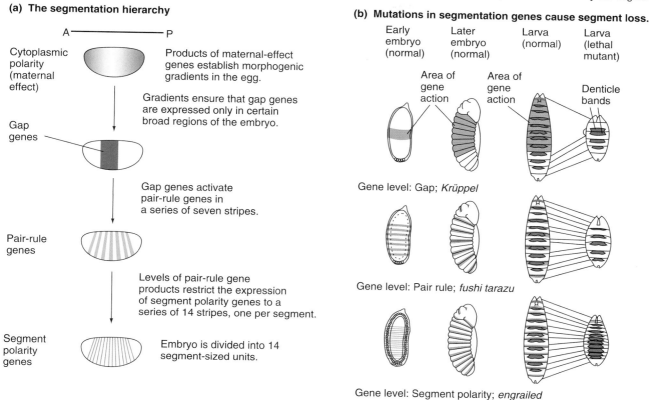

(a) The segmentation hierarchy

A ——————— P

Cytoplasmic polarity (maternal effect) — Products of maternal-effect genes establish morphogenic gradients in the egg.

Gradients ensure that gap genes are expressed only in certain broad regions of the embryo.

Gap genes — Gap genes activate pair-rule genes in a series of seven stripes.

Pair-rule genes — Levels of pair-rule gene products restrict the expression of segment polarity genes to a series of 14 stripes, one per segment.

Segment polarity genes — Embryo is divided into 14 segment-sized units.

(b) Mutations in segmentation genes cause segment loss.

Early embryo (normal) / Later embryo (normal) / Larva (normal) / Larva (lethal mutant)

Area of gene action / Area of gene action / Denticle bands

Gene level: Gap; *Krüppel*

Gene level: Pair rule; *fushi tarazu*

Gene level: Segment polarity; *engrailed*

in the hierarchy or by members of the same class, never by genes of a lower class (**Fig. 18.24**). In this regulatory cascade, the maternal genes control the gap and pair-rule genes, the gap genes control themselves and the pair-rule genes, and the pair-rule genes control themselves and the segment polarity genes. The expression of genes in successively lower parts of the hierarchy is increasingly spatially restricted within the embryo.

The cellular blastoderm looks from the outside like a uniform layer of cells (as seen in Fig. 18.18a), but the coordinated action of the segmentation genes has actually already divided the embryo into segment primordia. A few hours after gastrulation, these primordia become distinguishable as clear-cut segments (Fig. 18.18c).

Most of the proteins produced by segmentation genes are transcription factors that control gene expression in the syncytial blastoderm. These factors are hierarchical, acting to restrict transcription of genes of the same or lower classes to increasingly narrow regions. After cellularization, pattern formation also depends upon intercellular communication mediated by secreted proteins.

Segment identity is established by homeotic genes

After the segmentation genes have subdivided the body into a precise number of segments, the homeotic genes help assign a unique identity to each segment. They do this by functioning as master regulators that control the transcription of batteries of genes responsible for the development of segment-specific structures. The homeotic genes themselves are regulated by the gap, pair-rule, and segment polarity genes so that at the cellular blastoderm stage, or shortly thereafter, each homeotic gene becomes expressed within a specific subset of body segments. Most homeotic genes then remain active through the rest of development, functioning continuously to direct proper segmental specialization.

Mutations in homeotic genes, referred to as **homeotic mutations,** cause particular segments, or parts of them, to develop as if they were located elsewhere in the body. Because some of the mutant homeotic phenotypes are quite spectacular, researchers noticed them very early in *Drosophila* research. In 1915, for example, Calvin Bridges found a mutant he called *bithorax* (*bx*). In homozygotes for this mutation, the anterior portion of the third thoracic

(a) Effects of bx or pbx mutations

(b) A fly with both bx and pbx mutations

Figure 18.25 Homeotic transformations. (a) In animals homozygous for the mutation *bithorax* (*bx*), the anterior compartment of T3 (the third thoracic segment that makes the haltere) is transformed into the anterior compartment of T2 (the second thoracic segment that makes the wing). The mutation *postbithorax* (*pbx*) transforms the posterior compartment of T3 into the posterior compartment of T2. **(b)** In a *bx pbx* double mutant, T3 is changed entirely into T2. The result is a four-winged fly.

segment (T3) develops like the anterior second thoracic segment (T2); in other words, this mutation transforms part of T3 into the corresponding part of T2, as illustrated in **Fig. 18.25a.** This mutant phenotype is very dramatic, as T3 normally produces only small club-shaped balancer organs called *halteres,* whereas T2 produces the wings. Another homeotic mutation is *postbithorax* (*pbx*), which affects only posterior T3, causing its transformation into posterior T2. (Note that in this context, *Drosophila* geneticists use the term "transformation" to mean a change of body form.) In the *bx pbx* double mutant, all of T3 develops as T2 to produce the now famous four-winged fly (**Fig. 18.25b**).

In the last half of the twentieth century, researchers isolated many other homeotic mutations, most of which map within either of two gene clusters. Mutations affecting segments in the abdomen and posterior thorax lie within a cluster known as the **bithorax complex (BX-C);** mutations affecting segments in the head and anterior thorax lie within the **Antennapedia complex (ANT-C)** (**Fig. 18.26**).

The bithorax complex

Edward B. Lewis shared the 1995 Nobel Prize for Physiology or Medicine with Christiane Nüsslein-Volhard and Eric Wieschaus for his extensive genetic studies of the BX-C. In his work, Lewis isolated BX-C mutations that, like *bx* and *pbx,* affected the posterior thorax; he also found novel BX-C mutations that caused anteriorly directed transformations of each of the eight abdominal segments. Lewis named mutations affecting abdominal segments *infra-abdominal* (*iab*) mutations, and he numbered these according to the primary

segment they affect. Thus, *iab-2* mutations cause transformations of A2 toward A1, *iab-3* mutations cause transformations of A3 toward A2, and so forth.

Researchers initiated molecular studies of the bithorax complex in the early 1980s, and in 15 years, they not only extensively characterized all of the genes and mutations in the BX-C at the molecular level but also completed the sequencing of the entire 315 kb region. **Figure 18.2**

Figure 18.26 Homeotic selector genes. Two clusters of genes on *Drosophila*'s chromosome 3—the Antennapedia complex and the bithorax complex—determine most aspects of segment identity. Interestingly, the order of genes in these complexes is the same as the order of the segments each gene controls.

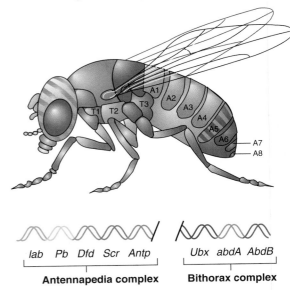

lab Pb Dfd Scr Antp   *Ubx abdA AbdB*

Antennapedia complex   **Bithorax complex**

Figure 18.27 315 kb of the bithorax complex. The complex contains only three homeotic genes: *Ubx, abd-A,* and *Abd-B.* Many homeotic mutations such as *bx* and *pbx* affect regulatory regions that influence the transcription of one gene in particular segments. For example, *bx* mutations prevent the transcription of *Ubx* in the anterior compartment of the third thoracic segment, whereas *iab-8* mutations affect the transcription of *Abd-B* in segment A8. Note that the order of these regulatory regions corresponds to the anterior-to-posterior order of segments in the animal.

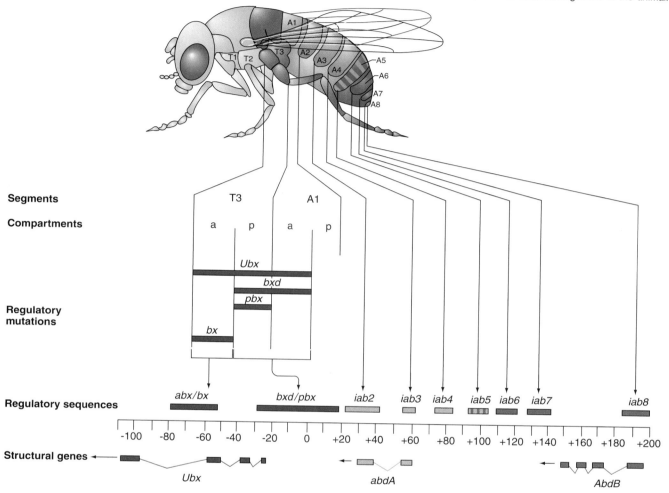

ummarizes the structure of the complex. A remarkable fea-
ure of the BX-C is that mutations map in the same order on
he chromosome as the anterior-posterior order of the segments each mutation affects. Thus, *bx* mutations, which affect
nterior T3, lie near the left end of the complex, whereas
bx mutations, which affect posterior T3, lie immediately to
heir right. In turn, *iab-2*, which affects A2, is to the right
f *pbx* but to the left of the A3-determining *iab-3*.

Because the *bx, pbx,* and *iab* elements are indepen-
ently mutable, Lewis thought that each was a separate
ene. However, the molecular characterization of the region
vealed that the BX-C actually contains only three protein-
oding genes: *Ultrabithorax* (*Ubx*), which controls the
dentity of T3; *abdominal-A* (*abd-A*), which controls the
entities of A1–A5; and *Abdominal-B* (*Abd-B*), which con-
ols the identities of A5–A8 (Fig. 18.27). The expression
atterns of these genes are consistent with their roles. *Ubx*
expressed in segments T3–A8 (but most strongly in T3);

abd-A is expressed in A1–A8 (most strongly in A1–A4);
and *Abd-B* is expressed in A5–A8. The *bx, pbx,* and *iab*
mutations studied by Lewis affect large *cis*-regulatory
regions that control the intricate spatial and temporal
expression of these genes within specific segments.

The Antennapedia complex

Genetic studies in the early 1980s showed that a second
homeotic gene cluster, the Antennapedia complex (ANT-C),
specifies the identities of segments in the head and anterior thorax of *Drosophila*. The five homeotic genes of the
ANT-C are *labial* (*lab*), which is expressed in the inter-
calary region; *proboscipedia* (*pb*), expressed in the maxillary and labial segments; *Deformed* (*Dfd*), expressed
in the mandibular and maxillary segments; *Sex combs
reduced* (*Scr*), expressed in the labial and T1 segments;
and *Antennapedia* (*Antp*), expressed mainly in T2, although

it is also active at lower levels in all three thoracic and most abdominal segments. (Figure 18.18c shows these head and thoracic segments, whereas Fig. 18.26 illustrates the order of the homeotic genes in the ANT-C.) As with the BX-C, the order of genes in the ANT-C is the same (with the exception of *pb*) as the order of segments each controls.

The homeodomain in development and evolution

As researchers started to characterize the genes of the ANT-C and the BX-C at the molecular level, they were surprised to find that all of these genes contained some closely related DNA sequences. Similar sequences were also found in many other genes important for development, such as *bicoid* and *eyeless,* that are located outside the homeotic gene complexes. The region of sequence homology, called the **homeobox,** is about 180 bp in length and is located in the protein-coding part of each gene. The 60 amino acids encoded by the homeobox constitute the *homeodomain,* a region of each protein that can bind to DNA (review Fig. 18.11). We now know that almost all proteins containing homeodomains are transcription factors

in which the homeodomain is responsible for the sequence-specific binding of the proteins to the *cis*-acting control sites of the genes they regulate.

Surprisingly, however, DNA-binding studies have shown that most of these homeodomains have very similar binding specificities. The homeodomains of the Antp and Ubx proteins, for example, bind essentially the same DNA sequences. Because different homeotic proteins are thought to regulate specific target genes, this lack of DNA-binding specificity seems paradoxical. Much current research is directed toward understanding how the homeotic proteins target specific genes that dictate different segment identities.

The discovery of the homeobox was one of the most important advances in the history of developmental biology because it allowed scientists to isolate by homology many other genes with roles in the development of *Drosophila* and other organisms. In the late 1980s and 1990s, the biological community was astonished to learn that the mouse and human genomes contain clustered homeobox genes called *Hox* genes with clear homologies to the ANT-C and BX-C genes in *Drosophila* (**Fig. 18.28**). Remarkably, in all mammals studied to date, the genes

Figure 18.28 The mammalian *Hox* genes are organized into four clusters. (a) Mammalian genomes contain multiple homologs of each of the ANT-C and BX-C homeobox genes in *Drosophila.* **(b)** Just as in *Drosophila,* the mammalian (mouse) *Hox* genes in each cluster are arranged in the order they are expressed along the anterior-posterior axis of the embryo. The *colored disks* represent somites—precursors of the vertebrae and other structures. The other colored areas are regions of the central nervous system. The colors represent the *Hox* genes expressed in that tissue.

Figure 18.29 Synpolydactyly caused by mutations in the human *HoxD13* gene.

within these clusters are arranged in a linear order that reflects their expression in particular regions along the spine of developing mammalian embryos (Fig. 18.28). In other words, these gene clusters in mice and humans are arranged in the genome and are regulated along the anterior-posterior axis in almost exactly the same way as the fly ANT-C and BX-C complexes.

As it turns out, all animal genomes, even those of sponges, the most primitive animals, contain *Hox* genes, so these genes are ancient and have played important (though not necessarily identical) roles in the developmental patterns of all animals. Generally, the more complex the body plan, the more *Hox* genes: Humans and other mammals have four *Hox* clusters that together contain 38 *Hox* genes (see Fig. 18.28). In just one demonstration that *Hox* genes mediate the developmental fate of specific regions in the body of animals other than *Drosophila*, it has recently been shown that the malformation of the digits in humans, in a condition called *synpolydactyly*, is caused by mutations in *HoxD13*, one of these 38 *Hox* genes (**Fig. 18.29**).

Homeodomain-containing proteins are transcription factors that often play key roles in the development of multicellular organisms. The genomes of animals contain clusters of *Hox* genes with homeoboxes that encode homeodomains. The particular set of *Hox* genes that is expressed in a segment or region of the embryo helps dictate its eventual developmental fate.

18.5 How Genes Help Control Development

The previously described analysis of *Drosophila* body plan development revealed some of the strategies by which genes control the development of multicellular organisms. These strategies form the basic underpinnings for many diverse developmental pathways in many organisms. Here are highlights of the lessons learned from *Drosophila*.

Development requires sequential changes in gene expression

The enormous diversity of cells within the body of a multicellular organism results in a remarkable variety of cell shapes and functions. Even a single tissue, such as the blood, harbors many different kinds of cells (**Fig. 18.30**).

How do cells that contain the same genes make such varied developmental decisions and become so different? As you saw in the introduction to this chapter, the reason is simple: Different cell types express different, characteristic subsets of genes. It is easy to understand this point when comparing cells whose function depends on the production of a large amount of a particular gene product. Red blood cells produce copious amounts of hemoglobin, the cone and rod cells in our eyes synthesize vast numbers of photoreceptor molecules, and certain pancreatic cells produce insulin and secrete it into the bloodstream. But the biochemical differences between cell types are not restricted to the expression of a single key gene. Instead, the differentiation of these various cells requires changes in the expression of many genes. **Figure 18.31** illustrates how complex these developmental patterns of expression can be. It shows that in *Drosophila* the many different proteins necessary for generating the structure of an adult wing are expressed in very precise, partially overlapping subsets of cells in larval imaginal discs that give rise to the wing.

Figure 18.30 Different types of blood cells. The *red* cells are erythrocytes, the oxygen-carrying red blood cells. The cells colored in *green* are macrophages that ingest and destroy invading microbes. The *yellow* cells are T lymphocytes involved in the immune system. The single *blue* cell is a monocyte, an immature cell that can develop into a macrophage. The colors other than red are computer-generated.

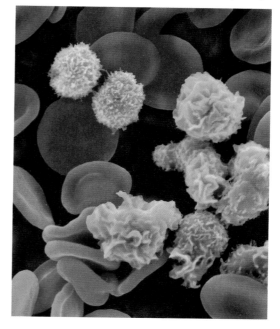

Figure 18.31 Development requires precise control of the expression of many genes. Each imaginal disc was stained with a fluorescently tagged antibody against a different specific protein important for patterning of the wing. Each protein is expressed in a unique set of cells in these imaginal discs.

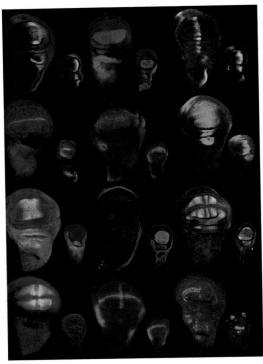

Progressive refinement of cell fate

Differentiation into many types of cells and tissues requires that cells undergo a successive restriction in developmental potential that affects both themselves and their descendents. For example, the two daughter cells of a human zygote can each generate descendents able to fulfill any fate in the adult. But later in development, cells must "decide" whether they and their descendents will adopt one kind of fate (say, that of neurons) or a different kind of fate (say, that of epidermal cells). Once a developmental decision is made, a cell and its descendents embark on a pathway of differentiation that excludes them from an alternative fate.

The hierarchic developmental system that determines the number of segments in *Drosophila* embryos provides a clear example (review Fig. 18.24). The gap genes such as *Krüppel* are expressed in broad regions covering roughly one-quarter to one-third of the embryo, but later, pair-rule genes are expressed in a fashion that subdivides the regions in which each gap gene was expressed. And later still, the segment polarity genes are expressed in even more sharply defined areas.

The key role of transcriptional regulation

The most efficient point at which protein production can be controlled is at the first step: the initiation of transcription.

Indeed, most of the processes that influence cellular fates culminate in decisions to turn on or off the transcription of "target" genes (such as those for hemoglobin) whose expression is important to that cell type (the red blood cell precursor).

We can make this generalization based on three kinds of observations. First, RNA *in situ* hybridization experiments, such as the one shown in Fig. 18.12, demonstrate that the mRNA for many developmentally important genes appears only in certain cells at certain times in development. Second, measurements of mRNA levels in many kinds of differentiated cells using techniques such as microarrays or quantitative PCR show that the levels of almost all proteins in those cells reflect the abundance of the mRNA encoding that protein. Third, many of the genes that play key roles in developmental decision-making encode proteins that function as transcription factors. For example, *bicoid* and most gap and pair-rule genes encode transcription factors. We have also seen that the homeodomain characteristic of proteins like the products of the BX-C and ANT-C genes, as well as other genes such as *eyeless/Pax-6,* allows these proteins to bind to DNA and thus act as regulatory transcription factors. Hierarchies of transcription factors allow an organism to provide its cells with increasingly specific information that guides them to specific fates.

Posttranscriptional gene regulation and development

Although regulation of transcriptional initiation is the most general strategy by which cells control gene expression during development, it is by no means the only one. The progression from gene to protein involves many subsequent steps, each of which is amenable to regulation. In eukaryotes, a gene's primary transcript has to be spliced into a mature mRNA. This mRNA must be translocated from the nucleus into the cytoplasm, and then it must be translated into a protein. The relative stability of an mRNA or protein can affect its concentration in the cell. And finally, once made, a protein can be altered after translation in ways that affect its activity. A number of molecular mechanisms underlying development exploit each of these steps of gene regulation. You saw one case of developmentally important posttranscriptional regulation in the comprehensive example: Bicoid and Nanos, two proteins encoded by maternal-effect genes in *Drosophila,* act as repressors of translation.

The contributions of both maternal and zygotic genes

The earliest stages of development require not only the regulation of the expression of genes in the developing individual's genome but also the regulation of gene expression in the mother's genome. Before fertilization the egg in most organisms already contains many of the mRNAs and proteins needed for the earliest stages of development. The egg must load up on these molecules because transcription of the zygotic genome does not begin immediately after fertilization. In *Drosophila,* for example, transcription of zygotic genes does not usually begin in earnest until the embryo contains roughly 6000 cells and has completed some of the earliest steps determining cell fates.

> During early embryonic development, the fate of cells becomes increasingly narrowed. This differentiation is based on successive changes in gene expression that are mostly, but not exclusively, regulated at the level of transcription. The earliest steps of development require maternal RNAs and proteins that are expressed from the mother's genome and deposited into the egg during oogenesis.

Development exploits asymmetries

For cells to differentiate into different types, they must either be exposed to different signals from their environment or they must be intrinsically biochemically distinct. Nature has used both strategies to guide the differentiation of cell types.

In some species, the egg is inherently asymmetric, providing a way for cells in the early embryo to receive information about their relative position. The *Drosophila* egg cell (the oocyte), for example, is part of a more complicated structure called an *egg chamber* (**Fig. 18.32**). Within the egg chamber, certain cells known as *nurse cells* act as factories that synthesize large amounts of mRNAs and proteins; the nurse cells then deposit these molecules into the oocyte.

Figure 18.32 A *Drosophila* egg chamber. Large nurse cells at the anterior of the egg chamber synthesize mRNA and proteins and transport them to the oocyte. The nurse cells and the oocyte are surrounded by a layer of *follicle cells*. Cell nuclei are in *purple*.

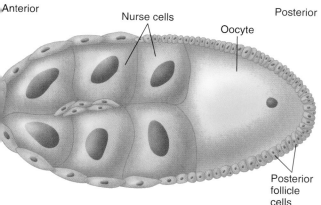

Anterior · Nurse cells · Oocyte · Posterior · Posterior follicle cells

The oocyte has an anterior-to-posterior (that is, head-to-tail) sense of direction in large part because it is connected to the nurse cells only at its anterior end. The mRNA of the *bicoid* gene is transcribed in the nuclei of the nurse cells and then transported into the oocyte. The *bicoid* mRNA, in association with certain proteins that bind to its 3'UTR, appears to become ensnared by microtubules within the egg cell. These microtubules act as tracks along which the mRNA and its associated proteins are transported to the cortex (the cytoplasm just beneath the cell membrane) at the oocyte's anterior end.

In other species, the first asymmetries important for development occur after fertilization. For example, in *C. elegans,* the site at which the sperm enters the egg to effect fertilization defines the posterior end of the embryo. Before fertilization, the egg has no polarity; sperm entry initiates rearrangements of the cytoplasm that establish the anterior-to-posterior axis of the embryo. The asymmetries affecting early mammalian development emerge even later, after four rounds of mitosis have produced a 16-cell embryo.

> In organisms like *Drosophila,* certain maternal RNAs and proteins are concentrated in particular parts of the egg before fertilization. In other organisms, like *C. elegans* or humans, the asymmetries required for differentiation are established after fertilization in response to signals provided by the entering sperm, or to emergent variations in the interactions between embryonic cells.

Cell-to-cell communication is essential for proper development

Construction of a large, complicated multicellular organism depends on more than broad, asymmetric cues such as morphogen gradients. Cells must "talk" to each other to obtain information about their relative positions in the organism. The information obtained from cell-to-cell communication enables cells to refine the decisions that guide their subsequent development.

Cells can communicate with each other either by direct contact or by diffusible factors (usually proteins) released from one cell and received by a second cell. Cell-to-cell communication usually takes place at the surface of the second cell when a ligand made by the signaling cell binds to a receptor embedded in the membrane of the receiving cell. One type of cell-to-cell communication, called *juxtacrine signaling,* takes the form of direct contact. In such signaling, the ligand is a cell surface molecule anchored in the membrane and extending outside of the signaling cell.

Other cellular interactions are mediated by *paracrine factors:* ligands secreted by the signaling cell. Ligands called *hormones,* or *endocrine factors,* circulate throughout the body in the blood and can affect tissues far removed from the gland that produces them. By contrast, some ligands diffuse only over short distances. The reciprocal interactions of *Drosophila* embryonic cells making the Wingless and Hedgehog segment polarity proteins (review Fig. 18.23b) illustrate this kind of short-range paracrine signaling. Both Wingless and Hedgehog are secreted by certain cells, and only nearby cells with appropriate receptors can respond to these ligands.

Figure 18.23b emphasizes another feature common to most kinds of cell-to-cell communication: The binding of the ligand to a cell-surface receptor initiates a signal transduction pathway that culminates in changes to the transcriptional regulation of suites of genes in the receiving cell's nucleus. Different ligand/receptor combinations activate different signal transduction pathways. For example, in Fig. 18.23b, the Smo and Ci proteins participate in the pathway activated by the binding of the Hedgehog ligand to its receptor (Patched), whereas the Dsh, Zw3, and Arm proteins are part of the pathway initiated by the binding of the Wingless ligand to its receptor (Frizzled).

In juxtacrine signaling, two adjacent cells communicate via a surface ligand on one cell that binds a receptor on the second cell. In paracrine signaling, the signaling cell secretes a hormone that can bind to receptors on cells elsewhere in the body. In either case, binding initiates a signal transduction pathway that alters gene expression in the receiving cell.

Genes explain much, but not everything, about development

Throughout this chapter, we have considered cells in developing multicellular organisms as complex computers. These cellular computers integrate a variety of inputs: the cell's history, its location within the organism, signals from neighboring cells, and signals from more distant cells. The outputs of the cellular computer are alterations to the transcription of a large suite of target genes, which determine the developmental fate of the cell. The central processors that convert the inputs into the outputs are located near the promoters of the target genes, where assessment of the combinatorial effects of many transcription factors determines the time and rate of target gene transcription.

This reductionist point of view has been remarkably successful in building our understanding of development. We now have lists of many genes that play important roles in development, and we are beginning to fathom how each of these genes works and how they interact with each other. Particularly remarkable in the

Figure 18.33 "cc," the cloned kitten.

recent past has been our growing appreciation for the way in which evolution has conserved critical genes and pathways, while at the same time creating new twists that underlie the enormous complexity and diversity of life-forms on earth.

Although genes clearly set the ground rules for an individual's development, the same set of genes does not inevitably lead to precisely the same result. Many events in development reflect the strong influence of environmental factors or chance on the execution of the genetic blueprint. For example, the name of the first kitten cloned from an adult cell (**Fig. 18.33**) is "cc" for "carbon copy," but this is somewhat of a misnomer. Though the kitten has exactly the same alleles of all genes as the cat that donated the adult cell, the coats of the two animals are dissimilar due to different prenatal environments.

Chance occurrences often influence expression of the genome as well as cellular behaviors. In mammalian females, for example, the decision of which X chromosome is inactivated in which cell is determined by stochastic (chance) events. Similarly, the choice of which cells adopt particular fates depends on small chance fluctuations in the concentrations of certain ligands and receptors. Finally, the incredibly complex connections between neurons in the developing brain are highly plastic and can be influenced by the environment, particularly through learning.

Chance events and environmental influences can significantly alter the course of the genetically determined programs underlying development.

Connections

This chapter has presented ample evidence for the conservation of genes that play important roles in development. The *eyeless/Pax-6/Aniridia* gene, for example, acts as a master switch to initiate the development of eyes in many types of organisms. Yet the eyes of various species show tremendous differences, from the compound eyes of *Drosophila* to the single camera-like organs of humans.

The themes of conservation and change have been central to our understanding of evolution since Darwin. Evolution creates and then preserves genetic solutions to problems organisms encounter in their development,

biochemistry, physiology, and behavior; but evolution also tinkers with these solutions to produce novel outcomes.

In the next two chapters, we shift our focus from the analysis of gene activity in individuals to an analysis of gene transmission in whole populations and an examination, at the molecular level, of how genes and genomes evolve over time. Chapter 19 describes why an understanding of evolution requires knowledge of gene transmission in populations. Chapter 20 then builds on ideas presented throughout the book to reconstruct the molecular strategies by which genes and genomes have evolved throughout the roughly 4 billion years of life on earth.

ESSENTIAL CONCEPTS

1. Developmental geneticists use model organisms as the basis for studying how a fertilized egg becomes a multicellular adult. The evolutionary relatedness of all organisms often makes it possible to extrapolate from model organisms to all living forms.

2. A key to the genetic dissection of development is the isolation of a comprehensive set of mutations. Loss-of-function mutations are especially useful in revealing genes whose action is critical for normal development, but gain-of-function mutants can also point to genes that participate in developmental processes. RNA interference provides a method to achieve loss of gene function without mutations.

3. Researchers first analyze the role of individual genes in development by characterizing the nature of the gene product, the locations in which the gene is transcribed and in which the protein product of the gene accumulates, and the phenotypes associated with mutations in the gene. Scientists then examine the interactions of multiple genes affecting the same process to elucidate developmental pathways.

4. The construction of genetic mosaics can help determine which cells need to express the gene so that the organism can develop normally.

5. Genetic analysis of the *Drosophila* body plan revealed several basic mechanisms by which genes help control development. A hierarchy of segmentation genes subdivides the body into an array of body segments; the expression of homeotic genes assigns a unique identity to each segment.

6. Cellular differentiation requires progressive changes in gene expression. These changes usually, but not always, result from decisions concerning the transcription of batteries of genes. The earliest stages of development require control of gene expression in both the maternal and zygotic genomes.

7. Differentiation requires either that cells have intrinsic differences at the biochemical level or that they are exposed to different information in their environment. Asymmetries in early embryonic development or in the distribution of molecules during cell division can generate intrinsic differences. Cell-to-cell communication, effected by the binding of ligands to receptors and mediated by signal transduction pathways, supplies cells with information about their position in the organism.

On Our Website   www.mhhe.com/hartwell4

Annotated Suggested Readings and Links to Other Websites

- Historical articles by Nüsslein-Volhard, Wieschaus, Lewis, and others, reporting their pathbreaking work on the development of the *Drosophila* embryo

- Links to images, databases, and interactive sites depicting details of *Drosophila* development

Specialized Topics

- Genetic portraits: Many of the fundamental findings in the genetics of development have depended on genetic manipulations specific to particular organisms. Our website contains chapter-length "genetic portraits" that discuss experimental techniques and key findings for the five most intensively investigated model organisms: the yeast *Saccharomyces cerevisiae,* the weedy plant *Arabidopsis thaliana,* the worm *Caenorhabditis elegans,* the fruit fly *Drosophila melanogaster,* and the house mouse *Mus musculus.*

- More on the genetic analysis of development: a description of advanced techniques for the discovery and analysis of genes important to development

Problems

Vocabulary

1. Match each of the terms in the left column to the best-fitting phrase from the right column.

a. mosaic determination	1. divide the body into identical units (segments)
b. regulative determination	2. initiated by the binding of ligand to receptor
c. haploinsufficiency	3. individuals with cells of more than one genotype
d. RNAi	4. the fate of early embryonic cells can be altered by the environment
e. ectopic expression	5. assign identity to body segments
f. homeodomain	6. substance whose concentration determines cell fates
g. green fluorescent protein	7. suppression of gene expression by double-stranded RNA
h. genetic mosaics	8. when a null allele is dominant to a wild-type allele
i. segmentation genes	9. a DNA-binding motif found in certain transcription factors
j. homeotic genes	10. encode proteins that accumulate in unfertilized eggs and are needed for embryo development
k. morphogen	11. early embryonic cells are assigned specific fates
l. maternal effect genes	12. a gene is turned on in an inappropriate tissue or at the wrong time
m. signal transduction pathways	13. a tag used to follow proteins in living cells

Section 18.1

2. a. If you were interested in the role of a particular gene in the embryonic development of the human heart, why would you probably study this role in a model organism, and which model organism(s) would you choose?

   b. If you were interested in finding new genes that might be required for human heart development, why would you try to find these genes in a model organism, and which model organism(s) would you choose?

3. Early *C. elegans* embryos display mosaic determination, whereas early mouse embryos exhibit regulative determination. Predict the results you would expect if the following treatments were performed on four-cell

embryos of each of these two species (assuming these manipulations could actually be performed):

a. A laser is used to destroy one of the four cells (this technique is called *laser ablation*).

b. The four cells of the embryo are separated from each other and allowed to develop.

c. The cells from two different four-celled embryos are fused together to make an eight-celled embryo.

Sections 18.2 and 18.3

Problems 4–7 concern a *Drosophila* gene called *rugose* (*rg*). Adult flies homozygous for recessive mutations in this gene have rough eyes in which the regular pattern of the eye segments called *ommatidia* is disrupted. The scanning electron micrographs below contrast the smooth eyes of wild-type flies on the *left* with the rough eyes of *rugose* mutants on the *right*. The disruption of the eye segment pattern is caused by the absence of one or more so-called *cone cells* from ommatidia; in the wild type, each ommatidium has four cone cells.

4. In 1932, H. J. Muller suggested a genetic test to determine whether a particular mutation whose phenotypic effects are recessive to wild type is a null (*amorphic*) or hypomorphic allele of a gene. Muller's test was to compare the phenotype of homozygotes for the recessive mutant alleles to the phenotype of a heterozygote in which one chromosome carries the recessive mutation in question and the homologous chromosome carries a deletion for a large region including the gene. In a recent study utilizing Muller's test, investigators examined two mutant alleles of *rugose* named rg^{41} and $rg^{\gamma3}$. The eye phenotypes displayed by flies of several genotypes is indicated in the following

table. *Df(1)JC70* is a large deletion that removes *rugose* and several genes to either side of it.

Genotype	Eye surface	Cone cells per ommatidium
wild type	smooth	4
rg^{41} / rg^{41}	mildly rough	2–3
$rg^{41} / Df(1)JC70$	moderately rough	1–2
$rg^{\gamma3} / rg^{\gamma3}$	very rough	0–1
$rg^{\gamma3} / Df(1)JC70$	very rough	0–1

a. Which allele (rg^{41} or $rg^{\gamma3}$) is "stronger" (that is, which causes the more severe phenotype)?

b. Which allele directs the production of higher levels of functional Rugose protein?

c. How would Muller's test discriminate between a null allele and a hypomorphic allele? Suggest a theoretical explanation for Muller's test. Based on the results shown in the table, is either of these two mutations likely to be a null allele of *rugose?* If so, which one?

5. The molecular identity of the fruit fly *rugose* gene is now known. cDNA clones corresponding to the *rugose* gene mRNA and antibodies that recognize the Rugose protein are also available. Outline several alternatives to the approach described in Problem 4 that might help you decide whether a newly discovered recessive allele of *rugose* is a null or a hypomorphic mutation.

6. In a *Drosophila* population of genotype $rg^{\gamma3}/rg^{\gamma3}$, it was noticed that about 35% of fertilized eggs develop into defective embryos that are unable to hatch into larvae. In contrast, only about 3% of fertilized wild-type eggs fail to develop into larvae.

a. In the light of this information as well as the data presented in Problem 4, predict which fly tissues at which stages of development require the function of the Rugose protein. (Note: The eyes of adult *Drosophila* are not pre-formed in embryos or larvae; instead, they develop from sacs of tissue in larvae called *imaginal discs.*)

b. How could you determine whether the *rugose* gene was expressed in the tissues you predicted in part *a*? Does the expression of the gene in those tissues establish that the Rugose protein plays an essential function there?

7. The *rugose* gene (*rg*) is located about midway between the centromere and telomere of the acrocentric *Drosophila* X chromosome. The *white* gene for eye color is located near the X chromosome telomere; the dominant w^+ allele specifies red color in eye cells, whereas w^- causes eye cells to be white. Mitotic recombination like that shown in Fig. 5.24 on p. 147 can be induced by exposing *Drosophila* larvae to X-rays.

a. Scientists can use mitotic recombination to create adult flies with mosaic eyes in which some eye cells would be simultaneously homozygous for mutant alleles of *rugose* and *white*, whereas the other cells in the eye would be heterozygous for the mutant and wild type alleles of both genes. Diagram an arrangement of mutant and wild type alleles of these two genes that would create such mosaic eyes upon X-ray-induced mitotic recombination.

b. How could you use this system of mitotic recombination to determine whether the lack of the Rugose protein in one ommatidium might affect the proper development of an adjacent ommatidium?

c. Suppose for the sake of argument that all animals homozygous for a true null mutation of *rugose* would die as embryos. How could you use this system of mitotic recombination to determine the effect of a complete lack of the Rugose protein on development of the adult eye?

Problems 8–11 concern a recombinant DNA construct called *myo-2::GFP* that *C. elegans* developmental geneticists have transformed into worms. Worms containing this construct express green fluorescent protein (GFP) in their pharynx, as shown in the following picture. The pharynx is an organ located between the mouth and the gut that grinds up the bacteria *C. elegans* eats so that these bacteria can be used as a food source. The *myo-2::GFP* construct was made by cloning the open reading frame for jellyfish GFP downstream of the promoter for *myo-2*, a gene that is specifically expressed in the muscle cells of the pharynx.

8. a. Explain how you could use worms transformed with *myo-2::GFP* to find mutations that disrupt the structure of the pharynx.

b. Nematodes homozygous for loss-of-function mutations in a gene called *pha-4* have no detectable pharyngeal structures. What do you think will be the fate of these worms?

c. How could you use *myo-2::GFP* to determine if *pha-4* is a master regulatory gene that directs development of the pharynx in a manner similar to the way *Pax-6/eyeless* controls eye development?

9. How could you use the pictured *myo-2::GFP* construct to find out what DNA sequence elements in the *myo-2* gene promoter are required for the pharynx-specific expression of the *myo-2* gene?

10. Suppose you wanted to determine whether a particular gene *X* was important for specification of the pharynx, but mutations in this same gene disrupt embryonic development well before pharyngeal structures appear. How could you use *myo-2::GFP*, the *myo-2* promoter, the DNA sequence of gene *X,* and your knowledge of RNA interference (RNAi) to generate worms that lack gene *X* expression in the pharynx but express gene *X* in all other tissues in which it is expressed in wild-type *C. elegans?*

11. The procedure normally used to transform *C. elegans* involves injection of DNA into the gonads of hermaphrodites. The DNA is incorporated into oocytes, but the injected DNA molecules usually recombine with each other, forming extrachromosomal arrays. These extrachromosomal arrays can be lost during mitosis at a low frequency, producing cells that lack the arrays. How could you use *myo-2::GFP* to create nematodes with mosaic pharynxes, such that some cells are homozygous for null mutations of gene *X* while other cells in the same pharynx have gene *X* activity? (Assume that null mutations and the genomic DNA of gene *X* are both available.)

12. Figure 18.5 on p. 622 shows how scientists can knock out any gene in mice using homologous recombination. An alternative and technically much simpler methodology to manipulate the mouse genome is an "add-on" strategy in which DNA is injected into a pronucleus of a fertilized egg, and the injected one-cell embryo is placed into an oviduct of a receptive female. In this add-on strategy, the injected DNA will integrate into various locations in the genome at random. For each of the following situations, indicate whether it would be preferable to use a knockout or add-on strategy, and explain both your decision and how you would employ the technology of your choice.
   a. You want to create a mouse model of a human genetic disease in which a particular missense mutation has a recessive deleterious effect on development.
   b. You want to create a mouse model of a human genetic disease in which a particular missense mutation has a dominant deleterious effect on development.
   c. You want to explore the potential effects of the ectopic expression of a gene in a tissue in which it is normally not expressed.
   d. You want to explore the potential deleterious haplo-insufficient effects of the deletion of a gene.

   e. You want to explore the potential deleterious effects of homozygosity for the deletion of a particular gene.
   f. You want to explore the potential effects of the absence of gene function associated with the expression of a dominant-negative allele of a gene.
   g. You want to suppress the function of a particular gene by RNA interference.
   h. You want to find *cis*-acting regulatory sequences that cause a certain gene to be expressed only in particular tissues.
   i. You want to prove that a polymorphism you have detected in the DNA of a particular candidate gene is responsible for a specific phenotype of abnormal development seen in mutant animals. (Assume that the mutation actually causing the phenotype is associated with a loss of function, but consider mutations that are recessive or dominant to wild type separately.)

13. As explained in Problem 12, when the "add-on" strategy is used to create transgenic mice, the injected DNA can insert at random into any chromosome. Subsequent matings produce animals homozygous for the transgene insertion, and sometimes an interesting developmental phenotype is generated by the insertion event itself. In one case, after injection of DNA containing the mouse mammary tumor virus (MMTV) promoter fused to the *c-myc* gene, investigators identified a recessive mutation that causes limb deformity. In this mouse, the distal bones were reduced and fused together; the mutation also caused kidney malfunction.
   a. The mutant phenotype could be due to insertion of the MMTV/*c-myc* transgene in a particular region of the chromosome or a chance point mutation that arose in the mouse. How could you distinguish between these two possibilities?
   b. The mutation in this example was in fact caused by insertion of the transgene. How could you use this transgene insertion as a tag for cloning and identifying a gene important for development?
   c. The insertion mutation was mapped to chromosome 2 of mice in a region where a mutation called limb deformity (*ld*) had previously been identified. Mice carrying this mutation are available from a major mouse research laboratory. How could you tell if the *ld* mutation was in the same gene as the transgenic insertion mutation?

Section 18.4

14. Which of the following is not a property of the *hunchback* gene in *Drosophila?*
   a. The *hunchback* mRNA is uniformly distributed in the egg by the mother.

b. Transcription of *hunchback* is enhanced by Bicoid (the anterior morphogen).

c. Translation of the *hunchback* mRNA is inhibited by Nanos (the posterior morphogen).

d. The Hunchback protein eventually is distributed in a gradient (anterior high; posterior low).

e. Hunchback protein directs the distribution of *bicoid* mRNA.

15. The *hunchback* gene contains a promoter region, the structural region (the amino acid coding sequence), and a 3′ untranslated region (DNA that will be transcribed into sequences appearing at the 3′ end of the mRNA that are not translated into amino acids).

a. What important sequences required to control *hunchback* gene expression are found in the promoter region of *hunchback?*

b. What sequence elements that encode specific protein domains are found in the structural region of *hunchback?*

c. There is another important kind of sequence that turns out to be located in the part of the gene transcribed as the 3′UTR (untranslated region) of the *hunchback* mRNA. What might this sequence do?

16. How do the segment polarity genes differ in their mode of action from the gap and pair-rule genes?

17. One important demonstration that Bicoid is an anterior determinant came from injection experiments analogous to those done by early embryologists. Injection experiments involve introduction of components such as cytoplasm from an egg or mRNA that is synthesized *in vitro* into the egg by direct injection. Describe injection experiments that would demonstrate that Bicoid is the anterior determinant.

18. In flies developing from eggs laid by a *nanos⁻* mother, development of the abdomen is inhibited. Flies developing from eggs that have no maternally supplied *hunchback* mRNA are normal. Flies developing from eggs laid by a *nanos⁻* mother that also have no maternally supplied *hunchback* mRNA are normal. If there is too much Hunchback protein in the posterior of the egg, abdominal development is prevented.

a. What do these findings say about the function of the Nanos protein and of the *hunchback* maternally supplied mRNA?

b. What do these findings say about the efficiency of evolution?

19. Mutant embryos lacking the gap gene *knirps* (*kni*) are stained at the syncytial blastoderm stage to examine the distributions of the Hunchback and Krüppel proteins. The results of the *knirps⁻* and wild-type embryos stained for the Hunchback and Krüppel proteins is shown schematically on the following figure.

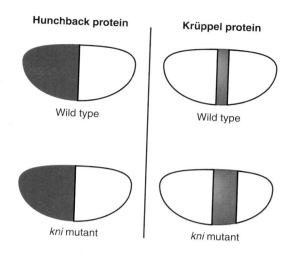

Hunchback protein   **Krüppel protein**

Wild type   Wild type

kni mutant   *kni* mutant

a. Based on these results, what can you conclude about the relationships among these three genes?

b. Would the pattern of Hunchback protein in embryos from a *nanos⁻* mutant mother differ from that shown? If yes, describe the difference and explain why. If not, explain why not.

20. In *Drosophila* with loss-of-function mutations affecting the *Ubx* gene, transformations of body segments are always in the anterior direction. That is, in *bx* mutants, the anterior compartment of T3 is transformed into the anterior compartment of T2, whereas in *pbx* mutants, the posterior part of T3 is transformed into the posterior compartment of T2. In wild type, the *Ubx* gene itself is expressed in T3–A8, but most strongly in T3.

a. The *Abd-B* gene is transcribed in segments A5–A8. Assuming the mode of function of *Abd-B* is the same as that of *Ubx*, what is the likely consequence of homozygosity for a null allele of *Abd-B* (that is, what segment transformations would you expect to see)?

b. Because *Abd-A* is expressed in segments A1–A8, there is some transcription of all three genes of the BX-C (*Ubx, Abd-A,* and *Abd-B*) in segments A5–A8. Why then are segments A5, A6, A7, and A8 morphologically distinguishable?

c. What segment transformations would you expect to see in an animal deleted for all three genes of the BX-C (*Ubx, Abd-A,* and *Abd-B*)?

d. Certain *contrabithorax* mutations in the BX-C cause transformations of wing to haltere. Propose an explanation for this phenotype based on the transcription of the *Ubx* gene in particular segments. Do you anticipate that *contrabithorax* mutations would be dominant or recessive to wild type? Explain.

e. During wild-type development, *Antp* is expressed in T1, T2, and T3, but most strongly in T2 and only weakly in T3. In animals with *Ubx* null mutations,

Antp is expressed at much higher levels in T3 as compared with wild type. In animals with deletions that remove both *Ubx* and *Abd-A*, *Antp* is expressed at high levels in T2, T3, and abdominal segments A1–A5. In animals with deletions that remove all three genes of the BX-C, *Antp* is expressed in T2, T3, and abdominal segments A1–A8. Given that the three genes of the BX-C encode proteins with homeodomains, suggest a model that explains how these genes dictate segment identity.

Section 18.5

21. If you were searching for mutations that affect early embryonic development in a model organism that had not been previously studied, why would you need to conduct separate genetic screens for genes encoding maternally supplied components and for genes whose transcription begins only after fertilization? What kinds of screens would you employ in both cases?

22. The unfertilized eggs of *C. elegans* have no predetermined anterior or posterior end. The polarity of the embryo instead depends on the site of sperm entry, which becomes the posterior end. Very soon after fertilization, so-called PAR (for "partitioning") proteins, which are uniformly distributed in unfertilized eggs, become localized to the embryonic cortex (the layer of cytoplasm just under the cell membrane) at one or the other end of the embryo. The following figure shows the distribution of two of these proteins, PAR-2 (which becomes localized to the posterior cortex) and PAR-3 (which goes to the anterior cortex). After the redistribution of these proteins has been achieved, the zygote divides so as to produce a two-cell embryo with an anterior cell and a posterior cell.

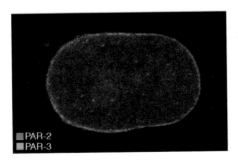

    PAR-2
    PAR-3

    a. How do these findings help explain why the early development of *C. elegans* embryos display mosaic, rather than regulative, determination?
    b. Mutations in the *par-2* or *par-3* genes cause the arrest of development in early embryonic stages. Would you be more likely to find mutations in these genes in screens looking for maternal-effect genes or in screens for zygotic genes?

    c. In zygotes produced by hermaphrodite mothers homozygous for loss-of-function *par-2* alleles, the PAR-3 protein is distributed uniformly around the cortex; the same is true of the PAR-2 protein in zygotes made by *par-3* mutant hermaphrodites. What does this information say about the establishment of early polarity in *C. elegans*?

23. At the end of two rounds of mitosis, the *C. elegans* embryo has four cells named ABa, ABp, P$_2$, and EMS (see the following figure). The ABa and ABp cells are originally developmentally equivalent, but they become different as a result of interactions between ABp and P$_2$ that involve two proteins called GLP-1 and APX-1, as shown in the figure. Both GLP-1 and APX-1 are membrane bound, with domains that lie outside of the cell. GLP-1 is expressed around the entire surface of ABa and ABp, whereas APX-1 is found at the membrane junction between ABp and P$_2$ as shown in the figure.

Key: ▬▬▬ GLP-1 protein
     ▬▬▬ APX-1 protein

ABa   ABp

P$_2$

EMS

    a. The mRNA for *glp-1* is found in all four cells, but the GLP-1 protein is found only in ABa and ABp. In light of your answer to Problem 22, provide an explanation for this observation.
    b. Based on the information in the figure, suggest a hypothesis to explain the localization of APX-1 in only one region of the membrane of the P$_2$ cell.
    c. Assuming that the effect of these proteins on the fate of ABp is caused by a signal transduction pathway, which of the two proteins GLP-1 and APX-1 is likely to be a ligand, and which a receptor for this ligand?
    d. Describe the effects on the fate of the ABp cell of the following: (i) Laser ablation of the P$_2$ cell; (ii) a null mutation in the *apx-1* gene; (iii) a null mutation in the *glp-1* gene; (iv) a null mutation in a gene encoding a component of the signal transduction pathway initiated by binding of the ligand to its receptor. (Assume here that the mutations in part ii–iv only affect the fate of the ABp cell and no other processes in the early nematode embryo.)

Variation and Selection in Populations

The enormous range of genetic diversity within our own species is easy to see.

Tuberculosis (TB) is an ancient and persistent human disease. Bone deformities typical of those produced by the infection are found in Egyptian mummies dating to 2000–4000 B.C.; and as recently as the mid–nineteenth century, TB was the leading cause of death in Europe and the urban United States. The microbe that causes TB is the bacterium *Mycobacterium tuberculosis.* In humans, populations of *M. tuberculosis* most often infect the lungs and lymph nodes, but sometimes they colonize the bones and skin of a patient (**Fig. 19.1a**). *M. tuberculosis* bacteria can spread from person to person through the air when an infected individual exhales bacteria from his or her lungs during coughing.

Beginning in the late nineteenth century, improved sanitation and the quarantine of TB patients led to a steady decline in the death rate from TB in Europe and the United States (**Fig. 19.1b**). The introduction of antibiotics during the 1940s and 1950s further reduced TB mortality in those areas, and by the 1960s, many people believed that the disease had been eradicated, at least in the United States. But 25 years later, the incidence of TB began to rise in urban areas around the globe. By 2000, TB accounted for more deaths worldwide than any other identifiable infectious disease, claiming close to 3 million lives annually. Three factors contributed to this rapid increase in TB incidence: the emergence of AIDS, which weakens the human immune system; protein deficiencies among the malnourished; and the widespread occurrence of *M. tuberculosis* strains that are resistant to one or more antibiotics.

Despite the cultural, technological, and medical advances of the twentieth century, infectious microorganisms such as *M. tuberculosis* are still among the leading causes of death in many human populations. And in a related arena, populations of plant pests (such as the mites that prey on strawberry plants and almond trees) destroy a substantial fraction of human food supplies.

How do new diseases emerge in human populations? Why do diseases persist in all living organisms? What causes diseases and pests long under control to resurge in frequency and intensity?

CHAPTER OUTLINE

- 19.1 The Hardy-Weinberg Law: Predicting Genetic Variation in Populations
- 19.2 Causes of Allele Frequency Changes
- 19.3 Analyzing Quantitative Variation

Figure 19.1 Tuberculosis in human populations. (a) Photograph of *M. tuberculosis* bacteria colonizing the lungs and bones. **(b)** Death rate from tuberculosis in the United States from 1900–2000.

(a)

(b)

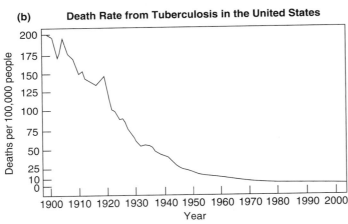

Prior to 1933 data are for only areas with death-registration; after 1933 data are for entire U.S.

One way to answer these questions is to examine genetic variation and its expression as phenotypes within populations of organisms. The scientific discipline that studies what happens in whole populations at the genetic level is known as **population genetics.** It encompasses the evolutionary ideas of Darwin, the laws of Mendel, and the insights of molecular biology.

In this chapter, we explore the nature of genotypic and phenotypic variation within populations and the role of this variation in evolution. We know from Chapter 2 that variation exists in all populations. To begin, we analyze the incidence of genetic diseases, such as cystic fibrosis and retinoblastoma, that are determined by a single gene. Through our analysis, we develop a framework for understanding how the frequency of a disease-causing allele determines the frequency of diseased individuals in a population. We next examine the effects of population size and chance on changes in allele frequency.

Finally, we consider variation in multifactorial traits, that is, in traits determined by two or more genes and their interaction with the environment (see Chapter 3). In fact, most aspects of disease susceptibility are multifactorial.

One general theme emerges from our discussion: Population geneticists rely on mathematical models in predicting a population's potential for stasis or change because most of the scientifically useful questions they ask are statistical. Simple mathematical models not only clarify the questions about frequency of genetic diseases or rate of spread of pathogens, but, they also serve as tools for analyzing data and making predictions about future populations.

19.1 The Hardy-Weinberg Law: Predicting Genetic Variation in Populations

Modern genetics began with Mendel's elucidation of formal rules of probability that describe the likelihood of transmission of genes and traits from parents to offspring in controlled breeding experiments. In this section, we describe an extension of Mendel's work that provides researchers with genetic tools for predicting transmission frequencies of traits and alleles in natural populations having an unlimited size.

Population geneticists describe populations with well-defined terms

To population geneticists, a **population** is a group of interbreeding individuals of the same species that inhabit the same space at the same time. An example would be all the white-tailed deer on Angel Island in San Francisco Bay in 1990 or all the rock cod at the mouth of the bay. The sum total of all alleles carried in all members of a population is that population's **gene pool.** In nature, the genetic makeup of a population changes over time as new alleles arise by mutation or are introduced by immigration and as rare, preexisting alleles disappear when all individuals carrying them leave the population or die. Changes in the frequency of alleles within a population are the basis of **microevolution:** alterations of a population's gene pool.

Suppose you were to look at a human population of 20 in which 4 people have blue-colored eyes because they are homozygous for the *B* allele at a particular "blue eyes" locus, where the alternative allele is *A*. To predict how the number of blue-eyed individuals in the population will change over time, you need to determine the frequencies of each genotype (homozygous *AA*, heterozygous *AB*, and homozygous *BB*), each phenotype (dark eyes and blue eyes), and each allele (*A* and *B*). Population geneticists define **phenotype frequency** as the proportion of individuals in a population that express a particular phenotype. For our hypothetical population, the phenotype frequencies are 4/20 = 20% blue eyes (the number of homozygous *BB* individuals expressing the recessive trait) and 16/20 = 80% dark-eyed (the remaining fraction with either *AA* or *AB* genotypes).

Genotype frequencies

Genotype frequency is the proportion of total individuals in a population that carry a particular genotype. To determine genotype frequencies, you simply count the number of individuals of each genotype and divide by the total number of individuals in the population (**Fig. 19.2a and b**). For recessive traits such as blue eyes, it is not possible to distinguish between homozygous dark eyes and heterozygous genotypes: Both give rise to individuals with dark eyes. Thus, the only way to determine genotype frequencies directly is to use a molecular assay that distinguishes between the different alleles. For our hypothetical population, molecular analyses showed that 12 individuals (of 20) are of genotype *AA*, 4 are of genotype *AB*, and 4 are *BB*. This means that the *AA* genotype frequency is 12/20 = 0.6; the *AB* genotype frequency is 4/20 = 0.2; and the *BB* genotype frequency is also 0.2. Note that these three frequencies (0.6 + 0.2 + 0.2) sum to 1, the totality of genotypes in the whole population.

Allele frequency

The definition of **allele frequency** is the proportion of gene copies in a whole population that are of a given allele type. (Initially, population geneticists used the term "gene frequency" to describe what is now more accurately called "allele frequency." Because each individual in a population has two copies of each chromosome, the total number of gene copies is two times the number of individuals in the population. Thus, for our hypothetical population of 20 people, there would be 40 gene copies or chromosomes. Of course, both homozygotes and heterozygotes contribute to the frequency of an allele. But homozygotes contribute to the frequency of a particular allele twice, while heterozygotes contribute only once (Fig. 19.2b). To find the frequencies of *A* and *B*,

you first use the number of people with each genotype to compute the number of *A* and *B* alleles.

$$12\ AA \rightarrow 24 \text{ copies of } A$$
$$4\ AB \rightarrow 4 \text{ copies of } A$$
$$4\ BB \rightarrow 0 \text{ copies } A$$

Together, 24 + 4 + 0 = 28 copies of the *A* allele. Similarly,

$$12\ AA \rightarrow 0 \text{ copies of } B$$
$$4\ AB \rightarrow 4 \text{ copies of } B$$
$$4\ BB \rightarrow 8 \text{ copies of } B$$

Together, 0 + 4 + 8 = 12 copies of the *B* allele. Next, you add the 28 *A* alleles to the 12 *B* alleles to find the total number of chromosome copies.

28 + 12 = 40 copies of the gene, which is twice the number of people in the population

Finally, you divide the number of each allele by the total number of gene copies to find the proportion, or frequency, for each allele.

For the *A* allele, it is 28/40 = 0.7
For the *B* allele, it is 12/40 = 0.3

Note that here again, the frequencies sum to a 1, representing all the alleles in the gene pool.

Gene pool

A gene pool is not a real material object. It is, rather, a conceptual term used by population geneticists. A **gene pool** represents all of the alleles present on the chromosomes of all members of a population and the relative prominence or rareness of each allele. Although an individual diploid organism can carry, at most, two alleles at a locus, a whole population of *N* individuals could, in theory, have a locus-specific gene pool of up to 2*N* alleles (Fig. 19.2a). In reality, the allele number is much smaller than 2*N* because nearly all children inherit unchanged alleles from their parents. A population is defined by its allele frequencies and genotype frequencies, which together make up a gene pool. The precise frequency measurements of a gene pool are fleeting, constantly changing over time as population components (that is, individual organisms) come into, or pass out of, existence.

The human cystic fibrosis transmembrane receptor (*CFTR*) locus provides an interesting example of a gene pool that is broad—with many disease-causing alleles— but shallow in the sense that none of these alleles are present at a very high frequency. Over 1600 disease-causing mutations have been identified in the genomes of individuals who express cystic fibrosis (**Fig. 19.2c**). The combined frequency of all disease-causing alleles is 0.02, which is quite small compared to the 0.98 frequency of the functional class of *CFTR* alleles.

Figure 19.2 From genotype frequencies to allele frequencies to genotype frequencies. (a) A first-generation population of 20 individuals who are each homozygous or heterozygous for alleles A and/or B at a locus. **(b)** Whole population numbers for genotypes and alleles at single locus of interest. **(c)** Gene pool of alleles at the *CFTR* locus in European-American populations. The structure of the *CFTR* gene is not drawn to scale; introns are much larger proportionally than shown. At the level of DNA sequence, thousands of nonfunctional biallelic SNP and InDel variants have been identified at this locus like all others (locations shown in the Seq. Var. row). Nonfunctional alleles are generally ignored in studies focused on disease phenotypes. The rows labeled missense, nonsense, frameshift, in-frame in/del, splicing, and promoter show the locations of mutations that affect each of these aspects of gene expression and CFTR protein structure and function.

One particular mutant allele, called ΔF508 because it deletes amino acid codon number 508, a phenylalanine (F) in normal CFTR polypeptides, accounts for approximately 70% of the total disease-causing chromosomes. This value corresponds to an individual allele frequency of 0.014; no other cystic fibrosis disease allele has a frequency of greater than 0.001. In contrast, other loci, like the genetic determinant of eye color that we will discuss shortly, have allelic forms that predominate in some human populations but are absent from others.

The scientific endeavor of genetics can be divided into subfields based on the unit object that is the focus of a geneticist's attention. To molecular geneticists, the unit entity is "the gene." To formal geneticists, the unit entity is the individual organism, which is defined by genotypes. To population geneticists, the unit entity is the population consisting of a group of interbreeding organisms.

Although an actual gene pool can only be determined empirically by counting all of its constituent alleles (which

is nearly impossible to do for a large wild population), population geneticists have developed analytical and computational models for estimating the genetic and phenotypic variations of a population and how they may change over time. The foundation for all of the more sophisticated models lies within the Hardy-Weinberg law that we discuss next.

The Hardy-Weinberg law is a binomial equation that correlates allele and genotype frequencies

Many rare diseases result from recessive disease-causing alleles. For scientists seeking to predict the potential incidence of such recessive conditions, an important question is, How common are the heterozygous carriers of the disease-causing allele in a population? At the start, the scientists know only the phenotypic frequencies of healthy and diseased individuals. Can they use this information to predict the frequency of heterozygous carriers?

The key to answering this question lies in establishing a quantitative relationship between phenotype, genotype, and allele frequencies within a population. The **Hardy-Weinberg law,** named for the two men—G. H. Hardy and W. Weinberg—who independently developed it in 1908, clarifies the relationships between genotype and allele frequencies within a generation and from one generation to the next. The derivation of this general law requires certain simplifying assumptions:

1. The population is composed of a very large number of individuals that, for all intents and purposes, is infinite.
2. An individual's genotype at the locus of interest has no influence on his or her choice of a mate—that is, mating is random.
3. No new mutations appear in the gene pool.
4. No migration takes place into or out of the population.
5. Different genotypes at the locus of interest have no impact on the ability to survive to reproductive age and transmit genes to the next generation.

The assumptions behind the Hardy-Weinberg equilibrium enable the mathematical derivation of an equation for predicting genotype (and thence phenotype) frequencies for a population of diploid individuals. Of course, no actual population is in perfect Hardy-Weinberg equilibrium. All populations are finite; alternative genotypes can make a difference in mating, mutations occur constantly; migration into and out of a population is common; and many genotypes of interest, such as those that cause diseases, affect the ability to survive or reproduce. Nevertheless, even when many of the assumptions of the Hardy-Weinberg equilibrium do not apply, the equation derived on the basis of these assumptions is remarkably robust at providing estimates of genotype and phenotype frequencies in real populations over a limited number of breeding generations. Furthermore, the reverse situation, where allele frequencies are found to be inconsistent with a Hardy-Weinberg equilibrium, can sometimes provide scientists with insight into special biological properties of the locus in question or the population as a whole. Indeed, the equation has always been the most powerful mathematical tool available to population geneticists.

Predicting frequencies from one generation to the next

For a population of sexually reproducing diploid organisms, two steps are needed in translating the genotype frequencies of one generation into the genotype frequencies of the next generation (**Fig. 19.2**).

First, if the likelihood that an individual will grow into an adult does not depend on the genotype (that is, if there is no difference in fitness among individuals), then the allele frequencies in the adults should be the same as in their gametes. For example, if p is the frequency of allele A, and q is the frequency of allele B in the adults, p and q will also be the frequencies of the two alleles in the combination of gametes produced by the whole population of those adults.

Second, the allele frequencies in the gametes can be used to calculate genotype frequencies in the zygotes of the next generation. An enhanced version of the Punnett square, which provides a systematic means of considering all possible combinations of uniting gametes, is the tool of choice (Fig. 19.2b). For example, if fertilization is random among individuals with any genotype and if the population of gametes is very large, then the following pattern emerges. Recall that AA zygotes result from fertilization of A-carrying eggs by A-carrying sperm. If p is the frequency of A gametes (eggs and sperm), then, applying the product rule, the frequency of AA zygotes is p (frequency of A eggs) $\times$ p (frequency of A sperm) $= p^2$. Similarly, BB zygotes result from fertilization of B-carrying eggs by B-carrying sperm. If q is the frequency of B gametes (eggs and sperm), the frequency of BB zygotes will be q (the frequency of B eggs) $\times$ q (the frequency of B sperm) $= q^2$. Finally, AB zygotes result either from fertilization of A eggs by B sperm, with a frequency of $p \times q = pq$, or from the fertilization of B eggs by A sperm, occurring at a frequency of $q \times p = pq$. The total frequency of AB zygotes is thus $pq + pq = 2pq$.

The resemblance of the Hardy-Weinberg square shown in **Fig. 19.3** to the Punnett square that we encountered in the visual representation of formal genetics is not a coincidence. The top and left sides of the Punnett square were divided into sectors representing the frequency of each genetically distinct class of sperm or egg produced by two individual parents. But to population geneticists, individual organisms are not significant. Instead, its the gametes produced by the population as a whole that matters.

In parallel to the Punnett square, the Hardy-Weinberg square represents a metaphorical mixture of sperm

Figure 19.3 Gametes and offspring of first-generation individuals.

(p): frequency of allele "A" = 0.7
(q): frequency of allele "B" = 0.3

		eggs	
		p	q
		0.7	0.3
sperm	p 0.7	"AA" 49%	"AB" 21%
	q 0.3	"AB" 21%	"BB" 9%

homozygote "AA" = p^2 = 0.49
homozygote "BB" = q^2 = 0.09
heterozygote "AB" = 2(pq) = 0.42
1.00

produced by all breeding males along one side, and a mixture of eggs produced by all breeding females along the second side.

To summarize: The genotype frequencies of zygotes arising in a large population of sexually reproducing diploid organisms are p^2 for AA, $2pq$ for AB, and q^2 for BB (see Fig. 19.2b). These genotype frequencies are known as the Hardy-Weinberg proportions; they exist in populations that satisfy the Hardy-Weinberg assumptions of a large number of individuals, mating at random, with no new mutations, no migration, and no genotype-dependent differences in fitness. Since these genotype frequencies represent the totality of genotypes in the population, they must sum to 1. Thus the binomial equation representing the Hardy-Weinberg proportions is

$$p^2 + 2pq + q^2 = 1 \qquad (19.1)$$

Because we have assumed no differences in fitness, the genotype frequencies of the zygotes will be the genotype frequencies of the adult generation that develops from those zygotes.

Predicting the frequency of albinism: A case study

This equation thus enables us to use information on genotype and allele frequencies to predict the genotype frequencies of the next generation. Suppose, for example, that in a population of 100,000 people carrying the recessive allele a for albinism, there are 100 aa albinos and 1800 Aa heterozygous carriers. To find what the frequency of heterozygous carriers will be in the next generation, you compute the allele frequencies in the parent population.

98,100 AA individuals; 1800 Aa individuals, and 100 aa individuals → 196,200 A alleles + 1800 A alleles; 1800 a alleles + 200 a alleles

Out of 200,000 total alleles the frequency of the A allele is

198,000/200,000 = 99/100 = 0.99; thus $p = 0.99$

and the frequency of the a allele is

2000/200,000 = 1/100 = 0.01; thus, $q = 0.01$

The Hardy-Weinberg equation for the albino gene in this population is

$$p^2 + 2pq + q^2 = 1$$
$$(0.99)^2 + 2(0.99 \times 0.01) + (0.01)^2 = 1$$
$$0.9801 + 0.0198 + 0.0001 = 1$$

It thus predicts that in the next generation of 100,000 individuals, there will be

100,000 × 0.9801 = 98,010 AA individuals

100,000 × 0.0198 = 1980 Aa individuals

100,000 × 0.0001 = 10 aa individuals

This example shows that in one generation, the genotype frequencies have changed somewhat. A natural question is, Have the allele frequencies also changed? Recall that the initial frequencies of the A and B alleles are p and q, respectively, and that $p + q = 1$. You can use the rules for computing allele frequencies from genotype frequencies (see Fig. 19.2) to compute the allele frequencies of the next generation. From the Hardy-Weinberg equation, you know that p^2 of the individuals are AA, whose alleles are all A, and $2pq$ of the individuals are AB, 1/2 of whose alleles are A. Similarly, q^2 of the individuals are BB, whose alleles are all B, and $2pq$ of the individuals are AB, 1/2 of whose alleles are B. If $p + q = 1$, then $q = 1 - p$, and the frequency of the A allele in the next-generation population is

$$p^2 + 1/2[2p(1 - p)] = p^2 + p(1 - p)$$
$$= p^2 + p - p^2 = p \quad (19.2)$$

Similarly, $p = 1 - q$, and the frequency of the B allele in the next-generation population is

$$q^2 + 1/2[2q(1 - q)] = q^2 + q(1 - q)$$
$$= q^2 + q - q^2 = q \quad (19.3)$$

Using these equations to calculate the allele frequencies of A and a in the second generation of 100,000 individuals, some of whom are albinos, we find

for p 0.9801 + 0.99 − 0.9801 = 0.99
= the frequency of the A allele

for q 0.0001 + 0.01 − 0.0001 = 0.01
= the frequency of the a allele

These frequencies are the same as those in the previous generation. Thus, even though the genotype frequencies have changed from the first generation to the next, the allele frequencies have not. Note that this is true of both the dominant and the recessive alleles.

Analysis of eye color shows the power and limitations of Hardy-Weinberg

As an example of dominant and recessive phenotypes that result from different genotypes and alleles at a single locus, let's consider the actual genetics of eye color in human populations. Until 10,000 years ago, eye color was not polymorphic—all of our ancestors from this period had brown irises.

Genetics of blue eyes

Blue eyes first appeared between 6000 and 10,000 years ago, probably in a population living near the north shore of the Black Sea, according to anthropological genetic data. Today, the trait predominates in northern European populations, appearing in more than 80% of the people

Figure 19.4 Blue-eye population genetics. (a) Geographical differences in the proportions of European populations expressing the "blue eyes" phenotype. **(b)** The SNP rs12913832 that controls blue eye color is located upstream from *OCA2* in an intron of *HERC2*. **(c)** Representation of haplotype structure and coinheritance of SNPs across extended DNA blocks in the *OCA2-HERC2* gene region of chromosome 15. The SNP allele rs12913832G is part of conserved 50 kb chromosomal block that spans the 3′ half of HERC2. **(d)** Pie diagrams depict frequencies of alleles G and A at the SNP locus rs12913832 in different Old World populations.

(a)

(c)

(d)

living around the Baltic Sea (**Fig. 19.4a**). Blue-eyed individuals can be seen throughout most of Europe with diminishing frequencies at lower latitudes. Outside of Europe and the Mediterranean region, the blue eye phenotype is rare, appearing sparsely in some central and northern Asian populations, but essentially absent from sub-Saharan Africa and east Asia.

High resolution linkage mapping has demonstrated an association of blue eyes with a single base substitution, from an A to a G, that defines the SNP locus rs12913832, located in an intron of the *HERC2* gene on chromosome 15 (**Fig. 19.4b**). The rs12913832G allele is always found as a part of a larger haplotype of conserved SNP alleles across a 50 kb chromosomal region (**Fig. 19.4c**).

The extent of the conserved DNA region and the limited distribution of the G allele primarily to European populations strongly suggests that this base substitution was a one-time event. All people with blue eyes today can trace themselves back genetically to the single individual in which the mutation occurred.

Scientists were puzzled at first by the association of rs12913832 to eye color because the product of the HERC2 a gene—within which the SNP lies—does not have any connection to pigment production and is not even expressed in the iris or its precursors. The puzzle was solved with studies that demonstrated transcription factor

binding to the DNA sequence surrounding rs12913832A, with a large reduction in binding affinity to the DNA sequence containing the G substitution. Further analysis showed that rs12913832 was inside a highly conserved enhancer of the *OCA2* gene, which plays a critical role in the biosynthesis of the dark pigment melanin. When a person is homozygous for the rs12913832G allele, which damages the iris-specific OCA2 enhancer, the OCA2 gene product is greatly reduced, melanin is not synthesized, and the resulting eye color in the absence of brown pigment is blue.

Pie diagrams illustrating allele frequencies

Pie diagrams provide an intuitive tool for visualizing allele frequency differences that distinguish one population from another. The two alleles of an SNP locus are represented in contrasting colors that occupy radial portions of a circle, or pie, corresponding to allele frequencies.

Pie diagrams are placed on an appropriate geographic map at the locations of the screened populations (**Fig. 19.4d**). To obtain useful data, researchers typically assign people to populations according to the geographic locations where their recent ancestors were born and lived.

By viewing Fig. 19.4d, you can see immediately that allele frequencies at the SNP locus rs12913832 are dramatically different in geographically separated populations. The highest frequency of the rs12913832G allele in populations screened for this locus is 0.84, associated with a population from northern Finland, whereas all of the Chinese and sub-Saharan African populations do not carry the G allele at all.

Use of the Hardy-Weinberg equation with mixed populations

To understand the implications of the Hardy-Weinberg law in the analysis of a population formed from a mixture of previously differentiated populations, imagine that 100 adults from northern Finland and 100 from the Yakut people of eastern Siberia (both men and women from both populations) decide to move to a newly built offshore oil rig in the Arctic Sea. Imagine further that the 200 men and women on the oil rig marry each other without regard to their ancestry.

Now let's ask two questions and see how the data we have obtained on allele frequencies can be combined with the Hardy-Weinberg law to provide answers. First, we can estimate how many adults on the oil rig have blue eyes. Second, we can estimate both the number of children with blue eyes and the allele frequency in this second generation.

Because the Finnish and Yakut populations have different rs12913832G allele frequencies, it is easiest to use the Hardy-Weinberg equation to determine the composition of each separately. Let's use p to represent the allele frequency of the brown eyes associated rs12913832A allele, and q to represent the allele frequency of rs12913832G. The data sampled from the Finnish yield $q = 0.84$. Blue eyes is recessive, which means that we can estimate the number of Finnish adults with blue eyes from the genotype frequency for *GG:*

$$q^2 = 0.84 \times 0.84 = 0.71$$

By multiplying 0.71 by the total number of Finns on the oil rig, we get an estimate for the number of blue-eyed Finns at

$$0.71 \times 100 = 71 \text{ individuals}$$

The frequency of brown-eyed Finnish carriers of the rs12913832G allele is calculated as

$$2pq = 2 \times .16 \times .84 = .27$$

which yields 27 carrier individuals on the oil rig.

Similarly, from the Yakut rs12913832G allele frequency of 0.10, we obtain

$$q^2 = (0.1)^2 = 0.01$$

which translates into a single Yakut adult with blue eyes, and

$$2pq = 2 \times 0.9 \times 0.1 = 0.18$$

for 18 Yakut adults who are carriers. Together, among the 200 people on the oil rig, $72(71 + 1)$ will have blue eyes, and $45(27 + 18)$ will be carriers. With this information, we can calculate the combined G allele frequency from a count of chromosomes—two from each blue-eyed person and one from each carrier yields

$$2 \times 72 + 45 = 189 \div 400 \text{ (the number of chromosomes is} \\ \text{twice the number of people) for} \\ \text{an answer of } q = 0.47$$

Now let's use the parental G allele frequency to predict the number of children expected with blue eyes. The frequency of blue eyes in this second generation is $q^2 = 0.47 \times 0.47 = 0.22$. If we assume that the population of children is equal in size to the population of adults, then the number of blue-eyed children is $0.22 \times 200 = 44$, far fewer than the 72 blue-eyed adults. Nevertheless, the G allele frequency remains unchanged at 0.47. If this second generation intermarries to produce a third generation of 200, the expected number with blue eyes will be the same as the second generation. Indeed, all future generations will have the same expected genotype and allele frequencies.

Properties of populations described by Hardy-Weinberg

The application of Hardy-Weinberg analysis to the study of eye color in human populations generates two important conclusions. First, even though the proportion of individuals expressing the blue-eye phenotype changed dramatically from the first generation of the mixed population to the second generation, no change in allele frequency occurred. The *conservation of allele proportions* principle holds from each generation to the next, as long as the population is sufficiently large, alleles are not lost by mutation or selection, and alleles are not gained by mutation or immigration.

Populations with the same allele frequency don't necessarily have the same genotype or phenotype frequencies. The reason is that a single allele can exist in homozygote or heterozygote genotypes, but a recessive phenotype is only expressed in homozygotes. In the most extreme hypothetical example, a population could have a blue-eyed allele frequency of 0.5 without actually having any people with blue eyes. This situation would arise if everyone in the population is a heterozygote.

Even in this extreme example, the Hardy-Weinberg equilibrium tells us that the Hardy-Weinberg genotype frequencies described by p^2, $2pq$, and q^2, will appear in the very next generation. This is the second significant Hardy-Weinberg implication: a population that is initially stratified because of its founding by individuals from two or more distinct populations will become completely balanced in a single generation.

Once a population is known in be in Hardy-Weinberg equilibrium, it becomes a simple task to predict allele frequencies from genotype frequencies, and genotype and phenotype frequencies from allele frequencies.

In studying populations, geneticists are interested in the frequencies with which different alleles and the resulting genotypes and phenotypes occur. The Hardy-Weinberg equation provides a mathematical method of evaluating these frequencies and predicting them from one generation to the next, based on equilibrium populations.

19.2 Causes of Allele Frequency Changes

If all populations of individuals within the same species were always in Hardy-Weinberg equilibrium, the Hardy-Weinberg equation would lead us to conclude that all allele frequencies would be forever unchanging, and allele frequencies at any particular locus would be equivalent across populations. And yet, as Fig. 19.4d shows, different populations of the human species are associated with dramatically different rs12913832G allele frequencies spanning the range from 0.0 to 0.84. A similar result is obtained for numerous other loci. What do these observations suggest about the applicability of Hardy-Weinberg to real populations?

Hardy-Weinberg provides a starting point for modeling population deviations

In natural populations, conditions always deviate at least slightly from the Hardy-Weinberg assumptions: New mutations do appear occasionally at every locus, no population is infinite, small groups of individuals sometimes migrate from the main group to become founders of new populations, separate populations can merge together, individuals do not mate at random, and different genotypes do generate differences in rates of survival and reproduction.

And yet, even with these deviations from ideal conditions, the Hardy-Weinberg equation provides remarkably good estimates of allele, genotype, and phenotype frequencies *over the short run,* through one or a few breeding generations of populations of all sizes (except for those so small as to be on the verge of extinction).

Over the *long run,* however, the Hardy-Weinberg equation is rarely applicable for predictive purposes. But it serves a critical role in providing the foundation for both analytical and stochastic methods that do incorporate factors responsible for deviation from equilibrium conditions. With simple modifications to the Hardy-Weinberg equation, or the manner in which it is used, the dynamics of realistic populations may be successfully modeled.

In finite populations, chance plays a critical role

A mutation is defined as a variant DNA sequence or chromosomal region in the genome of an individual that is not present in the genomes of either parent. Generally,

spontaneous mutations are so infrequent (on the order of once in 100,000 to 1 million offspring for each gene) that their impact on a population's allele frequencies can be safely ignored in the short run. Yet, mutations are the source of all alleles at all loci, which means that some mutations do come to matter in the long term.

Mutations that provide a relative benefit to an organism or population are in a rare category of an already rare phenomenon. Many mutations are deleterious, but even more are essentially neutral—that is, the novel allele formed by mutation provides neither a benefit nor a harm. The survival or nonsurvival of a neutral mutation is a stochastic phenomenon—it occurs by chance alone.

We now present the modifications to the Hardy-Weinberg law that are required to model the long-term consequences of mutations.

The Monte Carlo simulation

The derivation of the Hardy-Weinberg equation was accomplished by a "sleight-of-hand" extension of Mendel's first law of segregation. Mendel's first law does *not* actually determine which allele a heterozygous parent will transmit to an individual child. Instead, it tells us simply that allele inheritance is like a flip of a coin: A child can receive heads or tails with an equal prior probability. Mendel's law does determine the approximate proportion of a large cohort of offspring that will inherit a particular allele. The larger the cohort population, the more accurate the determination.

The required Hardy-Weinberg sleight of hand is the assumption that *precisely* 50% of the children in a population inherit each alternative allele from heterozygous parents in each generation. This assumption is only valid as the size of a population approaches infinity. Because no population is infinite, no population truly abides by the Hardy-Weinberg conditions for equilibrium.

To model long-term allele frequency changes in a finite population, the analytical Hardy-Weinberg equation is replaced by what is known as a **Monte Carlo simulation.** A Monte Carlo simulation is typically performed with a computer program that uses a random-number generator to flip a coin (metaphorically) to choose an outcome for each probabilistic event occurring in a dynamic system defined by predetermined rules of probability.

For population genetics simulations, a specialized Monte Carlo program is initialized with a starting population having a defined number of individuals of each homozygous and heterozygous class. In the simplest case of two alleles at a single locus with no effect on survival, mating, or reproduction, the program sets up matings between individuals chosen randomly with the use of a random number generator. If a chosen parent is a heterozygote, the program also flips a coin (metaphorically) to decide which allele will be transmitted to a child.

The birth of children is simulated to obtain a total number equal to the population size chosen for the analysis.

Then, the first-generation parents are eliminated, and the children are used as the progenitors for the subsequent generation. This process is continued for as many generations as requested by the investigator, or until one allele is lost from the population and every individual is homozygous for the surviving allele. The data are recorded, the program is terminated, and a new "run" is begun with the same initial conditions. A sufficient number of independent Monte Carlo simulations are performed in order for the investigator to get a sense of what outcomes are possible with what probabilities.

Genetic drift

In the first example shown in **Fig. 19.5a,** six Monte Carlo simulations have been initialized with populations of just 10 individuals who are all set to be heterozygotes; each population has $2 \times 10 = 20$ gene copies (two in each individual), and each allele (A or G) occurs initially with a frequency of 0.5. What allele frequencies are likely to be obtained in the first round of simulated offspring? Because of the particular way in which this example is structured, the Monte Carlo simulation in this first generation is mathematically equivalent to the results obtained from tossing a coin 20 times. As you can see in Fig. 19.5a, actual simulations yield first allele (A) frequencies that

Figure 19.5 Modeling genetic drift in populations of different sizes. (a) Population size is 10. Initial condition is equal numbers of alleles, no selection. **(b)** Population size is 500. Initial condition is equal numbers of alleles, no selection.

(a)

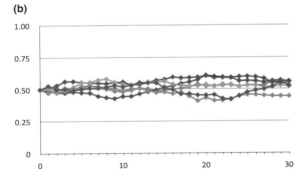

(b)

range from 0.25 (5 heads and 15 tails) to 0.65 (13 heads and 7 tails) with an average of 0.48.

Although the average of populations is not too far from the 0.5 predicted by the Hardy-Weinberg equation, the population-specific values guide each one down a different path of **genetic drift,** defined as a change in allele frequencies as a consequence of the randomness of inheritance from one generation to the next. Genetic drift occurs because the allele frequency in any one generation provides the median for possible allele frequencies in the next generation. So, for example, If one allele has already drifted to a high or low frequency, there's a 50% chance that it will go even higher or lower in the following generation.

In four of the six simulated runs shown in Fig. 19.5a, genetic drift has culminated in the loss, or extinction, of one of the two original alleles by generation 18. In each of these instances, a relatively small change in allele frequency from the previous generation caused extinction of one allele, and *fixation* of the remaining allele. A population is considered to be **fixed** at a locus when only one allele has survived and all individuals are homozygous for this allele. At this point, no further changes in allele frequency can occur (in the absence of migration or mutation).

Population size and time to fixation

The results that we would expect to get from a series of coin tosses can provide insight into the effect that the size of a population has on allele frequency changes and time to fixation. Let's start with an experiment that you repeat numerous times, in which you toss four coins in the air and record the frequency of heads each time. The possible frequency results are 0.0, 0.25, 0.5, 0.75, and 1.0. Getting an absolute difference of 4 between the heads and tails count is not so unusual ($1/16 + 1/16 = 1/8$). If heads represents one allele, and tails the other, then fixation occurs at two frequencies: 0.0 and 1.0, and the probability of fixation in any one experiment is 12.5%. If we repeat this experiment with 500 coins in each trial, instead of 4, there's still a good chance that the absolute difference between the heads and tails count may be 4 or more, but an absolute difference of 4 (that is, for example, 248 heads and 252 tails) translates into relative frequencies of 0.496 and 0.504. Extrapolation from this result leads to an important probabilistic conclusion concerning coin-toss-like models: the larger the sample size, the smaller the typical deviation from a 50:50 ratio.

The impact that population size has on allele frequency dynamics is readily observable in a comparison of the data presented in Fig. 19.5a and **19.5b.** Figure 19.5b shows results obtained with six simulations of populations with 500 individuals that are initially all heterozygous. If we follow the lines representing each population, we can see that single generation changes in allele frequency are always relatively small. Because these changes are small, the traditional Hardy-Weinberg equation provides good estimates of allele and genotype frequencies in large populations over the course of a few generations. But a series of small changes can still add up to large consequences over the long run, and eventually, each of these populations also became fixed for one allele or the other.

In populations with two alleles having equivalent phenotypic effects and present initially at equal frequencies, the median number of generations to fixation is roughly equal to the total number of gene copies in breeding individuals. For a population of 10, the median fixation time is 20 generations; for a population of 500, it's 1000 generations; and for a breeding population of 200 million people, it would be 400 million generations, or 8 billion years (assuming a birth-to-birth generation time of 20 years). Because the earth is expected to perish in flames when our sun becomes a red giant and expands into our planet's orbit in about 2 to 3 billion years, the implication is that neutral genetic drift is irrelevant to future human evolution.

Founder effect and population bottlenecks

One example of genetic drift in past human populations is the **founder effect,** which occurs when a few individuals separate from a larger population and establish a new one that is isolated from the original. The small number of founders in the new population carry only a fraction of the gene copies from the original population, and by chance, founder allele frequencies can be different.

About 200 individuals emigrated from Germany in the early eighteenth century to form the Amish community in eastern Pennsylvania. Since this founding population was completely cut off from Germany and people married only within the group, it was subjected to genetic drift. Today, the Amish number 14,000 in total, but the population exhibits a much higher incidence of manic-depressive illness than does the larger original European population, most likely because several founders carried alleles producing this disease.

Plant and animal populations are frequently subjected to **population bottlenecks,** which occur when a large proportion of individuals perish, often as a consequence of environmental disturbances. The surviving individuals are essentially equivalent to a founder population.

Consider the perpetuation of allele r, which occurs in 10% of the individuals in a population of sunflowers. If a chance occurrence such as a severe summer hailstorm strikes a population of 1 million plants and half die, it is likely that among the 500,000 survivors, roughly 50,000 (10%) will still carry the r allele. If the same storm hits a field of just 10 plants, only 1 of which carries the r allele, there is a 50% chance that the single plant bearing the r allele will not be among the survivors. The total loss of this one allele from the population would reduce the allele

frequency to 0. If, however, the lone individual carrying r does by chance survive, the frequency of allele r would increase to 20%.

> Over a few generations, Hardy-Weinberg almost always provides accurate estimates of allele and genotype frequencies. But in the long run, Hardy-Weinberg fails because the randomness of allele segregation causes genetic drift. Monte Carlo simulation takes account of random segregation and the impact of population size to provide estimates of the number of generations until an allele is lost or becomes fixed.

Natural selection acts on differences in fitness to alter allele frequencies

For many phenotypic traits, including inherited diseases, genotype does influence survival and the ability to reproduce, contrary to the Hardy-Weinberg assumptions. Thus, in real populations, not all individuals survive to adulthood, and some probability always exists that an individual will not live long enough to reproduce. As a result, the genotype frequencies of real populations change as their individual members mature from zygotes to adults.

Fitness and selection

To population geneticists, an individual's relative ability to survive and transmit its genes to the next generation is its **fitness.** But although fitness is an attribute associated with each genotype, it cannot be measured within the individuals of a population; the reason is that each animal with a particular genotype survives and reproduces in a manner greatly affected by chance circumstances. However, by considering all the individuals of a particular genotype together as a group, it becomes possible to measure the relative fitness for that genotype. Thus, for population geneticists, fitness is a statistical measurement only. Nevertheless, differences in fitness can have a profound effect on the allele frequencies of a population.

Fitness has two basic components: viability and reproductive success. The fitness of individuals possessing variations that help them survive and reproduce in a changing environment is relatively high; the fitness of individuals without those adaptive variations is relatively low. In nature, the process that progressively eliminates individuals whose fitness is lower and chooses individuals of higher fitness to survive and become the parents of the next generation is known as **natural selection.** The mechanisms of selection act independently of any individual; often, interactions between genetically determined phenotypes and environmental conditions are the agents of natural selection. For example, in a hypothetical population of giraffes browsing on the leaves of an ancient savanna, suppose that some of the animals had long necks and some short necks, and that each of these phenotypes resulted from variations in the

Figure 19.6 Giraffes on the savanna. A visible example of one outcome of natural selection for increased fitness.

genes contributing to neck length. If during a long drought, fewer low-hanging leaves were available on the shrubs and trees of the savanna, those long-necked individuals able to reach the higher leaves would have been able to harvest more food. Natural conditions would thus have selected the better adapted, long-necked giraffes—those with the higher fitness—to survive and become the parents of the next generation (**Fig. 19.6**). Similarly, in the laboratory, scientists can establish experimental conditions, such as the absence of a nutrient or the presence of an antibiotic, that become the agents of **artificial selection.**

Field studies show that natural selection occurs for phenotypic traits in all natural populations. Until recently genetic disease and genetic predisposition or resistance to infectious disease were major factors in determining a person's survival and reproduction. As a consequence, the potential for natural selection even in human populations was considerable. Today, the application of vaccines, the availability of antibiotics, and other medical advances have reduced but not eliminated the forces of natural selection. How does selection alter the conclusions that can be drawn from Hardy-Weinberg?

Modifications to Hardy-Weinberg

We can see how to apply the Hardy-Weinberg equation in populations undergoing selection with an analysis of the R gene in a population of zygotes in Hardy-Weinberg equilibrium. In this population, the genotype frequencies RR, Rr, and rr are p^2, $2pq$, and q^2, respectively. Now suppose that the viability, that is, the probability of surviving from zygote to adult, depends on genotype, while the second component of fitness—success at productive mating—is independent of genotype. If we define the relative fitness of the three genotypes as w_{RR}, w_{Rr}, and w_{rr}, respectively, the relative frequencies of the three genotypes at adulthood is p^2w_{RR}, $2pqw_{Rr}$, and q^2w_{rr} (**Fig. 19.7**).

The fitness of any one genotype is only defined in relation to the fitness of alternative genotypes, which means that the individual fitness coefficient values (W_{RR}, W_{Rr}, and

Figure 19.7 Changes in allele frequencies caused by selection. The uncalibrated frequency after selection is calculated by multiplying the zygote frequency by the relative fitness value. Adult frequencies are calibrated through division by the sum of the relative fitness values ($\overline{W}$).

Parental Gametes		
Allele	R	r
Frequency	p	q

First Generation Offspring		
Genotypes	RR	Rr	rr
Zygote frequency	p^2	$2pq$	q^2
Relative fitness	W_{RR}	W_{Rr}	W_{rr}
Relative frequency after selection	p^2W_{RR}	$2pqW_{Rr}$	q^2W_{rr}
Normalized adult frequency	$p^2W_{RR}/\overline{W}$	$2pqw_{Rr}/\overline{W}$	$q^2W_{rr}/\overline{W}$

Gametes from First Generation		
Allele	R	r
Frequency	$p' = (p^2W_{RR} + pqW_{Rr})/\overline{W}$	$q' = (q^2W_{rr} + pqW_{Rr})/\overline{W}$

Normalization factor $\quad \overline{W} = p^2W_{RR} + 2pqW_{Rr} + q^2W_{rr}$

W_{rr}) are arbitrary. For example, if an experimental result demonstrates a three-fold difference in fitness between the *RR* genotype and the rr genotype, the values of W_{RR} and wrr could be set to 15 and 5, or 6.9 and 2.3, or any of an infinite pair of numbers having a 3:1 ratio.

The fitness-modified Hardy-Weinberg equation is most useful when the fitness coefficients are adjusted so that the three terms sum to 1. In this "normalized" form, each terms represents an actual genotype frequency. Normalization is accomplished by calculating the value of a numerical factor that each Hardy-Weinberg term can be divided into so that the terms all add up to 1. The calculation consists simply in setting the sum of the terms in the modified equation to a new variable, designated $\overline{w}$.

$$p^2 w_{RR} + 2pq w_{Rr} + q^2 w_{rr} = \overline{w} \qquad (19.4a)$$

Since $\overline{w}$ represents the sum of the individual fitness values, each multiplied by their relative occurrence in the population, it in fact represents the average fitness of the population.

In populations that satisfy the conditions of the original Hardy-Weinberg equilibrium, when the fitness for each genotype is 1, the value of $\overline{w}$ is also 1. However, when fitness varies from one genotype to another, $\overline{w}$ can also vary, but in a way that can be calculated as long as the value of each of the variables in the equation is known. The modified Hardy-Weinberg equation is thus normalized by dividing each term by $\overline{w}$ such that the new equation becomes

$$\frac{p^2 w_{RR}}{\overline{w}} + \frac{2pq w_{Rr}}{\overline{w}} + \frac{q^2 w_{rr}}{\overline{w}} = 1 \qquad (19.4b)$$

Each term in this normalized equation represents the actual frequency that each genotype will assume in the generation following the one used for the original calculation. Figure 19.7 summarizes this process of calculation.

As an example, let's use the variables p' and q' to represent the frequencies of the *R* and *r* alleles in this next generation. Among the gametes produced by the original population, the frequency of allele *r* will be the result of contributions of *r* alleles from both *Rr* and *rr* adults relative to the number of individuals in the entire adult population. If q' represents the frequency of the *r* allele in the next generation adults, then

$$q' = \frac{q^2 w_{rr} + \frac{1}{2}(2pq w_{Rr})}{\overline{w}} = \frac{q(q w_{rr} + p w_{Rr})}{\overline{w}} \qquad (19.5)$$

Keep in mind,

1. Δq is defined as $q' - q$.
2. A useful identity in moving from Equation 19.5 to Equation 19.6 is $1 - 2q = 1 - q - q = (p - q)$.

Thus, in one generation of selection, the allele frequency of *r* has changed from *q* to q'. It is often useful to know the change in allele frequency over one generation of selection. We can represent this change as

$$\Delta q = \frac{pq[q(w_{rr} - w_{Rr}) + p(w_{Rr} - w_{RR})]}{\overline{w}} \qquad (19.6)$$

As these equations (19.5 and 19.6) show, selection can cause the frequency of an allele to change from one generation to the next. Equation 19.6 shows that the change in allele frequency resulting from one generation of selection depends on both the allele frequencies and the relative fitnesses (in this case, the viability component of fitness) of the three genotypes. Note that if the fitnesses of all genotypes are the same, as in populations at Hardy-Weinberg equilibrium, then the change in *q* (Δq) = 0; in other words, if there are no genotype-related differences in fitness, there is no possibility of selection, and if there is no possibility of selection then allele frequencies will be subjected only to genetic drift, as we described in an earlier section.

As an example, let us use Equation 19.6 to look at how a recessive genetic condition, such as thalassemia, influences the allele frequencies of a population. If the disease, which results from an *rr* genotype for the *R* gene, decreases fitness by decreasing the probability of surviving to adulthood, then the fitness of *RR* and *Rr* individuals is the same, while fitness of *rr* individuals is reduced. Because only the relative values of the fitnesses are important, it is useful to set the values of $w_{RR} = 1$, $w_{Rr} = 1$, and $w_{rr} = 1 - s$, where *s* is the *selection coefficient* against the *rr* genotype. This selection coefficient can vary from 0 (no selection against *rr*) to 1 (*rr* is lethal, and no *rr* individuals survive to adulthood). For this example, we can rewrite Equation 19.6 as

$$\Delta q = \frac{pq[q(1 - s - 1) + q(1 - 1)]}{\overline{w}} = \frac{-spq^2}{\overline{w}} \qquad (19.7)$$

Equation 19.7 has three interesting features. First, unless there is no selection and $s = 0$, Δq is always negative, and the frequency of the *r* allele decreases with time.

Second, the rate at which *q* decreases over time depends on the allele frequencies; in particular, because Δq varies with q^2, the rate at which *q* decreases diminishes as *q* becomes smaller. (Recall that because *q* is always less than 1, $q^2 < q$.) To understand the effect of this correlation between the allele frequency and the rate at which *q* decreases over time, consider the special case of a lethal recessive disease for which $s = 1$. The dotted line in **Fig. 19.8** shows the decrease in allele frequency predicted by Equation 19.7, starting from an initial allele frequency of 0.5. The decrease in allele frequency is rapid at first, and then slows. After 10 generations, the predicted frequency of the recessive disease allele is nearly 10%, even though the homozygous recessive genotype is lethal. The solid line in Fig. 19.8 plots actual data for the decrease in frequency of an autosomal lethal allele in a large experimental population of *Drosophila melanogaster*. In Fig. 19.8, the predicted and observed changes in allele frequency match quite closely.

Figure 19.8 Decrease in the frequency of a lethal recessive allele over time. The *dotted line* represents the mathematical prediction. The *blue line* represents the actual data obtained with an autosomal recessive lethal allele.

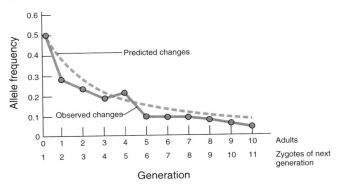

Figure 19.9 Monte Carlo modeling of natural selection. Each colored data line represents an independent Monte Carlo run on a population of 500 in which a new mutant allele appears in a single individual. In most runs, the mutant allele goes extinct in fewer than 100 generations. The few that survive longer inevitably move to fixation.

Why is selection less effective as the frequency of a recessive lethal allele moves closer to zero? The answer goes back to our consideration of the frequency of heterozygous carriers of a recessive disease allele. When q is small, individuals homozygous for the disease allele (at a frequency of q^2) are very rare because most copies of the r allele occur in Rr heterozygotes (at a frequency of $2pq$) who do not experience negative selection. (In mathematical terms, the ratio of q^2 to q decreases exponentially for all values of q less than 1.) By contrast, a lethal dominant allele will disappear from a population in a single generation of selection.

The third feature of Equation 19.7 is that it predicts that the allele frequency q should continue to decline, albeit more and more slowly over time as q moves closer and closer to a value of zero.

A Monte Carlo simulation of natural selection

Modifying the Hardy-Weinberg equation with coefficients of selection overcomes one limitation of the original Hardy-Weinberg equation: the assumption that all possible genotypes are equal in fitness. But the analytical solution of this equation and the derivation of Δq still suffer from a dependence on the assumption of an infinite population. Nevertheless, we can use the modified Hardy-Weinberg equation to develop a similarly modified Monte Carlo simulation to investigate the impact of natural selection on finite populations.

As an example, let's consider a population of 500 individuals in which 499 are homozygous initially for the r allele, and one is heterozygous with an R mutation on one chromosome that provides a slight dominant advantage in survival described by the following selection coefficients: $w_{RR} = 1.0$, $w_{Rr} = 0.98$, and $w_{rr} = 0.98$. These conditions can be modeled with a Monte Carlo approach that randomly eliminates 2% of Rr and rr individuals created in each generation, and replaces them with offspring from a new mating of the parental generation.

Figure 19.9 shows the results of six simulations of this population model. Notice first that in three of these, the new R allele never takes off, going extinct within 65 generations. But in the populations where the R allele increases in frequency to 0.10, it inevitably moves toward fixation.

This example illustrates several important points concerning the impact that a new mutant allele with a small, yet realistic, fitness advantage can have on a population. First, even though the original copy of the allele provides a selective advantage, it will often go extinct due to chance events of reproduction in the initial generations. But second, if the advantageous allele reaches a threshold frequency level that ensures its survival, it will always eventually increase all the way to fixation. Third, even a fitness advantage of just 2%—which is likely to be imperceptible at the individual level—will rise inevitably to fixation.

The fitness of alternative genotypes in different environments

When people migrated out of the East African region in which *H. sapiens* originated, beginning 70,000 years ago, founder populations encountered environmental conditions in Europe and Asia that were distinct from those in Africa. As a result, the relative fitness of alternative alleles at a number of genes became reversed. Among the most obvious changes were differences in allele frequencies at genes that determine skin pigmentation.

The ultraviolet rays of the sun provide people with a benefit as well as a harm. The benefit lies in the catalysis of vitamin D production. The harm is in the induction of skin cancer. Closer to the equator, the sun's rays are most intense. Alleles that cause a darkening of the skin are advantageous because they protect against skin cancer while allowing enough ultraviolet light through for vitamin D production. At higher latitudes, where the sun's rays are less intense, skin cancer is less of a problem, and alleles that lighten the skin allow enough UV penetration for sufficient vitamin D production.

Skin pigmentation is a complex quantitative trait determined by alleles at many genes, but about a half dozen genes are most influential. One fascinating question concerning our history as a species is whether European and Asian populations derived lighter skin pigmentation from a common ancestral population, or whether the trait evolved separately on the two continents. A mixed answer has been obtained by surveying allele frequencies at multiple pigmentation loci in populations indigenous to different geographical locations around the Old World.

The *KITLG* gene is among the small list with a prominent role in skin pigmentation. As you can see in the pie chart (**Fig. 19.10a**), Europeans and Asians share a common SNP variant responsible for a reduction in pigmentation, suggesting that they derived it from a common ancestor after crossing from Africa into the Arabian peninsula and prior to the separation of populations heading northwest and northeast. In contrast, Europeans and Asians independently accumulated variants at two other loci with a role in skin pigmentation (**Fig. 19.10b** and **c**), which is evidence that the same selective pressures existed in both populations, which took advantage of different mutations.

Cultural-genetic feedback

Less obvious, at first glance, but just as important to certain populations, has been a genetic response to the cultural innovation of domesticating cattle for milk production. In pre-agricultural societies, only very young children have a diet containing milk from lactating mothers. The lactase enzyme required to digest milk is not needed after weaning, and a DNA regulatory allele that turns it off is advantageous. People living in Turkey domesticated cattle approximately 8000 years ago, and cattle moved with agriculturalists across Europe. European adults who could digest cow's milk gained a survival advantage, and a DNA regulatory variant that maintains lactase production throughout life has increased to high levels. Scientists have identified the DNA change

Figure 19.10 Geographic distribution of allele frequencies at skin pigmentation loci. (a) Pie chart showing the distribution of alleles at the KITLG locus. **(b)** Pie chart showing the distribution of alleles at the SLC24A5 locus. **(c)** Pie chart showing the distribution of alleles at the MC1R locus. **(d)** Pie chart showing the distribution of alleles at the lactase (LCT) locus.

(a)

(c)

(b)

(d)

responsible for this allele, which occurred about 5000 years ago. Its advantage to northern Europeans is so great that its frequency is now greater than 90% in certain regions.

Eventually, genetic drift will take over and eliminate the mutant allele completely from a finite population.

In some cases, a recessive disease-causing allele remains in a population at a stable frequency, in opposition to expectations from both analytical and Monte Carlo predictions. What maintains these diseases despite continuing selection against them? One answer is that sometimes heterozygotes have a higher fitness than either homozygote, a situation referred to as **balancing selection.**

Balancing selection maintains deleterious alleles in a population

We have seen that sickle-cell anemia, which includes episodes of severe pain, serious anemia, and a probability of early death, is a recessive condition resulting from two copies of the sickle-cell allele at the β-globin locus. The disease allele has not disappeared from several African populations, where it seems to have existed for a very long time.

One clue to the maintenance of the sickle-cell allele in human populations lies in the observation that heterozygotes for the normal and sickle-cell alleles are resistant to malaria. This resistance is due, in part, to the fact that red blood cells infected by the malaria parasite, if they also contain a sickle-cell allele, break open, destroying the parasite as well as the red blood cell itself. By contrast, in cells with two normal hemoglobin alleles, the malaria parasite thrives.

To set up a model of heterozygous advantage, let B_1 represent the normal β-globin allele and B_2 stand for the abnormal recessive sickle-cell allele; and for simplicity, assume that B_1B_2 heterozygotes have the maximum relative fitness of 1, while the selection coefficient (representing the selective disadvantage) for B_1B_1 homozygotes is $1 - s_1$, and the selection coefficient for B_2B_2 homozygotes is $1 - s_2$. We can then represent the changes in allele frequency resulting from selection as

$$\Delta q = \frac{pq(s_1p - s_2q)}{\overline{w}} \quad (19.8)$$

To maintain both alleles in the population using this equation, Δq must be 0 for some value of q between 0 and 1. The q value at which $\Delta q = 0$ is known as the **equilibrium frequency** of allele B_2. The value of q when $\Delta q = 0$ and both alleles are present occurs when the term inside the parentheses of Equation 19.8 is 0, that is, when

$$s_1p - s_2q = 0$$

Substituting $1 - q$ for $p (p = 1 - q)$ and solving this equation for q reveals that the equilibrium frequency of B_2 (represented by q_e) is reached when

$$q_e = \frac{s_1}{s_1 + s_2} \quad (19.9)$$

Note that to find the equilibrium frequency, that is, the value of q at which $\Delta q = 0$ such that both alleles B_1 and B_2 persist in the population, you need know only the selection coefficients for the two homozygotes.

To understand the relationship between q, the change in q, and the equilibrium frequency q_e, you can formulate Δq using q_e.

$$\Delta q = \frac{-pq(s_1 + s_2)(q - q_e)}{\overline{w}} \quad (19.10)$$

From this formulation, you can see that when q is greater than q_e, Δq is negative. Under these circumstances, q, or the frequency of allele B_2, will decrease toward the equilibrium frequency. By contrast, when q is less than q_e, Δq is positive and the frequency of B_2 will increase toward the equilibrium. Thus, the equilibrium frequency stabilizes, because a change away from it is always followed by a change toward it.

Now, if you assume that the African populations in which sickle-cell anemia is prevalent are currently at equilibrium relative to their alleles at the β-globin locus, you can use the observed frequency of the sickle-cell allele in these populations to calculate the relative values of the selection coefficients. Field studies show that the actual value of q_e lies between 0.15 and 0.2 for an average value of 0.17. If you plug this number into Equation 19.9, you get

$$0.17 = \frac{s_1}{(s_1 + s_2)}$$

This equation makes it possible to express either selection coefficient in terms of the other. For example, $s_1 = 0.2s_2$.

If you assume that $s_2 = 1$ (that is, those with sickle-cell trait never reproduce), as was essentially true before medical advances enabled the survival of children expressing the sickle-cell trait, you will find that $s_1 = 0.2$, which, in turn, means that the relative fitness of the wild-type genotype is 0.8. Recall, however, that we set the fitness of the heterozygote at 1.0. By dividing 1.0 by 0.8, you get 1.25, which represents the relative advantage in fitness that heterozygotes for the sickle-cell allele have over people who do not carry this allele in African populations exposed to malaria. The use of simple statistical methods to calculate this heterozygous advantage demonstrates how medical geneticists can use the tools of population genetics (**Fig. 19.11**).

"Fitness" is a measure of relative likelihoods of survival and reproduction due to alternative genotypes at a particular locus in a particular population. More fit genotypes will reproduce more of themselves at each generation, which "drives" an increase in the frequency of the alleles they carry. In some instances, the same genotype can be more fit in one environment, but less fit in another relative to an alternative genotype.

Figure 19.11 Frequency of the sickle-cell allele across Africa where malaria is prevalent.

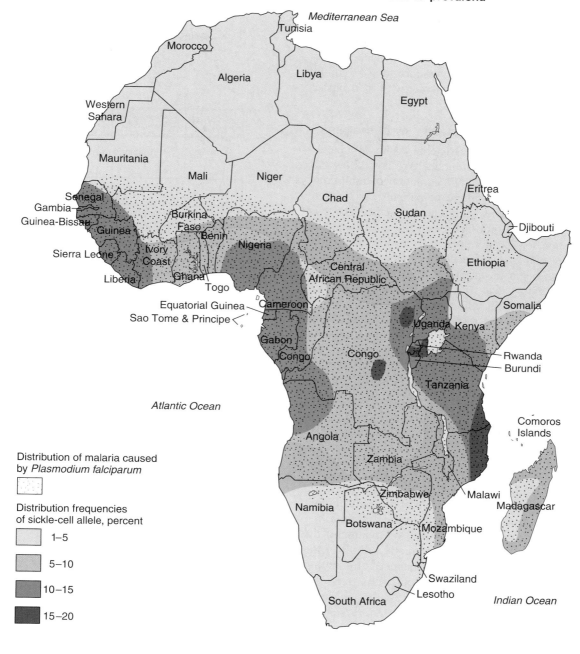

Distribution of malaria caused by *Plasmodium falciparum*

Distribution frequencies of sickle-cell allele, percent

- 1–5
- 5–10
- 10–15
- 15–20

A comprehensive example: Human behavior can affect evolution of pathogens and pests

Infectious diseases have been a major killer throughout human history, and as the AIDS epidemic illustrates, previously unknown diseases continue to emerge. In the twentieth century, the invention and discovery of a variety of vaccines, antibiotics, and other drugs made it possible to combat infectious diseases such as smallpox and tuberculosis with great success. In the last 25 years, however, many formerly surefire drugs have lost their effectiveness because populations of pathogens have evolved resistance to them. Similarly, populations of agricultural pests have evolved resistance to the pesticides used to control or eradicate them.

At the beginning of this chapter, we posed three questions: How do new diseases emerge in human populations? Why do diseases persist in all living organisms? What causes diseases and pests long under control to resurge in frequency and intensity? In previous sections, we have answered the first two. New diseases emerge in human populations as a consequence of new mutations. Diseases persist because changes in allele frequency tend toward an evolutionary equilibrium in which mutation balances selection. To answer the third question, we turn to an examination of how pathogens and pests interact with their hosts.

The evolution of drug resistance in pathogens

We have seen that many of the bacterial agents of tuberculosis are resistant to several antibiotics. We now know that a major factor contributing to the evolution of multidrug-resistant TB strains is the failure of patients to complete the lengthy drug regimens required for a cure. The two most widely used drugs for TB, isoniazid and rifampicin, require ingestion for six months and have side effects that include nausea and loss of appetite. However, the symptoms of TB can begin to disappear after only two to four weeks of treatment.

Imagine a TB patient with a persistent cough, shortness of breath, and general weakness. This individual harbors a large, actively growing and dividing population of TB bacteria in his lungs. At first, these bacteria are susceptible to antibiotics, but occasional mutations conferring partial resistance appear at random (**Fig. 19.12**). The patient's physician prescribes a six-month course of treatment with the antibiotic isoniazid. After a few weeks of treatment, the bacterial population in the patient's lungs has decreased considerably, and the patient's symptoms have abated, although the negative side effects of the drug continue to cause discomfort. However, the composition of the bacterial population has now changed so that the remaining bacteria are likely to include a high proportion of mutant bacteria possessing partial resistance to the antibiotic.

If the patient continues his course of treatment, the persistent dose of antibiotic will eventually kill all of the bacteria, even those with partial resistance, eliminating the infection. By contrast, if the patient stops treatment prematurely, the remaining (partially resistant) bacteria will proliferate and within three to four weeks reestablish a large population. Subsequent treatment of the same individual upon relapse or of a new patient to whom the partially resistant bacteria have spread would permit a second cycle of selection. New mutations could then convert the partially resistant bacteria to fully resistant microbes.

It is easy to see how repeated cycles of antibiotic treatment with multiple drugs, coupled with premature cessation of treatment, can promote the evolution of fully resistant bacterial populations, and even bacterial strains resistant to more than one drug, within a single patient. Initially individual mutant cells that express genes conferring partial resistance increase in frequency; subsequent mutations in some of the mutant bacteria will increase resistance, and incomplete drug dosages will select for the resistant strains.

Figure 19.12 The evolution of resistance in TB bacteria.

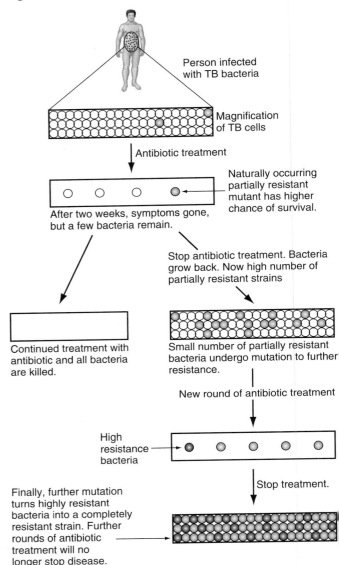

Several factors contribute to the rapid evolution of resistance in bacterial pathogens. The short generation times—often only a few hours—and rapid rate of reproduction under optimal conditions allow evolution to proceed quickly relative to a human life span. The large population densities typical of bacteria, which may exceed $10^9/cm^3$, ensure that rare resistance-conferring mutations will appear by chance in the population. The strong selection imposed by antibiotics increases the rate of evolution in each generation, unless the bacterial population is entirely eliminated.

The large variety of ways by which bacteria can acquire genes also contributes to the rapid evolution of resistance. Many genes for resistance are found on plasmids, and, as you saw in Chapters 9 and 14, the capacity of plasmids to replicate and be transmitted among bacteria allows the amplified expression of resistance genes in bacterial populations. Plasmids also provide a means for the genetic exchange of resistance genes among bacterial populations and species through transformation, conjugation, and transduction. Laboratory studies have demonstrated the ready transfer of plasmid-borne resistance genes to new bacterial species.

The evolution of pesticide resistance

Like infectious bacteria, many agricultural pests spawn large populations because of their short generation times and rapid rates of reproduction. These large, rapidly reproducing populations evolve resistance to the chemical pesticides used to control them via selection for resistance-conferring mutations. Our understanding of this familiar pattern of selection and rapid evolution is most complete for certain insecticides.

The large-scale, commercial use of DDT and other synthetic organic insecticides, begun in the 1940s, was initially highly successful at reducing crop destruction by agricultural pests, such as the boll weevil, and medical pests, such as the mosquitoes that transmit malaria and yellow fever. Within a few years, however, resistance to these insecticides was detectable in the targeted insect populations. Since the 1950s, resistance to every known insecticide has evolved within 10 years of its commercial introduction. By 1984 there were reports of more than 450 resistant species of insects and mites (**Fig. 19.13**). Because different populations within a species can become resistant independently of other populations, the number of times insecticide resistance has evolved probably exceeds 1000.

Genetic studies show that insecticide resistance often results from changes in a single gene, and that several significant mechanisms of resistance are similar to those seen in infectious bacteria. DDT, for example, is a nerve toxin in insects. House flies and some mosquitoes develop resistance to DDT from dominant mutations in a single, enzyme-encoding allele. The mutant enzyme detoxifies DDT, rendering it harmless to the insect. As we saw earlier, even at low frequencies, dominant alleles can experience strong selection because of heterozygous advantage. Consider, for example, dominant mutation *R* (for insecticide resistance), which occurs initially at low frequency in a population. Soon after the mutation appears, most of the *R* alleles are in *SR* heterozygotes (in which *S* is the wild-type susceptibility allele). With the application of insecticide, strong selection favoring *SR* heterozygotes rapidly increases the frequency of the resistance allele in the population.

A field study of the use of DDT in Bangkok, Thailand, to control *Aedes aegypti* mosquitoes, the carriers of yellow fever, illustrates the rapid evolution of resistance. Spraying of the insecticide began in 1964 (**Fig. 19.14**). Within a year, DDT-resistant genotypes emerged and rapidly increased in frequency. By mid-1967, the frequency of resistant *RR* homozygotes was nearly 100%.

Figure 19.13 Increase of insecticide resistance from 1908–1984. (a) Insecticide resistance evolved with the aerial spraying of DDT, which began in the 1940s. Within 10 years, resistance to an insecticide becomes widespread as the insects evolve defenses to the insecticides just as they would evolve defenses against infectious bacteria. **(b)** The evolution of resistance among Arthropoda.

(a)

(b)

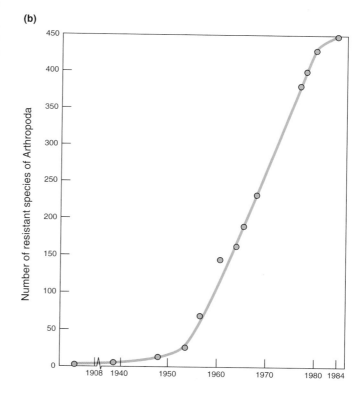

The biological balance of resistance and fitness

Since DDT no longer controlled mosquito populations in the region, the Bangkok insecticide program was stopped. The response of the mosquito population to the cessation of spraying was intriguing: The frequency of the *R* allele decreased rapidly, and by 1969, *RR* genotypes had virtually disappeared. The precipitous decline of the *R* allele suggests that in the absence of DDT, the *RR* genotype

Figure 19.14 How genotype frequencies among populations of *A. aegypti* mosquito larvae change in response to insecticide. (a) Mosquitoes and larvae. **(b)** Changing proportions of resistance genotypes of *A. aegypti* (larvae) under selection with DDT (1964–1967), and after selection was relaxed (1968), in a suburb of Bangkok, Thailand.

(a)

(b)

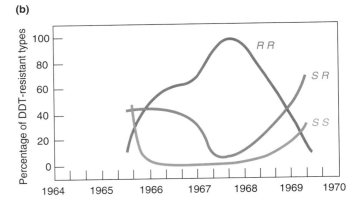

mechanism was maintaining both the *R* (resistance) and the *S* (susceptibility) alleles in the presence of warfarin.

Further study showed that in the presence of warfarin, the relative fitnesses were 0.37 for the *SS* genotype, 1.0 for the *SR* genotype, and 0.68 for the *RR* genotype. The greater relative fitness of the heterozygote is a driver that maintains both the *S* and *R* alleles at a particular equilibrium ratio. Further investigation revealed that two phenotypic factors cause the observed differences in fitness.

Both the *SR* and the *RR* genotypes are relatively resistant to the effects of warfarin, and thus, they provided higher fitnesses than the susceptible *SS* genotypes. However, *RR* homozygotes suffered from a vitamin K deficiency because of the less efficient vitamin K recycling during blood clotting, and this deficiency reduced the rate of survival when the diet did not contain a large amount of vitamin K. In the absence of warfarin, therefore, *RR* homozygotes had a lower fitness. The biological costs of fitness, which are widespread and occur by various mechanisms, are very likely a major reason why resistance alleles occurred in very low or undetectable frequencies before the routine use of pesticides.

> Rapid changes in resistance allele frequencies are driven by human use and subsequent disuse of pesticides and antibiotics to control organisms as different as bacteria and rats. The results suggest that fitness benefits often come with fitness costs, and the balance between the two is highly dependent on the environment in which the population lives.

19.3 Analyzing Quantitative Variation

We now examine how population geneticists study quantitative traits. The continuous variation of such traits depends on the number of genes that generate the trait, as well as the genetic and environmental factors that affect the penetrance and expressivity of these genes (see Chapters 3 and 11). One of the goals of quantitative analysis is to discover how much of the variation in a particular trait is the result of genotypic differences among individuals in a population and how much arises from differences in the environment.

Genetic variance can be separated from environmental variance

To sort out the genetic and environmental determinants of phenotypic variation in a population, consider a series of experiments on a population of dandelions, a common weedy plant in lawns and other disturbed areas throughout North America (**Fig. 19.15a**). Dandelions have a long tubular stem and a large, yellow composite flowering

produces a lower fitness than the *SS* genotype. In other words, the homozygous resistance genotype imposes a **fitness cost** on individuals such that in the absence of insecticide, resistance is subject to a negative selection that decreases the frequency of *R* in the population.

To understand the biological basis of fitness costs, consider how rats evolve resistance to warfarin, a pesticide introduced in the 1940s and 1950s to control small mammals, among other pests. Warfarin interferes with blood clotting by blocking the recycling of vitamin K (a cofactor in the clotting cascade). When a rat ingests warfarin, the inability to form a clot leads to a fatal loss of blood following any internal or external injury. In Europe in the 1960s, the extensive use of warfarin for rat control fueled the evolution of a single-gene resistance allele in many rat populations. The frequency of resistance, however, did not increase to 100%; instead, in most populations, it leveled off at 30% to 60%. Apparently, some

Figure 19.15 Studies of dandelions can help sort out the effects of genes versus the environment. (a) The familiar dandelion (*Taraxacum* sp.) is a useful model when studying population variations. (b) Finding the mean and variance of stem length. (c) Variance of genetically identical plants grown in a greenhouse and grown on a hillside. (d) Genetic variance of plants grown in a greenhouse. (e) Phenotype variance of plants grown on a hillside.

(a)

(c)

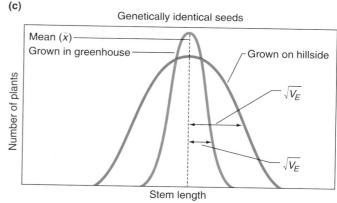

V_E is smaller among greenhouse-grown plants.

(b)

Finding the mean:

Let x_i = the stem length of the plant i in a population of N plants. The mean of stem length, $\bar{x}$, for the population is defined as

$$\bar{x} = \frac{\sum\limits_{i=1}^{N} x_i}{N}$$

Finding the variance:

The variance V_E of stem length for the population is defined as

$$V_E = \frac{\sum\limits_{i=1}^{N} (x_i - \bar{x})^2}{N}$$

(d)

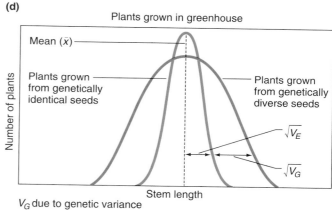

V_G due to genetic variance

(e)

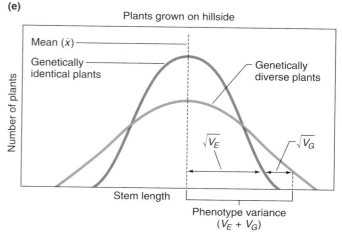

structure composed of many small individual flowers; each of these flowers can produce a single, tufted, diploid seed, dispersible by the wind. Most dandelion seeds arise from mitotic, rather than meiotic, divisions such that all the seeds from a single plant are genetically identical. Our goal is to compare the influence of genes and environment on the length of the stem at flowering.

To distinguish environmental from genetic effects on phenotypic variation, you need to quantify one variable, say the environment, while controlling for the other one; that is, while holding the genetic contribution steady. You could begin by planting half of the genetically identical seeds on a grassy hillside and allowing them to grow undisturbed until they flower. You then measure the length of the stem of each flowering plant and determine the mean and variance of the distribution of values for this trait in this dandelion population.

As **Fig. 19.15b** shows, you find the **mean** by summing the values of all stem lengths and dividing by the number of stems. You then find the **variance** by expressing the stem lengths as plus or minus deviations from the mean, squaring those deviations, and again dividing by the number of stems. Because all members of this population are genetically identical, any observed variation in stem length among individuals should be a consequence of environmental variations, such as different amounts of water and sunlight at different locations on the hillside (if we ignore rare mutations). When represented as a variance from the mean, these observed environmentally determined differences in stem length are called the **environmental variance,** or V_E.

To refine your estimate of environmental variance, you plant the second half of the genetically identical seeds from the single test plant in a controlled greenhouse in which growth conditions are everywhere the same (**Fig. 19.15c**). Because environmental conditions are much more similar for all these genetically identical plants, the amount of environmental variance (V_E) among greenhouse plants is much smaller than among hillside plants. In theory, in a perfectly controlled greenhouse, growth conditions would be the same for all plants, the V_E would be zero, and all plants would have identical stem lengths (within measurement error). In reality, there is no such thing as perfect control or a homogeneous environment, and the greenhouse V_E will have some value greater than zero. Nonetheless, the difference between the V_E of the dandelions grown on the hillside and the V_E of dandelions grown in the greenhouse is a measure of the impact of the more diversified hillside environment on the phenotypic variation of stem length.

Even though the greenhouse V_E will have some value greater than zero, for the sake of simplicity in the following discussion, we assume that it is small.

To examine the impact of genetic differences on stem length, you take seeds from many different dandelion plants produced in many different locations, and you plant them in a controlled greenhouse (**Fig. 19.15d**). Because you are raising genetically diverse plants in a relatively uniform environment, observed variation in stem length—beyond that found in the genetically identical population—is the result of genetic differences promoting **genetic variance,** or V_G.

Now, to determine the total impact on phenotype of genes and environment, you take the seeds of many different plants from many different locations and grow them on the same hillside (**Fig. 19.15e**). For the population of dandelions that grow up from these seeds, the **total phenotype variance** (V_P) in stem length will be the sum of the genetic variance (V_G) and the environmental variance (V_E). The environmental variance is determined directly from the phenotypic variance found in the initial population of genetically identical plants grown on the hillside. It thus becomes possible for you to calculate the genetic variance in the second, mixed population as the difference between the phenotypic variance found in this genetically mixed population and the phenotypic variance found in the genetically identical population. For natural populations of dandelions, both genetic variation among individuals and variation in the environmental conditions experienced by each plant contribute to the total phenotypic variation.

Heritability is the proportion of phenotypic variance due to genetic variance

With the ability to determine the relative contributions to phenotypic variation of genes and environment, geneticists have developed a mathematical definition of the **heritability** (h^2) of a trait: It is the proportion of total phenotypic variance ascribable to genetic variance.

$$h^2 = \frac{V_G}{V_G + V_E} = \frac{V_G}{V_P} \qquad (19.11)$$

Because the amounts of genetic, environmental, and phenotypic variation may differ among traits, among populations, and among different environments, the heritability of a trait is always defined for a specific population and specific set of environmental conditions. If you know any two of the three variables of total phenotypic variance, genetic variance, and environmental variance, you can find the remaining unknown variance.

Analysis of a quantitative trait begins by measuring the relative contributions of environmental and genetic variance. Because the combination of these two gives the total phenotypic variance, any two values can be used to calculate the third.

Heritability is measured in studies of groups with defined genetic differences

In analyzing the contributions of genes and environment to dandelion stem length, you measured the phenotypic variation among genetically identical individuals in a range of specified environments and compared it to the phenotypic variation among all individuals in the population. Of course, most organisms are not as easy to clone as dandelions. The key to generalizing from the dandelion example is to recognize that genetic clones are simply a special case of the broader notion of genetically related individuals, or genetic relatives, who share certain alleles because they have one or more common ancestors. To quantify this idea, we can define the **genetic relatedness** of two individuals as the average fraction of common alleles at all gene loci that the individuals share because they inherited them from a common ancestor.

To determine the genetic relatedness of two siblings, for example, you simply calculate the probability they received the same allele at any locus from the same parent. If you assume that one sibling received allele *A1* from an *A1/A2* heterozygous parent, the probability that the second sibling received the same allele is 0.5. Because this simple calculation holds for every locus transmitted by both parents, the total genetic relatedness of two siblings is 0.5. With an extension of this probabilistic analysis, we can see that an aunt and niece have 0.25 genetic relatedness, and first cousins 0.125.

If genetic similarity contributes to phenotypic similarity for some trait, it is logical to expect that a pair of close genetic relatives will be more phenotypically similar than a pair of individuals chosen at random from the population at large. Thus, by comparing the phenotypic variation among a well-defined set of genetic relatives with the phenotypic variation of the entire population over some range of environments, it is possible to estimate the heritability of a trait.

Heritability of bill depth in Darwin's finches

The finches observed by Darwin in the Galápagos Islands (often referred to as "Darwin's finches") provide an example of a population for which geneticists have measured the heritability of a trait under natural conditions in the field. Scientists studied the medium ground finch, *Geospiza fortis,* on the island of Daphne Major by banding many of the individual birds in the population (**Fig. 19.16a**). They then measured the depth of the bill for the mother, father, and offspring in each nest on the island and calculated how the bill depth of the offspring correlated with the average bill depth of the mother and father (called the *midparent value*).

The results, depicted in **Fig. 19.16b,** show a clear correlation between parents and offspring; parents with deeper bills had offspring with deeper bills, while parents with smaller bill depth had offspring with smaller bill depth. In the figure, the heritability of bill depth, as represented by the slope of the line correlating midparent bill depth to offspring bill depth, is 0.82. This means that roughly 82% of the variation in bill depth in this population of Darwin's finches is attributable to genetic variation among individuals in the population; the other 18% results from variation in the environment. If the environment had had no influence at all on the trait, then the slope of the line representing the heritability of bill depth, that is, correlating bill depth in parents with bill depth in offspring, would be 1.0 (**Fig. 19.16c**).

Now consider a population in which the bill depth for parents and their offspring is, on average, no more or less similar than the bill depths for any pair of individuals chosen from the population at random. In such a population, there is no correlation between the bill depth trait in parents and in offspring, and a plot of midparent and offspring bill depths produces a circular "cloud" of points (**Fig. 19.16d**).

Figure 19.16 Measuring the heritability of bill depth in populations of Darwin's finches. (a) *G. fortis* with bands placed by scientists. **(b)** The correlation between beak size of offspring and their midparent value (the average of the parents' beak size) is 0.90 both in 1976 (*red circles*) and 1978 (*blue circles*), even though the mean beak size increased due to a drought in 1978. This correlation shows constant high heritability independent of environmental change. Note that high heritability does *not* mean that a trait is constant: beak size is highly variable (note range of axes) and varies over time (displacement of slopes). **(c)** Results if heritability were 1.0. **(d)** Results if heritability were 0.0.

(a)

(b) Correlation between parents and offspring

(c) If the heritability were 1.0

Midparent bill depth (mm)

(d) If the heritability were 0.0

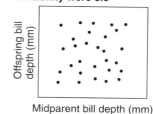

Midparent bill depth (mm)

From these examples, you can conclude that phenotypic similarity among genetically related individuals may provide evidence for the heritability of a trait. However, conversion of the phenotypic similarity among genetic relatives to a measure of heritability depends on a crucial assumption: that the distribution of genetic relatives is random with respect to environmental conditions experienced by the population. In the finch example, we assumed that parents and their offspring do not experience environments that are any more similar than the environments of unrelated individuals.

In nature, however, there may be reasons why genetic relatives violate this assumption by inhabiting similar environments. With finches, for example, all offspring produced by a mother and father during a breeding season normally hatch and grow in a single nest where they receive food from their parents. Because bill depth affects a finch's capacity to forage for food, the amount of feeding in a nest correlates with parental bill depth, for reasons quite distinct from genetic similarities.

One way to reduce the confounding variable of environmental similarity is to remove eggs from the nest of one pair of parents and randomly place them in nests built by other parents in the population; this random relocation of eggs is called **cross-fostering.** In heritability studies of animals that receive parental care, cross-fostering helps randomize environmental conditions. Controlling for both environmental conditions and breeding crosses is a fundamental part of the experimental design of heritability studies carried out on wild and domesticated organisms.

Measuring the heritability of polygenic traits in humans

Mating does not occur at random with respect to phenotypes in human populations, and researchers cannot apply techniques for controlling environmental conditions and breeding crosses to studies of such populations. Nonetheless, in most human societies, family members share similar family and cultural environments. Thus, phenotypic similarity between genetic relatives may result either from genetic similarities or similar environments or, most often, both. How can you distinguish the effects of genetic similarity from the effects of a shared environment?

One way is to study monozygotic, "identical" twins given up for adoption shortly after birth and raised in different families. In such a pair of identical twins, any phenotypic similarity should be the result of genetic similarity. At first glance, then, the study of adopted identical twins eliminates the confounding effects of a similar family environment. Further scrutiny, however, shows that this is often not true. Many pairs of twins are adopted by different genetic relatives; the adoptions often occur in the same geographic region (usually in the same state and even the same city); and families wishing to adopt must satisfy many criteria, including job and financial stability and a certain family

size. As a result, the two families adopting a pair of twins are likely to be more similar than a pair of families chosen at random, and this similarity can reduce the phenotypic differences between the twins. A valid scientific study of separated twins must take these factors into consideration.

A related approach is to compare the phenotypic differences between different sets of genetic relatives, particularly different types of twins (**Fig. 19.17a**). For example, monozygotic (MZ) twins, which are the result of a split in the zygote after fertilization, are genetically identical because they come from a single sperm and a single egg; they share all alleles at all loci and thus have a genetic relatedness of 1.0. By contrast, dizygotic (DZ) twins, which are the result of different sperm from a single father fertilizing two different maternal eggs, are like any pair of siblings born at separate times; they have a genetic relatedness of 0.5 (which actually means that their dissimilarity is only 50% of the average dissimilarity between two unrelated individuals). Comparing the phenotypic differences between a pair of MZ twins with the phenotypic differences between a pair of DZ twins can help distinguish between the effects of genes and family environment.

Consider a trait in which the differences in phenotype among individuals in the population arise entirely from differences in the environment experienced by each individual, that is, a trait for which the heritability is 0.0 (**Fig. 19.17b1**). For this trait, you would expect the phenotypic differences among many pairs of MZ twins to be as great as the differences among many pairs of DZ twins. The fact that the MZ twins are more closely related genetically has no effect.

Now consider a trait for which differences in phenotypes among individuals in a population arise entirely from genetic differences, that is, a trait for which the heritability is 1.0 (**Fig. 19.17b2**). Since MZ twins have a genetic relatedness of 1.0, they always show 100% concordance in expression: If one expresses the trait, the other does as well. The concordance of trait expression between unrelated individuals varies based on the commonality of the trait (as shown in Fig. 19.17b2). Dizygotic twins would display greater concordance than genetically unrelated individuals, but less than monozygotic twins. In the highly simplified case of a dominant trait caused by an allele at a single autosomal gene, dizygotic twins would show a level of concordance that is halfway between the unrelated value and 100%. In reality, nearly all traits are affected by multiple genes that may have dominant, recessive, semidominant, and interacting effects, and the heritabilities of nearly all traits lie between 0.0 and 1.0.

The concept of heritability is often used incorrectly by people who are not familiar with its scientific derivation. A measured heritability is a statistical value that is only meaningful in the context of a population, not an individual. Furthermore, the heritability of a trait applies only to a particular population in a particular environment, where environment includes every influence on organisms outside of their genomes.

Figure 19.17 The impact of heritability on the concordance of dominant trait expression in two children raised in the same family environment. **(a)** Monozygotic and dizygotic twins have different genetic origins. **(b)** The frequency with which a second child will share a trait expressed by a first child. *(1)* At one extreme are hypothetical traits associated with a heritability of 0.0. Irrespective of the frequency of trait expression, no differences would be observed in a comparison of monozygotic twins, dizygotic twins, or situations where one or both children are adopted. *(2)* At the opposite extreme are hypothetical traits associated with a heritability of 1.0. Monozygotic pairs would be concordant, whereas dizygotic pairs of twins would show a concordance halfway between 100% and the concordance found between genetically unrelated children.

(b) Probability that a second child will express a dominant trait that is expressed by a first child

(1) Trait with 0.0 heritability

(2) Trait with 1.0 heritability

MZ = monozygotic twins, DZ = dizygotic twins, UR = unrelated due to adoption

A good example of the impact of environment on heritability comes from an analysis of human height. When measured in a prosperous population with modern standards of food production, human height shows a very high heritability, greater than 0.9. In contrast, in a poor country where not everyone gets enough nutrition, heritability would be much lower.

The explanation comes from the fact that a person's genome determines their maximum height potential. If their nutrition is sufficient, they will reach this potential; further intake of food will make no difference. However, in some underdeveloped countries, great differences exist in the amount of nutrition that any individual is able to consume. This environmental difference will express itself as an increase in the environmental component of height variance.

> Genetic relatedness is a relative term that describes the degree of genetic similarity between two members of the same extended family that is greater than that expected for two unrelated members of the population. The degree to which genetic relatedness correlates with the expression of a trait provides a measure of the trait's heritability.

A trait's heritability determines its potential for evolution

We saw earlier how the selection of preexisting mutations generates evolutionary change. Because the heritability of a multifactorial trait is a measure of the genetic component of its variation, heritability quantifies the potential for selection and thus the potential for evolution from one generation to the next. A trait with high heritability has a large potential for evolution via selection.

To grasp the relationship between heritability, selection, and evolution, consider the number of bristles on the abdomens of fruit flies in a laboratory population of *D. melanogaster*. This fruit fly population exhibits some phenotypic variation in the trait of bristle number. If the trait has a high heritability in the population, the offspring of this original population will closely resemble their parents in bristle number (**Fig. 19.18**). If, however,

Figure 19.18 Relationship between midparent number of abdominal bristles and bristle number in offspring for a hypothetical laboratory population of *Drosophila*.

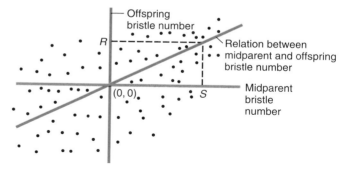

you select as parents of the next generation only those flies among the top 15% in bristle number, the average bristle number among these breeders of the next generation will be greater than the average bristle number in the population as a whole. This artificial selection in conjunction with the high heritability of the trait will produce an F_1 generation in which the average bristle number is greater than the average bristle number in the previous generation. In other words, the artificial selection imposed by the experimenter will induce an evolutionary change whose magnitude is related to the heritability of the trait. If the heritability of bristle number were zero, there would be no evolutionary change. (Figure 19.16 also shows the impact of natural selection on a trait with high heritability.)

A mathematical model of the relation between heritability and evolution

Let S represent the average trait value (in this case, the average bristle number) of breeding individuals in the parental population. This value is measured as the difference between the value of this trait for *parents* and the value of the trait in the entire parental population (both breeding and nonbreeding individuals). S is then a measure of the strength of selection on the trait; as such, it is called the **selection differential.** Now let R represent the average trait value in the offspring of these breeding parents, which is measured as the difference between the trait's value for *offspring* and its value in the entire parental population of breeding and nonbreeding individuals. Used in this way, R signifies the **response to selection,** that is, the amount of evolution, or change in mean trait value, resulting from selection.

The heritability of the trait (arbitrarily designated as h^2), as seen in the slope of the line relating parental to offspring trait values in Fig. 12.16, determines the relationship between S and R.

$$R = h^2 S \qquad (19.12)$$

In other words, the strength of selection (S) and the heritability of a trait (h^2) directly determine the trait's amount or rate of evolution in each generation. This relationship is the primary reason population and evolutionary geneticists consider the ability to measure heritability so important.

Variations in polygenic traits arise rapidly because of increased opportunities for change

Geneticists have long used bristle number in *Drosophila* as a model for understanding the variation, selection, and evolution of quantitative traits. Early laboratory studies of selection acting on bristle number showed that the trait has substantial heritability in *Drosophila*, and it evolves rapidly in response to selection for either high or low

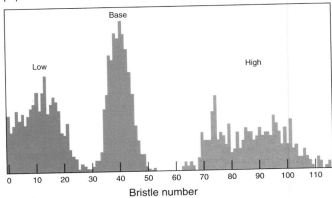

Figure 19.19 Evolution of abdominal bristle number in response to artificial selection in *Drosophila*. Bristle number distributions in different populations under selection for low (*green*) or high (*orange*) values, compared to distributions in a population not subjected to selection (base in *blue*).

bristle number (**Fig. 19.19**). Two results from these early studies were particularly striking. First, selection can rapidly lead to phenotypes not seen in the original population. After 35 generations of artificial selection for high or low bristle number, no overlap was evident between the unselected and the selected populations. Some of the change in bristle number probably arose from reassortment and changes in frequency of existing alleles, without the appearance of new alleles. However, traits such as bristle number continue to evolve in response to selection for many generations. This observation suggests that new mutation is an additional source of variation in the population.

Experimenters have examined the contribution of mutation to genetic variation in bristle number (and by extension, other quantitative traits) through studies of highly inbred lines of *Drosophila* that at first had low or no genetic variation in bristle number. With these inbred lines, selection could occur only in the presence of new mutations affecting bristle number. Quantitative analyses revealed a significant selection-driven evolution of bristle number, which means that new mutations affecting bristle number arise in a population at a substantial rate (**Fig. 19.20**). These results highlight a key characteristic of polygenic traits: If many polymorphic genes contribute to a trait, new variation in the trait may arise rapidly even if the mutation rate per gene is low, because a change at any one of many loci can cause a phenotypic difference.

Populations eventually reach a selective plateau

The bristle-number experiments with *Drosophila* showed that after many generations, populations eventually reach a selective plateau at which, even with continued selection, the average bristle number does not change for many

DNA Analysis and 9/11 Victim Identification

In the wake of the 9/11/01 World Trade Center (WTC) attacks in New York City, the scientific community refined techniques of DNA analysis to work successfully with badly damaged DNA and the lack of any prior tissue samples from some victims. Degraded DNA samples are common to forensic cases and missing persons investigations, and improvements have extended the range of information recoverable from highly degraded specimens.

The crime scene following the WTC disaster covered 17 acres from which searchers retrieved 19,893 separate body parts, including a single tooth. Fewer than 300 bodies were intact, and only 12 could be identified by sight. In addition, the DNA fragments in many of the recovered samples were very scarce and very small. The traditional means of DNA fingerprinting, which require long, intact pieces of DNA, would not be sufficient to identify the victims of 9/11.

To deal with this difficult situation, in October of 2001 the National Institute of Justice established the WTC Kinship and Data Analysis Panel (KADAP), a working group composed of 25 scientific experts. Over the next three and a half years, KADAP met monthly to develop and evaluate new technologies for the analysis of DNA remains.

The DNA analysis and victim identification process had three main phases. First, the researchers gathered as much information as possible about the missing individuals. Personal effects, such as the victims' hairbrushes, razors, combs, dirty clothes, and toothbrushes, were one source of information; DNA reference samples from family members—including children, spouses, siblings, and parents—were another.

In phase two, these personal effects and family reference samples were subjected to DNA typing tests, including PCR analysis of various microsatellite and SNP alleles, described previously in Chapter 11. In some cases, the allele constitution of the missing person could be reconstructed directly from DNA gathered from personal effects. In other cases, a victim's microsatellite and SNP alleles could be inferred only through genetic analysis of surviving children and spouses: Any allele that was present in a child and not in the surviving parent must have come from the victim's genome.

In phase three, the resultant DNA profiles were loaded into computer databases for matching with DNA extracted from the human remains found at the WTC site. Several companies contributed to this third phase, including Bode Technology Group, Celera Genomics, and Orchid GeneScreen. Gene Codes Forensics developed the Mass Fatality Identification System (M-FISys) software to deal with the need for high-throughput analysis.

In February 2005, the New York medical examiner's office announced that it had "exhausted all current technologies" and ended efforts to identify the remains. Of the 2749 people who died, 1100 remained unidentified. In addition, about 10,000 unidentified bone and tissue fragments had not yet been matched with the list of the missing. These will be held in the New York medical examiner's laboratory until identification is possible.

The technologies developed in the aftermath of the WTC disaster were applicable in the aftermath of the tsunami that struck Thailand on December 26, 2004, which killed an estimated 174,000–275,000 people. Thai forensic experts and disaster teams from more than 25 other nations have made positive matches on 2156 bodies, most of them tourists killed while on vacation. These identification efforts, based on continually improving strategies of DNA analysis, will continue well into the future.

Figure 19.20 The effect of new mutations on mean bristle number in *Drosophila*. The average bristle number in a population under artificial selection for a reduced number over many generations is indicated with the *diamond, pentagon,* and *up-triangle* data points (*green*): Populations not under selection are indicated with the *down-triangle, circle,* and *square* data points (*red*).

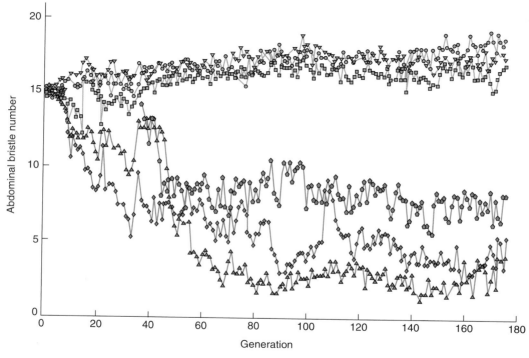

more generations. The existence of such evolutionary plateaus suggests that selection can, for a time, eliminate all genetic variation in a trait and that the potential for new mutations allowing further extremes in phenotypes has been exhausted, usually because the most extreme phenotypes are incompatible with viability.

A trait with high heritability has a large potential for leading to evolution by selection. In polygenic traits, new variation due to mutation may occur rapidly because of the number of loci involved. A selective plateau, at which the average phenotype does not change, is eventually reached.

Connections

We have seen that populations at Hardy-Weinberg equilibrium have unchanging allele frequencies, and in one generation, they achieve genotype frequencies of p^2, $2pq$, and q^2, which are subsequently maintained. In nature, where populations are rarely at complete Hardy-Weinberg equilibrium, however, natural selection acts on differences in fitness to alter allele frequencies. New mutations, genetic drift, and heterozygous advantage can also alter the allele frequencies of a population. For quantitative traits influenced by the alleles of two or more genes as well as by the interaction of those alleles with the environment, the heritability of a trait, that is, the proportion of its phenotypic variation attributable to genetic variation, determines its potential for evolution by mutation, selection, and genetic drift.

In Chapter 20, we look at evolution from the point of view of the molecular mechanisms that propel it. In that chapter, we examine the various ways in which changes at the genomic level continually reshuffle the genetic deck to create the ever-changing abundance of life-forms that inhabit the earth.

ESSENTIAL CONCEPTS

1. A population is defined as a unit entity by its allele frequencies and genotype frequencies, which together make up a gene pool. Although an actual gene pool can only be determined empirically by counting all existing alleles, population geneticists have developed analytical and computational models for estimating the genetic and phenotypic variations of a population and how they may change over time.

2. With the simplifying assumptions of an ideal population of very large size, where individuals mate at random, no new mutations appear, no individuals enter or leave, and there are no genotype-dependent differences in fitness, it becomes possible to derive a simple binomial equation that describes the precise relationships existing between allele, genotype, and phenotype frequencies. This equation, $p^2 + 2pq + q^2 = 1$, is called the Hardy-Weinberg law.

3. A population satisfying the Hardy-Weinberg assumptions is said to be at Hardy-Weinberg equilibrium. In such a population, allele frequencies remain constant from one generation to the next, and the genotype frequencies of p^2, $2pq$, and q^2 are achieved in one generation, after which they are maintained.

4. In natural populations, conditions always deviate at least slightly from the Hardy-Weinberg assumptions. And yet, even with these deviations from ideal conditions, the Hardy-Weinberg equation provides remarkably good estimates of allele, genotype, and phenotype frequencies over the *short run*. Over the *long run*, however, the Hardy-Weinberg equation is rarely applicable for predictive purposes. But it serves a critical role in providing the foundation for both analytical and stochastic methods that do incorporate the various factors responsible for deviation from equilibrium conditions.

5. Monte Carlo simulations provide a computational method for modeling allele frequencies in populations of finite size, which undergo genetic drift. In populations with two alleles having equivalent phenotypic effects and present initially at equal frequencies, the median number of generations to fixation is roughly equal to the total number of gene copies in breeding individuals. Evolution consists of changes in allele frequency over time. Selection acting on genotype-dependent differences in fitness can drive evolution. Selection does not entirely eliminate deleterious recessive alleles from a population. One reason for this is balancing selection.

6. For quantitative traits, the environmental variance is a measure of the influence of environment on phenotypic variation. Similarly, genetic variance measures the contribution of genes to phenotypic variation. Total phenotype variance is the sum of genetic variance and environmental variance.

7. Measures of environmental, genetic, and total phenotype variance make it possible to define the heritability of a trait as the proportion of total phenotype variance attributable to genetic variance. With traits for which the number and identity of contributing genes remain unknown and genetic clones cannot be obtained, it is possible to correlate phenotypic variation with the genetic relatedness of individuals—that is, the average fraction of common alleles at all gene loci that the individuals share because they inherited them from a common ancestor—to measure the heritability of a trait.

8. To ascertain the heritability of a human trait, population geneticists often turn to studies of twins. The most useful approach is to compare the phenotypic differences between pairs of monozygotic and dizygotic twins. Environmental changes can always influence the degree of heritability.

9. A trait's heritability determines its potential for evolution. In the case of polygenic traits, opportunities for mutation exist at many loci, therefore allowing relatively rapid changes to occur. Eventually a trait reaches a selective plateau at which no further average variation occurs.

On Our Website | www.mhhe.com/hartwell4

Annotated Suggested Readings and Links to Other Websites

- More on correlations between mutant hemoglobin alleles and malaria
- Monte Carlo simulations of effects of population size, drift, and unequal allelic fitness on changes in allele frequencies over time

Specialized Topics

- Modern changes in allele frequencies over time in Darwin's finches
- The use of data obtained from identical twins raised apart to determine genetic and nongenetic contributions to behavioral traits in human beings

Solved Problems

I. A population called the "founder generation," consisting of 2000 *AA* individuals, 2000 *Aa* individuals, and 6000 *aa* individuals is established on a remote island. Mating within this population occurs at random, the three genotypes are selectively neutral, and mutations occur at a negligible rate.

   a. What are the frequencies of alleles *A* and *a* in the founder generation?

   b. Is the founder generation at Hardy-Weinberg equilibrium?

   c. What is the frequency of the *A* allele in the second generation (that is, the generation subsequent to the founder generation)?

   d. What are the frequencies for the *AA*, *Aa*, and *aa* genotypes in the second generation?

   e. Is the second generation at Hardy-Weinberg equilibrium?

   f. What are the frequencies for the *AA*, *Aa*, and *aa* genotypes in the third generation?

Answer

This question requires calculation of allele and genotype frequencies and an understanding of the Hardy-Weinberg equilibrium principle.

   a. To calculate allele frequencies, count the total alleles represented in individuals with each genotype and divide by the total number of alleles.

Number of individuals	Number of *A* alleles	Number of *a* alleles
2000 *AA*	4000	0
2000 *Aa*	2000	2000
6000 *aa*	0	12,000
Total	6000	14,000

The frequency of the A allele (p) = 6000/20,000 = 0.3.
The frequency of the a allele (q) = 14,000/20,000 = 0.7.

   b. If a population is at Hardy-Weinberg equilibrium, the genotype frequencies are p^2, $2pq$, and q^2. We calculated in part *a* that $p = 0.3$ and $q = 0.7$ in this population. Therefore,

$$p^2 = 0.09$$
$$2pq = 2(0.3)(0.7) = 0.42$$
$$q^2 = 0.49$$

For a population of 10,000 individuals, the number of individuals with each genotype, if the population were at equilibrium and the allele frequencies were $p = 0.3$ and $p = 0.7$, would be *AA*, 900; *Aa*, 4200; and *aa*, 4900. *The founder population described therefore is not at equilibrium.*

   c. Given the conditions of random mating, selectively neutral alleles, and no new mutations, allele frequencies do not change from one generation to the next; $p = 0.3$, *and* $q = 0.7$.

d. *The genotype frequencies for the second genera-tion would be those calculated for part* b *because in one generation the population will go to equi-librium.* $AA = p^2 = 0.09$; $Aa = 2pq = 0.42$; and $aa = q^2 = 0.49$.

e. *Yes, in one generation a population not at equilib-rium will go to equilibrium if mating is random and there is no selection or significant mutation.*

f. *The genotype frequencies will be the same in the third generation as in the second generation.*

II. Two alleles have been found at the X-linked phos-phoglucomutase gene (*Pgm*) in *Drosophila persimilis* populations in California. The frequency of the Pgm^A allele is 0.25, while the frequency of the Pgm^B allele is 0.75. Assuming the population is at Hardy-Weinberg equilibrium, what are the expected genotype frequen-cies in males and females?

Answer

This problem requires application of the concept of allele and genotype frequencies to X-linked genes. For X-linked genes, males (XY) have only one copy of the X chromosome, so the genotype frequency is equal to the allele frequency. Therefore, $p = 0.25$ and $q = 0.75$. *The frequency of male flies with genotype* $X^{PgmA}Y$ *is 0.25; the frequency of males with genotype* $X^{PgmB}Y$ *is 0.75.* Three genotypes exist for females: $X^{PgmA} X^{PgmA}$, $X^{PgmA} X^{PgmB}$, and $X^{PgmB} X^{PgmB}$ corresponding to p^2, $2pq$, and q^2. *The frequencies of female flies with these three genotypes are* $(0.25)^2$, $2(0.25)(0.75)$, and $(0.75)^2$; or 0.0625, 0.375, and 0.5625, respectively.

III. Two hypothetical lizard populations found on oppo-site sides of a mountain in the Arizonan desert have two alleles (A^F, A^S) of a single gene *A* with the fol-lowing three genotype frequencies:

	$A^F A^F$	$A^F A^S$	$A^S A^S$
Population 1	38	44	18
Population 2	0	80	20

a. What is the allele frequency of A^F in the two populations?

b. Do either of the two populations appear to be at Hardy-Weinberg equilibrium?

c. A huge flood opened a canyon in the mountain range separating populations 1 and 2. They were then able to migrate such that the two populations, which were of equal size, mixed completely and mated at random. What are the frequencies of the three genotypes ($A^F A^F$, $A^F A^S$, and $A^S A^S$) in the next generation of the single new population of lizards?

Answer

This question requires calculation of allele frequencies and genotype frequencies in existing and in newly created populations.

a. The frequency of allele *A* is calculated in the fol-lowing way:

$$38 \ A^F A^F \times 2 \qquad 76 \ A^F \ alleles$$

$$44 \ A^F A^S \times 2 \qquad \frac{44 \ A^F \ alleles}{120 \ A^F \ alleles}$$

120 A^F alleles/200 total alleles $= 0.6$.

b. For population 1, the allele frequencies are $p = 0.6$ and $q = 0.4$. Genotype frequencies when the popu-lation is in equilibrium are

$$p^2 = (0.6)^2 = 0.36$$

$$2pq = 2(0.6)(0.4) = 0.48$$

$$q^2 = (0.4)^2 = 0.16$$

For population 1, which consists of 100 individu-als, the equilibrium would be 36 $A^F A^F$, 48 $A^F A^S$, and 16 $A^S A^S$ lizards. *Population 1 does seem to be at equilibrium.* (Sampling error and small population size could lead to slight variations from the expected frequencies.) For population 2, the allele frequency (*p*) is based solely on the number of A^F alleles from the 80 $A^F A^S$ individuals. The total number of alleles $= 200$, so the frequency of A^F alleles is 80/200 or 0.4. The genotype frequencies for a population at equilibrium would be

$$p^2 = (0.4)^2 = 0.16$$

$$2pq = 2(0.4)(0.6) = 0.48$$

$$q^2 = (0.6)^2 = 0.36$$

Population 2 does not seem to be at equilibrium.

c. The combination of the two populations of lizards results in one population with the following allele frequencies:

A^F *alleles*

$A^F A^F$	38×2	76
$A^F A^S$	44	44
$A^F A^S$	80	80
Total:		200

A^S *alleles*

$A^F A^S$	44	44
$A^F A^S$	80	80
$A^S A^S$	18×2	36
$A^S A^S$	20×2	40
Total:		200

The allele frequencies are 200/400, or 0.5, for both *p* and *q*. *The genotype frequencies in the next generation will therefore be*

$$p^2 = (0.5)^2 = 0.25$$

$$2pq = 2(0.5)(0.5) = 0.5$$

$$q^2 = (0.5)^2 = 0.25$$

Problems

Vocabulary

1. Choose the best matching phrase in the right column for each of the terms in the left column.

a. fitness	1. the genotype with the highest fitness is the heterozygote
b. gene pool	2. chance fluctuations in allele frequency
c. fitness cost	3. ability to survive and reproduce
d. allele frequency	4. proportion of total phenotypic variance representation attributed to genetic variance
e. genotype frequency representation	5. collection of alleles carried by all members of a population
f. heterozygote advantage	6. p^2 and q^2
g. equilibrium frequency	7. p and q
h. genetic drift	8. the advantage of a particular genotype in one situation is a disadvantage in another situation
i. heritability	9. frequency of an allele at which $\Delta q = 0$

Section 19.1

2. In a certain population of frogs, 120 are green, 60 are brownish green, and 20 are brown. The allele for brown is denoted G^B, while that for green is G^G, and these two alleles show incomplete dominance relative to each other.
   a. What are the genotype frequencies in the population?
   b. What are the allele frequencies of G^B and G^G in this population?
   c. What are the expected frequencies of the genotypes if the population is at Hardy-Weinberg equilibrium?

3. Which of the following populations are at Hardy-Weinberg equilibrium?

Population	AA	Aa	aa
a	0.25	0.50	0.25
b	0.10	0.74	0.16
c	0.64	0.27	0.09
d	0.46	0.50	0.04
e	0.81	0.18	0.01

4. A dominant mutation in *Drosophila* called *Delta* causes changes in wing morphology in *Delta /+* heterozygotes. Homozygosity for this mutation (*Delta / Delta*) is lethal. In a population of 150 flies, it was determined that 60 had normal wings and 90 had abnormal wings.
   a. What are the allele frequencies in this population?
   b. Using the allele frequencies calculated in part *a*, how many total zygotes must be produced by this population in order for you to count 160 viable adults in the next generation?
   c. Given that there is random mating, no migration, and no mutation, and ignoring the effects of genetic drift, what are the expected numbers of the different genotypes in the next generation if 160 viable offspring of the population in part *a* are counted?
   d. Is this next generation at Hardy-Weinberg equilibrium? Why or why not?

5. A large, random mating population is started with the following proportion of individuals for the indicated blood types:

   0.5 MM

   0.2 MN

   0.3 NN

   This blood type gene is autosomal and the *M* and *N* alleles are codominant.
   a. Is this population at Hardy-Weinberg equilibrium?
   b. What will be the allele and genotype frequencies after one generation under the conditions assumed for the Hardy-Weinberg equilibrium?
   c. What will be the allele and genotype frequencies after two generations under the conditions assumed for the Hardy-Weinberg equilibrium?

6. A gene called Q has two alleles, Q^F and Q^G, that encode alternative forms of a red blood cell protein that allows blood group typing. A different, independently segregating gene called R has two alleles, R^C and R^D, permitting a different kind of blood group typing. A random, representative population of football fans was examined, and on the basis of their blood typing, the following distribution of genotypes was inferred (all genotypes were equally distributed between males and females):

$Q^F Q^F R^C R^C$	202
$Q^F Q^G R^C R^C$	101
$Q^G Q^G R^C R^C$	101
$Q^F Q^F R^C R^D$	372
$Q^F Q^G R^C R^D$	186
$Q^G Q^G R^C R^D$	186
$Q^F Q^F R^D R^D$	166
$Q^F Q^G R^D R^D$	83
$Q^G Q^G R^D R^D$	83

   This sample contains 1480 fans.
   a. Is the population at Hardy-Weinberg equilibrium with respect to either or both of the Q and R genes?
   b. After one generation of random mating within this group, what fraction of the *next* generation of football fans will be $Q^F Q^F$ (independent of their R genotype)?

c. After one generation of random mating, what fraction of the *next* generation of football fans will be $R^C R^C$ (independent of their Q genotype)?

d. What is the chance that the first child of a $Q^F Q^G R^C R^D$ female and a $Q^F Q^F R^C R^D$ male will be a $Q^F Q^G R^D R^D$ male?

7. A population with an allele frequency (p) of 0.5 and a genotype frequency (p^2) of 0.25 is at equilibrium. How can you explain the fact that a population with an allele frequency (p) of 0.1 and a genotype frequency (p^2) of 0.01 is also at equilibrium?

8. When an allele is dominant, why does it not always increase to produce the phenotype proportion of 3:1 (3/4 dominant : 1/4 recessive individuals) in a population?

9. It is the year 1998, and the men and women sailors (in equal numbers) on the American ship the *Medischol Bounty* have mutinied in the South Pacific and settled on the island of Bali Hai, where they have come into contact with the local Polynesian population. Of the 400 sailors that come ashore on the island, 324 have MM blood type, 4 have the NN blood type, and 72 have the MN blood type. Already on the island are 600 Polynesians between the ages of 19 and 23. In the Polynesian population, the allele frequency of the *M* allele is 0.06, and the allele frequency of the *N* allele is 0.94. No other people come to the island over the next 10 years.

   a. What is the allele frequency of the *N* allele in the sailor population that mutinied?

   b. It is the year 2008, and 1000 children have been born on the island of Bali Hai. If the mixed population of 1000 young people on the island in 1998 mated randomly and the different blood group phenotypes had no effect on viability, how many of the 1000 children would you expect to have MN blood type?

   c. In fact, 50 children have MM blood type, 850 have MN blood type, and 100 have NN blood type. What is the observed frequency of the *N* allele among the children?

10. Alkaptonuria is a recessive autosomal genetic disorder associated with darkening of the urine. In the United States, approximately one out of every 250,000 people have alkaptonuria.

   a. Assuming Hardy-Weinberg equilibrium, estimate the frequency of the allele responsible for this trait.

   b. What proportion of people in the U.S. population are carriers for this trait? In this population, what is the ratio of carriers to individuals affected by alkaptonuria?

   c. If a woman without alkaptonuria who had a child with this trait with one husband then remarried, what is the chance that a child produced by her second marriage would have alkaptonuria?

d. Alkaptonuria is a relatively benign condition, so there is little selective advantage to individuals with any genotype; as a result, your assumption of Hardy-Weinberg equilibrium in part *a* is reasonable. Could you also use the assumption of Hardy-Weinberg equilibrium to estimate the allele frequencies and carrier frequencies of more severe recessive autosomal conditions such as cystic fibrosis? Explain.

11. The equation $p^2 + 2pq + q^2 = 1$ representing the Hardy-Weinberg proportions examines genes with only two alleles in a population.

   a. Derive a similar equation describing the equilibrium proportions of genotypes for a gene with three alleles. [*Hint:* Remember that the Hardy-Weinberg equation can be written as the binomial expansion $(p + q)^2$.]

   b. A single gene with three alleles (I^A, I^B, and i) is responsible for the ABO blood groups. Individuals with blood type A can be either $I^A I^A$ or $I^A i$; those with blood type B can be either $I^B I^B$ or $I^B i$; people with AB blood are $I^A I^B$, and type O individuals are ii. Among Armenians, the frequency of I^A is 0.360, the frequency of I^B is 0.104, and the frequency of i is 0.536. Calculate the frequencies of individuals in this population with the four possible blood types, assuming Hardy-Weinberg equilibrium.

12. a. Alleles of genes on the X chromosome can also be at equilibrium, but the equilibrium frequencies under the Hardy-Weinberg assumptions must be calculated separately for the two sexes. For a gene with two alleles A and a at frequencies of p and q, respectively, write expressions that describe the equilibrium frequencies for all the genotypes in men and women.

   b. Approximately 1 in 10,000 males in the United States is afflicted with hemophilia, an X-linked recessive condition. If you assume that the population is at Hardy-Weinberg equilibrium, what proportion of American females would be hemophiliacs? About how many female hemophiliacs would you expect to find among the 100 million women living in the United States?

13. In 1927, the ophthalmologist George Waaler tested 9049 schoolboys in Oslo, Norway for red-green color-blindness and found 8324 of them to be normal and 725 to be color-blind. He also tested 9072 schoolgirls and found 9032 that had normal color vision while 40 were color-blind.

   a. Assuming that the same sex-linked recessive allele *c* causes all forms of red-green color-blindness, calculate the allele frequencies of *c* and *C* (the allele for normal vision) from the data for the schoolboys. (*Note:* Refer to your answer to Problem 12a above.)

   b. Does Waaler's sample demonstrate Hardy-Weinberg equilibrium for this gene? Explain your answer by describing observations that are either consistent or inconsistent with this hypothesis.

On closer analysis of these schoolchildren, Waaler found that there was actually more than one c allele causing color-blindness in his sample: one kind for the "prot" type (c^p) and one for the "deuter" type (c^d) (protanopia and deuteranopia are slightly different forms of red-green color-blindness). Importantly, some of the "normal" females in Waaler's studies were probably of genotype c^p/c^d. Through further analysis of the 40 color-blind females, he found that 3 were prot (c^p/c^p), and 37 were deuter (c^d/c^d).

c. Based on this new information, what is the frequency of the c^p, c^d, and C alleles in the population examined by Waaler? Calculate these values as if the frequencies obey the Hardy-Weinberg equilibrium. (*Note:* Refer to your answer to Problem 11*a* above.)

d. Calculate the frequencies of all genotypes among men and women expected if the population is at equilibrium.

e. Do these results make it more likely or less likely that the population in Oslo is indeed at equilibrium for red-green color-blindness? Explain your reasoning.

14. A new university on a Caribbean island has recruited its 700 faculty members from colleges in France and Kenya. Five hundred came from France and 200 came from Kenya, with equal numbers of men and women in both groups. Upon arrival, you notice that 90 of the French and 75 of the Kenyans express a peculiar trait of rolling their eyes up into their sockets when asked a stupid question. Upon studying this trait, you discover that it is always due to the expression of a dominant allele at a single gene called *Ugh*. Field trips taken to both Kenya and France indicate that the two alleles at the *Ugh* locus are at Hardy-Weinberg equilibrium in both of these separate populations. All of the faculty members arrived on the island single, but after teaching for a few years, they all married other faculty members in a random manner. Among 1000 progeny from these marriages, how many children do you expect will express the eye-rolling phenotype?

15. In *Drosophila,* the vestigial wings recessive allele, *vg*, causes the wings to be very small. A geneticist crossed some true-breeding wild-type males to some vestigial virgin females. The male and female F_1 flies were wild type. He then allowed the F_1 flies to mate and found that 1/4 of the male and female F_2 flies had vestigial wings. He dumped the vestigial F_2 flies into a morgue and allowed the wild-type F_2 flies to mate and produce an F_3 generation.

a. Give the genotype and allele frequencies among the wild-type F_2 flies.

b. What will be the frequencies of wild-type and vestigial flies in the F_3?

c. Assuming the geneticist repeated the selection against the vestigial F_3 flies (that is, he dumped

them in a morgue and allowed the wild-type F_3 flies to mate at random), what will be the frequency of the wild-type allele and mutant alleles in the F_4 generation?

d. Now the geneticist lets all of the F_4 flies mate at random (that is, both wild-type and vestigial flies mate). What will be the frequencies of wild-type and vestigial F_5 flies?

16. A mouse mutation with incomplete dominance ($t = tailless$) causes short tails in heterozygotes (t^+/t). The same mutation acts as a recessive lethal that causes homozygotes (t/t) to die *in utero*. In a population consisting of 150 mice, 60 are t^+/t^+ and 90 are heterozygotes.

a. What are the allele frequencies in this population?

b. Given that there is random mating among mice, no migration, and no mutation, and ignoring the effects of random genetic drift, what are the expected numbers of the different genotypes in this next generation if 200 offspring are born?

c. Two populations (called Dom 1 and Dom 2) of mice come into contact and interbreed randomly. These populations initially are composed of the following numbers of wild-type (t^+/t^+) homozygotes and tailless (t^+/t) heterozygotes.

	Dom 1	Dom 2
Wild type	16	48
Tailless	48	36

What are the frequencies of the two genotypes in the next generation?

Section 19.2

17. Why is the elimination of a fully recessive deleterious allele by natural selection difficult in a large population and less so in a small population?

18. Would you expect to see a greater Δq from one generation to the next in a population with an allele frequency (q) of 0.2 or in a population with an allele frequency of 0.02? Assume relative fitness is the same in both populations and that the equilibrium frequency for q is 0.01.

19. You have identified an autosomal gene that contributes to tail size in male guppies, with a dominant allele B for large tails and a recessive allele b for small tails. Female guppies of all genotypes have similar tail sizes. You know that female guppies usually mate with males with the largest tails, but the effects of population density and the ratio of the sexes on this preference have not been studied. You therefore place an equal number of males in three tanks. In tank 1, the number of females is twice the number of males. In tank two, the numbers of males and females are equal. In tank 3, there are half as many females as males. After mating, you find the following proportions of small-tailed males among the progeny: tank 1, 16%; tank 2, 25%; tank 3, 30%.

a. In your original population, 25% of the males have small tails. Assuming that the allele frequencies in males and females are the same, calculate the frequencies of B and b in your original population.

b. Calculate Δq for each tank.

c. If $w_{BB} = 1.0$, what is w_{Bb} for each tank?

d. If $w_{BB} = 1.0$, is w_{bb} less than, equal to, or greater than 1.0 for each tank?

20. An allele of the *G6PD* gene acts in a recessive manner to cause sensitivity to fava beans, resulting in a hemolytic reaction (lysis of red blood cells) after ingestion of the beans. The same allele also confers dominant resistance to malaria. The heterozygote has an advantage in a region where malaria is prevalent. Will the equilibrium frequency (q_e) be the same for an African and a North American country? What factors affect q_e?

21. In Europe, the frequency of the CF^- allele causing the recessive autosomal disease cystic fibrosis is about 0.04. Cystic fibrosis causes death before reproduction in virtually all cases.

a. Determine values of fitness (w) and of the selection coefficient (s) for the unaffected, carrier, and affected genotypes.

b. Determine the average fitness at birth of the population as a whole with respect to the cystic fibrosis trait ($\overline{w}$) and the expected change in allele frequency over one generation (Δq) when measured at the birth of the next generation.

Now suppose that the mutation rate from CF^+ to CF^- alleles is 1×10^{-6}.

c. What is the expected evolutionary equilibrium frequency ($\hat{q}$) of the CF^- allele? Is this larger or smaller than the observed frequency?

d. Without changing the value of s for the CF^-/CF^- genotype you calculated in part *a*, propose an explanation that might resolve the discrepancy between the observed and expected frequencies of the CF^- allele you noted in part *c*.

Section 19.3

22. How can each of the following be used in determining the role of genetic and/or environmental factors in phenotypic variation in different organisms?

a. genetic clones

b. human monozygotic versus dizygotic twins

c. cross-fostering

23. Which of the following statements would be true of a human trait that has high heritability in a population of one country?

a. The phenotypic difference within monozygotic twin pairs would be about the same as the phenotypic differences among members of dizygotic twin pairs.

b. There is very little phenotypic variation between monozygotic twins but high variability between dizygotic twins.

c. The trait would have the same heritability in a population of another country.

24. a. Studies have indicated that for pairs of twins raised in the same family, the environmental similarity for monozygotic (MZ) twins is not significantly different from the environmental similarity for fraternal (dizygotic or DZ) twins. Why is this an important fact for calculations of heritability?

b. If you wished to determine the heritability of a particular trait in humans, would it be more useful to study MZ or DZ twins? Explain.

25. A study published in 1937 examined the average differences between pairs of twins [either monozygotic (MZ) or dizygotic (DZ)] and pairs of siblings for three different traits: height, weight, and intelligence quotient (IQ) as measured by the Stanford-Binet test. (The concept of "IQ" is extremely controversial as it is unclear to what extent IQ tests measure native intelligence, but for this problem, consider IQ as a measurable phenotype even if its significance is unknown.) Some of the MZ twins were raised together in the same household (RT), while other MZ twins were raised apart in different families (RA). The results of this study are as follows:

	MZ/RT	MZ/RA	DZ	Siblings
Height	1.7 cm	1.8 cm	4.4 cm	4.5 cm
Weight	1.86 kg	4.49 kg	4.54 kg	4.72 kg
IQ	5.9	8.2	9.9	9.8

a. Which of these three traits appears to have the highest heritability? The lowest heritability?

b. The Centers for Disease Control and Prevention (CDC) of the National Institutes of Health recently reported that in the United States during the period 1960–2002 the average weight of a 15-year-old boy increased from 135.5 pounds (61.46 kg) to 150.3 pounds (68.17 kg). During the same period, the average height of a 15-year-old boy increased from 67.5 inches (171.5 cm) to 68.4 inches (173.7 cm). How do these statistics match your estimates of heritability from part *a*?

26. Two different groups of scientists studying a rare trait in ground squirrels report very different heritabilities. What factors influencing heritability values make possible for both conclusions to be correct?

27. Human geneticists have found the Finnish population to be very useful for studies of a variety of conditions. The Finnish population is small; Finns have extensive church records documenting lineages; and few people have migrated into the population. The frequency of some recessive disorders is higher in the Finnish population than elsewhere in the world; and diseases such as PKU and cystic fibrosis that are common elsewhere do not occur in the Finnish population.

    a. How would a population geneticist explain these variations in disease occurrence?

    b. The Finnish population is also a source of information for the study of quantitative traits. The genetic basis of schizophrenia is one question that can be explored in this population. What advantage(s) and disadvantage(s) can you imagine for studying complex traits based on the Finnish population structure?

28. Two traits with similar phenotype variance exist in a population. If one trait has two major genes and six minor loci that influence the phenotype, and the second trait has 12 minor loci and no major genes affecting the phenotype, which trait would you expect to respond most consistently to selection? Explain.

29. Two alleles at one locus produce 3 distinct phenotypes. Two alleles of two genes lead to 5 distinct phenotypes. Two alleles of six genes lead to 13 distinct phenotypes. (These statements assume that the alleles at any one locus are codominant and that each gene makes an equal contribution to the phenotype.)

    a. Derive a formula to express this relationship. (Let n equal the number of genes.)

    b. Each of the most extreme phenotypes for a trait determined by two alleles at one locus are found in a proportion of 1/4 in the F_2 generation. If there are two alleles of two genes that determine a trait, each extreme phenotype will be present in the F_2 as

1/16 of the population. In common wheat (*Triticum aestivum*), kernel color varies from red to white and the genes controlling the color act additively, that is, alleles for each gene are semidominant and each gene contributes equally to the color. A true-breeding red variety is crossed to a true-breeding white variety, and 1/256 of the F_2 have red kernels and 1/256 have white kernels. How many genes control kernel color in this cross?

30. In a certain plant, leaf size is determined by four independently assorting genes acting additively. Thus, alleles A, B, C, and D each adds 4 cm to leaf length and alleles A', B', C', and D' each adds 2 cm to leaf length. Therefore, an A/A, B/B, C/C, D/D plant has leaves 32 cm long and an A'/A', B'/B', C'/C', D'/D' plant has leaves 16 cm long.

    a. If true-breeding plants with leaves 32 cm long are crossed to true-breeding plants with leaves 16 cm long, the F_1 will have leaves 24 cm long, that is, A/A', B/B', C/C', D/D'. List all possible leaf lengths and their expected frequencies in the F_2 generation produced from these F_1 plants.

    b. Now assume that in a randomly mating population the following allele frequencies occur:

    frequency of A = 0.9
    frequency of A' = 0.1
    frequency of B = 0.9
    frequency of B' = 0.1
    frequency of C = 0.1
    frequency of C' = 0.9
    frequency of D = 0.5
    frequency of D' = 0.5

    Calculate separately the expected frequency in this population of the three possible genotypes for each of the four genes.

    c. What proportion of the plants in the population described in part *b* will have leaves that are 32 cm long?

Evolution at the Molecular Level

Charles Darwin spent 5 years circling the globe collecting specimens. The material acquired on this grand tour provided the basis for his comparative analysis in The Origin of Species, *published some 23 years after he returned to England.*

From December 1831 to October 1836, Charles Darwin circled the globe as naturalist for the HMS *Beagle.* He was 22 years of age when he set sail. With indefatigable energy and insatiable curiosity, he dredged the oceans of the world for samples of the myriad organisms they concealed. He scoured the pampas of Uruguay for fossils and unusual contemporary species; scouted the no-man's-land of Tierra del Fuego for signs of unexpected life-forms; and climbed the highest peaks of the Andes, where he found deposits of seashells thousands of feet above sea level. Darwin also collected specimens of the species inhabiting different islands of the Galápagos. Whenever possible, he preserved and shipped his discoveries back to England. Some 23 years later, in 1859, he published *On the Origin of Species by Means of Natural Selection,* a comprehensive distillation of his thinking on what he had observed. The first printing of 1250 copies sold out in one day.

CHAPTER OUTLINE

- 20.1 The Origin of Life on Earth
- 20.2 The Evolution of Genomes
- 20.3 The Organization of Genomes
- 20.4 A Comprehensive Example: Rapid Evolution in the Immune Response and in HIV

In *The Origin of Species,* Darwin uses an extensive comparative analysis of thousands of specimens and fossils as the basis for proposing that "the similar framework of bones in the hand of a man, wing of a bat, fin of the porpoise, and leg of the horse—the same number of vertebrae forming the neck of the giraffe and of the elephant—and innumerable other such facts, at once explain themselves on the theory of descent with slow and slight successive modifications." This observation leads him to the stunning conclusion that "all organic beings which have ever lived on this earth may be descended from some one primordial form."

While Darwin was not the first to suggest that species could undergo evolution, he was the first to suggest a mechanism by which evolution could occur. He based his theory of evolution on three principles that in combination had revolutionary implications. First, within any species, variation exists among the individuals of a population in the expression of numerous traits. Second, variant forms of traits can be passed down through inheritance from one generation to the next. Third, some variant traits give the individuals that express them a greater chance of surviving and reproducing. (This is the so-called "survival of the fittest" principle.)

Darwin recognized that an advantageous trait that at first appears in only one or a few individuals could allow those individuals and their descendants to outcompete others. This process of "natural selection," that is, of natural conditions selecting for an advantageous trait, would result in the transmission of the trait to a greater proportion of the population in each successive generation. Darwin's understanding of the process of continuous evolution by natural selection became the cornerstone of his theory of evolution. But in spite of the enormous range of his revolutionary insight, Darwin was at a loss to explain the source of the visible variation on which natural selection acts. Mendel published "Experiments on Plant Hybrids" in 1866, just seven years after Darwin's *The Origin of Species* appeared, but as noted in Chapter 2, although Darwin received a copy of Mendel's paper, he most likely never read it. Had he done so, perhaps his questions regarding inheritance might have been answered.

Today, more than 150 years after the publication of *The Origin of Species,* biologists accept Darwin's theory as a foundation of modern biology. Moreover, thanks to Mendel and many other geneticists, they now understand the basic principles of heredity. And thanks to Watson and Crick, along with many other molecular biologists, biologists know that ultimately, evolution is a process that begins at the molecular level, inside the double helix of DNA.

In Chapter 1, you read that the modular construction of genomes has had a major impact on the evolution of life. In this chapter, we examine in detail the basic components of evolution at the molecular level: **diversification** into many variants, followed by **selection** of one or a few variants for amplification (that is, differential reproduction) in a population over many generations. The same process is at work in nearly all organisms, from tiny, subcellular viruses to large, multicellular plants and animals. While we can see examples of evolution occurring over relatively short periods of time (months to years), most molecular evolution in higher, more complex organisms occurs over millions of years.

One of the themes that arises from the study of evolution and genetics is that all life on earth today has come from preexisting life. Life itself arose according to laws of chemistry and conditions of the early earth. Another theme is that species evolve—they appear and disappear according to genetic variability that may or may not allow adaptation to changing conditions. And finally, we can see that what happens in the genome is reflected in what happens to species. Study of genomes continues to refine and redefine species histories and relationships.

20.1 The Origin of Life on Earth

To many biologists, the similarity of all living things on earth is more striking than the differences among them. Not only are all organisms composed of cells, but these cells work in essentially the same way, using the same complex molecules and the same type of genetic material read according to virtually the same genetic code. As we have seen, the flow of information in most living organisms from DNA via RNA to protein follows a well-defined pathway. But how did this elegant pathway, and the cells in which it is contained, arise from nonliving material on the ancient earth? Scientists continue to speculate about the answer in the absence of direct evidence.

Self-replicating molecules may have led to the complexity of cells

No fundamental law of biochemistry says that all living cells have to be constructed in the way that they are; indeed, an imaginative biochemist could think of an almost infinite number of ways to build a functioning cell that, like the organic life-forms around us, is based on the laws of chemistry. The observation that the cells of all plants, animals, fungi, and microorganisms analyzed so far are extremely similar in subcellular organelles, biochemistry, and genetic processes suggests that the abundant variety of life-forms alive today descend from a single, original cell that happened to begin life with the genetic code scientists now consider universal (even with the minor differences seen in some organelles and microorganisms).

A molecule that could replicate itself was the first step

A key step in molecular evolution was the emergence of a molecule that could replicate itself. Although one can only speculate on the nature of the original replicator, it must have been simple enough to form spontaneously after a half billion years of atoms bumping into each other on the surface of the primordial earth.

To give rise to the living cells we see today, this molecule would have had to fulfill three requirements: (1) encode information by the variation of letters in strings of a simple digital alphabet; (2) fold in three dimensions to create molecules capable of self-replication and ultimately other functions; and (3) expand the population of successful molecules through selective self-replication. What was the original self-replicating molecule and where did it come into existence?

The "RNA world"

In the 1980s, Thomas Cech and colleagues discovered that RNA, in addition to its ability to carry genetic information like DNA, can catalyze chemical reactions. RNA molecules that can act as enzymes to catalyze specific chemical reactions are called **ribozymes (Fig. 20.1)**. Although the substrates of most naturally occurring ribozymes are other RNA molecules, their potential range of enzymatic activity may be much broader.

The discovery of ribozymes gave molecular biologists an ideal candidate for the original replicator: a hypothetical RNA molecule that on its own could have (1) encoded information as linear strings in a four-letter alphabet; (2) folded into three-dimensional molecular machines able to execute critical functions of life (such as those currently carried out by polymerases, nucleases, and ligases); and (3) reproduced itself. The hypothetical primordial world in which this RNA became the first replicator has been termed the **RNA world.** The fact that all living organisms share the four letters of the RNA alphabet (A, U, G, and C) is testimony to the idea that successful, self-replicating RNA strings probably had a single origin, which, in turn, could have provided the common evolutionary origin of the information in all living organisms.

The earliest RNA may have had informational motifs, or coding regions (for example, encoding a simple polymerase), separated by noncoding regions of "background noise." The ribozymes of contemporary organisms that can cleave, join, copy, and even modify informational strings may reflect these early RNA activities. The pattern of coding regions separated by noncoding introns could have been established by the early random assembly of RNA strings. The evolutionary challenge was how to use the information and separate it from the noninformational regions. Accordingly, evolutionary pressures would have led to RNA coding regions that could cut (like an endonuclease) and splice (like a ligase), as well as synthesize new RNA molecules (like a polymerase).

However, multipurpose RNA strings that both stored information and folded into molecular machines would have had several intrinsic disadvantages. First, RNA is a relatively unstable molecule, readily susceptible to chemical and enzymatic hydrolysis. Second, RNA has only four letters in its alphabet, which are chemically similar, and it is thus less capable of folding into complex three-dimensional structures than other polymers with more complex alphabets. Accordingly, evolutionary pressures would have led to more stable storage molecules (DNAs) and more flexible molecular machines (proteins).

Figure 20.1 Ribozyme. Some RNA molecules have enzymatic functions. Shown is a region of a hammerhead RNA found in many plant viruses. This RNA can cleave itself at the site indicated.

Site of cleavage

Missing intermediates

The lack of evidence makes it difficult to provide solid answers to questions about evolutionary events at the precellular stage. If RNA indeed had been the original replicator, was it available for the first cells to use as an informational molecule, with the DNA and protein alphabets evolving subsequently? How did membrane compartments that concentrate the molecules of life and facilitate their sorting arise? What metabolic pathways gave some of the early cells an evolutionary edge?

Many biologists speculate that life began around the volcanic thermal vents of the ancient seas more than 3.5 billion years ago. In this high-temperature environment, informational subunits could have emerged and then polymerized into strings of informational molecules. Each of these informational intermediates was a proto-life-form that reproduced itself into a large number of slightly different copies (diversification) until by chance one gained a better mode of survival and outcompeted all its cousins in the next round of reproduction (selection). This two-step process of diversification and selection could have repeated itself over and over again until the first cell appeared. From that point on, the history of life's evolution is easier to discern.

> Life may have begun when certain organic molecules became self-replicating. Some arguments suggest RNA as the original replicator; however, many questions remain unanswered about how life may have progressed from replicator molecules to cells.

The fossil record allows inferences about later evolution

It is an enormous jump from a microscopically small single-celled organism to, for example, a human being composed of 100 trillion cells. However, like Darwin, no current biologist doubts that the one evolved into the other. This confidence arises not just from what Darwin's theory says *should* happen but from the possibility of seeing the critical intermediate stages of biological complexity, all the way up the ladder from single cells to sponges, to worms, to fish, to reptiles, to mammals, to primates and humans.

The fossil record is very important in enabling us to date the initial appearance of each intermediate stage, but the living representatives of each stage, in conjunction with our ability to study them with the tools of molecular biology, give us a glimpse into how evolution occurs step by step. It is fortunate for the scientists who study evolution that so many critical intermediate forms of life kept on reproducing in their less complex state, even as their cousins went on to evolve to the next stage of complexity.

The earliest cells

Scientists agree that planet earth coalesced some 4.5 billion years ago. By 4.2 billion years ago, enormous oceans covered the planet, and the first informational RNA molecules may have emerged around the high-temperature volcanic ocean vents. The first living organisms, consisting of a membrane surrounding information-replicating and information-executing machinery, evolved about 3.7 billion years ago; these were the precursors of present-day cells.

Fossil cells laid down 3.5 billion years ago near North Pole, Australia (a small town in an arid, rocky region) are the earliest evidence so far uncovered of distinct cells (**Fig. 20.2**). Once life in cellular form emerged, living organisms evolved into three distinct domains: archaea, bacteria, and eukarya (**Fig. 20.3**). Contemporary representatives of archaea and bacteria include only single-celled organisms whose genomes carry tightly packed genes.

Complex cells and multicellular organisms

Eukaryotes emerged about 1.4 billion years ago with the symbiotic incorporation of certain single-celled organisms into other single-celled organisms and the complex compartmentalization of the cell's interior, including the segregation of DNA molecules into the nucleus. The incorporated single-celled organisms evolved to become intracellular organelles. The evolution of these relatively complex eukaryotes from the earliest cells thus took almost 2.3 billion years.

Figure 20.2 Fossilized cells. The oldest fossilized cells.

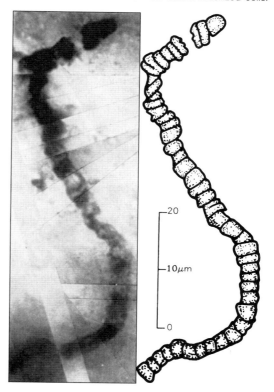

Figure 20.3 Three kingdoms. The distinct branches represent different organisms in each kingdom. The length of the branches is proportional to the times of species divergence.

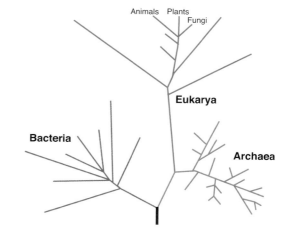

About 1 billion years ago, the single-celled ancestors of contemporary plants and animals diverged. The first primitive multicellular organisms appeared 600–900 million years ago. Then 570 million years ago, one of the most remarkable events in the evolution of life occurred: the explosive appearance of a multitude of multicellular organisms, both plants and animals. The multicellular animals are often referred to as **metazoans.**

The drama of metazoan evolution

The Burgess shale of southeastern British Columbia is one of the most amazing finds in paleontology. This shale was formed from a mud slide that trapped a wide variety of different organisms in a shallow Cambrian Sea. Events and conditions during and after the slide conspired to achieve the nearly perfect preservation of the three-dimensional structure of the entrapped specimens' soft body parts.

Three aspects of the Burgess organisms are remarkable. First, they represent a myriad of very different body plans (**Fig. 20.4**). For example, paleobiologists have distinguished 20–30 classes of arthropods in the Burgess sea shale, a striking contrast to the three contemporary classes of arthropods. Second, this emergence of metazoan organisms occurred over a remarkably short (in evolutionary terms) period, perhaps just 20–50 million years. This rapid evolution is an example of **punctuated equilibrium:** the tendency of evolution to proceed through long periods of stasis (lack of change) followed by short periods of explosive change. As we will see later, this rapid change in body plans reflects an equally rapid change in the regulatory networks that control the development of organisms. Third, it seems that all the basic body plans of contemporary organisms initially established themselves in the metazoan explosion. For example, the ancestor of contemporary vertebrates depicted in **Fig. 20.4c** probably emerged at about the same time as the ancestor of all contemporary invertebrates.

Mass extinctions

The enormous diversity of metazoan body plans that materialized about 500 million years ago has by now become tremendously reduced, in part through four to six abrupt extinction events that each destroyed 70% to 95% of the existing organisms. The most recent example was the global decimation 65 million years ago that led to the extinction of the dinosaurs. Many scientists believe this extinction was a consequence of a large meteorite impact in the Yucatan region of present-day Mexico that dramatically changed earth's climate by propelling enormous amounts of dust into the higher atmosphere. Scientists hypothesize that this thick cloud of dust dispersed and shrouded the globe for several years, preventing solar rays from reaching earth's surface. The lack of solar energy led to a global drop in temperatures and the demise of all green life, which in turn caused the demise of all large animals, such as dinosaurs, that depended for survival either directly on plants or on animals that ate plants.

Some smaller animals (like mammals' mouse-sized ancestors) presumably survived this long sunless winter because their lesser size allowed them to get by on seeds alone. When the sun returned, the seeds lying dormant on the ground sprang to life and the world again became an abundantly fertile environment. In the absence of competition from dinosaurs, mammals became the dominant large animal group, diverging into numerous species that could take advantage of all the newly unoccupied ecological niches. Some eventually evolved into our own species.

The evolution of humans

Humans arose from an ancestor common to most contemporary primates that existed 35 million years ago. They diverged from the ancestors of their closest primate relatives, the chimpanzees, about 6 million years ago.

Figure 20.4 Burgess shale organisms. Although all these life-forms are now extinct, fossils have revealed the enormous diversity of their body plans: **(a)** the *Nectocaris*, **(b)** the *Hallucigenia*, **(c)** the *Pikaia*, and **(d)** the *Anomalocaris*. The *Pikaia* contains a notochord, which makes it an ancestor to modern-day vertebrates.

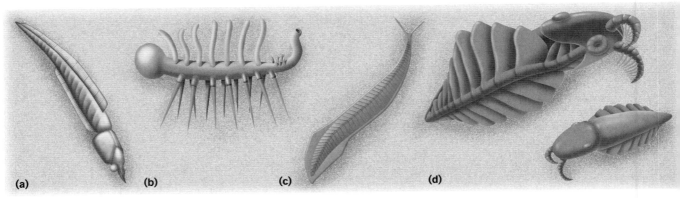

(a)   (b)   (c)   (d)

Figure 20.5 Humans diverged from an ancestor shared with chimpanzees about 6 million years ago. Representatives of primates alive today: **(a)** orangutan, **(b)** gorilla, **(c)** chimpanzee, and **(d)** human.

(a) (b) (c) (d)

(**Fig. 20.5**). While paleobiologists have not yet sorted out the immediate evolutionary ancestors of *Homo sapiens,* the recent typing of fossil DNA suggests that one previous candidate, the Neanderthal lineage, is not on the direct human evolutionary line.

Remarkably, on average, the chimpanzee and human genomes are approximately 99% similar. Moreover, as we saw in Chapter 12, the chimpanzee and human karyotypes are nearly the same (see Fig. 12.11). And in every comparison to date of chimpanzee and human DNA sequences, the observed differences between the two have been insignificant in terms of gene function. These data suggest that the evolution from a common primate ancestor to the modern human species might be accounted for by a few thousand isolated genetic changes yet to be uncovered.

Changes in regulatory circuits

While the changes bringing about divergence among the primates may have occurred in protein-coding sequences, many evolutionary biologists think it more likely that the changes occurred in regulatory sequences. Such changes would alter when and how master regulatory genes produce transcription factors, and when and how ordinary structural genes or batteries of genes respond to these regulatory molecules. For example, the brains of humans and chimps are quite different.

The human brain is larger, is far more convoluted (folded), and contains a significantly greater density of neurons (brain cells). Hence, the regulatory networks guiding chimp and human brain development have diverged strikingly in the 6 million years since the two species split from a common ancestor. These regulatory changes are presumably reflected in modified patterns of transcription factor binding sites in the promoter regions of genes that specify brain development. The rewiring of the regulatory

networks in less than 6 million years is a very rapid change in terms of evolutionary time. The same is true of the diversity of body plans generated during the Cambrian explosion of metazoa 570 million years ago.

The idea that evolution occurs primarily because of changes in regulatory networks and not structural genes is supported by the amazing ability of genes from one species to substitute for the absence of homologous genes in other species, in some cases even when the species are as different as yeast and humans. If homologous coding sequences from very different species are functionally indistinguishable, it is reasonable to speculate that species-specific differences in phenotype may arise, to a large degree, from species-specific differences in gene expression.

Multicellular life-forms diversified tremendously, although many lineages disappeared in mass extinction events. Humans diverged from a primate ancestor about 6 million years ago. What makes humans different from our closest relative, the chimpanzee, may not be the proteins that our genes encode but rather when, where, and at what level those proteins are expressed during development through evolutionary changes to master regulatory genes.

20.2 The Evolution of Genomes

Although Darwin developed his theory of evolution without any knowledge of the molecules that make up living systems, evolution is very much a molecular process that operates on genetic information. In particular, the variation that initiates each step in the evolutionary process occurs within the genetic material itself in the form of new mutations. Indeed, new mutations provide a continuous source of variation.

DNA alterations form the basis of genomic evolution

We have seen that mutations arise in several different ways. One is the replacement of individual nucleotides by other nucleotides. Substitutions occurring in a coding region are silent, or *synonymous,* when they have no effect on the amino acid encoded; by contrast, they are *nonsynonymous* when the change in nucleotide determines a change in an amino acid or creates a premature termination codon, leading to a truncated gene product. Molecular biologists further distinguish between nonsynonymous changes that cause conservative amino acid changes (for example, from one acidic amino acid to another) and those that cause nonconservative changes (for example, from a charged amino acid to a noncharged amino acid). Other gene mutations, arising from errors in replication or recombination, consist in the deletion from or insertion into genes of a DNA sequence of any length.

Changes can also occur in the order and types of transcription factor binding sites in the promoters of genes; such changes alter the patterns of gene expression. These expression-altering changes may occur very rapidly, which raises the question of whether such regulatory evolution can be explained merely by single-base mutations followed by selection.

Mutations can be classified according to effect

Different mutations can be *deleterious, neutral,* or *favorable* to the organisms that inherit them. In multicellular organisms with large genomes, such as corn or humans, genes and their regulatory sequences make up only a small fraction (<3%) of the total genetic material. As a result, random mutations occur most often in DNA that plays no role in the development or function of an organism. Such mutations are presumably neutral. It might seem that synonymous mutations within coding regions would also be neutral, but there is some evidence that even changes in the codon used to produce a particular amino acid can provide a minute advantage or disadvantage to the organism, possibly based on the availability of different tRNA molecules and their associated synthetases. While conservative amino-acid replacements were once considered neutral, current evidence suggests that they can have an impact on the growth and survival of an organism. Nonconservative amino-acid changes and changes such as deletions and insertions involving larger portions of a gene almost certainly have an impact on gene function.

Genetic changes that are truly neutral are unaffected by the agents of selection. They survive or disappear from a population through *genetic drift,* which is the result of chance reproductive events. The smaller the population, the more rapidly genetic drift exerts its effect.

Mutations with only deleterious effects disappear from a population by negative selection—that is, selection against an allele. As you saw in the preceding chapter, however, some mutations (such as those that cause sickle-cell anemia) are deleterious to homozygotes for the mutation but advantageous to heterozygotes. Because of this *heterozygous advantage,* selection retains these mutations in a population at a low equilibrium level (review Fig. 19.11). However, even deleterious mutations for which there is no heterozygous advantage are eliminated very slowly if they are fully recessive.

Some extremely rare mutations give an organism a significant advantage over other individuals. Because of this advantage, individuals carrying the mutation are more likely to reproduce, and in each succeeding generation, the frequency of the mutation increases. This is positive selection (selection for an allele). Ultimately, the allele that began as a mutation is present in nearly every member of the population on both chromosomes. At this stage, the allele has become *fixed* in the population.

Gene regulatory networks may dominate developmental evolution

Gene regulatory networks active in development receive informational signals from signal transduction pathways, integrate and modulate those signals, and then transmit them to protein networks that mediate various aspects of development. Eric Davidson, a pioneer in sea urchin studies (see the following chapter), has begun to study the evolution of a gene regulatory network in two invertebrate organisms with markedly different phenotypes: the sea urchin and the sea star (**Fig. 20.6a**). The lineages leading to these two invertebrates diverged about 500 million years ago (about the same time vertebrates diverged from invertebrates).

As **Figure 20.6b** shows, Davidson analyzed a portion of the gene regulatory network that specifies development of the endomesoderm. This subnetwork contains five transcription factors in the sea urchin and six in the sea star. Two observations are striking. First, except for the changes indicated by the lines outlined in red, the interactions among these transcription factors are highly conserved. Second, the Tbr transcription factor, which in the sea urchin specifies the expression of skeletogenic structural proteins, functions in the sea star as part of the endomesoderm network (as indicated by the brown arrows in Fig. 20.6).

Changes in transcription factor specificity and function can arise from changes to the DNA of *cis*-control elements or from changes to the amino acid sequences of the transcription factors themselves. Changes to the DNA include (1) the gain or loss of *cis*-control sequences to which the factors bind, (2) repositioning of *cis*-control elements on the regulatory DNA, (3) increases or decreases in a *cis*-control element's binding affinity for a particular transcription factor, and (4) mutations that make a *cis*-control element serve as the binding site for a different transcription

Figure 20.6 Sea urchin and sea star gene regulatory network. (a) Sea urchins and sea stars diverged about 500 million years ago. **(b)** Subnetwork of the gene regulatory networks governing mesoendodermal development in the sea urchin (top) and sea star (bottom). The transcription factors are in different colors; the *arrows* (positive influence) and *bars* (negative influence) indicate the effect each transcription factor has on those with which it interacts. The influence lines are in the same color as the transcription factors from which they arise. Note that the *red* lines shown with Krox, FoxA, and GataE represent the only interactions that have not been highly conserved.

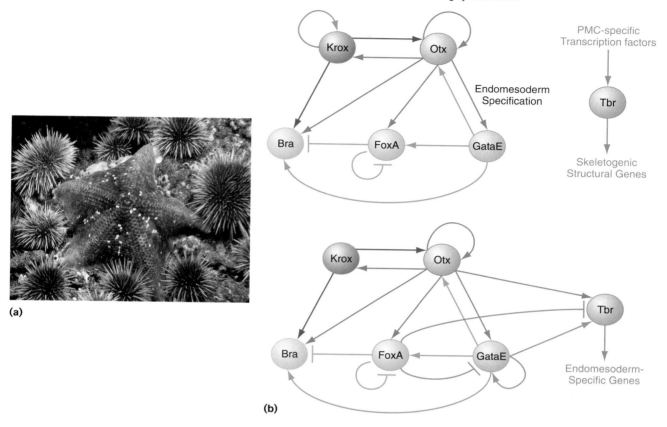

(a)

(b)

factor. The relevant amino acid modifications change the DNA binding specificity of the transcription factor.

These comparative evolutionary studies suggest that a subtle rewiring of a gene regulatory network and the joining together of elements from previously separate subnetworks can encode enormous phenotypic changes, including those that give rise to sea urchin versus sea star body plans. A fascinating possibility is that gene regulatory networks in humans may share much of their basic wiring with invertebrates. If this turns out to be true, a detailed study of invertebrate gene regulatory networks could provide powerful insights into the basic gene regulatory networks controlling development in higher organisms. Moreover, if the subtle rewiring of gene regulatory networks can lead to enormous phenotypic changes, it can also explain the evolution of considerable biological complexity.

Mutations in DNA are the basis of evolution; their effects may be deleterious, neutral, or favorable. Major phenotypic changes appear to result from mutations that affect developmental regulatory networks. Many of these basic networks have been conserved throughout evolution.

An increase in genome size generally correlates with evolution of complexity

Consider that although both bacteria and mammals evolved from a common cellular ancestor, the contemporary *Escherichia coli* genome is about 5 Mb in length, while in humans, the genome is about 3000 Mb long. How has evolution fashioned such different genomes from the same original material? The answer lies in the evolutionary potential for increasing the size of the genome through the duplication and diversification of genomic regions and, even more strikingly, through the acquisition of repetitive sequence elements that may represent more than 50% of the genome. In these processes, new DNA is born. Note, however, that although the increase in genome sizes from yeast to flies to vertebrates does reflect the increasing complexity of the organisms, there are examples of amoeba, plants, and amphibians with considerably more genomic DNA than humans.

Duplications can occur at random throughout the genome, and the size of the duplication unit can vary from a few nucleotides to the entire genome. When a duplicated segment contains one or more genes, either the original or the duplicated copy of each gene is free to accumulate function-destroying mutations (diversify) without harm to the organism, because the other "good" copy with original function is still present. With duplications acting as such an important force in evolution, it is critical to understand the two main ways in which they arise.

Duplications resulting from transposition

As we saw in Chapter 13, transposition, the transfer of one copy of a chromosomal sequence from one chromosomal site to another, can occur in various ways: through the direct movement of a DNA sequence; through an RNA intermediate that is copied into a DNA intermediate, leaving the original

DNA site intact; or through a DNA intermediate (**Fig. 20.7**). When the genomic DNA (rather than its RNA or DNA proxy) moves to a new site, the duplication of genetic material occurs only after the altered chromosome receiving the DNA segregates, together with the unaltered homolog of the chromosome containing the original locus, into an egg or sperm. When the gamete with the duplication unites with a normal gamete, the resulting zygote has three copies of the original locus (**Fig. 20.8**). In subsequent generations, the new transposition element may become fixed in the population.

Duplications resulting from unequal crossing-over

Normal crossing-over, or recombination, occurs between equivalent loci on the homologous chromatids present in a synaptonemal complex that forms during the pachytene

Figure 20.7 Duplication by transposition. Transposition may occur by **(a)** excising and reinserting the DNA segment; **(b)** making an RNA copy, which is then converted to a DNA copy for insertion; or **(c)** making a DNA copy for integration. In (b) and (c), the transposon is duplicated.

Figure 20.8 Transposition through direct movement of a DNA sequence. A DNA sequence may transpose from one chromosome to a second chromosome in a sex cell. In subsequent generations, this transposed element may become fixed.

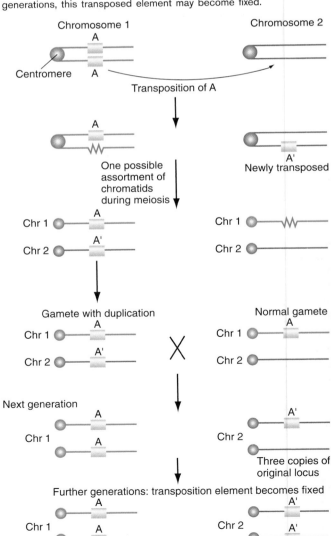

GENETICS AND SOCIETY

Evolution Versus Intelligent Design

Darwin's evolutionary theory maintains that the diversity and complexity of living organisms are the result of evolution by the natural selection of preexisting variations encoded by the genome in combination with random drift. Creationism is the belief that certain aspects of life are too complex to have evolved in this way; instead, it maintains that a divine being created the world, including the diversity and complexity of all life from microbes to people. Creationism is a religious belief, not a scientific theory, because the hypothesis at its foundation is not testable.

A battle has been ongoing between creationism and evolution ever since Darwin first proposed his theory of evolution by natural selection. In 1925, John Scopes, a rural high school biology teacher, was sued by the State of Tennessee for teaching evolution in the science classroom. The courtroom battle between two well-known attorneys, William Jennings Bryan for the state and Clarence Darrow for the defense, drew national attention. In the so-called "Monkey Trial," the forces for scientific evolution actually lost, but the decision was later overturned on a technicality.

More recently, the proponents of creationism have cast their argument in a new form known as Intelligent Design (ID). According to this idea, life is too complex to have been created by Darwinian evolution; instead, it must have been created by a higher agent or intelligence. Although not named as such, that intelligence is generally taken to be the Christian God by proponents of ID.

In 2005 the parents of eleven students sued the Dover, Pennsylvania, school board over the board's mandate that all science teachers must tell their students that evolution is "just a theory" and that intelligent design literature in the form of a textbook titled *Of Pandas and People* must be made available as an alternative hypothesis. The parents' lawsuit, *Klitzmer v. Dover Area School District*, argued that the mandate to give evolution and intelligent design equal time in the science classroom was inappropriate because intelligent design is not science, but religious belief. On December 20, 2005, Judge John E. Jones III of the federal district court hearing the case issued his decision: a sweeping repudiation of the teaching of intelligent design in the science classroom as an alternative to Darwinian evolution. In his decision, Judge Jones stated, "We find that ID . . . cannot be adjudged a valid, accepted scientific theory. . . . [It] is grounded in theology, not science. . . . It has no place in a science curriculum. . . . The goal of the ID movement is not to encourage critical thought, but to foment a revolution that would supplant evolutionary theory with ID."

Even as the proponents of Intelligent Design base their anti-evolution arguments on a supernatural explanation of how biological complexity emerged, biologists are making great strides toward understanding that complexity scientifically through the systems approach to biology.

---

stage of meiosis. *Unequal crossing-over,* also referred to as *illegitimate recombination,* occurs between nonequivalent loci (review Fig. 7.8a). Unequal crossing-over is most often initiated by related sequences located close to each other in the genome. Although the event is unequal in the exchange of nonequivalent segments of DNA, it is still mediated by the sequence similarities at the two separate loci.

So-called **nonhomologous unequal crossing-over** also occurs, although much less often than homologous crossing-over. A nonhomologous crossover may be mediated by at least a short stretch of sequence homology, coding or noncoding, at the crossover's two sites of initiation.

An initial duplication by unequal crossing-over that produces a two-unit cluster may be either homologous or nonhomologous, but as **Fig. 20.9** illustrates, once two units of related sequence are present in tandem, further rounds of homologous unequal crossing-over between nonequivalent members of the pair readily occur. Thus small clusters can easily expand to contain three, four, and many more copies of an original DNA sequence.

The result of unequal crossing-over between homologous chromosomes is always two reciprocal chromosomal products: one carrying a duplication of the region located between the two crossover sites and the other carrying a deletion that covers the exact same region. Regions duplicated by unequal crossing-over can vary from a few base pairs to hundreds of kilobases in length, and they may contain no genes, a portion of a gene, a few genes, or many genes.

Repeated duplications increase genome size. Transposition moves a copy of a sequence from one chromosomal site to another; unequal crossing-over results in duplication of one region, and deletion of the same region in the reciprocal chromosome.

Evolution of a duplicated gene: New functions or pseudogenes

Duplicated regions, like all other genetic novelties, must originate in the genome of a single individual. At first, the survival of a duplication in at least some animals in each subsequent generation of a population is, most often, a matter of chance. The reason is that the addition of one extra copy of a chromosomal region, including most genes, to the two already present in the diploid genome usually causes no significant harm to the individual. In the terminology of population genetics, the duplicated units are neutral with regard to genetic selection. They are thus subject to genetic drift, inherited at random by some offspring but not others. By chance again, most neutral genetic elements disappear from a population in several generations.

Development of pseudogenes

When a duplicated region that includes a functional gene survives for hundreds or thousands of generations, random

Figure 20.9 Duplications arise from unequal crossing-over. The crossover shown involved dispersed repeat elements (*blue boxes*). The *pink boxes* denote a unique gene. In the crossover event, this originally unique gene is deleted in one chromosome and duplicated in the other.

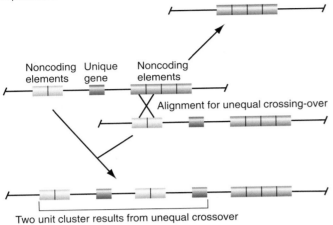

Noncoding elements   Unique gene   Noncoding elements

Alignment for unequal crossing-over

Two unit cluster results from unequal crossover

mutations in the gene may turn it into a related gene with a different function, or into a nonfunctional *pseudogene*. Some of the mutations generating a pseudogene lead to a loss of regulatory function; others change one or more critical amino acids in the gene product; still others cause premature termination of the growing polypeptide chain, or change the translational reading frame of the gene, or alter the RNA splicing patterns.

Pseudogenes, because they serve no function, are subject to mutation without selection and thus accumulate mutations at a far faster pace than the coding or regulatory regions of a functional gene. Eventually, nearly all pseudogene sequences mutate past a boundary beyond which it is no longer possible to identify the functional genes from which they have been derived. Thus, continuous mutation can turn a once functional sequence into an essentially random sequence of DNA.

Diversification leading to new functionality

Every so often, the accumulation of a set of random mutations in a spare copy of a gene leads to the emergence of a new functional gene that provides benefit and, consequently, selective advantage to the organism in which it resides. Because it provides a selective advantage, the new gene persists in the population. Although its function is usually related to that of the original gene, it almost always has a novel pattern of expression—in time, in space, or both—which most likely results from alterations in *cis*-regulatory sequences that occur along with codon changes. For example, a duplicated copy of the original human β-globin gene evolved into the myoglobin gene, whose protein product has a higher affinity for oxygen than the hemoglobin molecules composed in part of β-globin polypeptides. The myoglobin gene is active only in muscle cells, while the

β-globin gene is expressed only in red blood cell precursors. Thus, duplication, divergence, and selection generated a new gene function from a previously functional gene.

In many cases, mutations turn a duplicated gene into a nonfunctional pseudogene. In other cases, mutations may confer a new function on a duplicated gene on which selection can act. If the new function provides a selective advantage, the newly functional gene will be retained.

Molecular clocks allow inference of phylogenetic relationships

Before the advent of molecular biology, researchers determined the genealogies of organisms by calculating the rates of evolution in phenotypic traits such as teeth and vertebrae. Then, in the 1950s, Linus Pauling and Emile Zuckerkandl analyzed hemoglobin and cytochrome C protein sequences from different species and noted that the rates of amino acid substitution in each type of protein are similar for various mammalian lineages. On the basis of this observation, they postulated that for a given protein, the rate of evolution is constant across all lineages. They called this idea of a constant rate of change for each type of molecule a **molecular clock.** Its existence enables biologists to determine from molecular data the approximate times when species diverged and then use these dates to reconstruct genealogical phylogenetic trees.

Although the molecular clock hypothesis does not keep perfect time, in many instances where it has been tested, it has produced a reasonably good estimate of the time of divergence between two types of organisms. Today molecular biologists compare the nucleotide sequences of genes as well as the amino acid sequences of proteins to determine phylogenetic divergences.

Scientists use molecular data in various ways to construct **phylogenetic trees** that illustrate the relatedness of homologous genes or proteins. A phylogenetic tree consists of **nodes** and **branches** (**Fig. 20.10**). The nodes represent the taxonomic units, which may be species, populations, individuals, or genes, while the branches define the relationship of these units. The branch length suggests the amount of time that has elapsed based on the number of molecular changes that have occurred.

Because different genes accumulate changes at different rates, different types of genes are best suited to the construction of different types of phylogenetic trees. For example, in fibrinopeptides, the major components of wound-responsive blood clots, the exact amino acid sequences are not critical to function. As a result, the fibrinopeptides are not under strong selective pressure, and their genes evolve quickly. In contrast, the ribosomal genes, which are highly conserved, evolve slowly. Thus, the genes encoding fibrinopeptides are useful for looking at recent evolutionary events among very closely related species, while the

Figure 20.10 A phylogenetic tree.

This phylogenetic tree diagrams the evolutionary history of human hemoglobin genes. The *broken line* denotes a pseudogene linkage. Only one of the two α-hemoglobin genes is shown because their date of divergence is so recent.

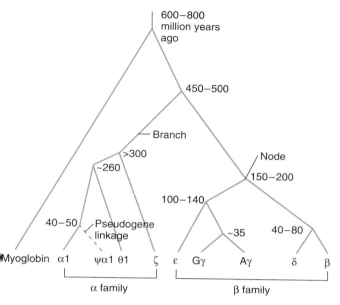

ribosomal genes are useful for looking at ancient evolutionary events such as the relationships of phyla to each other. Indeed, phylogenetic trees based on ribosomal genes helped rewrite the most fundamental domain classifications of multicellular organisms (see Fig. 20.3).

Individual proteins have been found to mutate at a constant rate across lineages. Biologists can use these molecular clocks to estimate times of divergence and to construct molecularly based phylogenetic trees. The genes of some proteins evolve more quickly than others, allowing analysis of distant divergences or more recent speciation.

20.3 The Organization of Genomes

With this understanding of the basic mechanisms by which genomes evolve, we turn our attention to the results of genome evolution as seen in the organization of contemporary genomes. Our focus is on the various organizational features of the enormous mammalian genome, which evolved from the much simpler bacteria-like genomes through eons of duplication, diversification, and selection.

Molecular geneticists have accumulated data on genome organization by analyzing the genomic sequences of chromosomal DNAs from completed sequences of more than 100 genomes, including those of humans, mice, puffer fish, rice, *Drosophila, C. elegans, Arabidopsis,* yeast, *E. coli,* and approximately 300 other organisms (mostly microbes). The single-celled organisms exhibit genomes

with densely packed genes and few, if any, introns. The mammalian genomes, with their far less densely packed genes, have several distinct features dominating their landscape: genes and families of genes; dispersed repetitive elements constituting more than a third of the genome; simple sequence repeats composed of single nucleotides or di-, tri-, tetra-, pentamers, and so forth; simple repetitive elements serving as a core for centromeres and telomeres; and unique nongene sequences. We now describe how these genomic features could have evolved.

Duplications have created multigene families and gene superfamilies

Four levels of duplication (followed by diversification and selection) have fueled the evolution of complex genomes. At the lowest level, exons duplicate or shuffle to change the size or function of genes. At the next three increasingly complex levels, entire genes duplicate to create multigene families; multigene families duplicate to produce gene superfamilies; and the entire genome duplicates to double the number of copies of every gene and gene family (**Fig. 20.11**). At each of these successively higher levels

Figure 20.11 Duplications increase genome size.

Genome size increases through duplication of exons, genes, gene families, and finally of entire genomes.

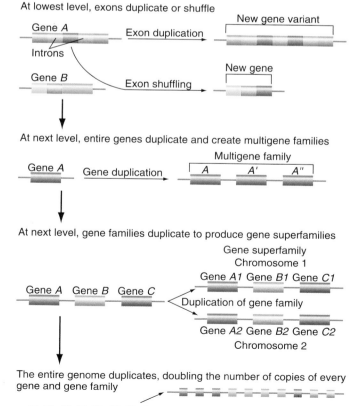

Figure 20.12 The basic structure of a gene. A typical eukaryotic protein-coding gene. The *light green boxes* represent the 5′ and 3′ untranslated mRNA sequences. The small *pink boxes* represent regulatory sequences where transcription factors bind.

of organization, the duplication of larger and larger units leads to the hierarchical generation of greater and greater amounts of new information.

Basic components of genes

Genes consist of many different components: exons containing coding regions and 5′ and 3′ untranslated regions; introns that will be spliced out; and associated control regions (**Fig. 20.12**). Many of the control regions lie just 5′ to the transcribed region; but some, such as the regulatory region (locus control region) of the β-globin gene family, lie far outside the gene and appear to play a role in opening up the chromatin of the gene family locus so that gene expression can proceed at the appropriate time and level. Until all associated regulatory elements have

been defined, the boundaries of a genetic locus remain uncertain.

The duplication and shuffling of exons

Many proteins carry discrete compact domains, some of which perform a specific function, while others sustain molecular structure. In many genes, the discrete exons encode the structural and functional domains of a protein. Genes may elongate by the duplication of these exons to generate tandem exons that determine tandem functional domains such as those seen in antibody molecules (**Fig. 20.13**). The functions of tandem domains may eventually diverge.

Entirely new genes may arise from **exon shuffling:** the exchange of exons among different genes. Exon shuffling produces mosaic proteins such as tissue plasminogen activator (TPA), a molecule with four domains of three distinct types: kringle (K), growth factor (G), and finger (F). The gene for TPA captured exons governing the synthesis of four domains from the genes for three other proteins: K from the gene for plasminogen, G from the gene for epidermal growth factor, and F from the gene for fibronectin (**Fig. 20.14**). The mechanism by which exon shuffling occurs is unclear: Because each distinct domain has a different function, one protein may have two or more different functions. Exon shuffling may create new proteins with different combinations of functions.

Figure 20.13 Domains in antibody proteins. The antibody molecule is composed of two identical pairs of light (*inner*) and heavy (*outer*) chains. The variable regions of each chain are shown in *tan;* the constant regions in *lavender.* The variable regions of a light and a heavy chain form a V domain. Likewise, the pairs of the CH1, CH2, and CH3 regions generate the CH1, CH2, and CH3 domains, respectively. Each domain carries out separate functions.

Figure 20.14 Duplication and shuffling of exons. The tissue plasminogen activator (TPA) gene has evolved by the shuffling of exons from the genes for plasminogen, fibronectin, and epidermal growth factor.

Figure 20.15 Multigene families. Tandem and dispersed multigene families on segments of the indicated chromosomes.

Tandem gene family: Members of the multigene family are clustered on the same chromosome

Dispersed gene family: Members of the multigene family are on different chromosomes

Figure 20.16 Evolution via crossovers within families. A schematic illustration of how a crossover can expand and contract gene numbers in a multigene family.

Number of members in this cluster increases

Number of members in this cluster decreases

Figure 20.17 Intergenic gene conversion. In intergenic gene conversion: one gene is changed, the other is not.

During synapsis gene *A* aligns with gene *C* because of homology between the two. Then a portion of gene *C* is changed to the sequence of gene *A*.

Note: Gene *A* remains unchanged, only gene *C* has a portion (*magenta*) of the gene *A* sequence.

Converted region

Alternative resolution: unequal crossing-over

Divergence

Creation of a multigene family

A **multigene family** is a set of genes descended by duplication and diversification from one ancestral gene. The members of a multigene family may be either arrayed in tandem (that is, clustered on the same chromosome) or distributed on different chromosomes (**Fig. 20.15**). Unequal crossing-over can expand and contract the number of members in a multigene family cluster (**Fig. 20.16**).

Genetic exchange between related DNA elements

The genome contains many places where a flow of genetic information appears to have occurred from one DNA element to other related, but nonallelic, elements located nearby or on different chromosomes. Such information flow between related DNA sequences occurs through an alternative outcome of the process responsible for unequal crossing-over. This alternative is known as **intergenic gene conversion** (**Fig. 20.17**). In Chapter 6, you learned that for meiosis to proceed, nonsister chromatids engaged in crossing-over must disengage, and that two resolutions via Holliday intermediates are possible (review Fig. 6.24, steps 7 and 8): One is straightforward crossing-over, and the other is gene conversion without crossing-over. The same alternative outcomes can occur with unequal recombination intermediates. The gene conversion outcome of unequal crossing-over allows the transfer of information from one gene to another. In special cases (such as the

Figure 20.18 Increasing the number of alleles. How gene conversion events from pseudo-class I genes could increase the polymorphism in functional MHC class I genes in mice.

ribosomal gene family that exists in every eukaryotic species), the flow of information from such intergenic gene conversion has been so extreme that it has caused all members of a gene family to coevolve with near identity. And in at least one case—that of the class I genes of the major histocompatibility complex (MHC)—selection has acted on information flow in only one direction, causing information transfer from a series of nonfunctional pseudogenes to a small subset of just two to three functional genes (**Fig. 20.18**). In this unusual case, the pseudogene family members served as a reservoir of genetic information that produced a dramatic increase in the amount of polymorphism (that is, the number of alleles) in the small number of functional gene members.

Concerted evolution and multigene homogeneity

A few multigene families have evolved under a special form of selective pressure that requires all family members to maintain essentially the same sequence. In these families, the high number of gene copies does not result in variations on a theme; rather it supplies a cell with a large amount of product within a short period of time. Among the gene families with identical elements is the one that produces RNA components of the cell's ribosomes, the one that produces tRNAs, and the one that produces the histones (which must rapidly generate enough protein to coat the new copy of the whole genome replicated during the S phase of every cell cycle).

Each of these gene families consists of one or more clusters of tandem repeats of identical elements. A strong selective pressure maintains the same sequence across all members of each family because all must produce the same product. Optimal functioning of the cell requires that the products of any individual gene be interchangeable in structure and function with the products of all other members of the same family. The problem is that

the natural tendency of duplicated sequences is to drift apart over time. How does the genome counteract this natural tendency?

When researchers first compared ribosomal RNA and other gene families in this class, both between and within species, a remarkable picture emerged: Between species, they saw clear evidence of genetic drift, but within species, all sequences appeared essentially equivalent. Thus it is not simply that some mechanism suppresses mutational changes in these gene families. Rather, there appears to be an ongoing process of **concerted evolution,** which allows changes in single genetic elements to spread across a complete set of genes in a particular family.

Concerted evolution appears to occur through two different processes. The first is based on the expansion and contraction of gene family size through sequential rounds of unequal crossing-over between homologous sequences (**Fig. 20.19**). Selection acts to maintain the absolute size of the gene family within a small range around an optimal mean. As the gene family becomes too large, the shorter of the unequal crossover products becomes selected; as the family becomes too small, the longer of the products becomes selected. This cyclic process causes a continuous oscillation around a size mean. However, each contraction results in the loss of divergent genes, whereas each expansion results in the indirect "replacement" of those lost genes with identical copies of other genes in the family. With unequal crossovers occurring at random positions throughout the cluster and with selection acting in favor of the least divergence among family members, this process can act to slow down dramatically the natural tendency of genetic drift between gene family members.

The second process responsible for concerted evolution is intergenic gene conversion between nonallelic family members. Although in each case, the direction of information transfer from one gene copy to the next is random, selection will act on this molecular process to ensure an increase in homogeneity among different gene family members (Fig. 20.19b). Information transfer (presumably by means of intergenic gene conversion) can also occur across gene clusters that belong to the same family but are distributed to different chromosomes.

> A gene family results from repeated duplication of a single gene and diversification among the copies. A few gene families have maintained homogeneity among members through concerted evolution, which occurs through two processes: selection that acts to keep the size of the gene family within an optimal range; and intergenic gene conversion that increases homogeneity among members.

The evolution of gene superfamilies

Molecular geneticists use the phrase **gene superfamily** to describe a large set of related genes that is divisible into smaller sets, or families, with the genes in each family

Figure 20.19 Concerted evolution can lead to gene homogeneity. Boxes with different colors and numbers represent gene family members with variant DNA sequences. Repeat cycles of unequal crossover events **(a)** or gene conversion **(b)** cause the duplicated genes on each chromosome to become progressively more homogenized.

(a)

(b)

the single myoglobin gene. The duplications and divergences that produced the three superfamily branches occurred early in the evolution of vertebrates; as a result, the three branches of the superfamily are found in all mammals. All functional members of this superfamily play a role in oxygen transport, as described at the beginning of Chapter 9. The products of the α- and β-globin genes are active in red blood cells, while the product of the myoglobin gene transports oxygen in muscle tissue.

The primordial globin gene gave rise to the myoglobin and α-/β-globin precursor genes by gene duplication and transposition. The primordial α- and β-globin genes probably arose by a large-scale genome duplication (tetraploidization).

The β-like branch of this gene superfamily arose by duplication via multiple unequal crossovers. In the mouse, all the β-like genes are present in a single cluster on chromosome 7, which contains four functional genes and three pseudogenes (Fig. 20.20). The β-like chains encode similar polypeptides, each of which has been selected for optimal function at a specific stage of mouse development: one functions during early embryogenesis, one during a later stage of embryogenesis, and two function in the adult.

The α-like branch also evolved by unequal crossovers and divergences that generated a cluster of three genes on mouse chromosome 11: one functions during embryogenesis, and two function in the adult (Fig. 20.20). The two adult α-globin genes are virtually identical at the level of DNA sequence, which suggests that the duplication producing them occurred very recently (on the evolutionary time scale). In addition to the primary α-like cluster, there are two nonfunctional α-like genes—pseudogenes—that have dispersed via transposition to locations on chromosomes 15 and 17.

Pseudogenes existing in isolation from their parental families are called *orphons*. Interestingly, the α-globin orphon on mouse chromosome 15 (named *Hba-ps3*) has no introns and thus appears to have arisen through a retrotransposition event involving mRNA copied back to DNA. In contrast, the α-globin orphon on chromosome 17 (*Hba-ps4*) does contain introns and may have arisen by a direct DNA-mediated transposition. The single mouse myoglobin gene on chromosome 15 has no close relatives either nearby or far away. The globin gene superfamily provides a view of the many different mechanisms that the genome can employ to evolve structural and functional complexity.

The mouse *Hox* gene superfamily (discussed in the genetic portrait of the house mouse on our website: www.mhhe.com/hartwell4) provides an alternative prototype for the evolution of a gene superfamily (**Fig. 20.21**). At first, a single *Hox* gene had evolved to produce a protein product that could bind to DNA enhancer regions and thereby regulate the expression of other genes. Unequal crossover events predating the divergence of insects and vertebrates some 600 million years ago produced a cluster of five related genes encoding DNA-binding proteins that

being more closely related to each other than to other members of the larger superfamily. The multigene (or single-gene) families that compose a gene superfamily reside at different chromosomal locations.

A prototypical small-size gene superfamily is the very well-studied globin genes illustrated in **Fig. 20.20**. The superfamily has three branches: the multigene family of β-like genes, the multigene family of α-like genes, and

Figure 20.20 Evolution of the mouse globin superfamily. Repeated gene duplication by various mechanisms gave rise to the globin supergene family in mice, with two multigene families (α and β) and one single gene (myoglobin). The α family has both tandemly arrayed and dispersed gene members.

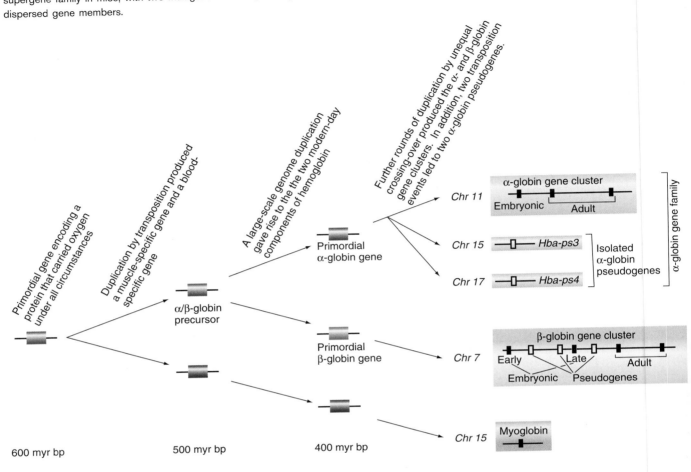

Figure 20.21 Evolution of the *Hox* gene superfamily of mouse and *Drosophila*. This gene superfamily arose by a series of gene duplications. Four multigene families are present in the mouse and one in *Drosophila*.

regulated the expression of other genes encoding spatial information (that is, instructions for the spatial positioning of tissues and organs) in the developing embryo.

The original *Hox* gene family then duplicated en masse and dispersed to four locations—on chromosomes in an ancestor common to all vertebrates. Because of the order of duplication events leading to the superfamily, an evolutionary tree would show that a single gene family within the superfamily has actually splayed out physically across the four gene clusters, as shown in Fig. 20.21.

After the en masse duplication that generated the gene superfamily, smaller duplications by unequal crossing-over added genes to some of the dispersed clusters and subtracted genes from others, thereby generating differences in gene number and type within a basic framework of homology among the different clusters. Each of the four *Hox* clusters in the mouse superfamily currently contains 9–12 homologous genes.

> A gene superfamily is a collection of related multigene families found at different chromosomal locations. One example is the globin superfamily that contains the myoglobin gene as well as different hemoglobin genes; another is the *Hox* gene superfamily that contains genes involved in regulation of gene expression.

Repetitive "nonfunctional" DNA families constitute nearly one-half of the genome

Many repetitive nonfunctional DNA families consist of retroviral elements. Retroviruses, to review, are RNA-containing viruses that can convert their RNA genome into circular DNA molecules through the viral-associated RNA-dependent DNA polymerase known as reverse transcriptase, which becomes activated upon cell infection. The resulting DNA can integrate itself at random into the host genome, where it becomes a provirus that retains the genetic information of the retroviral genome. Under certain conditions, the provirus can become activated to produce new viral RNA genomes and associated proteins, including reverse transcriptase, that can come together to form new virus particles. These particles are ultimately released from the cell surface by exocytosis. By contrast, many stably integrated retroviral elements appear to be inactive.

Once integrated into a host chromosome, the provirus replicates with every round of host DNA replication, regardless of whether the provirus itself is expressed or silent. Moreover, proviruses that integrate into the germ line, through the sperm or egg genome, segregate along with their host chromosome into the progeny of the host animal and into subsequent generations of animals as well. The genomes of all species of mammals contain inactive integrated proviral elements.

The LINE family: "Selfish DNA"

LINE is an acronym for <u>L</u>ong <u>IN</u>terspersed <u>E</u>lements. These elements, first described in Chapter 13, encode a reverse transcriptase. This enzyme, however, is not required for any normal cellular process of mammals. Geneticists speculate that its evolution benefitted what are termed "selfish DNA" elements that propagate themselves within the confines of the genome. The LINEs are one group of these elements.

The LINE family of DNA elements is very old. Homologous families of repetitive elements exist in a wide variety of organisms, including protists and plants. Thus, LINE-related elements, or other DNA elements of a similar nature, are likely to have been the source material that gave rise to retroviruses.

Dispersion to new positions in the germ-line genome presumably begins with the transcription of LINE elements in spermatogenic or oogenic cells. The reverse-transcriptase-encoding region on the transcript is translated into an enzyme that preferentially associates with and uses the transcript it came from as a template to produce LINE cDNA sequences; however, the reverse transcriptase often stops before it has made a full-length DNA copy of the RNA transcript. The resulting incomplete cDNA molecules can nevertheless form a second strand to produce truncated double-stranded LINE elements that integrate into the genome but remain forever dormant (**Fig. 20.22**).

The SINE family

The Alu family in the human genome is an example of a highly repetitive, widely dispersed SINE (<u>S</u>hort <u>IN</u>terspersed

Figure 20.22 Creation of a LINE gene family. A complete LINE sequence can be copied into RNA. It encodes a reverse transcriptase that can make cDNA copies from the RNA. These copies may be complete or truncated and may integrate into other sites on any chromosome.

Elements) family; SINEs were also described in Chapter 13. Over 500,000 Alu elements are dispersed throughout the human genome. At 300 bp in length, the Alu element is far too short to encode a reverse transcriptase. Nonetheless, like LINE elements, Alu and other SINE elements are able to disperse themselves throughout the genome by means of an RNA intermediate that undergoes reverse transcription and are considered selfish elements. Clearly, SINEs depend on the availability of reverse transcriptase produced elsewhere, perhaps from LINE transcripts or the proviral elements of retroviruses.

All SINE elements in the human genome, as well as in other mammalian genomes, appear to have evolved from small cellular RNA species, most often tRNAs, but also the 7S cytoplasmic RNA that is a component of the signal recognition particle (SRP) essential for protein translocation across the endoplasmic reticulum. The defining event in the evolution of a functional cellular RNA into an altered-function, self-replicating SINE element is the accumulation of nucleotide changes in the 3′ region that lead to self-complementarity with the propensity to form hairpin loops. Reverse transcriptase can recognize the open end of the hairpin loop as a primer for strand elongation. Because it is likely that the hairpin loops form only rarely among normal cellular RNAs, a cell will preferentially use its SINE transcripts as templates for the production of cDNA molecules that are somehow able to integrate into the genome at random sites (**Fig. 20.23**).

The potential selective advantage of selfish elements

While SINE and LINE elements may have amplified themselves for selfish purposes, they have had a profound impact on whole-genome evolution. In particular, homologous SINE or LINE elements located near each other can, and will, catalyze unequal but homologous crossovers that result in the duplication of single-copy genes located between the homologous elements. Such duplications initiate the formation of multigene families. In addition, some selfish elements appear to have evolved a regulatory role—acting as enhancers or promoters—through chance insertions next to open reading frames. Thus, selfish elements may confer a selective advantage by facilitating duplication through unequal crossing-over or by becoming regulatory elements.

Simple sequence repeats (SSRs)

Through large-scale sequencing and hybridization analyses of mammalian genomes, researchers have found tandem repeats of DNA sequences with no apparent function scattered throughout the genome. The size of the repeating units ranges from two nucleotides (CACACACA . . .) to 20 kb or more, and the number of tandem repeats varies from two to several hundred. As noted in Chapter 11, such sequences, including microsatellites, minisatellites, and macrosatellites, have proven very useful as tags in genome analysis and detection of individual genotype.

The mechanism by which these tandem repeats originate may be different for loci having very short repeat units as compared with loci having longer repeat units. Tandem repeats of short di- or trinucleotides can originate through random changes in nonfunctional sequences. By contrast, the initial duplication of larger repeat units is likely to be a consequence of unequal crossing-over. Once two or more copies of a repeat unit exist in tandem, an increase in the number of repeat units in subsequent generations can occur through unequal crossovers or errors in replication (see Figs. 20.9 and 20.16). It is not yet clear whether random mechanisms alone can account for the rich variety of tandem repeat loci in mammalian genomes or whether other selective forces are at play. Either way, tandem repeat loci continue to be highly susceptible to unequal crossing-over and, as a result, tend to be highly polymorphic in overall size.

Centromeres and telomeres contain many repeat sequences

Highly repetitive, noncoding sequences shorter than 200 bp are found in and around centromeres. For example, in the human genome, alphoid, a noncoding sequence 171 bp in length, is present in tandem arrays extending for over a megabase in the centromeric region of each chromosome. In addition, several similar-sized repetitive sequences unrelated to alphoid are found in some centromeres (review Fig. 12.22 on p. 422). These regions are sites of interaction with the spindle fibers that segregate chromosomes during meiosis and mitosis. Selection may have acted to retain the thousands of copies of centromere repeat elements in each centromeric region because they increase the efficiency and/or accuracy of chromosome segregation.

Figure 20.23 Creation of a SINE gene family. SINE elements can be transcribed, and because they form 3′ hairpin loops, they can be copied into cDNAs by LINE-encoded reverse transcriptase. These cDNA copies then integrate into the genome.

A second type of repeated genomic element with a special location is the hexamer TTAGGG found in the telomeres of all human chromosomes. The six-base unit is repeated in tandem arrays 5–10 kb in length at the ends of human and all other mammalian chromosomes. Selection may have conserved this repeat element because it plays an essential role in maintaining chromosomal length (review Figs. 12.18 and 12.19).

> Much of the genome consists of "nonfunctional" DNA, including the LINE and SINE families of repeated elements. In contrast, centromeres and telomeres contain highly repetitive noncoding sequences that presumably have benefited the function of these elements in chromosome replication.

20.4 A Comprehensive Example: Rapid Evolution in the Immune Response and in HIV

Much of our knowledge of evolution is based on inferences from observations of extinct organisms (fossils) and on comparisons between existing organisms, both phenotypically and at the molecular level. Examples in the viral and bacterial worlds can provide a view of evolution in progress.

An example of short-term competitive evolution at the molecular level is seen in the battle between HIV (the AIDS virus) and cells of the human immune system. Both the virus and the response of the immune system evolve through diversification of progenitor populations followed by selective amplification of some divergent forms.

When an invading virus activates the immune system, a virus-specific immune response ensues (described in the Fast Forward box in Chapter 13). Specific human immune responses depend on the cellular diversity of the immune system, which includes a trillion (10^{12}) circulating lymphocytes. These lymphocytes are of two types: T cells and B cells. Populations of lymphocytes have the genetic capacity to synthesize a large and varied group of cell surface immune receptors collectively capable of recognizing foreign (non-self) macromolecular structures (**Fig. 20.24**). Somatic mutations and gene rearrangements in the cells of the developing immune system enable enormous diversification of receptors from a relatively small repertoire of genes.

Although populations of lymphocytes carry a great diversity of immune receptors, each individual lymphocyte synthesizes only one type of immune receptor. This attribute is the key to the specificity of an immune response. When the multiple copies of that one type of receptor in a cell's membrane encounter complementary foreign structures (called *antigenic determinants*), interaction between the immune receptors and the antigenic determinants triggers that lymphocyte to divide and differentiate.

The immune system's response evolves according to the antigen present

The rapid proliferation, or cloning, of just a few selected lymphocytes is the first step of an immune response. Among the cells in each expanded clone are *memory cells,* which may live as long as 40 years, and *effector cells,* which actually carry out (or effect) the immune reactions that help dispose of the microorganisms. These effector cells include T effector cells that bind to the antigenic determinants of a bacterium or virus, and B effector cells that secrete antibodies, which in turn bind to antigenic determinants.

As the immune response progresses, some of the B effector cells mutate their membrane receptors, generating further diversification. The altered receptors with the closest fit to the antigenic determinants bind the determinants more tightly, and this high-affinity binding drives the amplification of the lymphocytes that carry the altered receptors—a process called *selective amplification.* The differentiated effector cells ultimately destroy the pathogenic organism carrying the antigenic determinants targeted by the immune response.

Figure 20.24 The immune response. Diverse receptors on lymphocytes recognize different molecular structures from invading pathogens. T cells employ T-cell receptors; B cells employ antibodies. Differentiated B cells secrete antibodies that destroy or neutralize antigens. Expanded numbers of memory T cells and B cells allow rapid response to an antigen encountered a second time.

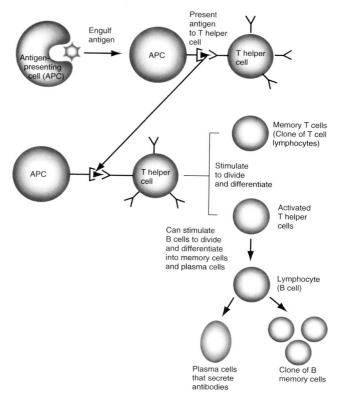

The immune system's generation of specific immune responses is a marvelous example of molecular evolution: the diversification of lymphocytes into many variants, followed by antigen-specific selection of just one or a few of these variants for amplification over a period of weeks to fend off the invader.

HIV also undergoes molecular evolution

HIV is a worthy adversary for the human immune system because it is able to diversify and amplify via selection far faster than the immune response itself. HIV, you may recall, is a retrovirus with an RNA genome (see Chapter 8). The virus makes its own reverse transcriptase available to the cells it infects (which include the T lymphocytes), forcing the cellular machinery first to copy the viral RNA genome into a DNA copy and then to generate a complementary DNA strand to form a proviral double helix. The infected cells integrate the double-stranded viral DNA into their own genomes (review Fig. B in the Genetics and Society box on p. 260). The HIV reverse transcriptase has a very high mutation rate of roughly 1 in 5000 nucleotides incorporated into the viral cDNA. Because the HIV genome is about 10 kb in length, each replicated virus carries an average of two mutations, which are the basis of rapid diversification.

When HIV replicates explosively on infection, it generates billions of variant viruses before the host's immune response has a chance to take hold. The antigenic determinants targeted by the initial response have mutated beyond recognition by the time the originally activated T cells and B cells have proliferated. Although some of the new antigenic determinants may be recognized by other cells among the diverse population of lymphocytes, subsequent viral mutations may alter these viral targets as well. Eventually, the speed of viral evolution outstrips the ability of the immune response to keep pace—not only because the viral genome mutates at a high frequency, but also because the viral generation time is so short.

Therapies attempt to tip the balance

A new therapeutic approach to AIDS has been remarkably effective in prolonging the initial symptom-free phase of the disease. Called highly active antiretroviral therapy (HAART), it entails the simultaneous delivery of three to four different anti-HIV drugs: In the triple-drug therapy, two drugs block the function of the HIV reverse transcriptase through different mechanisms, and the third blocks the functioning of a viral protease critical to HIV reproduction. By reducing the rate of viral replication, the triple-drug therapy significantly decreases the virus's ability to develop variants that are simultaneously resistant to the human immune response and all three drugs. As a result, the HIV population in patients diminishes dramatically with the initial treatment. The triple-drug therapy thus shifts the ability to diversify and amplify by selection in favor of the human immune response.

The immune system response involves selection for T and B cells that can bind a foreign antigen and their subsequent rapid proliferation. HIV evolves rapidly because of the very high mutation rate associated with its reverse transcriptase; this evolution keeps it ahead of the immune system's response. Treatments attempt to target the reverse transcriptase and other virus-specific elements.

Connections

A retrospective bird's-eye view of key events that led to an understanding of evolution at the molecular level goes something like this. In 1859, Charles Darwin published *The Origin of Species* in which he inferred from the visible evidence of descent through modification that the diverse organisms alive today evolved from a single primordial form, in large part, by a process of natural selection. Several years later, Mendel published "Experiments on Plant Hybrids" in which he applied the laws of probability to the visible evidence of heredity, inferring the existence of hereditary units that segregate during gamete formation and assort independently of each other. In the early twentieth century, Thomas Hunt Morgan and coworkers gave Mendel's units of heredity a physical location in the cell, establishing the chromosomal basis of heredity and showing not only that genes have chromosomal addresses but also that recombination can separate otherwise linked genes. In the 1940s several people, including Oswald Avery, Martha Chase, and Alfred Hershey, showed that the molecule of heredity is DNA. Then in 1953, James Watson and Francis Crick deciphered the structure of DNA and proposed a mechanism by which the molecule replicates. By the end of the twentieth century, extensive genomic analyses had made it possible to explain how DNA mutates, duplicates, diverges, and is acted on by selection to generate the diversity of life we see around us.

ESSENTIAL CONCEPTS

1. All forms of life on earth are descendants of a single cell—a common ancestor that existed approximately 3.7 billion years ago.

2. Charles Darwin explained how biological evolution occurs through a process of natural selection, which operates on variant forms of inherited traits. The variant that provides the highest degree of reproductive fitness is selected over many generations to become the predominant form in the entire population.

3. New mutations provide a continuous source of variation. Mutations with no effect on fitness are considered neutral. Neutral mutations are not acted on by selection and are subject instead to genetic drift. Selection operates against mutation with a deleterious effect, and operates in favor of the extremely rare mutations that have a positive effect on fitness. Selection can operate simultaneously at hundreds or thousands of variant loci within a population.

4. RNA can carry genetic information as well as catalyze chemical reactions. These two properties have led scientists to speculate that RNA may have predated the cell as the original independent replicator, or proto-life-form.

5. The fossil record as well as living organisms of all levels of complexity provide scientists with a detailed picture of the evolution of complex life from the first cell to human beings.

6. Preliminary studies on the evolution of gene regulatory networks suggest that it can account for the evolution of biological complexity.

7. The evolution of organismal complexity generally correlates with an increase in genome size, which occurs through repeated duplications. Some duplications result from transpositions, while others arise from unequal crossing-over.

8. Mutations rendering genes nonfunctional turn many duplicated genes into pseudogenes that over time diverge into random DNA sequences. However, rare advantageous mutations can turn a second copy of a gene into a new functional unit able to survive and spread through positive selection.

9. Sequence comparisons make it possible to construct phylogenetic trees illustrating the relatedness of species, populations, individuals, or molecules.

10. The mammalian genome contains genes, multigene families, gene superfamilies, genome-wide repetitive elements; simple sequence repeats; and repetitive elements in centromeres and telomeres.

11. Complex genomes arose from four levels of duplication followed by diversification and selection: exon duplication to create larger, more complex genes; gene duplication to create multigene families; multigene family duplication to create gene superfamilies; and the duplication of entire genomes.

12. Genetic exchange between related DNA elements by intergenic gene conversion most often increases the variation among members of a multigene family. Sometimes, however, it can contribute to concerted evolution, which creates a family of nearly identical genes.

13. The human immune system is capable of a response that evolves on the molecular level through cloning of T and B cells that match an antigen. HIV can undergo rapid evolution due to the high mutation rate of its reverse transcriptase. Therapies aim to slow the proliferation of HIV by targeting reverse transcriptase and other viral enzymes.

On Our Website   www.mhhe.com/hartwell4

Annotated Suggested Readings and Links to Other Websites

- Interesting historical papers on evolution
- Contemporary papers on evolution
- Papers on the ethical and social implications of evolution
- Interesting books on evolution

Solved Problems

I. The sequence of two different forms of a gene starting with the ATG is shown here. Which of the base differences in the second sequence are synonymous changes and which are nonsynonymous changes?

```
form 1        ATGTCTCATGGACCCCTTCGTTTG
form 2        ATGTCTCAAAGACCACATCGTCTG
```

Answer

The key to answering this question is understanding the difference between synonymous and nonsynonymous changes in DNA sequence.

Synonymous changes are nucleotide substitutions that do not change the amino acid specified by the DNA sequence. Nonsynonymous changes are nucleotide changes that result in a different amino acid in the protein.

Looking at the amino acids specified by the base sequence,

	Met	Ser	His	Gly	Pro	Leu	Arg	Leu
form 1	ATG	TCT	CAT	GGA	CCC	CTT	CGT	TTG
	Met	Ser	Gln	Arg	Pro	His	Arg	Leu
form 2	ATG	TCT	CAA	AGA	CCA	CAT	CGT	CTG

(The base substitutions in form 2 are underlined.) *The first, second, and fourth A substitutions are nonsynonymous changes; the third A substitution and the C substitution are synonymous changes.*

II. What difficulties would arise if you tried to derive a molecular clock rate using a noncoding sequence in some species and a coding sequence in other species?

Answer

To answer this question, you need to think about how molecular clocks are derived and the constraints on base changes in coding and noncoding sequences.

The evolution of coding sequences is restricted by the fact that the gene sequence needs to be maintained for the gene product to function. The sequence of noncoding regions generally can tolerate many base substitutions without selection acting on these sequences. *Therefore, you would expect more substitutions in the noncoding sequence. The result would be an inconsistency in your clock rate if you are using a coding region in some species and noncoding DNA in other species.*

III. If the chromosomes diagrammed below misalign by the pairing of repeated sequences (shown as solid blocks) and crossing-over occurs, what will be the products?

Answer

This question requires an understanding of crossing-over via homology. When you align the homologous repeated sequences out of register, one of the resulting products will have a duplication of the region between the repeats and three copies of the repeated sequence and the other product will be deleted for the DNA between the repeats and contain only one repeated sequence.

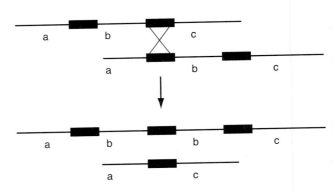

Problems

Vocabulary

1. For each of the terms in the left column, choose the best matching phrase in the right column.

a. ribozymes

b. retrotransposition

c. SINEs

d. punctuated equilibrium

e. molecular clock

f. phylogenetic trees

g. exon shuffling

1. constant rate of change in amino acid sequence

2. sudden explosive evolutionary changes

3. exchange of pieces of genes

4. RNA molecules that catalyze specific chemical reactions

5. short repeated sequences in human genomes

6. RNA intermediate in duplicatic of genetic material

7. representation of evolutionary relationships

Section 20.1

2. What observations support the unity of life concept that all life-forms evolved from a common ancestor?

3. Which of the following statements is support for RNA being the first replicator molecule?
a. RNA molecules can function as enzymes.
b. DNA is more stable than RNA.
c. Information can be encoded in RNA.

4. a. In what ways is RNA not a good information storage molecule?
b. In what ways is RNA not as good as protein as a molecular machine?

5. a. A particular chemical reaction that occurs between two proteins is sensitive to RNase treatment *in vitro* (that is, it will not occur if the reaction mix is pretreated with RNase), but it is not sensitive to protease treatment. What would you propose about the nature of the enzyme that carries out the reaction?
b. Another chemical reaction is sensitive to both RNase and protease treatment. What would you propose about the nature of the enzyme that carries out this reaction?

6. Humans and chimps have a 1% difference in their genomic sequence, while two humans have a 0.1% sequence difference. How could something as small as a 1% difference in DNA sequence lead to dramatic differences seen in chimps versus humans? Speculate on the types of differences the 1% variation may represent.

Section 20.2

7. Rates of nonsynonymous and synonymous amino acid substitutions for three genes that were compared in humans and mice or rats are shown here. (The rates are expressed as the average number of substitutions per base per year, with the standard deviation given. In each case, the number shown is the rate at which the human and rat sequences have diverged from each other, by either a nonsynonymous or a synonymous substitution.)
a. Why do the rates of nonsynonymous substitutions vary among these genes?
b. Why are the rates of synonymous substitutions similar?

Protein	Nonsynonymous substitutions	Synonymous substitutions
Histone 3	$0.0 \pm 0.0 \times 10^{-9}$	$6.38 \pm 1.10 \times 10^{-9}$
Growth hormone	$1.23 \pm 0.15 \times 10^{-9}$	$4.95 \pm 0.77 \times 10^{-9}$
β globin	$0.8 \pm 0.133 \times 10^{-9}$	$3.05 \pm 0.56 \times 10^{-9}$

8. Synonymous mutations are more prevalent than nonsynonymous mutations in most genes. The immunoglobulin (Ig) genes encoding antibody subunits are an exception where nonsynonymous base changes outnumber synonymous changes. Based on the function of the Ig genes, why do you think this might be true?

9. Mutations in the *CF* gene that cause cystic fibrosis are carried by 1 in 20 individuals of Caucasian ancestry. The disease is clearly detrimental, yet the allele is maintained at a relatively high level in the population. What does this paradox suggest about the effect of the mutation?

10. Unequal crossing-over between two copies of a gene can lead to duplication and deletion on the two homologs involved. How could a single gene become duplicated?

11. Human beings have three-color vision, while most other species of animals have two-color vision or one-color vision (that is, black and white). Three-color vision is produced by the products of a three-member, cross-hybridizing gene family that encodes light-sensitive pigments active in different ranges of the color spectrum (red, green, and blue). What is the most likely molecular explanation for the evolution of three-color vision in the ancestor to human beings?

12. How do transposition and unequal crossing-over differ based on the location of final copies of the duplicated sequence?

13. You have identified an interesting new gene that appears to be involved in human brain development. You have discovered three cross-hybridizing copies of this gene within the human genome (*A, B,* and *C*). In the mouse genome, there is only a single copy of this gene (named *M*) and in the frog *Xenopus,* there is also only a single copy (named *X*). You have sequenced the same 10,000 bp of open reading frame from each of these genes and calculated the number of base-pair differences that exist between different pairs with the following results:

Comparison	Number of base-pair differences
A versus *B*	300
B versus *C*	10
A versus *C*	300
A versus *M*	600
A versus *X*	3000

If you assume that a constant rate of evolution has occurred with all members of this gene family, and you assume that mice and humans evolved apart 60 million years ago:
a. How long ago did frogs split from the line leading to mice?

b. How many gene duplication events are observable within these data? At what time in the past did each of these duplication events occur?

c. Mapping of the *A*, *B*, and *C* genes shows that *A* and *C* are very closely linked, while *B* assorts independently from either of these genes. With this linkage information, what can you say about the molecular nature of the duplication events that occurred along the evolutionary line leading to human beings?

14. Phylogenetic trees of primates constructed using chromosome mutations (deletions, insertions, inversions, etc.) show the same relationships of species as those constructed using base substitutions within a gene. Which type of genetic alteration would you expect to have the greater impact on the evolution of chimp and human from a common ancestor. Why?

15. When a phylogenetic tree was constructed using comparisons of glucose-6-phosphate isomerase amino acid sequences from a wide variety of species including animals, plants, and bacteria, the bacterium *E. coli* was placed on a branch of the phylogenetic tree with a flower. What explanation could there be for this unusual association based on this one protein-coding sequence? (Recall that bacteria and plants are in very different locations on the evolutionary trees derived from analyses of several gene sequences or morphology and physiology.)

Section 20.3

16. Organisms have a characteristic percentage of GC bases in their genomes. In a species of halophilic (salt-loving) bacteria containing two essential plasmids and one chromosome, the plasmids have a different GC content than the chromosome. What could you hypothesize about the origin of the plasmids?

17. What is the unit that can be duplicated and modified to form
a. a new gene?
b. a multigene family?

18. It has been hypothesized that in the evolution of vertebrates, there were two successive doublings of the genome (tetraploidization) to produce the vertebrate genome.
a. How does the *Hox* superfamily fit with this hypothesis?
b. Among vertebrates, there is variation in the numbers of genes present within the *Hox* gene family clusters. How could this variation arise?

19. LINEs and SINEs are considered to be selfish DNA, yet they can, in some instances, confer a selective advantage on the organism. What are two ways in which a LINE or SINE can change the genome?

20. How is the size polymorphism of dinucleotide repeated sequences thought to occur?

21. a. What is an example of repetitive noncoding DNA for which we know no physiological function?
b. What is an example of repetitive noncoding DNA for which we know a cellular function?

22. Match the observation on the right with the event that it suggests occurred during evolution.

Event	Evidence in the genome
a. concerted evolution	1. genes in different individuals of the same species have 6, 8, or 10 homology units in an immunoglobulin gene family member
b. exons and introns of a gene	2. several copies of the same gene that are identical in the genome
c. unequal crossing-over	3. poly-A sequences at the end of coding regions in genomic DNA
d. retrotransposition	4. blocks of DNA sequence conserved between species separated by nonconserved blocks

Section 20.4

23. Indinavir sulfate is a viral protease inhibitor that is often a part of HAART to combat HIV infection. However, this drug has multiple possible side effects, including increased risk of kidney stones, redistribution of fat deposits in the body, and acute hemolytic anemia (bursting of red blood cells).
a. Based on these side effects, what can you say about the specificity of this protease inhibitor? Is its action restricted only to the viral target?
b. Redistribution of fat includes peripheral and facial wasting accompanied by increased fat deposition in the trunk and the dorsocervical region (i.e., a "buffalo hump"). These changes are often also seen in during aging and are associated with insulin resistance and diabetes. Speculate about some possible ways in which a protease inhibitor might bring about this fat distribution.
c. One underlying predisposition to hemolytic anemia unrelated to HIV is a hereditary enzymopathy resulting in a pathologically low level of glucose-6-phosphate dehydrogenase. This enzyme is especially critical in energy maintenance of red blood cells. What could you infer about the action of indinavir sulfate that might lead to hemolytic anemia? How would you test your hypothesis?

Systems Biology and the Future of Medicine

Systems biology explores biological phenomena using large-scale technologies to generate data and computational tools to analyze the data.

Smallpox is a deadly viral disease that has killed and disfigured humans for thousands of years. Its name comes from the many skin lesions, or pox, the disease produces. But people who managed to survive smallpox were immune to reinfection. By the 1600s, some practitioners in Africa, India, and China were attempting to avoid the disease through *inoculation*—the subcutaneous introduction of smallpox into healthy individuals. Pus from the lesions of an infected person was introduced by lancet or needle beneath the recipient's skin. But this coarse method was not without risk of contracting the full-blown disease and dying from it.

Edward Jenner (1749–1823), a dedicated English country doctor who had himself been inoculated with smallpox as a boy, was fascinated by reports that milkmaids could not get smallpox. These women often got the non-life-threatening cowpox, including blisters on their hands, but they did not become infected with smallpox. Jenner hypothesized that the pus in cowpox blisters somehow protects against smallpox. Others had used inoculation with cowpox as a preventive for smallpox, but no one had done scientific testing of this hypothesis.

To test this idea, Jenner took pus from cowpox blisters on the hands of a milkmaid who had regularly milked a cowpox-infected cow and injected some of this pus into a young boy named James Phipps. He repeated this process over a number of days in 1796, gradually increasing the amount of pus he put into the boy. James contracted and recovered from cowpox. Jenner then deliberately injected him with material from smallpox lesions. Although the boy fell ill, he fully recovered in a few days and suffered no negative side effects. Jenner termed his procedure **vaccination** because the Latin word for cow is *vacca*. We now know that related viruses cause cowpox and smallpox, but the cowpox virus is much less virulent. Vaccination now refers to inoculation with any nonvirulent or otherwise attenuated infectious agent for the purpose of producing immunity.

Jenner went on to publicize his findings with dissemination of a small booklet describing his experiments. He undertook a campaign to spread the word about vaccination, which was successful in bringing about its use throughout England and subsequently in Europe. Eventually, his vaccine found its way to America, where Thomas Jefferson set up the National Vaccination Institute to implement a national vaccination program in the early 1800s. A worldwide vaccination program in the 1970s eventually eliminated smallpox (**Fig. 21.1**).

Today, we understand surprisingly little about how to control the immune response to many pathogens. In the two centuries since Jenner's time, only about two dozen safe and effective vaccines have been developed. The inability to develop vaccines against any and every infectious disease is ironic because we know more about the molecular components of the vertebrate immune system than perhaps any other

CHAPTER OUTLINE

- 21.1 What Is Systems Biology?
- 21.2 Biology as an Informational Science
- 21.3 The Practice of Systems Biology
- 21.4 A Systems Approach to Disease

Figure 21.1 Smallpox victim. Ethiopian boy scarred by smallpox, 1970. Since 1977, vaccination has eradicated smallpox worldwide.

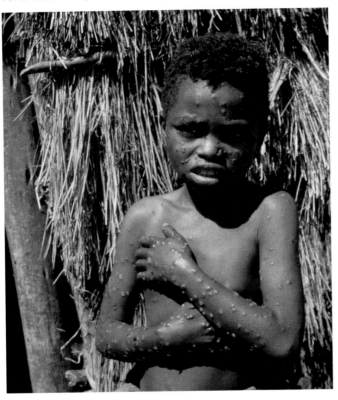

eukaryotic biological system. One reason for this discrepancy is that immunologists have studied the components of the immune system one gene and one protein at a time, but they have not yet studied them all together, as the system functions. Consequently, we do not yet understand the system's two most fundamental properties: **immunity,** the ability to generate immune responses to infections or vaccines; and **tolerance,** the ability to prevent the body from making immune responses to its own proteins.

Practitioners of the newly emerging field of **molecular systems biology** attempt to define all the components of a biological system and understand how they function in conjunction with one another. This pursuit relies on the tools and strategies of both genomics and proteomics, as well as the global data generated by these studies (see Chapter 10). It also employs computational and mathematical tools for the modeling and simulation of biological systems.

One main theme stands out in our overview of systems biology: By studying how the gene and protein components of a system function together, we can begin to understand how the system's interacting elements give rise to its emergent properties. When we accomplish this level of understanding for the immune system, as one example, we will likely acquire the insights to generate vaccines on demand against almost any infectious organism, including, perhaps, the AIDS virus.

21.1 What Is Systems Biology?

A **biological system** is a collection of interacting elements that carry out a specific biological task. These elements may include molecules such as proteins, mRNAs, metabolites and other small molecules, and the control elements of genes; or they may be cells such as immune system cells, hormonal network cells, and neuronal network cells that carry out a specific biological task. As mentioned earlier, the elements rarely act independently; rather, they most often function in association with one another.

Systems biology seeks to describe the multiple components of a biological system and analyze the complex interactions of these components both within the system and in relation to the components of other systems. For example, the nine proteins in yeast that help convert galactose to glucose constitute a system distinct from all other systems encoded by yeast's 6000 genes. These nine elements interact with the proteins of other systems to help regulate the timing and extent of the galactose-to-glucose conversion. In mammals, as another example, the cells of the innate immune system and the adaptive immune system function together to generate immune responses, and in carrying out these functions, they interact with cells of the nervous system. Thus, biological systems are defined by their discrete biological functions, but they often interact with other systems.

In reality, biologists have been practicing systems approaches to biology for more than 100 years. At the turn of the twentieth century, physiologists were interested in homeostasis, which is certainly a systems problem. So, too, have developmental biologists, neurobiologists, and immunologists been interested in problems that require thinking about systems. The systems biology approach of the twenty-first century is different in that it attempts both a "bottom-up" approach, starting with large molecular data sets, and a "top-down" approach employing computational modeling and simulations. The desired outcome is to trace complex observations of phenotype back to the digital core encoded in the genome. This approach is possible because the Human Genome Project, described in Chapter 10, has provided global data-gathering tools and genomic information on a scale never before available. These tools and data are central to the current practice of molecular systems biology.

Four questions help guide thinking about biological systems

Four fundamental questions can be asked about a biological system:

1. What are the *elements* of the system?
2. What are the *physical associations* among the elements?
3. How do *perturbations* affect the system and other systems connected to it?
4. How do a system's elements, associations, and relation to changes in the biological context explain its *emergent properties?*

We discuss each of these briefly.

What are the elements of a system?

Defining the elements or components of a system lays the fundamental groundwork for further analyses. We need to identify the proteins, genes, metabolites, cells, tissues, and organs that are involved. Modern systems biology uses the data sets generated by genomic and proteomics tools described in Chapter 10 to identify genes, mRNAs, and proteins. The systems biologist identifies specific genes involved by using the catalog of genes identified by genomic sequencing and transcriptional analysis using microarrays. Proteins are identified by mass spectrometry and two-dimensional gel analysis. Our ability to interrogate large basic data sets to find the components involved makes the systems approach possible.

What physical associations occur among elements?

What are the protein-protein interactions, protein-DNA interactions, and interactions between molecules in the system? The isotope-coded affinity tag (ICAT) and yeast two-hybrid analyses described in Chapter 10 are two of the tools that generate data on physical interactions. It is possible to depict the interactions of a system's elements in a graphic representation of a network where the nodes, or points, represent individual proteins and the connections represent physical interactions between the proteins (**Fig. 21.2**). A series of such network graphs can reveal how systems change throughout the development of an organism or during physiological responses to changing environments.

What happens when the system undergoes perturbation?

Delineating the dynamic behavior of systems is one of the central challenges of systems biology. One way to accomplish this is to ask how the relationships of the elements change when the system is subject to specific genetic or environmental perturbations.

Systems are most often studied in one of two *biological contexts:* within individual cell types (prostate cancer cells or embryonic stem cells) or within an entire organism

(a yeast, a nematode, a *Drosophila,* a mouse, or a human). The comprehensive knowledge of all the genes (and, hence, all the mRNAs and their predicted proteins) in a cell or organism, which is generated by each genome project, permits the study of systems in their biological contexts. This broad and yet detailed study may allow predictions about the effects of a disease state or other abnormal change in one system, termed a **perturbation,** upon other systems.

What gives rise to a system's emergent properties?

An **emergent property** is one that arises from the operation of the system as a whole. Examples are the ability of the immune system to generate immune responses, the ability of the heart to pump blood, and the ability of a metabolic pathway to convert galactose into glucose.

In some cases, an emergent property can be greater than the sum of individual properties of system components. An example is the action of the digestive system, in which many organs, tissues, and cellular components accomplish ingestion of food, absorption of nutrients, and elimination of wastes in a concerted, interdependent, and stepwise fashion.

Systems biology requires a cross-disciplinary approach

Systems biology is an immature science whose practitioners are still developing the tools and strategies of the discipline. To succeed in answering the basic questions just outlined, they must practice *cross-disciplinary biology,* in which teams of biologists, computer scientists,

Figure 21.2 Representation of a biological network. The nodes (*blue circles*) of the graph may represent molecules such as proteins and metabolites or cells (like those of the immune or nervous system). The *lines* connecting some nodes represent relationships between the elements.

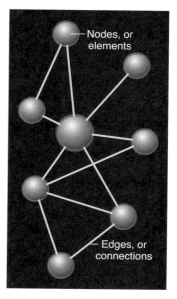

chemists, engineers, mathematicians, and physicists work together on common problems. Driven by the needs of systems biology, these teams must develop new high-throughput measuring instruments; use the new instruments to generate global data sets; and develop new computational tools to organize, annotate, analyze, integrate, and model the accumulated data.

New instruments and tools include more effective platforms for DNA sequencing and chip array technology that offer higher throughput, better quality data, greater sensitivity, and lower cost. Many of the techniques require the acquisition of large amounts of data and are best suited to nanotechnology. High-resolution techniques must be further developed to analyze single molecules and cells using advanced imaging techniques. More powerful computational and mathematical tools for storing, integrating, graphically displaying, analyzing, and mathematically modeling biological systems are needed and scientists must work together to gather and annotate their data in compatible formats. The development and implementation of these new technologies demands that scientists of varying backgrounds learn to speak the language of biology, and biologists learn to speak the languages of the physical and mathematical sciences.

> Systems biology is guided by four questions regarding system components, their associations, the effects of changes to the system, and the emergent properties of a system. Because complex biological systems encompass so many aspects, a cross-disciplinary approach is needed.

21.2 Biology as an Informational Science

A crucial consequence of the Human Genome Project has been the emerging view of biology as an informational science. The idea of analyzing biological systems in terms of the storage, transmission, and transformation of biological information is central to systems biology.

Biological information is hierarchical. It starts with the digital DNA informational core of the genome and progresses through mRNA, protein, molecular machines, networks, cells, networks of cells, and tissues to individual organisms, populations of organisms, and finally ecosystems. Environmental information impinges upon and modulates the core digital information at each of these successive steps. To understand biological systems, one must capture and integrate information from as many different hierarchical levels as possible. The most fundamental of the information is the digital information in the DNA of the genome.

Systems include molecular machines and functional networks

Digital genomic information consists of two types of sequences: the genes that encode proteins and untranslated

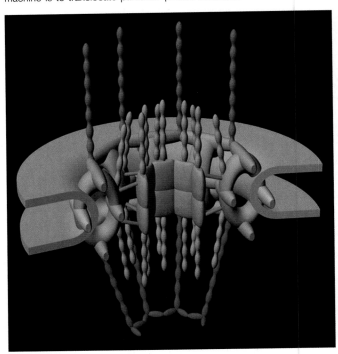

Figure 21.3 Drawing of a nuclear pore in yeast. This complex molecular machine contains about 60 proteins. One function of this machine is to translocate particular protein molecules into the nucleus.

RNAs, and short DNA sequences (6–15 base pairs long) that constitute the control elements adjacent (or *cis*) to the genes. These control elements are called *cis*-control elements. As with all systems elements, the gene-encoded proteins interact with other proteins and macromolecules to form complex molecular machines, such as spliceosomes, ribosomes, and nuclear pores (**Fig. 21.3**). These machines carry out specific activities, such as mRNA splicing, protein synthesis, and transport of proteins.

Associations between elements also establish **protein networks:** sets of interacting proteins and other molecules that execute a particular biological function (**Fig. 21.4**). These networks channel biological information and use it in functions such as signal transduction, physiological responses to environmental changes, development of tissues and organs, and metabolism. A key property of all networks is that they are dynamic, able to respond to conditions when activated. Understanding the two basic categories of protein interactions—in molecular machines and in networks—is a major challenge of systems biology.

Gene regulatory networks control information transmission

In addition to participating in protein networks, a class of proteins called *transcription factors* function along with their *cis*-control elements as key players in gene regulatory networks (see Chapters 8 and 16). **Gene regulatory networks** receive diverse inputs of information, integrate

Figure 21.4 A yeast protein network containing about 2500 proteins and 7000 linkages. New computational tools will enable biologists to focus on particular connections in the larger network.

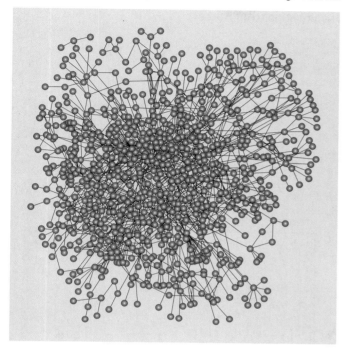

Figure 21.5 Multiple transcription factors regulate gene expression. Six transcription factors (tf1–tf6) bind to *cis*-control sites (*red squares*) to regulate when, where and how much mRNA of this hypothetical gene is produced. Because the gene depicted here is itself a transcription factor, the DNA-protein interactions are linkages in a gene regulatory network.

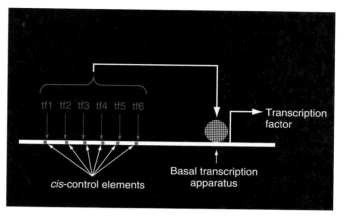

and modify those inputs, and then transmit the altered information to protein networks. The interaction of a transcription factor (protein) with its *cis*-control element (DNA) is the fundamental linkage relationship in a gene regulatory network. Each gene has from 3 to 30 or more *cis*-control elements, which collectively regulate its expres-

sion (**Fig. 21.5**). When transcription factors bind to the *cis*-control elements of a particular gene, they form a three-dimensional protein/DNA complex that regulates the expression of the corresponding gene through interactions with another complex protein/DNA machine, the basal transcription apparatus (see Chapter 16). The interactions of multiple *cis*-control elements and their cognate transcription factors determines where in space, when in time, and to what level the mRNA is expressed.

In interacting with *cis*-control elements, some transcription factors control the expression of two or more genes encoding other transcription factors (**Fig. 21.6**).

Figure 21.6 Gene regulatory network. In this network, transcription factors interact with transcription factor genes. The genes are represented by *horizontal lines* (*red, purple, blue,* and *green*) that fall into three layers. The transcription factor interactions may be positive (indicated by an *arrow* at the interaction site) or negative (indicated by a *bar* at the interaction site—see *2b* interacting with *2a*). A transcription factor may interact with another transcription factor in a lower layer or it may feed back to another gene in its layer or in an earlier layer.

Transient localized input

Gene 1

Gene 2a

Gene 2b

Gene 3

Differentiation genes

Figure 21.7 Endomesoderm gene regulatory network. About 50 proteins are represented in this network, and 35 of them are transcription factors. The schematic representation in this figure is similar to the one in Fig. 21.6. The particular network represented here makes it possible to understand many aspects of gut development in sea urchin larvae (depicted in Fig. 21.8).

Thus, a single transcription factor may affect the behavior of many other transcription factors and thereby create a complex network structure. Gene regulatory networks that encode both subcircuits of transcription factors and the *cis*-control elements with which the factors interact may generate complex feed-forward and feedback regulatory loops acting between different levels (**Fig. 21.7**).

The complexity of a gene regulatory network is specified in part by the number of layers in the network and the number of genes involved in each layer. They then transmit information from various signal transduction pathway and other inputs to batteries of genes that carry out metabolism, development, or physiological responses. **Figure 21.8** shows the most complex gene regulatory network analyzed to date: the network that controls endomesodermal, or gut, development in sea

urchin larvae. The network depicted in Fig. 21.7 accurately predicts the events required for gut development, shown in the blue territory in Fig. 21.8; that is, it explains the emergent properties of this developmental system. Because of the network's predictive power, it can be rationally reengineered by modifying the behavior of one or more genes to create predictable new emergent properties (for example, to convert all pigment cells to skeletal cells).

Proteins interact to form molecular machines for complex functions. Protein networks accomplish information transfer to implement specific actions such as signal transmission and physiological changes. Gene regulatory networks integrate and modulate inputs of biological information and transmit the transformed information to the protein networks.

Figure 21.8 Larval development of the sea urchin.
Development begins with the fertilized egg and in 72 hours generates a larva with 1800 cells. The drawings illustrate three separate stages of this process: blastula, gastrula, and differentiated larva. The four distinct territories of this development process are indicated by four distinct colors. Endomesodermal, or gut, development is indicated by the *blue*.

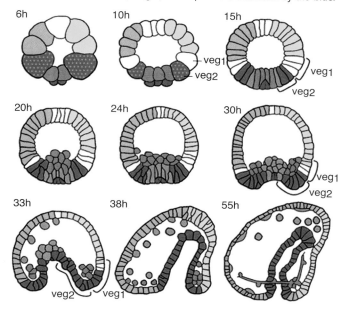

can study the energy-generating systems in one organism and compare them to those in other organisms.

In this section, we consider an algorithmic approach to biological systems and show how this approach can be applied to the example of the galactose conversion pathway of yeast.

Systems biology benefits from an algorithmic approach

The modern systems approach to biology incorporates the following interconnected steps.

Step 1. Scan the biological literature and databases for all that is known about the system of interest. A key aspect of this search is access to the entire genome sequence of the organism under consideration, because the discovery of all of the genes, RNAs, and proteins in a cell or organism, or as many as possible, is the foundation of systems analysis. Use the knowledge gained from discovery science and the literature to define the system of interest as best you can, identifying its elements, their relationships, and their contextual changes.

Step 2. Develop a preliminary model about how the system functions. This model may be descriptive (words), graphic (network diagrams), or mathematical, depending on how much information is available.

Step 3. Formulate a hypothesis-driven query about the model, and answer this query through genetic or environmental perturbations of the system. These perturbations may include alterations ranging from gene knockouts to changes to the environment such as the addition of nutrients, or a combination. In conjunction with these perturbations, collect comprehensive data sets from different levels of biological information (DNA sequence, mRNA levels, protein levels, protein-protein or protein-DNA interactions, and so forth).

Step 4. Integrate different types of data either graphically or mathematically and compare the results against the initially formulated model. Disparities will likely arise between the new experimental data and predictions based on the original model. Formulate new hypotheses that seek to resolve these discrepancies.

Step 5. Perform iterative perturbations. To test the new hypotheses, design a second round of genetic and environmental perturbations that will generate new global data sets whose integration will make it possible to resolve the discrepancies. Repeat steps 3–5 until model and experimental data are in accord.

Step 6. Evaluate whether the refined final model enables biologists to predict the behavior of the system, even with perturbations that have never before been tested. An accurate model should explain the emergent properties of the system and allow prediction of new emergent properties.

21.3 The Practice of Systems Biology

The following outcomes of the Human Genome Project serve as the foundation for the current practice of systems biology. The complete genome sequences of humans and model organisms provide genetics "parts lists" of all the genes in those organisms, as well as predictions of the proteins those genes encode.

- High-throughput platforms for genomics and proteomics (Chapter 10) enable the acquisition of global, or comprehensive, data sets of differing types of biological information (all genes, all mRNAs, all proteins, and so forth).
- Powerful computational tools make it possible to acquire, store, analyze, integrate, display, and model biological information.
- Studies of simple model organisms such as *E. coli* and yeast allow scientists to compile global data sets from experimental manipulations of less complex biological systems. From their analysis of these data, they can learn how to do systems biology in more complex organisms.
- Finally, comparative genomics allows scientists to begin to determine the logic of life for individual organisms and to discover how that logic has changed in different evolutionary lineages. For example, they

Figure 21.9 The yeast galactose-utilization system. This schematic depicts the chemical reactions that convert galactose to glucose-6-phosphate and indicates the enzymes that catalyze these reactions. Genes encoding the enzymes are indicated in parentheses.

Systems biology employs both discovery science and hypothesis-driven science. It requires both the *acquisition of global data sets* from different levels of biological information and the graphical or mathematical *integration of different types of data.*

An example: The systems approach reveals the process of galactose utilization in yeast

Researchers have successfully used the general systems approach just outlined to look at how yeast turns various genes on and off in the utilization of galactose. The galactose-utilization system in yeast converts the sugar galactose to a second sugar, glucose-6-phosphate, a major component in one carbohydrate pathway for energy production. The initial model, illustrated in **Fig. 21.9,** summarizes more than 30 years of galactose-utilization analysis in which researchers looked at one gene or one protein at a time.

Components and setup of the experimental system

The galactose-utilization system has nine elements:

- Four enzymes (encoded by the *GAL 1, GAL 5, GAL 7,* and *GAL 10* genes shown in Fig. 21.9) that catalyze the necessary chemical-modification reactions;
- One transporter molecule that carries galactose across the yeast membrane and also sets the activity state of the galactose system such that when galactose is absent, the system is shut down; and
- Four transcription factors that turn the system on and off.

To analyze the galactose-utilization system, researchers carried out three types of global experiments. They first constructed nine genetically perturbed yeast strains; in each strain, one of the nine genes encoding the protein elements

of the system had been knocked out. The investigators then used global microarrays with all 6000 yeast genes represented to analyze the nine knockout strains as well as the wild-type strain, in both the presence and absence of galactose. These analyses represented 20 perturbations (9 knockout + 1 wild type = 10 yeast strains × 2 system states).

Observations

Several interesting observations emerged from these experiments. First, more than eight unexpected gene expression patterns were recorded, which suggested that the galactose system has additional control features not captured in the original model. In two instances, researchers formulated new hypotheses, generated new perturbations (double knockouts), and carried out a second round of global microarray analyses, which afforded new insights on the regulation of galactose utilization that could be incorporated into the original model (**Fig. 21.10**). These fundamental new insights helped explain the operation of the galactose system.

Second, the expression patterns of 997 genes could be clustered into 16 groups, each exhibiting similar patterns of gene-expression change across the perturbations. Strikingly, some of the genes within each cluster were known to function in different systems in the yeast cell (for example, during the cell cycle, in amino acid synthesis, or in other aspects of carbohydrate metabolism). The investigators hypothesized that each of these systems was directly or indirectly connected to the galactose-utilization system such that perturbations in the galactose system caused changes in the others.

A second round of analyses using protein-protein and protein-DNA interactions confirmed this hypothesis. Databases cataloging more than 15,000 protein-protein interactions and thousands of protein-DNA (transcription factor/promoter region) interactions exist for yeast. Investigators correlated these cataloged interactions with the 997 genes perturbed in the knockout experiments.

Figure 21.10 Modeling and experimental tests. The top half of this figure depicts the experimental component of systems biology. One perturbs the biological system and analyzes the results experimentally. The bottom half shows the modeling component. Using a model, one predicts the outcome of a perturbation. Iterations of this process lead to greater understanding and predictability about the system.

They then constructed a graph or model of the integrated mRNA expression changes and the protein-protein and protein-DNA interactions. These data supported the hypothesis that interactions occur between the galactose system and many other metabolic and cellular systems (**Fig. 21.11**). This finding, in turn, pointed to additional global analyses—for example, to define in more detail how the different systems communicate with one another.

Finally, the researchers used the ICAT technology (see Chapter 10) to compare the concentrations of various proteins in two types of wild-type yeast cells: those with the galactose system running and those with the system shut off. They examined about 300 proteins, 30 of which exhibit significant changes in concentration; significantly,

15 of those 30 had no changes in their mRNA concentrations. One conclusion is that for these 15 proteins, the regulation of concentration must operate at the posttranscriptional level.

In studying biological systems, it is important to analyze many types of data and integrate the levels of information obtained. In the yeast studies, investigators looked at mRNA levels, protein levels, protein-protein interactions, and protein-DNA interactions and attempted to integrate their findings. The results have been both confirmation of existing theories and some surprises regarding where regulation takes place.

Figure 21.11 Interactions between networks. Genetic perturbations of the galactose-utilization system in yeast affect the network of interactions with other metabolic and functional systems. This network was developed by combining the clusters of mRNAs defined by knockout perturbation experiments and protein-protein and protein-DNA interaction data. The *yellow arrows* indicate protein-DNA interactions (transcription factor activity), and the *blue bars* show protein-protein interactions. The *red circle* indicates where the *GAL 4* gene has been knocked out. A *gray scale* depicts levels of mRNA expression: *black* = high levels; *white* = low levels.

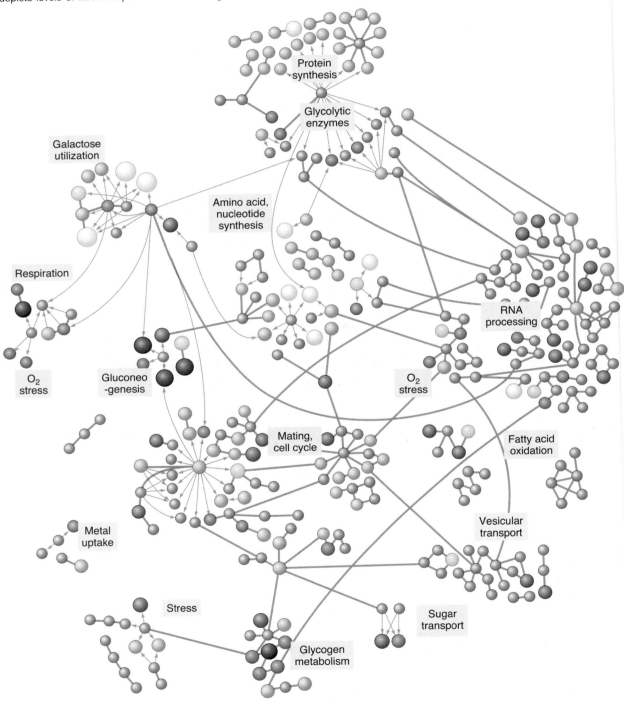

21.4 A Systems Approach to Disease

Genetic and environmental perturbations that cause cellular networks to alter their patterns of gene expression can lead to disease (**Fig. 21.12**). The disruptions that result in disease may arise from mutated genes, as in various types of cancer, or from infection by foreign agents as in AIDS, smallpox, and the flu. The view of disease as perturbations in cellular networks opens the door to new approaches to diagnostics, therapeutics, and, ultimately, prevention.

Identification of biomarkers is a first step

Molecules that are present under specific conditions or when a disease is present are referred to as **biomarkers.** In recent years the search for biomarkers associated with early stages of disease has intensified, because many diseases, including cancer, are highly treatable when detected at early stages. Patterns of mRNAs and proteins present in the body can be referred to as molecular fingerprints. Proteins are more stable and longer-lived than RNA molecules and are therefore the focus of most biomarker research, although advances have been made analyzing mRNAs (the transcriptome) and siRNAs as well.

Figure 21.12 A normal and a diseased cell. As in Fig. 21.2, the *blue circles* represent nodes (proteins), and the *lines* depict the connections (interactions) between nodes in this hypothetical network. Normal nodes are in *blue;* nodes perturbed by disease to differing extents are in *red, orange,* and *green.*

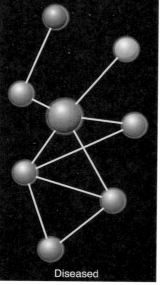

Nondiseased   Diseased

Many different bodily fluids, such as blood, urine, and saliva, can be sampled to identify altered molecular fingerprints. Of these, blood is probably the most information rich in that it bathes all tissues in the body. Through gene expression and proteomic approaches, researchers are discovering organ-specific products that are secreted into the blood. When an organ malfunctions, protein levels may change, indicating the start of disease or the progression of an organ-specific disease.

As one example, the altered patterns of gene expression in the disease-perturbed networks of a cancerous prostate gland cause changes in the levels and types of proteins expressed by various prostate cells. Normal prostate cells secrete a protein called prostate-specific antigen (PSA) into the blood, and this is one component of the blood protein fingerprint for the prostate. In cancer, the levels of PSA increase, and hence, blood measurements of this protein are routinely used to detect prostate cancer.

A more comprehensive systems approach is identification of many organ-specific proteins and monitoring levels of all these proteins to determine if the organ is diseased. A significant fraction (roughly 10%) of the proteins with disease-perturbed expression levels are secreted into the blood. There are probably 50 additional proteins in the prostate organ fingerprint beyond PSA, and measuring each of these in the future will give much more accurate diagnoses of prostate cancer. In addition, studies show that changes in blood concentration of several prostate-specific blood proteins reflect various stages of prostate cancer.

Each major organ or cell type in the body undoubtedly produces a molecular fingerprint. In this way, the blood becomes a window into health and disease.

Disease stratification may be identified

Many of the major human diseases, such as cancer or heart disease, are in fact several different disease subtypes that result in the same general phenotype. Cancer is typified by an uncontrolled growth of cells, but we know that many different genetic modifications may have occurred in a particular cell to cause it to become cancerous (see Chapter 17). Profiling the disease through molecular markers and analysis of the transcriptome and proteome gives important information that can be used to classify the type of cancer and even how far the disease has progressed.

Stratification of disease is seen in breast cancer. The diagnosis of breast cancer indicates the presence of a tumor—uncontrolled cell division—in the breast. Not all tumors are alike, but many can be grouped together based on the origin of the disease (what genetic changes occurred, what systems are perturbed). This knowledge allows us to more specifically and intelligently treat the patient. For example, in about 20% of breast cancer cases, there is an increased expression of a protein called HER2, which is found on the surface of cancer cells. The HER2-positive tumors grow faster and are more likely to recur. Knowing if the tumor is in the HER2-positive subclass directs the physician to treat the cancer differently. The drug trastuzumab (brand name Herceptin) targets the HER2 protein and decreases the disease recurrence. By understanding system networks we have a better diagnostic and treatment potential.

Knowledge of protein interactions can identify drug targets

Some of the proteins in a molecular fingerprint can point to the protein networks that have been perturbed by disease. An understanding of the protein interactions in these networks can lead to new candidates for *drug targets:* proteins whose interactions with specific drugs will either kill the cell (in the case of cancer) or alter the function of the network back toward normal. One can even imagine the future creation of drugs able to prevent disease by keeping networks from becoming perturbed in the first place.

This systems approach will undoubtedly lead to the integration of diagnosis and therapy. It will also lead to a revolution in medicine in which predictive, preventive, and personalized modes will replace the largely reactive current model in which physicians begin treatment only when a person is sick.

Advances in technology are needed for new medicine

This new medicine will require new technologies. Over the next 10 years or so, nanotechnology will revolutionize DNA sequencing, making it possible to rapidly sequence individual human genomes for well under $1000. More sensitive *molecular imaging* techniques will permit the noninvasive visualization of drug activity and function in model organisms and humans. *Microfluidics* and *nanotechnology* will produce devices that measure, identify, and inexpensively quantify in a fully automated high-throughput platform thousands of proteins from a small drop of blood or assess the information content of individual cells. We consider next one possible scenario for this revolution in medicine.

A systems approach to diseases involves identification of biomarkers that indicate the presence of disease at an early stage; classification of disease subtypes, which allows specific interventions; and clarification of protein interactions and pathways to help identify potential drug targets.

The systems approach leads to predictive, preventive, personalized medicine

As the ability to integrate vast amounts of biological data improves, medicine will continue to undergo a revolution in terms of prediction, prevention, and personalization of intervention and treatment.

Prediction

It is possible that within 10 years, physicians will have in place two major approaches to medical prediction. First, all patients will have their genome sequence determined by a nanotechnology device. It is now possible to sequence an individual human genome in weeks at a small fraction of the initial cost of the Human Genome Project. The time and cost of this endeavor will continue to decrease in coming years. From genome information and genetic analyses using SNPs and other molecular markers, we continue to identify more about single alleles or combinations of alleles that determine susceptibility to diseases or conditions.

From the individual's genomic sequence, it will then be possible to glean the information for predicting the individual's future health. For instance, a woman might learn that she has a 30% chance of developing cardiovascular disease by age 50; a 40% chance of getting ovarian cancer by age 60; and a 40% chance of developing rheumatoid arthritis by age 65. This knowledge may allow her and her doctor to plan strategies for her lifestyle and for medical interventions throughout her life to maximize her health and lower her risk of disease.

Second, quantitative measurements of the 1000–2000 proteins in a droplet of blood could be sent by wireless transmission to a server that will process the data in this molecular fingerprint and send the client/patient and the physician an e-mail stating, for example, "You are fine—do this again in six months" or "Consider additional tests for clarification of results." These blood fingerprints will allow the very early detection of disease as well as the stratification of particular disease types. The fingerprints will also make it possible to follow a patient's response to therapy and to detect adverse drug reactions in early stages. Because predictive medicine without the ability to treat or prevent is unsatisfactory to most patients, better therapies and prevention will have to emerge along with the predictive tools.

Prevention

The development of efficient nanolaboratories able to measure the protein and mRNA levels as well as protein-protein and protein-DNA interactions in individual cells will give rise to a new kind of preventive medicine that will work hand in hand with lifestyle measures used today.

The new prevention strategies will rely on the delineation of the networks in normal and diseased cells; analyses that clarify their differences; and the identification of key proteins (central nodes in the networks) as potential drug targets.

For instance, neuropsychiatrists had known for more than a decade that the protein serotonin (a neurotransmitter) plays a crucial role in the network whose perturbation contributes to clinical depression in humans, but they weren't sure how the serotonin functioned or what went wrong. Studies show that a protein designated p11 is another key player in that same network. It appears to modulate serotonin activity by influencing the number of serotonin receptors in the membranes of brain neurons that modulate mood. Although current drugs, such as Prozac and other selective serotonin reuptake inhibitors, slow the resorption of serotonin from the synapses, future antidepressive drugs that target the p11 node of the network may help the serotonin present in the synapses more effectively do its job.

Over the next two decades, the systems approach will not only produce more effective therapeutic agents for treating existing diseases, it will also lead to the development of drugs that can prevent disease by intervening to keep networks from becoming perturbed. Physicians will then be able to counsel patients with greater insight and sophistication. As a hypothetical example, a doctor might explain that although a woman has a 40% chance of developing ovarian cancer by the age of 60, taking a specific medication beginning when she is 40 can essentially prevent the disease by reducing that probability to 2%.

Personalization

Because the genome of one person differs from that of another by about 6 million base pairs, we are each susceptible to differing combinations of diseases. Increasingly, medical practitioners will be able to practice personalized medicine by applying the power of predictive and preventive medicine to our individual needs.

For treatment of breast cancer, we have already seen the power of the systems/biomarker approach. A set of 70–75 markers has been identified that can predict risk of metastasis of breast cancer. If the risk of metastasis is very low, surgery and tamoxifen treatment may be sufficient, making the systemic treatments unnecessary. The patient and doctor must then decide, based on the risk assessment, whether the systemic treatments (which have significant side effects) will be part of the patient's treatment.

> Predictive, preventive, and personalized medicine will transform the health-care industry and the practice of medicine. Striking changes based on the systems approach to biology will have a profound effect on the use of drugs and treatment options, as well as in the prevention of disease.

Connections

We began our study of genetics with the foundation of scientific discoveries beginning with Mendel. We have reviewed the experiments that determined the role and structure of DNA as the biological information molecule passed from one generation to the next. Modern developments allowing digital analysis of DNA and specification of genome and proteome details have given us the ability to map the genome down to the level of base pairs; we are now provided with new views into biological function. We have also seen how researchers determined the regulation of genes in prokaryotes and eukaryotes, and how molecular studies have led to clarification of the role of cell cycle regulation in cancer. Finally, we considered the implications and application of modern genetic knowledge to population genetics and evolutionary theory.

We have concluded this book with a view of the future of human medicine and ways in which this marvelous technology and newly elucidated body of knowledge can be applied to prediction and prevention of disease. Certainly we can say that the field of genetics has been, and continues to be, an exciting adventure into the frontiers of our scientific knowledge and abilities.

ESSENTIAL CONCEPTS

1. The practice of systems biology requires one to identify the elements of a biological system; measure their changing relationships; measure their relationships to the other systems functioning in the same context (organism or cell); and with this information, attempt to explain the system's emergent properties. The key point is that biological systems are dynamic entities that reflect changes that range across evolutionary, developmental, and physiological responses.

2. Biological information consists of the digital information of the genome and environmental signals from outside the genome, which modify the

genome's output. Gene regulatory networks integrate the inputs of information from signal transduction pathways and transmit information to the batteries of genes that encode protein networks. These networks carry out metabolism, development, and physiology. Ability to integrate biological information from many hierarchical levels is critical for understanding the system.

3. Researchers use genetic and environmental perturbations to study biological systems. A preliminary model of the system is created from preexisting knowledge; the system is then perturbed in a known way. Genomic, proteomic, genetic and biological assay data sets are collected and integrated, and comparison is made between a visualization of the integrated data and the model. Where discrepancies arise, new hypotheses are formulated that can be tested by another round of perturbations. This process is repeated until the experimental data and the model are in accord.

4. A study of the galactose-utilization system in yeast illustrates the effectiveness of the systems approach. The ultimate model resulting from this study demonstrates the interconnectedness of many networks within the yeast cell and the importance of posttranscriptional regulation, which could not have been predicted without the power of the systems approach.

5. A systems approach to disease encompasses the idea that disease arises from perturbed networks. From this simple idea come powerful new approaches to diagnosis, therapy, and prevention. The systems approach to disease is catalyzing a change from the current reactive mode of medicine to a future of predictive, preventive, and personalized medicine.

On Our Website   www.mhhe.com/hartwell4

Annotated Suggested Readings and Links to Other Websites

- Historical papers on the origins of systems biology
- Historical and contemporary papers on systems approaches to the biology of model organisms
- Historical and contemporary papers on the global and high-throughput technologies and computational tools integral to systems biology

- Contemporary papers on predictive, preventive, and personalized medicine

Specialized Topics

- Classic systems biology analyses

Solved Problems

I. You hypothesize that breast cancer that has been histologically classified as invasive ductal cancer can be further subclassified based on molecular signatures. If you can create such subcategorizations, you may be able to stratify the cancers and develop specific therapies for one or more of the subcategories. You and your collaborators have biopsy tissue from 63 invasive ductal breast cancer patients and clinical data on the course of disease in each of these patients. You plan to use microarray technology to measure gene expression in each of these samples, and then use the results to classify the tissues. When you analyze these samples with microarrays, what other samples should you analyze and why?

Answer

Controls are an important part of any scientific experiment. You need to choose control samples to provide confidence that the subcategories you identify truly reflect a stratification of invasive ductal breast cancer. In particular, you must ensure that the biopsies you receive are neither misdiagnosed nor improperly collected. For example, if some normal breast tissue is mistakenly included as a tumor in your analysis, you may identify normal tissue as a "subcategory of invasive cancer." Thus, you will want to include normal breast tissue as well as other types of breast cancer in your arrays. In addition, your analysis will require comparing gene expression in the cancer samples to a standard reference, so your set of normal controls will serve this important function. Finally, analyzing a comprehensive set of control samples will also help to develop a statistical model for the variability of your measurements and thus increase confidence in your results.

You may also wish to approach other hypotheses with your data. For example, you may want to identify markers specific to breast cancer or breast tissue. Thus, you may wish to include some samples of other normal tissues as well as cancers of these tissues.

II. The following diagram is a small portion of the much larger computerized model of an interaction network in the yeast *Saccharomyces cerevisiae* that is shown as Fig. 21.11 on p. 724. The nodes in the diagram represent either proteins or the genes encoding those proteins. Blue lines connecting nodes indicate protein-protein interactions. Red arrows connecting nodes show protein-DNA interactions, with the protein at the base of the arrow and the DNA sequence at the arrowhead.

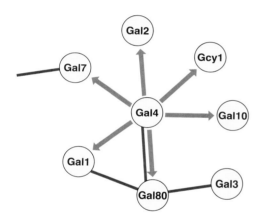

a. What kinds of techniques discussed in this chapter might have been involved in the collection of data for this interaction network?

b. What proteins in the diagram are likely to be in a complex with each other?

c. What protein(s) is (are) likely to act as a transcription factor, and how would this transcription factor operate?

d. The proteins and genes indicated in the diagram enable yeast cells to utilize the sugar galactose as a carbon source. You hypothesize that these genes

are regulated at the transcriptional level by the type of carbon source: for example, expression of many of these genes might be increased if the medium contained galactose, but expression might be repressed if the medium contained glucose. What kinds of genome-scale experiments might you do to test such hypotheses?

Answer

a. The data describing protein-protein interactions could have been derived in either of two ways. First, researchers might have used the affinity capture/mass spectrometry technique (see Chapter 10). A second method to uncover protein-protein interactions is the yeast two hybrid approach. Databases of the yeast interactome already exist that report the results of systematic tests of each yeast gene fused either to a DNA binding domain or to a DNA activation domain. Protein-DNA interactions could be identified by the ChIP/chip technique also described in Chapter 10, if antibodies that recognize the transcription factor(s) among the proteins in the diagram were available.

b. The proteins that could be in a complex must be linked by protein-protein interactions. These include Gal4, Gal80, Gal1, and Gal3.

c. The diagram indicates that the Gal4 protein can bind to DNA sequences in the vicinity of several genes, including the genes encoding Gal1, Gcy1, Gal2, Gal7, Gal10, and Gal80; the DNA sequences are presumably near the promoters of these genes. The binding of Gal4 to these DNA sequences in theory would regulate the transcription of these other genes.

d. One type of experiment to test your hypothesis is a microarray analysis. You would grow yeast cells in the presence of either galactose or glucose, and then compare the levels of the mRNAs for all yeast genes under these two conditions, with particular attention to those genes in the diagram that are potential targets for regulation by a protein complex containing Gal4. Even more interesting would be the microarray analysis of transcription in yeast that had some elements of the galactose utilization system "knocked out" by mutation.

Problems

Interactive Web Exercise

Systems biology depends on the computerized analysis of massive data sets to extract useful information. The interactive web exercise at www.mhhe.com/hartwell4 (click on Chapter 21) provides model data sets and

access to computer algorithms that will allow you to explore issues and techniques in systems biology such as the stratification (classification) of tumors by microarray analysis and the use of mass spectrometry to investigate proteomes.

Section 21.1

1. What are the four fundamental concepts related to defining a biological system?

2. Systems biology is a cross-disciplinary field.
   a. What role do the engineers have in this field?
   b. What role do the mathematicians have?

Section 21.2

3. What are the two types of digital genomic information?

4. If you were to catalog *cis*-control elements, would you be studying protein networks or gene regulatory networks? What other information would be required to gain an understanding of the kind of network you are studying?

Section 21.3

5. How has the Human Genome Project enabled systems biology in the twenty-first century?

6. Answer the following true or false:
   a. Systems biology employs both discovery science and hypothesis-driven science.
   b. Gene regulatory networks integrate information they receive from signal transduction networks and transmit it to protein networks.
   c. A transcription factor binds only a single *cis*-control region in the genome.
   d. DNA sequence may be modified by environmental information.
   e. The yeast cell contains only about 6000 proteins.
   f. The integration of different types of global sets may be carried out with graphical networks.
   g. The proteome of the organism is the sum of the proteomes of all cells in all developmental or physiological states.
   h. The mass spectrometer currently has the capacity to quantify globally all of the proteins in a given cell type.
   i. Protein chips are as global in their measurement capacity as DNA chips.

   j. The global localization procedure for identifying transcription factor binding sites also works for other proteins or protein complexes directly bound to DNA or indirectly bound to DNA through other DNA-binding proteins.
   k. The galactose utilization system is interconnected to many other cellular systems in yeast.

7. A friend of yours states that in his immunology research he is measuring the levels of 100 cytokines in response to knockout perturbations of interesting genes in his system. He claims that he is doing systems biology. What do you think?

8. Researchers carried out the following experiments on the galactose-utilization system in yeast. (1) They grew wild-type yeast in the presence and absence of galactose (that is, with the galactose-utilization system running and shut down, respectively). (2) They used microarrays to quantify all mRNA expression differences between these two states. (3) They used the ICAT approach to quantitate protein expression differences in 300 proteins in these two states. About 30 of the 300 proteins changed expression levels under these conditions. However, for 15 of these 300 proteins, there was no change in their corresponding mRNA levels between the two states. Suggest two explanations for these observations.

Section 21.4

9. Answer the following true or false:
   a. A systems approach to disease embodies the concept that diseased cells have some abnormal networks.
   b. A protein molecular fingerprint in the blood has the capacity to assess the state (for example, health or disease) of the cell type from which it was secreted.
   c. Systems approaches to disease provide new approaches for the discovery of drug targets.
   d. Predictive medicine without the ability to treat the predicted disease raises ethical concerns about whether insurance companies could use this information to modify insurance rates.
   e. Predictive, preventive, and personalized medicine will require medical education to be greatly modified.

Guidelines for Gene Nomenclature

There are inconsistencies within the various branches of genetics on some nomenclature—because it is a relatively new area of scientific investigation, the consistency present in more basic sciences has not been established. The authors debated whether they should try to impose a consistency on the entire topic area and decided against that path. As the study of genetics matures, the process itself will create a more consistent nomenclature. The following guidelines can be applied to all chapters in this book.

General Rules

- Names of genes are in italics (*lacZ, CDC28*)
- Names of proteins are in regular (Roman) type with an initial cap (LacZ, Cdc28)
- Chromosomes: sex chromosomes are represented by a capital letter in Roman type (X, Y); autosomes are designated by a cardinal number (1, 2, 21, 22)
- Names of transposons are in roman type (Tn10)

Specific Rules for Different Organisms

Human gene symbols are designated by uppercase Latin letters or by a combination of uppercase letters and Arabic numerals. The initial character should always be a letter and the whole symbol should have six or fewer characters. Greek letters in older gene symbols should be changed to the Latin equivalent. Thus, the hemoglobin-alpha gene was originally assigned the symbol HBα. The revised symbol is HBA. Alleles are limited to three characters using only capital letters or Arabic numerals. The allele designation is written on the same line as the gene symbol separated by an asterisk (e.g., *PGM1**1); the allele is printed as *1. More detailed nomenclature information is available at HGNC Guidelines (http:www.genenames.org/guidelines.html).

Brief Answer Section

Chapter 2

1. a. 4; b. 3; c. 6; d. 7; e. 11; f. 13; g. 10; h. 2; i. 14; j. 9; k. 12; l. 8; m. 5; n. 1.

3. For peas: (1) rapid generation time; (2) can either self-fertilize or be artificially crossed; (3) large numbers of offspring; (4) can be maintained as pure-breeding lines; (5) maintained as inbred stocks and two discrete forms of many phenotypic traits are known; (6) easy and inexpensive to grow. In contrast, for humans (1) generation time is long; (2) no self-fertilization, it is not ethical to manipulate crosses; (3) produce only a small number of offspring per mating; (4) although people that are homozygous for a trait exist, homozygosity cannot be maintained; (5) populations are not inbred so most traits show a continuum of phenotypes; (6) require a lot of expensive care to "grow" One advantage to the study of genetics in humans-a very large number of individuals with variant phenotypes can be recognized. Thus, the number of genes identified in this way is rapidly increasing.

5. Short hair is dominant to long hair.

7. The genotype can be determined by performing a testcross; that is, crossing your fly with the dominant phenotype (but unknown genotype) to a fly with the recessive (short wing) phenotype. If your fly has the homozygous dominant genotype the progeny in this case would be Ww and would have the dominant phenotype. If your fly had a heterozygous genotype, 1/2 of the progeny would be normal (Ww) and 1/2 of the progeny would be short (ww).

9. The dominant trait (short tail) is easier to eliminate from the population by selective breeding. You can recognize every animal that has inherited the allele, because only one dominant allele is needed to see the phenotype. Those mice that have inherited the dominant allele can be prevented from mating.

11. a. Dry is recessive, sticky is dominant; b. The 3:1 and 1:1 ratios are obscured because the offspring are then combined results of different crosses.

13. a. 1/6; b. 1/2; c. 1/3; d. 1/36; e. 1/2; f. 1/6; g. 1/9.

15. a. 2; b. 4; c. 8; d. 16.

17. a. aa Bb Cc DD Ee; b. a B C D E or a B c D E or a B C D e or a B c D e or a b C D E or a b C D e or a b c D E or a b c D e.

19. They must both be carriers (Pp); the probability that their next child will have the pp genotype is 1/4.

21. a. Rough and black are the dominant alleles (R = rough, r = smooth; B = black, b = white); b. a ratio of 1/4 rough black: 1/4 rough white: 1/4 smooth black: 1/4 smooth white.

23. a. 3/16; b. 1/16.

25. P = purple, p = white; S = spiny, s = smooth. a. Pp Ss × Pp Ss; b. PP Ss × P– ss or P– Ss × PP ss; c. Pp S– × pp SS or Pp SS × pp S–; d. Pp Ss × pp Ss; e. Pp ss × Pp ss; f. pp Ss × pp SS.

27. Cross 1: male: tt Nn, female: tt Nn; Cross 2: male: Tt nn, female: tt Nn; Cross 3: male: Tt nn, female: Tt Nn; Cross 4: male: Tt nn, female: Tt NN

29. a. Recessive. Two unaffected individuals have an affected child. It was a consanguineous marriage that produced the affected child. II-1 and V-2 are affected (aa); all unaffected individuals except II-2, II-4, III-4, III-5, and possibly V-1 are carriers (Aa). b. Dominant. The trait is seen in each generation and each affected child has an affected parent; if the trait were recessive it would not be possible for III-3 to be unaffected even though both his parents are affected. All affected individuals are Aa, though III-4, III-5, and III-6 could be AA; carrier, is not applicable when the mutation is dominant; c. Recessive. Unaffected parents have an affected child. I-2 and III-4 are affected (aa); II-4 and II-5 are carriers (Aa); all others could be AA or Aa, but I-1 is almost certainly AA if the disease is rare.

31. a. 2/3; b. 1/9; c. 4/9.

33. Recessive; common.

35. a. 1/16 = 0.0625; b. 0.067.

37. In about 40% of the families, both parents were Mm heterozygotes. In the remaining 60% of the families, at least one parent was MM.

Chapter 3

1. a. 2; b. 6; c. 11; d. 8; e. 7; f. 9; g. 12; h. 3; i. 5; j. 4; k. 1; l. 10.

3. One gene, 2 alleles, incomplete dominance; 1/2 $c^r c^w$ (yellow): 1/4 $c^r c^r$ (red): 1/4 $c^w c^w$ (white).

5. Long is completely dominant to short. Flower color trait shows incomplete dominance of two alleles.

7. a. Single-gene inheritance with incomplete dominance. Heterozygotes have intermediate serum cholesterol levels; homozygotes have elevated levels. The following people must have the mutant allele but do not express it (incomplete penetrance): family 2 I-3 or I-4; family 4 I-1 or I-2. b. Other factors are involved, including environment (particularly diet) and other genes.

9. a. ii (phenotype O) or iI^A (phenotype A) or iI^B (phenotype B); b. $I^B I^B$, $I^B i$ or $I^B I^A$; c. ii (phenotype O).

11. a. 1/4 spotted dotted: 1/2 marbled: 1/4 spotted; b. marbled and dotted.

13. a. Coat color is determined by three alleles of a single gene arranged in a dominance series with C (for chinchilla) > c^h (for himalaya) > c^a (for albino). b. Cross 1: $c^h c^a × c^h c^a$; Cross 2: $c^h c^a × c^a c^a$; Cross 3: $Cc^h × Cc^h$; Cross 4: $CC × c^h (c^h$ or $c^a)$; Cross 5: $Cc^a × Cc^a$; Cross 6: $c^h c^h × c^a c^a$; Cross 7: $Cc^a × c^a c^a$; Cross 8: $c^a c^a × c^a c^a$; Cross 9: $Cc^h × c^h c^h$; Cross 10: $Cc^a × c^h c^a$. c. 3/4 chinchilla (CC, Cc^h, and Cc^a) and 1/4 himalaya ($c^h c^a$).

15. a. 2/3 Curly: 1/3 normal; b. Cy/Cy is lethal; c. 90 Curly winged and 90 normal winged flies.

17. a. The 2:1 phenotypic ratio shows that the montezuma parents were heterozygous, Mm and homozygosity for M is lethal; b. 1/2 montezuma: 1/2 greenish, normal fin; c. 6/12 montezuma normal fin: 2/12 montezuma ruffled fin: 3/12 green normal fin: 1/12 green ruffled fin.

19. Incomplete penetrance or a spontaneous mutation during gamete or the father of the child is not the male parent of the couple.

21. Two genes are involved. The black mare was AAbb and the chestnut stallion was aaBB, the liver horses were aabb and the bay horses were AaBb.

23. a. There are two genes involved; homozygosity for the recessive allele of either or both genes causes yellow color. Green parent is AABB; yellow parent is aabb. b. AaBb, aaBb, Aabb and aabb in equal proportions: 1/4 green:3/4 yellow fruit.

25. Dominance relationships are between alleles of the same gene. Only one gene is involved. Epistasis involves two genes. The alleles at one gene affect the expression of a second gene.

27. 1/4 would appear to have O type blood, 3/8 have A, 3/8 have AB.

29.

	I-1	I-2	I-3	I-4	II-1	II-2	II-3	III-1	III-2
Phenotypes	AB	A	B	AB	O	O	AB	A	O
Genotypes	$I^A I^B$	I^A or $I^A I^A$	I^B or $I^B I^B$	$I^A I^B$	ii	I^B or $I^B I^B$	$I^A I^B$	$I^A i$	$I^A I^A$ or $I^A i$ $I^A I^B$ or $I^B i$
	Hh	Hh	$H-$	$H-$	$H-$	hh	Hh	Hh	hh

One or both of I-3 and I-4 must carry h.

31. 2/6 yellow: 3/6 albino: and 1/6 agouti progeny.

33. a. $A^Y aBbCc \times AabbCc$; b. six phenotypes: albino, yellow, brown agouti, black agouti, brown, black.

35. a. 27/64 wild type, 37/64 mutant; b. $AA\ Bb\ Cc$.

37. a. Two genes are involved. $A–B–$ and $aa\ B–$ are WR, $A–bb$ is DR, and $aa\ bb$ is LR. b. For these true-breeding strains, WR-1 is $AA\ BB$; WR-2 is $aa\ BB$; DR is $AA\ bb$, and LR is $aa\ bb$. c. The cross was $Aa\ Bb$ (WR) $\times aa\ bb$ (LR).

39. 44/56.

Chapter 4

1. a. 13; b. 7; c. 11; d. 10; e. 12; f. 8; g. 9; h. 1; i. 6; j. 15; k. 3; l. 2; m. 16; n. 4; o. 14; p. 5.

3. a. 7 centromeres; b. 7 chromosome; c. 14 chromatids; d. 3 pairs; e. 4 metacentric and 3 acrocentric; f. females are XX.

5. a. iii; b. i; c. iv; d. ii; e. v.

7. a. 1, 1 → 2, 2, 2, 2, 1, 1, b. yes, yes, yes, yes → no, no, no → yes; c. no, no, no, no → yes, yes, yes, yes → no; d. yes, yes, yes, yes → no, no, no, no → yes.

9. Meiosis produces 4 cells (*n*, haploid), each with 7 chromosomes.

11. a. Mitosis, meiosis I, II; b. mitosis, meiosis I; c. mitosis; d. meiosis II and meiosis I; e. meiosis I; f. none; g. meiosis I; h. meiosis II, mitosis; i. mitosis, meiosis I.

13. a. metaphase or early anaphase of meiosis I in a male (assuming X-Y sex determination in *Tenebrio molitor*); b. sister chromatids, centromeres, and telomeres (among others); c. five.

15. It is very realistic to assume that homologous chromosomes carry different alleles of some genes. In contrast, recombination almost always occurs between homologous chromosomes in any meiosis; thus the second assumption is much less realistic. The couple could potentially produce $2^{23} \times 2^{23} = 2^{46}$ or 70,368,744,177,664 different zygotic combinations.

17. Meiosis requires the pairing of homologous chromosomes during meiosis I.

19. a. 400 spermatozoa; b. 200; c. 100; d. 100; e. 100; f. none.

21. a. Only females; b. males; c. males; d. 1/5 ZZ males and 4/5 ZW females.

23. a. brown females and ivory-eyed males; b. females with brown eyes and males with ivory or brown eyes in a 1/2 to 1/2 ratio.

25. a. Nonbarred females and barred males; b. barred and nonbarred females and barred and nonbarred males.

27. The bag-winged females have one mutation on the X chromosome that has a dominant effect on wing structure and that also causes lethality in homozygous females or hemizygous males.

29.

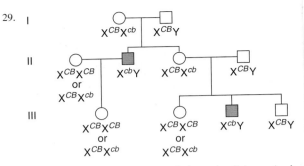

31. a. Recessive; b. autosomal; c. aa; d. Aa; e. Aa; f. Aa; g. Aa; h. Aa.

33. Vestigial wings is autosomal; body color is X-linked recessive.

35. a. X-linked dominant inheritance. b. Can exclude sex-linked recessive inheritance because affected females have unaffected sons. Can exclude autosomal recessive inheritance because the trait is rare and affected females have affected children with multiple husbands. Can exclude autosomal dominant inheritance because all the daughters but none of the sons of an affected male are affected. c. III-2 had four husbands and III-9 had six husbands.

37. a. 3; b. 1 or 3.

39. a. Purple is caused by homozygosity for a recessive allele of an autosomal gene (p), but the X-linked recessive white mutation is epistatic to p and to p^+. b. F_1 progeny: 1/2 white-eyed males and 1/2 wild-type (red) females; F_2 progeny: 1/4 white males, 1/4 white females, 3/16 red males, 3/16 red females, 1/16 purple males, 1/16 purple females.

41. a. Individual III-5; b. the BRCA2 mutation has a dominant effect on causing cancer; c. The data do not clearly distinguish between X-linked and autosomal inheritance BRCA2 is actually on autosome 13; d. The penetrance of the cancer phenotype is incomplete; e. The expressivity is variable; f. Ovarian cancer is sex-limited, the penetrance of breast cancer may be sex-influenced; g. low penetrance of the cancer phenotype, particularly among men.

Chapter 5

1. a. 8; b. 4; c. 1; d. 11; e. 2; f. 5; g. 6; h. 3; i. 10; j. 12; k. 9; l. 7.

3. a. parental gametes $B_1\ D_1$ and $B_3\ D_3$; b. recombinant gametes will be $B_1\ D_3$ and $B_3\ D_1$; c. the B and D DNA loci are linked.

5. a. $Oo\ Bb$; b. 9:3:3:1; c. not significant; d. between 0.5 and 0.1.

7. a. Notice that the null hypothesis is the same in both cases: that the genes are assorting independently; b. using 2 classes is a more sensitive test for linkage than using 4 classes; c. in a situation in which certain classes are sub-viable, you might see linkage with the 2 class test, but you would miss the even more important point that one allele causes reduced viability. This ability to see the relative viability of the alleles is an advantage to the 4 class method.

9. a. $Gs\ Bhd^+ / Gs^+\ Bhd\ ♀ \times Gs^+\ Bhd^+ / Y\ ♂ \rightarrow$ 49 $Gs\ Bhd^+\ ♂$: 48 $Gs^+\ Bhd\ ♂$: 2 $Gs\ Bhd\ ♂$: 1 $Gs^+\ Bhd^+\ ♂$. The rf = 3mu; b. genotypes, phenotypes and frequencies of the female progeny would be the same as their brothers.

11. 10%

13. a. A = normal pigmentation, a = albino allele, $Hb\beta^A$ = normal globin, $Hb\beta^S$ = sickle allele 49.5% $aHb\beta^A$, 49.5% $AHb\beta^A$, 0.5% $aHb\beta^A$, 0.5% $AHb\beta^A$; b. 49.5% $aHb\beta^A$, 49.5% $AHb\beta^A$, 0.5% $aHb\beta^A$, 0.5% $AHb\beta^A$; c. 0.0025.

15. a. 1/4 black, 1/2 albino, 1/4 brown; b. 34 m.u. apart.

17. a. Gametes: 20% Ab and aB, 30% AB and ab. F_2 generation: 59% $A–B–$, 16% $A–bb$ and $aa\ B–$, 9% $aa\ bb$. b. Gametes: 30% Ab and aB, 20% AB and ab. F_2 generation: 54% $A–B–$, 21% $A–bb$ and $aa\ B–$, 4% $aa\ bb$.

19. a. two genes are assorting independently; b. the two genes are on the same chromosome; yes; c. recombination occurs at the four

strand stage of meiosis, and so many crossovers occur between genes when they are far apart on the same chromosome that the linkage between alleles of these genes will be randomized; d. by summing up the values obtained for smaller distances separating other genes in between those at the ends.

21. The order of the genes is HIS4 − LEU2 − MAT − THR4.

23. the best map of these genes is:

25. a. 360 $a^+b^+c^+$; 360 abc; 90 a^+bc; 90 ab^+c^+; 40 a^+b^+c; 40 abc^+; 10 a^+bc^+; 10 ab^+c; b. 500 $a^+b^+c^+$; 500 abc.

27. a. $sceccv$ / + + + and b / +; b. $sceccv$ / + + +, sc–cv = 9 m.u., ec–cv = 10.5 m.u.; c. predicted DCO = 0.009, observed DCO = 0.001, interference = 0.89.

29. a. 39%; b. 39%; c. 0.5%; d. 8%.

31. $\dfrac{dwp/pld^+ \, rv^+ \, rmp}{dwp^+/pld \, rv \, rmp^+}$ rv–rmp 10 m.u.; pld/dwp–rv 5 m.u.

33. a. 334;

35. a. First group: met^+lys^+ and met^-lys^-; second group: $met^+ \, lys^+$, $met^+ \, lys^-$, met^-lys^+, met^-lys^-. b. 5.5 m.u. c. met^-lys^+ and met^+lys^-.

37. a. 100% 4; b. 100% 2; c. 50% 0 and 50% 2; d. 40% 0, 20% 1, and 40% 2; e. 100% 0; f. 80% 0 and 20% 1; g. 2.

39. a. (Unordered tetrads): PD = 2 $his^- \, lys^+$ and 2 $his^+ \, lys^-$; NPD = 2 $his^- \, lys^-$ and 2 $his^+ \, lys^+$; T = 1 $his^- \, lys^+$, 1 $his^+ \, lys^-$, 1 $his^- \, lys^-$ and 1 $his^+ \, lys^+$. b. 22.3 m.u. c. NCO = 222, SCO = 134; DCO = 44. d. 0.555 crossovers/meiosis. e. Two strand and three strand DCOs are missed. Map distance in map units = 1/2(T) + 3(NPD)/total asci; f. 27.8 m.u.

41. a. The sectors consist of $ade2^-/ade2^-$ cells generated by mitotic recombination. b. The sector size depends on when the mitotic recombination occurred during the growth of the colony. There should be many more small sectors because the mitotic recombinations creating them occur later in colony growth when there are many more cells.

43. a. Two mitotic crossovers occurred in succession in the same cell lineage. The first was between the sn and y genes, creating a patch of yellow tissue. The second was between the centromere and sn, creating a "clone within a clone" of yellow, singed cells. b. Yes.

Chapter 6

1. a. 6; b. 11; c. 9; d. 2; e. 4; f. 8; g. 10; h. 12; i. 3; j. 13; k. 5; l. 1; m. 7.

3. c.

5. Tube 1, nucleotides; tube 2, base pairs (without the sugar and phosphate) and sugar phosphate chains without the bases; tube 3, single strands of DNA.

7. a. 20% C; b. 30% T; c. 20% G.

9. Single stranded.

1. 5′.CAGAATGGTGCTCTGCTAT.3′.

3. 3′ GGGAACCTTGATGTTTCGGCTCTAATT 5′.

5. a. once every 4,096 nucleotides; b. once every 4,096 nucleotides; c. 256 nucleotides apart.

7. After one additional generation, 1/4 intermediate; after two additional generations, 1/8 intermediate.

19.

21. 5′ UAUACGAAUU 3′.

23. a. Relieves the stress of the overwound DNA ahead of the replication fork; b. unwinds the DNA; c. synthesizes a short RNA oligonucleotide; d. joins the sugar phosphate backbones.

25. The figure shows both strands of DNA are being replicated in the same direction relative to the replication fork.

27. a. no new DNAs will be formed; b. no new DNAs will be formed; c. the two DNA strands can pair with each other so two new DNA molecules will be formed; d. this single strand of DNA has two regions that have complementary base sequence so the DNA can form a so-called *hairpin loop* and the product will therefore be 5 nucleotides longer than the original:

29. Would not undergo recombination.

31. Regardless of which strands are cut during resolution (to result in crossing-over or no crossing-over) mismatches within the heteroduplex region can be corrected to the same allele, resulting in gene conversion.

33. If many short repeats are present in the double helix at the point where the invading strand is pairing, it is likely that the invading strand will not line up perfectly.

Chapter 7

1. 1. a, b, h; 2. b, c; 3. f, j; 4. g, j; 5. a, b, h; 6. f, i, k; 7. g, k; 8. d, i; 9. d, e, f, g, i.

3. The wild-type sequence is:
   5′ ACCGTA<u>G</u>TCGAC<u>T</u>GGT<u>A</u>AACTTTGCGCG

5. 9.5×10^{-5}; higher than normal rate.

7. If phages induce resistance, several appear in random positions on each of the replica plates. If the mutations preexist, the resistant colonies would appear at the same locations on each of the three replica plates.

9. Female A has a white-eyed mutation on the X. Female B has a recessive lethal mutation on the X. Female C is mosaic with a lethal mutation on one strand and wild-type sequence on the other strand of one X chromosome, or she on the other strand of one X chromosome, or she is heterozygenes for an incompletely penetrant lethal mutation.

11. a. 857 essential X-linked genes; b. 37.6% of the genes on the X chromosome are essential; c. the X-ray induced mutation rate = 1.4×10^{-4} a 40-fold increase.

13. a. two-way mutagen; b. one-way mutagen; c. two-way mutagen; d. two-way mutagen; e. two-way mutagen.

15. a. nucleotide excision repair and the SOS-type error-prone repair; b. AP endonuclease and other enzymes in the base excision repair system could remove the damage and the SOS repair systems can work at AP sites, adding any of the 4 bases at random.

17. Yes; Liver converts substance X into a mutagen.

19. a. complementation test; − is a lack of complementation; + means that the two mutations complemented each other; b. 1 × 4 = −, 1 × 6 = +, 2 × 3 = +, 2 × 4 = +, 2 × 5 = +, 3 × 5 = +, 3 × 6 = +, 4 × 5 = +, 4 × 6 = +; c. 3 genes (1, 3, and 4), (2 and 6), (5).

21. a. Deletions do not revert. Also, deletions will fail to recombine with either of two *rII⁻* mutations that can recombine with each other to produce *rII⁺* phage. b. The length of the T4 chromosome predicts the number of nucleotide pairs. Recombination analysis with the mutants suggests the total map units in the T4 genome. Thus, Benzer could estimate the number of map units per nucleotide pair. c. *rII⁻* mutations in the same nucleotide pair cannot recombine with each other to produce *rII⁺* phage.

23. a. two; b. (1, 4), (2, 3, 5).

25. a. 3, 6, and 7 are deletions (nonreverting);

    b.

    c. Use other deletions in crosses with mutants 2 and 5.

27. a. Parental ditype: All spores Arg⁻. Nonparental ditypes: 2 Arg⁻ : 2 Arg⁺; b. Two of the PD spores grow on either ornithine, citrulline, arginosuccinate, or arginine; the other two grow with arginine only; NPD Arg⁻ spores grow with arginine only.

29. 45 purple: 16 green: 3 blue.

31. a. In all four crosses, there are two unlinked genes involved with complete dominance at both loci. b. (Each arrow represents a biochemical reaction catalyzed by one of the two gene products.) (Cross 1) colorless → blue → purple; (Cross 2) colorless1 → colorless2 → purple; (Cross 3) colorless1 → red and colorless2 → blue, with red + blue = purple; (Cross 4) colorless1 → purple and colorless2 → purple. c. Cross 2. d. F₂ only. (Cross 1) 2 purple: 1 blue: 1 white; (Cross 2) 1 purple: 1 white; (Cross 3) 2 purple: 1 red: 1 blue; (Cross 4) all purple.

33. a.   18   14   9   10   21

    X → D → B → A → C → thymidine

    b. 9 and 10 accumulates B; 10 and 14 accumulates D.

35. a. successful, immediate, prolonged; b. unsuccessful; c. successful, delayed, prolonged; d. successful, immediate, prolonged; e. unsuccessful; f. unsuccessful; g. successful, delayed, prolonged; h. unsuccessful; i. successful, immediate, short term; j. successful, immediate, prolonged.

37. a. two; b. 1/16 α1α1 β1β1: 1/8 α1α2 β1β1: 1/16 α2α2 β1β1: 1/8 α1α1 β1β2: 1/4 α1α2 β1β2: 1/8 α1α2 β2β2: 1/16 α1α1 β2β2: 1/8 α1α2 β2β2: 1/16 α2α2 β2 β2.

39. One chromosome with β β/δ δ; another with β/δ only (where / signifies a protein part of which, for example, the N-terminal part, is one type of globin and the other part the other type of globin.)

Chapter 8

1. a. 5; b. 10; c. 8; d. 12; e. 6; f. 2; g. 9; h. 14; i. 3; j. 13; k. 1; l. 7; m. 15; n. 11; o. 4; p. 16.

3. a. GU GU GU GU GU or UG UG UG UG;

   b. GU UG GU UG GU UG GU UG GU;

   c. GUG UGU GUG U etc.;

   d. GUG UGU GUG UGU GUG UGU GUG UGU GU (depends on where you start);

   e. GUG UGU GU or UGU GUG UG (depends on where you start).

5. Hb^C therefore precedes Hb^S in the map of β-*globin* gene.

7. 5′ GGN GCA CCA AGG AAA 3′

9.

Stop Codon / Change	UAA		UAG		UGA	
1ˢᵗ position	<u>A</u>AA	Lys	<u>A</u>AG	Lys	<u>A</u>GA	Arg
	<u>C</u>AA	Gln	<u>C</u>AG	Gln	<u>C</u>GA	Arg
	<u>G</u>AA	Glu	<u>G</u>AG	Glu	<u>G</u>GA	Gly
2ⁿᵈ position	U<u>U</u>A	Leu	U<u>U</u>G	Leu	U<u>U</u>A	Leu
	U<u>C</u>A	Ser	U<u>C</u>G	Ser	U<u>C</u>A	Ser
	U<u>G</u>A	STP	U<u>G</u>G	Trp	U<u>A</u>A	STP
3ʳᵈ position	UA<u>U</u>	Tyr	UA<u>A</u>	STP	UG<u>U</u>	Cys
	UA<u>C</u>	Tyr	UA<u>C</u>	Tyr	UG<u>C</u>	Cys
	UA<u>G</u>	STP	UA<u>U</u>	Tyr	UG<u>G</u>	Trp

11. a. UGG changed to UGA or UAG so the DNA change was G to A. b. If the second base of the Trp codon UGG changes to A, a UAG stop codon will result. If the third base of the Trp codon UGG changes to A, a UGA stop codon will result. Mutation of A to T in the first base of the Lys codon leads to UAA. If the Gly codon is GGA, mutation of the first G to T creates a UGA stop codon.

13. Three.

15. a. Mutant 1: transversion changes Arg to Pro; mutant 2: single-base-pair deletion changes Val to Trp and then stop; mutant 3: transition Thr (silent); mutant 4: single-base-pair insertion changes several amino acids then stop; mutant 5: transition changes Arg to stop; mutant 6: inversion changes identity of 6 amino acids. b. EMS: 1, 3, 5; Proflavin: 2, 4.

17. Required to add the appropriate ribonucleotide to a growing RNA chain.

19. Gene *F*: bottom strand; gene *G*: top strand.

21. Base pairing between the codon in the mRNA and the anticodon in the tRNA is responsible for aligning the tRNA that carries the appropriate amino acid to be added to the polypeptide chain.

23. a. Translation. b. Tyrosine (Tyr) is the next amino acid to be added to the C terminus of the growing polypeptide, which will be nine amino acids long when completed. c. The carboxy-terminus of the growing polypeptide chain is tryptophan. d. The first amino acid at the N terminus would be f-met in a prokaryotic cell and met in a eukaryotic cell. The mRNA would have a cap at its 5′ end and a poly-A tail at its 3′ end in a eukaryotic cell but not in a prokaryotic cell. If the mRNA were sufficiently long, it might encode several proteins in a prokaryote but not in a eukaryote.

25. a. 1431 base pairs; b. 5′ ACCCUGGACUAGUGGAAAGUUAACU-UAC 3′; c. N Pro Trp Thr Ser Gly Lys Leu Thr Tyr.C.

27. Mitochondria do not use the same genetic code; mutate the 5′ CUA 3′ codons in the mitochondrial gene to 5′ ACN 3′.

29. Order: c e i f a k h d b j g.

31. a. Very severe; b. mild; c. very severe; d. mild; e. no effect; f. mild to no effect; g. severe; h. severe or mild.

33. Mutations possibly causing a detectable change in protein size: d, e, g, and i. In protein amount (assumes all mutant proteins are equally stable): e, f, j, and k. In mRNA size: i and j. In mRNA amount (assumes all mutant mRNAs with poly-A tails are equally stable): f and j.

35. If the met⁺ phenotype is due to a true reversion, then: *met⁻ x met⁺ → met⁺ / met⁻ → 2 met⁺; 2 met⁻*. If there is an unlinked suppressor mutation: *met⁻ su⁻* (phenotypically met⁺) × *met⁺ su⁺* (wild type) → *met⁻ / met⁺; su⁻ / su⁺* → 3/4 met⁺; 1/4 met⁻.

37. a. 3′ AUC 5′; b. 5′ CAG 3′, c. minimum two genes.

39. a. Missense mutations change identity of a particular amino acid inserted many times in many normal proteins but nonsense suppressors only make proteins longer b. (i) a mutation in a tRNA gene in a region other than that encoding the anticodon itself, so that the wrong aminoacyl-tRNA synthetase would sometimes recognize the tRNA and charge it with the wrong amino acid; (ii) a mutation in an aminoacyl-tRNA synthetase gene, making an enzyme that would sometimes put the wrong amino acid on a tRNA; (iii) a mutation in a gene encoding either a ribosomal protein, a ribosomal RNA or a translation factor that would make the ribosome more error-prone, inserting the wrong amino acid in the polypeptide; (iv) a mutation in a gene encoding a subunit of RNA polymerase that would sometimes cause the enzyme to transcribe the sequence incorrectly.

41. a. 5′ UUA 3′; b. 5′ UAG 3′ and 5′ UAA 3′ (due to wobble at the codon's 3′-most nucleotide); c. Gln, Lys, Glu, Ser, Leu, and Tyr.

Chapter 9

1. a. 10; b. 1; c. 9; d. 7; e. 6; f. 2; g. 8; h. 3; i. 5; j. 4.

3. Shorter molecules slip through pores more easily; large molecules get caught.

5. a. A; b. 10 kb; c. 10 kb.

7. a. 1.83 kb.

9. Selectable markers are genes that allow a vector to impart protection from an antibiotic on a host cell. When cells are transformed by a vector with a selectable marker, and then exposed to the appropriate antibiotic, only cells that have the vector will survive.

11. a. all; b. 1/4; c. none; d. 1/2 chance; e. 3/4.

13. a. Five; b. divide the number of base pairs in the genome by the average insert size, then multiply by 5.

15. After cloning: EcoRI: 42 and 2400 bp fragments; MboI: 705, 944, 500, and 300 bp or 905, 744, 500, and 300 bp fragments.

17. a. Alkaline phosphatase removes the 5′-phosphate groups so ligase can not join a hydroxyl group to the de-phosphorylated 5′ ends. The ligation with the non-phosphorylated vector reanneals to itself at a high frequency, leading to 99/100 blue colonies. The phosphorylated vector formed 99/100 white colonies, showing that almost all of the vectors had an insert; b. The dephosphorylation of the vector increased the number of clones (vector + insert) 100 fold; c. If the insert were dephosphorylated, it will not self-ligate, but the vector WILL self-ligate. The vector has the antibiotic resistance gene and ORI, so the "empty" vector will be propagated in *E. coli*, generating a high level of "background."

19. a. (1) 3.1, 6.9 kb; (2) 4.3, 4.0, 1.7 kb; (3) 1.5, 0.6, 1.0, 6.9 kb; (4) 4.3, 2.1, 1.9, 1.7 kb; (5) 3.1, 1.2, 4.0, 1.7 kb; b. The 6.9 kb fragment in the *Eco*RI+*Hin*dIII digest; the 2.1 and 1.9 kb fragments in the *Bam*HI+ *Pst*I, and the 4.0 kb fragment in the *Eco*RI+*Bam*HI digest.

21. probes should be between about 15 and 18 nucleotides long; (i) if you knew the sequence of the protein from several bacterial species you could choose a very highly conserved region on which to base a probe; (ii) find a region of 5 or 6 contiguous amino acids with low degeneracy.

23. a. You wish to know whether the PKU syndrome in this patient is caused by a mutation in the phenylalanine hydroxylase gene; b. there are 300 template molecules in 1 ng of DNA; c. 110 ng of a 1 kb section of the genome after the PCR!

25. a. the chance that one of the two primers will anneal to a random region of DNA that is not the targeted CFTR exon would be $(1/4)^{18}$, or about 1 chance in 7×10^{10} so an 18 base sequence will be present once in every 70 billion nucleotides; b. (i) the chance probability of a 16 base sequence in random DNA is $(1/4)^{16}$, or 1 chance out of 4×10^9. (ii) the longer the primers the more expensive they are to synthesize, the longer the primers the more likely they are to anneal

with each other, if the primer is too long it can hybridize with DNA with which it is not perfectly matched. Thus, longer primers might anneal to other regions of the genome than the region you actually want to amplify; c. the 5′-end. mismatches at the 3′-end would prevent DNA polymerase from adding any new nucleotides to the chain.

27. In well studied organisms such as *C. elegans, D. melanogaster,* yeast and mice the entire DNA sequence of the genomes is now available. To study any region in these genomes design PCR primers based on the genomic sequence. Having the genome sequence of an organism increases the importance of PCR. Restriction digestions remain the basis for many important applications of DNA cloning.

29. a. newly synthesized strand: 5′ TAGCTAGGCTAGCCCTTTATCG 3′ template strand: 3′ ATCGATCCGATCGGGAAATAGC 5′ b. 5′ CGAUAAAGGGCUAGCCUAGCTA 3′; c. There are stop codons in each frame so it is unlikely that this is an exon sequence of a coding region.

31. a. This terminal ddA, which is linked to a green fluorescent label, therefore becomes the 3′ end of this molecule; b. 5′...ACCTATTTTACAGGAATT...3′; c. "Residue Position" indicates a peak at a specific location in the scan so the size of the single-stranded DNA fragment is represented by the residue position; d. The double peak at position 370 is most likely caused by the fact that the original DNA actually had two different DNA sequences. One chromosome carrys a T-A base pair at this location while the homologue had a G-C base pair.

Chapter 10

1. a. 6; b. 3; c. 2; d. 5; e. 1; f. 4.

3.

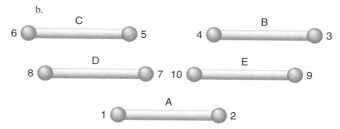

5. a. you could generate two sequencing primers that would hybridize in all of the clones to the BAC vector just on either side of the inserted monkey DNA. The same two primers would enable you to find thousands of different monkey STSs.

    b.

6 ●━━━━━━━● 5   4 ●━━━━━━━● 3
        C   B
8 ●━━━━━━━● 7 10 ●━━━━━━━● 9
        D   E
      1 ●━━━━━━━● 2
              A

c. BAC clones C, B, and A. d. the contig could range from somewhat less than 300 kb long to somewhat less than 1500 kb long.

7. Recall that you can read approximately 500-800 nucleotides from a single sequencing reaction. If the repetitive sequence of DNA is longer than this size, then all of the data obtained from the reaction will be derived from the repeated sequence. If the repetitive sequence is repeated many times in the genome, you might not be able to tell from where in the genome the copy you have sequenced is derived. The hierarchical shotgun strategy analyzes individual BACs that might contain only a single copy of the repetitive sequence, so shotgun sequencing of an entire BAC could proceed without complications. The whole genome shotgun strategy involves generating clones with known insert sizes of about 2 kb, 10 kb, and 200 kb. They then

sequence the two ends of each clone and retain the information that these two ends are related to each other (that is, one of the sequences is say ~200 kb away from the other sequence). Both types of sequencing strategies encounter major difficulties in dealing with tandemly repeated sequences. Regions around centromeres, for example, may have more than 1 Mb of tandemly repeated simple sequences.

9. some genomic sequences cannot be cloned (e.g. heterochromatin) and some sequences rearrange or delete when cloned (e.g. some tandemly arrayed repeats).

11. involves a single hybridization to a chromosome spread. FISH gives results quickly and can be used with any cloned piece of DNA.

13. the human genome contains a large amount of repeated DNA and introns can be quite large. There human genome also has many duplicated.

15. lack regulatory region information and intron DNA.

17. a. a difference in the amount of recombination in males and females; b. No, the same chromosomes are passed from generation to generation.

19. (i) centromeres and telomeres. (ii) Transposon-derived repeats have given rise to at least 47 different human genes. (iii) Certain genes have repeated sequences. (iv) Transposon-derived repeats have reshaped the genome by aiding the formation of chromosomal rearrangements.

21. a. the genome of yeast is very small. Yeast currently has a catalog tryptic peptides related to the genes which code for the as well as a catalog of >7,000 known protein-protein interactions and >500 protein-DNA interactions. b. The nematode is a fairly complex multi-cellular organism. c. The mouse is the closest model organism to humans.

23. a. suggesting that the protein is a transcription factor. b. the two genes arose by duplication.

25. the definition of 'gene' is somewhat imprecise; one gene can actually produce more than one type of protein, although the polypeptides produced by one gene are usually related to each other, and many genes are transcribed into RNAs that remain untranslated yet still have important functions. The most all-encompassing definition of 'gene' is a region of the chromosome that is transcribed into a discrete primary transcript that can subsequently be spliced or otherwise processed. It is possible to look for transcribed regions of the genome with techniques such as Northern blots or the sequencing of hundreds of thousands of clones from cDNA libraries. However, if a transcript is found only in very low abundance or if it is very small, these techniques do not ensure that it can be detected. Computer programs are much less successful in identifying genes with very short open-reading frames or the genes that are transcribed into very small non-coding RNAs.

27. a. If genes are vertically inherited, a cladogram that compared the DNA sequences of the gene should essentially match the accepted species cladogram, but if lateral gene transfer occurred then a cladogram of the protein sequences would unexpectedly show that the human gene was much closer in DNA sequence to the bacterial gene than to genes in more closely related species like primates or mammals. b. a gene of bacterial origin was found in humans and chimps, but not in any other primates or mammals. This suggests that the lateral transfer occurred before humans and chimps last shared a common ancestor (estimated to be about 5 million years ago), but before either of these two species last shared a common ancestor with any other current primate species (about 7 million years ago). c. if a large number of related species had a particular gene but one species in this group did not.

29. Not all human genes have been accurately identified. Genes that are rarely expressed or that have unusual codon usage patterns are difficult to find. The human proteome is much more complex and the human genome has more paralogs and chemical modifications of proteins.

31. a. <u>Black</u>—this gene is either, <u>green</u>—the mRNA for this gene accumulates to higher levels in normal tissue than in the tissue from the tumor, <u>red</u>—the mRNA for this gene accumulates to higher levels in cancerous tissue than in normal tissue, <u>yellow</u>—the mRNA for these genes accumulates to the same level in both kinds of tissue. b. a red signal.

Chapter 11

1. a. 5; b. 3; c. 8; d. 6; e. 2; f. 7; g. 1; h. 4.

3. Anonymous DNA markers are the DNA sequence of an individual. The terms dominant and recessive can only be used when discussing the phenotype of an organism, so in one sense this question is meaningless. Geneticists often say that DNA markers are inherited in a codominant fashion to denote that the both alleles can be seen in the DNA sequence.

5. a. Different numbers of simple sequence repeats; b. slippage of DNA polymerase during replication; c. a different mechanism: unequal crossing-over.

7. a. The polymorphism is within the short DNA sequence that is used as a probe; b. the polymorphism is in the nucleotide adjacent to the sequence used as a primer; c. the SNP polymorphism can be kilobases away from the probe sequence in a restriction site recognized by the restriction enzyme used to digest the genomic DNA.

9. The sequences of the ASOs would be

3′ GATATTTACCCGATCCGCA and 3′ GATATTTACGCGATC CGCA.

11. Sperm collected from man, eggs are collected from woman. After *in vetro* fertilization, embryos are allowed to develop to the eight-cell stage. A single cell from each eight-cell embryo is removed. DNA is prepared and genotype is analyzed using PCR and *Mst* II digestion. Embryos with the desired genotype are implanted into the woman's uterus.

13. Coworker 3 has the same DNA fingerprint as the crime sample and must be the perpetrator of the crime. The probability is essentially 100%.

15. a. Individuals A, B, C and E; b. Individuals D and F; c. 48 bp.

17. a. 10 kb; b. 10 kb; c. 0%; d. 50%.

19. Members of the disease family must be segregating two or more alleles at each DNA marker that is chosen.

21. a. 0% chance; b. 0.0075 probability of an affected child.

23. Mating W is not informative; mating X is informative – both parents are doubly heterozygous; mating Y is non-informative; mating Z is non-informative.

25. Identify sequences that are transcribed into RNA; use computational analysis to identify sequences that are conserved between distantly related species; use computational analysis to identify sequences that are open reading frames with appropriate codon usage and splice sites.

27. a. A, C and E, b. three different genes have been identified; c. Yes; d. fragments C and E; e. gene recognized by fragment E; f. If there is a mouse model of this disease you would transform the mice with the cDNA clone of the candidate gene and look for the normal human gene to rescue the mutant phenotype in the mice.

29. a. The disease is autosomal dominant; b. Yes, II-2, II-3 and III-1.

31. a. 12,500 different haplotypes; b. 156,250,000 possible diplotypes; c. The father's genotype is A25 C4 B7 / A23 C2 B35; the mother's genotype is A24 C5 B8 / A3 C9 B44; d. 1/4.

Chapter 12

1. a. 4; b. 9; c. 7; d. 8; e. 2; f. 3; g. 5; h. 1; i. 6.

3. Interphase: 40-fold compaction; metaphase: 10,000-fold compaction.

5. a. 1.2×10^8 molecules of H2A protein; b. during or just after S phase; c. more templates that the cells can transcribe simultaneously, allowing the more rapid production of histone proteins.

7. A deletion of one G band removes about 15 genes.

9. H1 is one the outside of the complex and locks the DNA to the core and interacts with H1 proteins from other nucleosomes to forming

the center of the coil that is thought to form the 300A fiber. The other histone proteins are coated with DNA and can not form the 300A fiber.

11. Mutate the DNA sequence so that the twelfth amino acid encoded is not lysine but another similar amino acid.

13. the Xist gene produces is a large, cis-acting mRNA causing inactivation of the X chromosome that produced it.

15. a. In the presence of a *Su(var)* mutant allele there will be fewer white patches in the eye and more red patches when the eyes are compared to a homozygous *Su(var)*⁺ fly. The situation would be reversed with more white patches and fewer red (wild type) patches if the fly were heterozygous for the *E(var)* mutation; b. the *Su(var)*⁺ genes encode proteins that establish and assist spreading of heterochromatin. The *E(var)*⁺ genes seem to encode proteins that restrict the spreading of heterochromatin.

17. These twin sisters could still be monozygotic twins. In the affected twin, the X^{Dmd+} homolog was inactivated in the cells that are affected by muscular dystrophy. In the unaffected twin, the other X chromosome (X^{Dmd}) was inactivated in those same cells.

19. a. $OO \times oY$ (orange females × black males), $oo \times OY$ (black females × orange males), $Oo \times oY$ (tortoiseshell females × black males), and $Oo \times OY$ (tortoiseshell females × orange males); b. XXY Klinefelter males who are heterozygous *Oo;* c. an autosomal gene called the *white-spotting* or *piebald* gene causes the white spotting— a dominant allele of this gene causes white fur, but in heterozygotes this allele has variable expressivity so some patches have a color dictated by the functional alleles of the *orange* gene.

21. choice b.

23. a. alpha satellite DNA; b. Cohesin holds sister chromatids together until anaphase, kinetochores attach chromosomes to the spindle poles and contain motor proteins that move the separated chromosomes to the poles.

25. a. genes encoding cohesin proteins, genes encoding kinetochore proteins, genes encoding motor proteins that help chromosomes move on the spindle apparatus and genes encoding components of the spindle checkpoint that makes the beginning of anaphase dependent upon the proper connections of spindle fibers and kinetochores. Mutations that alter the DNA comprising a centromere might also have similar effects; b. look for colonies that contained many cells that had lost the YAC because of mitotic chromosome mis-segregation; mutate the centromeric DNA of this YAC using in vitro mutagenesis. If the centromere were disrupted the YAC would not segregate properly and would be lost.

27. a. your DNA probe must contain unique DNA found next to the repeated 5′ TTAGGG (telomere) sequences; b. the blurriness indicates that the hybridizing fragments from the end of the chromosome in a population of cells are not homogeneous in length. The number of repeat sequences at the telomere, and therefore the telomere length, varies from cell to cell, especially in actively dividing cells.

29. a. CENP-A mutant dies while the CENP-B mutant is viable. Chromosome loss at elevated temperature cannot be measured in CENP-A because the cell dies. The CENP-B mutant, on the other hand, shows increased chromosome loss; b. cells with a marker which is on a chromosome, or on an artificial linear chromosome (YAC), or on a circular plasmid containing a centromere.

31. a. Use the yeast CBF1 protein to make antibodies and then use these antibodies to probe the human cDNA expression library. Alternatively, you could use the cloned yeast gene as a probe to hybridize to clones in a human cDNA library; b. Label or tag the antibody (with fluorescence for example). You can determine the location of the protein in the cell.

33. digest the BAC, the YAC, and the genomic DNA with several restriction enzymes and compare the restriction patterns of each when they are hybridized with a probe containing the BAC or YAC DNA.

Chapter 13

1. a. 4; b. 8; c. 6; d. 5; e. 7; f. 3; g. 2; h. 1.

3. In a duplication, there would be a repeated set of bands; in a deletion, bands normally found would be missing.

5.

⊢─3.0─⊣⊢──── 6.3 ────⊣⊢── 4.2 ──⊣⊢── 5.6 ──⊣⊢0.9⊣

apterous   *rolled*   *straw*   *thick*

7.

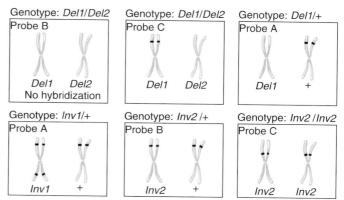

9. a. the parental types y^+ z^l w^{+R} spl^+ / Y (zeste) and y z^l w^{+R} spl / Y (yellow zeste split); b. crossing over anywhere between the *y* and *spl* genes; c. mispairing and unequal crossing over between the two copies of the w^+ gene; d. 5.9 mu.

11. a. 2, 4; b. 2, 4; c. 2; d. 1, 3.

13. a. 2 *URA3 ARG9* spores and 2 *ura3 arg9* spores;
   b. 2 spores die, 1 *URA3 ARG9* and one *ura3 arg9*;
   c. 4 viable spores, 2 *URA3 ARG9* spores and 2 *ura3 arg9* spores.

15. A two-strand double crossover with both crossovers in the inversion loop. One crossover must occur between *LEU2* and *HIS4*. The other crossover must occur on the other side of either of the two genes but still within the inversion loop.

17. a. 1, 3, 5 and 6; b. 2 and 4; c. 1 and 3; d. 5 and 6.

19. a. 1/4 fertile green, 1/4 fertile yellow-green, 1/4 semisterile green, 1/4 semisterile yellow-green; b. 1/2 fertile yellow-green, 1/2 semisterile green; c. from crossing-over events between the translocation chromosome and homologous region on the normal chromosome.

21. 1/2 *Lyra* males: 1/2 *Lyra*⁺ (wild type) females.

23. the 11 base long primers must be 5′ GTTCGCATACG 3′ and 5′ GTGTACGCACG 3′.

25. the arrows show the positions of hybridization.

27. *Ds* is a defective transposable element and *Ac* is a complete, autonomous copy.

29. Use a probe made of DNA from the sequence preceding the 200 A residues to hybridize to genomic DNA on Southern blots or to chromosomes by *in situ* hybridization.

31. a. the black *K. waltii* genes are duplicated in *S. cerevisiae.*
   b. At some time after the evolutionary lines for these two species separated a portion of the *S. cerevisiae* genome was duplicated in a progenitor of *S. cerevisiae*. Over time one copy was lost of

many of the duplicated genes. Occasionally both copies of a gene were retained

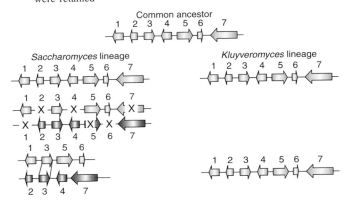

Common ancestor
1 2 3 4 5 6 7

Saccharomyces lineage
1 2 3 4 5 6 7

Kluyveromyces lineage
1 2 3 4 5 6 7

1 2 3 4 5 6 7

1 2 3 4 5 6 7

1 3 5 6

2 3 4 7

1 2 3 4 5 6 7

33. a. 7; b. sand oats: diploid, slender wild oats: tetraploid, cultivated oats: hexaploid; c. sand oats: 7, slender wild oats: 14, cultivated wild oats: 21; d. same answer as c.

35. a. (i) aneuploid, (ii) monosomic for chromosome 5, (iii) embryonic lethal; b. (i) aneuploid, (ii) trisomic for chromosomes 1 and 5, (iii) embryonic lethal; c. (i) euploid, (ii) autotriploid, (iii) viable but infertile; d. (i) euploid, (ii) autotetraploid, (iii) viable and fertile.

37. A: meiosis II in father; B: meiosis I in mother; C: meiosis I in father; D: meiosis II in mother.

39. You would actually expect more monosomies than trisomies, because meiotic nondisjunction would produce equal frequencies of monosomies and trisomies, but chromosome loss would produce only monosomies. The low frequency of monosomies observed is because monosomic zygotes usually arrest development so early that a pregnancy is not recognized. This may be due to a lower tolerance for imbalances involving only a single copy of a chromosome than for those involving three copies, or because recessive lethal mutations are carried on the remaining copy.

41. a. Mate putative mutants that are $ey\ ci^+ / ey^+\ ci$ with flies that are $ey\ ci / ey\ ci$. b. Nondisjunction during meiosis I will produce wild-type progeny; nondisjunction during meiosis II cannot be recognized. c. 2 eyeless: 2 cubitus interruptus: 1 eyeless, cubitus interruptus: 1 wild type. d. Mate putative mutants that are $ey\ ci^+ / ey^+\ ci$ with flies that have an unmarked attached chromosome 4. Nondisjunction during meiosis II would yield eyeless or cubitus interruptus progeny, but you could not recognize progeny resulting from nondisjunction during meiosis I. If the attached chromosome 4 carried two copies of ey and two copies of ci, you could recognize and discriminate some of the products of nondisjunction during the two meiotic divisions.

43. Treat with colchicine.

45. In autopolyploids, the banding patterns of homologs should be the same; in allopolyploids, different banding patterns will be seen for chromosomes from different species.

Chapter 14

1. a. 4; b. 5; c. 2; d. 7; e. 6; f. 3; g. 1.

3. 200 colonies on the first plate and 20 colonies on the second plate.

5. a. iv; b. iii; c. ii.

7. The $purE$ and $pepN$ genes will be cotransformed at a lower frequency if the *H. influenzae b* pathogenic strain was used as a host donor strain.

9. plasmid transformation into *Shigella dysenteriae*, bacteriophage infection of *Staphylococcus*, *Streptococcus* or *E. coli* species and transposition of DNA (pathogenicity island) into *Vibrio cholerae*.

11. Do a mating between the mutant cell with 3-4 copies of F and a wild-type F⁻ recipient. A mutation in the F plasmid means the exconjugant will have the higher copy number. If the mutation is in a chromosomal

gene the higher copy number phenotype would not be transferred into the recipient. You could isolate the F plasmid DNA from the mutant cell, and then transform this plasmid into new recipient cells. By examining the number of copies of the F factor in the transformed cells, you could tell whether the trait was carried by the plasmid.

13. a. (i) transformation, (ii) conjugation and (iii) transduction;. b. if the donor DNA used in the transformation includes plasmids recipient cells may take up the entire plasmid and acquire the characteristics conferred by the plasmid genes. Conjugation requires the presence of a conjugative plasmid in the donor cell. c. Bacteriophages are required for transduction. d. natural transformation with DNA fragments, conjugation with an Hfr and generalized transduction.

15. Transform the plasmid into a nontoxin-producing recipient strain and assay for toxin production.

17. order: *ilv bgl mtl*.

19. a.

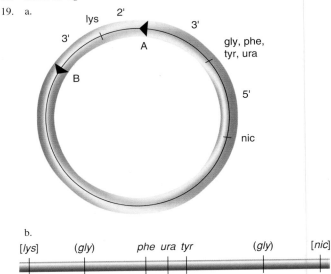

b.

[lys]   (gly)   phe ura tyr   (gly)   [nic]

c. To map the *gly* gene with respect to other markers, select for Gly⁺ transductants on min + lys + phe + tyr + ura+ nic. Then score the other markers to determine which genes are cotransduced with Gly⁺ at the highest frequency.

21. this assay detects *recA⁻* mutants in the F⁻ cell based on the inability to form stable exconjugants.

23. a. *in vitro* portion; b. *in vivo*; c. *in vivo*; d. *in vitro*.

25. a. both; b. both; c. neither; d. both.

27. a.

		Trp	His	Ile	Met
mRNA	5′	UGG	CAU/C	AUU/C/A	AUG
nDNA mRNA-like	5′	TGG	CAT/C	ATT/C/A	ATG
nDNA template	3′	ACC	GTA/G	TAA/G/T	TAC

b.

		Trp	His	Ile	Met
mRNA	5′	UGA/G	CAU/C	AUC/U	AUG/A
mtDNA mRNA-lik	5′	TGA/G	CAT/C	ATC/T	ATG/A
mtDNA template	3′	ACT/C	GTA/G	TAG/A	TAC/T

29. a and d.

31. a. Introns would have to be removed, some of the codons in the nuclear gene would have to be changed since the genetic code in the nucleus and in mitochondria is not identical, a mitochondrial translational start site and a transcriptional termination site must be added, the open reading frame of the altered nuclear gene would have to be placed under the control of a mitochondrial promoter, and the cloned gene must be introduced into the yeast mitochondria. b. Such a strain can then be used to select for function of the mitochondrial genetic system in mutants that are unable to respire;

try to find arginine auxotrophs that could no longer make arginine because there was a DNA change that obliterated the function of the promoter. Such mutations allow analysis of the function of regulatory elements in the mitochondrial genome.

33. The small size of the sperm can mean that organelles are excluded; cells can degrade organelles or organellar DNA from the male parent; early zygotic mitoses distribute the male organelles to cells that will not become part of the embryo; the details of the fertilization process may prevent the paternal cell from contributing any organelles (only the sperm nucleus is allowed into the egg); and in some species that zygote destroys the paternal organelle after fertilization.

35. If the mutation is very debilitating to the cell, either because of the loss of energy metabolism in the case of mitochondria or of photosynthetic capability in the case of chloroplasts, a cell that is homoplasmic for the mutant genome will die.

37. a. The zygote that formed this plant was heteroplasmic, containing both wild type chloroplast genomes and mutant chloroplast genomes. These two types of genomes can segregate as tissue is propagated mitotically. b. many of the ovules generated on this branch are heteroplasmic and give rise to variegated plants. Some of the cells on the variegated branch gave rise to ovules that segregated one or the other chloroplast genomes. The phenotype of the progeny will reflect the type(s) of chloroplast genome(s) in the ovules; white leaved plants cannot make chlorophyll and since they cannot conduct photosynthesis they will die. c. part of the plant can conduct photosynthesis then these carbohydrates can be made and transported to tissues that are unable to conduct photosynthesis.

39. a. If one of the parental inbred lines is male sterile, then this line can not self-fertilize and the seed companies would not have to do anything more to prevent self-fertilization. b. the sterile inbred line in part a must also be homozygous for the recessive for the *rf* allele of *Restorer*. The other inbred line, the male parent supplying the pollen for the cross, would have to have at least one (and preferable two) dominant *Rf* alleles of *Restorer*. c. make a fertile "Maintainer" line that has mitochondria with a normal (non-CMS) genome but whose nuclear genomes are the same as the CMS plants and also *rf/rf*. The *rf/rf* CMS plants are used as the female parent (they can not produce pollen). When pollen from Maintainer plants fertilizes the CMS plants, the progeny will have CMS mitochondria and will also be *rf/rf*; in other words, these progeny will be identical to their maternal parents. d. farmers are now dependent upon the seed companies to provide their seed; the genetic variation of the corn crop overall is reduced.

41. a. The mother (I-1) may have had very low levels of mutant mitochondrial chromosomes or there may have been a spontaneous mutation either in the mitochondrial genome of the egg that gave rise to individual II-2 or in the early zygote of individual II-2. b. You could look at the mitochondrial DNA from somatic cells from various tissues in the mother. If the mutation occurred in her germline and was inherited by II-2, the mother's somatic cells would not show any defective DNA.

43. The variation in affected tissues is due to differences in where and when during development the mutation occurred. Variation in the severity of the disease can be due to the proportion of mutant genomes (the degree of heteroplasmy) in the cells of different tissues.

45. Gel electrophoresis is better suited for an overview of the differences between mitochondrial genomes. Deletions can be very large and might not be amplified by PCR. In addition, sequences to which primers bind might be deleted in some mutations

Chapter 15

1. a. 4; b. 8; c. 5; d. 2; e. 7; f. 1; g. 3; h. 6.

3. a. i, ii, iii; b. iv, v, vi.

5. Mutations in the promoter region can only act in cis to the structural genes immediately adjacent to this regulatory sequence. This promoter mutation will not affect the expression of a second, normal operon.

7. b.

9. Nonlysogenic recipient cell did not have the cI (repressor) protein, so incoming infecting phage could go into the lytic cycle.

11.

	β-galactosidase	*Permease*
a.	constitutive	constitutive
b.	constitutive	inducible
c.	inducible	inducible
d.	no expression	constitutive
e.	no expression	no expression

13.

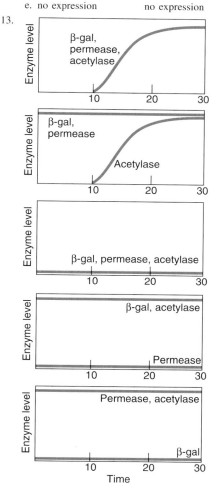

15. If the three genes make up an operon, they are cotranscribed to one mRNA and only one band should appear on a hybridization analysis using any of the three genes as a probe versus mRNA. If the genes are not part of an operon, there would be three differently sized hybridizing bands.

17. a. 4; b. 6; c. 7; d. 2; e. 3; f. 5; g. 1.

19. a. i, iii, v and vi, b. mutations ii, iii and iv; c. mutation 1 is i; mutation 6 is ii; mutation 2 is iii; mutation 4 is iv; mutation 5 is v; and mutation 3 is vi.

21. a. Mutations in O_2 or O_3 alone have only small effects on synthesis levels; b. Small DNA insertions between O_1 and O_2 may change the face and either change the ability of the repressor to bind one of the sites or change the ability of the bound repressor to bend the DNA leading to an O^c mutant phenotype; c. insensitive to a I^s repressor protein.

23. The protein-coding region of your gene must be in the same frame as the *lacZ* gene.

25. Seven His codons (CAC or CAU), in a row.

27. a. This seems to be a biosynthetic operon, the operon is repressible.

b.

Condition	Gene A	Gene B	Gene C	Gene D
Wildtype	completely repressible	constitutive	completely repressible	completely repressible
Nonsense in A	not expressed	constitutive	completely repressible	not expressed
Nonsense in B	partially repressible	not expressed	partially repressible	partially repressible
Nonsense in C	not expressed	constitutive	not expressed	not expressed
Nonsense in D	completely repressible	constitutive	completely repressible	not expressed
Deletion of region incl. E	partially repressible	constitutive	partially repressible	partially repressible
Deletion of F	partially repressible	constitutive	partially repressible	partially repressible
Deletion of G	not expressed	constitutive	not expressed	not expressed

c.

29. negative regulation.

31. a. two probes, one consists of labeled cDNA corresponding to the mRNA extracted from the culture grown at the higher osmolarity, and the other consists of cDNA corresponding to the mRNA in the culture grown at the lower osmolarity; b. each spot on the microarray would have a DNA sequence representing a single *E. coli* gene; c. use microarrays to compare the gene expression changes in cells grown under different osmotic conditions and those that are heat-shocked.

33. a. All of these turn out to be early genes; b. early genes; c. transcription of the large majority of *E. coli* genes would be drastically decreased; d. the *motA* gene prevents transcription of the middle genes, *asiA* should lower the transcription of middle and late T4 genes, the 55 gene should prevent the transcription of late transcripts but have little effect on the transcription of host genes; e. the *reg-A*-encoded ribonuclease is specifically required for the rapid destruction of T4 early mRNAs.

Chapter 16

1. a. 7; b. 4; c. 6; d. 2; e. 9; f. 8; g. 5; h. 3; i. 1.

3. include transcript processing (including alternate splicing of the RNA), export of mRNA from the nucleus, changes in the efficiency of translation (including miRNAs), chemical modification of the gene products and localization of the protein product in specific organelles.

5. a. i; b. ii.

7. a *GAL80* mutation in which the protein is not made or is made but cannot bind to the GAL4 protein will prevent repression and lead to constitutive synthesis. A *GAL4* mutation which inhibits binding to the GAL80 protein will also be constitutive. A mutation of the DNA at the binding site for the GAL4 protein will also give constitutive synthesis.

9. a. DNA binding; b. DNA binding; c. dimer formation; d. transcription activation; e. DNA binding.

11. If *Id* acts by quenching it interacts with *MyoD*, whereas if it blocks access to an enhancer it binds to DNA. Experimentally, look for binding to the regulatory DNA of a gene regulated by *MyoD*.

13. a. a *Drosophila* promoter sequence with the promoter added somewhere upstream of the DNA encoding the initiating AUG. Other helpful elements are a *Drosophila* poly-A addition sequence and a transcription termination signal downstream of the *lacZ* coding sequence; b. The type of construct you made is called an *enhancer trap*; these different insertions signal a position in the genome adjacent to a tissue-specific enhancer. In strains in which *lacZ* is expressed in the head, your construct must have integrated into the genome very near to an enhancer that helps activate transcription in the head. In other strains, your construct integrated into the genome near enhancers that are specific for other tissues like the thorax. Since the density of enhancer elements in the genome is low, most of the time new integrations of your construct would be located too far from an enhancer, so there would be no *lacZ* expression and no blue color.

15. differing levels of gene expression depending on their association with highly compacted, heterochromatic DNA vs. euchromatic; one example is Position Effect Variegation in *Drosophila*; another is Barr body formation in human females. Decompaction affects the location of the nucleosomes, and gives rise to DNase I hypersensitive sites where nucleosomes have been removed and the DNA is available for binding by RNA polymerase or regulatory proteins. Transcriptional silencing, on the other hand, involves methylation of the DNA.

17. Liver cell DNA has a DNaseI hypersensitive (DH) site 4 kb from 1 end of the *Eag*I fragment. This site is probably the promoter region for your gene.

19. a. 1, 2 and 4; b. 1 and 4; c. 1 and 4; d. 3.

21. a. half of his sons and half of his daughters will be affected; b. True; c. False; d. False.

23. {} represents an allele that is transcriptionally inactivated (imprinted); a. Bill Sr's genotype is 50K/{60K} and Joan's genotype (*60K*/{*?*}); b. Joan's genotype is *60K*/{*50K*} and Bill Sr's genotype is *50K*/{*60K*}.

25. a. The alleles of the gene are not expressed in the germ cells of male I-2. b. The allele of the gene from male I-2 will not be expressed in the somatic cells of II-2. c. The allele of the gene from male I-2 will be expressed in the germ cells of II-2. d. The allele of the gene from male I-2 will not be expressed in the somatic cells of II-3. e. The allele of the gene from male I-2 will not be expressed in the germ cells of II-3. f. The allele of the gene from male I-2 will be expressed in the germ cells of III-1. g. The allele of the gene from male I-2 will not be expressed in the germ cells of III-1.

27. Introns are spliced out, ribonuclease cleaves the primary transcript near the 3′ end and a poly-A tail is added, 5′ methl CAP is added.

29. The 5′ and 3′ untranslated regions could be cloned at the 5′ or 3′ ends of a reporter gene that is transformed back into *Drosophila* early embryos to see if either of the sequences affect the translatability of the reporter protein.

31. The protein in the fat cells may be post-translationally modified (for example, phosphorylated or de-phosphorylated) so that it is only active in fat cells. Alternatively, the protein may need a cofactor to be activated, and this cofactor is only transcribed in fat cells.

33. a. the difference in first detection of the mRNAs probably results from the different sensitivity in detecting mRNA versus protein. The difference in duration of the mRNA vs protein: the proteins are more stable than the mRNAs so they remain in the cells for several days longer; if the normal protein disappears at day 10.5 then the *lacZ* mRNA is more stable; or the β-galactosidase protein is more stable; or the transgene is transcribed until day 12; b. onset.

Chapter 17

1. a. 7; b. 6; c. 8; d. 2; e. 1; f. 9; g. 3; h. 5; i. 4.

3. a. a RAS mutant that stays in the GTP-bound state is permanently activated and will cause the cell to continue dividing. b. under the restrictive conditions the cells will not divide.

5. a. the effect of the T antigen is minimized. b. decrease the ability of p53 to function in cell cycle control. c. in a functional domain other than those that bind the T antigen and the transcription factor.

7. a. Use two different probes- one representing the specific sequence that you are analyzing and the other representing an unamplified control sequence. b. alterations in the chromosomal banding patterns in a karyotype analysis.

9. the role of diet, studies can be set up within the recent immigrant population vs. the United States-based native Indian population examining the effect of a Westernized diet vs. a diet resembling that of the ethnic group. Also, the effects of the same diets on non-Indian Westerners should be examined. To assess the role of genetic differences, you need to keep other factors, for example, diet, as constant as possible. You could look at the incidence in Indians and Americans who have similar diets.

11. order: d; a; b, c.

13. a. predisposition to colon cancer in this family could be an autosomal dominant trait. If this is true, then individuals II-2, and either I-1 or I-2 must have the mutation, but not express it. b. Individuals I-1, I-2 and II-2 are not among the high coffee consumers. Perhaps the predisposition to colon cancer is a combination of a particular genotype and the environmental factor of consumption of the special coffee.

15. Technique d.

17. If one PCR primer binds to one of the chromosomes at one side of the translocation while the other primer binds to the other chromosome on the other side of the breakpoint then your PCR primers will span the translocation. This would amplify a PCR fragment only if there were still cells in the blood that had the translocated chromosomes.

19. Both. These instabilities can be caused by somatic or germline mutations in genes such as *p53* or the genes for DNA repair enzymes, genome and karyotype instability can then result in additional problems that can contribute to cancer progression; mutations in DNA repair enzymes lead to a high rate of mutation and such mutations might inactivate a tumor suppressor gene or activate a protooncogene.

21. a. M (mitosis); b. M; c. S phase; d. G_1 phase.

23. three complementation groups.

25. cyclical regulation of and cyclical regulation of translation and cyclical control of posttranslational modifications.

27. a. 2; b. 3; c. 1.

29. In the M phase checkpoint molecules made by unattached kinetochores prevent the anaphase promoting complex (APC) from being activated. APC must become activated at the beginning of anaphase to destroy M phase cyclin, allowing cells to leave M phase. The activated APC adds ubiquitin to protein substrates. When this happens the ubiquinylated proteins are rapidly destroyed by the proteosome. One simple hypothesis is that cohesin is also targeted by the APC since it must be destroyed at the beginning of anaphase.

Chapter 18

1. a. 11; b. 4; c. 8; d. 7; e. 12; f. 9; g. 13; h. 3; i. l; j. 5; k. 6; l. 10; m. 2.

3. a. In *C. elegans,* laser ablation at this early stage of development would almost certainly be lethal, while in mice the loss of one out of four early embryonic cells would have no effect; b. lethal to *C. elegans* and it is possible that the separated cells could develop into a mouse; c. in *C. elegans* would likely be lethal, in mice, such a fusion would be tolerated giving rise to a chimeric animal.

5. Make RNA preparations from homozygotes for the new null allele and then analyzing these preparations on Northern blots; RT-PCR or the mutation could be null but the gene would still be transcribed. Analyze protein extracts from the homozygous mutant animals by Western blot using the antibody against the rugose protein as a probe.

7. a.

b. As a result of the mitotic crossover developing ommatidia in the eye would be simultaneously homozygous for the mutations in *rugose* and *white,* while adjacent ommatidia would be heterozygous for the wild type and mutant alleles of both genes. If the red ommatidia are abnormal even though their genotype predicts a normal structure, then the lack of rugose in the adjacent white ommatidia affects the red ommatidia; c. If these patches were normal in appearance, then rugose does not have an important role in eye development. If the white patch is abnormal, then rugose is important for eye development.

9. Mutate possible regulatory DNA elements.

11. Make DNA constructs that place a wild type genomic copy of gene X adjacent to *myo-2::GFP.* You then transform these constructs into worms that are homozygous for a null allele of gene X (and that did not contain any *GFP* source). The constructs form extrachromosomal arrays as described. Pharyngeal cells containing the arrays would be wild type for gene X and express GFP. Pharygeal cells that had lost the arrays would be homozygous mutant for gene X and would not express GFP.

13. a. If the mutation was due to an insertion of the transgene the MMTV *c-myc* gene should segregate with the phenotype; b. Clones containing the *c-myc* fusion could be identified by hybridization of MMTV sequences versus a library of genomic clones produced from the cells of the mutant mouse; c. The sequence of the gene into which the MMTV *c-myc* fusion inserted could be analyzed in the *ld* mutant to determine if there were mutations in the gene.

15. a. promoter, binding sites for transcription factors such as Bicoid and binding sites for other transcription factors that ensure the *hb* gene is transcribed in the proper cells in the mother; b. the amino acids in Hunchback that comprise DNA binding domains and domains involved in the transcriptional regulation of gap and pair rule genes; c. translational repression carried out by Nanos protein.

17. The cytoplasm from the anterior of a wild type embryo could be injected into the anterior end of a *bicoid* mutant embryo to see if there was rescue of the mutant phenotype. Alternately, purified *bicoid* mRNA injected into the anterior end of a *bicoid* mutant embryo would be a more definitive experiment. Finally, purified *bicoid* mRNA could be injected into the posterior end of a wild-type embryo.

19. a wild-type Knirps protein is needed to restrict the posterior limit of the zone of Kruppel expression; b. Hunchback protein would be seen throughout the embryo.

21. A mutation in the genes encoding a maternally supplied component which affects early development must be in the mother's genome. If the mutation affecting early development is in a gene whose transcription begins after fertilization then the mutation must be in the genome of the zygote (these are thus sometimes called "zygotic genes"). You would need two different kinds of genetic screens to make mutations either in the mothers' genome or the zygotes' genome.

23. a. the presence of PAR-3 and absence of PAR-2 from these cells indirectly dictates their ability to translate *glp-l* mRNA into GLP-1 protein; b. Such an interaction could occur through the extracellular domains of both proteins; c. receptor is the GLP-1 protein. Thus APX-1 would be the ligand; d. (i) the ablation of P_2 would make ABp and its descendants would have the same fate shown by ABa and its descendants, (ii) a null mutation of *apx-1* would have the same effect (iii) same, (iv) same.

Chapter 19

1. a. 3; b. 5; c. 8; d. 7; e. 6; f. 1; g. 9; h. 2; i. 4.

3. a, e.

5. a. the initial population is not in equilibrium; b. genotype frequencies in the F_1 will be $0.36\ MM + 0.48\ MN + 0.16\ NN = 1$, allele frequencies in the F_1 generation $M = 0.6$ and $N = 0.4$; c. the same as in part b.

7. Each allele frequency has a different set of genotype frequencies at equilibrium.

9. a. $N = 0.1$; b. 478 MN children on the island; c. $N = 0.525$.

11. a. $p^2 + 2pq + q^2 + 2pr + r^2 + 2qr = 1$; b. 0.516 A, 0.122 B, 0.075 AB and 0.287 O.

13. a. $C = 8324/9049 = 0.92$, $c = 725/9049 = 0.08$; b. this sample does not demonstrate Hardy-Weinberg equilibrium; c. the frequency of $cP = 0.018$, the frequency of $c^d = 0.064$, frequency of the C allele $= 0.918$; d. in boys $C = 0.918$ (normal vision), $c^d = 0.064$ (colorblind) and $cP = 0.018$ (colorblind). In the girls the genotype frequencies are: $CC = 0.843$ (normal vision), $Cc^d = 0.118$ (normal vision), $CcP = 0.033$ (normal vision), $cPcP = 3.3 \times 10\text{-}4$ (colorblind), $c^dc^d = 0.004$ (colorblind) and $c^dcP = 0.002$ (normal vision); e. the population is in equilibrium. As seen in part c, the allele frequency of C is the same in boys and girls and the allele frequency of c in the boys is the same as the total frequencies of $c^d + cP$ in girls.

15. a. the genotype frequencies in the F_2 are $0.33\ vg^+ vg^+$ and 0.67 $vg^+ vg$; the allele frequencies in the F_2 for $vg^+ = 0.33 + 1/2\ (0.67) = 0.67$ and for $vg = 1/2\ (0.67) = 0.33$; b. genotype frequencies in the F_3 progeny are $0.449\ vg^+ vg^+ + 0.442\ vg^+ vg + 0.109\ vg\ vg = 1$, or 0.891 wild type and 0.109 vestigial; c. F_4 allele frequencies are $vg^+ = 0.753$ and $vg = 0.249$; d. If all of the F_4 flies are allowed to mate at random then there is no selection and the population will be in Hardy-Weinberg equilibrium $-0.566\ vg^+ vg^+ + 0.373\ vg^+ vg + 0.062\ vg\ vg = 1$; $vg^+ = 0.753$ and $vg = 0.247$.

17. Selection against the homozygous recessive genotype will decrease the frequency of the recessive allele in the population, but it will never totally remove it, as the recessive allele is hidden in the heterozygote, recessive allele sometimes confers an advantage when present in the heterozygote, mutation can produce new recessive alleles in the population.

19. a. $b = \sqrt{0.25} = 0.5$, $B = 0.5$; b. Δq for tank 1 $= -0.1$, q for all tanks $= 0.5$; Δq for tank 2 $= 0$; Δq for tank 3 $= 0.05$.

	Tank 1	Tank 2	Tank 3
b. Δq	-0.1	0.0	0.05
c. w_{Bb}	1.0	1.0	1.0
d. w_{bb}	<1.0	1.0	>1.0

21. a. fitness value $(w) = 0$ and the selection coefficient $(s) = 1$ for the affected genotype. There is no selection pressure against the carrier or the homozygous normal genotypes, so for both of these $w = 1$ and $s = 0$; b. $\Delta q = -1.54 \times 10^{-3}$; c. 1.02×10^{-3}. This number (1.02×10^{-3}) is smaller than the observed q which is 0.04; d. CF^+/CF^- heterozygotes may be better able to survive outbreaks of cholera.

23. b.

25. a. Height has the highest heritability and weight has the lowest heritability; b. The data from the CDC is roughly in line with the conclusions from part a.

27. a. founder effect; b. advantages: genetic homogeneity and fewer genes that may affect a polygenic trait; disadvantages: some mutations are not found in the population that are in the general population.

29. a. $2n + 1$ where $n =$ number of genes; b. $(1/4)^n = 1/256$, so $n = 4$.

Chapter 20

1. a. 4; b. 6; c. 5; d. 2; e. 1; f. 7; g. 3.

3. a, c.

5. a. The enzyme consists of an RNA molecule; b. the enzyme has both an RNA and a protein component.

7. a. Different constraints on the functions of each of the proteins; b. rates are more constant because these base changes do not affect function of the gene product.

9. Suggests there is some benefit to the *CF* allele in the heterozygous state.

11. Duplication followed by evolutionary divergence.

13. a. 240 million years; b. two; *C* allele arose 30 million years ago; *B* allele arose 1 million years ago; c. duplication of *B*: transposition; duplication of *C*: misalignment and crossing-over.

15. This gene was introduced from a different species.

17. a. Exons; b. genes.

19. They mediate genome rearrangements or contribute regulatory elements adjacent to a gene.

21. a. SINEs or LINEs; b. centromere satellite DNA.

23. a. The side effects suggest that the protease inhibitor is not completely specific to the HIV protease. Presumably the HIV protease may have distant evolutionary relationships with other proteases found in normal cells. b. Protease cleavage could be involved in the generation of a hormone like cortisol that could affect fat distribution. Many hormones are generated from prohormones by protease cleavage. c. Perhaps the indinavir sulfate affects the processes needed for energy metabolism, such as the function or the integrity of the mitochondria. This hypothesis could be tested by analyzing the energy content of the cells from patients treated with the drug.

Chapter 21

1. The elements of the system; the physical associations among the elements; the biological context of the system; how the association of the system's elements and their relation to changes in the biological context explain its emergent property.

3. genes that encode proteins and untranslated RNAs and the short DNA sequences that make up the control elements adjacent to the genes.

5. The sequences of the entire genomes of humans and other model organisms like *E. coli,* yeast and mice provide a genetics parts list of all the genes and the proteins they encode. The study of human genome defined the basic blocks of DNA, proteins and other molecules that systems biology hopes to fit together into networks. This also defined many of the complex molecular machines and protein networks, and enforced the idea that biological information is hierarchic. The Genome Projects also drive the development of powerful computational tools which make it possible to acquire, store, analyze, integrate, display and model biological information. The high-throughput platforms for genomics and proteomics enable the acquisition of global data sets of differing types of biological information.

7. What exactly is the biological system that he is perturbing? Does he know all of the elements in this system? Some of the cytokines may be the output of the system, but does he know all of the outputs? Or all of the inputs? If he is measuring protein levels, he has only one type of biological information. Also your friend is not looking at the other systems whose behaviors will be altered by the knockout perturbations. Your friend's research is not systems biology.

9. a. **True;** b. **True;** c. **True;** d. **True;** e. **True.**

Glossary

Note: An italicized word in a definition indicates that word is defined elsewhere in the glossary.

A

acentric fragment a *chromatid* fragment lacking a *centromere;* usually the result of a crossover in an *inversion loop.*

acrocentric a *chromosome* in which the *centromere* is close to one end.

activator a type of *transcription factor* that can bind to specific cis-*acting* enhancer elements and increase the level of transcription from a nearby gene.

adaptation the ability to stop responding when the stimulus is present.

adenine (A) a nitrogenous base; one member of the *base pair* A–T (adenine–thymine).

adjacent-1 segregation pattern one of two patterns of *segregation* resulting from the normal disjunction of homologs during *meiosis I.* Homologous *centromeres* disjoin so that one *translocation* chromosome and one normal chromosome go to each pole. Contrast with *alternate segregation pattern.*

adjacent-2 segregation pattern a pattern of *segregation* resulting from a *nondisjunction* in which homologous centromeres go to the same pole during meiosis I.

allele frequency the proportion of all copies of a *gene* in a *population* that are of a given allele type.

alleles alternative forms of a single *gene.*

allele-specific oligonucleotides (ASOs) short *oligonucleotides* that hybridize with alleles distinguished by a single base difference.

allopolyploids *polyploid* hybrids in which the chromosome sets come from two or more distinct, though related, species.

allosteric proteins proteins that undergo reversible changes in conformation when bound to another molecule.

α-globin locus chromosomal region carrying all of the α-globin-like genes.

alternate segregation pattern one of two patterns of *segregation* resulting from the normal disjunction of homologs during *meiosis I.* Two *translocation* chromosomes go to one pole, while two normal chromosomes move to the opposite pole, resulting in *gametes* with the correct haploid number of genes.

alternative splicing production of different mature *mRNAs* from the same *primary transcript* by joining different combinations of *exons.*

Ames test screens for chemicals that cause mutations in bacterial cells.

amino acids the building blocks of proteins.

aminoacyl (A) site site on a *ribosome* to which a *charged tRNA* first binds.

aminoacyl-tRNA synthetases enzymes that catalyze the attachment of tRNAs to their corresponding amino acids, forming *charged tRNAs.*

amniocentesis medical procedure in which a sample of amniotic fluid is taken from a pregnant woman to determine the condition of an unborn baby. A hollow needle is inserted through the woman's abdomen and uterine wall, and the fluid, which contains cells shed by the embryo, is drawn off.

amorphic mutations changes that completely block the function of a *gene* (synonym for *null mutations*).

amphidiploids organisms produced by two *diploid* parental species; they contain two diploid genomes, each one derived from a different parent.

amplification spread of a molecular variant throughout a population over many generations.

anaphase the stage of *mitosis* in which the connection of *sister chromatids* is severed, allowing the chromatids to be pulled to opposite spindle poles.

anaphase I phase of *meiosis I* during which the *chiasmata* joining *homologous chromosomes* dissolve, allowing maternal and paternal homologs to move toward opposite spindle poles; the *centromeres* do not divide so that the *chromosomes* moving toward the poles each consist of two *chromatids.*

anaphase II phase of *meiosis II* when the dismantling of *cohesin* complexes allows *sister chromatids* to move to opposite spindle poles.

aneuploid an individual whose chromosome number is not an exact multiple of the *haploid* number for the species.

angiosperm plant descriptive meaning the seeds of the plant are enclosed in an ovary within the flower.

angstrom (Å) a unit of length equal to one ten-billionth of a meter.

anonymous locus a designated position on a chromosome with no known function; see *locus.*

Antennapedia complex (ANT-C) in *Drosophila,* a region containing several *homeotic genes* specifying the identity of segments in the head and anterior thorax.

anticodons groups of three *nucleotides* on *transfer RNA (tRNA)* molecules that recognize codons on the mRNA by *complementary base pairing* and *wobble.*

antigen foreign substance (or a particular part of a foreign substance) that induces an *immune response* when introduced into the body.

antisense the sequence of a single-stranded RNA or DNA molecule that is complementary to—and can base pair with—a portion of a transcribed RNA molecule.

apical meristem a group of undifferentiated plant cells that divide continuously, located at the growing points of both shoots and roots.

apoptosis programmed cell death; a process in which DNA is degraded and the nucleus condenses; the cell may then be devoured by neighboring cells or phagocytes.

archaea one of the three major evolutionary lineages (domains) of living organisms.

artificial selection the purposeful control of mating by choice of parents for the next generation. Contrast with *natural selection.*

artificial transformation a process to transfer genes from one bacterial strain to another, using laboratory procedures to weaken cell walls and make membranes permeable to DNA. Contrast with *natural transformation.*

ascospores in some fungi, the *haploid* cells that result from *meiosis.* Also known as *haplospores.*

ascus saclike structure in some varieties of fungi that houses all four *haploid* products of *meiosis.*

astral microtubules short, unstable microtubules that extend out from a *centrosome* toward the cell's periphery to stabilize the *mitotic spindle.*

attenuation a type of gene regulation in which *transcription* of a gene terminates in the regulatory region before a complete mRNA *transcript* is made.

autocrine stimulation process by which many tumor cells make their own signals to divide, rather than waiting for signals from neighboring cells.

autonomous elements intact transposable elements that can move from place to place in the genome by themselves. Contrast with *nonautonomous elements.*

autopolyploids a kind of *polyploid* that derives all of its chromosome sets from the same species.

autosome a *chromosome* not involved in sex determination. The *diploid* human genome consists of 46 chromosomes, 22 pairs of autosomes, and 1 pair of sex chromosomes (the X and Y chromosomes).

autotroph a plant that is nutritionally self-sufficient; it produces its own food via photosynthesis.

auxotroph a mutant microorganism that can grow on minimal medium only if it has been supplemented with one or more growth factors not required by wild-type strains.

B

bacterial chemotaxis bacterial movement up and down gradients of chemical attractants or repellents.

bacterial chromosome essential component of a bacterial *genome;* usually a single circular molecule of double-helical DNA.

bacteriophage See *phage.*

balancer chromosome special *chromosome* created for use in genetic manipulations; helps maintain *recessive lethal* mutations in stocks.

balancing selection situation in which heterozygotes have a higher selective advantage, or fitness, than either homozygote.

Barr bodies inactive X chromosomes observable at interphase as darkly stained *heterochromatin* masses.

barriers sites that block the spread of heterochromatin by various methods such as binding of specific proteins, attachment to a nuclear pore, or transcription of small RNA molecules.

basal factor a type of *transcription factor* that can associate nonspecifically with all *promoters* in a *genome.* A complex of basal factors associated with a promoter is required for the initiation of *transcription* by *RNA polymerase.* See *basal transcription apparatus.*

basal transcription apparatus complex protein machine that interacts with complexes of *transcription factors* and cis-*control elements* to mediate the synthesis of an RNA *transcript.* This RNA transcript is spliced and edited to produce a *messenger RNA (mRNA).*

base analogs *mutagens* that are so similar in chemical structure to the normal nitrogenous bases in DNA that the replication mechanism can incorporate them into DNA in place of the normal bases. This can cause base *substitutions* on the complementary strand synthesized in the next round of DNA replication.

base excision repair homology-dependent mechanism in which specific enzymes cleave an altered base from the sugar of its *nucleotide* to create an apurinic or apyrimidinic (AP) site in the DNA chain; nick the DNA backbone at the AP site; and remove nucleotides from the vicinity of the nick. DNA polymerase fills in this gap by copying the undamaged strand, restoring the original DNA sequence. See *nucleotide excision repair.*

base pair (bp) two nitrogenous bases on complementary DNA strands held together by *hydrogen bonds. Adenine* pairs with *thymine,* and *guanine* pairs with *cytosine.*

base sequence the order of nucleotide bases in a DNA or RNA strand.

base sequence analysis a method for determining a *base sequence.*

basic chromosome number (x) the number of different chromosomes that make up a single complete set. See *x.*

β-globin locus chromosomal region carrying all the β-globin-like genes.

B-form DNA the most common form of DNA in which molecular configuration spirals to the right. Compare with *Z-form DNA.*

biased random walk bacterial movement resulting from the addition of an attractant or repellant. The time spent in a straight run is longer immediately after the addition, so the movement over time is biased toward or away from the chemical gradient, though each direction change continues to be random.

bidirectional describes a mechanism of *DNA replication* in which two *replication forks* move in opposite directions away from the same *origin of replication.*

biochemical pathway an orderly series of reactions that allows an organism to obtain simple molecules from the environment and convert them step by step into successively more complicated molecules.

bioinformatics the science of using computational methods—specialized software—to decipher the biological meaning of information contained within organismal systems.

biological context the context in which a *biological system* operates within a cell or organism.

biological information consists of the digital information of the *genome* and environmental signals that activate or modulate the output of genomic information. These two types of information interact to mediate biological activity across the three time scales of *evolution,* development, and physiological responses.

biological system any complex network of interacting molecules or groups of cells that function in a coordinated manner through dynamic signaling.

biomarker molecule that is present when a disease is present or is present under specific conditions.

biotechnology a set of biological techniques developed through basic research and now applied to research and product development. In particular, the use by industry of recombinant DNA, cell fusion, and new bioprocessing techniques.

biparental inheritance inheritance of organelles from both parents. Occurs in single-celled yeast and some plants.

bithorax complex (BX-C) in *Drosophila,* a cluster of *homeotic genes* that control the identity of segments in the abdomen and posterior thorax.

bivalent a pair of synapsed homologous chromosomes during *prophase* of *meiosis I.*

blastocysts describes the embryo at the 16-cell stage of development through the 64-cell stage, when the embryo implants.

blastomeres early embryonic cells.

blunt end the 5′ or 3′ end of a double-stranded DNA molecule without *sticky ends.*

branched-line diagram a method for systematically listing the expected results of multigene crosses.

branches (of a *phylogenetic tree*) lines that define the relationship between the taxonomic units represented by the *nodes* of the tree; their length represents an estimate of the time that has elapsed based on the number of molecular changes that have occurred.

branch sites special sequence of RNA nucleotides within an *intron* that helps form the "lariat" intermediate required for *RNA splicing.*

C

cancer genes *genes* having mutant *alleles* that lead to cancer.

carpels structures in a plant comprising the fourth whorl; usually two are fused together; house the female gametes in the form of ovules. The fused carpels are part of a cylinder known as the *pistil.*

carriers *heterozygous* individuals of normal *phenotype* that have a *recessive allele* for a trait.

catabolite repression repression of expression in sugar-metabolizing *operons* like the *lac* operon when glucose or another preferred catabolite is present.

CDK inhibitors inhibit the activity of *cyclin-dependent kinases.*

cDNA complementary DNA has a base sequence that is complementary to that of the mRNA template and contains no *introns.*

cDNA library a large collection of cDNA clones that are representative of the *mRNAs* expressed by a particular cell type, tissue, organ, or organism.

cell autonomous trait a trait for which the *phenotype* expressed by a cell depends solely on the *genotype* of that cell and not that of any other nearby cell. Compare with *nonautonomous trait.*

cell-bound signals signals requiring direct contact between cells for transmission.

cell cycle repeating pattern of cell growth, replication of genetic material, and *mitosis.*

cell plate membrane-enclosed disk that forms inside a plant cell near the equator of the *mitotic spindle* and

grows rapidly outward to divide the cell in two during *cytokinesis.*

cellular blastoderm in *Drosophila* embryos, the one-cell-deep epithelial layer resulting from cellularization of the *syncytial blastoderm.*

cellular clone an isolated colony of cells that are all descendants from a single progenitor cell.

centimorgan (cM) a unit of measure of *recombination frequency.* One cM is equal to a 1% chance that a marker at one genetic *locus* will be separated from a marker at a second locus due to *crossing-over* in a single generation.

centrioles short cylindrical structures that help organize microtubules. Two centrioles at right angles to each other form the core of a *centrosome.* Each centrosome serves as a pole of the *mitotic spindle.*

centromere a specialized chromosome region at which *sister chromatids* are connected and to which spindle fibers attach during cell division.

centrosomes microtubule organizing centers at the poles of the *spindle apparatus.*

charged tRNA a tRNA molecule to which the corresponding *amino acid* has been attached by an *aminoacyl-tRNA synthetase.*

checkpoints mechanisms that prevent cells from continuing to the next phase of the *cell cycle* until a previous stop has been successfully completed, thus safeguarding genomic integrity.

chiasmata observable regions in which nonsister chromatids of homologous chromosomes cross over.

chimera an embryo or animal composed of cells from two or more different organisms.

chi-square (χ^2) test a statistical test to determine the probability that an observed deviation from an expected outcome occurs solely by chance.

chromatid one of two copies of a *chromosome* that exist immediately after *DNA replication.* See *sister chromatids.*

chromatin the generic term for any complex of *DNA* and *protein* found in a cell's nucleus.

chromatin immunoprecipitation (ChIP)
Uses a combination of genomic and proteomic techniques to measure transcription factor interactions with their *cis*-control elements or interactions of complex protein machines with their chromosome binding sites.

chromocenter the dense heterochromatic mass formed by the fusing of the *centromeres* of *polytene chromosomes.*

chromosomal interference the phenomenon of crossovers not occurring independently. Refer to *crossing-over.*

chromosomal puff the region of a *polytene chromosome* that swells to form a large, diffuse structure when high rates of gene *transcription* cause bands to decondense.

chromosomal rearrangement change in the order of *DNA sequence* along one or more *chromosomes.*

chromosome loss a mechanism causing *aneuploidy* in which a particular *chromatid* or *chromosome* fails to become incorporated into either daughter cell during cell division.

chromosome theory of inheritance the idea that *chromosomes* are the carriers of *genes.*

chromosomes the self-replicating genetic structures of cells containing the *DNA* that carries in its *nucleotide* sequence the linear array of *genes.*

chromosome walking using the ends of unconnected *contigs* as probes to retrieve *clones* that extend into an unmapped region.

***cis*-control elements** (sometimes referred to as cis-*acting elements*) short DNA sequences (6–15 base pairs long) that constitute the control elements adjacent to *genes.* Through their binding to *transcription factors,* cis-control elements control or modulate transcription initiation at one or more nearby *genes.* Promoters, enhancers, and *locus control regions* are three types of *cis*-control elements.

cistron a term sometimes used as a synonym for *complementation group* or *gene.*

cleavage stage in early embryonic development, the stage of the first four equal cell divisions.

clone a group of biological entities— cells or DNA molecules—that are genetically identical to each other.

cloning the process by which cellular clones or DNA clones are formed.

cloning vector DNA molecule into which another DNA fragment of appropriate size can be integrated without loss of the vector's capacity for replication. Vectors introduce foreign DNA into host cells, where it can be reproduced in large quantities. See *vector.*

coactivator a type of *transcription factor* or other molecule that binds to *transcription factors* rather than to *DNA* and plays a role in increasing levels of *transcription.*

codominant expression of *heterozygous* genotype resulting in hybrid offspring that resemble both parents equally for a particular trait.

codon nucleotide triplet that represents a particular *amino acid* to be inserted in a specific position in the growing amino acid chain during *translation.* Codons can be either in the *mRNA* or in the *DNA* from which the RNA is transcribed.

coefficient of coincidence the ratio between the actual frequency of double crossovers observed in an experiment and the number of double crossovers expected on the basis of independent probabilities.

coenocyte a plant cell containing multiple nuclei.

cohesin a multisubunit protein complex that associates with *sister chromatids* in eukaryotic cells and holds the chromatids together until *anaphase;* can be found at both the *centromere* and along the *chromosome* arms.

cohesive ends short, single-stranded unpaired flaps protruding from the ends of a cut DNA molecule. Each flap can reform *hydrogen bonds* with a complementary sequence protruding from the end of another piece of DNA.

colinearity the parallel between the sequence of *nucleotides* in a *gene* and the order of *amino acids* in a *polypeptide.*

colony a mound of genetically identical cells.

competent description of state of cells able to take up DNA from the medium.

complement (used as a verb) when a *heterozygote* for two *recessive mutations* displays a normal *phenotype* because the dominant *wild-type alleles* on each of the two homologs make up for a defect in the other *homologous chromosome.* Mutations that complement are usually in different genes, whereas mutations that fail to complement are usually in the same gene.

complementation process in which heterozygosity for *chromosomes* bearing mutant *recessive alleles* for two different *genes* produces a normal *phenotype.*

complementary base pairing during *DNA replication,* base pairing in which a complementary strand aligns opposite the exposed bases on the parent strand to create the nucleotide sequence of the new strand of DNA. Refer to *base pair, complementary sequences.*

complementary gene action genes working in tandem to produce a particular trait.

complementary sequences nucleic acid base sequences that can form a double-stranded structure by matching base pairs; the complementary sequence to 5′ GTAC 3′ is 3′ CATG 5′.

complementation group a collection of *mutations* that do not complement each other. Often used synonymously for *gene.*

complementation table a method of collating data that helps visualize the relationship among a large group of mutants. See Fig. 7.18b.

complementation test method of discovering whether two mutations are in the same or separate genes.

complete coverage in mapping of DNA, when the number of *markers* on a *linkage map* is sufficient so that the *locus* controlling any *phenotype* can be linked to at least one of those markers.

complete digest digesting a sample of DNA molecules with a *restriction enzyme* such that cleavage has occurred at every DNA site recognizable by the enzyme.

complete genomic library a hypothetical collection of *DNA clones* that includes one copy of every sequence in the entire *genome.*

complex refers to the multiple types of variation that can exist at alternative *alleles,* including more than one nucleotide *substitution,* a substitution in combination with a small *deletion,* a *duplication,* or another *insertion.*

complex haplotype a set of linked DNA variations along a *chromosome,* with the possibility of many differences in alternative *alleles.* See *haplotype.*

concerted evolution process that allows changes in single genetic elements to spread across a complete set of *genes* in a particular *gene family.*

condensation cellular process of *chromatin* compaction that results in the visible emergence of individual *chromosomes.*

condensin a multisubunit complex of proteins in eukaryotic cells that compacts *chromosomes* during *mitosis.*

conditional lethal an *allele* that is lethal only under certain conditions.

conjugation one of the mechanisms by which bacteria transfer genes from one strain to another; in this case, the *donor* carries a special type of *plasmid* that allows it to transfer DNA directly when it comes in contact with the recipient. The recipient is known as an exconjugant. Contrast *transformation.*

conjugative plasmids *plasmids* that initiate *conjugation* because they carry the genes that allow the *donor* to transfer genes to the *recipient.*

consanguine related by a common ancestor.

consanguineous mating mating between blood relatives sharing a recent common ancestor.

conservative substitutions mutational changes that substitute an amino acid in a protein with a different amino acid with similar chemical properties. Compare with *nonconservative substitutions.*

conserved synteny state in which the same two or more *loci* are found to be linked in several species. Compare *syntenic, syntenic segments.*

constitutive expression refers to a state of gene activation that remains at a constant high level and is not subject to modulation.

constitutive heterochromatin chromosomal regions that remain condensed in *heterochromatin* at most times in all cells.

constitutive mutants synthesize certain enzymes all the time, irrespective of environmental conditions.

constitutive mutation a mutation in a *cis*-acting or *trans*-acting element that causes an associated gene to remain in a state of activation irrespective of environmental or cellular conditions that modulate gene activity in nonmutant cells.

contig a set of two or more partially overlapping cloned DNA fragments that together cover an uninterrupted stretch of the *genome.*

continuous trait inherited trait that exhibits many intermediate forms; determined by segregating alleles of many different *genes* whose interaction with each other and the environment produces the *phenotype.* Also called a quantitative trait. Compare with *discontinuous trait.*

contractile ring transitory organelle composed of actin microfilaments aligned around the circumference of a dividing animal cell's equator; contraction of the filaments pinches the cell in two.

copy number polymorphism (CNP) or copy number variant (CNV) category of genetic variation arising from large regions of duplication or deletion, depending on frequency of occurrence in a population.

core histones proteins that form the core of the *nucleosome:* H2A, H2B, H3, and H4.

corepressor a type of *transcription factor* or other molecule that binds to transcription factors rather than DNA and prevents transcription above basal levels.

cosmids hybrid *plasmid-phage vectors* that make use of a virus capsule to infect bacteria; constructed with plasmid-derived selectable markers and two specialized segments of phage λ DNA known as *cos* (for co*hesive end*) sites.

cotransformation simultaneous transformation of two or more genes. See *transformation.*

crisscross inheritance inheritance pattern in which males inherit a trait from their mothers, while daughters inherit the trait from their fathers.

cross the deliberate mating of selected parents based on particular genetic traits desired in the offspring.

cross-disciplinary biology a type of biology in which teams of biologists, computer scientists, chemists, engineers, mathematicians, physicists, and others work together on the problems of *systems biology.*

cross-fertilization brushing the pollen from one plant onto the female organ of another plant.

cross-fostering random relocation of offspring to the care of other parents, typically done with animal studies to randomize the effects of environment on outcome.

crossing-over during *meiosis,* the breaking of one maternal and one paternal *chromosome,* resulting in the exchange of corresponding sections of DNA and the rejoining of the chromosome. This process can result in the exchange of *alleles* between chromosomes. Compare *recombination.*

crossover suppression result of heterozygosity for *inversions,* in which no viable recombinant progeny are possible.

C terminus the end of the *polypeptide* chain that contains a free carboxylic acid group.

cyclin-dependent kinases (CDKs) a *protein kinase* is an enzyme that adds a phosphate group to a target protein molecule; in this case, the kinases are dependent on proteins known as cyclins for the targeting of their activity to a specific substrate. CDKs regulate the transition from G_1 to S and from G_2 to M through phosphorylations that activate or inactivate target proteins.

cyclins family of proteins that combine with *cyclin-dependent kinases* and thereby determine the substrate specificity of the kinases. By directing kinases to the right substrates, the cyclins help regulate passage of the cell through the *cell cycle.*

Concentrations of the various cyclins rise and fall throughout the cell cycle.

cytokinesis the final stage of cell division, which begins during *anaphase* but is not completed until after *telophase*. In this stage, the daughter nuclei emerging at the end of telophase are packaged into two separate daughter cells.

cytosine (C) a nitrogenous base; one member of the base pair G–C (guanine–cytosine).

D

dauer larva in nematodes, an alternate L3 form that does not feed and has a specialized cuticle that resists desiccation; dauer larvae can survive more than six months when food is scarce.

deamination the removal of an amino (—NH_2) group from normal DNA.

degeneracy property of the *genetic code* in which several different *codons* can specify the same amino acid.

degrees of freedom (df) the measure of the number of independently varying parameters in an experiment.

deletion occurs when a block of one or more nucleotide pairs is lost from a DNA molecule. Compare *insertion*.

deletion loop an unpaired bulge of the normal *chromosome* that corresponds to an area deleted from a paired homolog. Contrast *duplication loop*.

denaturation (denature, denatured) the disruption of hydrogen bonds within a macromolecule that normally uses hydrogen bonds to maintain its structure and function. Hydrogen bonds can be disrupted by heat, extreme conditions of pH, or exposure to chemicals such as urea. When normally soluble proteins are denatured, they unfold and expose their nonpolar amino acids, which can cause them to become insoluble. When DNA is denatured, double-stranded molecules break apart into two separate strands.

deoxyribonucleic acid (DNA) See *DNA*.

deoxyribonucleotide See *nucleotide*.

depurination DNA alteration in which the hydrolysis of a purine base, either A or G, from the deoxyribose-phosphate backbone occurs.

developmental geneticists biologists who use *genetics* to study how the fertilized egg of a multicellular organism becomes an adult.

developmental genetics the use of *genetics* to study how the fertilized egg of a multicellular organism becomes an adult.

developmental hierarchy a *developmental pathway* in which the product of one *gene* regulates the expression of another gene.

developmental pathway a detailed description of how many *genes* interact biochemically to produce a particular outcome in development.

diakinesis substage of *prophase I* during which *chromosomes* condense to the point where each *tetrad* consists of four separate *chromatids;* at the end of this substage, the nuclear envelope breaks down and the microtubules of the *spindle apparatus* begin to form.

dicentric chromatid a *chromatid* with two *centromeres*.

Dicer a cytoplasmic enzyme component of the *RNAi* machinery present in all eukaryotic cells. Dicer recognizes double-stranded RNA duplexes and trims off both ends to create duplex products 21–24 base pairs long that contain a *miRNA* strand and a complementary miRNA* strand. Dicer passes the miRNA:miRNA* to *RISC*.

dicotyledonous plant descriptive meaning that the mature embryo carries two leaves.

dideoxynucleotide nucleotide analogue lacking the 3′-hydroxyl group that is critical for the formation of *phosphodiester bonds*. The four types of dideoxynucleotides are abbreviated ddTTP, ddATP, ddGTP, and ddCTP. Dideoxynucleotides are key components of the most common methods of DNA sequencing.

digestion the enzymatic process by which a complex biological molecule (DNA, RNA, protein, or complex carbohydrate) is broken down into smaller components.

dihybrid an individual that is *heterozygous* for two *genes* at the same time.

dimerization domain region of a *polypeptide* that facilitates interactions with other molecules of the same polypeptide or with other polypeptides. Certain motifs such as the leucine zipper often serve as dimerization domains.

dipeptide two *amino acids* connected by a *peptide bond*.

diploid *zygotes* and other cells carrying two matching sets of chromosomes are described as diploid (compare *haploid*).

diplotene substage of *prophase I* during which there is a slight separation of regions of *homologous chromosomes* but the aligned homologous chromosomes of each *bivalent* remain tightly merged at *chiasmata*.

discontinuous traits *phenotypes* that are expressed in clear-cut variations. Compare with *continuous trait*.

discovery science an approach to biology in which one seeks to identify all the elements of a *biological system* and place them in a database to enrich the infrastructure of biology.

discrete trait inherited trait that clearly exhibits an either/or status (that is, purple versus white flowers).

disease stratification the process of dividing a single general condition into different diseases on the basis of the underlying molecular defects.

diversification evolution of many variants from one progenitor molecule.

DNA deoxyribonucleic acid; the molecule of heredity that encodes genetic information.

DNA clone a purified sample containing a large number of identical *DNA* molecules.

DNA fingerprint the multilocus pattern produced by the detection of *genotype* at a group of unlinked, highly *polymorphic* loci.

DNA marker See *marker*.

DNA polymerase III complex enzyme that forms a new DNA strand during *replication* by adding *nucleotides,* one after the other, to the 3′ end of a growing strand.

DNA polymorphisms two or more *alleles* at a *locus* detected with any method that directly distinguishes differences in DNA sequence. The sequence variations of a DNA polymorphism can occur at any position on a chromosome and may, or may not, have an effect on *phenotype*. See *polymorphisms*.

DNA probe a purified fragment of DNA labeled with a radioactive isotope or fluorescent dye and used to identify complementary sequences by means of *hybridization*.

DNase hypersensitive (DH) sites sites on DNA that contain few, if any, *nucleosomes;* these sites are susceptible to cleavage by DNase enzymes.

DNA replication process by which a double-helical DNA molecule is duplicated into two identical double-helical DNA molecules.

DNA sequence the relative order of *base pairs,* whether in a fragment of DNA, a *gene,* a *chromosome,* or an entire *genome*.

DNA topoisomerases a group of enzymes that help relax *supercoiling* of the DNA helix by nicking one or both strands to allow the strands to rotate relative to each other.

domain a discrete region of a *protein* with its own function. The combination of domains in a single protein determines its overall function.

domain architecture the number and order of a protein's functional domains.

dominance series dominance relations of all possible pairs of *alleles* are arranged in order from most dominant to most recessive.

dominant allele an *allele* whose *phenotype* is expressed in a *heterozygote*. See *recessive allele*.

dominant epistasis the effects of a *dominant allele* at one *gene* hide the effects of alleles at another gene. Compare with *recessive epistasis*.

dominant negative mechanism of dominance in which some alleles of genes encode subunits of *multimeric proteins* that block the activity of the subunits produced by *wild-type alleles*.

dominant-negative (or antimorphic) alleles (or mutations) *alleles* that block the activity of *wild-type alleles* of the same gene, causing a loss of function even in *heterozygotes*.

dominant trait the trait that appears in the F_1 hybrids (*heterozygotes*)

resulting from a mating between pure-breeding parental strains showing antagonistic *phenotypes*.

donor in gene transfer in bacteria, the cell that provides the genetic material. See *recipient, transformation, conjugation, transduction*.

dosage compensation mechanism that equalizes levels of *X-linked* gene expression independent of the number of copies of the X chromosome; in mammals, the dosage compensation mechanism is *X chromosome inactivation*.

double helix the shape that two linear strands of DNA assume when bonded together.

double minutes small chromosome-like bodies lacking centromeres and telomeres.

downstream the direction traveled by RNA polymerase as it moves from the promoter to the terminator. Compare with *upstream*.

Drosha a nuclear enzyme component of the *RNAi* machinery present in all eukaryotic cells. Drosha recognizes and processes stem-loop structures associated with primary *miRNA*-containing transcripts. Drosha products are transported into the cytoplasm where they are further processed by *Dicer* into mature miRNAs.

duplication events that result in an increase in the number of copies of a particular chromosomal region. See *tandem duplications, nontandem duplications*.

duplication loop a bulge in the *duplication*-bearing chromosome that has no similar region with which to pair in the unduplicated normal homologous chromosome. Contrast with *deletion loop*.

E

ecotypes plant varieties analogous to animal strains.

ectopic expression gene expression that occurs outside the cell or tissue where the gene is normally expressed.

electrophoresis a method of separating large molecules (such as DNA fragments or proteins) from a mixture of similar molecules. An electric current

is passed through a medium containing the mixture, and each kind of molecule travels through the medium at a different rate, depending on its size and electrical charge. See *gel electrophoresis*.

elements components of a *biological system*.

elongation phase of *DNA replication, transcription,* or *translation* that successively adds nucleotides or amino acids to a growing macromolecule. Compare *initiation*.

elongation factors proteins that aid in the *elongation* phase of *translation*.

embryonic stem cells (ES cells) cultured embryonic cells that continue to divide without differentiating.

emergent properties traits and behaviors that arise from the operation of a *biological system* as a whole; *immunity* and *tolerance* are two emergent properties of the immune system.

endosymbiont theory proposes that chloroplasts and mitochondria originated when free-living bacteria were engulfed by primitive nucleated cells. Host- and guest-formed cellular communities in which each member adapted to the group arrangement and derived benefit.

enhancer mutations mutations in a *modifier gene* that worsen the phenotypic effects of a mutation in another gene.

enhancer trapping in *Drosophila,* the identification of P-element insertion lines with particular β-galactosidase expression patterns.

enhancers *cis*-acting elements that can regulate *transcription* from nearby genes. In yeast, enhancers are called upstream activation sites, or UASs. Enhancers function by acting as binding sites for *transcription factors*.

enhancesome a completely assembled set of *transcription factors* (which may include *activators, repressors, coactivators,* and *corepressors*) associated with an *enhancer* or *locus control region* in a structure that is able to modulate transcription activity.

environmental variance (V_E) deviation from the mean attributed to the influence of external, noninheritable factors. Compare with *genetic variance*.

epigenetic a state of gene functionality that is not encoded within the DNA sequence but that is still heritable from one generation to the next. It can be accomplished and maintained through a chemical modification of DNA such as methylation.

episomes *plasmids*, like the F plasmid, that can integrate into the host genome.

epistasis a gene interaction in which the effects of an *allele* at one gene hide the effects of alleles at another gene. See *dominant epistasis* and *recessive epistasis*.

epistatic describes an *allele* of one gene that masks the effects of one or more alleles of another gene.

equational division cell division that does *not* reduce the number of *chromosomes*, but instead distributes *sister chromatids* to the two daughter cells. *Mitosis* and *meiosis II* are both equational divisions.

equilibrium frequency the q value at which $\Delta q = 0$; the *allele* frequency required to maintain an allele in the *population*.

euchromatin chromosomal region of cells that appears much lighter and less condensed when viewed under a light microscope. Contrast with *heterochromatin*.

eukaryotes one of the three major evolutionary lineages of living organisms known as domains; organisms whose cells have a membrane-bounded nucleus. Contrast with *prokaryotes*.

eukaryotic gene regulation the control of gene expression in the cells of *eukaryotes*.

euploid describes cells containing only complete sets of *chromosomes*.

excision repair DNA repair mechanism in which specialized proteins recognize damaged base pairing and remove the damaged section so that DNA *polymerase* can fill in the gap by complementary base pairing with the information from the undamaged strand of DNA. See *base excision repair* and *nucleotide excision repair*.

exconjugants *recipient* cells resulting from gene transfer in which *donor* cells carrying specialized *plasmids* establish contact with and transfer DNA to the recipients.

exit (E) site one of three *transfer RNA* binding sites in ribosomes. The E site is occupied by tRNAs during the period just after their disconnection from *amino acids* by the action of *peptidyl transferase* and just before the release of the tRNAs from the *ribosome*.

exons sequences that are found both in a gene's DNA and in the corresponding mature *messenger RNA* (*mRNA*). See *introns*.

exon shuffling the exchange of *exons* among different genes during evolution, producing mosaic proteins with two or more distinct functions.

expressed sequence tag (EST) 600 to 1000 bp long single-sequence run on cDNA inserts.

expressivity the degree or intensity with which a particular *genotype* is expressed in a *phenotype*.

extracellular signals signals that are able to diffuse from cell to cell or by cell-to-cell contact; can occur in the form of steroids, peptides, and proteins and are collectively known as hormones.

F

facultative heterochromatin regions of *chromosomes* (or even whole chromosomes) that are heterochromatic in some cells and euchromatic in other cells of the same organisms.

filial generations the successive offspring in a controlled sequence of breeding, starting with two parents (the P generation) and selfing or intercrossing the offspring of each subsequent generation.

fine structure mapping recombination mapping of *mutations* in the same gene; in some *bacteriophage* experiments, fine structure mapping can resolve mutations in adjacent nucleotide pairs.

first-division segregation pattern a *tetrad* in which the arrangement of *ascospores* indicates that the two *alleles* of a *gene* segregated from each other in the first meiotic division.

first filial (F₁) generation progeny of the *parental generation* in a controlled series of crosses.

FISH (fluorescence *in situ* hybridization) a *physical mapping* approach that uses fluorescent tags to detect *hybridization* of nucleic acid probes with *chromosomes*.

fitness the relative advantage or disadvantage in reproduction that a particular *genotype* provides to members of a *population* in comparison to alternative genotypes at the same *locus*.

fitness cost negative impact of the development of a homozygous resistance *genotype*.

fixed describes a population in which no further changes in allele frequency can occur (in the absence of mutation or migration).

5′-untranslated leader in *eukaryotes*, mRNA region between the 5′ *methylated cap* and the *initiation codon*.

fluctuation test the Luria-Delbrück experiment to determine the origin of bacterial resistance. Fluctuations in the numbers of resistant colonies growing in different petri plates showed that resistance is not caused by exposure to bactericides.

focus of action the cells in which a gene of interest must be active to allow the animal to develop and function normally.

forward mutation a mutation that changes a *wild-type allele* of a gene to a different *allele*.

founder cells in nematode development, progenitors of the major embryonic lineages.

founder effect variation of *genetic drift*, occurring when a few individuals separate from a larger *population* and establish a new one that is isolated from the original population, resulting in altered *allele frequencies* in the new population.

F plasmid a *conjugative plasmid* that carries many genes required for the transfer of DNA. Cells carrying F plasmid are called F⁺ cells. Cells without the plasmid are called F⁻ cells.

F′ plasmids *F plasmid* variants that carry most F plasmid genes plus some bacterial DNA; particularly useful in genetic complementation studies.

frameshift mutations *insertions* or *deletions* of base pairs that alter the grouping of *nucleotides* into *codons*. Refer to *reading frame*.

free duplications small DNA fragments maintained extrachromosomally in a genetic stock.

fusion proteins proteins encoded by parts of more than one gene.

G

G$_0$ in the cell cycle, a resting form of G_1. Cells in G_0 normally do not divide.

gain-of-function alleles (or mutations) rare *mutations* that enhance a gene's function or confer a new activity on the gene's product.

gametes specialized *haploid* cells (eggs and sperm or pollen) that carry genes between generations.

gametogenesis the formation of *gametes*.

gastrulation folding of the cell sheet early in embryo formation; usually occurs immediately after the blastula stage of development.

gel electrophoresis a process used to separate DNA fragments, RNA molecules, or polypeptides according to their size. Electrophoresis is accomplished by passing an electrical current through agarose or polyacrylamide gels. The electrical current forces molecules to migrate into the gel at different rates dependent on their sizes.

gene basic unit of biological information; specific segment of DNA in a discrete region of a chromosome that serves as a unit of function by encoding a particular RNA or protein.

gene amplification an increase from the normal two copies to hundreds of copies of a *gene;* often due to *mutations* in *p53,* which disrupt the G$_1$-to-S *checkpoint.*

gene conversion any deviation from the expected 2:2 *segregation* of parental *alleles.*

gene dosage the number of times a given *gene* is present in the cell nucleus.

gene expression the process by which a gene's information is converted into *RNA* and then (for protein-coding genes) into a *polypeptide.*

gene family set of closely related genes with slightly different functions that most likely arose from a succession of gene *duplication* events.

gene function generally, to govern the synthesis of a *polypeptide;* in Mendelian terms, a gene's specific contribution to *phenotype.*

generalized transduction a type of *transduction* (gene transfer mediated by bacteriophages) that can result in the transfer of any bacterial gene between related strains of bacteria.

gene pool the sum total of all *alleles* carried in all members of a *population.*

gene regulatory network a set of interacting *transcription factors* and their cognate cis-*control elements* that receive diverse inputs of biological information; integrate and modify those inputs; and transmit the transformed information to various *protein networks.* The fundamental link in a gene regulatory network is the interaction of a transcription factor with its cognate *cis*-control element.

gene superfamily a large set of related genes that is divisible into smaller sets, or families, with the genes in each family being more closely related to each other than to other members of the larger superfamily. The single-gene or *multigene families* that compose a superfamily reside at different chromosomal locations. The families of genes encoding the globins and the *Hox* transcription factors are examples of gene superfamilies.

genetic code the sequence of *nucleotides,* coded in triplets (*codons*) along the *mRNA,* that determines the sequence of *amino acids* in *protein* synthesis.

genetic drift unpredictable, chance fluctuations in *allele* frequency that have a neutral effect on *fitness* of a *population.*

genetic imbalance situation when the *genome* of a cell or organism has more copies of some genes than other genes due to *chromosomal rearrangements* or *aneuploidy.*

genetic linkage See *linkage.*

genetic markers *genes* identifiable through phenotypic variants that can serve as points of reference in determining whether particular progeny are the result of *recombination.* Compare with *physical markers.*

genetic mosaic See *mosaic.*

genetic relatedness the average fraction of common *alleles* at all gene loci that individuals share because they inherited them from a common ancestor.

genetics the science of heredity.

genetic screen an examination of each individual in a *population* for its *phenotype.*

genetic variance (V$_G$) deviation from the mean attributable to inheritable factors. Compare with *environmental variance.*

genetic variant describes alleles of a polymorphic locus.

genome the sum total of genetic information in a particular cell or organism.

genomic equivalent the number of clones—with inserts of a particular size—that would be required to carry a single copy of every sequence in a particular genome.

genomic imprinting the phenomenon in which a gene's expression depends on the parent that transmits it.

genomic library a collection of *DNA clones* that together carry a representative copy of every DNA sequence in the *genome* of a particular organism.

genomics the study of whole *genomes.*

genotype the actual *alleles* present in an individual.

genotype frequency proportion of total individuals in a *population* that are of a particular *genotype.*

genotypic class a grouping defined by a set of related *genotypes* that will produce a particular *phenotype.* The term is most useful in describing progeny of *dihybrid* or *multihybrid* crosses involving complete dominance; for example, in a cross between *Aa Bb* individuals, the genotypic classes are *A- B-, A- bb, aa B-,* and *aa bb.*

germ cells specialized cells that incorporate into the reproductive organs, where they ultimately undergo *meiosis,* thereby producing *haploid* *gametes* that transmit genes to the next generation. Compare *somatic cells.*

germ line all the *germ cells* in a sexually reproducing organism. In animals, the germ line is set aside from the *somatic cells* during embryonic development. The germ cells in the germ line divide by *mitosis* to produce a collection of specialized *diploid* cells that then divide by *meiosis* to produce *haploid* cells, or *gametes.* The germ line thus includes the precursors of the gametes such as *oogonia, spermatagonia, primary* and *secondary oocytes,* and *primary* and *secondary spermatocytes* as well as the *gametes.*

germ-line gene therapy a genetic engineering technique that modifies the DNA of *germ cells* that are passed on to progeny.

globular stage embryo stage of development in a plant in which cell divisions give rise to the first evidence of differentiation found in the mature embryo. The innermost group of cells acquire an elongated shape, and a discrete outer cell layer is present.

G_1 phase stage of the cell cycle from the birth of a new cell until the onset of chromosome replication at *S phase.*

G_2 phase stage of the cell cycle from the completion of *chromosome replication* until the onset of cell division.

growth factors extracellular hormones and cell-bound *ligands* that stimulate or inhibit cell proliferation.

guanine (G) a nitrogenous base; one member of the base pair G–C (guanine–cytosine).

gynandromorph a rare genetic *mosaic* with some male tissue and some female tissue, usually in equal amounts.

H

hairpin loops structures formed when a single strand of DNA or RNA can fold back on itself because of *complementary base pairing* between different regions in the same molecule.

haploid a single set of *chromosomes* present in the egg and sperm cells of animals and in the egg and pollen cells of plants (compare with *diploid*).

haploinsufficiency a rare form of dominance in which an individual *heterozygous* for a *wild-type allele* and a *null* allele shows an abnormal *phenotype* because the level of gene activity is not enough to produce a normal phenotype.

haplospores See *ascospores.*

haplotype specific combination of *linked alleles* in a cluster of related *genes.* A contraction of the phrase "haploid genotype."

Hardy-Weinberg law defines the relationships between *genotype* and *allele frequencies* within a generation and from one generation to the next.

hemizygous describes the *genotype* for genes present in only one copy in an otherwise *diploid* organism, such as *X-linked* genes in a male.

heredity the way *genes* transmit physiological, physical, and behavioral traits from parents to offspring.

heritability (h^2) the proportion of *total phenotype variance* ascribable to *genetic variance.*

hermaphrodite an organism that has both male and female organs and produces both male *gametes* (sperm) and female gametes (eggs). The organism can have both types of organs at the same time (simultaneous hermaphrodite) or have one type early in life and the other type later in life (sequential hermaphrodite).

heterochromatin highly condensed chromosomal regions within which genes are usually transcriptionally inactive.

heterochromatic DNA genomic DNA from heterochromatic regions; this DNA is often difficult to clone.

heterochronic mutations mutations resulting in the inappropriate timing of cell division and cell-fate decisions during development.

heteroduplex region a region of double-stranded DNA in which the two strands have nonidentical (though similar) sequences. Heteroduplex regions are often formed as intermediates during *crossing-over.*

heterogametic sex the gender of a species in which the two *sex chromosomes* are dissimilar; e.g., males are the heterogametic sex in humans

because they have an X and a Y chromosome. Compare with *homogametic sex.*

heterogeneous trait occurs when a *mutation* at any one of a number of genes can give rise to the same *phenotype.*

heteromers multimeric proteins composed of nonidentical *subunits.* Compare *homomers.*

heteroplasmic genomic makeup of a cell's organelles characterized by a mixture of organelle *genomes.* Contrast *homoplasmic.*

heterothallic strains of organisms with stable *haploid* mating types; progeny of successive mitotic divisions always have the same mating type as their parents. Contrast *homothallic.*

heterozygote individual with two different *alleles* for a given *gene* or *locus.*

heterozygous a *genotype* in which the two copies of the gene that determine a particular trait are different *alleles.* See *hybrid.*

heterozygous carrier unaffected parents who bear a *dominant* normal *allele* that masks the effects of an abnormal *recessive* one.

Hfr bacteria that produce a high *frequency* of *recombinants* for chromosomal genes in mating experiments because their *chromosomes* contain an integrated *F plasmid.*

high-density linkage map a *linkage map* that shows one *gene* or *marker* for each centimorgan of a *genome.*

histocompatibility antigens cell surface molecules that play a critical role in stimulating a proper *immune response.*

histones small DNA-binding proteins with a preponderance of the basic, positively charged amino acids lysine and arginine. Histones are the fundamental protein components of *nucleosomes.*

homeobox in *homeotic genes,* the region of homology, usually 180 bp in length that encodes the *homeodomain.*

homeodomain a conserved DNA-binding region of *transcription factors* encoded by the *homeobox* of *homeotic genes.*

homeotic gene a gene that plays a role in determining a tissue's identity during development.

homeotic mutation mutation that causes cells to misinterpret their position in the blueprint and become normal organs in inappropriate positions; such a mutation can alter the overall body plan.

homeotic selector genes genes that control the identity of body segments.

homogametic sex the gender of a species in which the two *sex chromosomes* are identical; in humans, females are the homogametic sex because the have two X chromosomes. Compare with *heterogametic sex*.

homologous chromosomes (homologs) chromosomes that match in size, shape, and banding. A pair of chromosomes containing the same linear gene sequence, each derived from one parent.

homologs genes or regulatory DNA sequences that are similar in different species because of descent from a common ancestral sequence.

homologous genes genes in different species with enough sequence similarity to be evolutionarily related.

homomers *multimeric proteins* composed of identical *subunits*. Compare with *heteromers*.

homoplasmic genomic makeup of a cell's organelles characterized by a single type of organelle DNA. Contrast with *heteroplasmic*.

homothallic strains of organisms that can switch mating types; progeny of successive mitotic divisions may not have the same mating type as their parents. Compare with *heterothallic*.

homozygote individual with identical *alleles* for a given *gene* or *locus*.

homozygous a *genotype* in which the two copies of the gene that determine a particular trait are the same *allele*.

hormone a small molecule or polypeptide that is made and released by certain secretory cells in multicellular organisms. Secreted hormones diffuse or move via bodily fluids to other cell types that contain specific receptors. Hormone-receptor binding can elicit changes in gene function and differentiation in the target cells.

hot spots sites within a gene that mutate more frequently than others, either spontaneously or after treatment with a particular *mutagen*.

Human Genome Project initiative to determine the complete sequence of the human *genome* and to analyze this information.

hybrid dysgenesis phenomenon in which high *transposon* mobility causes reduced fertility in hybrid progeny; the result of crossing *Drosophila* males carrying the P element with females that lack the P element.

hybrids offspring of genetically dissimilar parents; often used as synonym for *heterozygotes*.

hydrogen bonds weak electrostatic bonds that result in a partial sharing of hydrogen atoms between reacting groups.

hypermorphic mutation produces an allele generating either more protein than the *wild-type allele* or the same amount of a more efficient protein. If excess protein activity alters *phenotype*, the hypermorphic allele is dominant. Compare with *hypomorphic mutation*.

hypomorphic mutation produces either less of a protein or a protein with a weak but detectable function. Compare with *hypermorphic mutation*.

I

idiogram black-and-white diagram of the chromosomes converted from the light and dark bands observed under the microscope.

imaginal discs flattened epithelial sacs that develop from small groups of cells set aside in the early embryo from which adult-specific structures like wings, legs, eyes, and genitalia develop; in *Drosophila*, they undergo extensive growth and development during the larval and pupal stages.

immune response physiological response to the immune system's activation by *antigen*. Immune responses include the production of antibodies by B lymphocytes and the ability of killer T cells to destroy foreign or cancerous cells by direct cell-to-cell contact.

immunity ability to generate immune responses to infectious agents or vaccines. Such a response protects against serious disease.

incomplete dominance expression of *heterozygous phenotype* resulting in offspring whose phenotype is intermediate between those of the parents.

inDel or DIP genetic variant with short deletions and insertions; a type of SNP.

indels *deletions, duplications,* and *insertions* at non-repeat loci.

independent assortment the random distribution of different genes during gamete formation. See *Mendel's second law*.

inducer small molecule that causes *transcription* from a gene or set of genes.

induction process by which a signal induces expression of a gene or set of genes.

inflorescence in a plant, the flower or group of flowers at the tip of a branch.

initiation first phase of *DNA replication, transcription,* or *translation* needed to set the stage for the addition of nucleotide or amino acid building blocks during *elongation*.

initiation codon nucleotide triplet that marks the precise spot in the nucleotide sequence of an *mRNA* where the code for a particular *polypeptide* begins. Compare *nonsense codon*.

initiation factors a term usually applied to proteins that help promote the association of *ribosomes, mRNA,* and initiating *tRNA* during the first phase of *translation*.

insertion the addition to a DNA molecule of one or more nucleotide pairs.

insertional mutagenesis method of mutagenesis in which a foreign DNA sequence (viral, *plasmid, transposon,* or cloned fragment) is used as the mutagenic agent. Mutations result when the foreign sequence integrates into a gene. The disrupted gene can be easily identified and cloned based on its association with the foreign DNA.

insertion sequences (ISs) small *transposable elements* that dot the chromosomes of many types of bacteria; they are *transposons* that do not contain selectable markers.

insulator a transcriptional regulation element in *eukaryotes* that stops communication between *enhancers* on one side of it with *promoters* on the other side. Insulators play an important role in limiting the *chromatin* region over which an enhancer can operate.

interactome the network of all or many of the protein interactions in a cell or organism.

intercalators class of chemical *mutagens* composed of flat, planar molecules that can sandwich themselves between successive *base pairs* and disrupt the machinery of *replication, recombination,* or repair.

intergenic gene conversion information flow between related DNA sequences that occurs through an alternative outcome of the process responsible for *unequal crossing-over.*

interkinesis brief *interphase* between *meiosis I* and *meiosis II.*

interphase the period in the cell cycle between divisions.

intragenic suppression the restoration of gene function by one *mutation* canceling the effects of another mutation in the same *gene.*

introns the DNA base sequences of a *gene* that are spliced out of the *primary transcript* and are therefore not found in the mature mRNA. See *exons.*

inversion a 180-degree rotation of a segment of a *chromosome* relative to the remainder of the chromosome.

inversion heterozygotes cells or organisms in which one *chromosome* is of a normal gene order, while the *homologous chromosome* carries an *inversion.*

inversion loop formed in the cells of an *inversion heterozygote* when the inverted region rotates to pair with the similar region in the normal homolog.

K

karyotype the visual description of the complete set of *chromosomes* in one cell of an organism; usually presented as a photomicrograph with the chromosomes arranged in a standard format showing the number, size, and shape of each chromosome type.

kinetochore a specialized chromosomal structure composed of DNA and proteins that is the site at which *chromosomes* attach to the spindle fibers. See *kinetochore microtubules.*

kinetochore microtubules microtubules of the *mitotic spindle* that extend between a *centrosome* and the *kinetochore* of a *chromatid. Chromosomes* move along the kinetochore microtubules during cell division.

knockout constructs cloned genes modified so that they no longer function. Used in *targeted mutagenesis.*

knockout mice mice homozygous for an induced mutation in a targeted gene; the mutation destroys (knocks out) the function of the gene. See *targeted mutagenesis.*

L

lac **operon** a single DNA unit in *E. coli,* composed of the *lacZ, lacY,* and *lacA* genes together with the *promoter* (*p*) and *operator site* (*o*), that enables the simultaneous regulation of the three structural genes in response to environmental changes.

lagging strand during *replication,* DNA strand whose polarity is opposite to that of the *leading strand.* The lagging strand must be synthesized discontinuously as small *Okazaki fragments* that are ultimately joined into a continuous strand.

lambda (λ) see *phage lambda.*

λ repressor protein protein that binds to *operator sites* on phage λ DNA, preventing the transcription of genes needed for the lytic cycle; this protein makes λ lysogens immune to infection with incoming λ phage.

late-onset a genetic condition in which symptoms are not present at birth, but manifest themselves later in life.

lateral gene transfer the introduction and incorporation of DNA from an unrelated individual or from a different species.

law of independent assortment See *Mendel's second law.*

law of segregation See *Mendel's first law.*

lawn bacteria immobilized in a nutrient agar, used as a field on which to test for the presence of viral particles.

leader sequence DNA sequence that precedes the coding sequence and contains signals that regulate *transcription termination* in an *operon* controlled by *attenuation.*

leading strand during *replication,* DNA strand synthesized continuously 5′ to 3′ toward the unwinding Y-shaped *replication fork.* Compare with *lagging strand.*

leptotene first definable substage of *prophase I* during which the long, thin, already duplicated *chromosomes* begin to thicken.

library see *genomic library* or *cDNA library.*

ligands molecules such as *growth factors* or *hormones* that are produced by one cell and bind to receptors on a different cell, initiating a *signal transduction pathway.*

LINE long *in*terspersed *e*lements; one of the two major classes of *transposable elements* in mammals. Contrast with *SINE.*

lineage compartments regions of an organism in which cells have a restricted developmental potential.

linkage the proximity of two or more *markers* on a *chromosome;* the closer together the markers are, the lower the probability that they will be separated by *recombination.* Genes are *linked* when the frequency of parental-type progeny exceeds that of recombinant progeny.

linkage disequilibrium when *alleles* at separate *loci* (such as *marker* alleles and disease alleles) are associated with each other at a significantly higher frequency than would be expected by chance. Linkage disequilibrium at particular loci in a *population* can be evidence of common ancestry.

linkage group a group of genes chained together by linkage relationships. See *linkage.*

linkage map depicts the distances between *loci* as well as the order in which they occur on the organism.

linked describes *genes* whose *alleles* are inherited together more often than not; linked genes are usually located close together on the same *chromosome.*

linker DNA a stretch of ≈40 base pairs of DNA that connect one *nucleosome* with the next.

locus a designated location on a *chromosome*. See α-*globin locus* and β-*globin locus.*

locus control region (LCR) a *cis*-acting regulatory element that operates to enhance *transcription* from individual genes within a gene complex such as the β-globin complex.

loss-of-function mutation (or allele) DNA *mutation* that reduces or abolishes the activity of a gene; most (but not all) loss-of-function alleles are *recessive.*

lysate population of *phage* particles released from the host bacteria at the end of the *lytic cycle.*

lysogenic bacterium bacterial cell that carries a *prophage;* lysogen.

lysogenic cycle occurs when *bacteriophage* integrate their DNA into the host *genome* such that it multiplies along with that genome, but does little harm to the host.

lysogeny the integration of *bacteriophage* DNA into the host *chromosome.*

lytic cycle bacterial cycle of *phage*-infected cells resulting in cell lysis and release of progeny phage. Compare with *lysogenic cycle.*

M

major groove in a space-filling representation of the DNA *double helix* model, the wider of the two grooves resulting from the vertical displacement of the two backbone threads. See *minor groove.*

MAP kinase cascade trio of three protein kinases that activates a transcription factor.

mapping function mathematical equation that compensates for the inaccuracies inherent in relating *recombination frequencies* to physical distance.

mapping panels a set of DNA samples used in multiple *linkage* analysis tests.

map unit (m.u.) synonymous with *centimorgan.*

marker an identifiable physical location on a *chromosome,* whose inheritance

can be monitored. Markers can be expressed regions of DNA (genes) or any segment of DNA with variant forms that can be followed.

maternal-effect mutations mutations in genes encoding maternal components (those supplied by the egg to the mother) that disrupt the development of her progeny.

maternally supplied components molecules synthesized by the mother that are supplied to the egg and that are needed for early development of the progeny.

mean statistical average; the middle point.

meiosis the process of two consecutive cell divisions starting in the *diploid* progenitors of sex cells. Meiosis results in four daughter cells, each with a *haploid* set of *chromosomes.*

meiosis I (or division I of meiosis) the parent nucleus divides to form two daughter nuclei; during meiosis I, the previously replicated *homologous chromosomes* segregate to different daughter cells.

meiosis II (or division II of meiosis) each of the two daughter nuclei resulting from *meiosis I* divide to produce four nuclei; because the *chromosomes* do not duplicate at the start of meiosis II, these four daughter nuclei are *haploid.*

Mendel's first law the law of segregation states that the two alleles for each trait separate (segregate) during gamete formation and then unite at random, one from each parent, at fertilization.

Mendel's second law the law of independent assortment states that during gamete formation, different pairs of *alleles* (genes) segregate independently of each other.

merodiploids partial diploids in which there are two copies of some genes.

messenger RNA (mRNA) RNA that serves as a template for protein synthesis. See *genetic code.*

metabolism the chemical and physical reactions that convert sources of energy and matter to fuel growth and repair within a cell.

metacentric a *chromosome* in which the *centromere* is at or near the middle.

metamorphosis a dramatic reorganization of an organism's body plan; for example, transition from larval stage to adult insect stage.

metaphase a stage in *mitosis* or *meiosis* during which the *chromosomes* are aligned along the equatorial plane of the cell.

metaphase I phase of *meiosis I* when the *kinetochores* of *homologous chromosomes* attach to microtubules from opposite spindle poles, positioning the *bivalents* at the equator of the *spindle apparatus.*

metaphase II second phase of *meiosis II* during which *kinetochores* of *sister chromatids* attach to microtubule fibers emanating from opposite poles of the *spindle apparatus.* Two characteristics distinguish metaphase II from its counterpart in *mitosis:* (1) the number of chromosomes is one-half that in mitotic metaphase of the same species, and (2) in most chromosomes, the two sister chromatids are no longer identical because of the recombination through crossing-over that occurred in *meiosis I.*

metaphase plate imaginary equator of the cell toward which *chromosomes* move during *metaphase.*

metazoans multicellular animals that first appeared about 0.57 billion years ago.

methylated cap formed by the action of capping enzyme and methyl transferases at the 5′ end of eukaryotic *mRNA,* critical for efficient *translation* of the mRNA into protein.

methyl-directed mismatch repair DNA repair mechanism that corrects mistakes in *replication,* discriminating between newly synthesized and parental DNA by the methyl groups on the parental strand.

microevolution alterations of a population's *gene pool.* Contrast *macroevolution.*

micro-RNA (miRNA) an *RNA* molecule 21–24 bases in length that is encoded in the genome of an organism and used by a cell to modulate gene expression through the process of *RNA interference.*

microsatellite DNA element composed of 15–100 tandem repeats of one-, two-, or three-base-pair sequences.

minimal tiling path the result of the final step in the *shotgun* sequencing strategy, a minimally overlapping set of BAC clones.

minisatellite DNA element composed of 10–40 bp tandem repeating units of identical sequence.

minor groove in a space-filling representation of the DNA *double helix* model, the narrower of the two grooves resulting from the vertical displacement of the two backbone threads. See *major groove.*

miRISC a functional *RNA-induced silencing complex (RISC)* loaded with a *micro-RNA.*

missense mutations changes in the *nucleotide* sequence of a *gene* that change the identity of an *amino acid* in the *polypeptide* encoded by that gene.

mitosis the process of division that produces daughter cells that are genetically identical to each other and to the parent cell.

mitotic nondisjunction the failure of two *sister chromatids* to separate during mitotic *anaphase* generates reciprocal trisomic and monosomic daughter cells.

mitotic spindle structure composed of three types of microtubules (*kinetochore microtubules, polar microtubules,* and *astral microtubules*). The mitotic spindle provides a framework for the movement of *chromosomes* during cell division.

model organisms used in genomic analysis because they have many genetic mechanisms and cellular pathways in common with each other and with humans. These organisms lend themselves well to classical breeding experiments and direct manipulation of the genome.

modification the phenomenon in which growth on a restricting host changes a *phage* so that succeeding generations grow more efficiently on that same host.

modification enzymes enzymes that add methyl groups to specific DNA sequences, preventing the action of specific *restriction enzymes* on that DNA.

modifier genes genes that produce a subtle, secondary effect on *phenotype.*

There is no formal distinction between major and modifier genes, rather it is a continuum of degrees of influence.

molecular clock hypothesis stating that one can assume a constant rate of *amino acid* or *nucleotide* substitution as a means of determining the genealogies of organisms.

molecular cloning the process by which a single DNA fragment is purified from a complex mixture of DNA molecules and then amplified into a large number of identical copies.

molecular machine complex of different *proteins* or of proteins and *RNAs* that carry out a particular process; examples are the *ribosome* and the *spliceosome.*

molecular marker a segment of DNA found at a specific site in a *genome* that has variants which can be recognized and followed. See *physical marker, genetic marker.*

molecular systems biology newly emerging field that attempts to define biological system components and understand how they function with one another.

monohybrid crosses crosses between parents that differ in only one trait.

monohybrids individuals having two different alleles for a single trait.

monomorphic a gene with only one *wild-type allele.*

monoploid describing cells, nuclei, or organisms that have a single set of unpaired *chromosomes.* For *diploid* organisms, monoploid and *haploid* are synonymous.

monosomic individual lacking one *chromosome* from the *diploid* number for the species.

Monte Carlo simulation a computer simulation that uses a random number generator to choose an outcome for probabilistic events in an dynamic system defined by predetermined rules of probability; allows multiple runs of generational sequences.

morphogens substances that define different cell fates in a concentration-dependent manner.

mosaic an organism containing tissues of different *genotypes.*

mosaic determination where the embryo is a collection of self-differentiating cells that at their formation receive a specific set of molecular instructions governing their unique fates. Contrast with *regulative determination.*

mRNA See *messenger RNA.*

multifactorial traits determined by two or more factors, including multiple genes interacting with each other or one or more genes interacting with the environment.

multigene family set of *genes* descended by *duplication* and *diversification* from one ancestral gene. The members of a multigene family may be either clustered on the same chromosome or distributed on different chromosomes.

multihybrid crosses crosses between parents that differ in three or more traits.

multimeric protein a protein made from more than one *polypeptide;* each polypeptide in the multimeric protein is called a *subunit.*

multiple alleles set of *alleles* of a gene with more than two variant forms.

mutagen any physical or chemical agent that raises the frequency of *mutations* above the spontaneous rate.

mutant allele (1) an *allele,* or DNA variant, whose frequency is less than 1% in a *population;* (2) an allele that dictates a phenotype seen only rarely in a population. See *allele frequency.*

mutant tumor-suppressor genes recessive *mutant alleles* that contribute to the formation of cancer.

mutations heritable alterations in *DNA sequence.*

N

n number of *chromosomes* in a normal *gamete;* for organisms that are not *polyploids, n* is the number of chromosomes in any *haploid* cell and is also equal to *x* (the number of chromosomes in a single complete set of non-homologous chromosomes). *n* and *x* are *not* identical in polyploid organisms.

natural selection in nature, the process that progressively eliminates individuals whose fitness is low and chooses individuals of high fitness to survive and become the parents of the next generation. Contrast with *artificial selection.*

natural transformation a process by which a few species of bacteria transfer genes from one strain to another by spontaneously accepting DNA from their surroundings. Contrast with *artificial transformation.*

neomorphic mutations rare mutations that produce a novel *phenotype* due to production of a protein with a new function or due to *ectopic expression* of the protein.

***N*-formylmethionine (fMet)** a modified methionine whose amino end is blocked by a formyl group; fMet is carried by a specialized *tRNA* that functions only at a *ribosome's* translation initiation site.

nodes (of a *phylogenetic tree*) representations of taxonomic units such as species, *populations,* individuals, or *genes.*

nonallelic noncomplementation (also called second-site noncomplementation) failure of *mutations* in two different genes to complement each other, causing a mutant *phenotype* in *heterozygotes.* Usually indicates that the two polypeptide products cooperate with each other, for example as *subunits* of the same *multimeric protein.*

nonautonomous elements defective *transposable elements* that cannot move unless the genome contains nondefective *autonomous elements* that can supply necessary functions like tranposase enzymes.

nonautonomous trait when the *phenotype* expressed by a particular cell depends upon the genotypes of neighboring cells. Compare with *cell autonomous trait.*

nonconservative substitutions mutational changes that substitute an *amino acid* in a *protein* with a different amino acid with different chemical properties. Compare with *conservative substitutions.*

nondisjunction failures in *chromosome segregation* during *meiosis;* responsible for defects such as trisomy. (See *trisomic*).

nonhomologous end-joining mechanism for stitching back together ends formed by double-strand breaks. It relies on proteins that bind to the ends

of the broken DNA strands and bring them close together. Overhanging ends are often "trimmed during nonhomologous end-joining, resulting in DNA loss.

nonhomologous unequal crossing-over exchange between nonequivalent chromosomal segments with little sequence homology. A nonhomologous crossover may be mediated by at least a short stretch of sequence homology—coding or noncoding—at the crossover's two sites of initiation. For example, related repeat sequences in the *genome* may mediate nonhomologous unequal crossing-over.

non-Mendelian inheritance pattern of inheritance that does not follow *Mendel's laws* and does not produce Mendelian ratios among the progeny of various crosses.

nonparental ditype (NPD) a *tetrad* containing four recombinant spores.

nonsense codons the three stop codons that terminate *translation.* Compare with *initiation codon.*

nonsense mutations mutational changes in which a codon for an amino acid is altered to a *stop codon,* resulting in the formation of a *truncated protein.*

nonsense suppressor tRNAs *tRNAs* encoded by mutant tRNA genes; these tRNAs contain *anticodons* that can recognize *stop codons,* thus suppressing the effects of *nonsense mutations* by inserting an *amino acid* into a *polypeptide* in spite of the stop codon.

nontandem duplications two or more copies of a region that are not adjacent to each other and may lie far apart on the same chromosome or on different chromosomes. Contrast with *tandem duplications.*

Northern blot analysis protocol for determining whether a fragment of DNA is transcribed in a particular tissue. In this protocol, RNA *transcripts* in the cells of a particular tissue are separated by *gel electrophoresis.* Compare *Southern blot.*

N terminus the end of a *polypeptide* chain that contains a free amino group that is not connected to any other amino acid.

nuclear envelope envelope composed of two membranes that surrounds the nucleus of a eukaryotic cell.

nuclear lamins proteins that underlie the inner surface of the nuclear membrane and serve as CDK substrates.

nucleoid body a folded bacterial *chromosome.*

nucleolar organizer clusters of *rRNA* genes on long loops of DNA within a *nucleolus.*

nucleolus large sphere-shaped organelle visible in the nucleus of *interphase* eukaryotic cells with a light microscope; formed by the *nucleolar organizer.*

nucleosome rudimentary DNA packaging unit; composed of DNA wrapped around a *histone protein* core.

nucleotide a subunit of DNA or RNA consisting of a nitrogenous base (adenine, guanine, thymine, or cytosine in DNA; adenine, guanine, uracil, or cytosine in RNA), a phosphate group, and a sugar (deoxyribose in DNA; ribose in RNA).

nucleotide excision repair homology-dependent mechanism that removes DNA alterations/errors, such as thymine-thymine dimers that *base excision repair* cannot take care of. Depends on process-specific enzyme complexes that patrol the DNA for irregularities and cut the damaged strand in two places that flank the error, releasing s short single-stranded region containing the alteration. DNA polymerase fills in the resultant gap.

null hypothesis a statistical hypothesis to be tested and either accepted or rejected in favor of an alternative.

null mutations (or alleles) mutations that abolish the function of a protein encoded by the *wild-type allele.* Such mutations either prevent synthesis of the protein or promote synthesis of a protein incapable of carrying out any function.

O

octads asci produced in *Neurospora* containing eight *ascospores* because of an extra round of *mitosis* that occurs after *meiosis* is completed.

octant stage embryo early stage of embryo formation during cell divisions of a plant.

Okazaki fragments during *DNA replication,* small fragments of about 1000 bases that are joined after synthesis to form the *lagging strand.*

oligonucleotide a short single-stranded DNA molecule (containing less than 50 bases); can be synthesized by an automated DNA synthesizer. Oligonucleotides are used as *DNA probes* and as *primers* for DNA sequencing or PCR.

oligopeptide several *amino acids* linked by *peptide bonds.*

oncogene a gene, one or more forms of which is associated with cancer. Many oncogenes are involved, directly or indirectly, in controlling the rate of cell growth.

oogenesis formation of the female gametes (eggs).

oogonia *diploid germ cells* in the ovary.

open reading frames (ORFs) DNA sequences with long stretches of codons in the same reading frame uninterrupted by *stop codons;* suggest the presence of genes.

operator site a short DNA sequence near a *promoter* that can be recognized by a *repressor* protein; binding of repressor to the operator blocks *transcription* of the gene.

operon a unit of DNA composed of specific genes, plus a *promoter* and/or *operator,* that acts in unison to regulate the response of the structural genes to environmental changes.

operon theory theory explaining the repression and induction of genes in *E. coli.*

ordered tetrads *tetrads* in fungi such as *Neurospora* in which the order of *ascospores* in the *ascus* reflects the geometry of the meiotic divisions.

origin of replication short sequence of *nucleotides* at which the *initiation* of DNA *replication* begins.

orthologous genes with sequence similarities in two different species that arose from the same gene in the two species' common ancestor.

ovum *haploid* female *germ cell* (the egg).

oxidative phosphorylation a set of reactions requiring oxygen that creates portable packets of energy in the form of ATP.

P

pachytene substage of *prophase I* that begins at the completion of *synapsis* and includes the *crossing-over* of genetic material that results in *recombination.*

paracentric inversions *inversions* that exclude the *centromere.* Compare with *pericentric inversions.*

paralogous genes that arise by *duplication* within the same species, often within the same *chromosome;* paralogous genes often constitute a *multigene family.*

parental classes combinations of *alleles* present in the original *parental generation.*

parental ditype (PD) a *tetrad* that contains four parental class *haploid* cells.

parental (P) generation pure-breeding individuals whose progeny in subsequent generations will be studied for specific traits. Refer to *filial generations.*

parental types *phenotypes* that reflect a previously existing parental combination of genes that is retained during gamete formation.

parthenogenesis reproduction in which offspring are produced by an unfertilized female. Parthenogenesis is common in ants, bees, wasps, and certain species of fish and lizards.

pathogenicity islands segments of DNA in disease-causing bacteria that encode several genes involved in pathogenesis. Pathogenicity islands appear to have been transferred into the bacteria by lateral gene transfer from a different species.

pedigree an orderly diagram of a family's relevant genetic features, extending through as many generations as possible.

penetrance indicates how many members of a *population* with a particular *genotype* show the expected *phenotype.*

peptide bond a covalent bond that joins *amino acids* during protein synthesis.

peptide motifs stretches of *amino acids* conserved in many otherwise unrelated *polypeptides.*

peptidyl (P) site site on a *ribosome* to which the initiating *tRNA* first binds

and at which the tRNAs carrying the growing *polypeptide* are located during *elongation.*

peptidyl transferase the enzymatic activity of the *ribosome* responsible for forming *peptide bonds* between successive *amino acids.*

pericentric inversions *inversions* that include the *centromere.* Compare with *paracentric inversions.*

permissive condition an environmental condition that allows the survival of an individual with a *conditional lethal* allele. Contrast with *restrictive condition.*

petals the structure composing the second *whorl* of a flower, leaf-shaped but containing no photosynthetic cells, therefore not green.

phage short for *bacteriophage;* a *virus* for which the natural host is a bacterial cell; literally "bacteria eaters."

phage induction process of phage DNA excision from the bacterial chromosome in a *lysogen* and entry into the *lytic cycle.*

phage lambda (λ) a naturally occurring double-stranded DNA virus that infects *E. coli.* A common *plasmid vector* used to clone DNA from other organisms.

phenocopy a change in *phenotype* arising from environmental agents that mimic the effects of a mutation in a gene. Phenocopies are not heritable because they do not result from a change in a gene.

phenotype an observable characteristic.

phenotype frequency the proportion of individuals in a population that are of a particular phenotype.

phenotype variance (V_P) see *total phenotype variance.*

pheromones molecules produced by one sex that serve as agents to elicit mating behaviors in individuals of the opposite sex.

phosphodiester bonds covalent bonds joining one *nucleotide* to another. Phosphodiester bonds between nucleotides form the backbone of DNA.

photomorphogenesis light-regulated developmental program of a plant.

photoperiod day length; period of light exposure for plants.

phylogenetic tree diagram composed of *nodes,* which represent the taxonomic units, and *branches,* which represent the relationship of these units.

physical associations protein or regulatory interactions in a *biological system.*

physical map a map of locations of identifiable landmarks on DNA (for example, restriction enzyme cutting sites, genes). For the human genome, the lowest-resolution physical map is the banding patterns on the 24 different chromosomes; the highest resolution map is the complete *nucleotide* sequence of the *chromosomes.* See *karyotype.*

physical markers cytologically visible abnormalities that make it possible to keep track of specific *chromosome* parts from one generation to the next. Compare *genetic markers.*

pilus hollow protein tube that protrudes from an F^+, *Hfr,* or F' bacterial cell and binds to the cell wall of an F^- cell. Retraction of the pilus into the F^+ cell draws the two cells close together in preparation for gene transfer.

pistil floral structure that consists of fused *carpels,* with pollen receptive *stigma* at the top, and a short neck or style, leading to the ovary.

plaque a clear area on a bacterial *lawn,* devoid of living bacterial cells, containing the genetically identical descendants of a single *bacteriophage.*

plasmids small circles of double-stranded DNA that can replicate in bacterial cells independently of the *bacterial chromosome;* commonly used as *cloning vectors.*

pleiotropy phenomenon in which a single gene determines a number of distinct and seemingly unrelated characteristics.

point mutation a mutation of one base pair.

polar body a cell produced by *meiosis I* or *meiosis II* during oogenesis that does not become the *primary* or *secondary oocyte.*

polarity an overall direction.

polar microtubules microtubules that originate in *centrosomes* and are directed toward the middle of the cell; polar microtubules that arise from

opposite centrosomes interdigitate near the cell's equator and push the spindle poles apart during *anaphase.*

poly-A tail the 3′ end of eukaryotic *mRNA* consisting of 100–200 angstroms, believed to stabilize the mRNA and increase the efficiency of the initial steps of *translation.*

polycistronic mRNA an *mRNA* that contains more than one protein coding region; often the transcriptional product of an *operon* in bacterial cells.

polygenic trait trait controlled by multiple genes. See *continuous trait.*

polymer a linked chain of repeating subunits that form a larger molecule; DNA is a type of polymer.

polymerase chain reaction (PCR) a fast inexpensive method of replicating a DNA sequence once the sequence has been identified; based on a reiterative loop that amplifies the products of each previous round of *replication.*

polymerases, DNA or RNA enzymes that catalyze the synthesis of nucleic acids on preexisting nucleic acid templates, assembling *RNA* from ribonucleotides or *DNA* from deoxyribonucleotides.

polymerization the linkage of subunits to form a multi-unit chain. In DNA *replication,* the polymerization of nucleotides occurs through the formation of *phosphodiester bonds* by DNA polymerase III.

polymorphic a *locus* with two or more distinct *alleles* in a *population.*

polymorphism variant of a gene or non-coding region that has two or more *alleles.* Molecular geneticists use this term to describe a variant of a *locus* within a *population* of organisms that has two or more alleles. Population geneticists reserve the term for variants at a locus where two or more alleles are present at a frequency of 1% or greater; for example, to describe the alternative forms of a gene that has more than one *wild-type* allele.

polypeptides amino acid chains containing hundreds to thousands of *amino acids* joined by *peptide bonds.*

polyploids *euploid* species that carry three or more complete sets of *chromosomes.*

polyproteins *polypeptides* produced by *translation* that can subsequently be cleaved by protease enzymes into two or more separate proteins.

polyribosomes structures formed by the simultaneous *translation* of a single *mRNA* molecule by multiple *ribosomes.*

polytene chromosome giant *chromosome* consisting of many identical *chromatids* lying in parallel register.

population a group of interbreeding individuals of the same species that inhabit the same space at the same time.

population bottleneck occurs when a large proportion of individuals in a population die, often because of environmental disturbances, resulting in survivors who essentially are equivalent to a founder population.

population genetics scientific discipline that studies what happens in whole *populations* at the genetic level.

positional cloning the process that enables researchers to obtain the clone of a gene without any prior knowledge of its protein product or function. It uses genetic and physical maps to locate *mutations* responsible for particular *phenotypes.*

position-effect variegation variable expression of a gene in a population of cells, caused by the gene's location near highly compacted *heterochromatin.*

posttranslational modifications changes such as phosphorylation that occur to a *polypeptide* after *translation* has been completed.

primary oocytes/spermatocytes *germ-line* cells in which *meiosis I* occurs.

primary structure the linear sequence of *amino acids* within a *polypeptide.*

primary transcript the single strand of *RNA* resulting from *transcription.*

primer short, preexisting *oligonucleotide* chain to which new DNA can be added by DNA polymerase.

primer walking a common approach to directed sequencing of DNA in which *primers* are synthesized using the information from each previous round of DNA sequencing.

product rule states that the probability of two or more independent events occurring together is the product of the probabilities that each event will occur by itself.

programmed cell death (PCD) see *apoptosis.*

prokaryotes one of the three major evolutionary lineages of living organisms known as domains; characterized by the lack of a nuclear membrane. Contrast with *eukaryotes.*

prokaryotic gene regulation control of gene expression in a bacterial cell via mechanisms to increase or decrease the *transcription* and *translation* of specific *genes* or groups of genes.

prometaphase the stage of *mitosis* or *meiosis* just after the breakdown of the *nuclear envelope,* when the chromosomes connect to the *spindle apparatus* and begin to move toward the *metaphase plate.*

promoters DNA sequences near the beginning of *genes* that signal *RNA polymerase* where to begin transcription. Compare with *terminators.*

prophage the integrated *phage genome.*

prophase the phase of the *cell cycle* marked by the emergence of the individual *chromosomes* from the undifferentiated mass of *chromatin,* indicating the beginning of *mitosis.*

prophase I the longest, most complex phase of *meiosis* consisting of several substages.

prophase II first phase of *meiosis II;* if the *chromosomes* decondensed during interkinesis, they recondense. At the end of prophase II, the *nuclear envelope* breaks down and the *spindle apparatus* re-forms.

protein domains discrete functional units of a protein, encoded by discrete regions of DNA.

protein kinases enzymes that add phosphate groups to their protein substrates.

protein network set of proteins (and often other molecules such as metabolites) that interact in executing a particular biological function.

proteins large polymers composed of hundreds to thousands of *amino acid* subunits strung together in a specific order into long chains. Proteins are required for the structure, function, and regulation of the body's cells, tissues, and organs.

proteome the complete set of *proteins* encoded by a *genome.*

proteomics global analysis of most (or ideally, all) the *proteins* in a particular cell type or organism.

proteosome large multiprotein complex in the cytoplasm of eukaryotic cells that contains proteolytic enzymes that degrade proteins tagged with *ubiquitin.*

proto-oncogene a *gene* that can mutate into an *oncogene*—an *allele* that causes a cell to become cancerous.

prototroph a microorganism (usually wild type) that can grow on minimal medium in the absence of one or more growth factors. Compare with *auxotroph.*

pseudodominance expression of a *phenotype* caused by a *recessive allele* in a deletion heterozygote because the other homolog has no copy of that gene.

pseudogene a nonfunctioning gene. The result of *duplication* and divergence events in which one copy of an originally functioning *gene* has undergone *mutations* such that it no longer has an intact *polypeptide* coding sequence.

pseudolinkage characteristic of a heterozygote for a *reciprocal translocation,* in which genes located near the translocation breakpoint behave as if they are linked even though they originated on nonhomologous chromosomes.

pulse-field gel electrophoresis a special type of electrophoretic protocol that allows an extreme extension of the normal separating capacity of the gels. In this protocol, the DNA sample is subjected to pulses of electrical current that alternate between two directions. The range of sizes separated in this manner is a function of pulse length. Compare *electrophoresis.*

punctuated equilibrium the tendency of evolution to proceed through long periods of stasis (lack of change) followed by short periods of explosive change.

pure-breeding lines families of organisms that produce offspring with specific parental traits that remain constant from generation to generation.

p value numerical probability that a particular set of observed experimental results represents a chance deviation from the values predicted by a particular hypothesis.

Q

quantitative trait See *continuous trait.*

quantitative trait loci (QTLs) loci that control the expression of *continuous traits.*

quaternary structure structure made up of the three-dimensional configuration of subunits in a *multimeric protein.*

R

radial loop-scaffold model the model of looping and gathering of DNA by nonhistone proteins that results in high compaction of *chromosomes* at *mitosis.*

random amplification of polymorphic DNA (RAPD) a protocol designed to detect single-base changes at *polymorphic* loci throughout a *genome.*

random walk description of movement of bacteria to achieve chemotaxis reflecting nonpredictable changes in the direction of movement. Contrast *biased random walk.*

reading frame the partitioning of groups of three *nucleotides* from a fixed starting point such that the sequential interpretation of each succeeding triplet generates the correct order of *amino acids* in the resulting *polypeptide chain.*

rearrangements events in which the *genome* is reshaped by the reorganization of *DNA sequences* within one or more *chromosomes.*

receptors proteins embedded in the membrane of a cell that bind to *growth factors* and other *ligands,* initiating a *signal transduction pathway* in the cell.

recessive allele an *allele* whose *phenotype* is not expressed in a heterozygote. See *dominant allele.*

recessive epistasis special case of *epistasis,* in which the *allele* causing the epistasis is *recessive.* Compare with *dominant epistasis.*

recessive lethal allele an *allele* that prevents the birth or survival of *homozygotes,* though *heterozygotes* carrying the allele survive.

recessive trait the trait that remains hidden in the F_1 hybrids (*heterozygotes*) resulting from a mating between purebreeding parental strains showing antagonistic *phenotypes;* the recessive trait usually reappears in the *second filial* (F_2) generation.

recipient during gene transfer in bacteria, the cell that receives the genetic material. See *donor, transformation, conjugation,* and *transduction.*

reciprocal crosses *crosses* in which the traits in the males and females are reversed, thereby controlling whether a particular trait is transmitted by the egg or the pollen.

reciprocal translocation results when two breaks, one in each of two *chromosomes,* yield DNA fragments that do not re-ligate to their chromosome of origin; rather, they switch places and become attached to the other chromosome. Compare with *translocation.*

recombinant classes reshuffled combinations of *alleles* that were not present in the *parental generation.*

recombinant DNA molecules a combination of DNA molecules of different origin that are joined using *recombinant DNA technologies.*

recombinants *chromosomes* that carry a mix of *alleles* derived from different *homologous chromosomes.*

recombinant types *phenotypes* reflecting a new combination of genes that occurs during gamete formation.

recombination the process by which offspring derive a combination of genes different from that of either parent; the generation of new allelic combinations. In higher organisms, this can occur by *crossing-over.*

recombination frequency (RF) the percentage of *recombinant* progeny; can be used as an indication of the physical distance separating any two genes on a chromosome. See *centimorgan.*

recombination nodules structures that appear during *pachytene* of *prophase I.* An exchange of parts between non-sister *chromatids* occurs at recombination nodules.

reduction(al) division cell division that reduces the number of *chromosomes,* usually by segregating *homologous chromosomes* to two daughter cells. *Meiosis I* is a reductional division.

regulative determination where the embryo is a collection of cells that can alter, or "regulate," their fates according to the environment, for example, to make up for missing cells. Contrast with *mosaic determination.*

regulon a group of *genes* that are regulated by a common signal and regulator.

release factors *proteins* that recognize *stop codons* and help end translation.

remodeling complex a complex of proteins that remove promoter-blocking nucleosomes or reposition them in relation to the gene, helping to prepare a gene for transcriptional activation.

replication see *DNA replication.*

replication bubble unwound area of the original DNA *double helix* during *replication.*

replication fork Y-shaped area consisting of the two unwound DNA strands branching out into unpaired (but complementary) single strands during *replication.*

replicon (replication unit) the DNA running both ways from one *origin of replication* to the endpoints where it merges with DNA from adjoining *replication forks.*

reporter gene a protein-coding gene incorporated into a recombinant DNA molecule along with putative DNA regulatory elements. After transformation of cells, the reporter gene "reports" the activity of the putative regulatory elements to molecular biologists.

repressor a type of *transcription factor* that can bind to specific *cis*-acting elements such as *operator sites* and thereby diminish or prevent *transcription.*

reproductive cloning creation of a cloned embryo by insertion of the nucleus of a *somatic cell* from one individual into an egg cell whose nucleus has been removed. The hybrid egg is stimulated to begin embryonic cell divisions, and the resulting cloned embryo is transplanted into the uterus of a foster mother and allowed to develop to term. Contrast with *therapeutic cloning.*

reproductive development period in plant development that produces flower and seed. Contrast *vegetative development.*

response to selection (R) the amount of evolution, or change in mean trait value, resulting from *selection.* Compare with *selection differential.*

restriction the bacterial capacity for limiting viral growth.

restriction enzymes proteins made by bacteria that recognize specific, short *nucleotide* sequences and cut DNA at those sites.

restriction fragment length polymorphism (RFLP) variation between individuals in DNA fragment size cut by specific *restriction enzymes; polymorphic* sequences that result in RFLPs are used as markers on both *physical maps* and *genetic linkage* maps.

restriction fragments DNA fragments generated by the action of *restriction enzymes.*

restriction map a linear diagram that illustrates the positions of *restriction enzyme* recognition sites along a DNA molecule.

restrictive condition an environmental condition that prevents the survival of an individual with a *conditional lethal* allele. Contrast with *permissive condition.*

retroposons genetic elements that transpose via *reverse transcription* of an RNA intermediate. One class of *transposable elements.* Contrast with *transposons.*

retroviruses viruses that hold their genetic information in a single strand of *RNA* and carry the enzyme *reverse transcriptase* to convert that RNA into DNA within a host cell.

reverse mutation a mutation that causes a novel mutant to revert back to wild type.

reverse transcriptase an RNA-dependent DNA *polymerase* that synthesizes DNA strands complementary to an RNA *template.* The product of reverse transcriptase is a *cDNA* molecule.

reverse transcription the process by which *reverse transcriptase* synthesizes DNA strands complementary to an RNA *template*. The product of reverse transcription is a cDNA molecule.

reversion See *reverse mutation.*

ribonucleic acid (RNA) a *polymer* of ribonucleotides found in the nucleus and cytoplasm of cells; it plays an important role in protein synthesis. There are several classes of RNA molecules, including *messenger RNA (mRNA), transfer RNA (tRNA),* ribosomal RNA (rRNA), and other small RNAs, each serving a different purpose.

ribosomal RNAs (rRNAs) *RNA* components of *ribosomes,* which are composed of both rRNAs and proteins.

ribosome binding sites regions on *prokaryotic mRNAs* containing both an *initiation codon* and a *Shine-Dalgarno box; ribosomes* bind to these sites to start *translation.*

ribosomes cytoplasmic structures composed of *ribosomal RNA* (rRNA) and protein; the sites of protein synthesis.

ribozymes RNA molecules that can act as enzymes to catalyze specific chemical reactions.

RISC See *RNA-induced silencing complex.*

RNA See *ribonucleic acid.*

RNA-dependent DNA polymerase See *reverse transcriptase.*

RNA editing specific alteration of the genetic sequence carried within an *RNA* molecule after *transcription* is completed.

RNA-induced silencing complex (RISC) a large enzymatic complex in the cytoplasm of all eukaryotic cells that binds to an *miRNA* and performs sequence-specific *RNA interference.*

RNA interference (RNAi) the sequence-specific modulation of eukaryotic gene expression by a 21–24 nucleotide-long RNA molecule referred to as *micro-RNA* if it is encoded within the genome and *short-interfering RNA* if it is introduced into the cell by scientists or infectious agents. These small, specialized RNAs prevent the expression of specific genes through complementary base pairing. In the most common

natural form of RNAi, primary miRNA-containing transcripts are processed sequentially with the enzymes *Drosha* and *Dicer* to produce a mature miRNA that is loaded onto an *RNA-induced silencing complex (RISC).* The RISC complex binds to complementary mRNA targets, causing mRNA degradation or reduced translational activity.

RNA-like strand strand of a double-helical DNA molecule that has the same nucleotide sequence as an *mRNA* (except for the substitution of T for U) and that is complementary to the *template strand.*

RNA polymerases enzymes that transcribe a DNA sequence into an RNA transcript. *Eukaryotes* have three types of RNA polymerases called pol I, pol II, and pol III that are responsible for transcribing different classes of genes.

RNA splicing a process that deletes *introns* and joins together adjacent *exons* to form a mature *mRNA* consisting of only exons.

RNA world hypothetical primordial world in which RNA became the first replicator.

Robertsonian translocation *translocation* arising from breaks at or near the *centromeres* of two *acrocentric chromosomes.* The reciprocal exchange of broken parts generates one large *metacentric* chromosome and one very small chromosome.

S

satellite DNAs blocks of repetitive, simple noncoding sequences, usually around *centromeres;* these blocks have a different *chromatin* structure and different higher-order packaging than other chromosomal regions.

saturation mutagenesis an attempt to isolate *mutations* in all of the *genes* that direct a particular biological process.

scaffold-associated regions (SARs) special, irregularly spaced repetitive base sequences of DNA that associate with nonhistone proteins to define chromatin loops. SARs are most likely the sites at which DNA is anchored to the condensation scaffold.

secondary oocytes/spermatocytes *germ-line* cells in which meiosis II occurs.

secondary structure localized region of a *polypeptide* chain with a characteristic geometry, such as an α-helix or β-pleated sheet.

second-division segregation pattern a *tetrad* in which the arrangement of *ascospores* indicates that the two *alleles* of a gene segregated from each other in the second meiotic division.

second filial (F_2) generation progeny resulting from self-crosses or inter-crosses between individuals of the F_1 generation in a series of controlled matings.

sectors portions of a growing *colony* of microorganisms that have a different *genotype* than the remainder of the colony.

segmentation gene in *Drosophila,* a large group of genes responsible for subdividing the body into an array of body segments.

segregation equal separation of alleles for each trait during *gamete* formation, in which one *allele* of each *gene* goes to each gamete.

selectable markers *vector* genes that make it possible to pick out cells harboring a *recombinant DNA molecule* constructed with that vector.

selection a process that establishes conditions in which only the desired mutant will grow.

selection differential (S) measure of the strength of selection on a trait. Compare *response to selection.*

self-fertilization (selfing) fertilization in which both egg and pollen come from the same plant.

semiconservative replication a pattern of double helix duplication in which *complementary base pairing* followed by the linkage of successive nucleotides yields two daughter double helixes that each contain one of the original DNA strands intact (conserved) and one completely new strand.

semisterility a condition in which the capacity of generating viable offspring is diminished by at least 50%.

sense describes a laboratory-designed single-strand RNA molecule, or portion of an RNA molecule, with a sequence equivalent to that present in a cellular mRNA. A laboratory-designed *short interfering RNA (siRNA)* mediator of RNA interference will contain both sense and *antisense* components.

sepals green leaflike structure composing the first *whorl* of a flower.

sequence tagged sites (STSs) one-of-a-kind markers that tag positions along the DNA molecule.

sequencing determining the order of *nucleotides* (base sequences) in a *DNA* or *RNA* molecule or the order of *amino acids* in a *protein.*

serial analysis of gene expression (SAGE) sequencing technique for determining the quantities of different RNAs in a mixture.

sex chromosomes the X and Y *chromosomes* in human beings, which determine the sex of an individual. Compare with *autosome.*

sex-influenced traits traits that can show up in both sexes but are expressed differently in each sex due to hormonal differences.

sex-limited traits traits that affect a structure or process that is found in one sex but not the other.

Shine-Dalgarno box a sequence of six nucleotides in *mRNA* that is one of two elements comprising a *ribosome binding site* (the other element is the *initiation codon*).

short-interfering RNA (siRNA) an RNA molecule 21–24 bases in length that originates outside an organism and can co-opt the natural *RNAi* machinery to effect *RNA interference.*

shotgun sequencing approach in which the overlapping insert fragments to be sequenced have been randomly generated in one of three ways: from large insert clones known as BACs; from the shearing with sound of the whole *genome;* or from partial digestion of the whole genome with *restriction enzymes.*

signal transducers cytoplasmic proteins that relay signals inside the cell.

signal transduction the activation and inhibition of intracellular targets after binding of *growth factors* or other *ligands* to *receptors.*

signal transduction pathway form of molecular communication in which the binding of proteins to receptors on cell surfaces constitutes a signal that is converted through a series of intermediate steps to a final intracellular regulatory response, usually the activation or repression of *transcription* in target genes.

silent mutations *mutations* without effects on *phenotype;* usually denotes *point mutations* that change one of the three bases in a *codon* but that do not change the identity of the specified *amino acid* because of the *degeneracy* of the *genetic code.*

simple sequence repeat (SSR) two- or three-base-long SNP.

SINE short *i*nterspersed *e*lements; one of the two major classes of *transposable elements* in mammals. Contrast with *LINE.*

single nucleotide polymorphism (SNP) a single *nucleotide* locus with two naturally existing *alleles* defined by a single base pair *substitution.* SNP loci are useful as DNA-based *markers* for formal genetic analysis.

sister chromatids the two identical copies of a chromosome that exist immediately after DNA replication. Sister chromatids are held together by protein complexes called *cohesins.*

SNP see *single nucleotide polymorphism.*

somatic cells any cell in an organism except *gametes* and their precursors. Compare with *germ cells.*

somatic gene therapy remedial measures in which a replacement *gene* is inserted into affected tissue to compensate for a faulty gene.

SOS system an emergency repair system in bacteria that relies on error-prone ("sloppy") DNA *polymerases;* these special SOS polymerases allow cells with damaged DNA to divide, but the daughter cells carry many new mutations.

Southern blot protocol for transferring DNA sequences separated by *gel electrophoresis* onto a nitrocellulose filter paper for analysis by *hybridization* with a *DNA probe.* Compare *Northern blot analysis.*

specialized transduction *bacteriophage*-mediated transfer of a few

bacterial genes located next to the bacteriophage DNA in the bacterial chromosome.

specialized transducing phages *bacteriophage* carrying mainly phage DNA but also one or a few of the bacterial genes that lie near the site of *prophage* insertion. They can transfer these genes to another bacterium in the process known as *specialized transduction.*

sperm a *haploid* male *gamete* produced by *meiosis.*

spermatids *haploid* cells produced at the end of *meiosis* that will mature into *sperm.*

spermatogenesis the production of *sperm.*

spermatogonia *diploid* germ cells in the testes.

S phase stage of the *cell cycle* during which *chromosome replication* occurs.

spindle apparatus microtubule-based structure responsible for *chromosome* movements and *segregation* during cell division.

splice acceptors *nucleotide* sequences in a *primary transcript* at the border between an *intron* and the downstream *exon* that follows it; required for proper *RNA splicing.*

splice donors *nucleotide* sequences in a *primary transcript* at the border between an *intron* and the upstream *exon* that precedes it; required for proper *RNA splicing.*

spliceosome a complicated intranuclear machine that ensures that all of the splicing reactions take place in concert.

stamen structure comprising the third *whorl* of a flower that bears the male *gametes* in the form of pollen.

stem cells relatively undifferentiated cells that undergo asymmetric mitotic divisions. One of the daughter cells produced by such a division is another stem cell, while the other daughter cell can differentiate. In this way, stem cells are self-renewing but can also give rise to differentiated cells.

sticky end the result achieved after digestion by many *restriction enzymes* that break the *phosphodiester bonds* on the two strands of a double helix DNA molecule at slightly different locations. The resulting double-stranded DNA molecule has a single protruding strand at each end that is usually one to four bases in length.

stigma pollen-receptive structure at the top of the *pistil* of a flower.

stop codons see *nonsense codons.*

substitution occurs when a base at a certain position in one strand of the DNA molecule is replaced by one of the other three bases.

substrate the target of an enzyme, usually cellular proteins.

subunit a single *polypeptide* that is a constituent of a *multimeric protein.*

sum rule the probability that any of two or more mutually exclusive events will occur is the sum of their individual probabilities.

supercoiling additional twisting of the DNA molecule caused by movement of the *replication fork* during unwinding. Refer to *DNA topoisomerases.*

suppressor mutations *mutations* that alleviate the phenotypic abnormality caused by another mutation. The two mutations can be in the same gene (see *intragenic suppression*), or the suppressor mutation can be in a second, *modifier gene.*

suspensor in plants, a structure analogous to the umbilical cord in mammals.

synapsis process during which *homologous chromosomes* become aligned and zipped together; occurs during *zygotene* of *prophase I.*

synaptonemal complex structure that helps align *homologous chromosomes* during *prophase* of *meiosis I.*

syncytial blastoderm in *Drosophila* embryos, formed when most of the nuclei migrate out to the cortex just under the surface of the embryo.

syncytium an animal cell with two or more nuclei.

syntenic relationship of two or more *loci* found to be located on the same chromosome. Compare with *conserved synteny* and *syntenic segments.*

syntenic blocks blocks of *linked loci* within a *genome.*

syntenic segments in the comparison of two *genomes,* large blocks of DNA sequences in which the identity, order, and transcriptional direction of the *genes* are almost exactly the same.

synthetic lethality when an individual carrying mutations in two different genes dies, even though individuals carrying either mutation alone survive.

systems biology definition of all (or as many as possible) of the components of a *biological system* followed by an attempt to understand how they interact among themselves and with the components of other systems.

T

TAFs *T*BP-*a*ssociated *f*actors; one type of basal factor.

tandem duplications repeats of a chromosomal region that lie adjacent to each other, either in the same order or in reverse order. Contrast with *nontandem duplications.*

TBP *T*ATA *b*ox–binding *p*rotein; key basal factor that assists the binding of RNA polymerase II to the promoter and the initiation of basal levels of *transcription.*

telomerase an enzyme critical to the successful replication of *telomeres* at *chromosome* ends.

telomeres specialized terminal structures on eukaryotic *chromosomes* that ensure the maintenance and accurate replication of the two ends of each linear chromosome.

telophase the final stage of *mitosis* in which the daughter *chromosomes* reach the opposite poles of the cell and reform nuclei.

telophase I phase of *meiosis I* when nuclear membranes form around the *chromosomes* that have moved to the poles; each incipient daughter nucleus contains one-half the number of chromosomes in the original parent cell nucleus, but each of these chromosomes consists of two *sister chromatids* held together by *cohesin* protein complexes.

telophase II final phase of *meiosis II* during which membranes form around each of the four daughter nuclei, and *cytokinesis* places each nucleus in a separate cell.

temperate bacteriophages after infecting the host, these *phages* can enter either the *lytic cycle* or the alternative *lysogenic cycle,* during which their DNA integrates into the host *genome.* Compare with *virulent bacteriophages.*

template a strand of *DNA* or *RNA* that is used as a model by DNA or RNA *polymerase* or by *reverse transcriptase* for the creation of a new complementary strand of DNA or RNA.

template strand the strand of the double helix that is complementary to both the RNA-like *DNA* strand and the *mRNA.*

10-fold sequence coverage the sequencing of every chromosomal region from 10 independently cloned inserts results in 10-fold sequence coverage.

teratype (T) a *tetrad* carrying four kinds of *haploid* cells; two different *parental class* spores and two different recombinants.

terminalization shifting of the *chiasmata* from their original position at the *centromere* toward the *chromosome* end or *telomere.*

termination phase of *translation* that brings *polypeptide* synthesis to a halt.

terminators sequences in the *RNA* products that tell RNA *polymerase* where to stop *transcription.* Compare with *promoters.*

tertiary structure ultimate three-dimensional shape of a *polypeptide.*

testcross a *cross* used to determine the *genotype* of an individual showing a *dominant phenotype* by mating with an individual showing the *recessive phenotype.*

tetrad (1) in some fungi, the assemblage of four *ascospores* (resulting from *meiosis*) in a single *ascus.* (2) a pair of synapsed homologous *chromosomes* during *prophase* of *meiosis I,* also known as a *bivalent.*

tetrad analysis the use of *tetrads* to study gene *linkage* and *recombination* during *meiosis* in fungi.

tetraploid describes cells or organisms with four complete sets of chromosomes. See *haploid, diploid,* and *triploid.*

tetrasomic otherwise *diploid* organism with four copies of a particular *chromosome.*

tetratype (T) a fungal *ascus* that carries four kinds of spores, or haploid cells: two different *parental types* and two different *recombinant types*.

therapeutic cloning creation of an embryo by the method described for *reproductive cloning,* with the exception that the embryo is not allowed to develop to term. Instead it is cultured in a Petri plate to the *blastocyst* stage, at which point the *embryonic stem (ES) cells* are collected and placed in culture. The cultured ES cells can be induced to differentiate into many kinds of cells that might be of therapeutic value.

thymine a nitrogenous base; one member of the base pair A–T (adenine–thymine).

tolerance ability to prevent the body from making *immune responses* to its own proteins.

torpedo stage embryo stage of embryonic development in plants where two protuberances expand and differentiate into two well-defined, discrete cotyledons.

total phenotype variance (V_P) population deviation calculated as the sum of the *genetic variance* and the *environmental variance.*

totipotent description of cell state during early embryonic development in which the cells have not yet differentiated and retain the ability to produce every type of cell found in the developing embryo and adult animal.

*trans***-acting element** a gene that codes for a *transcription factor.*

transcript the product of *transcription.*

transcription the conversion of *DNA*-encoded information to its *RNA*-encoded equivalent.

transcriptional silencing hypercondensation of *chromatin* domains makes it impossible to activate genes within those domains, no matter what *transcription factors* are active in the cell.

transcription bubble the region of DNA unwound by RNA *polymerase.*

transcription factor protein (or RNA) whose binding to or indirect association with a cis-*control element* helps regulate the timing, location, and level of a particular gene's *transcription.* Functional categories include

activators, repressors, coactivators, and *corepressors.*

transcriptome the population of *mRNAs* expressed in a single cell or cell type.

transductants cells resulting from gene transfer mediated by *bacteriophages.*

transduction one of the mechanisms by which bacteria transfer genes from one strain to another; *donor* DNA is packaged within the protein coat of a *bacteriophage* and transferred to the recipient when the phage particle infects it. Recipient cells are known as *transductants.*

transfection transformation of mammalian cells via the uptake of DNA from the medium.

transfer RNA (tRNA) small RNA adaptor molecules that place specific *amino acids* at the correct position in a growing *polypeptide* chain.

transformants cells that have received naked *donor* DNA.

transformation one of the mechanisms by which bacteria transfer genes from one strain to another; occurs when DNA from a *donor* is added to the bacterial growth medium and is then taken up from the medium by the recipient. The recipient cell is known as a *transformant.* Contrast with *conjugation.*

transgene any piece of foreign *DNA* that researchers have inserted into the *genome* of an organism.

transgenic any individual carrying a *transgene.*

transgenic technology the tools for inducing a specific change in a gene and confirming that this change causes the predicted *phenotype.* Transgenic technology includes experimental methods that allow scientists to add laboratory-constructed *DNA sequences* to the *genomes* of animals or plants.

transient- (or triangular-) stage embryo stage following *globular stage* in plant development; embryo becomes self-sufficient for growth, having used up most of its maternally deposited reserves.

transition a type of *substitution* mutation that occurs when one purine (A or G) replaces the other purine, or one pyrimidine (C or T) replaces the other pyrimidine. Contrast with *transversions.*

translation the process in which the *codons* carried by *mRNA* direct the synthesis of *polypeptides* from *amino acids* according to the *genetic code.* Compare with *transcription.*

translocation a rearrangement that occurs when parts of two nonhomologous *chromosomes* change places. Compare with *reciprocal translocation.*

translocation Down syndrome occurs in individuals affected by Down syndrome who have inherited three copies of a part (rather than all) of chromosome 21 because one of their parents was *heterozygous* for a *translocation* involving chromosome 21.

*trans***-splicing** a rare type of *RNA splicing* that joins together *exons* of the *primary transcripts* of two different genes.

transposable elements (TEs) all DNA segments that move about in the *genome,* regardless of mechanism.

transposition the movement of *transposable elements* from one position in the *genome* to another.

transposons units of DNA that move from place to place within the *genome* without an RNA intermediate, sometimes causing a change in gene function when they insert themselves in a new chromosomal location.

transversions a type of *substitution* mutation that occurs when a purine (A or G) replaces a pyrimidine (C or T) or when a pyrimidine replaces a purine.

triploid describes cells or organisms with three complete sets of *chromosomes.* See *haploid, diploid,* and *tetraploid.*

trisomic individual having one extra *chromosome* in addition to the normal *diploid* set of the species.

truncated proteins *polypeptides* with fewer amino acids than normal encoded by genes containing *nonsense mutations.*

twin spots adjacent patches of tissue that are phenotypically distinct from each other and from the surrounding tissue; can be produced as a result of mitotic recombination.

2n number of *chromosomes* in a normal *diploid* cell.

U

ubiquitin highly conserved protein whose covalent attachment to other proteins marks them for degradation by the *proteosome.*

unequal crossing-over change in DNA caused by erroneous *recombination* in which one *homologous chromosome* ends up with a *duplication,* while the other homolog sustains a *deletion.*

uniparental inheritance transmission of organelle genes via one parent. Most species transmit mitochondrial DNA and chloroplast DNA through the mother. (See *biparental inheritance.*)

unordered tetrads *tetrads* in yeast in which the four *ascospores* are randomly arranged in the *ascus.*

5′- and 3′-untranslated regions (UTRs) these sequences are located just after the methylated cap and just before the poly-A tail, respectively.

upstream movement opposite the direction *RNA* follows when moving along a gene. Compare with *downstream.*

uracil a nitrogenous base normally found in *RNA* but not in *DNA;* uracil is capable of forming a *base pair* with adenine.

V

vaccination inoculation with a nonvirulent or virulent but attenuated infectious agent that stimulates a protective *immune response.*

variance statistical measurement of deviation from the mean (middle); typically expressed in plus or minus terms referring to the relationship to the mean.

variolation injection with live smallpox virus obtained from a patient with a mild case of smallpox.

vector a specialized DNA sequence that can enter a living cell, signal its presence to an investigator by conferring a detectable property on the host cell, and provide a means of replication for itself and the foreign DNA inserted into it. A vector must also possess distinguishing physical traits by which it can be purified away from the host cell's *genome.* See *cloning vector.*

vegetative development in plants, the period of growth before flowering. Contrast with *reproductive development.*

vernalization the process of exposing plants to cold early in vegetative development to promote earlier flowering.

virulent bacteriophages after infecting the host, these phages always enter the *lytic cycle,* multiply rapidly, and kill the host. Compare with *temperate bacteriophages.*

virus a noncellular biological entity that can reproduce only within a host cell. Viruses consist of nucleic acid covered by protein. Inside an infected cell, the virus uses the synthetic capability of the host to produce progeny virus.

W

whorls in the structure of a flower, the concentric regions of modified leaves including *sepals, petals, stamens,* and *carpels.*

wild-type allele (1) an *allele,* or DNA variant, whose frequency is more than 1% in a *population;* (2) an allele that dictates the most frequently observed phenotype in a population. Wild-type alleles are often designated by a superscript "plus" sign ($^+$).

wobble ability of the 5′-most nucleotide of an anticodon to interact with more than one nucleotide at the 3′-end of codons; helps explain the *degeneracy* of the *genetic code.*

X

x indicates the number of chromosomes in a complete set of nonhomologous chromosomes.

X chromosome inactivation in mammals, a mechanism of *dosage compensation* in which all X *chromosomes* in a cellular genome but one are inactivated at an early stage of development through the formation of heterochromatic *Barr bodies.*

X chromosome reactivation in mammals, a mechanism by which X *chromosomes* that were inactivated become reactivated in *oogonia* so that the *haploid* cells in the *germ line* all have an active X chromosome.

X-linked carried by the X *chromosome.*

Y

YAC See *yeast artificial chromosome.*

yeast artificial chromosome (YAC) a vector used to clone DNA fragments up to 400 kb in length; it is constructed from *telomeric, centromeric,* and *origin-of-replication* sequences needed for replication in yeast cells. Compare with *cloning vector, cosmid.*

Z

Z-form DNA DNA in which the *nucleotide sequences* cause the structure to assume a zigzag shape due to the helixes spiraling to the left. Compare with *B-form DNA.* The significance of this variation on DNA structure is unknown at this time.

zygote the *diploid* cell formed by the fertilization of the egg by the *sperm* during sexual reproduction.

zygotene substage of *prophase I* when *homologous chromosomes* become zipped together in *synapsis.*

Credits

Chapter 1

Opener: © James Strachan/Stone/Getty Images; **1.1(a):** © David M. Phillips/Visuals Unlimited; **1.1(b):** © Vol. 44/Photo Disc/Getty Images RF; **1.1(c):** © Corbis RF; **1.1(d):** GenomeSystems Inc./Photo provided by Kearns Communication Group; **1.1(e):** © Vol. 24/PhotoDisc RF; **1.3:** © Applied Biosystems/Peter Arnold, Inc./Photolibrary.com; **1.4:** © Biophoto Associates/Photo Researchers, Inc.; **1.9a:** © Carolina Biological/Photo Researchers, Inc.; **1.9b:** © Vol. OS02/PhotoDisc RF; **Table 1.1a:** © J. William Schopf, UCLA. Reprinted with permission from *Science* 260: 640–646, 1993. "Microfossils of the Early Archean Apex Chert: New Evidence of the Antiquity of Life." © 1993 American Association for the Advancement of Science; **Table 1.1c-d:** Prof. Andrew Knoll; **Table 1.1e:** © Brand X Pictures/PunchStock; **Table 1.1f:** © Alan Sirulnikoff/Photo Researchers, Inc.; **1.11a-b:** © Edward Lewis, California Institute of Technology; **1.12(1):** © David M. Phillips/Visuals Unlimited; **1.12(2):** Lee Hartwell; **1.12(3):** © Sinclair Stammers/SPL/Photo Researchers, Inc.; **1.12(4):** Courtesy Debra Nero/Cornell University; **1.12(5):** © Myung Shin/Bergman Collection.

Chapter 2

Opener: © Lawrence Manning/Corbis RF; **2.1:** © Bruce Aryes/Stone/Getty Images; **2.2:** © Science Photo Library/Photo Researchers, Inc.; **2.3:** © Saudjie Cross Siino/Weathertop Labradors; **2.4:** © The Metropolitan Museum of Art, Gift of John D. Rockefeller, Jr., 1932 (32.143.2), **Photograph** © 1996 The Metropolitan Museum of Art; **2.5a:** © Malcolm Gutter/Visuals Unlimited; **2.5b:** James King-Holmes/Photo Researchers, Inc.; **2.6:** © Klaus Gulbrandsen/SPL/Photo Researchers, Inc.; **2.7a:** © Dwight Kuhn Photography; **Page 20:** Reprinted from Bhattacharyya MK, et al. Cell. 1990 Jan 12: 60(1):115–22, with permission from Elsevier; **2.19a:** © Science Photo Library/Photo Researchers, Inc.; **2.19b-d:** © Mendelianum Institute, Moravian Museum.

Chapter 3

Opener: © Vol. 8/PhotoDisc/Getty Images RF; **3.1:** © Jerry Marshall; **3.3a:** © John D. Cunningham/Visuals Unlimited; **3.7a (left):** © McGraw-Hill Higher Education Group, Inc./Jill Birschbach, Photographer; Arranged by Alexandra Dove, McArdle Laboratory, Universiity of Wisconsin-Madison; **3.7a (right & bottom):** © Charles River Laboratories; **3.10a:** © Stanley Flegler/Visuals Unlimited; **3.12a:** © William H. Allen, Jr./Allen Stock Photography; **3.19a:** © Radu Sigheti/Reuters/Landov; **3.20a:** © Renee Lynn/Photo Researchers, Inc.; **3.21a:** © Rudi Von Briel/Photo Edit.

Chapter 4

Opener: © Adrian T. Sumner/Stone/Getty Images; **4.1:** © Richard Hutchings/Photo Researchers, Inc.; **4.4:** © Scott Camazine/Photo Researchers, Inc.; **4.5:** © L. West/Photo Researchers, Inc.; **4.6a:** © Biophoto Association/Photo Researchers, Inc.; **4.8a-f:** Photographs by Dr. Conly L. Rieder, Division of Molecular Medicine, Wadsworth Center, NYS Dept. Of Health, Albany, NY; **4.9a:** © David M. Phillip/Visuals Unlimited; **4.9b:** © R. Calentine/Visuals Unlimited; **4.10:** © Dr. Byron Williams/Cornell University; **Page 91 Figure A-B:** © Dr. Michael Goldberg/Cornell University; **4.15:** © Dr. Leona Chemnick, Dr. Oliver Ryder/San Diego Zoo, Center for Reproduction of Endangered Species; **4.21 (both):** Color deficit simulation courtesy of Vischeck (www.vischeck.com). Source image courtesy of NASA; **4.23a:** © Bettmann/Corbis; **4.23b:** © The Corcoran Gallery of Art/Corbis.

Chapter 5

Opener: © Rudy Von Briel/Photo Edit; **5.14a:** © J. Forsdyke, Gene Cox/SPL/Photo Researchers, Inc.; **5.14a(2):** © & Courtesy of Dr. Aaron Neiman, Stony Brook University; **5.14b:** © James W. Richardson/Visuals Unlimited; **5.19:** © Dr. Eric Alani/Cornell University; **5.25:** Image courtesy of B.A. Montelone, Ph.D. and T.R. Manney, Ph.D.

Chapter 6

Opener: © Stone Imaging/Stone/Getty Images RF; **6.1a:** © George Bernard/Animals Animals; **6.1b:** © William Hauswirth; **6.1c:** © Archivo Iconografico, S.A./Corbis; **6.3:** Used with permission from: Arnold et al; New Associations With Pseudomonas Luteola Bacteremia: A Veteran With A History Of Tick Bites And A Trauma Patient With Pneumonia. *The Internet Journal of Infectious Diseases* 2005: Volume 4 Number 2. © & Courtesy of Dr. Forest Arnold, University of Louisville; **6.5b:** © PHANIE/Photo Researchers, Inc.; **6.8:** © Science Source/Photo Researchers, Inc.; **6.11a:** © A. Barrington Brown/Science Source/Photo Researchers, Inc.; **6.13a:** © Biophoto Assoicates/Science Source/Photo Researchers, Inc.; **6.13b:** © Microworks/Dan/Phototake.com; **6.13c:** © Ross Inman & Maria Schnös, University of Wisconsin, Madison, WI; **6.13d:** © Jack D. Griffith/University of North Carolina Lineberger Comprehensive Cancer Center; **6.14b:** © Dr. Tim Evans/Photo Researchers, Inc.

Chapter 7

Opener: © Milkie Studio, Inc.; **7.1:** © Dr. Don Fawcett/J.R. Paulson & U.K. Laemmli/Photo Researchers, Inc.; **7.3 (both):** © Charles River Laboratories; **Page 208 Figure A:** © Science VU/Visuals Unlimited; **7.15:** © Dr. Ken Greer/Visuals Unlimited; **7.17 (all):** © Carolina Biological/Photo Researchers, Inc.; **7.20a.1:** © The Bergman Collection; **7.20a.3:** © Bruce Iverson; **7.20b.1:** © Seymour Benzer; **7.30:** Color deficit simulation courtesy of Vischeck (www.vischeck.com). Source image courtesy of NASA.

Chapter 8

8.1: © Sinclair Stammers/SPL/Photo Researchers, Inc.; **8.11b.2:** © Professor Oscar Miller/SPL/Photo Researchers, Inc.; **8.17b:** © Dr. Thomas Maniatis, Thomas H. Lee Professor of Molecular and Cellular Biology, Harvard University; **8.24:** Cech TR. *Science* 11 August 2000: Vol. 289. no. 5481, pp. 878–879; **8.31a:** Courtesy of & © Dr. Karen Artzt/Artzt Lab/The University of Texas at Austin; **8.31c:** © Tom Vasicek; **8.31d1:** © Science VU/Dr. F.R. Turner/Visuals Unlimited; **8.31d2:** © Eye of Science/Photo Researchers, Inc.

Chapter 9

Opener: © Cytographics/Visuals Unlimited; **9.1a:** © Stanley Flegler/Visuals Unlimited; **9.4b (both):** © Lee Silver, Princeton University; **9.10a:** © Hank Morgan/Photo Researchers, Inc.; **9.11 (all):** © Lee Silver, Princeton University; **9.14b:** © Jean Claude Revy/Phototake.com; **9.15b** © 2010 Illumina, Inc. All Rights Reserved. **9.20a.3:** © Omikron/Science Source/Photo Researchers, Inc; **9.20b.3:** © Professor Sir David Weatherall, University of Oxford.

Chapter 10

10.2a: © Lee Silver, Princeton University; **10.3:** Section of Cancer Genomic Genetics Branch/CCR/NCI/NIH; **10.4b:** © Dr. Gopal Murti/SPL/Photo Researchers, Inc.; **10.17b:** Image courtesy Patrick O. Brown and Joe Derisi; **10.21a:** © Phototake.com; **10.24a-b:** Courtesy of & © Dr. Mike Snyder, Molecular Biophysics and Biochemistry Department, Yale University.

Chapter 11

Opener: © Lee Silver, Princeton University; **11.1 (egg):** © M. I. Walker/Photo Researchers, Inc.; **11.1 (sperm):** © Dr. David M. Phillips/Visuals Unlimited; **11.1 (embryo):** Courtesy of Ronald Carson, The Reproductive Science Center of Boston/IntegraMed America, Inc.; **11.1 (plate, PCR):** Permission to reproduce and publish this image has been granted by Bio-Rad Laboratories, Inc. solely for inclusion in the 4th edition of *Genetics: From Genes to Genomes*. Any further uses of the image, such as copying, downloading, distributing, reproducing, republishing, uploading, posting and transmitting, is prohibited unless written permission from Bio-Rad Laboratories is obtained. **11.4b & 11.12b:** © Lee Silver, Princeton University; **11.13:** Reprinted by permission from *Nature*, 394, **figure 1**, (1998), © 1998, Nature Publishing Group. Image courtesy Esther N. Signer; **11.14a:** Reprinted by permission from *Nature Genetics,* vol. 40 (10) pp. 1253–1260, 2008. © 2008, Nature Publishing Group; **11.15:** Trask et al, Extensive Copy-Number Variation of the Human Olfactory Receptor Gene Family (The American Journal of Human Genetics 83, 228–242, August 8, 2008). © 2008, with permission from Elsevier Science; **11.20:** Reprinted with permission from *Nature Genetics* (2009) vol. 41 (1) pp. 25–34. © 2009, Nature Publishing Group. Page 399: © Lee Silver, Princeton University. **Page 400:** Lee Silver, from http://www.geninfo.no/undervisning/DNA-fingerprinting.asp.

Chapter 12

Opener: © David M. Phillips/Visuals Unlimited; **12.1:** © Biophoto Associates/Photo Researchers, Inc.; **12.2:** © Dr. Don Fawcett/J.R. Paulson, U.K. Laemmli/Photo Researchers, Inc.; **12.3:** © Daniel A. Starr/University of Colorado; **12.4:** © Ada L. Olins/Biological Photo Services; **12.6:** © Dr. Gerard J. Bunick, Oak Ridge National Laboratory; **12.7a1:** © Dr. Barbara Hamkalo/University of California-Irvine, Department of Biochemistry; **12.7a2:** © Dr. Don Fawcett/ H. Ris and A. Olins/Photo Researchers, Inc.; **12.8:** © Dr. Don Fawcett/J.R. Paulson, U.K. Laemmli/Photo Researchers, Inc.; **12.9:** © Jacques Giltay, Center for Medical Genetics, Utrecht; **12.12:** © Doug Chapman, University of Washington Medical Center Cytogenetics Laboratory; **12.13a (both):** © Dr. Clinton Bishop, Department of Biology, West Virginia University; **12.15:** © H. Kreigstein and D.S. Hogness "Mechanism of DNA Repication in Drosophila Chromosomes: Structure of Replication Forks and Evidence of Bidirectionality", Proceedings of the National Academy of Sciences USA, 71(1974): 135–139; **12.17:** © Dr. Robert Moyzis/University of California-Irvine, Department of Biochemistry.

Chapter 13

Opener: © Michael Goldberg/Cornell University; **Figure C:** © Courtesy of The Centers for Disease Control; **13.7:** © Dr. Ross MacIntyre, Cornell University; **13.9a:** © Dr. Michael Goldberg, Cornell University; **13.10:** Courtesy of Dr. Philip Cotter; **13.13 (top):** © Cabisco/Visuals Unlimited; **13.13 (middle):** Courtesy of Dr. Brian R. Calvi; **13.13 (bottom):** © Cabisco/Visuals Unlimited; **13.15:** © Provided by M.J. Moses, Duke University, from Poorman, Moses, Davisson and Roderick: Chromosoma (Berl.) 83:419–429 (1981); **13.18b:** © Lisa G. Shaffer, PhD/Baylor College of Medicine; **13.20a (left):** © Dr. E. Walker/SPL/Photo Researchers, Inc.; **13.20a (right):** © J. Carrillo-Farg/Photo Researchers, Inc.; **13.21d:** © M.G. Neuffer, University of Missouri; **13.23:** © Corbis; **13.24 (both):** © Dr. Michael Goldberg, Cornell University; **13.25b:** © Dr. Nina Fedoroff; **13.30a-b:** Britton-Davidian et al, Environmental genetics: Rapid chromosomal evolution in island mice, *Nature* 403, 158 (13 January 2000). Reproduced with permission. © 2000, Nature Publishing Group; **13.37:** © Leonard Lessin/Peter Arnold, Inc./Photolibrary.com; **13.38b:** © Davis Barber/PhotoEdit.

Chapter 14

Opener: © Pat O'Hara/Stone/Getty Images; **14.1:** © Stephen Frish Photography; **14.2:** © Dr. Jeremy Burgess/SPL/Photo Researchers, Inc.; **14.3:** © David M. Phillips/Visuals Unlimited; **Figure A:** © Veronika Burmeister/Visuals Unlimited: **Figure B** © Oliver Meckes/Photo Researchers, Inc. **14.6:** © Dr. Gopal Murti/SPL/Photo Researchers, Inc.; **14.10:** © US Landmarks and Travel 2/V74 Robert Glusic/Getty Images RF; **14.11:** © SPL/Science Source/Photo Researchers, Inc.; **14.25:** © Jack D. Griffith/University of North Carolina Lineberger Comprehensive Cancer Center; **14.29:** © Newcomb & Wergin/Biological Photo Service; **14.30:** Electron micrograph by Dr. Stephen Hajduk/University of Alabama at Birmingham; **14.33:** © Eric L. Heyer/Grant Heilman Photography; **14.36 (both):** © Jim Strawser/Grant Heilman Photography; **14.38:** © Reprinted from Trends in Genetics, January 1989, Vol. 5, No.1, Dr. Douglas C. Wallace, **p. 11.** © 1989, with permission from Elsevier Science.

Chapter 15

Opener: © & Courtesy of Mitchell Lewis, University of Pennsylvania. Reprinted with permission from *Science* 271:1247, from M. Lewis, et al, © 1996 American Association for the Advancement of Science; **15.1:** © London School of Hygiene & Topical Medicine/SPL/Photo Researchers, Inc.; **15.4:** © Bettmann/UPI/CORBIS;

Index

Page numbers followed by an *f* indicate figures; page numbers followed by a *t* refer to tables.

A

A. *See* Adenine
AAAS. *See* American Association for the Advancement of Science
abdominal-A (abd-A) gene, of *Drosophila melanogaster,* 644, 644f
abdominal-B (abd-B) gene, of *Drosophila melanogaster,* 644, 644f
Ableson leukemia, 598t
abl gene, 598t
ABO blood group
  alleles of, 47–49, 47f, 48f
  Bombay phenotype, 58, 58f
Abortion
  genetic testing and, 33, 83, 393, 624
  spontaneous, 174, 458, 465, 618
Acentric fragment, 441, 442f
Achondroplasia
  in humans, 627
  in mice, 627f
Acidic carboxyl group, 3f
Acrocentric chromosome, 81, 82f, 91, 412, 413f
Actin, 4
Activator
  binding to enhancer, 556–558, 557f
  dimerization domain of, 558, 558f
  DNA-binding domain of, 557, 557f
  transcription-activator domain of, 557, 557f
Adaptivity of immune response, 716
ADE2 gene, of yeast, 147–148, 148f
Adenine (A), 1, 2f, 169f, 210f
Adenine methylase, 213
Adenyl cyclase, 528
Adherence, of bacterial pathogen, 543
Adjacent-1 segregation pattern, 446, 447f
Adjacent-2 segregation pattern, 446, 447f
β-Adrenergic receptor, 572, 575f
Adult hemoglobin, 230, 290, 291f
Adult stem cells, 623–624
Aedes aegypti, pesticide resistance in, 673, 673f
Affinity capture/mass spectrometry method, 356, 356f
Affinity chromatography, 355
Affymetrix oligonucleiotide array, 350
Africa
  HIV in, 360
  prehistoric human migration from, 669, 669f
AGAMOUS (AG) gene, of *Arabidopsis thaliana,* 631, 631f
Agar-medium plates, 479, 479f
Agarose, 295, 296f, 297f, 308f
Age of onset, of genetic disease, 387t, 388, 389
Aging
  cancer incidence and, 594, 595f
  mitochondrial mutations and, 509–520
agouti gene, of mice, 49, 49f, 68–69, 621f
Agriculture
  applied genetics and, 15
  artificial selection in, 15
  lentils in, 43
  nitrogen fixation and, 540, 541f
  pesticide resistance and, 304
  polyploid plants and, 462, 463f
AIDS. *See* HIV/AIDS
Alanine, 3f

Albinism
  in humans, 63–64, 63f
  in mice, 62–63, 62f, 69
  ocular-cutaneous, 63–64, 63f
Alfalfa, 462, 540, 541f
Alkaptonuria, 224, 224f
Alkylating agent, 210f–211f
Alkyltransferase, 209
Allele(s)
  antimorphic, 278, 280t
  blood group, 47–49, 47f, 48f
  coining of term, 44
  conditional lethal, 64 (*See also* Conditional lethal mutants)
  dominant
    designation of, 21, 22f
    pedigree of, 32–33, 32f
    relative nature of, 51
  dominant negative, 278, 279f
  fixed, 665, 696
  gain-of-function, 278–279, 280t, 627–628
  lethal
    conditional, 64
    recessive, 51–52, 51f
  loss-of-function, 277, 280t
  in Mendel, 20
  Mendel's discovery of, 20
  multiple (*See* Multiple alleles)
  mutant, 49f, 53
  mutations and, 49–51, 50f
  premutation, 208–209
  recessive
    decrease in frequency over time, 667, 668f
    designation of, 21, 22f
    51–52, 51f, 54, 51–52, 51f
    pedigree of, 34, 34f, 34t
    relative nature of, 51
  segregation and, 19–20–19f
  sources of new alleles, 49–51, 50f
  wild-type, 49, 200, 249f
Allele frequency, 49, 50–51, 50f
  definition of, 49
  and genetic drift, 664, 664f
  Hardy-Wienberg Law, 658–659, 663
  heterozygous advantage and, 670
  natural selection and, 665–670, 668f, 669f
Allele-specific oligonucleotide (ASO)
  hybridization, 374–375, 375f
  detection of SNPs, 371t, 373
Alligators, sex determination in, 85t
Allolactose, 522, 523f
Allopolyploid, 462, 463f
Allosteric protein, 525
α chains, 322, 323f
α helix, 175f
α-thalassemia, 290, 323, 324f
α tubulin, 230f, 231
Alphoid DNA, 708
ALS. *See* Amyotrophic lateral sclerosis
Alternate segregation pattern, 446, 447f
Alternative RNA splicing, 277f
Alu sequence, 448, 452, 596, 597f, 636–637
Alzheimer's disease
  genetic testing and, 393
  mitochondrial mutation and, 508, 510

Amber codon, 254
American Association for the Advancement of Science (AAAS), 507
American Society for Reproductive Medicine, 393
Ames test, 215–216, 216f
Amino acids
  codon-amino acid correspondences, 267–268, 267f
  codons representing, 248, 248f
  in proteins, 3f, 4
  protein structure and, 229–231
Aminoacyl (A) site, on ribosome, 269f, 270f–271f
Aminoacyl-tRNA synthetase, 266f
Amino group, 3f, 205f, 226, 227f
Amish community, genetic disease in, 665
Amniocentesis, 82, 83f, 209f, 374
Amniocytes, 83
Amoeba dubia, genome of, 336
Amorphic mutation. *See* Null mutation
Amphidiploid, 462, 463f
Ampicillin resistance, 300f, 301, 485f, 535f
Amplification, combinatorial
  at DNA level, 347, 347f
  at RNA level, 347–348, 347f
Amyotrophic lateral sclerosis (ALS), RNA interference therapy for, 573
Anaerobic organisms, 215, 540
Analogs, base, 208–209, 211f
Anaphase
  of meiosis I, 92, 94f, 96, 421f
  of meiosis II, 92, 94f, 97, 99f
  of mitosis, 88f, 89, 99f, 421f
Anaphase-promoting complex (APC), 605, 709
Ancient DNA, 162, 163f
Anderson, Anna, 381
Anemia
  molecular basis of, 228, 228f
  sickle-cell (*See* Sickle-cell disease)
  in sickle-cell disease, 54
Anemone fish, sex determination in, 85t
Aneuploid mosaic, 458
Aneuploids, 455
Aneuploidy, 431t, 454–456, 455f
  autosomal, 455
  in cells lacking checkpoints, 450, 451f
  in humans, 454–455, 465t
  from meiotic nondisjunction, 456, 456f
  X chromosome, 455, 455f, 465t
Angelman syndrome, 558
Angiogenesis, in cancer, 592f
Animal(s)
  breeding, history of, 15, 29
  Hox gene in, 705, 706f
  monoploidy in, 458
  polyploidy in, 458
Aniridia gene, of humans, 619, 620, 628
Anomalocaris, 694f
Anonymous locus, 372
Ant(s), monoploidy in, 458
Antagonistic pairs, 17–18, 18f
Antennapedia (Antp) gene, of *Drosophila melanogaster,* 279, 280, 440, 627–628, 641–642, 642f
Antennapedia complex (ANT-C), of *Drosophila melanogaster,* 642f, 643–644

E